THEORY OF
FLOW AND FRACTURE OF SOLIDS

ENGINEERING SOCIETIES MONOGRAPHS

Bakhmeteff: *Hydraulics of Open Channels*
Bleich: *Buckling Strength of Metal Structures*
Crandall: *Engineering Analysis*
Elevatorski: *Hydraulic Energy Dissipators*
Leontovich: *Frames and Arches*
Nadai: *Theory of Flow and Fracture of Solids*
Timoshenko and Gere: *Theory of Elastic Stability*
Timoshenko and Goodier: *Theory of Elasticity*
Timoshenko and Woinowsky-Krieger: *Theory of Plates and Shells*

Five national engineering societies, the American Society of Civil Engineers, the American Institute of Mining, Metallurgical, and Petroleum Engineers, the American Society of Mechanical Engineers, the American Institute of Electrical Engineers, and the American Institute of Chemical Engineers, have an arrangement with the McGraw-Hill Book Company, Inc., for the production of a series of selected books adjudged to possess usefulness for engineers and industry.

The purposes of this arrangement are: to provide monographs of high technical quality within the field of engineering; to rescue from obscurity important technical manuscripts which might not be published commercially because of too limited sale without special introduction; to develop manuscripts to fill gaps in existing literature; to collect into one volume scattered information of especial timeliness on a given subject.

The societies assume no responsibility for any statements made in these books. Each book before publication has, however, been examined by one or more representatives of the societies competent to express an opinion on the merits of the manuscript.

Ralph H. Phelps, CHAIRMAN
Engineering Societies Library
New York

ENGINEERING SOCIETIES MONOGRAPHS COMMITTEE

A. S. C. E.

Howard T. Critchlow
H. Alden Foster

A. I. M. E.

Nathaniel Arbiter
John F. Elliott

A. S. M. E.

Calvin S. Cronan
Raymond D. Mindlin

A. I. E. E

F. Malcolm Farmer
Royal W. Sorensen

A. I. Ch. E.

Joseph F. Skelly
Charles E. Reed

To the memory of my dear
Elisabeth

THEORY OF FLOW
AND FRACTURE
OF SOLIDS

BY

A. NADAI

Pittsburgh, Pennsylvania

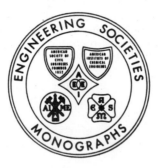

VOLUME TWO

McGRAW-HILL BOOK COMPANY, Inc.

New York   Toronto   London

THEORY OF FLOW AND FRACTURE OF SOLIDS, Volume II
(Revision of Plasticity)

45750

II

PREFACE

Several years have passed since the publication of the first volume of this book. Although progress in applied mechanics, during the last decades, has been marked by the publication of an imposing array of papers and several new books devoted to the mathematical theory of plastic deformation of solids, many of these developments have been directed toward abstract trends, concentrating on proofs of principles, the practical usefulness of which has been little explored. Very little that has been written recently has been aimed at opening up new perspectives in the mechanics of deformable solid substances, which would lead to a better understanding of those problems in which the time rate of permanent deformation, the temperature as variables of state, or the influence of time on flow strength of solids play an important role. Surprisingly, the fulfillment of the growing need for a few concise treatises offering the essential facts in the deformation range of solid matter up to the melting point, and endeavoring to explain the laws of interrelation between the speed of permanent deformation and the temperature, has not kept pace with the tremendous accumulation of empirical data in this field, scattered through special journals. Likewise, incidentally, one wonders as an engineer that the concepts of and useful observations on the slow creep of metals at elevated temperatures, which became known during the past years, have been little appreciated by those interested in the extremely slow distortion phenomena in the rock strata making up the outer crust of the earth, in the lower regions and levels of which, because of the steady increase of temperatures with depths, the rocks deform slowly under very small pressure differences, and thus essentially behave mechanically not unlike the ductile metals in their creep range.

This second volume aims to offer information on selected questions about the flow of solids influenced by the rate of permanent strain and temperature, briefly presenting, wherever possible, experimental evidence tied to theory from the viewpoint of mechanics, leaving aside discussion of atomic thermal agitation and propagation of dislocations within crystal-lattice structure, treated extensively in physics of the solid state, on which the author felt incompetent to report. In the first chapter, a brief review of the classical theory of thermoelasticity is included, distinguishing adiabatic and isothermal moduli of elasticity, covering the small adiabatic changes in temperature upon sudden stressing or unstressing of an elastic solid along the lines of the thermal analysis of these effects by LORD KELVIN (1855), illustrated and confirmed by early experiments made by the author in Berlin (1911), in which the neutral axis of a steel beam was observed by measuring its temperature during sudden, elastic bending.   Furthermore, a simplified theory of isotherms and adiabates in elastic solids applicable to the earth's rock shell is developed.   In relation to formulating expressions for mechanical work, elastic or plastic, in the second chapter a thorough analysis of the general states of strains of finite magnitude is presented.   Concerning the effects of speed of permanent deformation, throughout the book great emphasis is laid on exploring the applicability of the fundamental hyperbolic sine speed law, embracing the wide relative range 1 to 10^8 of the rates of strain in plastic substances, and the scale of homologous temperatures between zero absolute and the melting points of solids, discovered by LUDWIG PRANDTL in Göttingen as early as 1913, and supported and beautifully verified by an extensive series of experimental investigations by the author's former collaborators EVAN A. DAVIS and M. MANJOINE at the Westinghouse Research Laboratories in Pittsburgh, Pa., on many metals tested in uniaxial and biaxial states of stress over wide ranges of speeds and temperatures.   While some of their commendable efforts do not seem to have received from the profession the attention that they greatly deserve, perhaps the same may be true of OTTO MOHR's classical theory of the equilibria of idealized loose, gravitating material, proposed more than half a century ago.   The author has described this theory and endeavored to illustrate it with a few new, exact solutions which he developed for the ridge and the valley in a loose substance, and to show that MOHR's straight enveloping lines of the major principal stress circles may be generalized for defining enveloping curves and for what the author termed the theory of PRANDTL's generalized, ideally plastic substances, covering the influence of the mean stress or pressure upon the yield stress, which was envisaged by PRANDTL in 1923.   In the absence of bodily gravitational forces, the isogonal fields of nonorthogonal lines or surfaces of slip are easily derivable in useful applications, which can be constructed in quite a number of interesting cases through the exact solutions discovered by W. HARTMANN in his remarkable doctoral dissertation (Göttingen, 1925).

Several chapters in this second volume may appear, at first glance, as inappropriate in a book devoted primarily to plasticity, since in them the fundamentals of the mathematical theories of elasticity and viscosity are briefly reviewed in conjunction with a number of exact solutions. But an attentive reader will perhaps notice that several solutions covering elastic plates, concentrated pressure, trains of single loads resting on a plate, the theory of thermal stresses, etc., are presented in greatly improved, concise, exact forms and that new ones are developed for purely viscous and viscoelastic plates resting on a buoyant substratum.

In Chap. 13 on thermal stresses, the elegant way of writing the solutions in terms of the "displacement potential," proposed by ERNST MELAN (Vienna, 1950), is presented, postulating nonsteady heat flow. Among the practical applications, many curve sheets are included, illustrating in charts the temperature distributions in thin disks, cylinders, and spheres of steel during cooling, which the author evaluated many years ago but never found occasion to publish, and which serve for the quick computation of the maximum thermal stresses in large steam-turbine rotors. Turning these charts upside down allows estimation of the maximum thermal stresses in cold rotors, on the surface of which superheated steam impinges. Thermal shocks causing or associated with plastic strains are treated. In this respect, a very strange and interesting phenomenon might be mentioned, to which E. T. WESSEL recently called attention, namely, the extremely fine, densely spaced, regular serrations which appear in the tensile stress-strain curves of several ductile metals, if one tests them at the extremely low temperature of liquid helium, at 4 degrees absolute. The author has advanced the explanation that they are due to short thermal shocks, associated with layerwise yielding, caused by the very peculiar thermal conditions, the very low value of the specific heat, and the steep drop of the heat conductivity toward zero with approach to the absolute zero of the temperature scale.

The author feels that the similitude in the equations of isotropic elasticity, viscosity, and viscoelasticity should be brought into play in a book of this type, because the linear equations of the purely viscous substance throw considerable light on the theory of slow creep of solids at elevated temperatures, and these interrelations broaden the concepts in the minds of younger readers.

Chapter 16 on creep attempts to correlate the behavior of metals stressed in various types of tests at elevated temperatures, elucidating the power function, the logarithmic and the hyperbolic sine creep-speed laws, and their corresponding relaxation laws, allowing for strain hardening, creep recovery, etc. Based on these preliminaries, a special theory of steady creep is developed in three- and two-dimensional states of stress, illustrated with solutions, leading to synthesis of anelastic aftereffects, expressed by the BECKER, BOLTZMANN, and VOLTERRA type of definite integrals, exemplifying the direct and inverse aftereffect problem.

The evolution of prominent distortion and transgression phenomena on a grand scale in the outer solid rock shell of the earth inspired the author to compile an outline of selected problems of geomechanics in the last chapter of this volume, describing the mechanism of trans-current faults in mountain building, simple hypotheses for evaluation of pressures in the earth's interior, the causes of rocksalt rising in the prominent underground domes of the Gulf Coast planes, and analogous phenomena of flow in volcanic masses.   Having been for many years deeply impressed by venerable master ALBERT HEIM's monumental work on the geology of the Swiss Alps and by imaginative genius ALFRED WEGENER's theory of the impulsive splitting of the earth's primeval crust and the subsequent drifting apart of the continental block-massifs, the author has made an effort to assemble convincing mechanical evidences supporting HEIM's concepts in regard to the evolution of the great alpine nappes and to WEGENER's theory of continental drift.   As to the controversial bodily forces that activated these grand movements in the earth's crust, the author advances again the solid-tide-generating attraction forces exerted by the moon, in spite of some adverse opinions that came to light against this theory. His new, exact solution for the retreating wave of distortion in the rock slab, bent downward under the weight of a receding glacial front above substratum responding with buoyancy pressures, presumably may encounter less opposition.   In these efforts the author has let himself be guided by the principle he followed in the first volume, that mathematics in engineering applications and problems in geomechanics serves primarily as an excellent tool, not as an object in itself.

The author humbly admits how much he owes to his revered alma mater, the Eidgenössisches Polytechnikum in Zurich, remembering the spiritually high levels on which it spread knowledge while he studied at this old school during one of its brilliant epochs, when A. HEIM, A. HERZOG, A. HIRSCH, F. PRASIL, and A. STODOLA taught at the Swiss Federal Institute.   And he wishes to express in this preface, once more, his devoted respects and deepest feelings of gratitude to PROF. LUDWIG PRANDTL in Göttingen, to one of the great, creative, most original-thinking spirits in applied mechanics in the twentieth century, who was familiar with and creatively active in almost all branches of mechanics, who influenced more deeply than anyone else the author's way of thinking since 1919, and whose genial personality the author had the privilege of counting among his closest friends from 1929 until his death on Aug. 23, 1953.   His deeply penetrating spirit and straightforward manner were admired by all who knew him.   The author still recalls vividly the frequent, long discussions on problems of plasticity which he had with PRANDTL in Göttingen—the profound look in his dark eyes during any conversation, his instantaneous grasp of the essentials in any problem that arose.

Lastly, sincerest acknowledgments are due to the Westinghouse Electric Corporation for the continued interest and most generously offered assistance at their Research Laboratories the author has received since his retirement, in his efforts to complete the manuscript of the second volume of this book; to Director Emeritus DR. L. W. CHUBB, who passed away in April, 1952; and primarily to Vice-president DR. J. A. HUTCHESON, in charge of engineering, who generously granted the author the great privilege of enjoying the use of the vast facilities at the new Westinghouse Research Laboratories for preparing the typed manuscript and tracing and reproducing all the illustrations of the second volume, apart from the inspiring personal contacts with members of the scientific staff and the help of the outstanding reference library. To my friend, MRS. JOLAN M. FERTIG, Chief Librarian, I am deeply grateful for her invaluable help in assisting me in my bibliographical searches with her broad knowledge during all these many past years. My sincerest thanks are due to my former faithful collaborators EVAN A. DAVIS and M. J. MANJOINE, who since 1933 assisted me so actively in our joint experimental and theoretical investigations on the creep of metals at elevated temperatures and on the theories of mechanical strength, and with whom I have enjoyed continuing utilization of their experiences after my retirement in 1949; to J. GETSKO and MISS JEAN HOFFMAN for having helped to trace all the illustrations so perfectly; to D. W. GLASSER and G. PLAVETICH for reproducing many difficult photographs; to MISS BLANCHE RILING and, lastly, especially, to MRS. JANICE RAMAGE for all the tedious care devoted to preparing and typing the manuscript.

A. Nadai

CONTENTS

PART II: Elasticity and Viscosity

PART III: Subsidence and Postglacial Uplift of Ground. Flow of Substances Deforming under General Speed Laws. Thermal Stresses and Thermal Shocks. Residual Stresses

PART IV: Theory of Perfectly Loose and of Generally Plastic Substance

PART V: Creep of Metals at Elevated Temperatures

A. Rate of strain hardening and of increase of flow stress with rate
of permanent strain. B. Utilizing the stress surface. C. Considering a pure speed law. (1) For the power function speed law.
(2) Using the logarithmic law. (3) For the hyperbolic sine speed
function. D. Allowing for a uniform rate of strain hardening.
E. Constant-strain-rate tests. F. Creep of semifinite magnitude.
G. Comparing power function with hyperbolic sine speed law.
H. Allowing for variable rate of strain hardening and variable
viscosity. I. Creep recovery. J. The influence of time on change
of yield strength at elevated temperature.

A. Radial flow in a hollow cylinder. (1) Steady creep in hollow
cylinder under internal pressure. (2) Relaxation of stress in a hollow cylinder. B. Stresses around a cylindrical cavity. C. Concentration of stress around a circular hole in a thin, plane disk in a
steady stage of creep or in a plastic state of stress while the disk is
stretched uniformly. D. Creep in revolving de Laval turbine disk.
E. Creep in rotating disk of uniform thickness. F. Plastic deformation in rotating cylinders of strain-hardening metal.
A. Synthesis of aftereffects. (1) Steady load. (2) Steady strain.
B. The Richard Becker, Ludwig Boltzmann, and Vito Volterra
integrals. (1) In conceiving the direct problem. (2) In conceiving
the inverse problem of finding stress $\sigma(t)$ that deforms a solid along
a given, continuously rising, transient straining path $\varepsilon(t)$.

PART VI: Outline of Selected Problems in Geomechanics

A. The streaks and veins in granites. B. Jointing. C. Parallel
tension cracks caused by movement along a transcurrent fault.
D. Ordered arrangement of feldspar tablets in an extinct volcano.
A. System of bodily forces active in outer hollow, spherical solid
rock shell. B. Evaluation of elastic state of stress and strain in the
outer hollow, spherical, solid rock shell of the earth. (1) First case.
(2) Second case.

Part I

VARIABLES OF STATE IN SOLIDS. PRINCIPLES OF MECHANICAL WORK

CHAPTER 1

THERMAL PHENOMENA ASSOCIATED WITH STRESS AND STRAIN

1-1. Introduction. Whereas in Vol. I we assumed that during the process of elastic and permanent straining of a solid substance the temperature remained constant, in this chapter we shall consider various cases in which the temperature changes during loading or unloading of solids. We may encounter in the applications a number of simpler thermal phenomena in which it is sufficient to include the temperature as a variable of state in the group of equations connecting the elements of the tensor of strain with those of the tensor of stress, as, for example, when the thermal stresses in unequally heated bodies have to be determined. In other cases it will be necessary to make use also of the first and second laws of thermodynamics and to consider the conversion of external mechanical work or internal elastic strain energy in heat, or vice versa, as, for example, when the changes of temperature in an elastic solid or fluid which are associated with sudden elastic straining or stressing have to be determined. Only homogeneous states of strain and stress will be treated in a general way. In this chapter we shall primarily be concerned with the effects of temperature on the elastic properties of solids; the effects on plasticity, viscosity, or on the rate of change of strain with time will be treated later. Similarly, as in the thermal theory of ideal gases, it will be useful to introduce special processes of straining and stressing of solids and to describe, for example, the thermal changes when an elastic substance is *heated or cooled while the strain or the stress is held constant* or to distinguish in solids *isothermal and adiabatic sequences of stress and strain* as special loading processes. Under an isothermal change of state the temperature is maintained constant. Reversible changes require that the body in question be brought in contact with other bodies acting merely as thermal reservoirs from or into which heat must be drawn or transmitted under infinitely small differences of temperature. The adiabatic changes of state are carried out by preventing an exchange of heat with surrounding bodies. The latter occur on rapid (instantaneous) loading or unloading.

3

1-2. Adiabatic Temperature Changes in Solids. Since the classical experiments on the determination of the mechanical equivalent of heat by JAMES PRESCOTT JOULE, it has been known that on rapid loading or unloading the temperature in an elastic solid changes by small amounts in a reversible manner. He discovered that a bar of metal becomes slightly colder on the sudden application of a tensile load and warmer on rapid unloading within the elastic range of strain and that, similarly, a short column of metal becomes slightly warmer on the sudden application of a compression stress and colder on unloading.[1] However, when he tested vulcanized india rubber, Joule observed, when placing weights on a short column of this material and taking them off, that, on the contrary, the temperature of the rubber decreased and increased, respectively.[2] Furthermore, Joule found that the temperature of a helical spring of hardened steel drops slightly when it is suddenly loaded by a force in the axial direction and increases in a reversible way when it is rapidly unloaded. Hence, the distribution of simple shearing stresses in a wire of metal already twisted elastically causes it to become cooler on further sudden elastic twisting and warmer on untwisting.[3]

These observations on thermoelastic behavior of elastic solids may be summed up in the words of WILLIAM THOMSON (LORD KELVIN)[4] as follows: "It is concluded that cold is produced whenever a solid is strained by opposing, and heat when it is strained by yielding to any elastic force of its own, the strength of which would diminish if the

[1] J. P. JOULE, Proc. Roy. Soc. (London), vol. 8, pp. 564–569, 1857; Phil. Mag., vol. 15, ser. 4, pp. 538–544, 1858; Phil. Trans. Roy. Soc. London, vol. 149, p. 91, 1859.

[2] WILLIAM THOMSON, "Mathematical and Physical Papers," vol. 3, p. 65, Cambridge University Press, London, 1890, describes some striking experiments on thermoelasticity of rubber as follows: "Place an india rubber band in slight contact with the edges of the lips, then suddenly extend it—it becomes perceptively warmer; hold it for some time stretched nearly to breaking and suddenly allow it to shrink—it becomes quite startlingly colder, the cooling effect being sensible not merely to the lips but to the fingers holding the band." The curious, exceptional behavior of rubber in its response to heating or cooling, according to W. THOMSON, was first noticed by GOUGH (Mem. Lit. Phil. Soc. Manchester, ser. 2, vol. 1, p. 288), who hung a weight on an india-rubber band and observed that, when he moved a red-hot poker up and down close to it, the weight would rise when the red-hot body was near to the band and would sink when it was removed. Thus rubber, held under a constant stress, contracts on heating and stretches on cooling.

[3] Some tests on the alteration of temperature in steel wires that were stressed in the elastic range by twisting them were reported by WASSMUTH (Sitzber. Akad. Wiss. Wien, Abt. IIa, vol. 3, p. 996, 1902).

[4] Thermo-elastic Properties of Matter, Quart. J. Math., April, 1855, republished in Phil. Mag., 1877, second half year. Or see his "Mathematical and Physical Papers," vol. 3, pp. 63–82, Cambridge University Press, London, 1890.

FIG. 1-1. LORD KELVIN.†
(Born at Belfast, Ireland,
June 26, 1824; died at
Largs, Scotland, Dec. 17,
1907.)

temperature were raised; but that, on the contrary, heat is produced when a solid is strained against, and cold when it is strained by yielding to, any elastic force of its own, the strength of which would increase if the temperature were raised" (*op. cit.*, pp. 63–64) and "When the strain is a condensation or dilatation, uniform in all directions, a fluid may be included in the statement."

Thus an adiabatic cubical dilatation (compression) of an elastic fluid or solid causes an absorption (evolution) of heat in a normal substance, i.e., in material that under a constant hydrostatic stress expands when the temperature is raised. Most elastic solids and fluids have this property, namely, a positive rate of thermal cubical expansion. To the exceptions belong rubber and water which, within the temperature range of 0° to 4°C, contract on heating. As to the behavior of elastic solids under a state of pure or simple shear (under a deviator of stress), heat is absorbed if the modulus of rigidity of the substance under constant shearing stress decreases when the temperature is raised.

Alterations of temperature of a strictly reversible nature, accompanying processes of straining in elastic solids, are contrasted by the thermal

† WILLIAM THOMSON, knighted Lord Kelvin in 1866, was professor of natural philosophy at the University of Glasgow from 1846, which position he held for 53 years. He introduced the concept of absolute temperature and was one of the founders of the dynamical theory of heat and dissipation of energy. He developed the theory of thermo-elasticity, based on JAMES PRESCOTT JOULE's classic observations of the small changes of temperature upon sudden loading or unloading of elastic solids, in 1855. He invented many ingenious instruments utilized in laying submarine cables. With P. G. TAIT he was coauthor of the "Treatise on Natural Philosophy," published in 1867. In this book he advanced an instructive, simple explanation of one of the boundary conditions of an elastic deflected plate, proposed by G. KIRCHHOFF.

phenomena associated with the permanent deformation of solids, for example, with the yielding of ductile metals, which constitute irreversible processes of the conversion into heat of the mechanical work expended to deform a metal permanently.   The well-known fact that when a tensile bar of a ductile metal is rapidly stretched within the plastic range of the strains it becomes warmer, particularly in its necked portion, has been subjected first to a precise calorimetric determination of the heat evolved by H. HORT.[1]   He, G. I. TAYLOR, W. S. FARREN, and H. QUINNEY[2] have shown that the mechanical work done in a tensile test of ductile metallic bars, however, is not entirely converted to heat but that a measurable portion (about 10 per cent or less for a mild-steel bar) of the work becomes latent in the form of elastic energy which is stored in some manner, probably within the elastically bent lamellae of the plastically distorted crystal grains of the strain-hardened metal.   EWALD RASCH,[3] by applying increments of load rapidly in succession to tensile specimens of mild steel having a sharply defined yield stress and by recording their temperatures, found first, during the elastic range of the strains, a drop in temperature and at the instant at which the yield point was reached in the bars a sudden increase in temperature.

The absolute temperature θ of a bar of elastic material, when it is suddenly loaded by a tensile stress σ within the elastic range of strains, decreases by an amount $\theta - \theta_0$ which, according to a formula proposed by WILLIAM THOMSON (see Sec. 1–9, page 38), is expressed by

$$\theta - \theta_0 = -\frac{\alpha\theta_0\sigma}{Jcw},\qquad\qquad (1\text{-}1)$$

where α coefficient of linear thermal expansion

    θ_0 initial absolute temperature

    c specific heat (heat required to raise temperature by 1° in a unit of weight of substance under constant stress)

    w specific weight (weight per unit volume)

    J mechanical equivalent of heat

The proportional changes of temperature with stress, according to Eq. (1-1), were verified in a series of tensile and compression tests made by the author in 1911 in Berlin with mild-steel bars having a

[1] Wärmevorgänge beim Längen von Metallen, Forschungsarb. Ver. deut. Ing., no. 41, 53 pp., 1907.

[2] Proc. Roy. Soc. (London), Ser. A, vol. 107, p. 422, 1925; vol. 143, p. 307, 1934; vol. 163, p. 157, 1937.   See also Vol. I, pages 55 and 56.

[3] Die Bestimmung der kritischen Spannungen in festen Körpern, Sitzber. kgl. preuss. Akad. Wiss., vol. 10, 1908; also Mitt. intern. Verbandes für Materialprüfungen der Technik, Wien, vol. 3, p. 996, 1902.

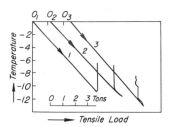

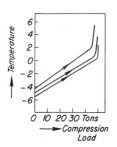

FIG. 1-2. Tensile tests.   FIG. 1-3. Compression   tests.   Observed changes of temperature in mild steel bars on rapid loading.

sharply determined yield stress.[1]   The temperatures were recorded by several thermocouples whose junctions were fused to the steel bars at equal distances along the axis and by means of a string galvanometer of EDELMANN.   The observed temperatures in three tensile and three compression specimens of the same mild steel are reproduced in Figs. 1-2 and 1-3 at various loads.   The latter were applied rapidly and increased in increments.   The cusps in the curves and the sudden increase of temperature in Figs. 1-2 and 1-3 corresponded exactly with the instant at which the yield point was observed by the drop of the beam of the testing machine.[2]

[1] Untersuchungen der Festigkeitslehre mit Hilfe von Temperaturmessungen, 51 pp., Dissertation, Technische Hochschule, Berlin, 1911.   Considering a bar of mild steel tested at room temperature (17°C) or at $\theta_0 = 290°$, for which the coefficient of linear thermal expansion was $\alpha = 0.000011$ per degree, the specific heat $c = 0.105$ kcal/kg deg, the specific weight $w = 0.0078$ kg/cm^3, and $J = 42,700$ kg cm/kcal, when a tensile stress $\sigma = 1,000$ kg/cm^2 is suddenly applied, the temperature, according to Eq. (1-1), drops by $\theta - \theta_0 = -0.0913°$C or approximately by 0.1°C.

[2] In a long mild-steel bar just starting to yield, heat is evolved, and the temperature rises locally in the slip bands that have first formed.   If a thermojunction coincides with this region, the thermocurrent will indicate a sudden rise.   Since steel is a comparatively good conductor of heat, the heat evolved at the yielded region is fairly rapidly conducted away to the adjoining colder portions of the bar, but this requires a certain time.   If several thermojunctions are attached along the bar, their thermocurrents will increase with time lags as the heat spreads along the bar axis.   This was indeed observed.

It is of interest to note that the temperature lines 2 and 3 in Fig. 1-2 show distinct *cusps* at the yield point and that a *reversible increase* of temperature occurred first before it rose discontinuously.   Clearly this was due to the fact that the steel had an *upper and lower yield point* and that the thermojunction whose record is reproduced in lines 2 and 3 in Fig. 1-2 first disclosed *the elastic drop* of stress from the upper to the lower yield stress before the heat generated in the yielded portion of the bar arrived at the junction. The ordinates indicate relative readings of the temperature proportional to the currents read in the galvanometer.

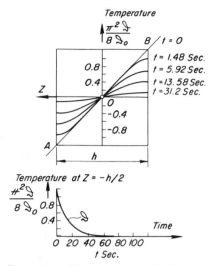

FIG. 1-4. Evanescence of thermo-elastic distribution of temperature across section of a steel beam subjected to bending.

If a prismatic bar of mild steel is suddenly loaded in the elastic range of strains by two equal and opposite moments, bending it uniformly over its length, the fibers parallel to its axis in which tensile stresses act will become slightly colder, those in which compression stresses are transmitted will become slightly warmer than in the unloaded condition, and a temperature distribution across the beam will be observable in which the temperatures are proportional to the bending stresses. They should disclose the straight-line law of the bending stresses. Figure 1-4 reproduces a distribution of temperatures which was observed by the author in a steel beam of rectangular cross section by suddenly bending it, after precautions were taken to record it instantaneously by thermoelectric means.

Suppose that the height of a beam is h, that σ denotes the stress, and ϑ is the temperature at distance z from the neutral axis, $\vartheta = -\vartheta_0$ being the temperature at the extreme fiber $z = h/2$ of the cross section in which the maximum tensile bending stress $\sigma = \sigma_0$ acts on sudden application of the bending moment. Then the temperature in the beam at time $t = 0$ is given by

$$\vartheta = -\frac{2\vartheta_0 z}{h}, \qquad \text{where} \qquad \vartheta_0 = \frac{\alpha\vartheta_0\sigma_0}{Jcw} \qquad (1\text{-}1a)$$

is to be computed from Eq. (1-1).

Suppose that the beam is perfectly insulated. Since steel is a good conductor of heat, this linear temperature distribution across the beam can persist only for an instant and must rapidly evanesce within its interior. At some subsequent time t the temperature ϑ must satisfy Fourier's differential equation for the conduction of heat[1]:

$$\frac{\partial^2\vartheta}{\partial z^2} = \frac{1}{q}\cdot\frac{\partial\vartheta}{\partial t}, \qquad (1\text{-}1b)$$

where q $k/cw = $ const.

     k heat conductivity

     c specific heat

     w specific weight of material

Since the bar is thermally insulated, the solution of Eq. (1-1b) is required, for which at any time t, for $z = \pm h/2$, $\partial\vartheta/\partial z = 0$ and at time $t = 0$, $\vartheta = -2\vartheta_0 z/h$.

[1] See W. E. BYERLY, "An Elementary Treatise on Fourier's Series and Spherical, Cylindrical and Ellipsoidal Harmonics," 287 pp., Ginn & Company, Boston, 1893.

It is expressed by the Fourier's series

$$\vartheta = -\frac{8}{\pi}\vartheta_0 \sum_{n=1}^{\infty} \frac{(-1)^{(n-1)/2}}{n^2} \cdot e^{-q(n^2\pi^2t/h^2)} \sin\frac{n\pi z}{h}, \qquad (n = 1, 3, 5, \ldots), \quad (1\text{-}1c)$$

in which n are the odd integers. Equation (1-1c) determines the distribution of the temperature ϑ across the beam section in dependence on the coordinate z at time t. Figure 1-4 shows such curves of the temperature which were computed at the times $t = 0, 1.48, 5.92, \ldots$ sec after sudden loading of a steel beam. The decay of ϑ in the extreme fiber $z = h/2$ is indicated in the lower curve in Fig. 1-4.[1]

FIG. 1-5. Distribution of temperature ϑ across section of a beam subjected to bending.

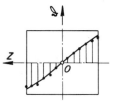

If the length of the beam is denoted by l, after the elementary theory of elastic bending, the beam will deflect in the middle of the span l by the amount

$$f_a = \frac{\sigma_0 l^2}{4E_a h}, \qquad (1\text{-}1d)$$

where, it must be expressly noted, E_a denotes the *adiabatic* modulus of elasticity which is valid for instantaneous loading. After the temperature distribution given by Eq. (1-1c) evanesces and the originally uniform temperature is again restored, the deflection of the beam increases slightly to

$$f = \frac{\sigma_0 l^2}{4Eh}, \qquad (1\text{-}1e)$$

where E denotes the *isothermal* modulus of elasticity. While this occurs, the fibers in the beam have readjusted their lengths: Those in tension, which were colder, have further expanded and those in compression, which were warmer, have further contracted while the values of the bending stresses σ remain unchanged. As will be shown in Sec. 1-9, since

$$\frac{E_a}{E} = \kappa = \frac{c_\sigma}{c_e} \qquad (1\text{-}1f)$$

is greater than unity {the quantity κ denotes the ratio of the specific heats at constant stress c_σ and constant volume c_e which is slightly greater than unity for a mild steel [cf. Eq. (1-73) and page 38 below]}, we therefore note that *a thermoelastic aftereffect must make itself conspicuous in the deflection of the beam.* While the external bending moment is held constant, the original deflection f_a increases to f. We may add that after a sudden unloading of the beam, owing to the same

[1] Figure 1-5 reproduces the changes of the temperature ϑ as observed an instant after application of a bending moment to a steel beam.

causes, its deflection cannot vanish instantaneously; rather, a very small, residual deflection will be discernible which subsequently vanishes gradually, so that *a thermoelastic recovery of a creeping character* must be observable after a complete rapid unloading of the bar. This must be true, generally, for *adiabatic* processes of cyclic stressing and unstressing of elastic solids which must be accompanied by narrow hysteresis loops of a purely thermoelastic nature.[1]

If a long cylindrical bar of a ductile metal is struck a heavy blow in the axial direction at one end either in tension or in compression, the bar deforms locally and necks down or bulges in the neighborhood of the struck end. The mechanical work of deformation is converted into heat in this case in a comparatively short portion of the bar, and the temperature may suddenly rise appreciably in the deformed region. In comparatively short tensile bars of steel that were broken in the high-speed tensile machine described in Vol. I, page 23, at a rate of permanent strain equal to 500 per sec a rise of temperature by approximately 50°C was observed.[2]

1-3. Variables of State in Thermoelasticity.

Denote by V the volume and by θ the absolute temperature $\theta = 273 + \vartheta, \vartheta$ being the temperature, in centigrade, of an isotropic elastic solid subjected to a state of homogeneous stress. It will be convenient to split the tensor of stress into two parts, an isotropic part consisting of a uniform tension equal to the mean normal stress, which will be denoted by σ and the remaining deviatoral part[3] of the state of stress, and to treat these parts separately.

Consider a uniform, cubical dilatation or compression in an elastic solid or fluid. The volume V is determined by the mean stress σ and the absolute temperature θ. Any two of these three variables of state may be chosen as the independent variables and the third as the dependent variable. But it is important to note that, apart from the isotropic state of strain, the deviatoral part of the resulting elastic

---

[1] Some exact experiments with thin metal wires, about which F. SAYRE (Elastic and Inelastic Behavior in Spring Materials, ASME 1930 Annual Meeting) reported, may have been partially influenced by these thermal phenomena. Sayre tested, among other metals, 0.67% C heat-treated thin steel wires, having the exceptionally long gauge length of 15.74 m, which were protected from air currents by a 55-ft-long steel pipe standing in vertical position in which the wires were stressed suddenly by hanging dead weights on them. On sudden application of a tensile stress by a weight, the wire should become colder by $\theta - \theta_0$ and subsequently, while the atmosphere warms it up again to its original temperature, its length should increase by thermal expansion by a strain $-\alpha(\theta - \theta_0)$ representing the thermoelastic aftereffect. On the rather complex elastic aftereffects and hysteresis loops which Sayre observed on loading and unloading, however, the effects of viscosity and plasticity were superposed and contributed more to the former than the pure thermal effects. Incidentally, it may be added that heat-treated high-carbon steels do not comply well or at all with Hooke's law of elasticity even at moderately small strains. Consequently, Sayre found a continuous decrease of Young's modulus with stress from $E = 30.1$ to 29.0×10^6 lb/in.² and substantial hysteresis loops in cyclic tests with the high-carbon steel.

[2] Familiar examples of the heat produced by rapid plastic forming in metals are encountered in the machining operations of cutting tools, in which the metal chips are rapidly bent away by the edges of cutting tools, necessitating the use of "cutting fluids" for their cooling.

[3] Cf. Vol. I, page 105.

distortion of a solid, in general, must also depend on two of the aforementioned three variables, for example, on the mean stress σ and on the
temperature θ as independent variables, since it is known that the
moduli of elasticity and rigidity of solids increase in their values to some
extent if the mean stress takes on high negative values $\sigma = -p$, that is,
under high hydrostatic pressures[1] p, and because the moduli decrease
considerably if the temperature θ approaches the melting temperature
θ_m of a solid.   Both effects must influence, for example, the elastic
behavior of the rock strata of the outer solid shell of the earth at great
depths under the surface where high pressures and temperatures
prevail.

Consequently, if the mean stress σ and the absolute temperature θ
are increased by the differentials $d\sigma$ and $d\theta$, the volume V of an elastic
solid under an isotropic state of stress will change by

$$dV = \frac{\partial V}{\partial \sigma}\,d\sigma + \frac{\partial V}{\partial \theta}\,d\theta. \tag{1-2}$$

If this equation is divided by V, the ratio dV/V expresses the increment
de of the *natural cubical dilation* e of a unit of volume $de = dV/V$ and
hence

$$de = \left(\frac{\partial e}{\partial \sigma}\right)_\theta d\sigma + \left(\frac{\partial e}{\partial \theta}\right)_\sigma d\theta. \tag{1-3}$$

$(\partial \sigma/\partial e)_\theta$ measures the rate of increase of the mean stress σ with the
dilatation of volume e at a constant temperature or *the isothermal bulk
modulus K of the elastic solid*,[2] and the quantity $(\partial e/\partial \theta)_\sigma$ measures *the
rate of thermal increase of a unit volume at constant stress* when the
temperature is raised or the increase of unit volume per degree, which
may be denoted by a.   Thus

$$de = \frac{d\sigma}{K} + a\,d\theta, \qquad K = \left(\frac{\partial \sigma}{\partial e}\right)_\theta, \qquad a = \left(\frac{\partial e}{\partial \theta}\right)_\sigma. \tag{1-4}$$

Conforming with practice in thermodynamics, the subscript affixed to
the partial derivatives indicates the variable that is held at a constant
value among the three variables of state e, σ, θ in the partial derivative,
a rule which is carried through in the following developments.

If K and a in their dependence on σ and θ were known and if Eq.
(1-3) were a complete differential which could be integrated, a general
equation of state of an elastic solid or fluid $F(e,\sigma,\theta) = 0$ would be

---

[1] Cf. Vol. I, page 34.

[2] The differential ratio $(\partial e/\partial \sigma)_\sigma$ or the reciprocal value of the bulk modulus
measures the "compressibility" of a solid.   See Vol. I, page 32.

known.[1] Unfortunately, comparatively little experimental information is available for solids concerning the exact dependence of K and a
on the mean stress σ and the temperature θ over a wider range of these
variables.   Some results of tests on the dependence of the parameters of
elasticity on the temperature will be given in Sec. 1-7.

When the cubical dilatation of unit volume e is quite small, as in
several applications, we may define it in the usual manner by

$$e = (V - V_0)/V_0$$

(V_0 = volume at some reference temperature θ_0 and stress σ_0) and may
express the cubical thermal change a of a unit volume by means of
the *linear* thermal expansion $\alpha = (\partial\varepsilon/\partial\theta)_\sigma$ of the edge of a unit cube.
For small e, a,

$$e = (1 + \varepsilon)^3 - 1 = 3\varepsilon, \qquad a = \left(\frac{\partial e}{\partial\theta}\right)_\sigma = 3\left(\frac{\partial\varepsilon}{\partial\theta}\right)_\sigma = 3\alpha. \qquad (1\text{-}6)$$

When the cubical dilatation e is small, the quantities a and α are called
the coefficients of cubical and of linear thermal expansion, respectively.
We see that the former is equal to three times the latter.[2]

Suppose that we consider first the behavior of an elastic solid under
isotropic states of stress and strain, after assuming that the cubical
dilatation of volume e remains small (a quantity small compared with
unity).   In Eqs. (1-3) and (1-4) or

$$de = \left(\frac{\partial e}{\partial\sigma}\right)_\theta d\sigma + \left(\frac{\partial e}{\partial\theta}\right)_\sigma d\theta = \frac{d\sigma}{K} + a\, d\theta \qquad (1\text{-}8)$$

the variable e then denotes the conventional cubical dilatation of
volume defined by $e = (V - V_0)/V_0$ and the mean stress σ may be
computed by dividing the normal force acting in an element of a
surface of a body by the original area that it possessed in the cold and
unloaded condition (at some low reference temperature θ_0 and the

---

[1] Such an equation, if it were explicitly known, would, in the theory of isotropic
stress of elastic solids, correspond to the equation of state for an ideal gas,

$$pv = R\theta, \qquad (1\text{-}5)$$

in the theory of gases (p = pressure, v = specific volume, θ = absolute temperature, R = gas constant).

[2] The variability of a or α with temperature is usually observed in the dilatom-
eters of metallurgists in which the linear thermal expansion of a rod is recorded.
By letting it equal $\varepsilon = \alpha_a(\theta - \theta_0)$, θ_0 serving as reference temperature, an average
value of the coefficient of linear expansion α_a in the temperature range θ_0 to θ is
determined from

$$\alpha_a = \frac{\varepsilon}{\theta - \theta_0} = \frac{\displaystyle\int_{\theta_0}^{\theta} \alpha\, d\theta}{\theta - \theta_0} \qquad (1\text{-}7)$$

stress $\sigma = 0$), instead of by the actual area of the surface in the heated and stressed condition (at θ, σ).   In particular this will be in order if the temperatures θ change only comparatively little, as in a number of important practical applications.[1]

A path of sequences of strain may be visualized as a curve in space, referred to a system of rectangular coordinates e, σ, θ, by plotting the absolute temperatures θ as the ordinates of the curve above the values of the cubical dilatation e and the mean stress σ represented in an e,σ plane.   The sequences of strain for loading or unloading the solid during which the temperature θ does not change ($\theta = $ const) are called *the isotherms of the solid*, and they may be represented by their normal projections on the e,σ plane as the family of curves for which $\theta = $ const.

If the solid is not permitted to expand, $e = $ const, $\partial e = 0$, on heating or cooling, the stress σ, according to Eq. (1-8), must change with the temperature θ at a rate

$$\left(\frac{\partial \sigma}{\partial \theta}\right)_e = -\left(\frac{\partial e}{\partial \theta}\right)_\sigma \bigg/ \left(\frac{\partial e}{\partial \sigma}\right)_\theta = -aK. \qquad (1\text{-}10)$$

The product aK in a body measures the increase of stress when the temperature is lowered by $1°$ while the body is prevented from contracting.[2]

---

[1] When, on the contrary, the temperature θ varies over a wide range and considerable changes of state between low values of θ and those near the melting point θ_m of the solid occur, as, for example, when the static conditions of the equilibrium of the stresses deep underground within the rocks of the solid, outer shell of the earth at depths of 50 to 100 km are to be investigated, then the density of the rocks ρ at great depths, corresponding to high pressures p (at $\sigma = -p$) and at high temperature, should be corrected according to the relation

$$\rho = \frac{\rho_0}{1 + e}, \qquad (1\text{-}9)$$

where ρ_0 denotes the density at $\theta = \theta_0$ and $\sigma = 0$.

When rocks are heated at atmospheric pressure ($\sigma = 0$) from atmospheric temperature $\theta_0 = 273°$ to near their melting temperature θ_m, the thermal dilatation e increases by amounts perhaps of the order of 8 to 12 per cent or more and their volume decreases at $\theta = \theta_0 = $ const with increasing pressures p perhaps by 4 to 6 per cent at a pressure $p = 10{,}000$ atm.   These circumstances become important when, for example, certain interesting mechanical questions related to the convective cooling processes near the earth's surface during the earliest geologic history of its cooling period are considered.   Then there arises the problem of how deep a rock could sink after it became solid and its density ρ increased because of freezing and the pressure under the weight of the overlying masses but decreased because of the thermal expansion of the rock when it sank to levels of higher temperatures.

[2] For mild steel, for example, at room temperature, having a bulk modulus $K = 1.75 \times 10^6$ kg/cm^2 and a cubical coefficient of thermal expansion $a = 3.3 \times 10^{-5}$ per °C, the mean stress σ would increase by $aK = 57.7$ kg/cm^2 per °C, if the temperature is lowered by $1°$.

For the deviatoral part of the state of strain in an elastic solid an equation corresponding to Eq. (1-8) may be postulated:

$$d\gamma = \left(\frac{\partial \gamma}{\partial \tau}\right)_\theta d\tau + \left(\frac{\partial \gamma}{\partial \theta}\right)_\tau d\theta, \tag{1-11}$$

where γ denotes a unit shear and τ a shearing stress. The quantity $(\partial \tau/\partial \gamma)_\theta = G$ defines the isothermal modulus of rigidity. Since G decreases generally, if the temperature is raised while the shearing stress τ is held constant, a change in the unit shear γ may be produced even though the stress remains constant. Under extreme hydrostatic pressures $p = -\sigma$, a further term $(\partial \gamma/\partial \sigma)_{\theta,\tau}$ should be added in Eq. (1-11).

1-4. Theory of Thermal Stresses. *If the bulk modulus K and the coefficient of cubical thermal expansion a do not depend on σ and θ and are constants*, the differential ∂e expressed by Eq. (1-8) is a complete differential and it might be integrated along any path between two points in the e,σ plane. If the thermal dilatation e at the stress $\sigma = 0$ is being measured from a reference temperature $\theta_0 = 273 + \vartheta_0$, where ϑ_0 may be taken equal to room temperature in degrees centigrade, Eq. (1-8) integrated between the points $e = 0$, $\sigma = 0$, $\theta = \theta_0$, and e, σ, θ gives

$$e = \frac{\sigma}{K} + a(\theta - \theta_0) \tag{1-12}$$

which is the equation of state for isotropic stress and strain in a solid, for which furthermore Hooke's law of elasticity is valid. For a set of temperatures held at constant values, Eq. (1-12) expresses, in terms of the variables e and σ, the equation of *the family of isotherms $\theta = const$* for such a solid. *It consists of parallel straight lines* (Fig. 1-6).

A linear equation of state such as Eq. (1-12) must be considered as a first approximation of its general form, valid only within a limited range of the variables e, σ, θ. In other words, the field of parallel and straight *isotherms* can be valid only over a limited range of the temperatures θ (and mean stresses σ). Obviously, if the temperature changes in the body between greater extremes, since the isothermal bulk modulus measures the slope of the isotherms in the e,σ plane and it is known that the bulk modulus at $\sigma = 0$ decreases materially as the melting temperature is approached, the isotherms must converge toward each other and consist of a family of curves whose spacing decreases continuously in the direction of the negative σ axis.

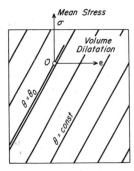

FIG. 1-6. Isotherms.

If σ_x, σ_y, σ_z, τ_{yz}, τ_{zx}, τ_{xy} and ε_x, ε_y, ε_z, γ_{yz}, γ_{zx}, γ_{xy} denote the components of stress and of small elastic strain, if $\alpha = a/3 = $ const, and if the bulk modulus K and Poisson's ratio ν are assumed constant (not dependent on σ and θ), the isothermal moduli of elasticity E and of rigidity G will also be constant, and the components of the strain tensor may be expressed by the six linear relations.[1]   Expressing Hooke's law, after adding the terms of the thermal expansion for ε_x, ε_y, and ε_z; thus

$$\varepsilon_x = \frac{1}{E}\left[\sigma_x - \nu(\sigma_y + \sigma_z)\right] + \alpha(\theta - \theta_0), \ldots , \qquad \gamma_{yz} = \frac{\tau_{yz}}{G}, \ldots \quad (1\text{-}13)$$

Since the sum of the normal strains

$$e = \varepsilon_x + \varepsilon_y + \varepsilon_z = \frac{1-2\nu}{E}(\sigma_x + \sigma_y + \sigma_z) + 3\alpha(\theta - \theta_0)$$

$$= \frac{\sigma}{K} + a(\theta - \theta_0) \qquad (1\text{-}14)$$

satisfies the equation of state (1–12),

$$E = 3(1 - 2\nu)K = 2(1 + \nu)G. \qquad (1\text{-}15)$$

The deviatory part of the state of elastic strain under these assumptions is expressed by the six relations

$$\varepsilon_x - \frac{e}{3} = \frac{\sigma_x - \sigma}{2G}, \ldots , \qquad \frac{\gamma_{yz}}{2} = \frac{\tau_{yz}}{2G}, \ldots \quad (1\text{-}16)$$

We may note that Eq. (1-15) may serve as the definition of the isothermal moduli of elasticity and rigidity in the general case of a solid for which K and ν are not constant but vary with the mean stress σ and the absolute temperature θ; however, in this case Eqs. (1-13) must be expressed for the differentials $\partial\varepsilon_x, \ldots , \partial\gamma_{yz}, \ldots$

Equations (1-13) and (1-14) usually serve for *computing the distribution of thermal stresses in an elastic body which is heated unequally in its interior*, provided that the temperature does not change between great extremes.   They are not general enough if the moduli E, G, K, and α and ν depend on the mean stress σ and on the absolute temperature θ and when the latter varies considerably in the body.

1-5.   General Field of Isotherms of a Solid Substance, Assuming Compressibility and Thermal Expansion as Pressure- and Temperature-dependent.   Let us now consider this case for isotropic stress and strain σ, e in an elastic solid in which the bulk modulus $K = (\partial\sigma/\partial e)_\theta$ and the coefficient of cubical thermal expansion $a = (\partial e/\partial\theta)_\sigma$ depend on the mean stress σ and on the absolute

[1] Cf. Vol. I, Eqs. (24-2) and (24-5), page 381.

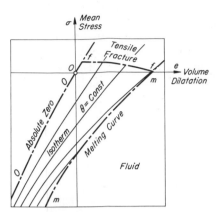

FIG. 1-7. Isotherms of a solid.

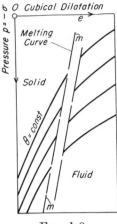

FIG. 1-8

temperature θ while the dilatation e still remains a comparatively small quantity and the variables of state σ and θ may now vary over a wide range.   Suppose that the field of the isotherms $\theta = $ const has been determined.   Corresponding to the solid state of a crystalline substance not having allotropic changes of its structure, this field in the e,σ plane is obviously limited.   It must be limited by three boundary curves: On the left side of Fig. 1-7 it cannot extend beyond the isotherm OO which corresponds to the *absolute temperature* $\theta = 0 = $ const, since no temperature exists smaller than absolute zero; on the right side of Fig. 1-7 the field is limited by a certain curve $\sigma_m = f(e_m)$, namely, *the melting curve mm of the solid*, beyond which the fluid states are located; and on the top of Fig. 1-7, by the fracture curve ff situated above the e axis where $\sigma > 0$, corresponding to the brittle fractures of the solid under triaxial equal tensile stresses.[1]   Since the melting temperature θ_m of solids increases with high hydrostatic pressures p, the melting curve mm must run slightly steeper than the isotherms and since the slope of the isotherms $(\partial\sigma/\partial e)_\theta$ measures the bulk modulus K in the solid or fluid condition of a substance, it is noted that the slope of the isotherm decreases on crossing the melting curve mm into the fluid regions (Fig. 1-8) because the reciprocal value $1/K = (\partial e/\partial \sigma)_\theta$ measures the compressibility of a substance and it is known that a fluid is more compressible than the solid which crystallizes out of it.   It should be noted that the fluid state on the right side of Fig. 1-8 starts beyond a certain second curve shown by a dotted line, because of the discontinuous increase of volume at the melting of a crystalline solid.

[1] In Fig. 1-7 the origin O of the e,σ plane has been taken to lie on the isotherm $\theta = 0$, that is, when the stress $\sigma = 0$, the thermal strains e are measured from the volume of the solid at absolute zero temperature.

In an attempt to define a family of curves inclined toward each other under increasing values of pressure (i.e., when $\sigma < 0$), we may perhaps postulate the existence of an equation of state in the form

$$e = \sum_{n=0}^{m} \phi_n \left(\frac{\theta}{\theta_1}\right) \cdot \left(\frac{\sigma}{K_0}\right)^n, \qquad (n = 0, 1, 2, \ldots, m), \qquad (1\text{-}17)$$

where the functions $\phi_n(\theta/\theta_1)$ depend on the temperature only and θ_1 and K_0 are two chosen constants. This may be written in terms of the dimensionless variables:

$$\vartheta = \frac{\theta}{\theta_1}, \qquad s = \frac{\sigma}{K_0}, \qquad e = \sum_{n=0}^{m} \phi_n(\vartheta) \cdot s^n. \qquad (1\text{-}18)$$

ϑ may be called the *homologous temperature*[1] after a term which was introduced by P. LUDWIK if θ_1 designates the melting temperature of the solid. In practical applications it may be sufficient to limit the series to its first three terms, by postulating an equation of state

$$e = \phi + \phi_1 s + \phi_2 s^2 \qquad (1\text{-}19)$$

which would permit considering cases, for example, in the rocks underground at great depths in the upper solid earth crust, i.e., in elastic solids under very high hydrostatic pressures p (for large negative values of the mean stress $\sigma = -p$) and when the temperature θ varies between any value and the melting temperature θ_1 of the solid. When the temperature is held constant, $\vartheta = $ const, Eq. (1-19) expresses for a set of values $\vartheta = $ const *the equation of the system of the isotherms of a solid.*

Assuming Eq. (1-19) to be valid, the compressibility $(\partial e/\partial \sigma)_\theta = 1/K$ and the coefficient of cubical thermal expansion $a = (\partial e/\partial \theta)_\sigma$ may be computed from

$$\frac{1}{K} = \left(\frac{\partial e}{\partial \sigma}\right)_\theta = \frac{1}{K_0}\left(\frac{\partial e}{\partial s}\right)_\vartheta = \frac{\phi_1 + 2\phi_2 s}{K_0}, \qquad (1\text{-}20)$$

$$a = \left(\frac{\partial e}{\partial \theta}\right)_\sigma = \frac{1}{\theta_1}\left(\frac{\partial e}{\partial \vartheta}\right)_s = \frac{\phi' + \phi_1' s + \phi_2' s^2}{\theta_1}, \qquad (1\text{-}21)$$

where the primes denote the derivatives with respect to ϑ. It may be seen that two of the three functions, namely, ϕ and ϕ_1, may be evaluated if the bulk modulus K and the thermal expansion e of the solid are known (if they have been determined experimentally, for example, at atmospheric pressure which we may identify with $\sigma = 0$ in their

---

[1] The dimensionless symbol ϑ herewith introduced and to be utilized in the subsequent equations (1-18) to (1-44) is not to be confused with the symbol ϑ in $\theta = 273° + \vartheta$ representing the temperature in degrees centigrade used in other parts of Chap. 1.

dependence on temperature $\theta = \theta_1\vartheta$, since, when $\sigma = s = 0$,

$$e = \phi(\vartheta), \qquad a = \frac{d\phi}{\theta_1 \, d\vartheta},$$

$$\frac{1}{K} = \frac{1}{K_0}\phi_1(\vartheta). \tag{1-22}$$

Let us now illustrate this with a more definite example, assuming that the bulk modulus K and the thermal dilatation e would vary with the homologous temperature ϑ, according to the simple functions

$$\frac{K_0}{K} = 1 + (\tfrac{1}{4})\vartheta + (\tfrac{3}{4})\vartheta^2 = \phi_1(\vartheta),$$

$$e = a_0\theta_1[\vartheta + (\tfrac{1}{2})\vartheta^2] = \phi(\vartheta), \qquad \text{when} \qquad \sigma = s = 0, \tag{1-23}$$

where K_0 and a_0 are given constants representing the values of the bulk modulus and of the coefficient of cubical thermal expansion of the solid, respectively, at zero stress and temperature $s = \vartheta = 0$. Also, from Eqs. (1-22) and (1-23) the coefficient of cubical thermal expansion for $\sigma = s = 0$ is

$$a = a_0(1 + \vartheta). \tag{1-24}$$

Incidentally, Eqs. (1-23) determine the abscissas e of the intercepts and the slopes $\partial\sigma/\partial e$ of the isotherms (Fig. 1-9) in the e,σ plane along the abscissa axis $\sigma = 0$. The values of K and e prescribed by Eqs. (1-23) are therefore obtained by assuming

$$\phi = a_1\vartheta + a_2\vartheta^2 \qquad \text{where} \qquad a_1 = 2a_2 = a_0\theta_1,$$

$$\phi_1 = b_0 + b_1\vartheta + b_2\vartheta^2 \qquad \text{where} \qquad b_0 = 1, \quad b_1 = \tfrac{1}{4}, \quad b_2 = \tfrac{3}{4}. \tag{1-25}$$

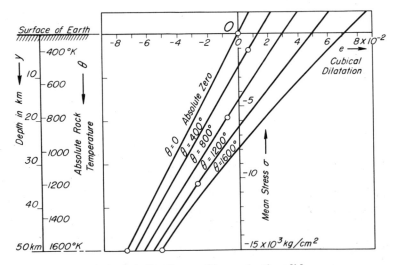

FIG. 1-9. Isotherms for an elastic solid.

Suppose that we choose for ϕ_2

$$\phi_2 = c_0 + c_1\vartheta + c_2\vartheta^2, \qquad (1\text{-}26)$$

where c_0, c_1, c_2 are constants. If we let $\vartheta = 0$, from Eq. (1-19) the corresponding dilatation of volume becomes

$$e = b_0 s + c_0 s^2. \qquad (1\text{-}27)$$

A relation precisely of this form has been found to be adequate for expressing the comparatively small decrease in the compressibility of solids at room temperature with high hydrostatic pressures p when $s = -p/K_0$ and has been verified by tests on several solids and fluids.[1] The quadratic term in Eq. (1-27) being insignificant even at pressures of the order of 15,000 atm in the low temperature range, we shall take the constant $c_0 = 0$ for the sake of simplicity, thus neglecting the small increase of the bulk modulus at the absolute zero temperature with pressures p up to $p = 15,000$ atm and assuming that the isotherm $\theta = 0$ corresponding to the absolute zero is the straight line $e = s$ (b_0 being equal to 1) passing through the origin O (Fig. 1-9).

Lastly, in order to find the values of the constants c_1 and c_2 in Eq. (1-26), after assuming $c_0 = 0$, we may perhaps proceed as follows: Suppose that the system of the isotherms $\vartheta = \text{const}$ represented in Eq. (1-19) tends to become more or less tangent to a pencil of rays emanating from a distant point A situated on the straight isotherm $\vartheta = 0$ (having the equation $e = s$) when the variable s in Eq. (1-19) has reached a certain negative value $s = -s_0$, which would correspond to some high pressure p_0. Since $s = \sigma/K_0$, this would make, at this pressure p_0, $\sigma = -p_0$ and $s_0 = p_0/K_0$. If e_a and s_a denote the coordinates of point A, a pencil of rays emanating from A is represented by the equation

$$e - e_a = \psi \cdot (s - s_a), \qquad (1\text{-}28)$$

where $\psi = \psi(\vartheta)$ is a function of ϑ. Suppose that we choose for the coordinates of A

$$e_a = s_a = -2s_0 = -\frac{2p_0}{K_0}. \qquad (1\text{-}29)$$

Equation (1-19) then may also be written as

$$e = -2s_0 + \psi \cdot (s + 2s_0). \qquad (1\text{-}30)$$

On the system of the isotherms [Eq. (1-19)],

$$e = \phi + \phi_1 \cdot s + \phi_2 \cdot s^2, \qquad (1\text{-}31)$$

---

[1] Cf. Vol. I, Chap. 4, on the behavior of matter under high hydrostatic pressures p. There the relation (1-27) was, conforming with our present notation, expressed by

$$e = -bp + cp^2$$

(b, c are constants) at room temperature.

apart from the conditions already mentioned, the additional condition may now be imposed that it become tangent to the pencil of rays expressed by Eq. (1-30) when $s = -s_0$. This requires that the values of e and of the derivatives $\partial e/\partial s$, computed from the preceding two equations, be equal when s is taken equal to $-s_0$ or that

$$\phi - \phi_1 s_0 + \phi_2 s_0^2 = -2s_0 + \psi s_0, \tag{1-32}$$

$$\phi_1 - 2\phi_2 s_0 = \psi, \tag{1-33}$$

or, after solving these two equations for ϕ_1 and ϕ_2, that

$$s_0 \phi_1 - 2\phi - 4s_0 + 3\psi s_0 = 0, \tag{1-34}$$

$$s_0^2 \phi_2 - \phi - 2s_0 + 2\psi s_0 = 0. \tag{1-35}$$

In order to satisfy the two conditions in which the first and second powers of ϑ enter in the functions ϕ, ϕ_1, ϕ_2, according to Eqs. (1-25) and (1-26), one has to choose the unknown function $\psi(\vartheta)$:

$$\psi = 1 + d_1\vartheta + d_2\vartheta^2, \tag{1-36}$$

where d_1, d_2 are constants. [The first term in Eq. (1-36) has to be taken equal to 1 in order to obtain, when $\vartheta = 0$, $\psi = 1$, from Eq. (1-30), the equation $e = s$ of the zero absolute isotherm.] After substituting the full expressions of ϕ_1, ϕ_2, ψ given in the preceding text, one obtains finally for the two conditions [Eqs. (1-34) and (1-35)]

$$(s_0^2 c_1 + 2s_0 d_1 - a_1)\vartheta + (s_0^2 c_2 + 2s_0 d_2 - a_2)\vartheta^2 = 0, \tag{1-37}$$

$$(s_0 b_1 + 3s_0 d_1 - 2a_1)\vartheta + (s_0 b_2 + 3s_0 d_2 - 2a_2)\vartheta^2 = 0, \tag{1-38}$$

which will be satisfied for all values of ϑ if the expressions enclosed in the four parentheses vanish, thus prescribing four linear equations for the four unknown constants c_1, c_2, d_1, d_2. The two parentheses in Eq. (1-38) give immediately for the intermediary constants

$$d_1 = \frac{2a_1 - s_0 b_1}{3s_0}, \qquad d_2 = \frac{2a_2 - s_0 b_2}{3s_0}, \tag{1-39}$$

and those in Eq. (1-37) give

$$c_1 = \frac{2s_0 b_1 - a_1}{3s_0^2}, \qquad c_2 = \frac{2s_0 b_2 - a_2}{3s_0^2}, \tag{1-40}$$

with which *the system of the isotherms* has explicitly been defined, within a range $s \geqq -s_0 = -p_0/K_0$ of the variable $s = \sigma/K_0$, by

$$e = \phi + \phi_1 s + \phi_2 s^2 = a_1\vartheta + a_2\vartheta^2 + (b_0 + b_1\vartheta + b_2\vartheta^2)s$$
$$+ (c_1\vartheta + c_2\vartheta^2)s^2. \tag{1-41}$$

The bulk modulus K and the coefficient of cubical thermal expansion a for the solid may, according to Eqs. (1-20) and (1-21), readily be computed at any stress σ and temperature θ within the prescribed range.

When, for example, $s = -s_0$, we find

$$\frac{K_0}{K} = \left(\frac{\partial e}{\partial s}\right)_\vartheta = b_0 + b_1\vartheta + b_2\vartheta^2 - 2(c_1\vartheta + c_2\vartheta^2)s_0, \tag{1-42}$$

$$a\theta_1 = \left(\frac{\partial e}{\partial \vartheta}\right)_s = a_1 + 2a_2\vartheta - (b_1 + 2b_2\vartheta)s_0 + (c_1 + 2c_2\vartheta)s_0^2. \tag{1-43}$$

A system of isotherms was constructed after these equations and reproduced in Fig. 1-9, using the numerical values of the material constants given in the footnote.[1]

1-6. Application of Preceding Chart of Isotherms to the Elastic Equilibrium in Outermost Solid Shell of the Earth. The mechanical properties of the solid material whose thermal behavior is reproduced in Fig. 1-9 are perhaps comparable to those of a strong, consolidated rock having a rather high melting temperature (1327°C at $\sigma = 0$), a comparatively moderate thermal expansion, and a fairly high volume elasticity. In an attempt to utilize the information disclosed in Fig. 1-9 *for describing the elastic state in the rocks of the outer shell of the earth,* let us assume, in a first approximation, that the density of the rocks and the gravity acceleration are uniform within the first 50 km of depth. If we assume their average density three times that of water or their specific weight equal to $\gamma = 0.003$ kg/cm³, an all-sided pressure equal to $p_0 = 15,000$ kg/cm² $= \gamma y$ is reached in the earth crust under the weight of the rocks just at

[1] At zero stress and absolute temperature, at the origin O in Fig. 1-9 the value of the bulk modulus $K = 2 \times 10^5$ kg/cm² and a coefficient of cubical thermal expansion $a_0 = 2 \times 10^{-5}$ per °C were assumed. If the absolute melting temperature of the solid at vanishing stress is assumed equal to $\theta_1 = 1,600°$K, $a_0\theta_1 = a_1 = 2a_2 = 0.04800$. For the pressure p_0 at which the conditions of Eqs. (1-37) and (1-38) hold, the fairly high value of $p_0 = 15,000$ kg/cm² was assumed, corresponding to which the constants $s_0 = p_0/K_0 = 0.075$, $c_1 = -0.6220$, $c_2 = 5.243$ were computed. With these values and using $b_0 = 1$, $b_1 = 0.250$, $b_2 = 0.750$, the following table was evaluated:

Absolute temperature θ ...... Homologous temperature ϑ ...	0 0	$\theta_1 = 1,600°$K 1
Cubical dilatation e: At $\sigma = 0$...............	0	0.072
At $\sigma = -p_0$	0.0750	0.0520
Bulk modulus K/K_0: At $\sigma = 0$...............	1	0.500
At $\sigma = -p_0$	1	0.765

This shows that, whereas the volume of the solid at $\theta = \theta_1 = 1600°$K in the unstressed condition increased by 7.2 per cent, under a pressure of $p_0 = 15,000$ kg/cm², it is augmented by thermal expansion by only 2.30 per cent and that, whereas the value of the bulk modulus for a raise of temperature by 1600°K in the former case is reduced by 50 per cent, in the latter it is only 23.5 per cent less than at $\theta = 0$.

the depth $y = 50$ km.   Since both the pressure p and the underground tempera-ture[1] θ increase proportionally with the depths y, a uniform vertical scale may be constructed in a downward direction along the chart of the isotherms in Fig. 1-9 on which the depths y and absolute earth temperatures θ corresponding to the pressure ordinates in Fig. 1-9 may be inscribed.   Then by projecting horizontally the scale points marked $\theta = 400, 800, 1200, 1600°$K of this vertical scale, for example, on the corresponding isotherms, the four points marked on them by large circles may be obtained; in the field of the isotherms, these obviously must define the state of the rocks at the corresponding depths y.   Their abscissas define the elastic strains e including the thermal dilatation, and the slopes of the isotherms define at these points the correct values of the local bulk modulus K at the prevailing pressures and temperatures.   Thus, it is noted that such a chart may prove helpful for discussing the elastic equilibria in the rocks of the earth's outer shell.

If we presume, furthermore, that some information were available on the increase of Poisson's ratio ν with the absolute temperature θ for rocks, then the values of the modulus of elasticity E and of rigidity G could be computed, using Eq. (1-15) at any depths y of the outer shell of the earth.   Since this information is of particular interest in geophysics, let us suppose, hypothetically, that Poisson's ratio ν would increase with θ within the uppermost 50 km of depths independently of the pressure p according to the function

$$\nu = \nu_0\left(1 + \frac{3\theta^2}{4\theta_1^2}\right) = \nu_0[1 + (\tfrac{3}{4})\vartheta^2], \tag{1-44}$$

where the constant ν_0 or Poisson's ratio at $\theta = \vartheta = 0$ for consolidated rocks may be estimated to be equal to $\nu_0 = \tfrac{1}{4}$ and thus, when $0 \leq \vartheta = \theta/\theta_1 \leq 1$, $\tfrac{1}{4} \leq \nu \leq \tfrac{7}{16}$.[†]

Concerning the shape of the curve representing the variation of Poisson's ratio $\nu = f(\theta)$ with the temperature θ at vanishing pressure for crystalline solids, one sees that this curve must terminate when the melting temperature θ_m is gradually approached from below *at a value ν_m which must be distinctly smaller than the value $\nu_f = \tfrac{1}{2}$ corresponding to the fluid state.*   The bulk modulus K of a substance retains its significance in both its solid and fluid state.   It decreases abruptly from a value K_m to a finite value smaller than K_f when a crystalline solid melts, because the compressibility $\partial e/\partial\sigma = 1/K$ is known to be greater in the fluid than in the solid state.   The moduli E and G, on the other hand, vanish in the fluid state since a fluid cannot sustain shearing stresses of any duration when it is at

---

[1] If the absolute surface temperature of the earth, for the sake of rounded figures, is assumed to be $\theta = 300°$K, obviously the gradient of the temperature $d\theta/dy$ must be $1600° - 300° = 1300°$ divided by 50 km or $26°$/km, a figure which is a little less than the figure of the geothermal gradient $30°$/km usually quoted in geophysics in the outer layers of the earth shell.

[†] See also Sec. 1-7, page 24.   It is well known that, in loose, very porous materials under low pressures, ν tends to approach the value $\nu = 0$.   When small uniaxial or multiaxial pressures are applied to such solids the pore spaces are first closed down.   In compact solids under low pressures, an increase of ν with temperature has been observed. It seems rational to assume that, on the contrary, when the pressures reach extreme values of the order of several hundred thousand atmospheres, such as must act in the central core of the earth, ν tends to become equal to $\tfrac{1}{4}$ at all temperatures, because these parts of the earth do not transmit more shear waves in earthquakes and in these regions the modulus of rigidity G must vanish in spite of a very high value of the bulk modulus K, which is the case when $\nu = \tfrac{1}{2}$.

rest. For physical reasons one must, however, expect that E and G converge toward finite values[1] E_m and G_m when, in a solid, θ approaches the melting temperature θ_m. Since

$$E = 2(1 + \nu)G = 3(1 - 2\nu)K, \qquad (1\text{-}45)$$

E and G at constant σ decrease with increasing θ for two reasons: because ν increases and because K decreases with θ. That the modulus of elasticity E retains a measurable, finite value E_m in a crystalline solid, when the temperature θ is gradually raised to the melting temperature θ_m, has been beautifully verified in the tests by W. Köster (reported in Sec. 1-7) who was able to measure the modulus of elasticity E a trifle below the melting temperature θ_m of several metals.

The curve $\nu = f(\theta)$ must satisfy a further condition. If the derivatives of E,

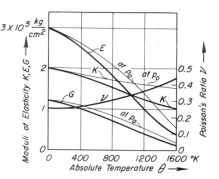

Fig. 1-10. Moduli of elasticity E and rigidity G, bulk modulus K, and Poisson's ratio ν at various absolute temperatures θ. The thick curves refer to pressure $p = 0$, the thin curves to a pressure $p_0 = 15,000$ kg/cm².

K, and ν with respect to the temperature θ are denoted by primes, after differentiating Eq. (1-45) one sees that

$$\frac{K'}{K} = \frac{E'}{E} + \frac{2\nu'}{1 - 2\nu}. \qquad (1\text{-}46)$$

According to tests, $dE/d\theta$ is always negative for metals (not having an allotropic transformation) and $d\nu/d\theta$ is positive. In order that the curve representing the values of the bulk modulus should also drop monotonously with increasing temperature, i.e., that $dK/d\theta < 0$, a condition must be satisfied by the curve $\nu = f(\theta)$, namely, that along it nowhere

$$\frac{d\nu}{d\theta} > \frac{1 - 2\nu}{2E} \cdot \left| \frac{dE}{d\theta} \right|; \qquad (1\text{-}47)$$

otherwise the curve representing the values of the bulk modulus K in the range $0 < \theta < \theta_m$ would obtain an analytic extremum. Obviously, also $K \gtrless E$ as long as in the curve $\nu = f(\theta)$, for a constant σ, Poisson's ratio $\nu \gtrless \frac{1}{3}$. These details are mentioned because of certain erroneous assertions which have been expressed regarding the shape of the curve $\nu = f(\theta)$ and the values ν_m and E_m in solids.

Curves representing Poisson's ratio ν, the bulk modulus K, and the moduli of elasticity E and of rigidity G are plotted in Fig. 1-10, using Eqs. (1-15) and (1-44) in dependence on the absolute temperature θ for the rock-type solid whose properties were described above. The curves drawn in heavy lines refer to $\sigma = -p = 0$, and those drawn in thin lines represent the values of K, E, and G

[1] An ice slab above which the air is held at 0°C and which is floating on water of 0°C has certainly a measurable rigidity, may sustain a weight placed on it, deflects elastically when a weight is placed on it, and deflects back when it is removed.

when the solid is subjected to a pressure $p_0 = 15{,}000$ kg/cm^2 at various tempera-tures.[1] It may be instructive to note the much steeper drop in the two curves for Young's modulus E and for G compared with that of the bulk modulus K.

In summing up, we may state, in regard to the conditions encountered in the earth's upper crust, that whereas the value of the bulk modulus K decreases only moderately with depth y on account of the increase of the temperature (by approximately 18 per cent[2]) the modulus of elasticity E drops in its value more appreciably (by approximately 79 per cent) from the respective values of K and E on the earth's surface when the depth of 50 km is reached[3] at which the temperature increases to 1600°K and the pressure to 15,000 kg/cm^2.

1-7. Dependence of Elasticity and Thermal Expansion on Temperature.
Reports on the experimental determination of the moduli of elasticity and rigidity at comparatively high temperatures approaching the melting temperature θ_m of solids are scarce in the litera-ture. The values of the moduli determined by static tests at elevated temperatures are liable to be too low, owing to the unavoidable plastic strains and creep which become pronounced, particularly in the ductile metals, at higher temperatures. More reliable values were observed in dynamic tests by letting specimens vibrate elastically.

[1] The following values, which were computed by using Eqs. (1-15), (1-23), (1-42), and (1-44), may be quoted (assuming $K_0 = 2 \times 10^5$ kg/cm^2, $\theta_1 = 1600$°K; see also Fig. 1-10):

Absolute temperature θ, °K	0	400	800	1200	1600
Homologous temperature $(\vartheta = \theta/\theta_1)$ ..	0	0.25	0.50	0.75	1
Bulk modulus K/K_0:					
At $\sigma = 0$	1	0.902	0.762	0.621	0.500
At $\sigma = -p_0$ ($-15{,}000$ kg/cm^2)	1	0.923	0.860	0.808	0.765
Poisson's ratio ν	0.250	0.262	0.297	0.355	0.4375
Modulus of elasticity E/K_0:					
At $\sigma = 0$	1.500	1.28	0.93	0.51	0.186
At $\sigma = -p_0$ ($15{,}000$ kg/cm^2)	1.500	1.32	1.05	0.70	0.285
Modulus of rigidity G/K_0:					
At $\sigma = 0$	0.600	0.507	0.358	0.187	0.064
At $\sigma = -p_0$ ($15{,}000$ kg/cm^2)	0.600	0.545	0.405	0.260	0.098

[2] We have to recall that the values of K in the earth's crust or the slopes of the iso-therms in the chart Fig. 1-9 have to be taken at the points which were marked on it by large circles, corresponding to the depths y and temperatures θ inscribed on the scales at the left of Fig. 1-9.

[3] At depths much greater than 50 km, beyond which the isotherm chart of Fig. 1-9 cannot represent the conditions correctly on account of the various restrictive assump-tions under which it was constructed, the following may be noted:

1. The isotherms will tend to be crowded together and to obtain nearly equal slopes for the same pressure which will increase considerably with depth and pressure.

2. Consequently the bulk modulus K, instead of decreasing, will start to increase with depth and pressure.

3. Thus the influence of pressure will tend to become predominant and that of tem-perature less significant.

4. At great depths in the earth core, the moduli E and G will cease to have significant values, conditions which are beyond the scope of this chapter.

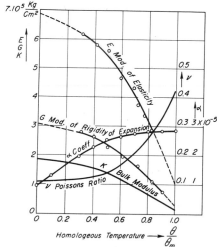

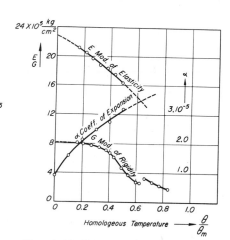

FIG. 1-11. Dependence of the moduli of elasticity E and rigidity G, of the bulk modulus K, of Poisson's ratio ν, and of the coefficient of linear, thermal expansion α of pure aluminum on the homologous temperature ratio θ/θ_m. (*Tests by Koch and Dieterle.*)

FIG. 1-12. Dependence of E, G, and α on the homologous temperature ratio θ/θ_m for iron. (*Tests by Koch and Dannecker.*)

Some early work was reported by KOCH and DIETERLE[1] who recorded the frequencies of vibrating strings and oscillating wires (in torsion) of aluminum from which they computed the values of the moduli of elasticity E and of rigidity G. They are reproduced in Fig. 1-11 above the homologous temperature θ/θ_m, in which the values of Poisson's ratio ν and of the bulk modulus K were also plotted. The full part of the curves is based on their tests. The coefficient of linear thermal expansion α for aluminum has also been plotted in Fig. 1-11. The values of Poisson's ratio ν computed from their tests have probably been underestimated at low and overestimated at high temperatures. More recent tests by KÖSTER (see below) do not verify the trend of their curve for E (and for G) which drops to much smaller values of E than the newer tests indicate (see Fig. 1-16) when the melting temperature θ_m is approached.

Figure 1-12 reproduces the test results of KOCH and DANNECKER for E, G, and α for iron. The discontinuity in the curve for G corresponds to the change from α to γ iron.

[1] The variation of the modulus of elasticity E with temperature has been determined by KOCH and DIETERLE, Ann. Physik, vol. 68, p. 441, 1922, and that of the modulus of rigidity G by KOCH and DANNECKER, Ann. Physik, vol. 41, p. 197, 1915.

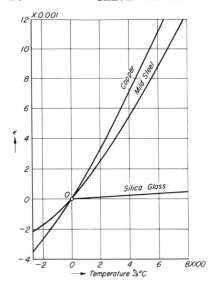

FIG. 1-13. Thermal strain. (*After* Holborn, Scheel, and Henning, 1919.)

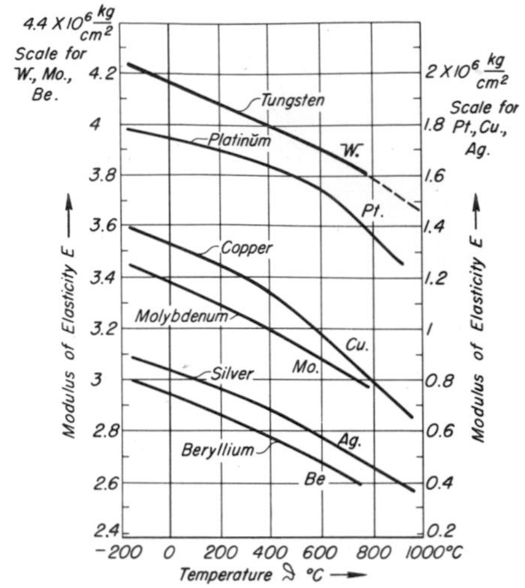

FIG. 1-14. Modulus of elasticity E at various temperatures. (*After* W. Köster.)

The thermal strain [extension of a unit length: $\varepsilon = (l - l_0)/l_0$] for copper, mild steel, and silica glass, measured from 0°C, is shown at various temperatures ϑ (in degrees centigrade) in Fig. 1-13, after tests reported by HOLBORN, SCHEEL, and HENNING.[1] The slope of the tangents drawn to the curves shown in Fig. 1-13 determines the coefficient of linear, thermal expansion[2] α.

By far the most complete and thorough determinations of the temperature dependency of the modulus of elasticity of pure metals are

[1] "Wärmetabellen der Physikalisch Technischen Reichsanstalt," Friedr. Vieweg und Sohn, Brunswick, Germany, 1919.

[2] Whereas, for example, for mild steel at $\vartheta = 0$°C, $\alpha = 1.02 \times 10^{-5}$ per °C, at $\vartheta = 700$°C, $\alpha = 1.92 \times 10^{-5}$ per °C. By means of a crude extrapolation of the curve of the thermal strain ε *for steel* (neglecting the shrinkage in volume corresponding to the α–γ phase transformation) a value of the coefficient of linear, thermal expansion $\alpha = 2.86 \times 10^{-5}$ per °C and of the coefficient of cubical, thermal expansion $a = 3\alpha = 8.58 \times 10^{-5}$ per °C at the melting temperature of mild steel (assumed to be $\vartheta_m = 1450$°C) was estimated. The volume of steel thus would increase roughly by 8 to 9 per cent just before it melts. E. GRÜNEISEN (quoted by A. EUCKEN, "Grundriss der physikalischen Chemie," 6th ed., p. 68, Akademische Verlagsgesellschaft m.b.H., Leipzig, 1944) states that the cubical dilatation of volume due to thermal expansion for most metals between absolute zero and their melting temperature amounts to about 7 per cent. It is well known that the patternmakers in foundry shops use a so-called *shrink scale*, the divisions of which are 2 per cent longer than those of an inch scale, when they make the wooden patterns for steel castings, thus allowing for the thermal contraction of the castings in their molds during their cooling.

those by WERNER KÖSTER.[1]   He subjected round bars, 4 to 10 mm in diameter and 100 to 200 mm in length, of 32 different, pure metals to elastic flexural vibrations of small amplitudes, which were excited to resonance by an electromagnetic device.   The bars were supported in horizontal position in two wire loops in the two nodes of the first fundamental oscillation form in which the ends of the rods were free and they could be made to vibrate at temperatures over a range from −180° to 1000°C.[2]   Köster's test results are reproduced in Fig. 1-14 for tungsten, molybdenum, beryllium, platinum, copper, and silver; in Fig. 1-15 for nickel, iron, and cobalt, and in Fig. 1-16 for zinc, aluminum, and magnesium.   The curves representing the values of the modulus of elasticity E in Figs. 1-14 and 1-16 appear as extremely smooth lines

[1] Die Temperaturabhängigkeit des Elastizitäts-moduls reiner Metalle, Z. Metallk., vol. 39, pp. 1–9, also 9–12 and 145–160, 1948. The equipment which served for these tests is described by him in Z. Metallk., vol. 29, pp. 109–123, 1937. In these papers numerous references to older related work may also be found.

[2] The modulus of elasticity was determined from the frequency n of the fundamental mode from the formula

$$E = \frac{n^2 \rho A l^4}{\beta^4 I}$$

(ρ density; l length; A area; I moment of inertia of cross section of rod; $\beta = 4.730$ for rod having both ends free). Köster also determined the damping factor of the flexural oscillations for several metals at various temperatures.

It is noted that the value of the modulus of elasticity E, determined in these acoustic tests through rapid transversal vibrations of rods, represent the *adiabatic* values of E which are slightly higher than their isothermic values. The difference is insignificant for practical purposes.

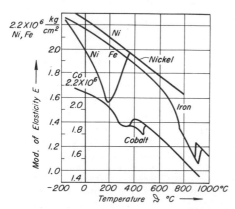

FIG. 1-15. Modulus of elasticity E at various temperatures. (*After W. Köster.*)

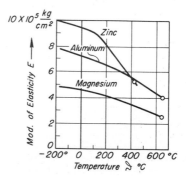

FIG. 1-16. Modulus of elasticity E at various temperatures. (*After W. Köster.*)

bent gently, with their concave side toward the temperature axis.   It is
most remarkable that his observations of E for silver and for metals
having low melting temperatures (see the curves in Fig. 1-16 for Zn, Al,
and Mg) extend almost to the melting points (marked by circles), thus
definitely proving that the modulus of elasticity of a crystalline solid
tends to take on a finite value (for pure aluminum, for example, the
comparatively high value $E_m = 4.00 \times 10^5 \,\text{kg/cm}^2$, whereas at $-180°\text{C}$
$E = 7.80 \times 10^5 \,\text{kg/cm}^2$ was observed) when the melting temperature
is approached from below and thus demonstrating the fallacy of
Poisson's ratio ν becoming equal to ½ when the melting point θ_m is
approached from below.   The ferromagnetic metals Ni, Fe, and Co,
however, disclose quite anomalous curves (Fig. 1-15): The values of the
modulus of elasticity E of annealed nickel drop first to a dip at 200°C and
increase subsequently until the Curie point is reached, after which they
decrease linearly with the temperature; the curve for the modulus of
iron starts to bend down more rapidly before the Curie point (760°C), at
which the slope of the curve suddenly becomes less steep until the α–γ
transformation point around 900°C is reached, at which the modulus
abruptly increases on further heating, whereas E suddenly decreases
during the γ–α transformation on cooling.   The ferromagnetic properties as well as a polymorphic transformation upset the smoothness of
the curves for the modulus of elasticity.   (See also the corresponding

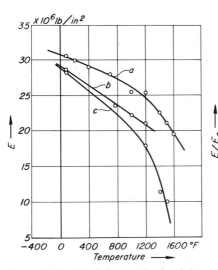

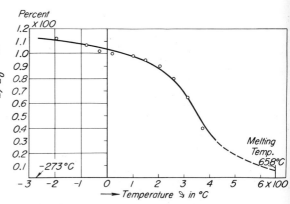

FIG. 1-17. Modulus of elasticity
E. (a) Westinghouse refractaloy 26.
(b) Westinghouse discaloy 25. (*Tests
by M. J. Manjoine.*) (c) 16% Cr,
25% Ni, 6% Mo steel. (*After Fleischmann.*)

FIG. 1-18. Modulus of elasticity E of aluminum
alloys. (*After R. L. Templin.*)

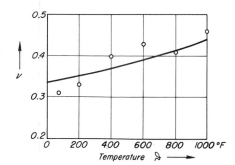

FIG. 1-19. Poisson's ratio ν for SAE steel. (*After Everett and Miklowitz.*)

irregularities in the observed values of E for cobalt in Fig. 1-15.)   These anomalies were also confirmed in the trend of the damping factor of the latter metals.

A few observations of the modulus of elasticity of alloys resistant to creep at high temperatures are reproduced in Fig. 1-17 after tests by M. J. MANJOINE[1] and M. FLEISCHMANN.[2]

Figure 1-18 shows the variation of the modulus of elasticity of aluminum alloys, with the temperature ϑ in degrees centigrade.   The points marked by circles represent the average values of the ordinates E in per cent of the value of E_0 at room temperature $\vartheta_0 = 21°C$, which have been determined at the temperatures indicated in their abscissas in various elasticity tests in American industrial laboratories, according to information received from R. L. TEMPLIN.[3]   The interpolating curve in Fig. 1-18 was plotted by the author.

By subjecting small cantilever rods, by means of hung-on weights, simultaneously to combined elastic bending and torsion, F. L. EVERETT and J. MIKLOWITZ[4] determined from the observed values of E and G Poisson's ratio $\nu = (E/2G) - 1$ for five SAE steel specimens between room temperature and 1000°F (537°C).   A curve $\nu = f(\vartheta)$ interpolating the average values of their observations is shown in Fig. 1-19.

[1] Unpublished work of the Westinghouse Research Laboratories.
[2] Quoted from F. H. CLARK, "Metals at High Temperatures," p. 171, 1950.   Reinhold Publishing Corporation, New York, 1950.
[3] Acknowledgment is due to R. L. TEMPLIN of the Research Laboratories of the Aluminum Company of America in New Kensington, Pa., for supplying the above data of observations.   In a paper by R. L. TEMPLIN and E. C. HARTMANN, The Elastic Constants for Wrought Aluminum Alloys, NACA Tech. Note 966, January, 1945, exact values of E in tension and in compression, of G, and of Poisson's ratio ν were found for a number of aluminum alloys, which were observed at room temperature.

Alloy	E, lb/in.^{2}		G, lb/in.^{2}	ν
	Tension	Compression		
2S	9.9	10.0	3.8×10^6	0.32
75S	10.3	10.5	3.9×10^6	0.33
24S	10.5	10.7	4.0×10^6	0.32

The stress σ_x versus strain ε_x curves of these aluminum alloys have a well-defined proportional limit.   The values just given and those represented in Fig. 1-18 for E/E_0 refer to the straight portion of the stress-strain curves below the proportional limit.

[4] Poisson's Ratio at High Temperatures, J. Appl. Phys., vol. 15, pp. 592–598, 1944.

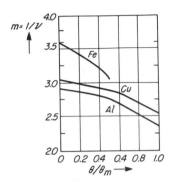

FIG. 1-20. Reciprocal value $m = 1/\nu$ of Poisson's ratio ν. (*After F. Vitovec.*)

By considering the energy of an atomic lattice and the resulting variation of the bulk modulus and of its thermal dilatation with the absolute temperature, F. VITOVEC[1] has computed the reciprocal values $m = 1/\nu$ of Poisson's ratio for the metals iron, copper, and aluminum in their dependence on the homologous temperature ratio θ/θ_m (θ_m = absolute melting temperature), which are reproduced in the curves based on his computations in Fig. 1-20. He gave also a table of the values of $m = 1/\nu$ for a number of metals from which we quote the values (see table below).

Further observations of the dependence of the moduli of elasticity and rigidity and of Poisson's ratio on the temperature for 21 different commercial steels were reported in a paper by F. GARO-FALO, P. R. MALENOCK, and G. V. SMITH.[2] Their tests were made in an apparatus similar to that used by EVERETT and MIKLOWITZ, quoted above, in which they subjected horizontal cantilever rods of steel simultaneously to static bending and torsion and determined the moduli of elasticity

VALUES OF $m = 1/\nu$

	Al	Mo	W	Ni	Cu	Ag	Zn	Pb
At absolute zero..	3.00	3.28	4.30	3.50	2.90	3.20	3.77	2.33
At melting point..	2.50	2.64	2.75	2.70	2.35	2.70	2.90	2.15

E and rigidity G at intervals of 200°F up to 900°F for carbon steels, to a maximum temperature of 1100°F for ferritic low-alloy and high-chromium steels, and of 1500°F for austenitic stainless steels. They found that E and G for these steels (except for two austenitic stainless steels) decrease approximately linearly with temperature within the interval over which they ran their tests, but at higher temperatures they noted that E and G would start to drop faster than linearly with the temperature. From their tests one may thus conclude that Poisson's ratio in a first approximation remains practically constant within the observed range of temperature (in contrast to the test results by Everett and Miklowitz, quoted in Fig. 1-19). They also attributed the observed departure from linearity in ferritic alloys to the changing magnetic properties as the temperature increases.

[1] Über die Temperaturabhängigkeit der Querzahl der Metalle, Österr. Ing. Arch., vol. 6, no. 2, pp. 1932–1934, 1952. Vitovec quotes a formula proposed by CLEMENS SCHAEFER (Drudes Ann., p. 1124, 1902) expressing the variation of Poisson's ratio ν with the temperature ϑ:

$$1 + \nu = (1 + \nu_{20}) \frac{1 - \alpha(\vartheta - 20)}{1 - \beta(\vartheta - 20)},$$

where α and β denote the temperature coefficients of the moduli of elasticity and of rigidity and ν_{20} the value of ν at $\vartheta = 20$°C. But G. ANGENHEISTER (Drudes Ann., vol. 11, p. 188, 1903) has already shown that a linear extrapolation of E and G with temperature, on which the formula is based, cannot be valid over a wider range of the temperature ϑ.

[2] The Influence of Temperature on the Elastic Constants of Some Commercial Steels, presented at the 55th Annual Meeting of the American Society for Testing Materials, June, 1952, Preprint 159, 18 pp. This paper also includes some test results of previous investigators on this subject, to which references may be found in it.

For details and the numerical values of E, G, ν the reader must be referred to the figure charts published in this paper.[1]

1-8. Variation of Poisson's Ratio ν in Transition Region from Elastic to Plastic Range of Strains. The preceding brief review of elasticity constants under various conditions may be supplemented by a few remarks about the increase of Poisson's ratio ν in metals when the permanent strains gradually develop in them at normal temperature in uniaxial tension or compression. A. H. STANG, M. GREENSPAN, and S. B. NEWMAN[2] determined the ratio of the total lateral contraction $-\varepsilon_y$ to the total axial elongation ε_x, using for both the conventional definition of strain in specimens of several metals (24S-T aluminum alloy, a chrome molybdenum, and two fully killed low-carbon steels), which they tested in tension beyond the elastic range—in some cases up to 18 per cent axial, permanent strain at room temperature and at $-44°C$. When they

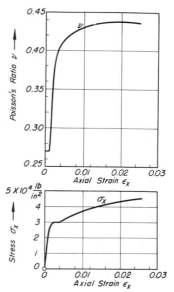

FIG. 1-21. Fully killed low-carbon steel (C 0.22%) stress-strain curve and Poisson's ratio ν in plastic range. (*After A. H. Stang, M. Greenspan, and S. B. Newman.*)

plotted this ratio $-\varepsilon_y/\varepsilon_x$ above the axial strain ε_x they found that beyond the elastic range it would increase rapidly from a value of the order of 0.3 to a maximum of the magnitude of 0.46 and subsequently decrease slowly. Anisotropy in the rolled metals considerably influenced this ratio in specimens cut at different angles relative to the direction of rolling. One of their curves representing $-\varepsilon_y/\varepsilon_x$ in the beginning of the plastic range of strains for a fully killed low-carbon steel, together with its stress-strain curve, is reproduced in Fig. 1-21.

Similar exact measurements of Poisson's ratio have been reported by G. GERARD and S. WILDHORN[3] within the transition region from the elastic to the initial plastic range of strains of specimens tested axially in tension and in compression for three aluminum alloys (rolled 24S-T4, extruded 14S-T6, and 75S-T6) at room temperature. These alloys possessed a well-determined elastic

---

[1] From their observations, as a practical rule, the designer of machine parts exposed to elevated temperature in steam or gas turbines may, in a first approximation, thus assume a constant rate of decrease in the tensile modulus $dE/d\vartheta$ with temperatures varying between -5.0×10^3 and -7.0×10^3 lb/in.² per °F and Poisson's ratio ν equal to its value at room temperature.

[2] Poisson's Ratio of Some Structural Alloys for Large Strains, J. Research, Natl. Bur. Standards, vol. 37, pp. 211–221, 1946.

[3] A Study of Poisson's Ratio in the Yield Region, New York Univ. rep. NAw-5753, sponsored by National Advisory Committee for Aeronautics, October, 1950.

range in their stress-strain curves which had a shape similar to the curve for $\sigma_x = f(\varepsilon_x)$ (σ_x = axial normal stress, $\varepsilon_x = \varepsilon_x' + \varepsilon_x''$ total axial strain, where $\varepsilon_x' = \sigma_x/E$ is the elastic and ε_x'' the permanent part of ε_x), reproduced from their observations for a 24S-T4 aluminum alloy in Fig. 1-22, having two gradually bent transition curves leading to the plastic ranges of the strain ε_x for tension and for compression.

For the evaluation of Poisson's resultant ratio ν within the transition region from the elastic to small plastic strains these authors used the equation

$$\varepsilon_y = \varepsilon_z = -\nu\varepsilon_x = -\nu'\varepsilon_x' - \nu''\varepsilon_x'', \qquad (1\text{-}47a)$$

from which

$$\nu = \frac{\nu'\varepsilon_x' + \nu''\varepsilon_x''}{\varepsilon_x' + \varepsilon_x''}, \qquad (1\text{-}47b)$$

where ν' and ν'' denote Poisson's ratio corresponding to the elastic (ε_x') and to the permanent (ε_x'') part of the strain ε_x, respectively, an equation which was developed for isotropic flow in the synthesis of small elastic and permanent strains in Vol. I [see Eqs. (24-11) and (24-11a), page 383] in the equivalent form [see Eq. (24-23), page 387]:

$$\nu = \nu'' - \frac{(\nu'' - \nu')\varepsilon_x'}{\varepsilon_x} \qquad (1\text{-}47c)$$

If the *total dilation of volume* is denoted by e, the elastic and permanent dilation by e' and e'', one has for uniaxial tension or compression ε_x

$$e = e' + e'' = (1 - 2\nu)\varepsilon_x = (1 - 2\nu')\varepsilon_x' + (1 - 2\nu'')\varepsilon_x'', \qquad (1\text{-}47d)$$

from which one also obtains Eq. (1-47c). A typical example of a curve representing the variations of Poisson's ratio ν within the transition portions of the tensile and compression stress-strain curve with the strains ε_x is illustrated in Fig. 1-22, taken from the observations of the authors. It is interesting to note that the branch of the curve for ν corresponding to tensile strains ($\varepsilon_x > 0$) has smaller ordinates than the branch in which the strains were compressions ($\varepsilon_x < 0$) and that the latter branch of the ν curve crosses the horizontal line $\nu = \frac{1}{2}$, corresponding to the limiting value of Poisson's ratio ν for an *incompressible* material. Thus values of ν (and of ν'') greater than $\frac{1}{2}$ were observed within the compression range of the strains beyond the strain $\varepsilon_x = -0.012$. This would point to the fact that *the permanent dilatation of volume* $e'' = (1 - 2\nu'')\varepsilon_x''$ *under increasing compression strains became a positive quantity*, greater than the absolute value of the elastic dilatation of volume $e' = (1 - 2\nu')\varepsilon_x'$, which for the observed value of $\nu' = 0.34$ was negative in the compression range of the strains ($\varepsilon_x' < 0$). Since $\varepsilon_x'' < 0$, ν'' had to be greater than $\frac{1}{2}$ to make the quantity $e'' = (1 - 2\nu'')\varepsilon_x''$ a positive dilatation greater than the absolute value of e'. This is corroborated by some old observations according to which it is known that cold-worked and strain-hardened polycrystalline ductile metals very slightly increase their volume permanently,[1] even when they have been deformed by uniaxial or multiaxial compression stresses enabling them to flow. It must be added, however, that the conditions encountered in these tests were very complex on account of the plastic anisotropy inherent in the extruded or rolled stock of the metals from which the test specimens were made, as the authors themselves have definitely

---

[1] This is because of the formation of minute voids between the packages of the layers displaced by slip within the individual crystal grains when the metal has been deformed plastically.

shown.[1]   In any case, these and the tests reported previously clearly bring out the great sensitivity of a quantity such as Poisson's ratio ν to structural anisotropy.

It may perhaps be of interest to compare the trend of the ν curve as illustrated by the observed values in Fig. 1-22 with a curve which was computed *for an isotropic substance for Poisson's ratio ν for an idealized and simplified, symmetric stress-strain curve for tension and compression consisting of three straight-line portions* as represented in Fig. 1-23 and after making the simplifying assumption

[1] They found systematic deviations in the values of ν in test specimens in which the direction of the stress σ_x was perpendicular to the direction of extrusion or rolling from the values of ν that they observed in specimens in which the load acted parallel to this direction.   In the specimens loaded parallel to the direction of extrusion—according to the authors—a value of Poisson's ratio ν'' corresponding to the permanent parts of the strains, approximately equal to $\nu'' = 0.56$ in tension and $\nu'' = 0.63$ in compression and assumed to be approximately constant (independent of the magnitude of the permanent strains ε_x''), would account for the observed shapes of both branches of the curve for Poisson's resultant ratio ν in Fig. 1-22 (for the 24S-T4 alloy).   A constant $\nu'' > \frac{1}{2}$ would, however, imply that the permanent dilatation of volume

$$e'' = (1 - 2\nu'')\varepsilon_x'' \qquad\qquad (1\text{-}47e)$$

would vary linearly with the permanent strains ε_x'' and *that the volume of a metal would decrease permanently when the stresses are tensile and increase when they are compressions.* It is surmised that for compact and isotropic material (not containing voids, etc.) the former statement is not very probable, but, on the contrary, that the volume very slightly increases permanently, also under tensile stresses (i.e., that the quantity ν'' remains below the limiting value of $\frac{1}{2}$, $\nu'' < \frac{1}{2}$ in the tensile region of strains ε_x'').   The assertion of the authors, namely, that $\nu'' > \frac{1}{2}$ when $\varepsilon_x'' > 0$, may perhaps be understandable as a consequence of lack of isotropy in the extruded stock of the metals with which they dealt.   One may surmise that certain zones of weakness (the streaks in which the weaker impurities of slag were aligned) in the fibrous structure of an extruded metal responded to the action of tensile stresses differently from that of compression stresses when both acted parallel to the direction of rolling.   In the former case the permanent dilatation of volume would become negative because the "holes" (crushed or broken-up brittle inclusions oriented parallel to the tension direction) would be partially closed under stress, whereas under compression stresses, the permanent dilatation would become positive in the latter case, because the formation of new voids between the displaced layers in the plastically deformed crystal grains exceeded the loss of space due to the closing of the "holes."

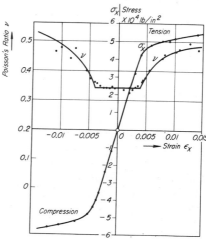

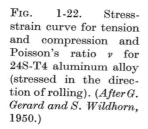

Fig.   1-22.   Stress-strain curve for tension and compression and Poisson's ratio ν for 24S-T4 aluminum alloy (stressed in the direction of rolling). (*After G. Gerard and S. Wildhorn*, 1950.)

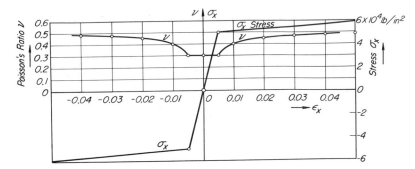

FIG. 1-23. Idealized stress-strain curve for tension and compression and corresponding ratio ν. Strain $\varepsilon_x = \pm 0.5 \quad \pm 1 \quad \pm 2 \quad \pm 3 \quad \pm 4 \times 0.01$
$$\nu = 0.300 \quad 0.400 \quad 0.450 \quad 0.475 \quad 0.483$$

that $\nu' = 0.3$ and $\nu'' = \frac{1}{2} = \text{const}$. Suppose that we denote by ε_0 the elastic strain just when the yield point is reached at the stress $\sigma_x = \sigma_0$ in tension, by E the modulus of elasticity in the steep portion of the stress-strain curve in Fig. 1-23, and by E_0 the slope $d\sigma_x/d\varepsilon_x = E_0 = \text{const}$ in the plastic ranges. One easily verifies then that the ratio of the elastic strain ε_x' and total strain ε_x at a point in the plastic range $\varepsilon_x > \varepsilon_0$ is expressed by

$$\frac{\varepsilon_x'}{\varepsilon_x} = \frac{E_0}{E} + \left(1 - \frac{E_0}{E}\right)\frac{\varepsilon_0}{\varepsilon_x}. \tag{1-47f}$$

If this value of the ratio $\varepsilon_x'/\varepsilon_x$ is substituted in Eq. (1.47c), Poisson's resultant ratio ν in terms of the total strain ε_x is expressed by two branches of ordinary hyperbolas having the straight line $\nu = \frac{1}{2}$ as their horizontal asymptote (see Fig. 1-23). Or if one assumed a constant value for ν'' slightly greater than $\frac{1}{2}$ in the region of compression ($\varepsilon_x'' < 0$) and smaller than $\frac{1}{2}$ in the region of tensile strains ($\varepsilon_x'' > 0$), one may express analytically by means of two noncongruent branches of ordinary hyperbolas the variation of Poisson's resultant ratio ν for a ductile metal whose volume slightly increases permanently both under axial tension and under compression.

1-9. Theory of Thermoelasticity. Just as the states through which an ideal gas passes when it is doing work by expanding or is being compressed by external forces in an engine are described by applying the first and second laws of thermodynamics to certain ideal cycles or processes of the gas, it will now be in order to consider the conversion of mechanical work or elastic strain energy into heat, or vice versa, to determine how the variables of state change in *an elastic solid* when it is subjected to prescribed modes of straining and stressing. Considering first isotropic states of stress and strain, using the notation of Sec. 1-3, the stress σ and the absolute temperature θ as the independent variables, and the elastic dilatation of volume e as the dependent variable, with reference to Eq. (1-8), we shall assume that in

$$de = \left(\frac{\partial e}{\partial \sigma}\right)_\theta d\sigma + \left(\frac{\partial e}{\partial \theta}\right)_\sigma d\theta \tag{1-48}$$

the partial derivatives defining the bulk modulus K and the coefficient of cubical thermal expansion a,

$$\left(\frac{\partial \sigma}{\partial e}\right)_\theta = K, \qquad \left(\frac{\partial e}{\partial \theta}\right)_\sigma = a, \qquad \text{also} \left(\frac{\partial \sigma}{\partial \theta}\right)_e = -aK, \qquad (1\text{-}49)$$

are material constants, since the changes of temperature with which we shall be concerned in this section are quite small. Consequently, de being a complete differential, Eq. (1-48) may be integrated at once along any path from an initial state $e = \sigma = 0, \theta = \theta_0$, to any state e, σ, θ, and an equation of state

$$e = \frac{\sigma}{K} + a(\theta - \theta_0) \qquad (1\text{-}50)$$

may be postulated.

Let dQ denote the heat taken in *per unit volume* of a solid for changing its state e, σ, θ by $de, d\sigma, d\theta$, and let $d\omega = \sigma\, de$ denote the mechanical work expended to deform it. If A denotes the thermal equivalent of mechanical work, then, according to the first law of thermodynamics or the principle of conservation of energy, the sum of dQ and $A\, d\omega$ must appear as the amount du by which the intrinsic energy u per unit volume (including the potential elastic strain energy) has changed, or

$$dQ + A\, d\omega = dQ + A\sigma\, de = du. \qquad (1\text{-}51)$$

If we choose θ and σ as the independent variables, we may express dQ by

$$dQ = \left(\frac{\partial u}{\partial \theta}\right)_\sigma d\theta + \left(\frac{\partial u}{\partial \sigma}\right)_\theta \cdot d\sigma - A\, d\omega \qquad (1\text{-}52)$$

or else, if θ and e are used as the independent variables, by

$$dQ = \left(\frac{\partial u}{\partial \theta}\right)_e d\theta + \left[\left(\frac{\partial u}{\partial e}\right)_\theta - A\sigma\right] de. \qquad (1\text{-}53)$$

Suppose that the temperature θ is raised by $d\theta$ in a body while the volume is held constant by constraining it from expanding and that the heat dQ taken in under this condition by a unit volume of the substance having the specific weight w (reckoned in kilograms per cubic centimeter) is expressed by $dQ = wc_e\, d\theta$, where c_e denotes the specific heat (capacity) of the solid or the heat required to raise the temperature θ of 1 kg weight by 1° at constant volume $e = $ const. When $de = 0$, no external work is done, and from Eq. (1-53)

$$dQ_e = wc_e\, d\theta = \left(\frac{\partial u}{\partial \theta}\right)_e d\theta, \qquad \left(\frac{\partial u}{\partial \theta}\right)_e = wc_e. \qquad (1\text{-}54)$$

On the other hand, if the temperature is raised by $d\theta$ while the stress σ is held at a constant value, from

$$du = \left(\frac{\partial u}{\partial \theta}\right)_e d\theta + \left(\frac{\partial u}{\partial e}\right)_\theta de \qquad (1\text{-}55)$$

after dividing by $d\theta$ and using Eq. (1-54), when $\sigma = \text{const}$, one obtains

$$\left(\frac{\partial u}{\partial \theta}\right)_\sigma = \left(\frac{\partial u}{\partial \theta}\right)_e + \left(\frac{\partial u}{\partial e}\right)_\theta \cdot \left(\frac{\partial e}{\partial \theta}\right)_\sigma = wc_e + \left(\frac{\partial u}{\partial e}\right)_\theta \cdot \left(\frac{\partial e}{\partial \theta}\right)_\sigma. \qquad (1\text{-}56)$$

If the specific heat at constant stress is denoted by c_σ, using Eq. (1-52) and taking $de = (\partial e/\partial \theta)_\sigma\, d\theta$, since $d\sigma = 0$, the heat dQ_σ taken in by the solid is expressed by

$$dQ_\sigma = wc_\sigma\, d\theta = \left(\frac{\partial u}{\partial \theta}\right)_\sigma d\theta - A\sigma\left(\frac{\partial e}{\partial \theta}\right)_\sigma d\theta \qquad (1\text{-}57)$$

or, after substituting here the value of $(\partial u/\partial \theta)_\sigma$ from Eq. (1-56), we see that the difference of the specific heats $c_\sigma - c_e$ of a solid may be computed from the equation

$$w(c_\sigma - c_e) = \left[\left(\frac{\partial u}{\partial e}\right)_\theta - A\sigma\right]\left(\frac{\partial e}{\partial \theta}\right)_\sigma, \qquad (1\text{-}58)$$

provided that $(\partial u/\partial e)_\theta$ is known.

In order to evaluate $(\partial u/\partial e)_\theta$ we shall follow standard procedure[1] by making use of the second law of thermodynamics and of the entropy ϕ of the substance, defined by

$$d\phi = \frac{dQ}{\theta} = \frac{du - A\sigma\, de}{\theta}, \qquad (1\text{-}59)$$

and by evaluating the second derivative of ϕ, $\partial^2\phi/\partial\theta\, \partial e$, for an elastic solid whose equation of state is expressed by Eq. (1-50). Again assuming e, θ as variables, one sees from Eq. (1-59) that

$$\left(\frac{\partial \phi}{\partial \theta}\right)_e = \frac{(\partial u/\partial \theta)_e}{\theta} = \frac{wc_e}{\theta}, \qquad \left(\frac{\partial \phi}{\partial e}\right)_\theta = \frac{(\partial u/\partial e)_\theta - A\sigma}{\theta}. \qquad (1\text{-}60)$$

After equating the expressions for $\partial^2\phi/\partial\theta\, \partial e$ computed from the preceding two first derivatives of ϕ, one obtains, by reference to Eq. (1-49),

$$\left(\frac{\partial u}{\partial e}\right)_\theta = A\left[\sigma - \theta\left(\frac{\partial \sigma}{\partial \theta}\right)_e\right] = A(\sigma + aK\theta), \qquad (1\text{-}61)$$

and, if this expression is substituted in Eq. (1-58), for *the difference of the two specific heats $c_\sigma - c_e$ of a solid*

$$\underline{w(c_\sigma - c_e)} = -A\theta\left(\frac{\partial \sigma}{\partial \theta}\right)_e \cdot \left(\frac{\partial e}{\partial \theta}\right)_\sigma = \underline{Aa^2K\theta}. \qquad (1\text{-}62)$$

---

[1] Cf. MAX PLANCK, "Vorlesungen über Thermodynamik," 2d ed., p. 55, Veit & Co., Leipzig, 1905 (English edition).

If, as in gas dynamics, the ratio of the two specific heats is denoted by the letter κ, after dividing Eq. (1-62) by c_e, one sees that for a solid

$$\kappa = \frac{c_\sigma}{c_e} = 1 + \frac{Aa^2K\theta}{wc_e}. \qquad (1\text{-}63)$$

The term to be added to the one in this expression of κ, however, turns out to be quite small, and thus the difference $c_\sigma - c_e$ is frequently insignificant when only small changes of temperature are considered.

We wish to utilize the preceding formulas now *for computing the small changes of temperature* which have been observed *in solids that are stressed suddenly, i.e., adiabatically, and uniformly in all directions* from an initial state $e_1 = a(\theta_1 - \theta_0)$, $\sigma_1 = 0$, θ_1 to a stress σ. In an adiabatic process no heat is exchanged between the solid and surrounding bodies. Using Eq. (1-53), assuming that dQ vanishes,

$$dQ = du - A\sigma \, de = \left(\frac{\partial u}{\partial \theta}\right)_e d\theta + \left[\left(\frac{\partial u}{\partial e}\right)_\theta - A\sigma\right] de = 0, \qquad (1\text{-}64)$$

we may substitute for the two partial derivatives of u their expressions which were computed in Eqs. (1-54) and (1-61) and obtain for the adiabatic the differential equation

$$\frac{AaK \, de}{wc_e} = -\frac{d\theta}{\theta} \qquad (1\text{-}65)$$

and, after integration,

$$e - e_1 = \frac{wc_e}{AaK} \ln \frac{\theta_1}{\theta}. \qquad (1\text{-}66)$$

The difference of temperatures $\theta_1 - \theta$ being small compared with θ or θ_1, we may replace $\ln(\theta_1/\theta)$ by $\ln[1 + (\theta_1 - \theta)/\theta] = (\theta_1 - \theta)/\theta$ and can also write, instead of Eq. (1-66)

$$e - e_1 = \frac{wc_e(\theta_1 - \theta)}{AaK\theta}, \qquad (1\text{-}67)$$

where we may substitute from the equation of state for

$$e - e_1 = \frac{\sigma}{K} - a(\theta_1 - \theta) \qquad (1\text{-}68)$$

which gives, after using Eq. (1-62), the following formula for the change of temperature in a solid under adiabatic stressing:

$$\theta - \theta_1 = -\frac{Aa\theta\sigma}{wc_e + Aa^2K\theta} = -\frac{Aa\theta\sigma}{wc_\sigma}. \qquad (1\text{-}69)$$

Under θ in the right-hand term, either the arithmetic mean of the initial and final temperature $(\theta_1 + \theta)/2$, or simply θ_1, may be understood.   In other words, we may consider the specific heat c_σ and the ratio $\kappa = c_\sigma/c_e$ as given by their initial values at temperature θ_1, assuming that

$$\kappa = 1 + \frac{Aa^2 K \theta_1}{wc_e} = \text{const.} \qquad (1\text{-}70)$$

With these stipulations, one obtains from Eqs. (1-67), (1-68), and (1-70)

$$a(\theta - \theta_1) = e - e_1 - \frac{\sigma}{K} = -\frac{Aa^2 K \theta_1 (e - e_1)}{wc_e} = -(\kappa - 1)(e - e_1)$$

or, for *the equation of the adiabatic,*

$$\underline{\underline{e - e_1 = \frac{\sigma}{\kappa K} = \frac{\sigma}{K_a}}}, \qquad (1\text{-}71)$$

and for *the change of temperature in the adiabatic,*

$$\underline{\underline{\theta - \theta_1 = -\frac{Aa\theta_1 \sigma}{wc_\sigma}}}. \qquad (1\text{-}72)$$

This shows that the system of the adiabatics of a solid subjected to a uniform stress σ consists of a family of parallel straight lines in the e, σ plane having a slightly steeper slope $d\sigma/de = \kappa K = K_a$, κ times greater than the slope K of the isotherms [Eq. (1-50)], or *that the adiabatic bulk modulus K_a of a solid is κ times greater than the isothermal bulk modulus K.*

When $\sigma = -p$, Eq. (1-72) is also valid for a fluid, disclosing that the temperature θ_1 in a fluid is raised on a sudden application of pressure p and lowered on release of the pressure.   Eq. (1-72) coincides with the formula which was first proposed by W. THOMSON.[1]

Suppose now that a cylindrical specimen of metal is suddenly strained elastically in tension or compression in the axial direction by a stress σ_x while $\sigma_y = \sigma_z = 0$.   Since the coefficient of linear thermal expansion $\alpha = a/3$ and for uniaxial stress σ_x, the mean stress, is equal to $\sigma = \sigma_x/3$, after substituting these values in Eq. (1-72), *the change in temperature in a solid bar which is suddenly loaded by a stress σ_x in the axial direction is found equal to*

$$\underline{\underline{\theta - \theta_1 = -\frac{A\alpha\theta_1 \sigma_x}{wc_\sigma}}}. \qquad (1\text{-}73)$$

We may add, since $K_a = \kappa K$, that the adiabatic modulus of elasticity $E_a = \kappa E$ is κ times the isothermal modulus E (assuming that Poisson's ratio ν for the small changes of state that we are considering is not

[1] Page 4 of this book (*loc. cit.*).

dependent on thermal effects).   In applying Eq. (1-72) to a uniaxial state of stress resulting in Eq. (1-73), we have implicitly assumed that only the isotropic part $\sigma = \sigma_x/3$ of the tensor of axial stress σ_x contributes essentially to the adiabatic cooling or heating effect, or that, in other words, the deviatoric part of the state of stress, which in the case considered consists of the sum of two states of pure shear, namely, $\sigma_1 = -\sigma_2 = \sigma_x/3$, $\sigma_3 = 0$ and $\sigma_1 = -\sigma_3 = \sigma_x/3$, $\sigma_2 = 0$, has a negligible influence on the thermal effects.   In this conclusion we believe we have followed W. THOMSON, although the author could verify this only indirectly because he could not find in Thomson's elaborate developments on thermoelasticity an example in which the thermal effects due to a state of pure shear (a pure deviator of stress not involving a volume dilatation) were explicitly determined.   The illustrious physicist stated only that his general equation of the thermal effects [see Eq. (1-81) below] was valid for any type of stress.

We shall list lastly the *amounts of heat taken in* to raise the temperature from θ_1 to θ:

(1). *On the isopicnic surface*, i.e., when the surface is held fixed or at a constant dilatation $e = e_1 = a(\theta_1 - \theta_0) = $ const (along the path AB of Fig. 1-24).   From Eqs. (1-54) and (1-50),

$$Q_e = wc_e(\theta - \theta_1), \tag{1-74}$$

while the stress drops to a value

$$\sigma = -Ka(\theta - \theta_1).$$

(2). *On the isobar*, when the stress is held constant (along the path CD in Fig. 1-24).   Since from Eq. (1-57), in conjunction with Eq. (1-62),

$$dQ_\sigma = wc_\sigma \, d\theta = (wc_e + Aa^2K\theta) \, d\theta,$$

after integrating,

$$Q_\sigma = wc_e(\theta - \theta_1) + \frac{Aa^2K(\theta^2 - \theta_1^2)}{2}. \tag{1-75}$$

We may add that both Q_e and Q_σ are independent of the values of e or σ, respectively, at which the lines AB and CD bridge the space in the plane of Fig. 1-24 between two given isotherms $\theta_1 = $ const and $\theta = $ const.

(3). *On the isotherm*.   If the stress is raised from an unstressed condition of the solid to a stress σ [from point E at $e = a(\theta - \theta_0)$, $\sigma = 0$ to point F in Fig. 1-24] while the temperature θ is held constant, an amount of heat Q_θ has to be supplied to the solid equal to

$$Q_\theta = Aa\theta\sigma, \tag{1-76}$$

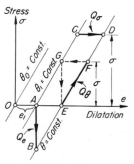

FIG.   1-24.   Sequences of   strain $e = $ const, $\sigma = $ const, $\theta = $ const.

which can be verified by applying Eq. (1-51), expressing the first law of thermodynamics, to a closed path around a thermal cycle, such as is indicated by $EFGE$ in Fig. 1-24.   In this figure the amounts of heat to be disposed of along the short sides of the triangle FG and GE are given by the formulas for Q_e and Q_σ which were just derived, and the area of the triangle EFG represents the work per unit volume that the elastic solid gives up after the cycle is completed.

The simple expressions for Q_e, Q_σ, and Q_θ are useful when thermal changes of state have to be evaluated or when thermal cycles are described whose reversible branches follow prescribed sequences of strain. This may be illustrated in an example.   Consider the closed thermal cycle of three consecutive operations enclosing a triangle in the e,σ plane in Fig. 1-25, which starts at a point A $(e_1, \sigma = 0, \theta_1)$.   Let a solid be stressed first adiabatically to a stress σ and temperature θ (to point B, having e, σ as coordinates); subsequently heated, while its volume is held constant, until its temperature is raised from θ back to θ_1 to a point C (e,σ_1,θ_1); and finally be unstressed, while the temperature is held constant (along the isotherm $\theta_1 = \text{const}$ from point C back to A). Since along the adiabatic AB no heat is exchanged, along BC an amount of heat Q_1 is taken in, and along CA an amount Q_2 taken out, according to the first law of the thermodynamics, after the cycle is completed,

$$Q_1 + Q_2 + \frac{A(\sigma - \sigma_1)(e - e_1)}{2} = 0, \qquad (1\text{-}77)$$

where the third term expresses the thermal equivalent of the mechanical work represented by the shaded area of the triangle ABC and expended from outside sources in the solid for returning it to its original state. But, according to Eqs. (1-74) and (1-76),

$$Q_1 = wc_e(\theta_1 - \theta), \qquad Q_2 = -Aa\theta_1\sigma_1, \qquad (1\text{-}78)$$

and, after Eq. (1-50),

$$K(e - e_1) = \sigma_1 = \sigma - \sigma_1 + aK(\theta - \theta_1). \qquad (1\text{-}79)$$

With these values one computes from Eq. (1-77)

$$\theta - \theta_1 = -\frac{Aa\sigma(\theta + \theta_1)/2}{wc_e + Aa^2K(\theta + \theta_1)/2} \qquad (1\text{-}80)$$

where the denominator of the fraction on the right side represents wc_σ [see Eq. (1-62)] at the mean temperature $(\theta + \theta_1)/2$.   Thus we have

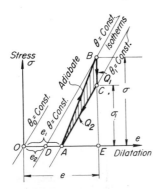

FIG. 1-25. Thermal cycle.

derived an expression for the change of temperature $\theta - \theta_1$ during adiabatic stressing which we find in agreement with the formula (1-69) previously given [after assuming $(\theta + \theta_1)/2 \sim \theta_1$].

In conclusion, it may be remarked that W. THOMSON proposed a general formula based on the first and second thermal laws[1] for the heat taken in by a solid stressed while its temperature θ is held constant which he expressed as follows:

$$Q = -A\theta\left(\frac{\partial\omega}{\partial\theta}\right)_e. \tag{1-81}$$

ω in Eq. (1-81) denotes the work done along the isotherm $\theta = $ const from an unstressed initial state to a final state under any type of stress.

If we utilize Eq. (1-81) for isotropic stress, by assuming the initial state in Fig. 1-25 at point D with $e_2 = a(\theta - \theta_0)$, $\sigma = 0$, and the final state at point B (e,σ,θ), the mechanical work done on the isotherm (equal to the area of the triangle DBE) is expressed by

$$\omega = \frac{(e - e_1)\sigma}{2} = \frac{[e - a(\theta - \theta_0)]\sigma}{2}, \tag{1-82}$$

but since
$$\sigma = K[e - a(\theta - \theta_0)],$$

$$\omega = \frac{K[e - a(\theta - \theta_0)]^2}{2} = \frac{\sigma^2}{2K},$$

and
$$\left(\frac{\partial\omega}{\partial\theta}\right)_e = -Ka[e - a(\theta - \theta_0)] = -a\sigma, \tag{1-83}$$

therefore, we find from Thomson's equation (1-81) that *the heat Q taken in on the isotherm $\theta = $ const* is equal to

$$Q = Aa\theta\sigma, \tag{1-84}$$

in agreement with our Eq. (1-76).   Also, if one considers, as Thomson did, the product $wc_\sigma(\theta - \theta_1)$ computed from (Eq. 1-69) as "a loss or gain of heat" Q *while a body is adiabatically stressed or unloaded, one may compute $\theta - \theta_1$ by dividing the heat taken in on the isotherm Q*, as expressed by Thomson's equation (1-81) by wc_σ, and may evaluate $\theta - \theta_1$ under any type of stress.

This brings us to a final remark.   Suppose that we should wish to evaluate the temperature change due to a state of pure shear τ $(\sigma_1 = -\sigma_2 = \tau$, $\sigma_3 = 0)$ producing a unit shear γ adiabatically, when no change of volume $(e = 0)$ is involved.   In order to establish a theory for this case, one needs an equation of state for pure shear.   If one

[1] Mathematical and Physical Papers, vol. 1, art. 48, On the Dynamical Theory of Heat, part 7, pp. 182–210, Cambridge University Press, London.   For the quoted equation, see p. 201.

plots γ and τ as rectangular coordinates (in a manner analogous to what we did with e and σ under isotropic states of stress), clearly, one cannot postulate that the isotherms $\theta = $ const in the γ,τ plane are represented by a family of parallel straight lines[1] (as was the case for isotropic states e, σ). Assuming Hooke's law as valid, one sees that the isotherms consist of a bundle of straight lines passing through the origin ($\gamma = \tau = 0$):

$$\gamma = \frac{\tau}{G},\qquad(1\text{-}85)$$

where the isothermal modulus of rigidity G must depend on the absolute temperature θ. Suppose, in a limited range of θ, that $G = G_0[1 - \beta(\theta - \theta_0)]$, where β is a very small, positive constant. One may then postulate for the isotherms $\theta = $ const for a deviator of stress the equation

$$\gamma = \frac{\tau[1 + \beta(\theta - \theta_0)]}{G_0}.\qquad(1\text{-}86)$$

One sees, however, that the thermal effects due to adiabatic stressing by a pure shear which would result from this assumption, and which might be evaluated in a manner analogous to that applied to isotropic states of stress, would become smaller by an order of magnitude compared with those due to volume dilatation, which makes the former practically insignificant.

[1] This would imply that an unloaded body (when $\tau = 0$) could suffer unit shears merely by raising or decreasing the temperature, which is absurd. The isotherms for a pure shear must therefore pass through the origin $\gamma = \tau = 0$, as in Eq. (1-86).

CHAPTER 2

MECHANICAL WORK.
CONSIDERING STATES OF SMALL AND OF FINITE STRAIN

Here is my present notion about plasticity of homogeneous amorphous solids.

Let α, β, γ be the 3 principal strains at any point, P, Q, R the principal stresses connected with them by symmetrical linear equations the same for all axes. Then the whole work done by P, Q, R in developing α, β, γ may be written:

$$U = A(\alpha^2 + \beta^2 + \gamma^2) + B(\beta\gamma + \gamma\alpha + \alpha\beta),$$

where A and B are coefficients, the nature of which is foreign to our inquiry. Now we may put

$$U = U_1 + U_2,$$

where U_1 is due to a symmetrical compression ($\alpha_1 = \beta_1 = \gamma_1$) and U_2 to distortion without compression ($\alpha_2 + \beta_2 + \gamma_2 = 0$) and

$$\alpha = \alpha_1 + \alpha_2, \qquad \beta = \beta_1 + \beta_2, \qquad \gamma = \gamma_1 + \gamma_2.$$

It follows that $U_1 = (\frac{1}{3})(A + B)(\alpha + \beta + \gamma)^2$,

$$U_2 = (\frac{1}{3})(2A - B)[\alpha^2 + \beta^2 + \gamma^2 - (\beta\gamma + \gamma\alpha + \alpha\beta)].$$

Now my opinion is that these two parts may be considered as independent, U_1 being the work done in condensation and U_2 that done in distortion. Now I would use the old word "resilience" to denote the work necessary to be done on a body to overcome its elastic forces.

Letter from J. C. MAXWELL to LORD KELVIN, Dec. 18, 1856. (From Sir Joseph Larmor, "Origin of Clerk Maxwell's Electric Ideas," p. 32. Cambridge University Press, London, 1937.)

In this and the following chapter general expressions for mechanical work and several theorems concerning the energies required for straining solid substances under static conditions will be developed. In a number of the applications to be given, cases will be considered in

43

Fig. 2-1a. Paul Ludwik.[†]
(Born Jan. 15, 1878, in
Schlan, Bohemia; died July
28, 1934, in Vienna.)[‡]

which the strains reach finite magnitudes. The following sections therefore also contain many details about finite strains and the general methods for dealing with and for analyzing homogeneous, finite distortions in elastic and plastic substances.

2-1. The Differential of Mechanical Work. When a body is deformed by a system of external forces in equilibrium, mechanical work is done by them equal to the work consumed by the internal stresses required for overcoming the resistance with which the material elements of the body react. Let x, y, z be the rectangular coordinates of a point P in the strained state of the body, referred to axes fixed in space, and let the state of stress in an infinitesimal element of material dx, dy, dz be given through the components of normal stress σ_x, σ_y, σ_z and of shearing stress τ_{yz}, τ_{zx}, τ_{xy}. Suppose, while the stresses may have constant

[†] Ludwik, director of the Technische Versuchsanstalt and professor at the Technical University in Vienna, was one of the founders of the celebrated Viennese school of investigators of mechanical strength (L. Tetmajer, P. Ludwik, Karl Terzaghi, Alfons Leon, Ernst Melan). In 1909 he proposed, in collaboration with A. Leon, the concept of the logarithmic strain $\bar{\varepsilon} = \int dl/l = \ln(1 + \varepsilon)$ as a new measure for the finite elongations of bars subjected to tension, in his most remarkable small book "Elemente der technologischen Mechanik" (57 pp., Julius Springer, Berlin, 1909), in which he defined the general flow curve (*Fliesskurve*) $\bar{\sigma} = f(\bar{\varepsilon})$, characterizing the plastic distortion of the ductile metals in their strain-hardening range, utilizing it for predicting their behavior in comparative tensile, compression, torsion, and rolling tests. Ludwik's strain $\bar{\varepsilon}$ became one of the outstanding tools for defining general states of finite strains which the author of this book named in 1937 the "*natural strains.*" Ludwik was the discoverer of the logarithmic speed law which he found by pulling wires of tin at various rates, also described in his book of 1909.

[‡] Courtesy of Franz Vitovec, Vienna.

FIG. 2-1b. ALFONS LEON.†
(Born Sept. 9, 1881, in
Ragusa, Dalmatia; died
May 30, 1951, in Vienna.)‡

values, as in an ideally plastic substance, or while they increase by the differentials $d\sigma_x, \ldots, d\tau_{yz}, \ldots$, as in an elastic material or in a strain-hardening metal, that the state of strain in an element of material changes infinitesimally by the differentials of the components of strain $d\varepsilon_x$, $d\varepsilon_y$, $d\varepsilon_z$ and of unit shear $d\gamma_{yz}$, $d\gamma_{zx}$, $d\gamma_{xy}$. *If the strain is of finite magnitude, the increments of strain should be taken as those of the components of the natural strains and shears* as defined in Vol. I, page 130; it is understood that they refer to those line elements of material points, which—while the distortion progresses—*successively* sweep through a frame of axes held in a position parallel to the fixed directions of the x, y, z axes at point $P(x,y,z)$. As the body is deformed, new material points will, in general, sweep through this frame of mutually perpendicular directions. The state of stress may, alternatively, be given through the principal stresses denoted by σ_1, σ_2, σ_3, and their directions and the change of the state of strain may be defined by the principal values $d\varepsilon_1$, $d\varepsilon_2$, $d\varepsilon_3$ of the differentials of natural strain whose directions coincide instantaneously with the principal directions of stress, whereas

† LEON became professor of mechanics and mechanical technology at the Technical University, Graz, in 1918. In 1945 he was appointed director of the Technische Versuchsanstalt at the Technical University of Vienna. In early times he collaborated with PAUL LUDWIK. A nice review of his life work may be found in "Alfons Leon. Gedenkschrift" (88 pp., Verlag Allgemeine Bau-Zeitung, Vienna, 1952). Alfons Leon will also be remembered for his outstanding investigations on cleavage and shear fracture, through his extension of MOHR's theory of strength, by proposing a parabola as an envelope of the principal stress circles which he verified in tests on cast iron, and for his extensive work on stress concentration.

‡ Courtesy of Franz Vitovec, Vienna.

the three directions of the principal, finite, natural strains themselves, in general, differ from the former ones.

If the mechanical work is denoted by ω per unit of volume of material,[1] the differential $d\omega$ of the work done by the stresses $\sigma_x, \ldots, \tau_{yz}, \ldots$ is equal to

$$d\omega = \sigma_x \, d\varepsilon_x + \cdots + \tau_{yz} \, d\gamma_{yz} + \cdots = \sigma_1 \, d\varepsilon_1 + \sigma_2 \, d\varepsilon_2 + \sigma_3 \, d\varepsilon_3. \quad (2\text{-}1)$$

In this equation we have omitted, for the sake of brevity, all three terms in the sums, such as $\sigma_x \, d\varepsilon_x + \sigma_y \, d\varepsilon_y + \sigma_z \, d\varepsilon_z$ and $\tau_{yz} \, d\gamma_{yz} + \tau_{zx} \, d\gamma_{zx} + \tau_{xy} \, d\gamma_{xy}$, and we shall exercise this liberty in the following equations when sums of terms containing stress or strain components appear in which the subscripts x, y, z are merely to be interchanged in cyclic order. We shall also omit the bars above ε and γ denoting the natural components of strain[2] as long as this causes no ambiguity in distinguishing the former from other types of strain.

For *isotropic materials* Eq. (2-1) may be expressed in a more condensed form by making use of the octahedral components of stress and of the increments of strain referred to the planes of a regular octahedron oriented with its three axes in the directions of principal stress.   Denote by σ the normal and by τ_0 the tangential component of stress in an octahedral plane,

$$\sigma = \frac{\sigma_x + \sigma_y + \sigma_z}{3} = \frac{\sigma_1 + \sigma_2 + \sigma_3}{3}, \quad\quad (2\text{-}2)$$

$$\tau_0 = (\tfrac{1}{3})\sqrt{(\sigma_x - \sigma_y)^2 + \cdots + 6(\tau_{yz}^2 + \cdots)} = (\tfrac{1}{3})\sqrt{(\sigma_1 - \sigma_2)^2 + \cdots}, \quad (2\text{-}3)$$

[1] Although the strains that we wish to consider may have finite magnitudes, it is understood that in these present applications the assumption is made that the density of mass ρ, if it changes at all during a distortion in solids, varies only a little (the element of volume $dV = dx\,dy\,dz$ contains practically the same mass density in subsequent, strained conditions and ρ is considered a constant).   Thus the element of volume dV in volume integrals $\int \omega \, dV$ need not be subjected to a variation, according to the rules of the calculus of variations, when the total work of deformation in a body is to be varied.   The amount ω may be considered as a density of work or of energy throughout a strained mass associated practically with the same amount of inert mass.

When writing the second expression in Eq. (2-1) in terms of the principal values for the increment of work $d\omega$, we may conceive that an infinitesimal prismatic element of material, oriented with its six mutually perpendicular faces according to the principal axes of stress, is stretched first by the increments of strain $d\varepsilon_1$, $d\varepsilon_2$, $d\varepsilon_3$ in the directions of its edges and subsequently is turned as a rigid body into its new, infinitesimally near, slightly tilted position.   Since during this infinitesimal rotation of the element no work is done, the work $d\omega$ in terms of the principal stresses is expressed precisely by Eq. (2-1).

[2] These were formerly denoted by $\bar{\varepsilon}$, $\bar{\gamma}$ (see Vol. I, page 130).

and by $d\varepsilon$ the increment of the natural strain in the direction normal to and by $d\gamma_0$ in the tangential direction to an octahedral plane as previously defined[1]:

$$d\varepsilon = \frac{d\varepsilon_x + d\varepsilon_y + d\varepsilon_z}{3} = \frac{d\varepsilon_1 + d\varepsilon_2 + d\varepsilon_3}{3}, \tag{2-4}$$

$$d\gamma_0 = (\tfrac{2}{3})\sqrt{(d\varepsilon_x - d\varepsilon_y)^2 + \cdots + (\tfrac{3}{2})(d\gamma_{yz}^2 + \cdots)}$$

$$= (\tfrac{2}{3})\sqrt{(d\varepsilon_1 - d\varepsilon_2)^2 + (d\varepsilon_2 - d\varepsilon_3)^2 + (d\varepsilon_3 - d\varepsilon_1)^2}, \tag{2-5}$$

where σ mean normal stress
$d\epsilon$ mean natural normal strain increment
$d\gamma_0$ natural octahedral unit shear increment

The differential of mechanical work per unit volume $d\omega$ may, for a state of homogeneous stress, be expressed as the sum of the work done by the forces acting normally (the work of dilatation of volume) $d\omega_v$ and tangentially (the work of distortion) $d\omega_d$ to the eight octahedral planes:

$$d\omega = d\omega_v + d\omega_d. \tag{2-6}$$

(the subscripts v and d refer to volume and distortion of shape, respectively). Since a unit of volume under the mean normal stress σ is increased by the amount $3\,d\varepsilon$, the former is equal to

$$d\omega_v = 3\sigma\,d\varepsilon = \sigma(d\varepsilon_x + d\varepsilon_y + d\varepsilon_z) = \sigma(d\varepsilon_1 + d\varepsilon_2 + d\varepsilon_3), \tag{2-7}$$

whereas the latter is equal to

$$d\omega_d = d\omega - d\omega_v = (\sigma_x - \sigma)\,d\varepsilon_x + \cdots + \tau_{yz}\,d\gamma_{yz} + \cdots$$

$$= (\sigma_1 - \sigma)\,d\varepsilon_1 + (\sigma_2 - \sigma)\,d\varepsilon_2 + (\sigma_3 - \sigma)\,d\varepsilon_3. \tag{2-8}$$

The differential of the work of distortion $d\omega_d$ may be expressed in terms of τ_0 and $d\gamma_0$ as

$$d\omega_d = (\tfrac{3}{2})\tau_0\,d\gamma_0, \tag{2-9}$$

after remembering a general rule, governing the distortion of *isotropic* materials, according to which the infinitesimal increment $d\gamma$ of any shearing strain is always directed in the direction in which the corresponding shearing stress τ causing it acts.[2] τ_0 and $d\gamma_0$ are therefore

[1] Cf. Vol. I, pages 103 and 115.
[2] Cf. Vol. I, page 233.

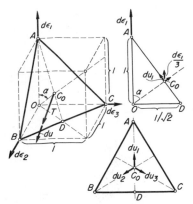

FIG. 2-2. Tangential displacements du_1, du_2, du_3 of center C_0 of octahedral plane ABC corresponding to strain increments $d\varepsilon_1$, $d\varepsilon_2$, $d\varepsilon_3$.

represented in an octahedral plane by separate parallel vectors.[1] If Eq.

[1] In fact, if T denotes the resultant force and du the resultant displacement of the center point C_0 of the equilateral triangle ABC (Fig. 2-2) representing an octahedral plane, in the tangential direction, and V the volume of one octant $OABC$ of the octahedron, since T and du must coincide with each other, the work of T per unit of volume is expressed by

$$dw_d = \frac{T\,du}{V}. \qquad (2\text{-}9a)$$

If we choose the lengths of the semiaxes of the octahedron (Fig. 2-2) equal to $OA = OB = OC = 1$, the equilateral triangle ABC has the area $A = \sqrt{3}/2$, an octant $OABC$ the volume $V = \frac{1}{6}$, and the force T is equal to $T = A\tau_0 = \sqrt{3}\tau_0/2$. In order to evaluate du, suppose that the octant $OABC$ of material is stretched only in the direction parallel to OA by a uniform extension $d\varepsilon_1$. Then the center C_0 of the triangle ABC is displaced in the same direction by the amount $d\varepsilon_1/3$ having the components $(d\varepsilon_1/3)\cos\alpha$ and $(d\varepsilon_1/3)\sin\alpha$ in normal and tangential directions to the plane ABC. Since $\cos\alpha = 1/\sqrt{3}$, $\sin\alpha = \sqrt{2/3}$, the former is $d\varepsilon_1/3\sqrt{3}$ and the latter $(d\varepsilon_1/3)\sqrt{2/3} = du_1$. If the extensions $d\varepsilon_1$, $d\varepsilon_2$, $d\varepsilon_3$ act simultaneously, the point C_0 is displaced in the tangential directions to the plane ABC by the three amounts

$$du_1, du_2, du_3 = \frac{(d\varepsilon_1, d\varepsilon_2, d\varepsilon_3)\sqrt{2/3}}{3} \qquad (2\text{-}9b)$$

along the three symmetry axes (heights) of the equilateral triangle ABC, respectively; this causes the resultant displacement du of these three coplanar vector components inclined at 120° to one another:

$$du = \frac{1}{\sqrt{2}}\sqrt{(du_1 - du_2)^2 + (du_2 - du_3)^2 + (du_3 - du_1)^2}. \qquad (2\text{-}9c)$$

After substituting here the values of du_1, du_2, du_3 taken from Eq. (2-9b) and after making use of Eq. (2-5), we obtain

$$du = \frac{1}{3\sqrt{3}}\sqrt{(d\varepsilon_1 - d\varepsilon_2)^2 + (d\varepsilon_2 - d\varepsilon_3)^2 + (d\varepsilon_3 - d\varepsilon_1)^2} = \frac{d\gamma_0}{2\sqrt{3}} \qquad (2\text{-}9d)$$

and, from Eq. (2-9a), for the work of distortion

$$dw_d = \frac{T\,du}{V} = \frac{\sqrt{3}\tau_0}{2} \times \frac{d\gamma_0}{2\sqrt{3}} \times 6 = (\tfrac{3}{2})\tau_0\,d\gamma_0, \qquad (2\text{-}9e)$$

which is the amount given in Eq. (2-9).

(2-9) is divided by the differential of time dt and if a differentiation with respect to the time t is denoted by a dot, from Eq. (2-9) *the rate at which the work of distortion is done* is found equal to

$$\dot{\omega}_d = (\tfrac{3}{2})\tau_0\dot{\gamma}_0, \tag{2-10}$$

where $\dot{\gamma}_0$ denotes the rate of octahedral unit shear.

The differential of the work $d\omega$ done in an infinitesimal element of material $dV = dx\,dy\,dz$ per unit of volume is thus expressed as the sum of the differentials of the work of dilatation of volume $d\omega_v$ and of distortion of shape $d\omega_d$,

$$d\omega = d\omega_v + d\omega_d = 3\sigma\,d\varepsilon + (\tfrac{3}{2})\tau_0\,d\gamma_0, \tag{2-11}$$

and the total work of deformation done during a sequence of loading (a sequence of consecutive infinitesimal increments of strain) in an element of material by the sum

$$\omega = \omega_v + \omega_d = 3\int \sigma\,d\varepsilon + (\tfrac{3}{2})\int \tau_0\,d\gamma_0 \tag{2-12}$$

in which the two integrals are to be computed along the prescribed path of straining. In order to evaluate these two integrals it will be necessary to consider the dependence between the components of stress and strain or rate of strain characterizing special cases of solid substances.

2-2 Elastic Strain Energy. A. SMALL COMPONENTS OF STRAIN. In an isotropic, elastic material let us first assume small components of strain which increase or decrease linearly in a reversible manner with the components of stress. The symbols $\varepsilon_x, \ldots, \gamma_{yz}, \ldots$ in this sectioned note the conventional components of small strain, which, according to Hooke's law of elasticity, satisfy the linear stress-strain relations

$$\varepsilon_x = \frac{\sigma_x - \nu(\sigma_y + \sigma_z)}{E}, \ldots, \qquad \gamma_{yz} = \frac{\tau_{yz}}{G}, \ldots \tag{2-13}$$

or, in terms of the principal stresses,

$$\varepsilon_1 = \frac{\sigma_1 - \nu(\sigma_2 + \sigma_3)}{E}, \ldots, \tag{2-13a}$$

where E and $G = E/2(1 + \nu)$ are the moduli of elasticity and of rigidity and ν is Poisson's ratio. Owing to the linearity of the stress-strain relations and to the principle of superposition postulated in them, the mechanical work ω per unit of volume may, independently of the path of straining or stressing, be expressed directly as the sum of finite terms:

$$\omega = (\tfrac{1}{2})(\sigma_x\varepsilon_x + \cdots + \tau_{yz}\gamma_{yz} + \cdots) = (\tfrac{1}{2})(\sigma_1\varepsilon_1 + \sigma_2\varepsilon_2 + \sigma_3\varepsilon_3). \tag{2-14}$$

This work ω represents the elastic (potential) strain energy stored in a unit of volume of material.   Since the mean strain

$$\varepsilon = \frac{\varepsilon_x + \varepsilon_y + \varepsilon_z}{3} = \frac{(1 - 2\nu)(\sigma_x + \sigma_y + \sigma_z)}{3E} = \frac{(1 - 2\nu)\sigma}{E} \qquad (2\text{-}15)$$

and the octahedral unit shear

$$\gamma_0 = \frac{\tau_0}{G} \qquad (2\text{-}16)$$

are proportional to the mean stress σ and to the octahedral shearing stress τ_0, respectively, the integrals in Eq. (2-12) for any path of straining may be evaluated at once.   The strain energy ω is expressed either in terms of the octahedral stresses σ, τ_0 by

$$\omega = \frac{3(1 - 2\nu)\sigma^2}{2E} + \frac{3\tau_0^2}{4G} \qquad (2\text{-}17)$$

or in terms of the octahedral strains ε, γ_0,

$$\omega = \frac{3E\varepsilon^2}{2(1 - 2\nu)} + (\tfrac{3}{4})G\gamma_0^2, \qquad (2\text{-}18)$$

where the first and second terms represent the elastic strain energy of dilatation of volume ω_v and of distortion ω_d, respectively. σ and τ_0 are given by Eqs. (2-2) and (2-3), the mean strain ε by Eq. (2-15), and the octahedral unit shear γ_0 by

$$\gamma_0 = (\tfrac{2}{3})\sqrt{(\varepsilon_x - \varepsilon_y)^2 + \cdots + (\tfrac{3}{2})(\gamma_{yz}^2 + \cdots)}$$

$$= (\tfrac{2}{3})\sqrt{(\varepsilon_1 - \varepsilon_2)^2 + (\varepsilon_2 - \varepsilon_3)^2 + (\varepsilon_3 - \varepsilon_1)^2}. \qquad (2\text{-}19)$$

The elastic strain energy ω, according to Eqs. (2-17) and (2-18), is a quadratic, homogeneous function either of the six components of stress or of strain.   Its differential $d\omega$ is a complete differential, and one verifies by using Eq. (2-17) or (2-18) that either the six relations

$$\frac{\partial \omega}{\partial \sigma_x} = \varepsilon_x, \dots, \qquad \frac{\partial \omega}{\partial \tau_{yz}} = \gamma_{yz}, \dots \qquad (2\text{-}20)$$

or

$$\frac{\partial \omega}{\partial \varepsilon_x} = \sigma_x, \dots, \qquad \frac{\partial \omega}{\partial \gamma_{yz}} = \tau_{yz}, \dots \qquad (2\text{-}21)$$

hold, respectively.

The total elastic strain energy W stored in a body is computed from the integral of ω taken over the volume V of the body.   In terms of σ and τ_0, using Eq. (2-17),

$$W = \int \omega \, dV = \frac{3(1 - 2\nu)}{2E} \int \sigma^2 \, dV + \frac{3}{4G} \int \tau_0^2 \, dV. \qquad (2\text{-}22)$$

If u, v, w denote the small components of displacement of a point, these may be introduced in the preceding equations containing the components of strain by means of Eqs. (25-1) of Vol. I:

$$\varepsilon_x = \frac{\partial u}{\partial x}, \ldots, \qquad \gamma_{yz} = \frac{\partial w}{\partial y} + \frac{\partial v}{\partial z}, \ldots \qquad (2\text{-}23)$$

The elastic strain energy W in a body, in terms of the octahedral strain components ε, γ_0, is expressed by the volume integrals, using Eqs. (2-19) and (2-23):

$$W = \frac{3E}{2(1-2\nu)} \int \varepsilon^2 \, dV + \frac{3G}{4} \int \gamma_0^2 \, dV,$$

$$W = \frac{E}{6(1-2\nu)} \int \left(\frac{\partial u}{\partial x} + \frac{\partial v}{\partial y} + \frac{\partial w}{\partial z}\right)^2 dV$$

$$+ \frac{G}{3} \int \left\{ \left(\frac{\partial u}{\partial x} - \frac{\partial v}{\partial y}\right)^2 + \cdots + (\tfrac{3}{2})\left[\left(\frac{\partial w}{\partial y} + \frac{\partial v}{\partial z}\right)^2 + \cdots \right] \right\} dV. \quad (2\text{-}24)$$

B. STRAIN ENERGY OF GENERAL ELASTIC SUBSTANCE, ASSUMING FINITE STRAINS. A generally elastic, isotropic substance may be characterized by the property that the differentials of the components of natural strain are proportional to the differentials of the components of true stress:

$$d\varepsilon_x = \frac{d\sigma_x - \gamma(d\sigma_y + d\sigma_z)}{E}, \ldots, \qquad d\gamma_{yz} = \frac{d\tau_{yz}}{G}, \ldots \qquad (2\text{-}25)$$

The moduli of elasticity E and of rigidity $G = E/2(1+\nu)$ and Poisson's ratio ν in these six stress-strain relations are variable quantities, dependent on the state of stress (or strain). Letting the differential of the natural dilatation of volume $de = d\varepsilon_x + d\varepsilon_y + d\varepsilon_z = 3\,d\varepsilon$, denoting the mean natural strain by ε, the mean stress by $\sigma = (\sigma_x + \sigma_y + \sigma_z)/3$, the octahedral shearing stress and natural unit shear by τ_0 and γ_0, after adding the first three relations in Eqs. (2-25),

$$de = \frac{3(1-2\nu)\,d\sigma}{E}, \qquad (2\text{-}26)$$

the bulk modulus of the substance is defined by

$$K = \frac{d\sigma}{de} = \frac{E}{3(1-2\nu)} \qquad (2\text{-}27)$$

and the modulus of rigidity by

$$G = \frac{E}{2(1+\nu)} = \frac{d\tau_0}{d\gamma_0}. \qquad (2\text{-}28)$$

One may postulate that the mean stress σ is a function of the natural dilatation of volume e or of the mean natural strain ε, while the shearing stress τ_0 is a function of the unit shear γ_0,

$$\sigma = g(\varepsilon), \qquad \tau_0 = f(\gamma_0), \tag{2-29}$$

both of these monotonously increasing functions being valid for their increasing and decreasing arguments. Since these two equations in their derivatives prescribe that

$$G = \frac{E}{2(1+\nu)} = \frac{df}{d\gamma_0} = f', \qquad 3K = \frac{E}{(1-2\nu)} = \frac{dg}{d\varepsilon} = g', \tag{2-30}$$

after eliminating E from the last two equations and solving for ν, one sees that Poisson's ratio for this solid is defined by

$$\nu = \frac{g' - 2f'}{2(g' + f')}, \tag{2-31}$$

and the modulus of elasticity E by

$$E = 2(1+\nu)G = \frac{3f'g'}{g' + f'}. \tag{2-32}$$

The differential of the strain energy,

$$d\omega = \sigma_x \, d\varepsilon_x + \cdots + \tau_{yz} \, d\gamma_{yz} + \cdots, \tag{2-33}$$

after making use of Eqs. (2-25), may be expressed in terms of the components of stress $\sigma_x, \ldots, \tau_{yz}, \ldots$, but ω may preferably be split into the sum of the work of dilatation of volume ω_v,

$$\omega_v = 3 \int \sigma \, d\varepsilon = 3 \int g(\varepsilon) \, d\varepsilon, \tag{2-34}$$

and the work of distortion [using Eq. (2-9)],

$$\omega_d = (\tfrac{3}{2}) \int \tau_0 \, d\gamma_0 = (\tfrac{3}{2}) \int f(\gamma_0) \, d\gamma_0, \tag{2-35}$$

their sum $\omega_v + \omega_d = \omega$ representing the elastic strain energy stored in an element of material per unit of volume.

2-3. Isotropic, Perfectly Elastic, Incompressible Substance under Finite Strains. A special case of the type of material considered in Sec. 2-2B is an elastic solid having Poisson's ratio $\nu = \tfrac{1}{2} = $ const and constant moduli of elasticity E and rigidity $G = E/3$ while the elastic strains can increase to finite values. A perfectly elastic, rubberlike, isotropic substance, not showing any elastic aftereffects or creep under a moderate distortion, should behave in this manner. Since E, G, and ν now are material constants, one may think of rewriting the stress-strain relations (2-25) in finite form after integrating them. Thus in a state of homogeneous, finite strain,

$$\varepsilon_x = \frac{\sigma_x - \nu(\sigma_y + \sigma_z)}{E}, \ldots, \qquad \gamma_{yz} = \frac{\tau_{yz}}{G}, \ldots \qquad (2\text{-}36)$$

Although these relations coincide with those which express Hooke's law if the strains are infinitesimal, it must be borne in mind that, in them, the $\varepsilon_x, \ldots, \gamma_{yz}, \ldots$ represent components of natural strain and shear, complying with their definitions in Vol. I, page 130. Thus, for example, the strain ε_x represents the integrated increments $d\varepsilon_x$ of those line elements of material points which swept through an imaginary axis of a frame, attached to a material point $P(x,y,z)$ of the body, and held in the direction parallel to the x axis of a fixed system of rectangular coordinates x, y, z in space while the body was deformed; similarly, for example, the natural unit shear γ_{yz} represents the integrated angular changes $d\gamma_{yz}$ of the line elements which swept through a right angle whose two edges were held in positions parallel to the y and z axes. Thus, while finite values of $\varepsilon_x, \ldots$ or $\gamma_{yz}, \ldots$ accrue, generally speaking, neither the $\varepsilon_x, \ldots$ nor the $\gamma_{yz}, \ldots$ refer to line elements consisting of identical material points of the deforming body while it distorts. If we desire to express the strain along a line element of given material points ds which elongates to ds' or the change that a right angle between two such line elements suffers during a finite distortion, we have to revert to the quadratic elongation $\lambda = (ds'/ds)^2$ and to the herewith defined natural strain $\bar{\varepsilon} = \ln \sqrt{\lambda}$ and to the conventional unit shear $\gamma = \tan \psi$ (ψ is the angle by which the right angle changes), respectively.[1]

We may add that this furnishes a deeper insight into the deformation than the one that Eqs. (2-36) are supposed to convey, which, however, are sufficient for the evaluation of the mechanical work done by the stresses. Since in an incompressible material no work of dilatation of volume is done, $\omega_d = 0$ and since Eqs. (2-36) are identical in their form with those for infinitesimal elastic strains Eq. (2-13), the total work done in this type of elastic substance under finite strain is equal to the work of distortion ω_d or to *the strain energy stored* in a unit of volume:

$$\omega = \omega_d = (3\!\!/\!2) \int \tau_0 \, d\gamma_0 = \frac{3\tau_0^2}{4G} = \frac{3G\gamma_0^2}{4}. \qquad (2\text{-}37)$$

In order to illustrate a few cases of the finite distortion of a perfectly elastic substance for which $E = 3G = \text{const}$, $\nu = \frac{1}{2}$, consider the following simple examples. We shall denote in them natural strains and shears by the symbols $\bar{\varepsilon}$ and $\bar{\gamma}$ in order to distinguish these from the conventional strains and shears ε and γ.

---

[1] Cf. Vol. I, Chap. 12.

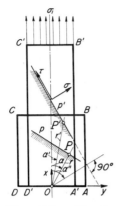

FIG. 2-2a. Simple tension.

A. SIMPLE TENSION OR COMPRESSION. The stress-strain law for a bar of an ideally elastic, incompressible substance which is tested by pulling or compressing it in the axial direction is expressed[1] by

$$\sigma_1 = E\bar{\varepsilon}_1. \tag{2-38}$$

σ_1 is the true stress, and $\bar{\varepsilon}_1 = \ln(1 + \varepsilon_1)$ is the natural strain in the axial direction.

The strain energy stored in the bar per unit of volume is

$$\omega = \frac{\sigma_1 \bar{\varepsilon}_1}{2} = \frac{\sigma_1^2}{2E} = \frac{E(\bar{\varepsilon}_1)^2}{2}. \tag{2-39}$$

It may be instructive to investigate the relation connecting the shearing stress τ in an oblique section of the bar with the corresponding unit shear γ for this ideally elastic, incompressible substance when the axial strain ε_1 increases to finite magnitudes. Let the x axis coincide with the bar axis and denote by $x, y, z = 0$ the coordinates of a point P in the unstrained condition and by $x', y', z' = 0$ the coordinates in the strained condition of the bar when point P has been displaced to $P'(x', y')$, assuming the origin O at the fixed end of the bar (Fig. 2-2a). Denote also by a_x, a_y, a_z the direction cosines of radius vector $r = \overline{OP}$ in the unstrained bar and by $a_{x'}, a_{y'}, a_{z'}$ the direction cosines of radius vector $r' = \overline{OP'}$ in the strained bar. A plane section p, which was originally normal to $\overline{OP}$, becomes in the strained condition a plane p'. In order to evaluate the shearing strain γ in this plane p' in which a normal stress σ and a shearing stress τ act, let us denote the direction cosines of the normal to plane p' by a_x'', a_y'', a_z''. For a simple extension the principal stresses are $\sigma_1, \sigma_2 = \sigma_3 = 0$, and in an incompressible substance the principal natural strains are equal to $\bar{\varepsilon}_1, \bar{\varepsilon}_2 = \bar{\varepsilon}_3 = -\bar{\varepsilon}_1/2$. Remembering that a simple extension is expressed by the linear transformation

$$x' = (1 + \varepsilon_1)x = e^{\bar{\varepsilon}_1} \cdot x, \quad y' = (1 + \varepsilon_2)y = e^{-\bar{\varepsilon}_1/2} \cdot y, \quad z' = (1 + \varepsilon_3)z = e^{-\bar{\varepsilon}_1/2} \cdot z, \tag{2-40}$$

after making use of the angles α, α', and α'' indicated in Fig. 2-2a, we have

$$\tan \alpha' = \frac{y'}{x'} = e^{-3\bar{\varepsilon}_1/2} \cdot \frac{y}{x} = e^{-3\bar{\varepsilon}_1/2} \tan \alpha. \tag{2-41}$$

According to the rules laid down in Vol. I, Chap. 12, for a state of homogeneous finite strain, we may evaluate the (quadratic) elongation λ in the direction of radius vector r' or $\overline{OP'}$ as $\lambda = r'^2/r^2 = (1 + \varepsilon)^2 = e^{2\bar{\varepsilon}}$, utilizing the principal

---

[1] Cf. also Vol. I, page 76, where the conventional stress-strain curve for such a bar,

$$\sigma_0 = E\bar{\varepsilon}_1 e^{-\bar{\varepsilon}_1} = \frac{E \ln(1 + \varepsilon_1)}{1 + \varepsilon_1}, \tag{2-38a}$$

was plotted. σ_0 denotes the stress under the load P referred to the original area A_0 of the cross section, $\sigma_0 = P/A_0$, and ε_1 is the conventional strain.

elongations for a simple extension $\lambda_1 = e^{2\bar{\varepsilon}_1}$, $\lambda_2 = \lambda_3 = e^{-\bar{\varepsilon}_1}$ (satisfying the incompressibility condition $\lambda_1 \lambda_2 \lambda_3 = 1$), and the direction cosines a_x, a_y, a_z of $\overline{OP}$, $a_x = \cos \alpha$, $a_y = \sin \alpha$, $a_z = 0$ (assuming $z = z' = 0$) from Eqs. (2-40):

$$\lambda = \frac{r'^2}{r^2} = a_x^2 \lambda_1 + a_y^2 \lambda_2 + a_z^2 \lambda_3. \tag{2-42}$$

This, with the values just stated, is found equal to

$$\lambda = e^{2\bar{\varepsilon}} = e^{\bar{\varepsilon}_1/2} \left(\cosh \frac{3\bar{\varepsilon}_1}{2} + \cos 2\alpha \sinh \frac{3\bar{\varepsilon}_1}{2} \right), \tag{2-43}$$

determining the natural strain $\bar{\varepsilon}$ in the direction $\overline{OP'}$ inclined at the angle α' with respect to the x axis in the strained bar. If the bar is pulled under the true stress $\sigma_1 = E\bar{\varepsilon}_1$, the expressions for the normal stress σ and shearing stress τ acting across an oblique section (the plane p') whose normal is inclined under the angle α'' with respect to the x axis are

$$\sigma = \frac{\sigma_1}{2} (1 + \cos 2\alpha''),$$
$$\tag{2-44}$$
$$\tau = -\frac{\sigma_1}{2} \sin 2\alpha''.$$

In order to evaluate α'', we make use of the relations for the direction cosines a_x'', a_y'', a_z'' of the normal to plane p' which were derived in Vol. I, in Eqs. (12-23), page 122. Since (when $z = z' = 0$, $a_z'' = 0$)

$$a_x'' = \cos \alpha'' = \frac{a_x / \sqrt{\lambda_1}}{\sqrt{(a_x^2/\lambda_1) + (a_y^2/\lambda_2)}} = \frac{e^{-\bar{\varepsilon}_1} \cos \alpha}{\sqrt{e^{-2\bar{\varepsilon}_1} \cos^2 \alpha + e^{-\bar{\varepsilon}_1} \sin^2 \alpha}},$$
$$\tag{2-45}$$
$$a_y'' = \sin \alpha'' = \frac{a_y / \sqrt{\lambda_2}}{\sqrt{(a_x^2/\lambda_1) + (a_y^2/\lambda_2)}} = \frac{e^{-\bar{\varepsilon}_1} \sin \alpha}{\sqrt{e^{-2\bar{\varepsilon}_1} \cos^2 \alpha + e^{-\bar{\varepsilon}_1} \sin^2 \alpha}},$$

we note that

$$\sin 2\alpha'' = \frac{e^{-3\bar{\varepsilon}_1/2} \sin 2\alpha}{\cosh (3\bar{\varepsilon}_1/2) + \cos 2\alpha \sinh (3\bar{\varepsilon}_1/2)}. \tag{2-46}$$

The conventional unit shear γ, which expresses the relative slip between the plane p' and a plane parallel to it a unit of length apart, or $\gamma = -\tan (\alpha'' - \alpha')$, is computed from Eq. (12-28) in Vol. I, page 123 (after letting the direction cosine $a_z = 0$), or from the formula

$$\gamma = -(\lambda_1 - \lambda_2) \sqrt{\lambda_3} \sin \alpha \cos \alpha = -\sin 2\alpha \sinh \frac{3\bar{\varepsilon}_1}{2}, \tag{2-47}$$

whereas *the shearing stress* τ in plane p' is given, after substituting the value of $\sin 2\alpha''$ which has been computed in Eq. (2-46) in the formula (2-44), by the expression

$$\tau = -\frac{(E\bar{\varepsilon}_1/2)e^{-3\bar{\varepsilon}_1/2} \sin 2\alpha}{\cosh (3\bar{\varepsilon}_1/2) + \cos 2\alpha \sinh (3\bar{\varepsilon}_1/2)} \tag{2-48}$$

The last equations define in parametric form the function sought, $\tau = f(\gamma)$, connecting a shearing stress τ with the corresponding unit shear γ. The reader will note that, whereas the stress-strain law could be expressed for the normal

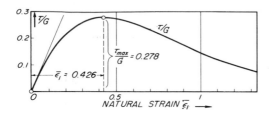

Fɪɢ. 2-3. Shearing stress $\tau = F(\bar\varepsilon_1)$ in dependence on natural axial strain $\bar\varepsilon_1$ for plane section inclined at angle $\alpha = 45°$ with respect to axis of tensile bar of perfectly elastic substance.

stress σ_1 and the natural strain $\bar\varepsilon_1$ in Eq. (2-38) simply by $\sigma_1 = E\bar\varepsilon_1$, under a finite distortion the function $\tau = f(\gamma)$ in Eq. (2-48) turns out to be much more involved. For example, for $\alpha = \pi/4$;

$$\gamma = -\sinh\frac{3\bar\varepsilon_1}{2}, \qquad \tau = -\frac{(E\bar\varepsilon_1/2)e^{-3\bar\varepsilon_1/2}}{\cosh(3\bar\varepsilon_1/2)} \qquad (2\text{-}49)$$

determine the shearing stress τ and unit shear γ in a plane section of the tensile bar that originally, in the unstrained condition of the bar, was inclined at an angle $\alpha = \pi/4$ with respect to the bar axis. While the unit shear γ increases monotonously with the axial strain $\bar\varepsilon_1$, the shearing stress τ soon reaches a maximum value in the oblique section and subsequently decreases with increasing $\bar\varepsilon_1$, owing to the fact that the plane p' is tilted in steeper positions in which the factor $\sin 2\alpha''$ in the expression for $\tau = -(\sigma_1/2)\sin 2\alpha''$ decreases more rapidly than $\sigma_1 = E\bar\varepsilon_1$ increases with $\bar\varepsilon_1$.*

B. Pᴜʀᴇ Sʜᴇᴀʀ. Supposing that the material is compressed uniformly in the direction of the x axis and extended parallel to the y axis, these being the principal directions of strain, the state of a finite pure shear is defined by choosing the principal, natural strains in these directions $\bar\varepsilon_1 = -\bar\varepsilon_0$ and $\bar\varepsilon_2 = \bar\varepsilon_0$ and assuming $\bar\varepsilon_3 = 0$. The corresponding principal elongations being $\lambda_1 = 1/\lambda_2 = e^{-2\bar\varepsilon_0}$, $\lambda_3 = 1$, a pure shear having the intensity $\bar\varepsilon_0$ is expressed by the linear transformation[1]

$$x' = x\sqrt{\lambda_1} = xe^{-\bar\varepsilon_0}, \qquad y' = \frac{y}{\sqrt{\lambda_1}} = ye^{\bar\varepsilon_0}, \qquad z' = z, \qquad (2\text{-}50)$$

x, y denoting the coordinates of a point P in the unstrained condition and x', y', in the strained condition. This results in the angular transformations

$$\tan\alpha = e^{-2\bar\varepsilon_0}\tan\alpha' = e^{2\bar\varepsilon_0}\tan\alpha'', \qquad (2\text{-}51)$$

α denoting the angle of radius vector $r = \overline{OP}$ in the unstrained body, α' the angle of radius vector $r' = \overline{OP'}$ in the strained body with the x axis, and α'' the angle of inclination of the normal to the plane which

* One verifies when $\alpha = \pi/4$ that τ becomes a maximum when $\bar\varepsilon_1$ satisfies the condition $e^{-3\bar\varepsilon_1} = 3\bar\varepsilon - 1$, which is the case for $\bar\varepsilon_1 = 0.426$ or for a conventional strain $\varepsilon_1 = 0.531$ or when the bar is extended by 53 per cent. The maximum $|\tau_{max}| = 0.278G$ occurs at a unit shear $|\gamma| = 0.683$. The formulas (2-47) and (2-48) converge toward $\tau = -G\gamma = -E\gamma/3$ when the strains are infinitesimal, as one would expect. The curves for $\tau = F(\bar\varepsilon_1)$ and for $\tau = f(\gamma)$ are reproduced in Figs. 2-3 and 2-4.

[1] Cf. Vol. I, page 133.

Fig. 2-4. Shearing stress $\tau = f(\gamma)$ in dependence on unit shear for plane section inclined at angle $\alpha = 45°$ with respect to axis in bar of perfectly elastic substance pulled in simple tension.

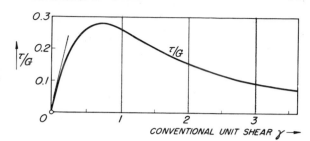

originally was perpendicular to $\overline{OP}$. For a pure shear having the principal stresses $\sigma_1 = -\sigma_2 = -\tau_0$, $\sigma_3 = 0$, in incompressible, elastic material having constant moduli E and $G = E/3$, the stress-strain relations [Eq. (2-25)] for finite strain may be written in finite terms. For a pure shear,

$$\bar{\varepsilon}_1 = -\bar{\varepsilon}_2 = \frac{\sigma_1 - (\sigma_2/2)}{E} = -\frac{3\tau_0}{2E} = -\frac{\tau_0}{2G} = -\bar{\varepsilon}_0, \qquad (2\text{-}52)$$

the elastic strain energy per unit volume is equal to

$$\omega = \frac{\sigma_1 \bar{\varepsilon}_1 + \sigma_2 \bar{\varepsilon}_2}{2} = \tau_0 \bar{\varepsilon}_0 = \frac{\tau_0^2}{2G} = 2G(\bar{\varepsilon}_0)^2. \qquad (2\text{-}53)$$

We have already evaluated the elongation λ along OP', λ'' along the normal inclined at the angle α'', and the conventional unit shear[1] $\gamma = \tan(\alpha' - \alpha'')$ and since the components of normal stress σ and of shearing stress τ in a plane whose normal makes the angle α'' with the x axis are equal to

$$\sigma = -\tau_0 \cos 2\alpha'', \qquad \tau = \tau_0 \sin 2\alpha'', \qquad (2\text{-}54)$$

since $\tau_0 = 2G\bar{\varepsilon}_0$, after utilizing the expressions quoted in the footnote, we have

$$\sigma = -2G\bar{\varepsilon}_0 c'' = -\frac{2G\bar{\varepsilon}_0(S + Cc)}{C + Sc}, \qquad (2\text{-}55)$$

$$\tau = 2G\bar{\varepsilon}_0 s'' = \frac{2G\bar{\varepsilon}_0 s}{C + Sc}. \qquad (2\text{-}56)$$

[1] With particular reference to Eqs. (13-16) through (13-18a and b) in Vol. I, page 137, we find there for

The elongation:

$$\lambda = e^{2\bar{\varepsilon}} = C - Sc, \qquad (2\text{-}57)$$

The elongation:

$$\lambda'' = \frac{1}{C + Sc''} \qquad (2\text{-}58)$$

The unit shear:

$$\gamma = Ss = \frac{Sc''}{C - Sc''}, \qquad (2\text{-}59)$$

where the abbreviating symbols denote

$$\begin{aligned} s &= \sin 2\alpha, & s'' &= \sin 2\alpha'', & S &= \sinh 2\bar{\varepsilon}_0, \\ c &= \cos 2\alpha, & c'' &= \cos 2\alpha'', & C &= \cosh 2\bar{\varepsilon}_0, \end{aligned} \qquad (2\text{-}60)$$

and on account of Eq. (2-51) we note that

$$s'' = \frac{s}{C + Sc}, \qquad c'' = \frac{S + Cc}{C + Sc}. \qquad (2\text{-}61)$$

Thus, by combining the expression for the shearing stress given in Eq. (2-16) with the one in the footnote [Eq. (2-59)] for γ, we may determine the function $\tau = f(\alpha, \gamma)$ in parametric form (considering the intensity of the pure shear $\bar{\varepsilon}_0$ as the parameter), and *the dependence of the shearing stress τ on the unit shear γ in the plane sections of the body consisting of the same material points* is given by

$$\tau = \frac{2G\bar{\varepsilon}_0 s}{C + Sc}, \qquad \gamma = Ss, \qquad (2\text{-}62)$$

holding α at a constant value in these last two expressions.[1]

Whereas in the examples in Sec. 2-3A and B no rotation of the principal directions of stress and of finite strain occurred which coincided with each other and the stress–natural-strain relations for them in an elastic material could be postulated in the linear form in which Hooke's law appeared to be preserved, it is noted that the relation connecting a shearing stress τ with the corresponding conventional unit shear γ is far from being linear and depends also on the orientation of the plane section. Let us now consider a state of finite strain involving a rotation of the principal directions of strain.

C. SIMPLE SHEAR.   Denoting again by x, y and x', y' the coordinates of a point P in the unstrained and P' in the strained body, respectively, a simple shear parallel to the x axis is expressed by

$$x' = x + \gamma_s y, \qquad y' = y, \qquad (2\text{-}63)$$

where $\gamma_s = \tan \delta$ measures the intensity of the shear.   *A state of simple shear* may be produced by holding the components of normal stress σ_x and σ_y at vanishing values and increasing the components of shearing stress τ_{xy}, that is, by a state of plane stress in which the principal stresses are equal to xy

$$\sigma_1 = -\sigma_2 = \tau_{xy}, \qquad \sigma_3 = 0. \qquad (2\text{-}64)$$

The principal stresses σ_1 and σ_2 stay inclined at the angles $\pi/4$, $3\pi/4$ with respect to the x axis.   On account of τ_{xy} being the only nonvanishing component of stress in the directions x, y, z, the stress-strain relations [Eqs. (2-25)] expressing *the elasticity law* show that $\bar{\varepsilon}_x = \bar{\varepsilon}_y = \bar{\varepsilon}_z = 0$, that the increment $d\bar{\gamma}_{xy}$ of the natural shear $\bar{\gamma}_{xy}$ is equal to

$$d\bar{\gamma}_{xy} = d\gamma_s = \frac{d\tau_{xy}}{G}, \qquad (2\text{-}65)$$

and that also, in finite terms,

$$\bar{\gamma}_{xy} = \gamma_s = \frac{\tau_{xy}}{G}; \qquad (2\text{-}66)$$

[1] For example, when $\alpha = \pi/4$,

$$\tau = \frac{2G\bar{\varepsilon}_0}{\cosh 2\bar{\varepsilon}_0}, \qquad \gamma = \sinh 2\bar{\varepsilon}_0 \qquad (2\text{-}62a)$$

define the shearing stress τ and unit shear γ in those planes consisting of the same material points in the distorted body which originally, in its unstrained condition, were perpendicular to a direction OP inclined at the angle of $\alpha = 45°$ with respect to the x axis. Equations (2-62) show that τ reaches a maximum value when $d\tau/d\bar{\varepsilon}_0 = 0$, $2\bar{\varepsilon}_0 = \coth 2\bar{\varepsilon}_0$ or when $2\bar{\varepsilon}_0$ is approximately equal to 1.20 or $\bar{\varepsilon}_0 = 0.60$, at a value $\tau_{max} = 0.66G$, corresponding to which $\gamma = 1.51$.

hence the *mechanical work* done by the shearing stresses τ_{xy} or *the elastic strain energy* stored per unit of volume is equal to

$$\omega = \frac{\tau_{xy}\gamma_s}{2} = \frac{\tau_{xy}^2}{2G} = \frac{G\gamma_s^2}{2}. \tag{2-67}$$

Incidentally, by utilizing the expressions for the octahedral shearing stress τ_{oct} and for the increment of the natural octahedral unit shear $d\gamma_{\text{oct}}$, after using Eqs. (2-3) and (2-5) which give

$$\tau_{\text{oct}} = \sqrt{\frac{2}{3}} \cdot \tau_{xy}, \qquad d\gamma_{\text{oct}} = \sqrt{\frac{2}{3}}\, d\gamma_s, \qquad \gamma_{\text{oct}} = \sqrt{\frac{2}{3}}\, \gamma_s = \sqrt{\frac{2}{3}} \cdot \frac{\tau_{xy}}{G}, \tag{2-68}$$

from Eq. (2-9),

$$\omega = (\tfrac{3}{2}) \int \tau_{\text{oct}}\, d\gamma_{\text{oct}} = \frac{\tau_{xy}^2}{2G}, \tag{2-69}$$

the same work is computed.

Remembering[1] that the elongation $\lambda = e^{2\bar{\varepsilon}}$ in the direction α' (angle of $\overline{OP'}$ with x axis) and the conventional unit shear γ may be expressed for a state of simple, finite shear γ_s either by

$$\lambda = 1 + \frac{\gamma_s^2}{2} - \frac{\gamma_s^2}{2}\cos 2\alpha + \gamma_s \sin 2\alpha,$$

$$\gamma = \frac{\gamma_s^2}{2}\sin 2\alpha + \gamma_s \cos 2\alpha \tag{2-70}$$

(where α denotes the angle of $\overline{OP}$ with the x axis), or by

$$\frac{1}{\lambda} = 1 + \frac{\gamma_s^2}{2} - \frac{\gamma_s^2}{2}\cos 2\alpha' - \gamma_s \sin 2\alpha',$$

$$\frac{\gamma}{\lambda} = -\frac{\gamma_s^2}{2}\sin 2\alpha' + \gamma_s \cos 2\alpha', \tag{2-71}$$

showing that *the strain circle corresponding to a finite simple shear* γ_s *has the equation*

$$\left(\lambda - 1 - \frac{\gamma_s^2}{2}\right)^2 + \gamma^2 = \gamma_s^2\left(1 + \frac{\gamma_s^2}{4}\right), \tag{2-72}$$

we note that *its principal elongations* $\lambda_1,\ \lambda_2$ are obtained [after letting $\gamma = 0$ in Eq. (2-72)] from

$$\lambda_1 = e^{2\bar{\varepsilon}_1} = 1 + \frac{\gamma_s^2}{2} + \gamma_s\sqrt{1 + \frac{\gamma_s^2}{4}} = \left(\frac{\gamma_s}{2} + \sqrt{1 + \frac{\gamma_s^2}{4}}\right)^2,$$

$$\lambda_2 = e^{2\bar{\varepsilon}_2} = 1 + \frac{\gamma_s^2}{2} - \gamma_s\sqrt{1 + \frac{\gamma_s^2}{4}} = \left(\frac{\gamma_s}{2} - \sqrt{1 + \frac{\gamma_s^2}{4}}\right)^2, \tag{2-73}$$

[1] Cf. Vol. I, Eqs. (13-41) to (13-49), pages 147, 148.

satisfying the condition of incompressibility of the material $\lambda_1 \lambda_2 = 1$ or $\bar{\varepsilon}_1 + \bar{\varepsilon}_2 = 0$. Furthermore, we see that

$$\frac{\lambda_1 + \lambda_2}{2} = \frac{e^{2\bar{\varepsilon}_1} + e^{-2\bar{\varepsilon}_1}}{2} = \cosh 2\bar{\varepsilon}_1 = 1 + \frac{\gamma_s^2}{2} \qquad (2\text{-}74)$$

and that [after letting $\gamma = 0$ in Eqs. (2-70) and (2-71)] the principal directions of strain of a simple, finite shear γ_s are determined by the two conditions

$$\tan 2\alpha = -\frac{2}{\gamma_s} = -\tan 2\alpha' \qquad (2\text{-}75)$$

defining two angles

$$\alpha_1, \; \alpha_2 = \alpha_1 + \frac{\pi}{2}$$

and two angles

$$\alpha_1', \; \alpha_2' = \alpha_1' + \frac{\pi}{2}$$

or two sets of mutually perpendicular directions, the former ones describing those perpendicular lines in the unstrained condition of the body which, after the strain is applied, turn in the two mutually perpendicular directions α_1', α_2' along which the principal elongations λ_1 and λ_2 and principal, natural strains $\bar{\varepsilon}_1$ and $\bar{\varepsilon}_2$ act[1] (Figs. 2-5 and 2-7).

[1] These two mutually perpendicular sets of lines appear in the diagonals of the two "unstretched" rhombuses which were introduced in Vol. I, Fig. 13-11, page 148. Their construction, reproduced in Fig. 2-7, furnishes also the values of the square roots of the principal elongations $\sqrt{\lambda_1} = 1 + \varepsilon_1$, $\sqrt{\lambda_2} = 1 + \varepsilon_2$ and thereby the principal conventional strains ε_1, ε_2 corresponding to a finite, simple shear, graphically using only triangles and a compass. Lay out (Fig. 2-7) the lengths $OA = 1$, $AB = AC = \gamma_s/2$, draw a circle around the origin O of a rectangular system of coordinates x, y as center with the unit of length as radius, also construct with the unit of length $OG = 1$ as the base the two unstretched rhombuses $OG12$ traced by thin lines in Fig. 2-7, and draw the four diagonals $O1$ and $G2$ in them. The sides $O2$ of the rhombuses lie on the rays OB and OC. In reference to the directions of the diagonals $O1$ and $G2$ of the left rhombus, trace the unit square $ODEF$ shown in thick dashed lines in Fig. 2-7, assuming that this unit square lies imbedded in the yet unstrained material. Now construct in reference to the directions of the diagonals $O1$ and $G2$ of the right rhombus the rectangle $OD'E'F'$ shown in thick lines. Then it obviously must represent the figure in its correct orientation into which the unit square $ODEF$ has been distorted by the finite, simple shear γ_s. The corners of this rectangle may be constructed simply by projecting the corners D and F of the square horizontally (parallel to the x axis, since in a simple shear all points move in this direction) onto the two rays drawn from O which are parallel to the diagonals of the right rhombus, furnishing the corners D' and F' of the rectangle. The two lengths $\overline{OD'}$ and $\overline{OF'}$ thus obtained determine the principal conventional strains ε_1 and ε_2 since $\overline{OD'} = 1 + \varepsilon_1$ and $\overline{OF'} = 1 + \varepsilon_2$.

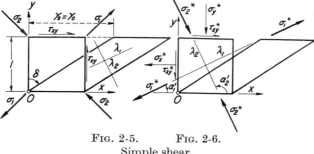

FIG. 2-5.   FIG. 2-6.
Simple shear.

States of finite, simple, and pure shear belong to the class of finite plane strains characterized—as far as the geometry of their distortion is concerned—in an incompressible substance by two equal principal natural strains of opposite sign $\bar{\varepsilon}_1 = -\bar{\varepsilon}_2$ while the third vanishes, $\bar{\varepsilon}_3 = 0$.

Let us call a series of continuously increasing distortions *a sequence of strains*. A sequence of simple shears defined by the linear transformations of Eq. (2-63) is obtained by increasing γ_s. Suppose that it is terminated at some finite value $\gamma_s = \gamma_{s0}$. In an elastic material under a simple shear, according to Eq. (2-66), the shearing stress τ_{xy} is proportional to the natural unit shear $\bar{\gamma}_{xy}$ and also to the conventional unit shear γ_s, since both are equal to τ_{xy}/G, and owing to $0 \leq \gamma_s \leq \gamma_{s0}$ the principal stresses $\sigma_1 = -\sigma_2 = G\gamma_s$ will increase in their absolute values as τ_{xy} increases from zero to $\tau_{xy} = G\gamma_{s0}$, with the result that at the end of the sequence of simple shears the principal, natural strain $\bar{\varepsilon}_1$, according to Eq. (2-74), has the value one computes from

$$\cosh 2\bar{\varepsilon}_1 = 1 + \frac{\gamma_{s0}^2}{2}. \qquad (2\text{-}76)$$

After what has just been said, the same principal strains $\bar{\varepsilon}_1 = -\bar{\varepsilon}_2$ may be produced by deforming the material through a sequence of pure

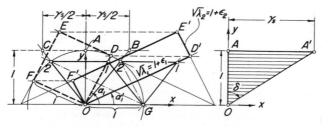

FIG. 2-7. Constructing the principal elongations λ_1, λ_2 for a simple shear λ_s (distorting the unit square $ODEF$ into the rectangle $OD'E'F'$).

shears[1] $\bar{\varepsilon}_1{}^* = -\bar{\varepsilon}_2{}^* = \bar{\varepsilon}_0$ by increasing the intensity $\bar{\varepsilon}_0$. In order that the material be brought from its unstrained condition precisely into the position that it has acquired at the end of the sequence of the simple shears ($\gamma_s = \gamma_{s0}$), the pure shear $\bar{\varepsilon}_0$ must be applied in the proper direction, namely, along the lines OD and OF (Fig. 2-7) whose directions were defined by the angles α_1 and α_2 (by stretching the material in the former direction by the principal stress $\sigma_1{}^*$ and by compressing it in the latter direction by the stress $\sigma_2{}^* = -\sigma_1{}^* = -\tau_0$) and subsequently, after $\bar{\varepsilon}_0$ has reached its required greatest value, namely, $\bar{\varepsilon}_0 = \bar{\varepsilon}_1{}^* = \bar{\varepsilon}_1$, by turning the strained material as a rigid body into that position $OD'E'F'$ (Fig. 2-7) in which the first principal direction of the pure shear coincides with that of the simple shear and with a line inclined at the angle $\alpha_1{}'$ defined by Eq. (2-75). The value of $\bar{\varepsilon}_0$ at which the sequence of the pure shears must be terminated is thus determined by substituting $\bar{\varepsilon}_0$ in Eq. (2-76) for $\bar{\varepsilon}_1$ or from the condition

$$\frac{\gamma_{s0}^2}{4} = (\tfrac{1}{2})(\cosh 2\bar{\varepsilon}_0 - 1) = \sinh^2 \bar{\varepsilon}_0$$

or from

$$\sinh \bar{\varepsilon}_0 = \frac{\gamma_{s0}}{2} \qquad\qquad (2\text{-}77)$$

expressing *the condition of the equivalence of a pure shear $\bar{\varepsilon}_0$ and a simple shear γ_{s0}* as derived in Vol. I, Eq. (13-51). In order to produce this distortion, an elastic material has to be stressed *by pure shear*, according to Sec. 2-3B, Eq. (2-52), up to the principal stresses,

$$\sigma_1^* = -\sigma_2^* = \tau_0 = 2G\bar{\varepsilon}_0, \qquad\qquad (2\text{-}78)$$

and τ_0 must become equal to

$$\tau_0 = 2G\bar{\varepsilon}_0 = 2G \sinh^{-1} \frac{\gamma_{s0}}{2} = 2G \ln \left(\frac{\gamma_{s0}}{2} + \sqrt{1 + \frac{\gamma_{s0}^2}{4}} \right). \quad (2\text{-}79)$$

While the final distortions thus produced either by the simple or by the pure shear are exactly the same, both having identically coinciding material lines along which the principal strains appear, however, *we note that the corresponding states of stress are by no means the same*, the simple shear having the principal stresses $\sigma_1 = -\sigma_2 = \tau_{xy} = G\gamma_{s0}$ and inclined at the angles $\pi/4$ and $3\pi/4$ with respect to the x axis (Fig. 2-5), whereas the pure shear has the stresses $\sigma_1{}^* = -\sigma_2{}^*$ prescribed in Eqs. (2-78) and (2-79), acting in the principal strain directions of $\bar{\varepsilon}_1$ and $\bar{\varepsilon}_2$ defined

---

[1] The reader should note that, in order to obtain a positive principal strain $\bar{\varepsilon}_1$ for the simple shear, the principal strains of the pure shear must be chosen as stated above in the text, whereas they had the opposite signs in the example treated in Sec. 2-3B.

by the angles α_1' and α_2' (Fig. 2-6). *This example convinces us, then, that it is possible in the domain of finite strains to produce one and the same distortion or state of strain in a perfectly elastic material by means of two (or more) different states of stress, depending on the strain path along which the substance has been deformed.* In other words, the state of finite strain does not yet determine uniquely, in general, the state of stress, even in a perfectly elastic substance, in those cases in which a rotation of the principal directions of stress or strain or of both, relative to the material, is involved unless a definite path of straining is also prescribed. We shall consequently expect to find that the mechanical work required for deforming an elastic substance through different sequences of strain ending at the same finite state of strain may or may not be the same. We find, indeed, here that *the work done in the sequence of pure shears* which we have just considered, according to Sec. 2-3B, Eq. (2-53), amounts to

$$\omega_p = \tau_0 \bar\varepsilon_0 = \frac{\tau_0^2}{2G} = 2G(\bar\varepsilon_0)^2, \tag{2-80}$$

while *the work done in the sequence of simple shears* is equal to

$$\omega_s = \frac{\tau_{xy}^2}{2G} = \frac{G\gamma_{s0}^2}{2}. \tag{2-81}$$

Thus, we see that the ratio ω_s/ω_p, according to Eq. (2-77), since

$$\sinh \bar\varepsilon_0 = \frac{\gamma_{s0}}{2},$$

is always greater than 1:

$$\frac{\omega_s}{\omega_p} = \frac{\gamma_{s0}^2}{4(\bar\varepsilon_0)^2} = \left(\frac{\sinh \bar\varepsilon_0}{\bar\varepsilon_0}\right)^2 > 1. \tag{2-82}$$

The work done in the sequence of simple shears ω_s is greater than the work done in the sequence of pure shears ω_p. (Only when the strain $\bar\varepsilon_0$ is of infinitesimal order is the work equal.)

Let us finally compute the components of stress $\sigma_x{}^*$, $\sigma_y{}^*$, $\tau_{xy}{}^*$ required to maintain the equilibrium in the final position of the material after completing the sequence of pure shears $\sigma_1{}^* = -\sigma_2{}^* = \tau_0 = 2G\bar\varepsilon_0$ and after having carried out the necessary rotation of the body. In a plane state of stress the sum $\sigma_x{}^* + \sigma_y{}^* = \sigma_1{}^* + \sigma_2{}^*$, but the latter sum for a pure shear vanishes and $\sigma_y{}^* = -\sigma_x{}^*$. Since, furthermore, the principal directions of stress for the pure shear coincide with those of the finite principal strains for the simple shear, two conditions are prescribed for the two unknown components of stress $\sigma_x{}^*$ and $\tau_{xy}{}^*$, namely,

$$\tau_{\max}^2 = \sigma_x^{*2} + \tau_{xy}^{*2} = \tau_0^2 \tag{2-83}$$

and the condition for the coincidence of the principal axes of stress and of strain which is expressed by

$$\frac{2\tau_{xy}^*}{\sigma_y^* - \sigma_x^*} = \frac{\tau_{xy}^*}{\sigma_x^*} = \frac{2}{\gamma_{s0}}. \tag{2-84}$$

From this, after using Eqs. (2-77) and (2-79), we find the values

$$\sigma_x^* = -\sigma_y^* = \frac{\tau_0 \gamma_{s0}}{2\sqrt{1 + (\gamma_{s0}^2/4)}}, \qquad \tau_{xy}^* = \frac{\tau_0}{\sqrt{1 + (\gamma_{s0}^2/4)}} \tag{2-85}$$

which may also be expressed in the equivalent form[1]

$$\sigma_x^* = -\sigma_y^* = 2G\bar{\varepsilon}_0 \tanh \bar{\varepsilon}_0, \qquad \tau_{xy}^* = \frac{2G\bar{\varepsilon}_0}{\cosh \bar{\varepsilon}_0}, \tag{2-86}$$

whereas the sequence of the finite simple shears terminates at the stresses

$$\sigma_x = \sigma_y = 0, \qquad \tau_{xy} = G\gamma_{s0}. \tag{2-87}$$

We may conceive of deforming the material through a sequence of pure shears in an alternative way. Instead of first straining the body and then carrying out with it the necessary rotation in a single step into the prescribed final position, *we may consider an alternative sequence of pure shears by straining and simultaneously turning the body in infinitesimal steps by such angles.* It is shown below (see Sec. 2-5K) that the linear transformation

$$x' = x\sqrt{\overline{\lambda_x}} + \frac{y\gamma_s}{\sqrt{\overline{\lambda_x}}}, \qquad y' = \frac{y}{\sqrt{\overline{\lambda_x}}}, \qquad z' = z, \tag{2-88}$$

will deform a square into an oblong rhomboid if the two constants λ_x and γ_s representing the elongation in the direction of the x axis and the conventional unit shear parallel to this axis are made to depend on each other, that is, if a function $f(\lambda_x, \gamma_s) = 0$ defining a special sequence of these types of plane strains is postulated. We shall prove later [see Eq. (2-188), page 92] that through Eqs. (2-88) *a sequence of pure shears may be defined in which the principal directions of stress will continuously coincide with those of the finite principal strains* (both are tied, in fact, to two mutually perpendicular lines of the *same* material

---

[1] Equations (2-85) and (2-86) should not be misinterpreted by assuming that they would represent the three components of stress σ_x^*, σ_y^*, and τ_{xy}^* needed actually to produce a *continuous* sequence of simple shears $0 \leqq \gamma_s \leqq \gamma_{s0}$. If one increases the parameter $\bar{\varepsilon}_0$ (or γ_{s0}) in these equations by an increment $d\bar{\varepsilon}_0$ (or $d\gamma_{s0}$), σ_x^* increases by $d\sigma_x^*$ and hence, according to Hooke's law, the strains $\bar{\varepsilon}_x^*$ and $\bar{\varepsilon}_y^*$ would change by $d\varepsilon_x^* = -d\varepsilon_y^* = d\sigma_x^*/2G$, violating the conditions $d\varepsilon_x = -d\varepsilon_y = 0$ valid during a *continuous* series of simple shears. σ_x^*, σ_y^*, τ_{xy}^* express the stresses *after completing the series of pure shears* carrying the substance into the position in which it coincides with a distortion of prescribed magnitude $\bar{\varepsilon}_x = \bar{\varepsilon}_y = 0$, $\gamma_s = \gamma_{s0}$ of a finite simple shear. This remark should be borne in mind when reading the text of the example treated in Vol. I, page 149.

points within the substance during the entire distortion[1]), provided that λ_x and γ_s satisfy the following quadratic equation:

$$\lambda_x^2 + \gamma_0 \lambda_x \gamma_s - \gamma_s^2 = 1 \qquad (2\text{-}89)$$

which, in the variables λ_x and γ_s, expresses the equation of an equilateral hyperbola. We shall prove, furthermore, that on the way of this particular strain path a body is brought from the unstrained condition ($\lambda_x = 1, \gamma_s = 0$) into a state of finite homogeneous, simple shear ($\lambda_x = 1$, $\gamma_s = \gamma_0$). Thus we may note that through this particular, continuous sequence of pure shears, characterized by the preceding two equations, *the distortion* of the state of a finite simple shear $\gamma_s = \gamma_0$ may also be produced in an elastic, incompressible substance. It is scarcely necessary to add that, through these pure shears combined with infinitesimal rotations, the same mechanical work is done and is stored as potential energy of strain in the elastic substance as the work $\omega_p = 2G(\bar{\varepsilon}_0)^2$ that we computed in Eq. (2-81) for the first type of pure shears, no work being consumed for any rotation, whether effectuated by a single, finite turn or in a series of consecutive, infinitesimal turns associated with simultaneous straining. The reader is well aware of the fact that, during the intermediate stages of this last sequence of pure shears combined with rotations, the elongation λ_x varies; it decreases first and increases subsequently (as a glance at Fig. 2-26 shows). That is, on the way of these pure shears the substance suffers first a certain compression, changing later to an extension, in the direction of the x axis (and corresponding changes in length parallel to the y axis).

Although two or more finite linear transformations applied in succession do not comply, in general, with the commutative rule of a summation, i.e., they will, in general, not furnish the same final transformation (configuration of the distorted body) when the order of their application is changed, they may well serve, after a proper adjustment of their constants, to show that a certain, prescribed homogeneous state of finite strain may be produced by deforming a substance along different pathways of straining. This may further be illustrated for an elastic substance in the following example.

D. VARIOUS SEQUENCES OF STRAINING. (1). *Suppose that such a substance is* strained first in a sequence of pure shears:

$$x' = x\sqrt{\lambda_x} = xe^{\bar{\varepsilon}_x},$$
$$y' = \frac{y}{\sqrt{\lambda_x}} = ye^{-\bar{\varepsilon}_x}, \qquad (2\text{-}90)$$

under the stresses $\sigma_x = -\sigma_y$, $\tau_{xy} = 0$ and satisfying the stress-strain relations

$$d\bar{\varepsilon}_x = -d\bar{\varepsilon}_y = \frac{d\sigma_x - (\tfrac{1}{2})d\sigma_y}{E} = \frac{3d\sigma_x}{2E} = \frac{d\sigma_x}{2G}$$

or

$$\bar{\varepsilon}_x = -\bar{\varepsilon}_y = \frac{\sigma_x}{2G}. \qquad (2\text{-}91)$$

[1] This type of distortion has been represented in Figs. 2-26 and 2-27 which should clearly depict what we are talking about here.

(2). *After $\bar{\varepsilon}_x$ reaches the value $\bar{\varepsilon}_x = \bar{\varepsilon}_0$*, interrupt the pure shear and deform the body in a sequence of simple shears (Fig. 2-8):

$$x'' = x' + \gamma_s y', \qquad y'' = y', \tag{2-92}$$

requiring the shearing stress $\tau_{xy} = G\gamma_s$ while the normal stresses stay at their last values $\sigma_x = -\sigma_y = 2G\bar{\varepsilon}_0 = \text{const}$. Suppose that the simple shear γ_s is terminated at the value $\gamma_s = \gamma_0$. After substituting Eq. (2-90) in (2-92), the final distortion is thus characterized by the linear transformation

$$x'' = xe^{\bar{\varepsilon}_0} + y\gamma_0 e^{-\bar{\varepsilon}_0}, \qquad y'' = ye^{-\bar{\varepsilon}_0}. \tag{2-93}$$

The mechanical work done by the pure shear is $\omega_p = 2G\bar{\varepsilon}_0^2$ and by simple shear $\omega_s = G\gamma_0^2/2$ (the normal stresses σ_x and σ_y during the second sequence of straining do not do additional work since the natural strains left from the first sequence $\bar{\varepsilon}_x = -\bar{\varepsilon}_y = \bar{\varepsilon}_0 = \text{const}$ remain unchanged) and the total work done is equal to

$$\omega_d = \omega_p + \omega_s = G\left(2\bar{\varepsilon}_0^2 + \frac{\gamma_0^2}{2}\right). \tag{2-94}$$

E.   DISTORTION CARRIED OUT IN REVERSE ORDER.   Consider now a distortion carried out in reverse order, by straining the substance first in a sequence of simple shears,

$$x' = x + \gamma_s' y, \qquad y' = y, \tag{2-95}$$

under the stresses $\sigma_x = \sigma_y = 0$, $\tau_{xy}' = G\gamma_s'$, stopping this distortion at $\gamma_s' = \gamma_0'$ and continuing it under a sequence of pure shears (Fig. 2-9):

$$x'' = x'\sqrt{\lambda_x} = e^{\bar{\varepsilon}_x}(x + \gamma_s' y),$$

$$y'' = \frac{y'}{\sqrt{\lambda_x}} = e^{-\bar{\varepsilon}_x} \cdot y. \tag{2-96}$$

F.   FINAL STATES OF STRAIN.   The final states of strain after the sequences of Sec. 2-3D and E are completed, represented in Eqs. (2-93) and (2-96), will be the same if the corresponding constants in these equations are made equal, namely,

$$\bar{\varepsilon}_x = \bar{\varepsilon}_0, \qquad \gamma_s' = e^{-2\bar{\varepsilon}_0} \cdot \gamma_0. \tag{2-97}$$

The body in E must be loaded first by the shearing stresses $\tau_{xy}' = G\gamma_0 e^{-2\bar{\varepsilon}_0}$ and subsequently by the normal stresses $\sigma_x = -\sigma_y = 2G\bar{\varepsilon}_0$ while the shearing stresses τ_{xy}' left from the simple shear will remain unchanged at the values just stated (the conditions of equilibrium during the application of the pure shear remain satisfied, although the body is elongated in the direction of the x axis and contracts in the direction of the y axis; one sees also that the stresses τ_{xy}' do work only during the sequence of the simple shears).   Consequently, the total work done under the conditions of Sec. 2-3E is

$$\omega_e = \omega_p + \omega_s' = G[2\bar{\varepsilon}_0^2 + (\tfrac{1}{2})\gamma_0^2 e^{-2\bar{\varepsilon}_0}]. \tag{2-98}$$

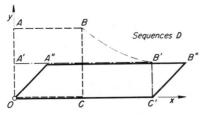

FIG. 2-8. Sequences D.   First pure, then simple shear applied.

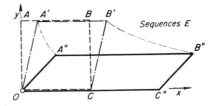

FIG. 2-9. Sequences E.   First simple, then pure shear applied.

The amounts of work ω_d and ω_e consumed under the series of distortions of Sec. 2-3D and E differ in the parts done by the shearing stresses τ_{xy}. To produce the final distortion in an elastic material, as indicated in Figs. 2-8 and 2-9, less work is needed when the body is first strained by simple shear (in the series of Sec. 2-3E) than if it is deformed first by pure shear and subsequently by a simple shear (series of Sec. 2-3D).

2-4. Rate of Dissipation of Energy in Viscous Substance.

As in Vol. I, Chap. 26, we shall assume that the distortion in a very viscous substance progresses as a steady creep while the internal stresses are in static equilibrium. We wish to consider only small changes of shape in the elements of material, neglecting the constant values of the elastic portions of the strains and considering the substance an incompressible solid or fluid. The stress components in a viscous substance are given by the relations[1]

$$\sigma_x = 2\mu\dot{\varepsilon}_x + \sigma, \ldots, \qquad \tau_{yz} = \mu\dot{\gamma}_{yz}, \ldots, \qquad \sigma = (\tfrac{1}{3})(\sigma_x + \sigma_y + \sigma_z),$$
$$(2\text{-}99a)$$

where the rates of strain and shear are expressed by

$$\dot{\varepsilon}_x = \frac{\partial u}{\partial x}, \ldots, \qquad \dot{\gamma}_{yz} = \frac{\partial w}{\partial y} + \frac{\partial v}{\partial z}, \ldots, \qquad \dot{\varepsilon}_x + \dot{\varepsilon}_y + \dot{\varepsilon}_z = 0, \quad (2\text{-}99b)$$

u, v, w denoting the components of velocity and μ the coefficient of viscosity. The dots above the symbols ε and γ refer to differentiation with respect to the time t. The tractions $\sigma_x, \ldots, \tau_{yz}, \ldots$ do mechanical work to overcome the substance's viscous resistance to a deformation, and the rate at which energy is dissipated in its interior and converted into heat is given per unit of volume by

$$\dot{\omega} = \sigma_x\dot{\varepsilon}_x + \cdots + \tau_{yz}\dot{\gamma}_{yz} + \cdots = \sigma_1\dot{\varepsilon}_1 + \sigma_2\dot{\varepsilon}_2 + \sigma_3\dot{\varepsilon}_3. \quad (2\text{-}100)$$

After substituting the relations of Eqs. (2-99a) in Eq. (2-100), this is found equal to

$$\dot{\omega} = \mu(2\dot{\varepsilon}_x^2 + 2\dot{\varepsilon}_y^2 + 2\dot{\varepsilon}_z^2 + \dot{\gamma}_{yz}^2 + \dot{\gamma}_{zx}^2 + \dot{\gamma}_{xy}^2). \quad (2\text{-}100a)$$

After subtracting here $(\tfrac{2}{3})(\dot{\varepsilon}_x + \dot{\varepsilon}_y + \dot{\varepsilon}_z)^2$ (which in an incompressible substance is zero) $\dot{\omega}$ may also be expressed by

$$\dot{\omega} = (\tfrac{2}{3})\mu[(\dot{\varepsilon}_x - \dot{\varepsilon}_y)^2 + \cdots + (\tfrac{3}{2})(\dot{\gamma}_{yz}^2 + \cdots)]. \quad (2\text{-}101)$$

But the expression in brackets, according to Eq. (2-19), being equal to $(9/4)\dot{\gamma}_0{}^2$, where $\dot{\gamma}_0$ denotes the octahedral rate of shear, we see that the rate of dissipation of energy in a viscous substance is also expressed by

$$\dot{\omega} = (\tfrac{3}{2})\mu\dot{\gamma}_0^2 = (\tfrac{3}{2})\tau_0\dot{\gamma}_0 = \dot{\omega}_d, \quad (2\text{-}101a)$$

indicating that the dissipated energy is entirely used up in changing the shape of the body, confirming our Eq. (2-10) since in an incompressible substance the work of dilatation vanishes, $\dot{\omega}_v = 0$.

[1] Vol. I, page 397, Eq. (26-6).

The rate $\partial W / \partial t$ at which energy is dissipated in a viscous body is expressed by the integral

$$\frac{\partial W}{\partial t} = \int \dot{\omega}_d \, dV = \frac{3\mu}{2} \int \dot{\gamma}_0^2 \, dV$$

$$= \mu \int \left[2\left(\frac{\partial u}{\partial x}\right)^2 + \cdots + \left(\frac{\partial w}{\partial y} + \frac{\partial v}{\partial z}\right)^2 + \cdots \right] dV \qquad (2\text{-}102)$$

to be taken over the volume V of the body.

2-5. Mechanical Work for Deforming a Plastic Substance. Stress and Strain Paths. A. SIMPLE CASES OF FINITE HOMOGENEOUS STRAINING. We shall consider first certain cases of finite, homogeneous straining in strain-hardening materials when the principal directions of stress and strain coincide and do not rotate relatively to each other and to the body. Suppose that the two monotonously increasing functions describing the dependence of the mean stress $\sigma = (\frac{1}{3})(\sigma_1 + \sigma_2 + \sigma_3)$ on the mean strain $\varepsilon = (\frac{1}{3})(\varepsilon_1 + \varepsilon_2 + \varepsilon_3)$ and of the octahedral shearing stress

$$\tau_0 = (\frac{1}{3})[(\sigma_1 - \sigma_2)^2 + (\sigma_2 - \sigma_3)^2 + (\sigma_3 - \sigma_1)^2]^{\frac{1}{2}}$$

on the unit shear

$$\gamma_0 = (\frac{2}{3})[(\varepsilon_1 - \varepsilon_2)^2 + (\varepsilon_2 - \varepsilon_3)^2 + (\varepsilon_3 - \varepsilon_1)^2]^{\frac{1}{2}}$$

$$\sigma = g(\varepsilon), \qquad \tau_0 = f(\gamma_0) \qquad (2\text{-}103)$$

(where σ_1, σ_2, σ_3 denote the principal stresses; ε_1, ε_2, ε_3 the principal natural strains; and γ_0 a natural unit shear) have been determined experimentally or are otherwise known. The mechanical work per unit volume done by the stresses to deform an element in a metal or in a plastic substance is evaluated, according to Eq. (2-12), from the curve integrals

$$\omega = 3 \int \sigma \, d\varepsilon + (\frac{3}{2}) \int \tau_0 \, d\gamma_0 \qquad (2\text{-}104)$$

to be taken along the path of straining or stressing, that is, over the sequence of the infinitesimal increments of strain through which the deformation has passed. Although Eq. (2-104) is valid in the general case in which the principal directions of stress or strain during a finite straining rotate relatively to each other or in space, provided that the components of natural strain are used, we shall first limit the discussion to cases of irrotational states of stress and finite strain. We may add that Eqs. (2-103) permit including generally the distortion of porous materials which are elastically as well as permanently compressible and in which a small fraction of the volume, apart from an elastic dilatation on first loading, may suffer an irreversible, permanent change. It is preferable in such cases to introduce as the arguments of the two functions postulated in Eqs. (2-103) the total natural strains [i.e., to understand under $\varepsilon = (\frac{1}{3})(\varepsilon_1 + \varepsilon_2 + \varepsilon_3)$ and γ_0 the sums of the elastic and permanent strains, without separating their respective parts a priori] and to introduce the plastic stress-strain relations in their deviatoral form[1] for a loading process according to

$$d\varepsilon_1 - d\varepsilon = (\tfrac{1}{2})(\sigma_1 - \sigma)\, d\psi,$$
$$d\varepsilon_2 - d\varepsilon = (\tfrac{1}{2})(\sigma_2 - \sigma)\, d\psi, \qquad (2\text{-}105)$$
$$d\varepsilon_3 - d\varepsilon = (\tfrac{1}{2})(\sigma_3 - \sigma)\, d\psi,$$

where the increment of the flow function for a shearing deformation $d\psi$ is equal to

$$d\psi = \frac{d\gamma_0}{\tau_0}. \qquad (2\text{-}106)$$

Should the need arise to evaluate the part of the mechanical work required for straining the material elastically, we may make use of Eq. (2-17) or (2-18) by computing the elastic strain energy stored in the substance from

$$\omega_{\text{elas}} = \frac{3(1 - 2\nu)\sigma^2}{2E} + \frac{3\tau_0^2}{4G}. \qquad (2\text{-}107)$$

However, since we shall be mostly concerned in the following with cases of distortion in which the permanent portions of the strains predominate, it will be permissible to neglect ω_{elas} and to consider compact materials such as the ductile metals as incompressible substances, assuming that $d\varepsilon = (\tfrac{1}{3})(d\varepsilon_1 + d\varepsilon_2 + d\varepsilon_3) = 0$, so that the total work of deformation ω consists only of the work of permanent distortion:

$$\omega = \omega_d = (\tfrac{3}{2})\int_0^{\gamma_0} \tau_0\, d\gamma_0. \qquad (2\text{-}108)$$

The lower limit of the integral $\gamma_0 = 0$ refers to the unstrained condition of the material and the upper limit γ_0 to the end of the deformation. Obviously, the integral in Eq. (2-108) represents the area under the general strain-hardening curve $\tau_0 = f(\gamma_0)$ between these limits. *Our principal attention in the following developments is to be directed to the determination of the upper limit of the integral in Eq. (2-108) which we shall find dependent on the path of loading,* i.e., on the intermediate, homogeneous states of stress or on the path of straining through which an element of material is being distorted.[2]

[1] Cf. Vol. I, page 385, utilizing Eqs. (24-19) after expressing them, however, for the differentials of the natural strains and of the flow function ψ.

[2] Strictly speaking, only such sequences of deformation are to be considered for which the differential of work $d\omega > 0$, that is, only loading processes. During an unloading, the curve $\tau_0 = f(\gamma_0)$ ceases to be valid and the strains temporarily decrease elastically, cases which must be excluded. But we shall see below that we may still include sequences of strain having abrupt discontinuities associated with sudden, instantaneous changes of the plastic state of stress and even with a reversal of stress, provided that the elastic parts of the strains are completely neglected and the stress-strain curve, after the discontinuity occurred, is correctly interpreted.

B. CORRELATION BETWEEN PATH OF STRESSING AND STRAINING.
After our introductory remarks, *let us investigate the correlation between
a path of stressing and of plastic straining,* basing the following considerations on the stress-strain relations for an incompressible material
for which the differentials of the principal, finite, natural strains may be
expressed by the equations:

$$d\varepsilon_1 = d\phi\left(\sigma_1 - \frac{\sigma_2 + \sigma_3}{2}\right) = (\tfrac{3}{2})\, d\phi(\sigma_1 - \sigma),$$

$$d\varepsilon_2 = d\phi\left(\sigma_2 - \frac{\sigma_3 + \sigma_1}{2}\right) = (\tfrac{3}{2})\, d\phi(\sigma_2 - \sigma), \qquad (2\text{-}109)$$

$$d\varepsilon_3 = d\phi\left(\sigma_3 - \frac{\sigma_1 + \sigma_2}{2}\right) = (\tfrac{3}{2})\, d\phi(\sigma_3 - \sigma),$$

with the increment of the flow function ϕ

$$d\phi = \frac{d\gamma_0}{3\tau_0} \qquad (2\text{-}110)$$

dependent on the increment $d\gamma_0$ of the octahedral natural unit shear γ_0
and on the shearing stress τ_0.   If a certain sequence of loading (stressing) is prescribed, we wish to determine the corresponding sequence of
straining, or vice versa, the upper limit γ_0 of the integral of Eq. (2-108),
and the mechanical work expended on the path.

To facilitate the discussion, let us represent in geometric manner,
similar to the way in which the cases of constrained flow were described[1]
previously, a state of stress and of finite strain by a point $P(\sigma_1,\sigma_2,\sigma_3)$
and $Q(\varepsilon_1,\varepsilon_2,\varepsilon_3)$ having the cartesian coordinates σ_1, σ_2, σ_3 and ε_1, ε_2, ε_3,
respectively, in space in these two rectangular systems, coinciding with
their corresponding axes so that a sequence of these two states is
represented by two curves, one traced by P in the σ_1, σ_2, σ_3 space, and
the other traced by Q in the ε_1, ε_2, ε_3 space.

Considering first an ideally plastic, incompressible substance—the
principal conclusions in regard to the evaluation of the states of finite
strains will retain their validity also for a strain-hardening material—a
sequence of stress is subject to the restraining condition

$$(\sigma_1 - \sigma_2)^2 + (\sigma_2 - \sigma_3)^2 + (\sigma_3 - \sigma_1)^2 = 9\tau_0^2 = 2\sigma_0^2 = \text{const} \quad (2\text{-}111)$$

which is the equation of the surface of yielding[2] and of a straight circular
cylinder having a radius r equal to $\sqrt{3}\tau_0 = \sqrt{\tfrac{2}{3}}\sigma_0$ (σ_0 = yield stress
in tension) and an axis that coincides with the space diagonal $\sigma_1 =
\sigma_2 = \sigma_3$.   A path of strain is subject to the condition of incompressi-
bility of the material,

$$\varepsilon_1 + \varepsilon_2 + \varepsilon_3 = 0, \qquad (2\text{-}112)$$

---

[1] Vol. I, page 428.
[2] Cf. Vol. I, page 211.

which, in the running coordinates ε_1, ε_2, ε_3, is the equation of a plane containing the origin O and normal to the space diagonal $\varepsilon_1 = \varepsilon_2 = \varepsilon_3$ coinciding with the axis of the cylinder [Eq. (2-111)].

A path of loading should, therefore, be describable as a curve traced on the surface of the cylinder and a sequence of strain as a curve drawn in the plane of Eq. (2-112). A little thought, however, convinces us that, as far as the stress path is concerned, the component of the movements of point $P(\sigma_1, \sigma_2, \sigma_3)$ up or down the cylinder in the axial direction is not essential, because that amounts to adding to or subtracting from the principal stresses σ_1, σ_2, σ_3 a uniform hydrostatic tension or compression, not having an effect on the yielding of the material. What matters are the components of the movements of point P normal to the axis; in other words, the stress path may be represented by a circle in a normal section of the cylinder, for example, in the plane

$$\sigma_1 + \sigma_2 + \sigma_3 = 0 \qquad (2\text{-}113)$$

containing the origin O, which coincides with the plane $\varepsilon_1 + \varepsilon_2 + \varepsilon_3 = 0$. In this plane, consider a point $P_0(\sigma_1', \sigma_2', \sigma_3')$ which is the projection of point $P(\sigma_1, \sigma_2, \sigma_3)$ on it or in which the generatrix of the cylinder passing through P intersects plane $\sigma_1' + \sigma_2' + \sigma_3' = 0$ (see Fig. 2-10†). When P moves on the cylinder, P_0 traces the circle of radius (r) equal to $\sqrt{3}\tau_0 = \sqrt{2/3}\sigma_0$ having the equation

$$2(\sigma_1'^2 + \sigma_1'\sigma_2' + \sigma_2'^2) = 3\tau_0^2 = (2/3)\sigma_0^2. \qquad (2\text{-}114)$$

For brevity, let us call the plane $\sigma_1' + \sigma_2' + \sigma_3' = 0$ *the stress plane* and $\varepsilon_1 + \varepsilon_2 + \varepsilon_3 = 0$ *the strain plane.*

The differential arc element of the strain path or of the curve traced by point $Q(\varepsilon_1, \varepsilon_2, \varepsilon_3)$ situated in the strain plane is an infinitesimal vector whose magnitude or absolute value, on account of $d\varepsilon_3 = -d\varepsilon_1 - d\varepsilon_2$, is equal to

$$d\varepsilon_s = \sqrt{d\varepsilon_1^2 + d\varepsilon_2^2 + d\varepsilon_3^2} = \sqrt{2(d\varepsilon_1^2 + d\varepsilon_1\,d\varepsilon_2 + d\varepsilon_2^2)}. \qquad (2\text{-}115)$$

But, according to Eq. (2-5), after using $d\varepsilon_3 = -d\varepsilon_1 - d\varepsilon_2$,

$$d\gamma_0 = 2\sqrt{(2/3)(d\varepsilon_1^2 + d\varepsilon_1\,d\varepsilon_2 + d\varepsilon_2^2)}. \qquad (2\text{-}116)$$

† Figure 2-10 shows the cylinder in its position relative to a cube whose corner O lies in the origin and whose three edges passing through O coincide with the σ_1, σ_2, σ_3 axes. The diagonal OD determines the orientation of the axis of the cylinder, whereas six corners of the cube having the edge lengths equal to σ_0 (yield stress in tension) lie on the surface of the cylinder. Its base plane, coinciding with the plane of Eq. (2-113) and with the circle of Eq. (2-114), is shown in Fig. 2-10. From point $P(\sigma_1, \sigma_2, \sigma_3)$ draw the perpendicular PC to the axis of the cylinder. Since the length $OC = (\sigma_1 + \sigma_2 + \sigma_3)/\sqrt{3}$, the three coordinates of point C are equal to $(1/3)(\sigma_1 + \sigma_2 + \sigma_3) = \sigma$ or to the mean stress σ in point $P(\sigma_1, \sigma_2, \sigma_3)$.

We see that the absolute value of vector $d\varepsilon_s$ or of the arc element of the strain path

$$d\varepsilon_s = (\tfrac{1}{2})\sqrt{3}\, d\gamma_0 \qquad (2\text{-}117)$$

is proportional to the increment of the natural octahedral unit shear $d\gamma_0$ defining the change in intensity of a finite permanent distortion.

The components $d\varepsilon_1$, $d\varepsilon_2$, $d\varepsilon_3$ of the arc element $d\varepsilon_s$ of the strain path, according to Eqs. (2-109), satisfy the proportions

$$d\varepsilon_1 : d\varepsilon_2 : d\varepsilon_3 = \sigma_1 - \sigma \,:\, \sigma_2 - \sigma : \sigma_3 - \sigma = \sigma_1' : \sigma_2' : \sigma_3', \qquad (2\text{-}118)$$

showing that the infinitesimal vector $d\varepsilon_s$ defining the strain path is parallel to and points in the same direction as the radii vectors of the circular stress path [Eq. (2-114)]

$$\overline{CP} = \overline{OP_0} = \sqrt{(\sigma_1 - \sigma_2)^2 + \cdots} = \sqrt{\sigma_1'^2 + \sigma_2'^2 + \sigma_3'^2} \qquad (2\text{-}119)$$

whose absolute value is equal to $\sqrt{3}\,\tau_0 = \sqrt{\tfrac{2}{3}}\,\sigma_0 = $ const.

An ideally plastic material may deform indefinitely while the principal stresses take on stationary, constant values satisfying Eq. (2-111). In this case, point P remains in its assumed position on the cylinder [Eq. (2-111)] indefinitely, the factors containing the stresses in Eqs. (2-109) are constants, Eqs. (2-118) may be integrated, and, if the distortion starts from the unstrained condition of the material, the principal

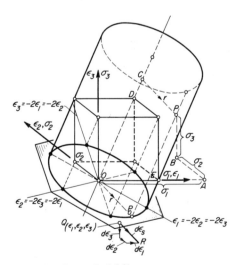

Fig. 2-10. Surface of yielding

$$(\sigma_1 - \sigma_2)^2 + (\sigma_2 - \sigma_3)^2 + (\sigma_3 - \sigma_1)^2 = 2\sigma_0{}^2 = 9\tau_0{}^2$$

and stress and strain plane

$$\sigma_1' + \sigma_2' + \sigma_3' = 0, \qquad \varepsilon_1 + \varepsilon_2 + \varepsilon_3 = 0.$$

natural strains will vary according
to the proportions

$$\varepsilon_1 : \varepsilon_2 : \varepsilon_3 = \sigma_1 - \sigma : \sigma_2 - \sigma : \sigma_3 - \sigma$$
$$= \sigma_1' : \sigma_2' : \sigma_3'. \qquad (2\text{-}120)$$

The strain path is a straight line
radiating from the origin O, and the
distance traveled on it by point
$Q(\varepsilon_1, \varepsilon_2, \varepsilon_3)$ is a measure of the octahedral unit shear γ_0 times the factor
$(\tfrac{1}{2})\sqrt{3}$, since

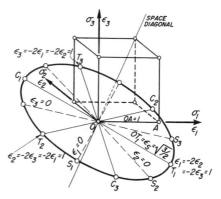

$$\varepsilon_s = \sqrt{\varepsilon_1^2 + \varepsilon_2^2 + \varepsilon_3^2}$$
$$= \sqrt{2(\varepsilon_1^2 + \varepsilon_1\varepsilon_2 + \varepsilon_2^2)}$$
$$= (\tfrac{1}{2})\sqrt{3}\gamma_0. \qquad (2\text{-}121)$$

FIG. 2-11. Strain plane $\varepsilon_1 + \varepsilon_2 + \varepsilon_3 = 0$
and circle $\varepsilon_s = \sqrt{3/2}$ = const.

Examples are the sequences of a simple extension, $\varepsilon_1 = -2\varepsilon_2 = -2\varepsilon_3$,
of a pure shear, $\varepsilon_1 = -\varepsilon_2$, $\varepsilon_3 = 0$, etc., distortions, in which the
principal, natural strains vary under constant ratios $\varepsilon_2/\varepsilon_1$ and $\varepsilon_3/\varepsilon_1$
(Fig. 2-10).[1]

One sees that six coplanar straight rays making equal angles of 60°
with each other represent the sequences of simple tension, compression,
and of pure shear. (Their directions may easily be inferred in their
relative orientation with respect to the cube indicated in Fig. 2-11.)
If a similar distortion, characterized by a straight-line path, should not
start from the unstrained condition of the material but from an initially,
permanently deformed state, from a point $Q^*(\varepsilon_1^*, \varepsilon_2^*, \varepsilon_3^*)$, we have the
proportions

$$\varepsilon_1 - \varepsilon_1^* : \varepsilon_2 - \varepsilon_2^* : \varepsilon_3 - \varepsilon_3^* = \sigma_1^* - \sigma^* : \sigma_2^* - \sigma^* : \sigma_3^* - \sigma^*. \qquad (2\text{-}122)$$

These kinds of plastic deformations, characterized by straight-line

[1] The strain plane $\varepsilon_1 + \varepsilon_2 + \varepsilon_3 = 0$ has been represented in Fig. 2-11 by a
circle shown in axonometric projection whose radius $\overline{OT_1} = \varepsilon_s = (\tfrac{1}{2})\sqrt{3}\gamma_0$ was
chosen equal to $\varepsilon_s = \sqrt{3/2}$ corresponding to a value of $\gamma_0 = \sqrt{2}$, assuming that
the edge length OA of a cube shown in Fig. 2-11 represents the natural strain
$\varepsilon_1 = 1$ and point T_1 on the circle represents the state of a simple extension of the
magnitude $\varepsilon_1 = -2\varepsilon_2 = -2\varepsilon_3 = 1$. The three points T_1, T_2, T_3 thus represent
the simple extensions of this magnitude in the direction of the 1, 2, 3 axes; the
points C_1, C_2, C_3, simple compressions in the same directions; and S_1, S_2, S_3, the
states of pure shear, all corresponding to the same value of $\varepsilon_s = \sqrt{3/2}$ or $\gamma_0 = \sqrt{2}$.
All points on the circumference of a family of circles concentric with the one
shown in Fig. 2-11 having the radius $\varepsilon_s = \sqrt{3/2}$ have in common the property
that they represent distortions of equal plastic intensity γ_0 = const and consequently of the same amount of mechanical work $\omega = (\tfrac{3}{2})\tau_0\gamma_0$ expended to
reach a point on the circumference of a circle on the straight strain path coinciding
with a radius of it.

strain paths, have been called *examples of unrestricted flow* (cf. Vol. I, page 427).[1]

C. MECHANICAL WORK TO DEFORM IDEALLY PLASTIC SUBSTANCE. *Let us compare the mechanical work ω expended to deform an ideally plastic substance from the unstrained condition in different ways to the same distorted state* in which the natural strains have prescribed, finite values ε_1, ε_2, $\varepsilon_3 = -\varepsilon_1 - \varepsilon_2$, assuming that during any of the distortions no rotation of the principal axes of stress and strain is involved and that both groups of corresponding principal directions continuously coincide with each other.   Suppose that the material is deformed in some general manner, by prescribing a curve on which point $Q(\varepsilon_1,\varepsilon_2,\varepsilon_3)$ moves on the strain path in the strain plane $\varepsilon_1 + \varepsilon_2 + \varepsilon_3 = 0$, originating from the point O, $\varepsilon_1 = \varepsilon_2 = \varepsilon_3 = 0$, and terminating in some given point Q. The strain plane is represented in the plane of Fig. 2-12.   In a substance in which $\tau_0 = \text{const}$, the mechanical work ω done by the stresses, according to Eq. (2-108), is equal to

$$\omega = (\tfrac{3}{2}) \int_0^{\gamma_0} \tau_0 \, d\gamma_0 = (\tfrac{3}{2})\tau_0\gamma_0 = \sqrt{3}\,\tau_0\varepsilon_s = \sqrt{\tfrac{2}{3}}\,\sigma_0\varepsilon_s. \qquad (2\text{-}123)$$

The upper limit γ_0 of the integral or the value of the octahedral, natural unit shear at the end of the distortion, according to Eq. (2-121), was taken equal to $\gamma_0 = 2\varepsilon_s/\sqrt{3}$, where ε_s, it is understood, represents the arc length measured along the given curve of the strain path connecting O with Q in Fig. 2-12.

Suppose that we connect the origin O with the end point Q of the strain-path curve (in Fig. 2-12) by a straight line and consider it as

---

[1] It may be important to add here a remark concerning sudden changes in the direction of a strain path, including the case of a sudden, complete reversal of a state of stress at a plastic limit.   Suppose that the material is yielding under simple tension $\sigma_1 = \sigma_0$, $\sigma_2 = \sigma_3 = 0$, while point Q traces the straight line OT_1 in Fig. 2-11.   After Q reaches a certain position Q^*, suppose that the stress σ_1 is suddenly reversed and that the material is subjected to a simple compression: $\sigma_1{}^* = -\sigma_0$, $\sigma_2{}^* = \sigma_3{}^* = 0$.   Since point P jumps suddenly from $\sigma_1 = \sigma_0$ to $\sigma_1{}^* = -\sigma_0$ along the σ_1 axis (this crosses the cylinder in an oblique direction intersecting it on the two opposite sides), vector OP reverses its direction and consequently point Q will start to recede from Q^* in the direction OC_1 in Fig. 2-11.   Therefore we may note that, hypothetically, our scheme of plotting pathways of strain may also be applied to cases in which a state of stress may suddenly be changed, discontinuously, from σ_1, σ_2, σ_3 to new values $\sigma_1{}^*$, $\sigma_2{}^*$, $\sigma_3{}^*$, provided that the elastic strains are completely neglected.   Examples are treated in the text to follow.

It is well known that the *Bauschinger effect* contradicts the simple facts just stated (see Vol. I, page 20); it is thought, however, from a logical viewpoint and provided that the elastic strains are neglected, the Bauschinger effect is excluded, and the new position of point P on the cylindrical surface of yielding [Eq. (2-111)] corresponding to the sudden change in the direction of the strain path is considered, that discontinuities in the strain paths should be included in our schemes of representing them generally.

another path on which Q may also be reached. This straight-line path constitutes, as we have seen, a sequence of unrestricted flow. Since the length of arc ε_s traveled by point $Q(\varepsilon_1,\varepsilon_2,\varepsilon_3)$ is greater on the curve than on the straight line connecting O with Q and since ω is proportional to ε_s, we see at once that *the minimum of work* ω_{min} needed to deform the substance to a prescribed state of finite strain ε_1, ε_2, ε_3 must be equal to

$$\omega_{min} = \sqrt{3}\tau_0\varepsilon_{s,min} = (3/2)\tau_0\gamma_{0,min}, \qquad (2\text{-}124)$$

where $\varepsilon_{s,min}$ is the straight distance between O and Q:

$$\varepsilon_{s,min} = \sqrt{\varepsilon_1^2 + \varepsilon_2^2 + \varepsilon_3^2} = \sqrt{2(\varepsilon_1^2 + \varepsilon_1\varepsilon_2 + \varepsilon_2^2)}. \qquad (2\text{-}125)$$

Thus

$$\underline{\underline{\omega_{min} = \tau_0\sqrt{6(\varepsilon_1^2 + \varepsilon_1\varepsilon_2 + \varepsilon_2^2)},}} \qquad (2\text{-}126)$$

the minimum work, is done by unrestricted flow or by increasing the strains under constant ratios $\varepsilon_2/\varepsilon_1$ and $\varepsilon_3/\varepsilon_1$ to their final values.

D. STRESS AND STRAIN PATH DEFINED. Regarding the stress path, with reference to Eqs. (2-114) and (2-119) and Fig. 2-10, suppose that we denote the direction cosines of radius vector $\overline{OP_0}$ in the stress circle by $\cos\alpha_1$, $\cos\alpha_2$, $\cos\alpha_3$. We may then express the relations just quoted by the equivalent set of equations,

$$\cos\alpha_1 + \cos\alpha_2 + \cos\alpha_3 = 0, \qquad (2\text{-}127)$$

$$2(\cos^2\alpha_1 + \cos\alpha_1\cos\alpha_2 + \cos^2\alpha_2) = 1, \qquad (2\text{-}128)$$

and the condition that vector OP_0 is parallel to the infinitesimal arc element $d\varepsilon_s$ in the strain path by

$$\cos\alpha_1 = \frac{\sigma_1'}{\sqrt{3}\tau_0} = \frac{d\varepsilon_1}{d\varepsilon_s} = \frac{\dot{\varepsilon}_1}{\dot{\varepsilon}_s},$$

$$\cos\alpha_2 = \frac{\sigma_2'}{\sqrt{3}\tau_0} = \frac{d\varepsilon_2}{d\varepsilon_s} = \frac{\dot{\varepsilon}_2}{\dot{\varepsilon}_s}, \qquad (2\text{-}129)$$

$$\cos\alpha_3 = \frac{\sigma_3'}{\sqrt{3}\tau_0} = \frac{d\varepsilon_3}{d\varepsilon_s} = \frac{\dot{\varepsilon}_3}{\dot{\varepsilon}_s},$$

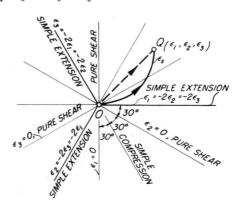

FIG. 2-12. Various strain paths represented in strain plane $\varepsilon_1 + \varepsilon_2 + \varepsilon_3 = 0$.

where $\dot{\varepsilon}_1$, $\dot{\varepsilon}_2$, $\dot{\varepsilon}_3$ denote the corresponding natural principal rates of permanent strain $d\varepsilon_1/dt, \ldots$, and $\dot{\varepsilon}_s$, according to Eq. (2-115), is equal to

$$\dot{\varepsilon}_s = \frac{d\varepsilon_s}{dt} = \sqrt{2(\dot{\varepsilon}_1^2 + \dot{\varepsilon}_1\dot{\varepsilon}_2 + \dot{\varepsilon}_2^2)}. \qquad (2\text{-}130)$$

We may note *that the preceding group of relations define the stress path corresponding to a given strain path.* In fact, suppose that the latter is given, in parameter form, through the equations of a plane curve situated in plane $\varepsilon_1 + \varepsilon_2 + \varepsilon_3 = 0$:

$$\varepsilon_1 = \int_0^t f_1(t)\,dt, \qquad \varepsilon_2 = \int_0^t f_2(t)\,dt, \qquad \varepsilon_3 = -\varepsilon_1 - \varepsilon_2. \qquad (2\text{-}131)$$

Then we see that the corresponding stress path is determined by Eqs. (2-129) and (2-130) or by

$$\sigma_1' = \frac{\sqrt{3}\tau_0\dot{\varepsilon}_1}{\dot{\varepsilon}_s} = \frac{\tau_0\dot{\varepsilon}_1}{\sqrt{(\tfrac{2}{3})(\dot{\varepsilon}_1^2 + \dot{\varepsilon}_1\dot{\varepsilon}_2 + \dot{\varepsilon}_2^2)}},$$

$$\sigma_2' = \frac{\sqrt{3}\tau_0\dot{\varepsilon}_2}{\dot{\varepsilon}_s} = \frac{\tau_0\dot{\varepsilon}_2}{\sqrt{(\tfrac{2}{3})(\dot{\varepsilon}_1^2 + \dot{\varepsilon}_1\dot{\varepsilon}_2 + \dot{\varepsilon}_2^2)}}, \qquad (2\text{-}132)$$

$$\sigma_3' = -\sigma_1' - \sigma_2',$$

where $\dot{\varepsilon}_1 = f_1(t)$, $\dot{\varepsilon}_2 = f_2(t)$ represent the natural principal rates of permanent strain under which the plastic distortion proceeded. We note, incidentally, that, if these given rates are multiplied by a factor, this has no effect on the resulting stress path or the time sequence according to which the load has to be varied, thus affirming the implicitly postulated property of an ideally plastic substance, namely, that its yield stresses do not depend on the absolute velocity of deformation. We may add that strain paths represented by geometrically similar curves [Eq. (2-131)] result in the same stress path.[1]

Conversely, if a stress path is given through the relations

$$\sigma_1' = \sigma_1 - \sigma = g_1(t) = \sqrt{3}\tau_0 \cos\alpha_1,$$

$$\sigma_2' = \sigma_2 - \sigma = g_2(t) = \sqrt{3}\tau_0 \cos\alpha_2, \qquad (2\text{-}133)$$

$$\sigma_3' = -\sigma_1' - \sigma_2',$$

where $g_1(t)$ and $g_2(t)$ are subject to the condition of Eq. (2-128), after

[1] Using terminology to which reference has already been made in connection with Eq. (2-120), the sequences of strain resulting in curved pathways that we have considered in Eqs. (2-131) might be called cases of *constrained flow* in contrast to those postulated in Eqs. (2-120), which we designated as cases of *unrestricted flow.* Since we have just prescribed for a distortion the principal natural strain rates $\dot{\varepsilon}_1 = f_1(t)$ and $\dot{\varepsilon}_2 = f_2(t)$, we may say *that Eqs. (2-132) solve the case of constrained flow* of an ideally plastic substance which is squeezed under prescribed combined rates of strain in two perpendicular directions. It would require special mechanisms to effectuate this type of distortion; hence the designation "constrained flow" seems appropriate.

solving Eqs. (2-132) for the strain rates,

$$\dot{\varepsilon}_1 = \frac{\sigma_1' \dot{\varepsilon}_s}{\sqrt{3}\tau_0}, \qquad \dot{\varepsilon}_2 = \frac{\sigma_2' \dot{\varepsilon}_s}{\sqrt{3}\tau_0}, \qquad (2\text{-}134)$$

using Eq. (2-130), we note that from them only the ratio of the rates of strain

$$\frac{\dot{\varepsilon}_1}{\dot{\varepsilon}_2} = \frac{\sigma_1'}{\sigma_2'} = \frac{\cos \alpha_1}{\cos \alpha_2} \qquad (2\text{-}135)$$

can be determined. Obviously, the inverse problem of finding the strain path for a given stress path is generally indeterminate (excepting the case of a straight-line path of unrestricted flow), unless one does not specify the resultant velocity $\dot{\varepsilon}_s = d\varepsilon_s/dt$ (or the equivalent shear rate $\dot{\gamma}_0 = 2\dot{\varepsilon}_s/\sqrt{3}$) under which the distortion is to be carried out.[1] Supposing a velocity given by

$$\dot{\varepsilon}_s = (\tfrac{1}{2})\sqrt{3}\dot{\gamma}_0 = h(t), \qquad (2\text{-}136)$$

the orbit of the strain path is defined by

$$\varepsilon_1 = \frac{1}{2\tau_0} \int_0^t \sigma_1' \dot{\gamma}_0 \, dt, \qquad \varepsilon_2 = \frac{1}{2\tau_0} \int_0^t \sigma_2' \dot{\gamma}_0 \, dt; \qquad (2\text{-}137)$$

for example, if the rate of octahedral shear is maintained at a constant value $\dot{\gamma}_0 = c$,

$$\varepsilon_1, \varepsilon_2 = \frac{c}{2\tau_0} \int_0^t (\sigma_1', \sigma_2') \, dt \qquad (2\text{-}138)$$

will describe the corresponding "constant rate of strain" deformations.

E. Sequences of Simple Extension and Pure Shear. Returning to the work done in these sequences of deformation, one sees that the mechanical work ω done in deforming an ideally plastic substance, for example, through a series of consecutive sequences of strain represented by *a polygon of straight lines in the strain plane* $\varepsilon_1 + \varepsilon_2 + \varepsilon_3 = 0$, is greater than the work done on the shortest straight path connecting the origin O with the end of the polygon. All sides of such a polygon represent unrestricted flows, and at each corner of it the principal stresses causing the yielding suffer sudden changes, point P_0 in Fig. 2-10 jumping from one position to another point on the stress circle.

Consider the simple example of a triangle OQQ_1 as the strain path (Fig. 2-13), the side $\overline{OQ}$ representing *a simple extension* $\varepsilon_1 = -2\varepsilon_2 = -2\varepsilon_3$ and the sides $\overline{OQ_1}$ and $\overline{Q_1Q}$ *two consecutive pure shears* through which the same final extension may be produced as in the simple extension. This may be illustrated by deforming two cubes of the material, one (Fig. 2-15) in simple tension $\sigma_1 = \sigma_0 = \text{const}$ to the final natural strains $\varepsilon_1 = -2\varepsilon_2 = -2\varepsilon_3 = \varepsilon_0$ along the "direct" strain

[1] Equations (2-129) or (2-135) define for the plane orbit of point Q only the direction of the velocity with which it moves; the plane orbit cannot be constructed unless its "hodograph" is completely given, i.e., including the magnitude of the resultant velocity $\dot{\varepsilon}_s$ with which point Q moves.

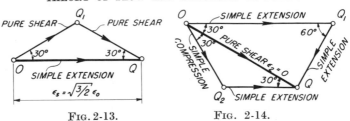

FIG. 2-13.   FIG. 2-14.

Various strain paths represented in strain plane

$$\varepsilon_1 + \varepsilon_2 + \varepsilon_3 = 0.$$

path $\overline{OQ}$, corresponding to which $\varepsilon_s = \sqrt{3/2}\,\varepsilon_0$, $\gamma_0 = \sqrt{2}\,\varepsilon_0$, requiring the work $\omega_t = \sigma_0\varepsilon_0$. Deform the other cube in two steps (Fig. 2-16) in a manner reminiscent of the way a blacksmith swages a piece to be forged by turning it alternately after each blow of his hammer, supposing, however, that the second cube will be deformed strictly according to the broken strain-path line OQ_1Q (Fig. 2-13) *first by a pure shear* $\sigma_1 = -\sigma_2 = \sigma_0/\sqrt{3}$, $\sigma_3 = 0$, $\varepsilon_1 = -\varepsilon_2 = \varepsilon_0/2$, $\varepsilon_3 = 0$ (until the cube edge $\overline{OB_1} = \overline{OB}$, Fig. 2-16) and *subsequently, after its plane is turned into the position shown in Fig. 2-16, by the pure shear,* $\sigma_1 = -\sigma_3 = \sigma_0/\sqrt{3}$, $\sigma_2 = 0$, straining it until edge $\overline{OC_2} = \overline{OC}$. This brings the second cube into a shape congruent with that of the first cube. Since in these two consecutive pure shears obviously the work is consumed,

$$\omega_1 = 2\int_0^{\varepsilon_0/2} \sigma_1\,d\varepsilon_1 = \frac{\sigma_0\varepsilon_0}{\sqrt{3}}, \qquad \omega_2 = 2\int_{\varepsilon_0/2}^{\varepsilon_0} \sigma_1\,d\varepsilon_1 = \frac{\sigma_0\varepsilon_0}{\sqrt{3}}, \qquad (2\text{-}139)$$

their sum

$$\omega_p = \omega_1 + \omega_2 = \frac{2\sigma_0\varepsilon_0}{\sqrt{3}} \qquad (2\text{-}140)$$

is $2/\sqrt{3} = 1.155$ times the work ω_t done in simple tension, confirming that the length of the broken path OQ_1Q is $1/\cos 30° = 2/\sqrt{3}$ times longer than that of the direct path $\overline{OQ}$ or that $\omega_p/\omega_t = 2/\sqrt{3}$.

The preceding remarks may perhaps throw some interesting additional light on *the common necking process of a round bar of a ductile metal pulled in tension.* We have mentioned in Vol I, page 85, that the tensile load, the resultant force of the axial stresses σ_a in the minimum section of the necked portion of a tensile bar in an advanced stage of the necking process, is the smallest resultant force of

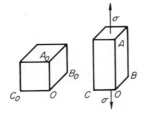

FIG. 2-15. Simple extension.

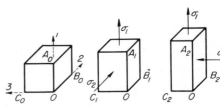

FIG. 2-16. Two consecutive pure shears.

the stresses σ_a (among the forces corresponding to various distributions of the axial σ_a, radial σ_r, and tangential σ_t normal stresses, satisfying the plasticity condition $\tau_0 = \text{const}$) when the two permanent strains in the lateral direction, namely, ε_r and ε_t, are equal to each other throughout the minimum cross section. DAVIDENKOV and SPIRIDONOVA first called attention to the fact that $\varepsilon_r = \varepsilon_t = \text{const}$ in the minimum cross section of a tensile bar just before it breaks. Thus their observations clearly indicated that all material elements in this section are subject to states of stress σ_a, $\sigma_r = \sigma_t$ of the type of a simple tension σ_1, $\sigma_2 = \sigma_3 = 0$ on which a triaxial or hydrostatic stress is superposed; these elements yield according to ε_a, $\varepsilon_r = \varepsilon_t$ or according to the direct strain path $\overline{OQ}$ in Fig. 2-13, corresponding to a simple extension $\varepsilon_1 = -2\varepsilon_2 = -2\varepsilon_3$. *Our previous example explains a mechanical cause for this type of deformation: It requires the least axial load and consequently the least mechanical work in this particular case of the yielding.* In his book[1] F. K. TH. VAN ITERSON states in this respect that a structure gives way at the least load "if the mechanical conditions make it possible that two of the principal stresses tend to equalize each other." Although this latter statement applies to the case just mentioned of the necking of a tensile specimen, it is, however, *generally not valid*, as can be demonstrated simply by interchanging the types of strain in the last example, supposing that in Fig. 2-14 a point Q is reached in a distortion on the direct path through the shortest distance $\overline{OQ}$ by states of pure shear and on either the polygonal path OQ_1Q or on OQ_2Q in two, consecutive, simple extensions or in a simple compression followed by a simple extension, respectively. In the latter example just the contrary would occur, namely, that a direct sequence of pure shears requires less work to be done than the two consecutive sequences of simple extensions. Thus we have to interpret the facts cautiously in applying these rules of flow. In this respect the reader is referred to Sec. 2-5J and K below where the minimum principle of mechanical work is further discussed for finite strains.

F. STRAIN-HARDENING MATERIAL. The developments subsequent to Eq. (2-123) postulated an ideally plastic substance, but they can be generalized at once to include also an incompressible strain-hardening metal, assuming that in it $\varepsilon_1 + \varepsilon_2 + \varepsilon_3 = 0$ and that it yields under a general strain-hardening law $\tau_0 = f(\gamma_0)$, where $f(\gamma_0)$ represents a monotonously increasing function of γ_0. The work ω done by the stresses is then to be evaluated from the integral,

$$\omega = (\tfrac{3}{2}) \int_0^{\gamma_0} \tau_0 \, d\gamma_0 = (\tfrac{3}{2}) \int_0^{\gamma_0} f(\gamma_0) \, d\gamma_0, \qquad (2\text{-}141)$$

the integral representing the area under the general strain-hardening function $\tau_0 = f(\gamma_0)$. The previous statements regarding the minimum-work paths do not lose their validity. We can utilize the stress plane $\sigma_1' + \sigma_2' + \sigma_3' = 0$ for the representation of a sequence of stress which now will be, however, a plane curve. The plasticity condition may be expressed for $\sigma_1' = \sigma_1 - \sigma$, $\sigma_2' = \sigma_2 - \sigma$ again by Eq. (2-114):

$$2(\sigma_1'^2 + \sigma_1'\sigma_2' + \sigma_2'^2) = 3\tau_0^2, \qquad (2\text{-}142)$$

describing at a given value of τ_0 a circle but, at continuously varying

---

[1] "Plasticity in Engineering," p. 83, Blackie & Son, Ltd., Glasgow, 1947.

radii r equal to $\sqrt{3}\tau_0 = \sqrt{3}f(\gamma_0)$, a family of concentric circles through which the stress path cuts a curve in which the radius vector $\overline{OP_0}$ is parallel to $d\varepsilon_s$. If, for example, the strain path is given by Eqs. (2-131), the velocity in the strain path may be found from Eq. (2-130),

$$\dot{\varepsilon}_s = \sqrt{2(\dot{\varepsilon}_1^2 + \dot{\varepsilon}_1\dot{\varepsilon}_2 + \dot{\varepsilon}_2^2)} = \frac{\sqrt{3}\dot{\gamma}_0}{2}, \qquad (2\text{-}143)$$

from which the values of the natural octahedral finite unit shears γ_0 may be computed by an integration

$$\gamma_0 = \frac{2\varepsilon_s}{\sqrt{3}} = 2\sqrt{\tfrac{2}{3}} \int_0^\lambda \sqrt{(\dot{\varepsilon}_1^2 + \dot{\varepsilon}_1\dot{\varepsilon}_2 + \dot{\varepsilon}_2^2)}\, d\lambda. \qquad (2\text{-}144)$$

This amounts to computing the arc length ε_s along the given strain-path curve now also needed and furnishes, at the end of the distortion, in the corresponding value the upper limit γ_0 of the work integral [Eq. (2-141)]. Equations (2-132) then supply the stresses determining the corresponding stress-path curve:

$$\sigma_1' = \frac{\sqrt{3}\tau_0\dot{\varepsilon}_1}{\dot{\varepsilon}_s} = \frac{\sqrt{3}f(\gamma_0)\dot{\varepsilon}_1}{\dot{\varepsilon}_s},$$

$$\sigma_2' = \frac{\sqrt{3}\tau_0\dot{\varepsilon}_2}{\dot{\varepsilon}_s} = \frac{\sqrt{3}f(\gamma_0)\dot{\varepsilon}_2}{\dot{\varepsilon}_s}. \qquad (2\text{-}145)$$

We may, for example, compare the work ω_t and ω_p required to deform a strain-hardening metal in simple tension and in the two consecutive pure shears, producing the same final distortion as the former in the sequences illustrated in Fig. 2-13, but we note that the ratio ω_p/ω_t is now determined by the ratio of the areas under the general strain-hardening curve $\tau_0 = f(\gamma_0)$ corresponding to the upper limits of the integral: $\overline{OA} = \gamma_0 = \sqrt{2}\varepsilon_0$ for a simple extension ε_0 and $\overline{OB} = \gamma_0 = 2\sqrt{\tfrac{2}{3}}\varepsilon_0$ for the consecutive two pure shears, which were indicated in Fig. 2-17 reaching from O to A and O to B, respectively, the excess area having been shaded, confirming again that $\omega_p/\omega_t > 1$.

G. Summary. *The preceding statements concerning the flow of an ideally plastic substance may be summed up as follows:*

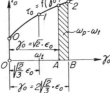

Fig. 2-17. General strain-hardening curve $\tau_0 = f(\gamma_0)$.

(1). Supposing that the principal axes of stress and of finite strain coincide with each other and with the same lines of material points and that no rotation of these axes is involved while the material distorts, a geometric rule determines the correlation between the stress and strain path: As point $P_0(\sigma_1', \sigma_2', \sigma_3')$ moves on the circumference of a circle having a radius (r) equal to $\sqrt{3}\tau_0 = \sqrt{\tfrac{2}{3}}\sigma_0$ in the stress plane $\sigma_1' + \sigma_2' + \sigma_3' = 0$, point $Q(\varepsilon_1, \varepsilon_2, \varepsilon_3)$ trails its movements in the strain plane $\varepsilon_1 + \varepsilon_2 + \varepsilon_3 = 0$ in such a manner that in tracing the strain path it always moves in the direction parallel to the radius vector $\overline{OP}_0$ (Fig. 2-10).

(2). The mechanical work ω done by the stresses, per unit of volume, is equal to the distance ε_s traveled by point Q (measured on the length of arc) on the strain path times $\sqrt{3}\tau_0 = \sqrt{2/3}\sigma_0$ [the radius (r) of the cylinder equals $\sqrt{3}\tau_0$].

(3). Consequently, in the domain of finite strains, not involving rotation of the principal directions of strain, the minimum amount of mechanical work is expended in deforming an ideally plastic substance from the unstrained condition to a finite state of strain ε_1, ε_2, ε_3 through the shortest sequence of unrestricted flow in which this state can be reached, i.e., by deforming it under constant ratios of strain $\varepsilon_2/\varepsilon_1$ and $\varepsilon_3/\varepsilon_1$. It may be added that in conclusion 3 a strain-hardening metal may also be included, deforming under a general, monotonously increasing strain-hardening function $\tau_0 = f(\gamma_0)$.

H. ENERGY ABSORBED TO DEFLECT THIN PLATES. During World War II some attention was given to the determination of the energy absorbed in permanently deflecting thin steel plates firmly clamped along their circumference and laterally loaded by hydrostatic pressure. Some of these investigations aimed also at the determination of the energy of plastic distortion absorbed by plates exposed to underwater explosions. We shall at least mention a group of greatly simplified cases of this kind, namely, the plastic distortion of thin membranes of a very ductile metal of equal thickness, assuming that they are firmly clamped down along their edges, while they are moderately deflected permanently by a static, uniform lateral pressure p. For the purpose of a simplified estimate of the work W required to deflect a membrane permanently, we shall assume that it is unstressed in its initially plane condition and approximately uniformly stressed by tensile stresses of equal magnitude in all tangential directions. It is known that this latter assumption cannot be true for two reasons: first, because the conditions prescribed on the boundary curve require that the strains in the direction of the tangents of this curve must vanish while they take on finite magnitudes normal to it and therefore the membrane stresses along the circumference have different values in these two directions and, secondly, because, due to the strain hardening of the metal, the membrane thickness in the later stages of the permanent distortion will change from point to point. In order to estimate the work approximately, we shall, however, disregard all these facts[1] and, in other words,

---

[1] Neglecting the strain energy for the elastic parts of the strains, assuming that the latter are permanent.

determine the estimated energy to deflect the membranes permanently as if they were thin skins bulged above a circle, a square, an ellipse, or a rectangle, excluding, however, very narrow ellipses or long rectangles (because in the latter cases, in which the contour line encloses a very oblong figure, obviously the membrane stresses in the longitudinal direction are approximately one-half the stresses in the transverse direction and the work is done primarily by the stresses in the latter direction, the strain parallel to the long axis vanishing).   Assuming the deflection w of the membrane as a function of rectangular coordinates x and y, the bulged surface has an area

$$A = \iint \sqrt{1 + \left(\frac{\partial w}{\partial x}\right)^2 + \left(\frac{\partial w}{\partial y}\right)^2} \, dx \, dy, \qquad (2\text{-}146)$$

which for not too great deflections w may be taken equal to

$$A = A_0 + J, \qquad J = (\tfrac{1}{2}) \iint \left[\left(\frac{\partial w}{\partial x}\right)^2 + \left(\frac{\partial w}{\partial y}\right)^2 \right] dx \, dy,$$

$$(2\text{-}147)$$

where A_0 denotes the area of the plane figure within the contour line. The average value of the natural strain ε_t in the deflected middle surface of the membrane may then be estimated as

$$\varepsilon_t = \ln \sqrt{\frac{A}{A_0}} = (\tfrac{1}{2}) \ln \left(1 + \frac{J}{A_0}\right) \cong \frac{J}{2A_0} . \qquad (2\text{-}148)$$

Since the principal strains are $\varepsilon_1 = \varepsilon_2 = \varepsilon_t$, $\varepsilon_3 = -2\varepsilon_t$, we have $\gamma_0 = 2\sqrt{2}\varepsilon_t = \sqrt{2}J/A_0$ and may compute $\tau_0 = f(\gamma_0)$ and the work of distortion:

$$W = (\tfrac{3}{2})V \int_0^{\gamma_0} \tau_0 \, d\gamma_0, \qquad (2\text{-}149)$$

where V denotes the material volume of the membrane, $V = A_0 h_0$, and h_0 is its original thickness.

Suppose that we approximate the deflected form of an elliptic membrane by

$$w_e = w_0\left(1 - \frac{x^2}{a^2} - \frac{y^2}{b^2}\right) \qquad (2\text{-}150)$$

and of a rectangular membrane by

$$w_r = w_0 \sin\frac{\pi x}{a} \sin\frac{\pi y}{b}, \qquad (2\text{-}151)$$

w_0 denoting the maximum deflection and a and b the semiaxes of the ellipse or the sides of the rectangle, respectively.   Then for the former we find, after carrying out the integration in Eq. (2-147),

$$J_e = \frac{\pi w_0^2}{2} \left(\frac{b}{a} + \frac{a}{b} \right), \qquad A_0 = \pi ab, \qquad \gamma_0 = \frac{\sqrt{2}J_e}{A_0} \qquad (2\text{-}152)$$

and for the latter

$$J_r = \frac{\pi^2 w_0^2}{8} \left(\frac{b}{a} + \frac{a}{b} \right), \qquad A_0 = ab, \qquad \gamma_0 = \frac{\sqrt{2}J_r}{A_0}, \qquad (2\text{-}153)$$

so that the work W given in Eq. (2-149) may be computed approximately by graphical quadrature for increasing deflections w_0.

For an ideally plastic substance in which $\tau_0 = $ const, we would find the work for an elliptic and a rectangular membrane, respectively, equal to

$$W_e = \frac{3\pi w_0^2 h_0 \tau_0}{2\sqrt{2}} \left(\frac{b}{a} + \frac{a}{b} \right), \qquad (2\text{-}154)$$

$$W_r = \frac{3\pi^2 w_0^2 h_0 \tau_0}{8\sqrt{2}} \left(\frac{b}{a} + \frac{a}{b} \right). \qquad (2\text{-}155)$$

When $\tau_0 = $ const, the ratio of W_e to W_r for an elliptic membrane and the one of the circumscribed rectangle at the same deflection w_0 is $W_e : W_r = 4 : \pi$, but for very oblong figures these estimates should not be used, after what has been said.

I. SIMPLE SHEAR IN PLASTIC SUBSTANCE. Finite plastic distortions with rotation of the principal axes of stress and finite strain have not yet been considered in this section. Endeavoring to define also for such plastic states of strain a geometric representation of a path of straining, consider a sequence of finite simple shears as an example of a case in which the directions of principal stress and strain rotate relatively to the material elements of a plastic substance and to each other. A simple shear is a case of plane strain with rotation. In incompressible material the states of homogeneous, finite, plane strain have two equal principal natural strains of opposite signs, the third principal strain vanishing, irrespective of whether the distortion is connected with a rotation or not. Since no provisions were foreseen in the geometric representation of irrotational states of stress and finite strain described in Sec. 2-5B for recording the directions in which either act, we may as well extend it to all states of plane, plastic strain, including those with rotation. The principal differentials of the incremental strain tensor of a state of plane strain satisfy Eqs. (2-115) to (2-119) with the conditions $d\varepsilon_1 = -d\varepsilon_2$ and $d\varepsilon_3 = 0$. Since there corresponds to them principal stresses $\sigma_1 = -\sigma_2$, $\sigma_3 = 0$ whose ratios remain constant during the entire distortion, Eqs. (2-118) may be integrated and expressed in the finite form[1] $\varepsilon_1 = -\varepsilon_2$, $\varepsilon_3 = 0$ and by the relations obtained by inter-changing the subscripts 1, 2, 3 in cyclic order. In the strain plane $\varepsilon_1 + \varepsilon_2 + \varepsilon_3 = 0$ these three groups of equations are represented by three straight lines inclined at equal angles of 60° intersecting each other at the origin O. This leads us then to propose that a sequence of simple shears γ_s (a state of plane strain with rotation) be represented by the straight-line path $\varepsilon_1 = -\varepsilon_2$, $\varepsilon_3 = 0$ that a point Q traces along $\overline{OS_3}$ in Fig. 2-11, whose coordinates ε_1, ε_2, ε_3 are plotted in the same directions as the principal stresses σ_1, σ_2, σ_3. Supposing a sequence of simple shears γ_s in the direction of the x axis, as in Sec. 2-3C, we may utilize those expressions already derived there which are valid for a state of simple shear irrespective of the nature of the material, namely,

$$d\gamma_s = d\gamma_{xy} = d\varepsilon_1 - d\varepsilon_2 = 2d\varepsilon_1, \qquad \gamma_s = \gamma_{xy} = 2\varepsilon_1, \qquad \sigma_1 = -\sigma_1 = \tau_{xy},$$

the octahedral shearing stress being equal to $\tau_0 = \sqrt{\tfrac{2}{3}}\tau_{xy}$ and the octahedral, natural unit shear $\gamma_0 = \sqrt{\tfrac{2}{3}} \cdot \gamma_{xy}$. We note that point $Q(\varepsilon_1, \varepsilon_2, \varepsilon_3)$ advances on the straight line $\varepsilon_1 = -\varepsilon_2$, $\varepsilon_3 = 0$, as the simple shear γ_s increases by the increment $d\gamma_s$, by a line element $d\varepsilon_s$ [see Eq. (2-115)],

$$d\varepsilon_s = \sqrt{d\varepsilon_1^2 + d\varepsilon_2^2 + d\varepsilon_3^2} = \sqrt{2}\,d\varepsilon_1 = \frac{d\gamma_s}{\sqrt{2}}, \qquad (2\text{-}156)$$

so that the distance traveled by point Q amounts to

$$\overline{OQ} = \varepsilon_s = \sqrt{2}\varepsilon_1 = \frac{\gamma_s}{\sqrt{2}}. \qquad (2\text{-}157)$$

Suppose that we choose a second point Q^* whose rectangular coordinates were made equal to the principal natural strains $\varepsilon_1^* = -\varepsilon_2^*$, $\varepsilon_3^* = 0$ of the equivalent pure shear ε_0 (having precisely the same principal, inherent natural strains as the simple shear γ_s) and whose magnitude ε_0 we defined generally by Eq. (2-77) by

$$2 \sinh \varepsilon_0 = \gamma_s. \qquad (2\text{-}158)$$

---

[1] Whereas the corresponding equation (2-120) deals with the values of the principal, inherent Eigen-natural strains in the irrotational case considered in Sec. 2-5B, the reader should note the different meaning attributed to the strains ε_1, ε_2 that we have just expressed in the text: While the distortion progresses and the principal axes of stress rotate relatively to the material and to fixed axes in space, these "apparent" natural strains ε_1 and ε_2 represent the integrated values of the principal differentials $d\varepsilon_1$ and $d\varepsilon_2$ of the incremental plastic strain tensors trailing the directions of σ_1 and σ_2 in those material lines which sweep through the former. These values ε_1 and ε_2 are to be distinguished clearly from the actual values of the principal, inherent *Eigen-natural strains*, say ε_1^* and $\varepsilon_2^* = -\varepsilon_1^*$ of the state of plane strain.

Obviously, this point Q^* would trace the same straight line along $\overline{OS_3}$ in Fig. 2-11 in its strain path as point Q did, but it is easy to see that *the former would trail the latter*, because Q^* would be displaced by a line element $d\varepsilon_s^* < d\varepsilon_s$, namely,

$$d\varepsilon_s^* = \sqrt{d\varepsilon_1^{*2} + d\varepsilon_2^{*2} + d\varepsilon_3^{*2}} = \sqrt{2}d\varepsilon_1^*, \qquad (2\text{-}159)$$

or by a finite distance

$$\overline{OQ}^* = \varepsilon_s^* = \sqrt{2}\varepsilon_1^* = \sqrt{2}\ln\left(\frac{\gamma_s}{2} + \sqrt{1 + \frac{\gamma_s^2}{4}}\right) \qquad (2\text{-}160)$$

since the principal, inherent, natural strain of the simple shear γ_s (and of the equivalent pure shear), according to Eqs. (2-73), equals

$$\varepsilon_1^* = \ln\left(\frac{\gamma_s}{2} + \sqrt{1 + \frac{\gamma_s^2}{4}}\right) \qquad (2\text{-}161)$$

and

$$d\varepsilon_1^* = \frac{d\gamma_s}{2\sqrt{1 + (\gamma_s^2/4)}} < d\varepsilon_s. \qquad (2\text{-}162)$$

Therefore, since $\varepsilon_s > \varepsilon_s^*$, *point Q representing the sequence of simple shears always shoots ahead of point Q^** representing the equivalent pure shear.[1]

The comparison of these two lengths ε_s and ε_s^* traveled by points Q and Q^* has the significance that, as we recall from Sec. 2-5B, they measure directly *the mechanical work* ω_s *and* ω_p *done in a simple shear* γ_s *and in the equivalent pure shear* ε_0, respectively, in an ideally plastic substance ($\tau_0 = $ const), which must amount to

$$\omega_s = \sqrt{3}\tau_0\varepsilon_s = \sqrt{3/2}\tau_0\gamma_s, \qquad (2\text{-}163)$$

$$\omega_p = \sqrt{3}\tau_0\varepsilon_s^* = \sqrt{6}\,\tau_0\ln\left(\frac{\gamma_s}{2} + \sqrt{1 + \frac{\gamma_s^2}{4}}\right). \qquad (2\text{-}164)$$

[1] When the simple shear γ_s is increased by the increment $d\gamma_s$, this causes in the incremental plastic strain tensor the changes $d\varepsilon_1 = -d\varepsilon_2$ in the directions of the principal stresses $\sigma_1 = -\sigma_2 = \tau_{xy}$. Figure 2-18 shows the corresponding two neighboring positions of an unstretched rhombus whose diagonals define the directions of the principal, inherent, finite strains $\varepsilon_1^* = -\varepsilon_2^*$ of the simple shear γ_s. The long diagonal prescribes the principal strain direction in which ε_1^* will act, the length OD' inclined at the angle α_1' represents $1 + \varepsilon_1^*$ (where this latter symbol ε_1^* here temporarily denotes the conventional principal strain), and the length OD'' is equal to $1 + \varepsilon_1^* + d\varepsilon_1^*$.

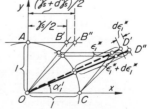

FIG. 2-18. Increment $d\gamma_s$ of simple shear γ_s.

Thus we note, after substituting here $\gamma_s = 2 \sinh \varepsilon_0$, that *the work ratio in an ideally plastic substance is*

$$\omega_s : \omega_p = \sinh \varepsilon_0 : \varepsilon_0, \tag{2-165}$$

whereas *in a perfectly elastic substance this ratio*, according to Eq. (2-82), was found equal to

$$\omega_s : \omega_p = (\sinh \varepsilon_0 : \varepsilon_0)^2. \tag{2-166}$$

In a strain-hardening metal deforming under the law $\tau_0 = f(\gamma_0)$ the work ω_s and ω_p is expressed by the two integrals

$$\omega_s, \ \omega_p = (\tfrac{3}{2}) \int_0^{\gamma_0, \gamma_0^*} \tau_0 \, d\gamma_0 \tag{2-167}$$

whose upper limits are proportional to the values ε_s and ε_s^* which were just evaluated and are equal to

$$\gamma_0 = \sqrt{\tfrac{2}{3}} \gamma_s = 2\sqrt{\tfrac{2}{3}} \sinh \varepsilon_0 \qquad \text{for simple shear,} \tag{2-168}$$

$$\gamma_0^* = 2\sqrt{\tfrac{2}{3}} \cdot \varepsilon_0 \qquad \text{for pure shear,} \tag{2-169}$$

respectively. Again we see that, in a ductile metal yielding under a monotonously increasing strain-hardening function $\tau_0 = f(\gamma_0)$, $\omega_s > \omega_p$, the work in simple shear is always greater than in the equivalent pure shear.

Thus, there is no paradox in attributing to the positions of two, distinct, representative points $Q(\varepsilon_1, \varepsilon_2, \varepsilon_3)$ and $Q^*(\varepsilon_1^*, \varepsilon_2^*, \varepsilon_3^*)$ the determination of the accumulated principal values of the infinitesimal incremental strain tensors and of the principal, inherent, natural strains encountered in a sequence of simple finite shears γ_s in a plastic substance. The movements of these two points Q and Q^* leave their precisely correct records in the strain plane $\varepsilon_1 + \varepsilon_2 + \varepsilon_3 = 0$.

J. Theorem of Minimum Mechanical Work for Finite, Homogeneous, Plastic Strains. The shearing stress τ_0 and natural unit shear γ_0 of the octahedral planes, apart from the various advantages of their use, references to which were presented in the preceding sections, namely, that they serve for defining the intensity of a homogeneous state of stress at a plastic limit and of the finite permanent strains in ductile materials, are also the two significant variables on which the mechanical work of distortion done by the stresses in incompressible plastic substances depends. After having shown that sequences of loading and distortion in them may be represented geometrically through the movements of a point P_0 whose rectangular coordinates are equal to the reduced principal stresses $\sigma_1' = \sigma_1 - \sigma$, $\sigma_2' = \sigma_2 - \sigma$, $\sigma_3' = \sigma_3 - \sigma$, satisfying the condition $\sigma_1' + \sigma_2' + \sigma_3' = 0$, and of a point Q whose coordinates are equal to the principal, natural strains ε_1, ε_2, ε_3 satisfying the condition $\varepsilon_1 + \varepsilon_2 + \varepsilon_3 = 0$, we have seen in Sec. 2-5B that a one-to-one correspondence could be established between the state of finite strain and the positions of point Q in the strain plane, provided that the condition is satisfied that the principal strain axes do not change their orientation relative to the elements of material and coincide during the distortion with the same material points and with the axes of principal stress. We noted also that, since the increment of the octahedral unit shear $d\gamma_0 = 2\, d\varepsilon_s/\sqrt{3}$ is proportional to the differential arc element $d\varepsilon_s$ in the curve representing the strain path and this must be true also for their integrated values $\gamma_0 = 2\varepsilon_s/\sqrt{3}$ along it, consequently *the integral expressing the mechanical work per unit of volume*

$$\omega = \left(\frac{3}{2}\right) \int_0^{\gamma_0 = 2\varepsilon_s/\sqrt{3}} \tau_0 \, d\gamma_0 \qquad (2\text{-}170)$$

increases with the length of arc ε_s measured along the strain-path curve. This led us to formulate a principle of minimum work for plastic substances strained homogeneously to finite amounts, after assuming that a general strain-hardening function $\tau_0 = f(\gamma_0)$ exists which monotonously increases (or at least remains stationary as for the ideally plastic substance, $\tau_0 = \text{const}$) with γ_0. This could be inferred from the shortest distance between the origin O and a point $Q(\varepsilon_1, \varepsilon_3, \varepsilon_3)$ representing the unstrained and strained condition of the body and from the longer arc lengths ε_s measured otherwise on the curved strain paths connecting these points, indicating that the minimum work is done on the straight path along which the ratios of the principal, natural strains $\varepsilon_2/\varepsilon_1$ and $\varepsilon_3/\varepsilon_1$ and of the reduced principal stresses σ_2'/σ_1' and σ_3'/σ_1' remain constant during a distortion.

Let us now consider the general case of a sequence of finite, homogeneous strains combined with a rotation of the principal axes of stress and strain in an incompressible substance. A state of pure strain is determined by six quantities: the quadratic elongations[1]

$$\lambda_x = (1 + \varepsilon_x')^2, \qquad \lambda_y = (1 + \varepsilon_y')^2, \qquad \lambda_z = (1 + \varepsilon_z')^2$$

and the unit shears

$$\gamma_{yz}', \quad \gamma_{zx}', \quad \gamma_{xy}',$$

(where the symbols $\varepsilon_x', \ldots, \gamma_{yz}', \ldots$ denote the conventional components of strain), and a rotation is defined by three quantities. Since the strains are subject to the condition of incompressibility, a strain path may be defined by expressing eight of these quantities as given functions of a variable parameter. Denote by $\lambda_1, \lambda_2, \lambda_3$ the principal elongations in an intermediate stage of distortion and by $\lambda_1^*, \lambda_2^*, \lambda_3^*$ their values at the end of the distortion. Whereas the three principal axes of strain take on, in general, positions distinct from those in which

[1] Cf. Vol. I, page 118.

the reduced principal stresses σ_1', σ_2', σ_3' act, it is recognized—provided that the range of variation between the strain paths leaves open a sufficient range of degrees of freedom—*that sequences of strains might be constructed in which the respective principal axes of stress, of the incremental strain tensor, and of the finite inherent strains in every point of the path will coincide with each other along the same lines of material points in the body.* We may conceive this type of distortion as made up of infinitesimal pure strains in these three mutually perpendicular directions followed by similar rotations by small angles. Since no work is being consumed during these small rotations, it is recognized that these distortions are exactly of the type which were considered in Sec. 2-5C, if one disregards these rotations. We may conclude that among these distortions there will be one in which the principal inherent natural strains ε_1, ε_2, ε_3 grow under constant ratios $\varepsilon_2/\varepsilon_1$, $\varepsilon_3/\varepsilon_1$ until they reach the final values ε_1^*, ε_2^*, ε_3^* and that this latter strain path requires the minimum work. Or viewed from a slightly different angle, we may substitute for this continuous path satisfying the conditions $\varepsilon_2/\varepsilon_1 = \varepsilon_2^*/\varepsilon_1^* = $ const, $\varepsilon_3/\varepsilon_1 = \varepsilon_3^*/\varepsilon_1^* = $ const a discontinuous path as follows: Remembering that a state of homogeneous finite strain is brought about by a linear transformation in which the coordinates x', y', z' of a point in the strained body are linear homogeneous functions of its coordinates x, y, z in the unstrained condition and that this distortion may be brought about by deforming the body first along three mutually perpendicular directions to the required amounts and subsequently rotating it as a rigid body into the position in which these directions coincide with the axes of the strain ellipsoid[1] $(\lambda_1^*, \lambda_2^*, \lambda_3^*)$, we may choose to produce ε_1, ε_2, ε_3 under these circumstances under constant strain ratios $\varepsilon_2/\varepsilon_1$, $\varepsilon_3/\varepsilon_1$. The first operation requires an amount of work which certainly, after what has been said in Sec. 2-5C, represents the absolute minimum of mechanical work ω^* for producing λ_1^*, λ_2^*, λ_3^* under any circumstance; since the former, continuous series carried out under constant $\varepsilon_2/\varepsilon_1$, $\varepsilon_3/\varepsilon_1$ and combined with infinitesimal rotations requires the same work, *the minimum-work principle is valid for it too.* It is admitted that no proof has been advanced here for the existence of this continuous sequence of strains characterized by the property postulated that, during it, the principal axes of stress and finite strain remain in mutual coincidence with a group of three perpendicular lines, consisting of the same material points, while they rotate from their original to their final position. A proof will, however, be given for the general state of a plane, finite strain in the following section.

K. FINITE HOMOGENEOUS PLANE STRAIN. THE PRINCIPLE OF MINI-MUM WORK APPLIED TO PLASTIC STATES OF FINITE, HOMOGENEOUS, PLANE STRAIN. (1). *A state of finite, homogeneous, plane strain* is brought

[1] Cf. Vol. I, page 112.

about by a linear transformation[1]

$$x' = c_{11}x + c_{12}y,$$
$$y' = c_{21}x + c_{22}y, \qquad (2\text{-}171)$$
$$z' = z,$$

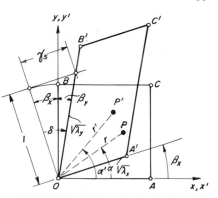

where x, y denote the rectangular coordinates of a point P in its original position and x', y' in its displaced position P'. In an incompressible substance which we wish to postulate, such a strain transforms a unit square $OABC$ (Fig. 2-19) into a rhomboid $OA'B'C'$ of unit area.

FIG. 2-19. Finite plane strain.

The four constants in the linear transformation may conveniently be expressed in terms of the strains or elongations and of the unit shear to be prescribed in those two directions which originally coincided with the x and y axes, after also making use of the condition of incompressibility. The straight lines OA and OB which were originally in the x and y direction suffer finite strains and will be tilted by the finite angles β_x and β_y toward each other.

Denote by ε_x' and ε_y' the conventional unit strains $\varepsilon_x' = OA'/OA - 1$, $\varepsilon_y' = OB'/OB - 1$, and the conventional unit shear by $\gamma_s = \tan \delta = \tan(\beta_x + \beta_y)$. Instead of dealing with the strains ε_x' and ε_y', we introduce the quadratic elongations along $\overline{OA'}$ and $\overline{OB'}$ $\lambda_x = (1 + \varepsilon_x')^2$ and $\lambda_y = (1 + \varepsilon_y')^2$. The area of the rhomboid $OA'B'C'$ being unity, the condition of incompressibility of the material is expressed by

$$(1 + \varepsilon_x')(1 + \varepsilon_y') \cos \delta = 1 \qquad \text{or} \qquad \lambda_x \lambda_y = \frac{1}{\cos^2 \delta} = 1 + \gamma_s^2. \quad (2\text{-}172)$$

By choosing two of the three quantities λ_x, λ_y, γ_s, for example, λ_x and γ_s, and one of the angles β_x or β_y, for example, β_x, the strain is fully determined. In the unstrained condition $\lambda_x = \lambda_y = 1$, $\gamma_s = 0$, $\beta_x = 0$. With these stipulations the four constants $c_{11}, c_{12}, c_{21}, c_{22}$ in Eqs. (2-171) are defined, and after inserting the prescribed values of the coordinates x, y, and x', y' of points A, B and A', B' one verifies easily that the general state of homogeneous finite plane strain is expressed by the linear transformation

$$x' = x\sqrt{\lambda_x} \cos \beta_x + y\sqrt{\lambda_y} \sin \beta_y,$$
$$y' = x\sqrt{\lambda_x} \sin \beta_x + y\sqrt{\lambda_y} \cos \beta_y, \qquad (2\text{-}173)$$
$$z' = z.$$

[1] Cf. Vol. I, Secs. 11-1, 12-1, 13-1, and 13-2.

An alternative form of it, avoiding λ_y and β_y, after using Eq. (2-172) and $\beta_x + \beta_y = \delta,\ \gamma_s = \tan \delta$ is

$$x' = x\sqrt{\lambda_x}\cos \beta_x + \frac{y(\gamma_s \cos \beta_x - \sin \beta_x)}{\sqrt{\lambda_x}},$$

$$y' = x\sqrt{\lambda_x}\sin \beta_x + \frac{y(\cos \beta_x + \gamma_s \sin \beta_x)}{\sqrt{\lambda_x}}, \qquad (2\text{-}174)$$

$$z' = z.$$

A line $\overline{OP} = r$ inclined under an angle α with respect to the x axis is brought in a position $\overline{OP'} = r'$ inclined under an angle α'. The elongation $\lambda = (r'/r)^2$ in the direction $\overline{OP'}$ may be expressed either in terms of the angle α (measured in the unstrained body) or of the angle α' (measured in the strained body). If the values of x' and y' taken from Eqs. (2-173) and $x = r\cos \alpha,\ y = r\sin \alpha$ are substituted in the expression defining the elongation $\lambda = (r'/r)^2 = (x'^2 + y'^2)/r^2$, this is found equal to

$$\lambda = \frac{\lambda_x + \lambda_y}{2} + \frac{\lambda_x - \lambda_y}{2}\cos 2\alpha + \sqrt{\lambda_x \lambda_y}\sin \delta \sin 2\alpha \qquad (2\text{-}175)$$

or, after making use of Eq. (2-172), and $\tan \delta = \gamma_s$, equal to

$$\lambda = \frac{\lambda_x + \lambda_y}{2} + \frac{\lambda_x - \lambda_y}{2}\cos 2\alpha + \gamma_s \sin 2\alpha. \qquad (2\text{-}176)$$

A unit square in the unstrained condition of the body with the sides inclined under the angles α and $\alpha + (\pi/2)$ is distorted into a rhomboid of unit area having the elongations λ_μ and λ_v, and if γ denotes the conventional unit shear in this latter rhomboid, we have also

$$\lambda_\mu \lambda_v = 1 + \gamma^2 \qquad (2\text{-}177)$$

serving for computing the value of the unit shear γ. We have

$$\lambda_\mu = \frac{\lambda_x + \lambda_y}{2} + \frac{\lambda_x - \lambda_y}{2}\cos 2\alpha + \gamma_s \sin 2\alpha,$$

$$\lambda_v = \frac{\lambda_x + \lambda_y}{2} - \frac{\lambda_x - \lambda_y}{2}\cos 2\alpha - \gamma_s \sin 2\alpha, \qquad (2\text{-}178)$$

and
$$\lambda_\mu + \lambda_v = \lambda_x + \lambda_y. \qquad (2\text{-}179)$$

After substituting $\lambda_\mu,\ \lambda_v$ from Eqs. (2-178) in Eq. (2-177), we obtain for the unit shear γ

$$\gamma = -\frac{\lambda_x - \lambda_y}{2}\sin 2\alpha + \gamma_s \cos 2\alpha, \qquad (2\text{-}180)$$

and, after squaring and adding the terms in Eqs. (2-176) and (2-180),

$$\left(\lambda - \frac{\lambda_x + \lambda_y}{2}\right)^2 + \gamma^2 = \frac{(\lambda_x - \lambda_y)^2}{4} + \gamma_s^2 = \frac{(\lambda_x + \lambda_y)^2}{4} - 1,$$

(2-181)

we obtain, in the variables λ, γ, *the equation of the elongation λ–unit shear γ circle of a plane strain* in which, on account of Eq. (2-172), the right side has also been expressed by $(\frac{1}{4})(\lambda_x + \lambda_y)^2 - 1$.

Assuming $\gamma = 0$, from Eq. (2-181) *the principal elongations* are found equal to

$$\lambda_1, \lambda_2 = \frac{\lambda_x + \lambda_y}{2} \pm \sqrt{\frac{(\lambda_x + \lambda_y)^2}{4} - 1}, \qquad \lambda_3 = 1, \qquad (2\text{-}182)$$

or in alternative form, in which λ_y is replaced by $\lambda_y = (1 + \gamma_s^2)/\lambda_x$ and $\lambda_x + \lambda_y$ by $(\lambda_x^2 + \gamma_s^2 + 1)/\lambda_x$,

$$\lambda_1, \lambda_2 = \frac{\lambda_x^2 + \gamma_s^2 + 1}{2\lambda_x} \pm \sqrt{\frac{(\lambda_x^2 + \gamma_s^2 + 1)^2}{4\lambda_x^2} - 1}, \qquad (2\text{-}183)$$

satisfying the condition of incompressibility $\lambda_1 \lambda_2 = 1$. Taking $\gamma = 0$ in Eq. (2-180),

$$\tan 2\alpha = \frac{2\gamma_s}{\lambda_x - \lambda_y} = \frac{2\lambda_x \gamma_s}{\lambda_x^2 - \gamma_s^2 - 1} \qquad (2\text{-}184)$$

defines two angles α, $\alpha + (\pi/2)$ of two directions in the unstrained body, corresponding to which the principal axes of strain will be found in the strained body. In order to determine the corresponding angles α' in the strained body one solves Eqs. (2-173) for x and y,

$$x = \sqrt{\lambda_y} \cdot (x' \cos \beta_y - y' \sin \beta_y),$$
$$y = \sqrt{\lambda_x} \cdot (-x' \sin \beta_x + y' \cos \beta_x); \qquad (2\text{-}185)$$

computes the reciprocal value of the elongation $1/\lambda = (r/r')^2$ in terms of $x' = r' \cos \alpha'$ and $y' = r' \sin \alpha'$,

$$\frac{1}{\lambda} = \frac{1 + \gamma_s^2}{2} \left[\frac{1}{\lambda_x} + \frac{1}{\lambda_y} + \left(\frac{\cos 2\beta_y}{\lambda_x} - \frac{\cos 2\beta_x}{\lambda_y} \right) \cos 2\alpha' \right.$$
$$\left. - \left(\frac{\sin 2\beta_y}{\lambda_x} + \frac{\sin 2\beta_x}{\lambda_y} \right) \sin 2\alpha' \right]; \qquad (2\text{-}186)$$

and, after letting $(d/d\alpha')(1/\lambda) = 0$, obtains for *the directions of the principal axes of strain in the strained condition of the body*

$$\tan 2\alpha' = \frac{\lambda_y \sin 2\beta_y + \lambda_x \sin 2\beta_x}{\lambda_x \cos 2\beta_x - \lambda_y \cos 2\beta_y},$$

$$\tan 2\alpha' = \frac{(1 + \gamma_s^2) \sin 2\beta_y + \lambda_x^2 \sin 2\beta_x}{\lambda_x^2 \cos 2\beta_x - (1 + \gamma_s^2) \cos 2\beta_y}. \qquad (2\text{-}187)$$

It was felt that the preceding formulas for one of the most frequently encountered, general states of finite strain in engineering and geophysical applications should be made available to readers here since they were not included in Vol. I.

(2). *Mechanical work for a prescribed sequence of plane strain.* In order to avoid writing nonessential constant terms and to clarify the facts in the simplest possible manner when evaluating the work of deformation, let us now conceive sequences of states of plane strain, supposing that in them the angle β_x stays at the value $\beta_x = 0$. This deformation thus consists of a *simple, finite shear* γ_s in the direction of the x axis *combined with a simultaneous extension or compression of the linear elements parallel to the x axis* (and the corresponding changes of length parallel to the oblique sides of the rhomboids $ORQS$ in Fig. 2-20). After letting $\beta_x = 0, \beta_y = \delta, \gamma_s = \tan \delta = \tan \beta_y$ in Eqs. (2-173), this type of plane strain is expressed by the linear transformation of simpler form:

$$x' = x\sqrt{\lambda_x} + \frac{y\gamma_s}{\sqrt{\lambda_x}}, \qquad y' = \frac{y}{\sqrt{\lambda_x}}, \qquad z' = z, \qquad (2\text{-}188)$$

on which the following computations will be based. This type, as well as the general state of plane strain [Eqs. (2-173)] for incompressible material, is *essentially a finite, pure shear combined with a rotation of its principal axes of strain* [their angle of rotation when postulating Eqs. (2-188) has been, in fact, diminished by the angle β_x which was present in the former state expressed by Eqs. (2-173)]. The type of strain considered distorts a unit square $OR_0S_0Q_0$ into a rhomboid $ORSQ$ of unit area, as represented in Fig. 2-20 by the intermediate rhomboids, all having one pair of their sides remaining parallel to the x axis. The angular transformations for this plane strain are

$$\tan \alpha = \frac{y}{x}, \qquad \tan \alpha' = \frac{y'}{x'} = \frac{\tan \alpha}{\lambda_x + \gamma_s \tan \alpha}. \qquad (2\text{-}189)$$

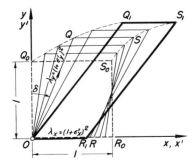

FIG. 2-20. A sequence of finite plane strains.

FIG. 2-21. Path $\gamma_s = f(\lambda_x)$.

For it *a sequence of strains may be defined* by a function

$$F(\lambda_x, \gamma_s) = 0 \tag{2-190}$$

or, graphically, by a curve in a plot of rectangular coordinates λ_x, γ_s (Fig. 2-21), connecting the point $P_0(\lambda_x = 1, \gamma_s = 0)$ with the point $P_1(\lambda_{x1}, \gamma_{s1})$, representing the initial, unstrained and the final, strained state. We may investigate various strain paths, instead of in the strain plane $\varepsilon_1 + \varepsilon_2 + \varepsilon_3 = 0$, by describing the curves that they trace in this plane having the rectangular coordinates λ_x, γ_s.

In order to express the mechanical work ω done by the stresses in a sequence of this plane strain, let us introduce the differentials $d\varepsilon_x$, $d\varepsilon_y$, $d\gamma_{xy}$ of the natural components of strain $\varepsilon_x = \ln (1 + \varepsilon_x') = \ln \sqrt{\lambda_x}$, $\varepsilon_y = \ln (1 + \varepsilon_y') = \ln \sqrt{\lambda_y}$ and shear γ_{xy}. $d\varepsilon_x = d\lambda_x/2\lambda_x$ and $d\varepsilon_y = d\lambda_y/2\lambda_y$ define the infinitesimal changes of a unit of length in the lines sweeping through the x and y axis, and $d\gamma_{xy}$ expresses the small change that their right angle suffers. In a state of homogeneous plane strain the components of shearing stress τ_{yz} and τ_{zx} vanish, and we may choose also the normal stress σ_z equal to zero.[1] On account of $\varepsilon_z = 0$, in incompressible material $d\varepsilon_x = -d\varepsilon_y$ and the plastic stress-strain relations

$$d\varepsilon_x = d\phi[\sigma_x - (\tfrac{1}{2})(\sigma_y + \sigma_z)],$$
$$d\varepsilon_y = d\phi[\sigma_y - (\tfrac{1}{2})(\sigma_x + \sigma_z)], \qquad d\gamma_{xy} = 3\,d\phi\tau_{xy}, \tag{2-191}$$
$$d\varepsilon_z = d\phi[\sigma_z - (\tfrac{1}{2})(\sigma_x + \sigma_y)]$$

may be considerably simplified; since $d\varepsilon_z = 0$, $\sigma_z = 0$, it follows that $\sigma_y = -\sigma_x$ and

$$d\varepsilon_x = -d\varepsilon_y = \frac{d\lambda_x}{2\lambda_x} = \frac{3d\phi\sigma_x}{2}, \qquad d\gamma_{xy} = 3d\phi\tau_{xy}, \tag{2-192}$$

where the differential of the flow function is $d\phi = d\gamma_0/3\tau_0$; τ_0, γ_0 are the octahedral shearing stress and natural shearing strain.

Considering first an ideally plastic material, the condition of plasticity $\tau_0 = $ const for a plane state of stress and strain takes the simpler form

$$\sigma_x^2 + \tau_{xy}^2 = \frac{3\tau_0^2}{2} = \frac{\sigma_0^2}{3} = \text{const} \tag{2-193}$$

(σ_0 is yield stress in tension) which in the variables σ_x and τ_{xy} is the

---

[1] This amounts to superposing a hydrostatic uniform normal stress not having an effect on the plasticity condition through which a nonvanishing normal stress σ_z may be canceled out.

equation of a circle (Fig. 2-22).   The principal stresses are $\sigma_1 = -\sigma_2 = \sigma_0/\sqrt{3}$, $\sigma_3 = 0$.

The differential of the natural unit shear $d\gamma_{xy}$ may be expressed in terms of the differentials $d\lambda_x$ and $d\gamma_s$ defining an increment of the plane strain as follows:

$$dγ_{xy} = dγ_s - \frac{γ_s\, dλ_x}{λ_x} = dγ_s - 2γ_s\, dε_x. \tag{2-194}$$

For evaluating this increment of the natural shear $d\gamma_{xy}$, consider a snapshot of the deformed body in Fig. 2-23 taken just after a vertical material line $\overline{OQ'} = 1$, which coincided instantaneously with the y axis, was slightly tilted into its new position $\overline{OQ''}$ in consequence of the increments of the strains $d\lambda_x$, $d\gamma_s$.   This amounts to finding the infinitesimal angle $d\alpha'$ by which the vertical ray $\alpha' = \pi/2$ $(\overline{OQ'})$ has turned. Using the angular transformation formula (2-189), we differentiate it, considering λ_x and γ_s as the independent variables and α' as the dependent variable while the angle α in the unstrained body is being held invariable.   This ties the direction $\alpha' = \pi/2$ to the corresponding material line $\alpha = \text{const}$ in the undeformed body,

$$d\tan α' = \frac{\partial}{\partial λ_x}(\tan α')\, dλ_x + \frac{\partial}{\partial γ_s}(\tan α')\, dγ_s \tag{2-195}$$

or

$$\frac{dα'}{\cos^2 α'} = -\frac{\tan α \cdot dλ_x + \tan^2 α \cdot dγ_s}{(λ_x + γ_s \tan α)^2}$$

or, after again using Eqs. (2-189),

$$dα' = -\sin^2 α' \left(\frac{1 - γ_s \tan α'}{λ_x \tan α'}\, dλ_x + dγ_s \right), \tag{2-196}$$

giving, for the small angle $d\alpha'$ by which the vertical ray $\alpha' = \pi/2$ turns, the increment of the natural shear

$$dγ_{xy} = -dα' = dγ_s - \frac{γ_s\, dλ_x}{λ_x} \tag{2-197}$$

FIG. 2-22.
Stress circle.

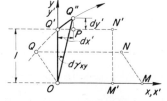

FIG. 2-23. Increment of
natural shear $d\gamma_{xy}$.

in accordance with Eq. (2-194). The corners of the rhomboid $OMNQ$ in Fig. 2-23 illustrate the original positions of the points in the unstrained body, which, after the finite strain λ_x, γ_s was applied to it, became the corners of the unit square $OM'N'Q'$ just before the increments $d\lambda_x$, $d\gamma_s$ were added.[1]

After substituting the value of $d\gamma_{xy}$ found in Eq. (2-194) and $d\varepsilon_z = 0$, $d\varepsilon_x = -d\varepsilon_y$ in the formula (2-5) for the differential of the natural octahedral unit shear $d\gamma_0$, this is found equal to

$$dy_0 = \sqrt{\frac{2}{3}} \sqrt{4d\varepsilon_x^2 + d\gamma_{xy}^2} = \sqrt{\frac{2}{3}} \sqrt{\frac{d\lambda_x^2}{\lambda_x^2} + \left(d\gamma_s - \frac{\gamma_s\,d\lambda_x}{\lambda_x}\right)^2},$$

(2-198)

which permits us to express *the mechanical work ω per unit of volume* for straining the material over a prescribed path[2] $F(\lambda_x,\gamma_s) = 0$ in a state of plane strain:

$$\omega = \frac{3}{2}\int \tau_0\,d\gamma_0 = \frac{\sigma_0}{\sqrt{3}}\int_1^{\lambda_{x1}} \sqrt{1 + \left(\frac{\lambda_x\,d\gamma_s}{d\lambda_x} - \gamma_s\right)^2} \cdot \frac{d\lambda_x}{\lambda_x}.$$

(2-199)

Before further applying this expression, let us write the formulas defining the principal directions of stress and of strain. The former are inclined at the angles α' for which (since $\sigma_y = -\sigma_x$)

$$\tan 2\alpha' = \frac{2\tau_{xy}}{\sigma_x - \sigma_y} = \frac{\tau_{xy}}{\sigma_x}.$$

(2-200)

In order to avoid confusing the angles α' of the principal axes of stress with those of the principal axes of finite strain, let us denote the angles of the latter by the symbol β' in the deformed state of the body. To find β', we solve Eqs. (2-188) for x and y, writing

$$x' = r'\cos\beta', \qquad y' = r'\sin\beta',$$

which gives

$$x = \frac{r'}{\sqrt{\lambda_x}}(\cos\beta' - \gamma_s\sin\beta'), \qquad y = \sqrt{\lambda_x}\,r'\sin\beta';$$

[1] Or if one computes alternatively from Eqs. (2-188) the coordinates $x = -\gamma_s/\sqrt{\lambda_x}$, $y = \sqrt{\lambda_x}$ of the corner $Q(x,y)$ of the rhomboid corresponding to point $Q'(x' = 0, y' = 1)$ and subsequently evaluates from Eqs. (2-188) the differential $dx' = Q'P$ (Fig. 2-23), one obtains for the infinitesimal angle $d\alpha' = dx':1 = Q'P:OQ'$ the same expression as found in Eq. (2-197) in the text above.

[2] Incidentally, we may note that the work done along a prescribed strain path after making use of Eqs. (2-193) and (2-203) may be expressed in the alternative form

$$\omega = \frac{\sigma_0}{\sqrt{3}}\int_1^{\lambda_{x1}} \sqrt{1 + \frac{\tau_{xy}^2}{\sigma_x^2}} \cdot \frac{d\lambda_x}{\lambda_x} = \frac{\sigma_0^2}{3}\int_1^{\lambda_{x1}} \frac{d\lambda_x}{\lambda_x\sigma_x} = \frac{2\sigma_0^2}{3}\int_0^{\varepsilon_{x1}} \frac{d\varepsilon_x}{\sigma_x}.$$

(2-199a)

we then compute the reciprocal value of the quadratic elongation

$$\frac{1}{\lambda} = \frac{x^2 + y^2}{r'^2} = \frac{1}{2\lambda_x} [1 + \gamma_s^2 + \lambda_x^2 + (1 - \gamma_s^2 - \lambda_x^2) \cos 2\beta' - 2\gamma_s \sin 2\beta'],$$

and make $1/\lambda$ an extremum, $(d/d\beta')(1/\lambda) = 0$, which gives for the angle β' of the principal strain axes

$$\tan 2\beta' = \frac{2\gamma_s}{\lambda_x^2 + \gamma_s^2 - 1} . \tag{2-201}$$

The principal elongations $\lambda_1 = e^{2\varepsilon_1}$, $\lambda_2 = e^{2\varepsilon_2}$ *for the plane strain* are expressed, using Eq. (2-183), by

$$\lambda_1 = \varphi + \sqrt{\varphi^2 - 1}, \qquad \lambda_2 = \varphi - \sqrt{\varphi^2 - 1}, \tag{2-201a}$$

satisfying the condition of incompressibility $\lambda_1\lambda_2 = 1$ and $\lambda_1 + \lambda_2 = 2\varphi$, where the abbreviating symbol φ stands for

$$\varphi = \frac{\lambda_x^2 + \gamma_s^2 + 1}{2\lambda_x} = \frac{\lambda_x + \lambda_y}{2} . \tag{2-201b}$$

By virtue of the stress-strain relations of Eq. (2-192), the stress ratio $\tau_{xy}/\sigma_x = \tan 2\alpha'$ is also equal to

$$\frac{\tau_{xy}}{\sigma_x} = \frac{\lambda_x \, d\gamma_{xy}}{d\lambda_x} = \frac{d\gamma_{xy}}{2 \, d\varepsilon_x} = \frac{\lambda_x \, d\gamma_s}{d\lambda_x} - \gamma_s \tag{2-202}$$

and will be a known function either of λ_x or of γ_s when a sequence of strains $F(\lambda_x, \gamma_s) = 0$ is prescribed.   Therefore the components of stress σ_x, σ_y, and τ_{xy} may be determined from Eq. (2-193), as follows:

$$\sigma_x = -\sigma_y = \frac{\sigma_0}{\sqrt{3}} \cos 2\alpha', \qquad \tau_{xy} = \frac{\sigma_0}{\sqrt{3}} \sin 2\alpha',$$

$$\sigma_x = -\sigma_y = \frac{\pm\sigma_0}{\sqrt{3}\sqrt{1 + (\tau_{xy}/\sigma_x)^2}}, \qquad \tau_{xy} = \frac{\pm\sigma_0}{\sqrt{3}} \frac{\tau_{xy}/\sigma_x}{\sqrt{1 + (\tau_{xy}/\sigma_x)^2}} . \tag{2-203}$$

(3). *Minimum-work path.*   We can now draw some interesting conclusions from the preceding equations.   Among the various sequences of plane strain $F(\lambda_x, \gamma_s) = 0$ there is one and only one path connecting the points $P_0(\lambda_x = 1, \gamma_s = 0)$ (Fig. 2-21), representing the initial, unstrained condition of the body, and $P_1(\lambda_{x1}, \gamma_{s1})$, corresponding to a given final state of strain, along which path we may prescribe that Eqs. (2-200) and (2-201) be simultaneously satisfied.   For this *particular strain path the principal axes of finite, plane strain will coincide with those of the incremental strain tensor and consequently also with the instantaneous axes of principal stress in every point of the path.*   For this path the angles $\beta' = \alpha'$ will equal each other, provided that λ_x and γ_s

are chosen so that both satisfy a certain differential equation which is obtained by equating the right-hand expressions of $\tan 2\alpha' = \tau_{xy}/\sigma_x$ and $\tan 2\beta'$ in Eqs. (2-202) and (2-201), namely,

$$\lambda_x \frac{d\gamma_s}{d\lambda_x} - \gamma_s = \frac{2\gamma_s}{\lambda_x^2 + \gamma_s^2 - 1}. \tag{2-204}$$

By letting $\xi = \lambda_x^2$, $\eta = \gamma_s^2$, this is transformed into the differential equation

$$\frac{d\eta}{d\xi} = \frac{\eta(\xi + \eta + 1)}{\xi(\xi + \eta - 1)} \tag{2-205}$$

having the integral

$$\xi + c\sqrt{\xi\eta} - \eta = 1 \tag{2-206}$$

or, in terms of λ_x, γ_s,

$$\underline{\underline{\lambda_x^2 + c\lambda_x\gamma_s - \gamma_s^2 = 1,}} \tag{2-207}$$

c being the integration constant. The latter equation represents in the λ_x, γ_s plane of rectangular coordinates *a family of equilateral hyperbolas*, all of which pass through the point A (Fig. 2-24), $\lambda_x = 1$, $\gamma_s = 0$. The constant c may be evaluated by substituting the values λ_{s1}, λ_{x1} in Eq. (2-207), and the stresses $\sigma_y = -\sigma_x$, τ_{xy} distorting the material along the hyperbolic strain paths may be computed from Eqs. (2-203). Since the integration constant c in Eq. (2-207) appears in the first power, one sees that there is only one strain path connecting the point $A(\lambda_x = 1$, $\gamma_s = 0)$ with a prescribed final state along which the stated conditions are satisfied.

This special sequence of states of pure shears defined by Eq. (2-207) is characterized by an additional property: We may note that the two pairs of coinciding principal axes remain continuously in coincidence with two straight lines in the substance consisting of the same material points while it is being deformed. For, if the expression

$$\lambda_x^2 - \gamma_s^2 - 1 = -c\lambda_x\gamma_s \tag{2-208}$$

taken from Eq. (2-207) of the hyperbolas is substituted in the denominator of the fraction on the right-hand side of Eq. (2-184) expressing $\tan 2\alpha$, where it also appears, it is seen that

$$\tan 2\alpha = \frac{2\lambda_x\gamma_s}{\lambda_x^2 - \gamma_s^2 - 1} = -\frac{2\lambda_x\gamma_s}{c\lambda_x\gamma_s}$$

$$= -\frac{2}{c} = \text{const}, \tag{2-209}$$

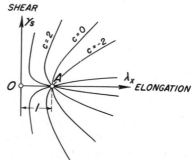

FIG. 2-24. Sequences of finite plane strain requiring minimum plastic work.

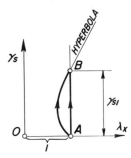

FIG. 2-25. Two ways of producing a simple finite shear γ_{s1}.

whereas the angles β' of the principal strain axes [Eq. (2-201)] in the strained body vary with their rotation in space. Thus, while β' varies, α remains constant, i.e., *the same material points in the body* (for which $\alpha = $ const, $\alpha + \pi/2 = $ const in two perpendicular straight lines in the unstrained condition of the substance) *remain attached to the principal axes of strain (and stress) during the distortion.*

In a pure shear without rotation ($\gamma_s = 0$) while the principal elongation $\lambda_1 = e^{2\varepsilon_1}$ increases and $d\varepsilon_1 = -d\varepsilon_2$, $\sigma_1 = -\sigma_2 = \sigma_0/\sqrt{3}$, in an ideally plastic substance $\sigma_0 = $ const, the mechanical work done, as we have seen, is

$$\omega = \int (\sigma_1 \, d\varepsilon_1 + \sigma_2 \, d\varepsilon_2) = \frac{2}{\sqrt{3}} \sigma_0 \varepsilon_1 = \frac{\sigma_0}{\sqrt{3}} \ln \lambda_1. \qquad (2\text{-}210)$$

In a pure shear with rotations (in an ideally plastic substance) we considered above, deforming along the strain path we prescribed by the function $F(\lambda_x, \gamma_s) = 0$ the same amount of work is done.[1]

After what has been said in Sec. 2-5C and G, since in these pure shears with rotation which follow the strain paths of the equilateral hyperbolas [Eq. (2-207)] the ratio of the principal natural strains $\varepsilon_1/\varepsilon_2 = -1$ remains constant, we expect that the work ω done in them just computed in Eq. (2-210) *represents the minimum work* in an ideally plastic substance for deforming it in a sequence of plane strains to prescribed finite elongations λ_1, $\lambda_2 = 1/\lambda_1$, $\lambda_3 = 1$.

Consider, for example, *a sequence of simple shears* γ_s. This is represented in the plane λ_x, γ_s by the vertical line AB, $\lambda_x = 1$ (Fig. 2-25). Let point B having an ordinate $\gamma_{s1} = AB$ represent the simple shear at the end of the distortion. But point B may be reached from point $A(\lambda_x = 1$, $\gamma_s = 0)$ also on the equilateral hyperbola [Eq. (2-207)] on another strain path. The constant c for it, $c = (1 + \gamma_{s1}^2 - \lambda_{x1}^2)/\lambda_{x1}\gamma_{s1}$, assuming $\lambda_{x1} = 1$, is equal to $c = \gamma_{s1}$. *Thus the minimum-work path for deforming the substance to the strains $\lambda_{x1} = 1$, γ_{s1} of a simple shear is the hyperbola*

$$\underline{\lambda_x^2 + \gamma_{s1}\lambda_x\gamma_s - \gamma_s^2 = 1.} \qquad (2\text{-}211)$$

---

[1] This is confirmed if use is **made** of the auxiliary variable φ which was introduced in Eq. (2-201b) since the work done by this type of pure shear computed from Eq. (2-199),

$$\omega = \frac{\sigma_0}{\sqrt{3}} \int_1^{\varphi_1} \frac{d\varphi}{\sqrt{\varphi^2 - 1}} = \frac{\sigma_0}{\sqrt{3}} \ln (\varphi_1 + \sqrt{\varphi_1^2 - 1}) = \frac{\sigma_0}{\sqrt{3}} \ln \lambda_1,$$

is equal to that given in Eq. (2-210).

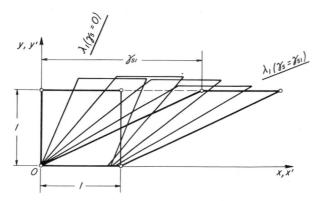

FIG. 2-26. A simple finite shear γ_{s1} produced by minimum-work strain sequence.

While the sequence of simple shears, according to Eq. (2-163), consumes the work

$$\omega_s = \frac{\sqrt{3}}{2}\,\tau_0\gamma_{s1} = \frac{\sigma_0}{\sqrt{3}}\,\gamma_{s1} \tag{2-212}$$

on the strain path of the hyperbola of Eq. (2-211), the same final distortion[1] $\lambda_{x1} = 1$, γ_{s1} is produced under the minimum of work:

$$\omega_{\min} = \frac{\sigma_0}{\sqrt{3}}\ln\lambda_1 = \frac{2\sigma_0}{\sqrt{3}}\ln\left[\frac{\gamma_{s1}}{2} + \sqrt{1 + \left(\frac{\gamma_{s1}}{2}\right)^2}\,\right]. \tag{2-213}$$

For example, if $\gamma_{s1} = 1$, $\omega_s = \sigma_0/\sqrt{3}$, whereas

$$\omega_{\min} = \frac{2\sigma_0}{\sqrt{3}}\ln\left(\frac{1 + \sqrt{5}}{2}\right) = \frac{0.96\sigma_0}{\sqrt{3}}.$$

We note that, along the hyperbola of Eq. (2-211), $\lambda_x < 1$ (except in the end points A and B in Fig. 2-25). The minimum-work path requires that the body first be compressed slightly in the direction of the x axis while the planes $y = $ const slip by the appropriate amounts and subsequently be expanded back until the original lengths are restored. This sequence of distortions consuming the least work $\omega_{\min}$ has been illustrated in Figs. 2-26 and 2-27 by tracing the rhomboids in one of these figures and the rectangles along the principal axes in the second figure. The latter disclose clearly the simultaneous rotation of the principal axes of the pure shears.

---

[1] The principal elongation λ_1 corresponding to a finite, simple shear γ_{s1} appearing in Eq. (2-213) was evaluated in Eqs. (2-73).

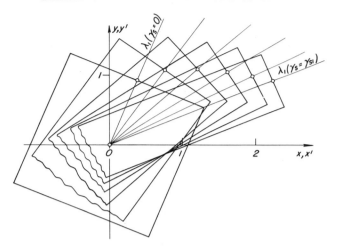

F<small>IG</small>. 2-27. Minimum-work strain sequence. A pure shear connected with a rotation of the distorted body. The rotation is indicated by the consecutive positions of the principal axes of stress and of the finite strain coinciding with each other.

We shall now prove, after postulating the general class of plane-strain distortions defined by Eqs. (2-188), that for the pathways of the family of equilateral hyperbolas [Eq. (2-207)] the mechanical work ω becomes an extremum. This amounts *to finding the sequence of plane, finite strains* $F(\lambda_x, \gamma_s) = 0$ *for which the definite integral expressing the mechanical work done by the stresses*

$$\omega = \frac{\sigma_0}{\sqrt{3}} \int_1^{\lambda_{x1}} \frac{d\lambda_x}{\lambda_x} \sqrt{1 + \left(\lambda_x \frac{d\gamma_s}{d\lambda_x} - \gamma_s\right)^2} \qquad (2\text{-}214)$$

becomes an analytic extremum, in fact a minimum, constituting a problem of the calculus of variations. In it the maximizing or minimizing functions $F(\lambda_x, \gamma_s) = 0$ are called the "extremal curves" of the integral[1] [Eq. (2-214)]. Proof will be established by showing that the extremal curves of the integral are identical with the family of our hyperbolas [Eq. (2-207)].

It will be convenient to change one of the variables, namely, λ_x, and to denote the new independent variable by u and the dependent variable by v:

$$u = \ln \lambda_x = 2\varepsilon_x, \qquad du = \frac{d\lambda_x}{\lambda_x}, \qquad (2\text{-}215)$$

$$v = \gamma_s = g(u).$$

[1] Cf. O. B<small>OLZA</small>, "Vorlesungen über Variationsrechnung," 705 pp, Verlag von B. G. Teubner, Leipzig, 1909, or F. S. W<small>OODS</small>, "Advanced Calculus," Ginn & Company, Boston.

Following the standard symbolism used in the calculus of variations, we shall denote the small change or variation of the work ω expressed by the definite integral [Eq. (2-214)] if a strain path is slightly changed (varied) by writing δ before the quantity to be varied; thus $\delta\omega$ expresses the (first) variation of the mechanical work ω. In order that ω become an extremum or that $\delta\omega$ vanish, we have to write the δ before the integral in Eq. (2-214), letting the variation of it vanish. After using Eqs. (2-215), this amounts, then, to finding the extremal functions $v = g(u)$ for which the first variation of the definite integral

$$\delta J = \delta \int_0^{u_1} \sqrt{1 + (v' - v)^2}\, du = \delta \int_0^{u_1} f(u,v,v')\, du = 0 \qquad (2\text{-}216)$$

vanishes, where v' denotes the derivative $v' = dv/du$ and the function f denotes the integrand of J. In the calculus of variations one shows that this mathematical problem $\delta J = 0$ is solved by *integrating* what is known as *Euler's differential equation* corresponding to Eq. (2-216), namely, the equation having the form

$$\frac{\partial f}{\partial v} - \frac{d}{du}\left(\frac{\partial f}{\partial v'}\right) = 0, \qquad \text{where} \qquad f(u,v,v') = \sqrt{1 + (v' - v)^2}. \quad (2\text{-}217)$$

But,
$$-\frac{\partial f}{\partial v} = \frac{\partial f}{\partial v'} = \frac{v' - v}{\sqrt{1 + (v' - v)^2}}. \qquad (2\text{-}218)$$

Thus denoting by:

$$U = \frac{v' - v}{\sqrt{1 + (v' - v)^2}}, \qquad (2\text{-}219)$$

we see that *Euler's equation* is expressed by

$$\frac{dU}{du} + U = 0 \qquad (2\text{-}220)$$

or explicitly by

$$\frac{d^2 v}{du^2} - v + \left(\frac{dv}{du} - v\right)^3 = 0. \qquad (2\text{-}221)$$

The integral of Eq. (2-220),

$$U = \frac{v' - v}{\sqrt{1 + (v' - v)^2}} = c_0 e^{-u}, \qquad (2\text{-}222)$$

after solving for $v' - v$, is

$$v' - v = \frac{c_0}{\sqrt{e^{2u} - c_0^2}}, \qquad (2\text{-}223)$$

where the $\pm$ sign has been suppressed since c_0 is an undetermined integration constant.   A second integration carried out on Eq. (2-223) furnishes

$$v = c_1 e^u + \frac{1}{c_0} \sqrt{e^{2u} - c_0^2}, \qquad (2\text{-}224)$$

with c_0, c_1 as integration constants.   After discarding the square root by squaring and after reinstituting the original symbols γ_s and λ_x for v and u and $e^u = \lambda_x$, the curves making the integral J [Eq. (2-216)] an extremum are expressed by *the general solution of Euler's equation*:

$$\gamma_s^2 - 2c_1\lambda_x\gamma_s - \left(\frac{1}{c_0^2} - c_1^2\right)\lambda_x^2 + 1 = 0. \qquad (2\text{-}225)$$

It contains two integration constants, c_0 and c_1, thus significantly permitting one to lay the curve $F(\lambda_x,\gamma_s) = 0$ through two given points, namely, $\lambda_x = 1$, $\gamma_s = 0$ and λ_{x1}, γ_{s1}.   It is readily seen, after choosing them accordingly, $c_0 = 2/\sqrt{4 + c^2}$ and $c_1 = -c/2$, that Eq. (2-225) coincides with Eq. (2-207) defining the family of the equilateral hyperbolas:

$$\gamma_s^2 + c\lambda_x\gamma_s - \lambda_x^2 + 1 = 0, \qquad (2\text{-}226)$$

proof having been herewith established that the mechanical work ω expressed by Eq. (2-214) *becomes an analytic extremum* by deforming the body from the unstrained condition $\lambda_x = 1$, $\gamma_s = 0$ to a prescrided strained condition λ_{x1}, γ_{s1} *in such a manner that during the plane-strain distortion the principal axes of stress remain continuously in coincidence with those of finite strain.*   That the extremum of work [expressed by Eq. (2-210)] represents a minimum has not been shown, but after what has been indicated previously it should be sufficiently evident and may be readily verified in examples.[1]

It may perhaps be instructive *to mention a few alternative sequences of plane strains* belonging to the class defined by Eqs. (2-188).   For example, the sequences for which *the principal axes of stress do not change their orientation* are determined by the condition [see Eqs. (2-200) and (2-202)] that

$$\tan 2\alpha' = \lambda_x \frac{d\gamma_s}{d\lambda_x} - \gamma_s = c = \text{const} \qquad (2\text{-}227)$$

---

[1] It may perhaps be in order here to call attention to the fact that, whereas the various sequences of distortion, which were compared in their mechanical work in this section *devoted to the domain of finite strains, satisfied all the exact conditions characteristic of the flow of an ideally plastic substance*, in other extremum or variational principles that have been advanced for such a substance *within the domain of infinitesimal strains* (to which references will be made in Chap. 3), the sequences of distortion which one usually admits in a variation are supposed *to differ from the exact solution* in one or the other respect.

or, after the preceding equation is integrated, by

$$\gamma_s = c(\lambda_x - 1) \tag{2-228}$$

representing a family of straight lines in the λ_x, γ_s plane (Fig. 2-28).

The sequences of plane strain for which, on the other hand, *the principal directions of strain remain unchanged* are defined by letting, in Eq. (2-201),

$$\tan 2\beta' = \frac{2\gamma_s}{\lambda_x^2 + \gamma_s^2 - 1} = c = \text{const}, \tag{2-229}$$

which is the equation of a family of circles (Fig. 2-29),

$$\lambda_x^2 + \left(\gamma_s - \frac{1}{c}\right)^2 = 1 + \frac{1}{c^2}. \tag{2-230}$$

In neither group of distortions do the principal axes of stress simultaneously coincide with those of strain.

In Fig. 2-30 three alternative sequences of plane strain are indicated in the λ_x, γ_s plane of coordinates through the paths A, B, and C while Fig. 2-31 reproduces the corresponding series of distortions ending in the same final configuration. Let point $D(\lambda_x = 1, \gamma_s = 0)$ in Fig. 2-30 represent the unstrained condition and point $F(\lambda_{x1} = 4, \gamma_{s1} = 1)$ the final, strained condition in the body and let it in path A be deformed along the broken line DEF first by simple shear to point $E(\lambda_x = 1, \gamma_s = \frac{1}{4})$ and subsequently by pure shear to point F. Along path B (the broken line DGF) the body is subjected first to pure shear and subsequently to simple shear. The hyperbola of path C represents the

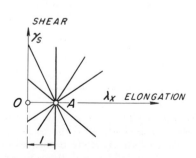

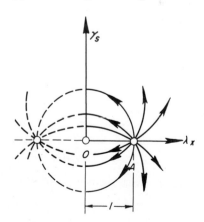

FIG. 2-28. Sequences of finite plane strain without rotation of principal stress directions.

FIG. 2-29. Sequences of finite plane strain without rotation of principal strain directions.

minimum-work path.   For these three, alternative methods of distortion (Fig. 2-30) the following amounts of work were computed:

$$\omega_A, \omega_B, \omega_C = (1.64, 2.39, 1.25)\frac{\sigma_0}{\sqrt{3}},$$

verifying again that for the hyperbola path C the least work was
necessary.

In conclusion, it may be added that the principle of minimum work,
as explained in the preceding theory and illustrated by various examples
of plane-strain sequences of an ideally plastic substance $\tau_0 = $ const, is
valid also for a material that strain-hardens according to a monotonously increasing function $\tau_0 = f(\gamma_0)$.   The geometry for resolving
the components of finite strain is the same in both cases but the evaluation of the mechanical work would require cumbersome quadratures of
the integrals expressing the work for different pathways of deformation.
The extremum (minimum) condition is not invalidated in the integrals
expressing the work when $\tau_0 = f(\gamma_0)$.

In the various applications that we have described in the preceding

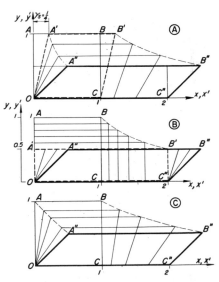

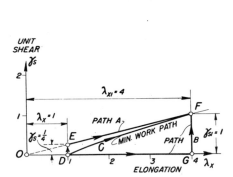

Fig. 2-30. Three sequences of finite
plane strains.

Fig. 2-31. Three sequences of finite
plane strain ending in the same final
configuration: A. Body deformed first
by a simple shear and then by pure
shear; B. body deformed first by a pure
shear and subsequently by simple shear;
C. minimum-work path.

sections devoted to plastic substances, we have considered only states of homogeneous, finite strain as the simplest cases that can be treated, and we raised the question of which among the competing states consumed the least work. It is conjectured that the principle of minimum work of plastic deformation may become a significant means of determining the particular sequences of nonhomogeneous straining in bodies which terminate in states of stress and strain for which a total distortion or the resultant forces are prescribed in the domain of non-homogeneous states of finite deformation—a field that, because of its mathematical difficulties, has barely been touched in the boundary-value problems of this type.

CHAPTER 3

EXTREMUM PRINCIPLES OF WORK IN THE THEORIES OF DEFORMABLE SUBSTANCES

3-1. Energy Principles of the Theory of Elasticity. In the mathematical theory of elasticity, principles have been established which utilize the condition that the potential energy of an elastic body in a stable position of equilibrium is a minimum, compared with its values in arbitrarily disturbed, nearby positions, in which the elastically distorted shape of the body has been slightly altered, or compared with the values of the strain energy in slightly disturbed equilibrium positions of an elastic system in which the external forces or the state of internal stress has been changed by small amounts.

The great physicist GUSTAV KIRCHHOFF was the first to introduce one of these principles in the theory of elasticity in one of his fundamental papers[1] published in 1850. Endeavoring to develop the theory of the bending of a thin, flat, elastic plate, in this remarkable paper he succeeded in deriving from the extremum condition of the potential energy at once the fourth-order linear partial differential equation for the small deflections of an elastic plate (*Lagrange's* equation) and the differential expressions for two complete boundary conditions for the deflected middle surface of a plate. He thus established for the first time the correct expressions of the latter conditions, after various unsuccessful attempts during the first half of the nineteenth century by mathematicians of the French schools, among them POISSON, who had failed to obtain them. They asserted that the elastic surface of a slightly bent plate and solution of the fourth-order differential equation for the deflections of a plate must satisfy three independent boundary conditions whereas Kirchhoff found that only two were sufficient.[2]

---

[1] Über das Gleichgewicht und die Bewegung einer elastischen Scheibe, Crelles J., vol. 40, p. 51, 1850; see also the thirtieth lecture, in the collected lectures of G. KIRCHHOFF: W. Wien (ed.), "Vorlesungen ueber Mechanik," 464 pp., 4th ed., p. 449, Verlag von B. G. Teubner, Leipzig, 1897.

[2] This paper of 1850 was KIRCHHOFF's Habilitationsschrift, the one for which he received the *Venia legendi*, the permit to lecture, according to the custom of German universities. While Kirchhoff devoted his life work to the varied fields in physics, in view of this early paper dealing with an eminently mechanical

Fig. 3-1. Gustav Kirchhoff.† (Born in Königsberg, Mar. 12, 1824; died in Berlin, Oct. 17, 1887.)‡

This he accomplished by applying the principle of virtual displacements, by letting the first variation of a definite integral vanish, expressing the total potential energy of a bent plate as the sum of the elastic strain energy of the internal stresses straining the plate in bending and of the potential energy of the system of the external forces (loads) deflecting it. After carrying out the variation behind the integral sign in the integrand, he found the differential equation for the

---

subject it may, incidentally, be remarked that he, as well as some of the contemporary, outstanding, theoretical physicists living in the second half of the nineteenth century (Hermann von Helmholtz, James Clerk Maxwell, Lord Kelvin), consecrated much laudable effort in their treatises and in parts of their lecture courses to expounding the principles of mechanics of continua. The first volume of Kirchhoff's ·collected university lectures cited above was a general course in mechanics in which the last, the thirtieth lecture dealt with the theory of bending of elastic plates. These courses, with their admirable language, brevity, and precision of expression, are still worth being studied by engineering students.

† Gustav Robert Kirchhoff, professor of physics in Breslau in 1850, in Heidelberg in 1854, and in Berlin in 1874, discovered, with Robert Wilhelm von Bunsen in 1859, the method of spectrum analysis and investigated the physical and chemical nature of heat and light. By applying calculus of variations in the principle of virtual displacements to the elastic surface of a flat, deflected plate, he defined for the first time the precise forms of the two boundary conditions of a slightly bent elastic plate (1850). In his collected courses on mathematical physics given at the University of Berlin, the first course is a classic example of an introduction to general mechanics.

‡ Photograph taken from Philipp Lenard, "Great Men of Science," The Macmillan Company, New York, 1933.

deflected middle surface and the expressions for the two boundary conditions of an elastic plate.[1]

The condition of the minimum of the potential energy involved in an elastic system under static equilibrium has led to the establishment of two related principles.

By applying the principle of virtual displacements, originally introduced in the statics of rigid bodies, to elastically deformed bodies, one can express the small changes of the potential energy of the internal and external forces, corresponding to small virtual displacements to be attributed to the points of an elastic body from their correct equilibrium positions, consistent with the conditions of support, while one assumes that the external forces acting on the body are left essentially undisturbed. Then the potential energy of the internal and extraneous forces in the stable equilibrium position of the body is a minimum (first energy principle).

Or one can compare the values of the strain energy in states of stress adjacent to the states of equilibrium of internal stress in an elastic body, by supposing that the external forces and boundary stresses which the elastic system carries in an equilibrium position are slightly changed or varied in such a way that the equilibrium of all forces is still preserved. Since the elastic strain energy stored in a body of a material that satisfies Hooke's linear law of elasticity (for which the stress-strain relations are expressed by linear functions) for small displacements might be expressed by a homogeneous, quadratic function of the stresses or the extraneous forces and boundary stresses, it is possible to compute the small variation of the strain energy of the elastic body when the stresses or forces are varied. The stresses or extraneous forces causing the true elastic displacements u, v, w of the material points in their

---

[1] By combining the aforementioned equation with Hamilton's principle of the variation of the kinetic energy of a vibrating, elastic plate, Kirchhoff also derived the differential equation of the deflected middle surface for the flexural small oscillations of circular plates in a group of their various modes of lateral vibrations. This led him to a determination of the multitude of their nodal circles and radii by means of Bessel's functions, thus again solving for the first time a celebrated mathematical problem, namely, the determination of CHLADNI's *Klangfiguren*, of the "sound figures," which the Austrian physicist had discovered around 1787, and had described in a book "Entdeckungen über die Theorie des Klanges," by sprinkling a very fine powder (the pollen of lycopodium) on plates excited to bending oscillations by skimming their edge with a violin bow. The plate problem had been proposed for an award by LAGRANGE and the Academy of Sciences in Paris around 1812, but among the competing mathematicians Miss SOPHIE GERMAIN, to whom the award was later granted, had unsuccessfully tackled it by arriving at a sixth-order partial differential equation for the elastic surface of a deflected plate and at wrong boundary conditions. Lagrange discovered her errors and proposed for the first time the correct, fourth-order equation named after this great mathematician.

equilibrium positions are those which make the strain energy a minimum (second energy principle).[1]

In Sec. 2-2A the elastic strain energy per unit of volume was expressed as a homogeneous, quadratic function either of the six components of strain or of stress in Eqs. (2-17) and (2-18). Considering the former as the independent variables, the differential of work is expressed by

$$d\omega = \frac{\partial \omega}{\partial \varepsilon_x} d\varepsilon_x + \cdots + \frac{\partial \omega}{\partial \gamma_{yz}} d\gamma_{yz} + \cdots \qquad (3\text{-}2)$$

and, if the latter are the independent variables, by

$$d\omega = \frac{\partial \omega}{\partial \sigma_x} d\sigma_x + \cdots + \frac{\partial \omega}{\partial \tau_{yz}} d\tau_{yz} + \cdots . \qquad (3\text{-}3)$$

In the last two equations we can substitute, provided that the linear stress-strain relations are considered valid, for the partial derivatives their expressions given in Eqs. (2-20) and (2-21) and obtain either

$$d\omega = \sigma_x d\varepsilon_x + \cdots + \tau_{yz} d\gamma_{yz} + \cdots \qquad (3\text{-}4)$$

or $$d\omega = \varepsilon_x d\sigma_x + \cdots + \gamma_{yz} d\tau_{yz} + \cdots , \qquad (3\text{-}5)$$

in which the terms standing one above the other are equal, provided that stress and strain are proportional to each other.

[1] In an equilibrium position of an elastic body sustaining small displacements three conditions are to be simultaneously satisfied, namely:

1. The stress components in every infinitesimal element of material must be in a state of equilibrium.

2. The stress-strain relations are linear functions.

3. The six components of strain ε_x, ε_y, ε_z, γ_{yz}, γ_{zx}, γ_{xy} must be derivable from three continuous functions of the coordinates x, y, z, namely, from the three components of displacement u, v, w, and satisfy the six conditions of geometric continuity:

$$\varepsilon_x = \frac{\partial u}{\partial x}, \ldots, \qquad \gamma_{yz} = \frac{\partial w}{\partial y} + \frac{\partial v}{\partial z}, \ldots . \qquad (3\text{-}1)$$

Since a valid expression for the work of deformation per unit volume done by the six components of stress σ_x, σ_y, σ_z, τ_{yz}, τ_{zx}, τ_{xy} in an infinitesimal element of elastic material cannot be established unless the stress-strain law has been postulated, the variational principles for the elastic substance in which the strain energy ω is involved assume the validity of the linear stress-strain relations (of the second necessary condition which was quoted above).

The reader, therefore, will note that the virtual displacements postulated in the first energy principle are such that they satisfy conditions 2 and 3. They may hence deviate from the true displacements in an elastic body in the respect that for them the six stress components may not satisfy the three conditions of equilibrium of the stresses (the condition 1 prescribed above).

The small variations of the state of stress in an elastic body, considered in the second variational principle of work, comply with condition 1 but they may deviate from the true distribution of stress in an elastic body in the respect that the strains in it, in general, will not satisfy either conditions 2 or 3, depending on the manner in which the variations are conceived.

If we now proceed to utilize these aforementioned relations for the purpose of expressing the small variations $\delta\omega$ of the unit work ω, we may replace in Eqs. (3-4) and (3-5) the straight d by substituting for it the variational sign δ.   However, we must be aware of the fact that in the corresponding expressions the variational sign δ may have different meanings and that if we subsequently make use of the two respective forms for the variation $\delta\omega$ of the strain energy in

$$\delta\omega = \sigma_x\,\delta\varepsilon_x + \cdots + \tau_{yz}\,\delta\gamma_{yz} + \cdots \qquad (3\text{-}6)$$

or $$\delta\omega = \varepsilon_x\,\delta\sigma_x + \cdots + \gamma_{yz}\,\delta\tau_{yz} + \cdots \qquad (3\text{-}7)$$

the latter expressions in a sense are more general than the former ones of Eqs. (3-4) and (3-5), in the respect that we do not need to postulate in them, for example, the validity of the linear stress-strain relations (or of the conditions of geometric continuity of the displacements u, v, w of condition 3 formerly mentioned, as the case may warrant), depending on the conditions to which we subject the new, variational states.   This is sometimes expressed by stating that the variation of ω is represented by Eq. (3-6) if the state of strain is being varied and by Eq. (3-7) if the state of stress is being varied, respectively.   Strictly speaking, if one has made use of neither Eq. (3-6) nor of (3-7) but, for example, uses the expression of the total strain energy, expressed as a volume integral taken over a body, in whose integrand the unit work ω has tacitly been expressed as the sum of quadratic terms of either the components of strain or of stress, one sees that, if one starts to vary such a volume integral, one has in fact already postulated implicitly the existence or validity of the linear stress-strain relations, since one cannot write an expression in *finite* terms for ω without having used a relation connecting stress with strain, or vice versa.   These remarks should clarify some conditions to which variations may be subjected in specific cases.

If we suppose first that the points of an elastic body are given small, virtual displacements δu, δv, δw *from their equilibrium positions, the* internal stresses σ_x, . . . will do some additional work and the strain energy $W_i = \int \omega\,dV$ will change by a certain amount

$$\delta W_i = \delta\int \omega\,dV, \qquad (3\text{-}8)$$

where the integral is to be taken over the volume V of the body.   Let us denote by W_e the potential energy of all the external forces (loads), the subscripts i and e of W referring to the systems of the internal and extraneous forces.   When the equilibrium configuration of the body is disturbed, the external and the body forces acting on it will likewise do work which must be equal to the decrease of their potential energy, that is, equal to $-\delta W_e$.   In order to express this work in the simplest way, we shall *stipulate that the external forces are not altered* by the virtual displacements $\delta u, \delta v, \delta w$, that they retain those values that they possessed in the undisturbed equilibrium position of the body. The same effect would result by imagining that each force were produced through an equal pull exerted in its direction by a wire led around a pulley, each wire being loaded by a dead weight.

This may seem to contradict experience in the theory of the small deflections of bent elastic beams or plates, where it is well known that the extraneous forces (loads) acting on an elastic body increase proportionally with the deflections that they produce in their direction. A little thought may convince us that it should not make a difference whether one computes the external work $-\delta W_e$ by using those given values of the external forces that they possessed in the undisturbed equilibrium position of the body or by letting them change to those new equilibrium values that they would take on after their points of application have been displaced by the amounts $\delta u, \delta v, \delta w$.

Since the strain energy ω can be expressed as a homogeneous quadratic function, either of the six components of stress or of strain, the potential energy W_e of a system of concentrated external forces $Q_1, \ldots,$ Q_m acting on an elastic body,

$$W_e = -(\tfrac{1}{2}) \sum_{n=1}^{m} Q_n q_n, \tag{3-9}$$

may be expressible as a homogeneous quadratic function either of the external loads Q_n or of the small displacements q_n in the directions caused by these forces. This follows from the fact that any deflection q_i under the force Q_i in an elastic body is a linear function of the forces Q_n,

$$q_i = \sum_{n=1}^{n=m} \alpha_{ni} Q_n; \tag{3-10}$$

and, vice versa, after solving these m linear expressions for Q_n, any force can be expressed also by

$$Q_i = \sum_{n=1}^{n=m} \beta_{ni} q_n, \tag{3-11}$$

where the "influence factors," on account of the principle of conservation of energy, must satisfy the Maxwellian theorem or the symmetry property

$$\alpha_{ij} = \alpha_{ji}, \qquad \beta_{ij} = \beta_{ji}, \qquad i, j = 1, 2, \ldots, n, \ldots, m, \tag{3-12}$$

so that the determinant of the preceding two systems of linear equations is symmetrical. Thus, after substituting either the m equation (3-10) or (3-11) in Eq. (3-9), a homogeneous, quadratic function of the Q_n or of the q_n for the expression of the potential energy W_e of the external forces is obtained. Consequently, one verifies by computing the partial derivatives of W_e with respect to the forces Q_n or displacements[1] q_n that they are found equal to

$$\frac{\partial W_e}{\partial Q_i} = -q_i, \qquad \frac{\partial W_e}{\partial q_i} = -Q_i, \qquad (3\text{-}13)$$

disclosing that the variation of the potential energy of the system of the external forces Q_n may be expressed either by

$$\delta W_e = \sum_{n=1}^{m} \frac{\partial W_e}{\partial Q_n} \delta Q_n = -\sum_{1}^{m} q_n \,\delta Q_n \qquad (3\text{-}14)$$

or by

$$\delta W_e = \sum_{n=1}^{m} \frac{\partial W_e}{\partial q_n} \delta q_n = -\sum_{1}^{m} Q_n \,\delta q_n \qquad (3\text{-}15)$$

or, after adding these last two sums, also by

$$\delta W_e = -\,(\tfrac{1}{2}) \sum (Q_n \,\delta q_n + q_n \,\delta Q_n) = -\,(\tfrac{1}{2})\delta \sum_{1}^{m} Q_n q_n, \qquad (3\text{-}16)$$

having shown herewith that, as far as the expression for the variation of the potential energy of the external forces δW_e is concerned, it does not make a difference whether or not one includes the external forces as quantities to be varied with the variations of the shape of an elastic body[2] $\delta u,\ \delta v,\ \delta w$.

In order to complete the expression of the variation of the potential energy to which, as we have just shown, the external forces Q_n contribute, according to Eq. (3-15), a variation

$$-\sum Q_n \,\delta q_n, \qquad (3\text{-}17)$$

likewise if, in certain parts of the boundary surface of the body, stresses are transmitted in an area A, their potential energy similarly will change by

$$-\int (s_x \,\delta u + s_y \,\delta v + s_z \,\delta w)\, dA, \qquad (3\text{-}18)$$

---

[1] One verifies Eq. (3-10) by assuming only two or only three loads, etc. In order to prove that, for example, $\partial W_e / \partial Q_i = -q_i$, after having substituted Eq. (3-10) in Eq. (3-9), one sees that when computing $\partial W_e / \partial Q_i$ the terms in the double sum will give either $\alpha_{in} Q_n$ or $\alpha_{ni} Q_n$ with the exception of one single term, namely, the one $\alpha_{ii} Q_i{}^2$ in which the square $Q_i{}^2$ appears, which gives $2\alpha_{ii} Q_i$. Thus, after computing the partial derivative term by term, one obtains

$$\frac{\partial W_e}{\partial Q_i} = -(\tfrac{1}{2})(\alpha_{i1} Q_1 + \alpha_{i2} Q_2 + \cdots + \alpha_{ii} Q_i + \cdots$$
$$+ \alpha_{1i} Q_1 + \alpha_{2i} Q_2 + \cdots + \alpha_{ii} Q_i + \cdots)$$

which, on account of the symmetry property $\alpha_{ij} = \alpha_{ji}$, becomes equal to

$$\frac{\partial W_e}{\partial Q_i} = -(\tfrac{1}{2})2 \sum_{n=1}^{n=m} \alpha_{ni} Q_n = -q_i,$$

which is the first of Eqs. (3-13).

[2] Cf. THEODOR VON KÁRMÁN, Physik. Z., p. 253, 1913; also A. STODOLA, "Dampf- und Gasturbinen," 5th ed., p. 914, Verlag von J. Springer, Berlin, 1922.

where $s_x = \sigma_x a_x + \tau_{xy} a_y + \tau_{xz} a_z$, $s_y = \cdots$, $s_z = \cdots$ denote the components of the oblique boundary stress, taken in the directions parallel to the x, y, z axes, and a_x, a_y, a_z are the direction cosines of the external normal to an element of area dA of the boundary surface and where the integral is to be taken over the area A.

If there are no body forces present, the potential energy of the preceding two systems of external forces will change by

$$\delta W_e = -\sum Q_n \, \delta q_n - \int (s_x \, \delta u + s_y \, \delta v + s_z \, \delta w) \, dA. \qquad (3\text{-}19)$$

The principle of virtual displacements, applied to an elastic body in a stable equilibrium, is then expressed by the condition that the variation of the total potential energy $W_i + W_e$ must vanish:

$$\delta(W_i + W_e) = \delta \int \omega \, dV + \delta W_e = 0, \qquad (3\text{-}20)$$

where δW_e is given by Eq. (3-19) (*first principle*). In order to simplify applications of Eq. (3-20), one may, if possible, subject the virtual distortion to such variations of shape for which the forces or stresses in the supports or the boundary of the body do not do virtual work.

Let us apply Eq. (3-20) to *the bending distortions of an elastic plate* of equal thickness h, taking the x,y plane coinciding with the middle plane of the plate, denoting its small deflection at x,y by w after assuming that the plate carries a distributed pressure $p = f(x,y)$ lb/in.[2] as external load in the surface $z = -h/2$ but no concentrated forces and that no forces act on the plate in the direction of its middle plane. After making use of the expressions of the bending strains in the planes $z = $ const (see Sec. 8-1),

$$\varepsilon_x = \frac{\partial u}{\partial x} = -z \frac{\partial^2 w}{\partial x^2}, \quad \varepsilon_y = \frac{\partial v}{\partial y} = -z \frac{\partial^2 w}{\partial y^2}, \quad \gamma_{xy} = \frac{\partial u}{\partial y} + \frac{\partial v}{\partial x} = -2z \frac{\partial w^2}{\partial x \, \partial y}, \qquad (3\text{-}21)$$

and of Hooke's law, neglecting the insignificant normal stress σ_z, the bending moments m_x and m_y and a twisting moment m_{xy} may be defined per unit of section width by the expressions[1]

$$m_x = \int \sigma_x z \, dz = -N \left(\frac{\partial^2 w}{\partial x^2} + \nu \frac{\partial^2 w}{\partial y^2} \right),$$

$$m_y = \int \sigma_y z \, dz = -N \left(\frac{\partial^2 w}{\partial y^2} + \nu \frac{\partial^2 w}{\partial x^2} \right), \qquad (3\text{-}22)$$

$$m_{xy} = \int \tau_{xy} z \, dz = -(1 - \nu) N \frac{\partial^2 w}{\partial x \, \partial y},$$

[1] See pp. 20 and 269 in the author's "Die elastischen Platten," 326 pp., Verlag von J. Springer, Berlin, 1925; see also Sec. 8-1 below.

where the integrals are to be taken between the limits $-h/2$ and $h/2$ and the constant N denotes the plate modulus $N = Eh^3/12(1 - \nu^2)$. In order to compute the expression for the strain energy W_i of a plate, we note that the work of the stress components in a thin plate, σ_z, τ_{xz}, and τ_{yz}, may be neglected and that, referring to Eq. (2-17), the strain energy per unit volume ω is expressed by

$$\omega = \frac{1}{2}\left[\frac{1}{E}\left(\sigma_x^2 + \sigma_y^2 - 2\nu\sigma_x\sigma_y\right) + \frac{1}{G}\tau_{xy}^2\right]. \tag{3-23}$$

Using $\sigma_x = 12m_x z/h^3$, $\sigma_y = 12m_y z/h^3$, $\tau_{xy} = 12m_{xy}z/h^3$, after multiplying this by $dx\,dy\,dz$ and after integrating with respect to z, one obtains for the strain energy of the plate

$$W_i = \frac{6}{Eh^3}\int\int[m_x^2 + m_y^2 - 2\nu m_x m_y + 2(1 + \nu)m_{xy}^2]\,dx\,dy \tag{3-24}$$

or, after substituting the expressions of m_x, m_y, m_{xy} from Eqs. (3-22),

$$W_i = N\int\int\left[(\tfrac{1}{2})(\Delta w)^2 - (1 - \nu)\left(\frac{\partial^2 w}{\partial x^2}\cdot\frac{\partial^2 w}{\partial y^2} - \left(\frac{\partial^2 w}{\partial x\,\partial y}\right)^2\right)\right]\,dx\,dy, \tag{3-25}$$

where the double integral is to be extended over the area within the boundary curve of the plate. In the absence of concentrated forces, furthermore, if no work is done along the supports or edges of the plate, the potential energy of the external forces acting on the plate (of the lateral pressure load p) is given by

$$W_e = -\int\int pw\,dx\,dy. \tag{3-26}$$

The first energy principle is then expressed for an elastic plate, using the two preceding expressions of W_i and W_e, by

$$\delta(W_i + W_e) = 0 \tag{3-27}$$

which coincides with *Gustav Kirchhoff's equation* quoted above.

The variation process may be carried into the integrands, omitting variation of the pressure p, and after transforming the integrals by successive integrations by parts, one shows that the minimum condition [Eq. (3-27)] is equivalent to prescribing for the deflection w of the plate the partial differential equation of fourth order (*Lagrange's equation*),

$$\Delta\Delta w = \frac{\partial^4 w}{\partial x^4} + 2\frac{\partial^4 w}{\partial x^2\,\partial y^2} + \frac{\partial^4 w}{\partial y^4} = \frac{p}{N}, \tag{3-28}$$

and two differential expressions dependent on w expressing the boundary conditions of the plate as follows:

$$m_n = -N\left(\frac{\partial^2 w}{\partial n^2} + \nu \, \frac{\partial^2 w}{\partial s^2}\right),$$

$$p_n' = -N\left[\frac{\partial^3 w}{\partial n^3} + (2 - \nu)\frac{\partial^3 w}{\partial n \, \partial s^2}\right], \tag{3-29}$$

coinciding with those found by this method by KIRCHHOFF.[1]

The first variational principle of energy served to establish integrals of the differential equations in the theory of elasticity, but its significance is more due to the fact that, with its help, approximate expressions for the distorted forms of elastic beams, plates, and other bodies could be constructed in many important applications for which exact solutions could not be found by integrating the differential equations. The Swiss mathematician WALTER RITZ,[2] regrettably deceased at an early age, showed how such approximate solutions could be obtained. For example, in the case of the bending of a plate, he proposed to express its deflected elastic surface approximately by a finite sum of terms:

$$w = c_1 w_1(x,y) + \cdots + c_n w_n(x,y), \tag{3-30}$$

in which, in order to obtain better approximations, the number of the terms would successively have to be increased. He chose the $w_i(x,y)$ in such a manner that they would exactly satisfy the prescribed boundary conditions along the edge of the plate and proposed to determine the constants $c_1, \ldots, c_n$ from the minimum condition of the potential energy $W_i + W_e$. For this purpose the finite sum of terms [Eq. (3-30)] is substituted in the definite integrals [Eqs. (3-25) and (3-26)] expressing the energies W_i and W_e of the internal and external forces. Before the sum of the integrals is evaluated, its partial derivatives with respect to the unknown constants $c_1, \ldots, c_n$ are taken, corresponding to the

[1] In Eqs. (3-29) n denotes the outward direction normal to and s the direction tangential to the boundary curve of the plate. m_n represents the bending moment whose axis coincides with s, and p_n' the "amended" shearing force perpendicular to the elastic surface of the plate, both taken per unit of width in the boundary cylinder circumscribed around the edge of the plate. For further details, see W. THOMSON and P. G. TAIT, "Natural Philosophy," 2d ed., Pt. 2, p. 267, 1879–1883. See also A. E. H. LOVE, "A Treatise on the Mathematical Theory of Elasticity," 2d ed., p. 441, Cambridge University Press, London, 1906, and the author's "Die elastischen Platten," p. 33.

[2] Crelles J., vol. 135, p. 1, 1908. In this remarkable paper RITZ developed the approximate expression for the deflection of a rectangular plate having firmly fixed (clamped) edges. In another paper (Ann. Physik, vol. 28, p. 737, 1909) Ritz determined the fundamental frequencies of the bending oscillations of a quadratic plate having free edges. See also Nachr. Ges. Wiss. Göttingen, p. 237, 1908.

variation $\delta(W_i + W_e) = 0$, this leading *to n linear equations for the determination of the* $c_1, \ldots, c_n$, after evaluating the integrals appearing as their factors for the given distribution of the distributed pressure p of the plate.   It may be added that by choosing properly the functions $w_j(x,y)$ in Eq. (3-30), as Ritz and others after him have shown, this method converges very rapidly and may also be used for evaluating the bending stresses or moments in plates after computing the second partial derivatives of w.   In the case of a plate with firmly clamped edges RITZ and STODOLA[1] have noted that the variation of the part of the integral of Eq. (3-25),

$$\delta \int \int \left(\frac{\partial^2 w}{\partial x^2} \cdot \frac{\partial^2 w}{\partial y^2} - \left(\frac{\partial^2 w}{\partial x \, \partial y} \right)^2 \right) dx \, dy, \qquad (3\text{-}31)$$

vanishes.   This is also the case in plates having straight polygonal edges along which the boundary conditions $w = 0$ and $\Delta w = 0$ are prescribed (corresponding to straightly supported edges).   In these cases the minimum condition of energy simplifies quite considerably, since the constants $c_1, \ldots, c_n$ are to be evaluated from the much simpler condition

$$\delta \int \int \left[(\tfrac{1}{2})(\Delta w)^2 - \frac{pw}{N} \right] dx \, dy = 0. \qquad (3\text{-}32)$$

The method has been extended to cases when the plate is loaded in its middle plane by forces which strain it in some region in compression and under whose action the plate may buckle.   Supposing that the plate is loaded by a system of stress resultants n_x, n_y, n_{xy} (n_x, n_y normal to the sections $h \, dx$, $h \, dy$, respectively; n_{xy} tangential in them) per unit of width acting exactly in the middle plane, after including in the strain energy that part which is due to the force resultants n_x, n_y, n_{xy} when the plate bends out from its plane, their critical values under which the plate buckles may be computed from the condition[2]

$$(\tfrac{1}{2}) \, \delta \int \int \left[n_x \left(\frac{\partial w}{\partial x} \right)^2 + 2 n_{xy} \cdot \frac{\partial w}{\partial x} \cdot \frac{\partial w}{\partial y} + n_y \left(\frac{\partial w}{\partial y} \right)^2 \right] dx \, dy$$

$$+ \, N \, \delta \int \int \left[(\tfrac{1}{2})(\Delta w)^2 - (1 - v) \left(\frac{\partial^2 w}{\partial x^2} \cdot \frac{\partial^2 w}{\partial y^2} - \left(\frac{\partial^2 w}{\partial x \, \partial y} \right)^2 \right) \right] dx \, dy = 0. \qquad (3\text{-}33)$$

[1] See page 112 (*loc. cit.*).

[2] Cf. G. H. BRYAN, Proc. London Math. Soc., vol. 22, p. 54, 1891; S. TIMOSHENKO, Sur la Stabilité des systèmes élastiques, in A. Dumas (ed.), Annales des ponts et chaussées, Fasc. III, IV, V, 174 pp., Paris, 1913, and S. TIMOSHENKO, "Theory of Elastic Stability," 1st ed., 518 pp. (see p. 306), McGraw-Hill Book Company, Inc., New York, 1936. In Eq. (3-33) it is assumed that no lateral loads act on the plate and that no virtual work is being done by the boundary stresses.

Equation (3-33) and various related conditions of buckling in beams and plates have been utilized for evaluating approximate values of the buckling loads or stresses in such bodies.

Whereas in the preceding paragraphs virtual displacements were considered in an elastic body, altering its deformed shape while the extraneous forces were left undisturbed, *we shall now assume that its state of internal stress is varied* slightly, causing a change of the strain energy,

$$\delta W_i = \int \delta \omega \, dV = \int (\varepsilon_x \, \delta\sigma_x + \cdots + \gamma_{yz} \, \delta\tau_{yz} + \cdots) \, dV, \qquad (3\text{-}34)$$

while the equilibrium of stress is preserved throughout the body, so that the small variations of stress $\delta\sigma_x, \ldots, \delta\tau_{yz}, \ldots$ satisfy the three equations of equilibrium. In order to express the variation of strain energy δW_i through the work done by the stresses acting in the boundary surface of the body, the volume integral [Eq. (3-34)] has to be transformed into a surface integral defining the variation of external work,

$$\delta W_i = \int \int \int \delta \omega \, dV = \int \int (u \, \delta s_x + v \, \delta s_y + w \, \delta s_z) \, dA = -\delta W_e, \qquad (3\text{-}35)$$

where s_x, s_y, s_z denote the components of the oblique stress $\mathbf{s} = \mathbf{i}s_x + \mathbf{j}s_y + \mathbf{k}s_z$ in the directions of the x, y, z axes, respectively, and are given by the equations $s_x = \sigma_x a_x + \tau_{xy} a_y + \tau_{xz} a_z, \ldots$, a_x, a_y, a_z denoting the direction cosines of the normal to the element of area dA in the surface or the components of unit vector $\mathbf{a} = \mathbf{i}a_x + \mathbf{j}a_y + \mathbf{k}a_z$, also defining the element of area $d\mathbf{A} = \mathbf{a} \, dA$. This may be shown by transforming the six product terms in the expression of $\delta\omega$ in a sum of three scalar products,

$$\delta\omega = \frac{\partial u}{\partial x} \, \delta\sigma_x + \cdots + \left(\frac{\partial w}{\partial y} + \frac{\partial v}{\partial z} \right) \delta\tau_{yz} + \cdots$$

$$= \frac{\partial}{\partial x} (\mathbf{v} \cdot \delta\mathbf{S}_x) + \frac{\partial}{\partial y} (\mathbf{v} \cdot \delta\mathbf{S}_y) + \frac{\partial}{\partial z} (\mathbf{v} \cdot \delta\mathbf{S}_z), \qquad (3\text{-}36)$$

where $\mathbf{v} = \mathbf{i}u + \mathbf{j}v + \mathbf{k}w$ denotes the displacement vector and the $\mathbf{S}_x = \mathbf{i}\sigma_x + \mathbf{j}\tau_{xy} + \mathbf{k}\tau_{xz}$, $\mathbf{S}_y = \cdots$, $\mathbf{S}_z = \cdots$ are the three resultant stress vectors in the sections parallel to the yz, zx, and xy planes or the three components of *stress tensor* or dyadic:

$$\mathbf{\Pi} = \mathbf{i}\mathbf{S}_x + \mathbf{j}\mathbf{S}_y + \mathbf{k}\mathbf{S}_z. \qquad (3\text{-}37)$$

But the three scalar products on the right side of Eq. (3-36) may be condensed to $\delta\omega = \operatorname{div}(\mathbf{v} \cdot \delta\mathbf{\Pi})$, and the volume integral [Eq. (3-34)], by the theorem of Gauss, may be expressed through the surface integral

$$\delta W_i = \int \delta\omega \, dV = \int \operatorname{div}(\mathbf{v} \cdot \delta\mathbf{\Pi}) \, dV = \int \int \mathbf{v} \cdot \delta\mathbf{s} \, dA = -\delta W_e, \qquad (3\text{-}38)$$

the last integral on the right side coinciding with the expression of the surface integral in Eq. (3-35).[1]

If there are single, concentrated forces (loads) $Q_1, \ldots, Q_n$ acting in the surface of the body, causing the displacements $q_1, \ldots, q_n$ in their directions in the equilibrium position, obviously, instead of the surface integral in Eq. (3-38), the sum of terms is written

$$\delta W_e = -\sum q_n\, \delta Q_n \quad \text{and} \quad q_n = -\frac{\partial W_e}{\partial Q_n}, \tag{3-39}$$

after what has been said with respect to Eqs. (3-13).

After having proved in Eq. (3-38) that $\delta W_i = -\delta W_e$, we thus conclude that, when concentrated forces are present,

$$q_n = \frac{\partial W_i}{\partial Q_n}, \tag{3-40}$$

i.e., the deflection q_n of an elastic body in the direction of an external force or load is equal to the partial derivative of the strain energy W_i with respect to the force Q_n, expressing the well-known *theorem by Castigliano*.

If one assumes such variations of the state of stress, under which the surface stress **s** is not changed, thus $\delta \mathbf{s} = 0$, Eq. (3-38) becomes

$$\delta W_i = 0 \tag{3-41}$$

expressing the theorem of least work which is so frequently used for the determination of the reaction forces in statically indeterminate cases of the bending of continuous elastic beams (*theorem by Menabrea*), following also from Eqs. (3-39) after assuming that $q_n = 0$ for a reaction force Q_n in an unmovable support[2] (*second energy principle*).

It has been pointed out in Vol. I, Chap. 26, that the differential equations for the velocity components in an *incompressible viscous solid*

---

[1] The reader is referred to Sec. 3-2 where very similar transformations and the intermediate steps are explained in detail.   From the preceding it is evident that, in arriving at Eq. (3-35) or (3-38), derived from Eq. (3-34), two of the three conditions stipulated in footnote 1 on page 127 in an elastic material were postulated namely, conditions 1 (equilibrium of the internal stresses) and 3 (geometric continuity or compatibility between the strain components), whereas condition 2 (linearity of the stress-strain relations) was not utilized.

[2] The theorem of least work was derived by FEDERICO MENABREA in a paper submitted to the Academy of Sciences of Turin in 1857, and the theorem expressed by Eq. (3-40) was announced by ALBERTO CASTIGLIANO in the latter's dissertation, submitted to the University of Turin in 1873 and published also in his "Théorie de l'équilibre des systèmes élastiques," Turin, 1879.   See GUSTAVO COLONETTI, "Scienza delle Construzioni," 562 pp., 2d ed., pp. 72, 77, Giulio Einauidi, Turin, Italy, 1948.

We have not proved in the text that the extrema with respect to $\delta(W_i + W_e) = 0$ and $\delta W_i = 0$ represent conditions of a minimum of total or of the strain energy, which seems rather evident in stable states of equilibrium.

in steady, slow motion under a system of equilibrium forces coincide in their form with those for the small displacement components in an incompressible elastic solid. One should therefore expect that certain theorems of the strain energy of an elastic solid should have their counterparts in theorems for the rate of dissipation of energy in a viscous solid in steady motion.

HERMANN VON HELMHOLTZ and LORD RAYLEIGH have indeed pointed out that in the slow, steady motion of a viscous fluid or solid, under

FIG. 3-1a. HERMANN VON HELM-
HOLTZ.† (Born in Potsdam, Aug. 31,
1821; died in Berlin, Sept. 8, 1894.)

FIG. 3-1b. LORD RAYLEIGH.‡ (Born
in Essex, Nov. 2, 1842; died in Essex,
June 30, 1919.)

† HERMANN LUDWIG FERDINAND VON HELMHOLTZ was educated as a surgeon for the Prussian Army; in 1849 he was appointed professor of physiology at Königsberg, in 1858 at Heidelberg, and from 1871 until his death he was professor of theoretical physics at the University of Berlin. Apart from his outstanding contributions to physiologic optics [he invented the eye mirror (ophthalmoscope)] and to acoustics [as author of "Lehre von den Tonempfindungen" (1862) he analyzed the functioning of the organs in the human ear and developed the principles of physiologic aesthetics controlling the sense for the harmonies in musics], in one of his first papers, Über die Erhaltung der Kraft (1847), he announced the principle of the conservation of energy. In the latter part of his life he devoted his investigations to mechanics, hydrodynamics [having defined the laws of vortical motion in fluids and of the interaction of vortices in his paper Ueber Integrale der hydrodynamischen Gleichungen, welche den Wirbelbewegungen entsprechen (Crelles J., vol. 55, 1958)], to meteorology (waves in the atmosphere along the boundary surfaces of broad streams of air), and to electric oscillations by sponsoring the work of his brilliant assistant HEINRICH HERTZ that led the latter to the discovery of electromagnetic waves. His collected courses in mechanics are still an outstanding example of the beauty of presentation of lectures through the perfection of the language in which the principles of mechanics were elucidated to students.

‡ JOHN WILLIAM STRUTT, third Baron Rayleigh, became after the death of JAMES

constant extraneous forces, provided that the inertia terms may be neglected, the least amount of energy is dissipated in the body, compared with the energy lost in any other motion consistent with the same values of the velocity components in the boundary surface of the body.[1]

To illustrate the analogy between two corresponding energy principles to be expressed for an elastic and for a perfectly viscous substance, consider the example of a state of infinitesimal simple shear in an elastic layer of material $0 \leqq y \leqq y_1$ under a constant shearing stress $\tau_{xy} = $ const causing the displacements

$$u = \frac{u_1 y}{y_1}, \qquad v = w = 0,$$

in the direction of the x axis under the unit shears

$$\gamma_{xy} = \frac{\partial u}{\partial y} + \frac{\partial v}{\partial x} = \frac{u_1}{y_1} = \frac{\tau_{xy}}{G} = \text{const.}$$

Suppose that this equilibrium position of the layer $0 < y < y_1$ is being disturbed by displacing the planes $y = $ const by additional amounts in the direction of the x axis to new positions in which

$$u' = u_1 \left[(1 + 4c) \frac{y}{y_1} - 4c \left(\frac{y}{y_1} \right)^2 \right], \qquad v' = w' = 0. \qquad (a)$$

For any positive or negative value of the constant c the distribution of the u' is represented by a parabola (Fig. 3-2) which has been chosen so that it passes through the points O and A and that, for $y = 0$, $u' = u = 0$, and for $y = y_1$, $u_1' = u_1$, thus leaving the two boundaries $y = 0$, $y = y_1$ of the body in their previous positions.

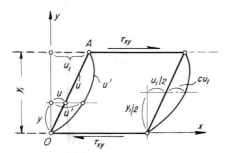

FIG. 3-2. Displacements u and u'.

[1] Cf. H. LAMB, "Hydrodynamics," 6th ed., p. 618, Dover Publications, New York, 1945.

The substitution of the displacements u' instead of the previous ones $u = u_1 y / y_1$ amounts to having varied the shape of the body (the difference $u' - u$ if c is given small values, in fact, defines a variation in shape δu). Then the displacements u' will generate the unit shears,

$$\gamma'_{xy} = \frac{\partial u'}{\partial y} = \frac{u_1}{y_1} \left[1 + 4c \left(1 - 2 \frac{y}{y_1} \right) \right],$$

and a strain energy per unit volume:

$$\omega' = (\tfrac{1}{2}) \tau_{xy} \gamma'_{xy} = \frac{G}{2} \gamma'^2_{xy} = \frac{G u_1^2}{2 y_1^2} \left[1 + 4c \left(1 - 2 \frac{y}{y_1} \right) \right]^2.$$

In a prism of material having a unit of area as base and a height equal to y_1, the strain energy stored will amount to

$$W'_i = \int_0^{y_1} \omega' \, dy = \frac{G u_1^2}{2 y_1^2} \int_0^{y_1} \left[1 + 4c \left(1 - 2 \frac{y}{y_1} \right) \right]^2 dy;$$

after evaluating the integral, this is found equal to

$$W'_i = \frac{G u_1^2}{2 y_1} \left(1 + \frac{16 c^2}{3} \right). \qquad (b)$$

Since the two boundary planes $y = 0$, $y = y_1$ have not been displaced and the shearing stresses in two plane sections normal to them, say $x = 0$ and $x = 1$, will not do any work, the work of the external forces vanishes, $W_e' = 0$, and the total potential energy will be equal to the strain energy W_i'. Thus, according to the first energy principle, the strain energy W_i' should become a minimum. This is the case when in the last equation the constant c is taken equal to zero, $c = 0$, showing that in the original distribution $u = u_1 y / y_1$ the strain energy $W_i' = W_i = G u_1^2 / 2 y_1$ is a minimum.

Now let us consider the state of a simple shear in a perfectly viscous substance, for which the rate of shear is

$$\dot{\gamma}_{xy} = \frac{\tau_{xy}}{\mu},$$

μ denoting the coefficient of viscosity. The rate at which energy is being dissipated per unit of volume is

$$\dot{\omega} = \tau_{xy} \dot{\gamma}_{xy}.$$

Let us vary this state, using Eq. (a). We need not repeat the calculation. If we interpret the u, v, w as the velocity components of the flow of the viscous substance, all that we have to do is to insert a dot above the quantities γ_{xy}', ω', W_i', to replace the symbol G by μ, and to note that in Eq. (c) below a factor $\tfrac{1}{2}$ is missing which was present in $\omega = \tau_{xy} \gamma_{xy} / 2$ and in Eq. (b). Thus, the rate at which energy is being dissipated in the varied system in the interior of the viscous layer of material is found from

$$\dot{W}'_i = \frac{\mu u_1^2}{y_1} \left(1 + \frac{16 c^2}{3} \right), \qquad (c)$$

showing again that this is a minimum when $c = 0$. In generalizing, we may state that in a steady, slow motion of a viscous substance under given constant extraneous forces the least amount of energy is dissipated compared with the energy lost in any other motion whose velocities in the boundary surface are the same as the prescribed ones.   We may add: If the external forces in the boundary surface of a viscous body do not do work under the virtually changed pattern of the internal velocities of flow, it suffices to make the rate of energy dissipation W_i of the internal stresses a minimum.[1]

3-2. Theorem of Maximum Plastic Work.

Variational principles for solving problems of the theory of the ideally plastic substance have been proposed by several investigators.   As mentioned in previous chapters, in the applications of this theory one may be interested to determine the distributions of stress in a body that yields completely or yields only in certain portions.   In the first case the elastic portions of the strains may frequently be neglected entirely, while in the case of partial yielding they must also be considered.   Both groups of problems may be treated by means of variational principles.

M. A. Sadowsky[2] derived for complete yielding exact expressions for the stresses in an ideally plastic material in certain cases, satisfying the differential equations of equilibrium under prescribed boundary conditions and the plasticity condition $\tau_0 = $ const, omitting, however, consideration of the stress–rate-of-strain relations which, in general cases of flow (when the former two groups of conditions do not furnish a sufficient number of equations for the determination of the unknown components of stress), must also be satisfied.   Instead of the latter relations, he introduced a maximum principle, stating that the correct plastic distribution of stress is characterized by the property that its external efforts (loads) are larger than the loads corresponding to any of the other distributions of stress that satisfy the first two, but not the latter, of the three above-mentioned conditions.

[1] We have assumed that body forces were not present.   It may perhaps be instructive to remark that the "varied" state of displacements (or of velocities) which we have just considered in Eqs. (a), (b), and (c) represents, in fact, an exact solution in an elastic (or viscous) material, satisfying the system of the differential equations in terms of the u, v, w, valid in the theory of elasticity and in the theory of a viscous solid, respectively [see Eqs. (25-5) and (26-8), Vol. I, pages 389 and 397 in the latter case], and that the virtual states which departed from an exact equilibrium state also represented such exact states. [Equation (a) expresses, in fact, the velocities of flow in a layer of a viscous substance, moving between two rigid parallel plates, one of which is displaced relatively to the other with a velocity u_1, when simultaneously a pressure gradient drives the fluid in laminar flow ahead in the direction of the x axis in Fig. 3-2.].   One ascertains easily in the case represented by Eq. (a) that the correct values of the stresses which correspond to this "varied" state in an elastic (viscous) substance involve a more complex distribution of stress, in which, apart from the changed values of τ_{xy}, normal stresses σ_x and σ_y also act, thus causing an increase of the energy W_i in the changed system of the u', v', w'. This then makes it plausible that, through the added new constraints, the energy increased in the varied states.

[2] A Principle of Maximum Plastic Resistance, J. Appl. Mechanics, December, 1942.   In this remarkable paper the solutions in several cases of yielding under combined tension and torsion in bars of circular and rectangular cross sections and of the yielding of hollow cylinders were developed by using the methods of the calculus of variations.

R. HILL[1] in Cambridge, England, in an equally remarkable paper established proof that the maximum condition just mentioned is equivalent to making use of a principle of maximum plastic work.

An example considered by Sadowsky may first illustrate the method. Suppose that *the distribution of normal stress σ and shearing stress τ in a round bar is to be determined for the case of complete yielding under combined tension-torsion.*   The bar is loaded simultaneously by

an axial force
$$P = 2\pi \int_0^a \sigma r \, dr$$

and a twisting moment
$$M = 2\pi \int_0^a \tau r^2 \, dr.$$

It is assumed that the elements in the interior of the circular cylinder of radius a yield under a constant octahedral shearing stress $\tau_0 = \text{const}$, σ and τ being functions of the radial distance r.   The exact solution for this case[2] is easily established.   Let ε and γ be the axial permanent strain and unit shear in the distance r from the axis of the bar.   Assuming infinitesimal strains, the tensors of stress and of plastic strain must satisfy the requirement that their principal directions should coincide.[3] This is the case if the normal strain in the axial direction ε and the unit shear γ are taken equal to

$$\varepsilon = \phi\sigma, \qquad \gamma = 3\phi\tau = \theta r. \tag{3-42}$$

θ denotes the angle of twist per unit of length.   Therefore also

$$\frac{3\tau}{\sigma} = \frac{\gamma}{\varepsilon} = \frac{\theta r}{\varepsilon} . \tag{3-43}$$

[1] A Variational Principle of Maximum Plastic Work in Classical Plasticity, Quart. J. Mechanics and Appl. Math., vol. 1, p. 1, March, 1948. (Also, British Ministry of Supply, Theoret. Research Rept. 10/46, December, 1946.) An unsatisfactory proof was given by A. H. PHILIPPIDES, J. Appl. Mechanics, June, 1948. See also R. HILL, "Mathematical Theory of Plasticity," p. 66, Oxford University Press, London, 1950.

[2] Cf. author's paper, On the Mechanics of the Plastic State of Metals, Trans. ASME, presented at the 1929 annual meeting. The case of tension and torsion in a round bar was treated by including the elastic portions of the strains by R. L'HERMITE and G. DAWANCE, Étude théorique et expérimentale sur la torsion composée, Compte rendu des recherches effectuées, Laboratoires du Batiment et des Travaux Publics, Paris, pp. 141–152, 1947. See also the synthesis of strains for this case in Vol. I, page 430, and H. W. SWIFT, Length Changes in Metals under Torsional Overstrain, Engineering, pp. 253–257, April 4, 1947.

[3] The stress-strain relations introduced in Eq. (3-42) postulate the stress–rate-of-strain relations $\dot{\varepsilon} = \phi\sigma$, $\dot{\gamma} = 3\phi\tau$, valid for this case of flow in an ideally plastic substance in which, after assuming steady flow and infinitesimal components of strain instead of the rates of strain $\dot{\varepsilon}$ and $\dot{\gamma}$, the permanent strains themselves, ε and γ, could be substituted (see Vol. I, page 237).

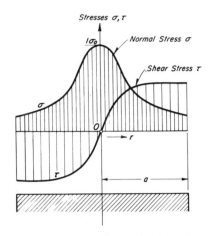

The principal stresses furthermore being equal to σ_1, $\sigma_2 = (\sigma/2) \pm \sqrt{(\sigma/2)^2 + \tau^2}$, $\sigma_3 = 0$, the condition of plasticity $\tau_0 = (\sqrt{2}/3)\sigma_0 = $ const or $(\sigma_1 - \sigma_2)^2 + (\sigma_2 - \sigma_3)^2 + (\sigma_3 - \sigma_1)^2 = 9\tau_0^2 = 2\sigma_0^2$ takes the form

$$\sigma^2 + 3\tau^2 = \sigma_0^2, \qquad (3\text{-}44)$$

where σ_0 is the yield stress in tension. From Eqs. (3-43) and (3-44), therefore, for complete yielding in combined tension-torsion in a round bar,

$$\frac{\sigma}{\sqrt{3}} = \frac{\sigma_0 \varepsilon}{\sqrt{3\varepsilon^2 + \theta^2 r^2}},$$

$$\sqrt{3}\tau = \frac{\sigma_0 \theta r}{\sqrt{3\varepsilon^2 + \theta^2 r^2}}. \qquad (3\text{-}45)$$

FIG. 3-3. Stress distribution for complete yielding in round bar under combined tension and torsion.

An example, reproduced in Fig. 3-3, illustrates and Eqs. (3-45) show that the center portion of the bar carries the greatest tensile axial stresses and the peripheral outer portion the largest shearing stresses. According to Sadowsky, the two functions of r expressing σ and τ in Eqs. (3-45) are characterized by the property that σ and $\tau = \sqrt{(\sigma_0^2 - \sigma^2)/3}$ will make the torsion moment

$$M = 2\pi \int_0^a \tau r^2 \, dr = 2\pi \int_0^a \sqrt{\frac{\sigma_0^2 - \sigma^2}{3}} \cdot r^2 \, dr \qquad (3\text{-}46)$$

a maximum, subject to the condition that the axial force in the round bar,

$$P = 2\pi \int_0^a \sigma r \, dr = P_0 = \text{const} \qquad (3\text{-}47)$$

($P_0 < \pi a^2 \sigma_0$), remains constant (or conversely, will make P a maximum when M is held $M = M_0 = \text{const} < 2\pi\sigma_0 a^3/3\sqrt{3}$).

This problem of the calculus of variations with a condition of constraint (isoperimetric problem),[1] requiring that the integral M in Eq. (3-46) be a maximum subject to the condition that the integral $P = $ const in Eq. (3-47), is reduced to an extremum problem by adding λP to M and requiring that the first variation of the resulting integral

$$\delta(M + \lambda P) = \delta \int_0^a f(r, \sigma) \, dr = 0 \qquad (3\text{-}48)$$

[1] F. S. WOODS, "Advanced Calculus," p. 324, Ginn & Company, Boston.

vanish. λ denotes a Lagrangian factor and $f(r,\sigma)$ the function of σ and of r:

$$f(r,\sigma) = 2\pi\left(\sqrt{\frac{\sigma_0^2 - \sigma^2}{3}} \cdot r^2 + \lambda\sigma r\right). \tag{3-49}$$

Since $f(r,\sigma)$ does not contain the derivative $\sigma' = d\sigma/dr$ of the unknown stress σ, the second term in EULER's equation,

$$\frac{\partial f}{\partial \sigma} - \frac{d}{dr}\left(\frac{\partial f}{\partial \sigma'}\right) = 0, \tag{3-50}$$

vanishes, and the latter equation does not require an integration but, after the first term is equated to zero, furnishes the equation from which the unknown normal stress σ is found equal to

$$\frac{\sigma}{\sqrt{3}} = \frac{\sigma_0\lambda}{\sqrt{3\lambda^2 + r^2}} \quad \text{and} \quad \sqrt{3}\tau = \sqrt{\sigma_0^2 - \sigma^2} = \frac{\sigma_0 r}{\sqrt{3\lambda^2 + r^2}}. \tag{3-51}$$

With these expressions for σ and τ, M and P may be computed. The value $\lambda = 0$ corresponds to the complete yielding of a round bar in simple torsion $\tau = \sigma_0/\sqrt{3}$, $\sigma = 0$, and the value $\lambda = \infty$ to that in pure tension $\sigma = \sigma_0$, $\tau = 0$. The physical meaning of the Lagrangian factor λ is, however, not clear until Eqs. (3-51) are compared with the complete expressions for σ and τ given in Eqs. (3-45). A comparison of these discloses that, by letting $\lambda = \varepsilon/\theta$, both groups of formulas become identical.

In order to formulate the general principle of maximum plastic work which served in the preceding example for the determination of a state of plastic equilibrium, consider first a system of stresses $\sigma_x, \ldots, \tau_{yz}, \ldots$ in an ideally plastic substance satisfying the three conditions of equilibrium

$$\frac{\partial \sigma_x}{\partial x} + \frac{\partial \tau_{xy}}{\partial y} + \frac{\partial \tau_{xz}}{\partial z} = 0, \ldots, \tag{3-52}$$

the condition of plasticity

$$(\sigma_x - \sigma_y)^2 + (\sigma_y - \sigma_z)^2 + (\sigma_z - \sigma_x)^2 + 6(\tau_{yz}^2 + \tau_{zx}^2 + \tau_{xy}^2) = 2\sigma_0^2 = 9\tau_0^2 = \text{const}, \tag{3-53}$$

and the six stress–rate-of-strain relations

$$\dot{\varepsilon}_x = \frac{\partial u}{\partial x} = \phi[\sigma_x - (\tfrac{1}{2})(\sigma_y + \sigma_z)], \ldots, \qquad \dot{\gamma}_{yz} = \frac{\partial v}{\partial z} + \frac{\partial w}{\partial y} = 3\phi\tau_{yz}, \ldots, \tag{3-54}$$

where $\phi(x,y,z)$ denotes the flow function for tension and u, v, w are the components of velocity. Suppose that the values of u, v, w are prescribed through given boundary conditions in the surface of the body.

The rate at which energy is dissipated in a unit volume of material,

$$\dot{\omega} = \sigma_x \dot{\varepsilon}_x + \sigma_y \dot{\varepsilon}_y + \sigma_z \dot{\varepsilon}_z + \tau_{yz} \dot{\gamma}_{yz} + \tau_{zx} \dot{\gamma}_{zx} + \tau_{xy} \dot{\gamma}_{xy}, \qquad (3\text{-}55)$$

in terms of the stress components, using Eqs. (3-54), is equal to

$$\dot{\omega} = \frac{\phi}{2} \left[(\sigma_x - \sigma_y)^2 + (\sigma_y - \sigma_z)^2 + (\sigma_z - \sigma_x)^2 + 6(\tau_{yz}^2 + \tau_{zx}^2 + \tau_{xy}^2) \right] \quad (3\text{-}56)$$

which, since the expression in the brackets, according to Eq. (3-53), is equal to $9\tau_0{}^2 = 2\sigma_0{}^2 = $ const at every point of the body, is also

$$\dot{\omega} = (\tfrac{9}{2})\tau_0^2 \phi = \sigma_0^2 \phi. \qquad (3\text{-}57)$$

Then, according to R. HILL, *the rate $\dot{W}$ at which the extraneous forces of this system do work is greater than the rate of energy $\dot{W}'$ dissipated in the body under any other system of stresses $\sigma_x{}', \ldots, \tau_{yz}{}', \ldots$ moving the material elements with the same velocities u, v, w, provided that the $\sigma_x{}', \ldots, \tau_{yz}{}', \ldots$ satisfy the equilibrium equations and the condition of plasticity.*

If again, as in Sec. 3-1, a_x, a_y, a_z denote the direction cosines of the outward normal to an element of area dA of the surface (or the components of a unit vector $\mathbf{a} = \mathbf{i}a_x + \mathbf{j}a_y + \mathbf{k}a_z$ drawn outward on the normal of the surface and coinciding with the vector $d\mathbf{A} = \mathbf{a}\, dA$ which may also represent an element of area), $\mathbf{v} = \mathbf{i}u + \mathbf{j}v + \mathbf{k}w$ is the velocity vector,[1] and

$$s_x = \sigma_x a_x + \tau_{xy} a_y + \tau_{xz} a_z,$$
$$s_y = \tau_{yx} a_x + \sigma_y a_y + \tau_{yz} a_z, \qquad (3\text{-}58)$$
$$s_z = \tau_{zx} a_x + \tau_{zy} a_y + \sigma_z a_z,$$

are the components of the oblique, resultant stress $\mathbf{s} = \mathbf{i}s_x + \mathbf{j}s_y + \mathbf{k}s_z$ in the directions of the x, y, z axes, respectively, the work $\dot{W}$ per unit of time done by the stresses $\mathbf{s}$ in the boundary surface of the body is expressed by the integral taken over the surface:

$$\dot{W} = \iint \mathbf{s} \cdot \mathbf{v}\, dA = \iint (s_x u + s_y v + s_z w)\, dA. \qquad (3\text{-}59)$$

This work must be equal to the energy dissipated in the interior of the

---

[1] The symbol v, one of the rectangular components u, v, w of the resultant velocity vector denoted here by $\mathbf{v}$, should not be confused with the absolute value of the latter vector $\mathbf{v}$ which is $\sqrt{u^2 + v^2 + w^2}$.

yielding body expressed by the integral[1] taken over its volume V [using Eqs. (3-53) and (3-54)]:

$$\dot{W} = \int\int\int \dot{\omega}\, dV = \sigma_0^2 \int\int\int \phi\, dV$$

$$= \int\int\int \frac{\phi}{2}\, [(\sigma_x - \sigma_y)^2 + (\sigma_y - \sigma_z)^2 + (\sigma_z - \sigma_x)^2 + 6(\tau_{yz}^2 + \tau_{zx}^2 + \tau_{xy}^2)]\, dV,$$

hence,

$$\int\int \mathbf{s}\cdot\mathbf{v}\, dA = \int\int\int \dot{\omega}\, dV. \tag{3-60}$$

[1] That the volume integral $\int \dot{\omega}\, dV$ may take the place of the surface integral $\int \mathbf{s}\cdot\mathbf{v}\, dA$ needs no further explanation in the absence of body or concentrated forces in the interior of the body.   But we may in this footnote show the standard proof for transforming the surface integral, expressing the rate of work done by the surface stresses, into the volume integral, expressing the rate of dissipation of energy in the interior of the body, by vector analysis.   With reference to Vol. I, Chap. 14, using the notation formerly introduced, denote by

$$\begin{aligned} \mathbf{S}_x &= \mathbf{i}\sigma_x + \mathbf{j}\tau_{xy} + \mathbf{k}\tau_{xz},\\ \mathbf{S}_y &= \mathbf{i}\tau_{yx} + \mathbf{j}\sigma_y + \mathbf{k}\tau_{yz},\\ \mathbf{S}_z &= \mathbf{i}\tau_{zx} + \mathbf{j}\tau_{zy} + \mathbf{k}\sigma_z, \end{aligned} \tag{a}$$

the three resultant stress vectors in the sections perpendicular to the axes x, y, z; by $\mathbf{\Pi}$, *the stress tensor or dyadic*:

$$\mathbf{\Pi} = \mathbf{i}\mathbf{S}_x + \mathbf{j}\mathbf{S}_y + \mathbf{k}\mathbf{S}_z = \begin{bmatrix} \sigma_x & \tau_{xy} & \tau_{xz} \\ \tau_{yx} & \sigma_y & \tau_{yz} \\ \tau_{zx} & \tau_{zy} & \sigma_z \end{bmatrix} \tag{b}$$

which must satisfy the condition of equilibrium in the interior of the body:

$$\frac{\partial \mathbf{S}_x}{\partial x} + \frac{\partial \mathbf{S}_y}{\partial y} + \frac{\partial \mathbf{S}_z}{\partial z} = \nabla \cdot \mathbf{\Pi} = 0. \tag{c}$$

One easily sees that the sum of six product terms in Eq. (3-55), equaling the rate of dissipation of energy $\dot{\omega}$ per unit volume in the interior of the body, is expressed by the sum of three scalar products appearing on the right side in the equation

$$\dot{\omega} = \mathbf{S}_x \cdot \frac{\partial \mathbf{v}}{\partial x} + \mathbf{S}_y \cdot \frac{\partial \mathbf{v}}{\partial y} + \mathbf{S}_z \cdot \frac{\partial \mathbf{v}}{\partial z} \tag{d}$$

by computing the preceding three scalar products term by term.   Furthermore, for the sum of these three scalar products we may write the sum of scalar products,

$$\dot{\omega} = \frac{\partial}{\partial x}(\mathbf{S}_x \cdot \mathbf{v}) + \frac{\partial}{\partial y}(\mathbf{S}_y \cdot \mathbf{v}) + \frac{\partial}{\partial z}(\mathbf{S}_z \cdot \mathbf{v}), \tag{e}$$

since, if we differentiate the first factors, their sum

$$\left(\frac{\partial \mathbf{S}_x}{\partial x} + \frac{\partial \mathbf{S}_y}{\partial y} + \frac{\partial \mathbf{S}_z}{\partial z}\right) \cdot \mathbf{v}$$

on account of Eq. (c) vanishes.

The right-hand expression of Eq. (e) may be condensed further by making use of the abbreviations for the scalar product of the nabla differential operator with

Similarly, the rate at which work is done by the varied system of stresses $\sigma_x', \ldots, \tau_{yz}', \ldots$ under the original velocities u, v, w or strain rates $\dot{\varepsilon}_x, \ldots, \dot{\gamma}_{yz}, \ldots$ is expressed by

$$\dot{W}' = \int \int \int (\sigma_x' \dot{\varepsilon}_x + \cdots + \tau_{yz}' \dot{\gamma}_{yz} + \cdots)\, dV \tag{3-61}$$

which is equal to

$$\dot{W}' = \int \int \int \frac{\phi}{2} \left[(\sigma_x' - \sigma_y')(\sigma_x - \sigma_y) + \cdots + 6(\tau_{yz}' \tau_{yz} + \cdots) \right] dV. \tag{3-62}$$

In this integral $\phi = \dot{\gamma}_0/3\tau_0$ is the same, positive quantity as in Eq. (3-60) [ϕ must be positive; otherwise it would not require a positive work $\dot{\omega} = (\tfrac{9}{2})\phi\tau_0{}^2$ to overcome the resistance of the plastic material for deforming it].

The principle of maximum plastic work is proved by showing that

$$\underline{\dot{W}' < \dot{W},} \tag{3-63}$$

which is verified below.[1]

---

a vector $\mathbf{w}$, by writing $\boldsymbol{\nabla} \cdot \mathbf{w} = \operatorname{div} \mathbf{w}$ and $\partial/\partial x = \boldsymbol{\nabla} \cdot \mathbf{i}$, $\partial/\partial y = \boldsymbol{\nabla} \cdot \mathbf{j}$, $\partial/\partial z = \boldsymbol{\nabla} \cdot \mathbf{k}$. Thus Eq. (e) for the rate of dissipation of energy is

$$\dot{\omega} = \frac{\partial}{\partial x}(\mathbf{S}_x \cdot \mathbf{v}) + \frac{\partial}{\partial y}(\mathbf{S}_y \cdot \mathbf{v}) + \frac{\partial}{\partial z}(\mathbf{S}_z \cdot \mathbf{v})$$

$$= \boldsymbol{\nabla} \cdot [(\mathbf{i}\mathbf{S}_x + \mathbf{j}\mathbf{S}_y + \mathbf{k}\mathbf{S}_z) \cdot \mathbf{v}] = \boldsymbol{\nabla} \cdot (\boldsymbol{\Pi} \cdot \mathbf{v}),$$

$$\underline{\dot{\omega} = \operatorname{div}(\boldsymbol{\Pi} \cdot \mathbf{v}).} \tag{f}$$

But in a vector field $\mathbf{w}$, after the theorem by GAUSS, the flux $\mathbf{w} \cdot d\mathbf{A}$ through the elements of area $d\mathbf{A} = \mathbf{a}\, dA$ integrated over a closed surface equals the fluid created in the sources (divergences) $\operatorname{div} \mathbf{w}$ within it, or

$$\int \int \mathbf{w} \cdot d\mathbf{A} = \int \int \int \operatorname{div} \mathbf{w}\, dV. \tag{g}$$

Thus by writing here $(\boldsymbol{\Pi} \cdot \mathbf{v})$ instead of vector $\mathbf{w}$ and after noting that $\mathbf{a} \cdot \boldsymbol{\Pi} = \mathbf{s}$ represents the oblique resultant stress $\mathbf{s}$ in an element $d\mathbf{A}$ of area in the surface:

$$d\mathbf{A} \cdot \mathbf{w} = dA\,\mathbf{a} \cdot \mathbf{w} = dA\,\mathbf{a} \cdot (\boldsymbol{\Pi} \cdot \mathbf{v}) = dA\,\mathbf{s} \cdot \mathbf{v},$$

we finally obtain from Eq. (g)

$$\int \int \mathbf{s} \cdot \mathbf{v}\, dA = \int \int \int \operatorname{div}(\boldsymbol{\Pi} \cdot \mathbf{v})\, dV = \int \int \int \dot{\omega}\, dV, \tag{h}$$

proving the equality claimed for the surface and volume integrals expressed in Eq. (3-60).

[1] The bracketed expression in the integrands in Eqs. (3-60) and (3-62) may be expressed in terms of the principal stresses, in the former equation by

$$(\sigma_1 - \sigma_2)^2 + (\sigma_2 - \sigma_3)^2 + (\sigma_3 - \sigma_1)^2 = 2\sigma_0^2 = \text{const}$$

or after letting $\xi = \sigma_2 - \sigma_3$, $\eta = \sigma_3 - \sigma_1$, $\zeta = \sigma_1 - \sigma_2$, $\rho = \sqrt{2}\sigma_0$, by

$$\xi^2 + \eta^2 + \zeta^2 = \rho^2.$$

After having applied in Sec. 3-1 the minimum principles of energy to the case of a state of simple shear in an elastic and in a perfectly viscous substance, let us consider now as a further illustration of the principle of maximum work the variation of a state of simple shear in an ideally plastic substance in a layer $0 \leqq y \leqq y_1$, yielding under a constant shearing stress

$$\tau_{xy} = k = \frac{\sigma_0}{\sqrt{3}} ; \qquad (a)$$

under the velocities,

$$u = \frac{u_1 y}{y_1} , \qquad v = w = 0 ,$$

and rates of shear,

$$\dot{\gamma}_{xy} = \frac{\partial u}{\partial y} + \frac{\partial v}{\partial x} = \frac{u_1}{y_1} = 3\phi k, \qquad (b)$$

showing that the flow function is $\phi = u_1/3ky_1$.

Suppose that we vary this state of stress by assuming, instead of it, a state of plane plastic strain [in which $\dot{\varepsilon}_z = 0$, $\sigma_z' = (\tfrac{1}{2})(\sigma_x' + \sigma_y')$] having the components of stress

$$\sigma_x' = \left(\frac{ckx}{y_1}\right) + 2k \cdot \sqrt{\frac{2cy}{y_1}} ,$$

$$\sigma_y' = \frac{ckx}{y_1} , \qquad (c)$$

$$\tau_{xy}' = k\left(1 - \frac{cy}{y_1}\right) .$$

In these expressions $0 \leqq y \leqq y_1$, y may not be taken $y < 0$, so that the boundary of the layer $y = 0$ is one of those "branch lines" of a plastic state of stress which

---

Similarly, letting $\xi' = \sigma_2' - \sigma_3'$, $\eta' = \sigma_3' - \sigma_1'$, $\zeta' = \sigma_1' - \sigma_2'$, we have also

$$\xi'^2 + \eta'^2 + \zeta'^2 = \rho'^2$$

representing two vectors $\rho = \mathbf{i}\xi + \mathbf{j}\eta + \mathbf{k}\zeta$ and $\rho' = \mathbf{i}\xi' + \mathbf{j}\eta' + \mathbf{k}\zeta'$ of equal lengths drawn to two distinct points ξ, η, ζ and ξ', η', ζ' situated on a sphere having the radius $\sqrt{2}\sigma_0$. But the integrand in Eq. (3-62) is $\phi/2$ times

$$\xi'\xi + \eta'\eta + \zeta'\zeta = \rho' \cdot \rho$$

which represents the scalar product $\rho' \cdot \rho$ that is certainly smaller than $2\sigma_0^2$, thus verifying the inequality (3-63).

The velocity components u, v, w were assumed to be continuous functions of x, y, z. It is well known in the theory of hyperbolic partial differential equations governing the problems of plasticity that, under given distributions of stress plastic flow layers may form involving discontinuous functions of the u, v, w. For example, in a bar, one layer or two or more distinct plastic layers, which may intersect each other, may form in simple tension or compression. These are not comparable cases in regard to the work consumed in the sense of the principle stated above and would require additional investigations.

That the principle of maximum efforts in the formulation that SADOWSKY gave for it, in fact, is equivalent to the principle of maximum plastic work may be seen in the example of combined tension-torsion by expressing the external work of the torsion moment M which is $M\theta$ if P and $\dot{\varepsilon}$ are kept constant. For a prescribed angular rate of twisting $\dot{\theta} = \text{const}$ the work is indeed a maximum if M becomes a maximum.

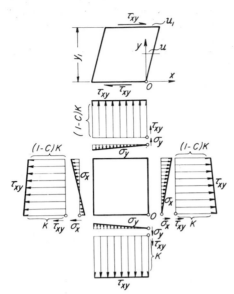

FIG. 3-4. Plastic state of
equilibrium of stresses
after variation.

were defined in Vol. I, page 546, beyond which a solution does not exist. Furthermore, the dimensionless constant c is an essentially positive small parameter to
be varied.[1] If c is taken equal to zero, Eqs. (c) coincide with Eq. (a). The
components of stress of the varied state have been chosen so that they satisfy
the two equilibrium conditions for the stresses σ_x', σ_y', τ_{xy}' and the condition of
plasticity

$$(\sigma_x' - \sigma_y')^2 + 4\tau_{xy}'^2 = 4k^2, \qquad (d)$$

provided that c remains small. Their distribution is reproduced in Fig. 3-4 and
may be interpreted by saying that after the constant shearing stresses τ_{xy} were
slightly disturbed, as indicated in Fig. 3-4, some additional normal stresses σ_x, σ_y
had to be applied in the body, in order to bring the stress values up to the yield
point again. Incidentally, it may be noted in this example that it would have
been senseless to increase the value of $\tau_{xy} = $ const by a positive increment,
because in a plastic body, according to Eq. (d), the absolute value of τ_{xy}' can
never become greater than k. If yielding is not to be interrupted, the variations
of the components of stress in a plastic body are subject to the condition of

---

[1] According to the postulated conditions under which the maximum energy principle
was formulated, the components σ_x', σ_y', τ_{xy}' of the varied state must satisfy the two
equilibrium conditions and the plasticity condition [Eq. (d)]. They must represent,
therefore, in a two-dimensional case of plane plastic strain an exact solution satisfying
these three conditions, which in general is not easy to write. The expressions of Eqs. (c)
were derived from an exact solution

$$\sigma_x = c_1 + \frac{kx}{a} \pm 2k\sqrt{1 - \left(\frac{y^*}{a}\right)^2}, \qquad \sigma_y = c_1 + \frac{kx}{a}, \qquad \tau_{xy} = -\frac{ky^*}{a},$$

for $-a \leq y^* < a$ which was discussed in Vol. I, Eq. (37-21), page 534, by developing
these expressions in the neighborhood of one of the two branch lines of the solution,
namely, $y^* = -a = $ const, in powers of $y = a + y^*$, supposing y to be a small positive
quantity. After denoting the small constant ratio y_1/a by $c = y_1/a$, this furnishes the
formulas (c), putting the insignificant constant $c_1 = 0$.

plasticity, that the constant c in Eqs. (c) is essentially positive. The rate at which the constant shearing stresses $\tau_{xy} = k$ do work (in a prism of unit area base and of height y_1), using $\phi = u_1/3ky_1$, is

$$\dot{W} = \tau_{xy}\dot{\gamma}_{xy}y_1 = 3\phi\tau_{xy}^2 y_1 = ku_1,$$

and the rate of work done by the varied stresses σ_x', σ_y', τ_{xy}' under the same velocities $u = u_1 y/y_1$, according to Eq. (3-62), is given by

$$\dot{W}' = 3\int_0^{y_1} \phi\tau_{xy}'\tau_{xy}\,dy = \frac{ku_1}{y_1}\int_0^{y_1}\left(1 - \frac{cy}{y_1}\right)dy = ku_1\left(1 - \frac{c}{2}\right),$$

thus showing, since c is an essentially positive constant that, indeed,

$$\dot{W}' < \dot{W},$$

verifying the maximum-work principle.

3-3. Principle of Virtual Displacements and Minimum Complementary Work Principle for Materials Having Nonlinear Stress-Strain or Stress–Rate-of-strain Relations.

Let us consider in this section variational work principles which are applicable to several general types of solid substances that have been discussed previously, endeavoring to formulate them for the cases when either the components of displacement or the state of stress in a body are varied. In order to have a definite case in mind, suppose that we consider an incompressible substance in which $\varepsilon_x, \ldots, \gamma_{yz} \ldots$ represent infinitesimal components of permanent strain, that their differentials are expressed by the relations

$$d\varepsilon_x = \frac{d\psi}{3}[\sigma_x - (\tfrac{1}{2})(\sigma_y + \sigma_z)], \ldots, \qquad d\gamma_{yz} = d\psi\cdot\tau_{yz}, \ldots, \qquad (3\text{-}64)$$

and that the octahedral shearing stress τ_0 and unit shear γ_0 [expressions of which were previously given in Eqs. (2-3) and (2-19)] are related by

$$d\gamma_0 = \tau_0\,d\psi, \qquad \tau_0 = f(\gamma_0), \qquad (3\text{-}65)$$

$d\psi$ denoting the differential of the flow function for shear. These relations obviously describe the yielding of a strain-hardening plastic solid under a general strain-hardening function $\tau_0 = f(\gamma_0)$, assumed as monotonously increasing.

The internal stresses do work. Consider the work per unit of volume

$$\omega = \frac{3}{2}\int \tau_0\,d\gamma_0 \qquad (3\text{-}66)$$

and *the complementary work* per unit of volume defined by

$$\omega' = \frac{3}{2}\int \gamma_0\,d\tau_0, \qquad (3\text{-}67)$$

represented by the vertically and horizontally shaded areas in Fig. 3-5 under the curve of the strain-hardening function $\tau_0 = f(\gamma_0)$ times the factor $\frac{3}{2}$. Corresponding to ω and ω', the deformation work W_i and complementary work W_i' done by the stresses $\sigma_x, \ldots, \tau_{yz}, \ldots$ in the interior of a body are given by

$$W_i = \iiint \omega \, dV, \qquad W_i' = \iiint \omega' \, dV, \qquad (3\text{-}68)$$

where the integrals are to be taken over the volume V of the body.

If again, using the notation of Sec. 3-1, $\mathbf{s} = \mathbf{i}s_x + \mathbf{j}s_y + \mathbf{k}s_z$ denotes the resultant stress in an element of area dA of the boundary surface and $\mathbf{v} = \mathbf{i}u + \mathbf{j}v + \mathbf{k}w$ is the vector of the displacement, the work done by the boundary stresses $\mathbf{s}$ per unit of area of the surface of the body is expressed by

$$\bar{w} = \int \mathbf{s} \cdot d\mathbf{v} = \int (s_x \, du + s_y \, dv + s_z \, dw), \qquad (3\text{-}69)$$

$$\bar{w}' = \int \mathbf{v} \cdot d\mathbf{s} = \int (u \, ds_x + v \, ds_y + w \, ds_z), \qquad (3\text{-}70)$$

and the external work W_e and complementary external work W_e' by

$$W_e = \iint \bar{w} \, dA, \qquad W_e' = \iint \bar{w}' \, dA, \qquad (3\text{-}71)$$

where the integrals are taken over the surface of the body. In a strain-hardening substance the work W represents irrecoverable energies lost in the irreversible yielding of the structure.

Assuming a stable equilibrium position of a deformed body, suppose that its points are displaced by small amounts $\delta u, \delta v, \delta w$ while the boundary stresses $\mathbf{s}$ and extraneous forces are left undisturbed. On these "virtual" displacements $\delta \mathbf{v}$, however, in a yielding material, the condition must be imposed that, in the body elements, nowhere $d\tau_0 < 0$, $d\gamma_0 < 0$ or an unloading has occurred, in order that Eqs. (3-64) and (3-65) shall not be violated, since we are not considering elastic parts of the strains. Although the work W_i and W_e represent lost energies in contrast to elastic works, they are uniquely determined by the displacements or strains suffered by the yielded material elements as long as the strains remain small; consequently *the principle of virtual displacements remains applicable* in a stable equilibrium, requiring that

$$\delta W_i - \delta W_e = 0, \qquad (3\text{-}72)$$

where

$$\delta W_i = \int \delta \omega \, dV, \quad \delta W_e = \int (s_x \, \delta u + s_y \, \delta v + s_z \, \delta w) \, dA = \int \mathbf{s} \cdot \delta \mathbf{v} \, dA. \quad (3\text{-}73)$$

If concentrated extraneous forces $Q_1, \ldots, Q_\kappa$ act in the surface, displacing their points of application in their directions by the amounts

$q_1, \ldots, q_\kappa$, the work in Eqs. (3-71) appear as the sums of the integrals,

$$W_e = \sum \int Q_i \, dq_i, \qquad W_e' = \sum \int q_i \, dQ_i, \qquad (3\text{-}74)$$

and δW_e in Eq. (3-72) is expressed by

$$\delta W_e = \sum_{i=1}^{i=k} Q_i \, \delta q_i. \qquad (3\text{-}75)$$

In the integrals of Eqs. (3-69) and (3-70) we assume that the boundary stress $\mathbf{s}$ is a certain function of the displacement vector $\mathbf{v}$, or vice versa, and similarly that this is the case for the forces Q_i in the integrals appearing in the sums in Eqs. (3-74) in their dependence on the corresponding displacements q_i of their points of application, or vice versa. A certain Q_i will increase monotonously with the displacement q_i under its point of application according to a certain curve, such as Figs. 3-6 and 3-7 indicate for Q_i and Q_{i+1}. The form of each of these curves essentially depends on the nature of the strain-hardening function $\tau_0 = f(\gamma_0)$ but is also definitely influenced by the sequence through which the other parameters of loading (the other forces present) are being increased to their final values. Since the principle of the superposition of the individual distortions, caused by several loads changing simultaneously, does not hold under the postulated nonlinear stress-strain law [Eq. (3-65)], it becomes obvious that a general discussion of the relation of external load Q_i versus displacement q_i involves quite a formidable problem in itself. A few instructive examples, however, may be considered below. We shall therefore be content to state that the total work W and W' may be uniquely expressible in terms of functions either of the loads Q_i or displacements q_i and that the principle of virtual displacements in the form expressed in Eqs. (3-72), (3-73), and (3-75) remains valid for the strain-hardening substance.

Secondly, let us *consider a small variation of the state of stress* in a body yielding under the law given in Eq. (3-65) subject to the condition that nowhere in the body $\delta\tau_0 < 0$, $\delta\gamma_0 < 0$, supposing, for example, that one of the external loads Q_i is being increased by δQ_i and assuming that the internal equilibrium of the stresses is not disturbed thereby (that the reaction forces will take care of this change without also doing work).

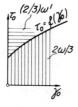
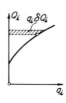

FIG. 3-5   FIG. 3-6   FIG. 3-7

Aiming at expressions equivalent to those derived in Sec. 3-2 in Eqs. (3-44) and (3-42), valid for an elastic material, the expression for the variation δW_e of the external work W_e given in Eq. (3-73) will not be of use, but suppose that we consider the variation $\delta W_e'$ of the complementary work W_e' expressed in Eqs. (3-74). A glance at Figs. 3-6 and 3-7 discloses that, if the load Q_i is increased by δQ_i *while all the other loads are unchanged*, the total *complementary* work W_e' in the body will increase by the area of the densely shaded horizontal strip in Fig. 3-6, which is equal to $q_i\,\delta Q_i$. It is true that, if force Q_i is increased by δQ_i, the other forces Q_κ will do additional work W_e (one of these, for example, Q_{i+1}, will do the work shown in the densely shaded vertical strip in Fig. 3-7), but since, according to our assumption, all Q_κ were held constant, neither Q_{i+1} nor the Q_κ do complementary work except Q_i. Assuming, furthermore, that the complementary work W_e' has been expressed as a pure function of the concentrated forces Q_κ, we see that the variation of W_e' if load Q_i has increased by δQ_i must be expressed by

$$\delta W_e' = \frac{\partial W_e'}{\partial Q_i}\,\delta Q_i = q_i\,\delta Q_i \qquad (3\text{-}76)$$

and hence $q_i = \partial W_e'/\partial Q_i$. In this partial derivative we may replace the external work W_e' by the internal complementary work W_i', amounting to that transformation of a surface integral into a volume integral of which we have repeatedly made use in previous sections, and write

$$\underline{\underline{q_i = \frac{\partial W_i'}{\partial Q_i}}}, \qquad (3\text{-}77)$$

stating that in a solid satisfying the conditions of flow in Eqs. (3-64) and (3-65) *the displacement q_i under the concentrated force Q_i is equal to the partial derivative of the complementary work W_i' of the internal stresses with respect to this force.* This is a counterpart of the theorem proved by CASTIGLIANO for the strain energy of an elastic body,[1] including those cases when one or the other of the displacements q_i vanishes above unmovable supports of statically indeterminate systems or when the

---

[1] In an elastic substance, obviously $\omega' = \omega$, $W' = W$, and it was superfluous to distinguish between the direct and the complementary work. The credit of having first introduced the complementary work W_i' in the variational problems dealing with materials not deforming according to the elasticity law is attributed to F. ENGESSER, Über statisch unbestimmte Träger bei beliebigem Formänderungsgesetz und über den Satz von der kleinsten Ergänzungsarbeit, Z. Architekten u. Ing. Ver. Hannover, vol. 35, 1889. See also H. M. WESTERGAARD, On the Method of Complementary Energy . . . , Trans. Am. Soc. Civil Engrs., vol. 107, pp. 765–793, 1942, and "Theory of Elasticity and Plasticity," p. 30, Harvard Monograph 3, John Wiley & Sons, Inc., New York, 1952. See also the papers quoted on page 153 below.

boundary stresses are not varied, $\delta W_e' = 0$, so that

$$\underline{\underline{\delta W_i' = 0}} \qquad (3\text{-}78)$$

expresses *the theorem of minimum complementary work*.[1]

We shall omit here proof that the principle of virtual displacements expressed in Eq. (3-72) by $\delta(W_i - W_e) = 0$ and of complementary work expressed in Eq. (3-78) by $\delta W_i' = 0$ for a material yielding according to Eqs. (3-64) and (3-65) involves a minimum of $W_i - W_e$ and of W_i', respectively, in a stable equilibrium position of the body.[2]

Nor shall we show generally that the aforementioned two minimum theorems are also valid for *a generally elastic, incompressible solid* characterized by the stress-strain relations,

$$d\varepsilon_x = \frac{1}{3G}[d\sigma_x - (\tfrac{1}{2})(d\sigma_y + d\sigma_z)], \ldots, \qquad d\gamma_{yz} = \frac{d\tau_{yz}}{G}, \ldots,$$

$$\tau_0 = f(\gamma_0), \qquad G = \frac{d\tau_0}{d\gamma_0}, \qquad (3\text{-}79)$$

the strains $\varepsilon_x, \ldots, \gamma_{yz}, \ldots$, now representing infinitesimal, recoverable, elastic strains and W_i, W_i' representing recoverable strain energies; furthermore, we shall not show that the theorems may be applied to the rates $\dot{W}_i$, $\dot{W}_i'$ of direct and of complementary work dissipated in a body of *a generally viscous substance* characterized by the relations

$$d\dot\varepsilon_x = \frac{1}{3\mu}[d\sigma_x - (\tfrac{1}{2})(d\sigma_y + d\sigma_z)], \ldots, \qquad d\dot\gamma_{yz} = \frac{d\tau_{yz}}{\mu}, \ldots,$$

$$\tau_0 = f(\dot\gamma_0), \qquad \mu = \frac{d\tau_0}{d\dot\gamma_0}, \qquad (3\text{-}80)$$

which, after having been integrated, may describe the slow creep at elevated temperatures in a ductile metal in which the coefficient of viscosity μ is assumed to be dependent on the state of stress or rate of strain.

Promising applications of these extremum principles may be found in *the theory of bending of slender beams of materials deforming according to either of the three laws formulated in* Eqs. (3-64), (3-79), and (3-80),

[1] Equation (3-77) fails in the case of an ideally plastic substance in which $\tau_0 = $ const since the complementary work W_i' for it vanishes unless one does not also include elastic parts of the strains we have not yet considered. See Sec. 3-4.

[2] The proofs may be found in several papers quoted in the bibliography at the end of this chapter, listed for referring the reader to quite a group of more or less related variational principles that authors have formulated during the past few years for various types of plastic solids. Lack of space prohibits reference to them here in detail; also some of these investigations dealt more with the formal side of the proposed principles, while no definite applications to specific or to new problems in the theory of plasticity, in which the advantages of the proposed extremum conditions would have become apparent, were considered.

respectively. In order to illustrate a few such practical applications in exactly computed examples, suppose that the functions $f(\gamma_0)$ and $f(\dot\gamma_0)$ were given *in the form of a power function*,

$$\tau_0 = f(\gamma_0) = c_1\gamma_0^{1/n} \quad \text{or} \quad \tau_0 = f(\dot\gamma_0) = c_2\dot\gamma_0^{1/n}, \quad (n > 1), \quad (3\text{-}81)$$

of their respective arguments γ_0, $\dot\gamma_0$. Incidentally, it may be added that, as far as the creep of metals at elevated temperatures is concerned, experimental evidence supports the validity of Eqs. (3-80) and (3-81) within a reasonable range of the permanent rates of creep in the long-time creep tests made under constant stress, justifying its being considered here especially since, after postulating a power function $c_2\dot\gamma_0^{1/n}$, solutions have been established also for more complex states of stress than those encountered in the simple bending of beams. The theories turn out as completely analogous for the three aforementioned types of solids leading to the same distributions of stress in identical cases of loading and shapes of bodies.

Since the case of bending of beams involves merely uniaxial states of stress, we may as well formulate the three deformation laws by expressing them as follows for the normal stress σ, permanent or elastic small strain ε, or rate of strain $\dot\varepsilon$ at a point of a cross section of the beam:

Cases 1, 2: $\sigma = \sigma_0\varepsilon^{1/n}$ or $\varepsilon = (\sigma/\sigma_0)^n$ (3-82)

Case 3: $\sigma = c\dot\varepsilon^{1/n}$ or $\dot\varepsilon = (\sigma/c)^n$ $(n > 1)$,   (3-83)

where Case 1 refers to a strain-hardening (ε = a permanent strain), Case 2 to an elastic (ε = an elastic, recoverable strain), and Case 3 to a viscous solid ($\dot\varepsilon$ = a permanent rate of strain) and where σ_0, c, n are given material constants.[1]

[1] In Case 2, when we have an elastic material in mind, the proportionality factor $\sigma_0 = E$ denotes a variable modulus of elasticity and in Case 3 for brevity's sake we let $\sigma = c\dot\varepsilon^{1/n}$ for the viscous substance instead of writing preferably

$$\sigma = \sigma_0\left(\frac{\dot\varepsilon}{\dot\varepsilon_0}\right)^{1/n}, \quad c = \sigma_0\dot\varepsilon_0^{-1/n}, \quad (3\text{-}84)$$

disclosing the dimensions of c.

The reader can verify that for incompressible material the stress- or strain-dependent flow function ψ, modulus of rigidity G, and coefficient of viscosity μ introduced in Eqs. (3-65), (3-79), and (3-80) in terms of the deformation laws formulated for uniaxial stress in Eqs. (3-82) and (3-83) are defined by

$$3\frac{d\varepsilon}{d\psi} = \sigma, \quad 3G = \frac{d\sigma}{d\varepsilon}, \quad 3\mu = \frac{d\sigma}{d\dot\varepsilon},$$

and hence

$$\frac{\psi}{3} = \int\frac{d\varepsilon}{\sigma} = \frac{n\varepsilon^{(n-1)/n}}{(n-1)\sigma_0}, \quad E = 3G = \frac{\sigma_0\varepsilon^{-(n-1)/n}}{n}, \quad 3\mu = \frac{c\dot\varepsilon^{-(n-1)/n}}{n},$$

respectively.

It has been remarked previously that a physical law, such as Eqs. (3-82) and (3-83) postulate, when the exponent n is greater than 1, fails at $\varepsilon = \sigma = 0$, since

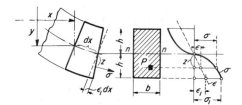

FIG. 3-8. Plastic bend-
ing of beam.

Having Case 1 of *the strain-hardening solid* in mind in the following
applications concerning the bending of beams,[1] in recapitulating briefly
a few needed, elementary formulas from the theory of bending of beams,
based on the usual assumption that after a beam deflects slightly its
plane sections remain planes, let us consider a beam having a rectangular cross section of the width b, the height $2h$, having the inertia
moment $I = (\tfrac{2}{3})bh^3$ referred to the center axis parallel to the sides b,
assuming that the beam is bent in the plane that coincides with the other
symmetry axis of the rectangle.   Denote by x the distance of a cross
section from one end of the beam, by l its length, by y its deflection, by
z the distance of a point P from the neutral axis nn of the cross section
(Fig. 3-8), and by ε_1 and σ_1 the strain and bending stress in the extreme
fibers $z = h$ of the cross section.   If the strain ε and stress σ at a point
$P(x,z)$ in a beam are expressed by

$$\varepsilon = \frac{\varepsilon_1 z}{h}, \qquad \sigma = \sigma_0 f(\varepsilon), \tag{3-85}$$

E, G, or μ become infinitely great there, contradicting the experimental facts,
requiring also that, when the material behaves equally under tensile as under
compression stresses, $\sigma = f(\varepsilon)$ or $\sigma = f(\dot{\varepsilon})$ be an *odd* function of ε or $\dot{\varepsilon}$. If n
is not an odd integer, for negative values of ε Eq. (3-82) must be interpreted by
writing

when $\varepsilon < 0$: $\sigma = -\sigma_0(-\varepsilon)^{1/n}, \qquad (\sigma_0 > 0).$

The choice of the power functions shall, however, not preclude that other simple
types of functions might just as effectively be considered for formulating laws of
distortion for the purpose of satisfying precisely certain known experimental
facts such as, for example, could be considered for eliminating the first-mentioned
defect of a pure power function by including an additive term proportional to
stress, assuming, for example, instead of Eq. (3-82), the function

$$\varepsilon = \frac{\sigma}{E} + \left(\frac{\sigma}{\sigma_0}\right)^n.$$

[1] Which may, as just stated, be equally referred to Case 3 of a *generally
viscous, slowly creeping solid* (a ductile metal at elevated temperatures) after
simply inserting a dot above the quantities ε, γ, γ_0, ω, W, ... and after replacing
the constant σ_0 by the constant c in all the formulas subsequently developed in
the text above.

the bending moment M, after substituting $z = h\varepsilon/\varepsilon_1$ and σ from the preceding equations and using $I = (\tfrac{2}{3})bh^3$, is given by

$$M = 2b \int_0^h \sigma z \, dz = \frac{3I\sigma_0}{h\varepsilon_1^2} \int_0^{\varepsilon_1} f(\varepsilon)\varepsilon \, d\varepsilon. \tag{3-86}$$

Since M is usually known as a given function of x along the beam, Eq. (3-86) shows that *the bending moments M in the beam may be expressed by two curves:* by plotting the ordinates M above the coordinates x (curve a) along the beam, and by plotting M in ordinates above the strains ε_1 (curve b) of the extreme fibers as abscissas (Fig. 3-9a and b), writing

$$M = \frac{3I\sigma_0}{h} \cdot F(\varepsilon_1), \qquad F(\varepsilon_1) = \frac{1}{\varepsilon_1^2} \int_0^{\varepsilon_1} f(\varepsilon)\varepsilon \, d\varepsilon. \tag{3-87}$$

These two curves for M then also permit expressing generally the strain ε_1 as a given quantity along the beam, as a function of the coordinate x, $\varepsilon_1 = \varphi(x)$, if the stress-strain law $\sigma = \sigma_0 f(\varepsilon)$ is known; this may be done graphically even if the latter law is only known empirically (see curve c in Fig. 3-9).

Since the curvature d^2y/dx^2 of the deflected center line of the beam for small deflections y is given by

$$\frac{d^2y}{dx^2} = \pm \frac{\varepsilon_1}{h} = \pm \frac{\varphi(x)}{h}, \tag{3-88}$$

this is *the differential equation for the deflections of the beam* consisting of a material that deforms according to a law $\sigma = \sigma_0 f(\varepsilon)$.

If the stress-strain law $\sigma = \sigma_0 f(\varepsilon)$ [Eqs. (3-85)] is expressed by a power function,

$$\sigma = \sigma_0 \varepsilon^{1/n}, \tag{3-89}$$

according to Eqs. (3-87) the bending moments are computed from

$$M = \frac{3\sigma_0 nI}{(2n+1)h} \cdot \varepsilon_1^{1/n}$$

and

$$F(\varepsilon_1) = \varepsilon_1^{-2} \int_0^{\varepsilon_1} \varepsilon^{(n+1)/n} \, d\varepsilon = \frac{n\varepsilon_1^{1/n}}{2n+1}. \tag{3-90}$$

The constant factor of $\varepsilon_1^{1/n}$ has the dimensions of a moment and may be abbreviated by the symbol M_0,

$$M_0 = \frac{3n\sigma_0 I}{(2n+1)h} = \frac{2nbh^2\sigma_0}{2n+1}. \tag{3-91}$$

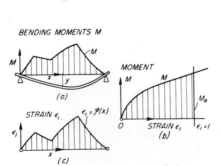

BENDING MOMENTS M

FIG. 3-9. Bending moments M and strain ε_1 of beam.

M_0 may be interpreted as that fictitious, constant bending moment which would produce in the rectangular area of the cross section of the beam the strain $\varepsilon_1 = 1$ and stress $\sigma_1 = \sigma_0$ in the extreme fiber $z = h$. We see therefore that the strain ε_1 and stress σ_1 in the extreme fibers along the beam for the power function law [Eq. (3-89)] are expressed by

$$\varepsilon_1 = \left(\frac{M}{M_0}\right)^n, \qquad \sigma_1 = \frac{\sigma_0 M}{M_0} \tag{3-92}$$

corresponding to which the differential equation of the deflected center line[1] takes the form:

$$\frac{d^2 y}{dx^2} = -\frac{\varepsilon_1}{h} = -\frac{1}{h}\left(\frac{M}{M_0}\right)^n, \tag{3-93}$$

assuming that M has positive values throughout the length of the beam.

If the deflections y have been determined for a set of given loads, one sees from Eqs. (3-93) that, if all the forces are multiplied by a common factor k without changing their relative ratios, the deflections of the beam become k^n times greater. Every load Q_i grows with the deflection y_i that it produces under its point of application as $y_i^{1/n}$, *that is, increases with the same power as the stress* $\sigma = \sigma_0 \varepsilon^{1/n}$ *changes with the strain* ε, provided that the relative ratios between the loads are not altered; this is also true if a uniformly distributed load $p = f(x)$ is increased k times.

The work per unit of volume corresponding to the stress-strain law $\sigma = \sigma_0 \varepsilon^{1/n}$ is equal to

$$\omega = \int_0^\varepsilon \sigma \, d\varepsilon = \frac{n \sigma_0 \varepsilon^{(n+1)/n}}{n+1} \tag{3-94}$$

and the complementary work per unit volume to

$$\omega' = \int_0^\sigma \varepsilon \, d\sigma = \frac{\sigma_0 \varepsilon^{(n+1)/n}}{n+1} = \frac{\omega}{n}. \tag{3-95}$$

Since the differential of the work dW_i required to bend an element of the beam of the length dx having the volume $2bh \, dx$ is

$$dW_i = 2b \, dx \int_0^h \omega \, dz = \frac{2bh}{\varepsilon_1} \int_0^{\varepsilon_1} \omega \, d\varepsilon, \tag{3-96}$$

after substituting ω from Eq. (3-94), integrating, and using Eqs. (3-92),

[1] It can be integrated by two successive quadratures or graphically for a given distribution of the bending moments M plotted above the coordinates x. If the beam carries single loads $Q_1, \ldots, Q_i, \ldots, Q_\kappa$, since the bending moments M are represented by the ordinates of a certain polygon of straight lines (funicular polygon), we see that these ordinates have to be raised to the nth power. Hence the integration of Eq. (3-93) has to be carried out twice in succession on a *distorted* polygon whose ordinates are the nth powers of the ordinates of the original funicular polygon.

the bending work for deforming the beam is found equal to

$$W_i = \frac{nM_0}{(n+1)h} \int_0^l \varepsilon_1^{(n+1)/n} \, dx = \frac{nM_0}{(n+1)h} \int_0^l \left(\frac{M}{M_0}\right)^{n+1} dx = nW_i'. \quad (3\text{-}97)$$

We note here that, when a power function law is postulated on account of $\omega' = \omega/n$, the complementary work W_i' is equal to the direct deformation work divided by the exponent n.

Let us apply the second work principle to a few cases of bending.

EXAMPLE 1.   Find the deflection under a concentrated load Q in a simply supported beam.   Denoting by a_1 and a_2 the distances of the load from the ends of the beam ($a_1 + a_2 = l$) and by x_1 and x_2 the coordinates in the left and right side of the span (Fig. 3-10), since the complementary work, according to Eq. (3-97), is expressed by

$$W_i' = \frac{M_0^{-n}}{(n+1)h} \int_0^l M^{n+1} \, dx, \quad (3\text{-}98)$$

the deflection y under the load Q, after Eq. (3-77), is found by computing the partial derivative of W_i' with respect to Q:

$$y = \frac{\partial W_i'}{\partial Q} = \frac{M_0^{-n}}{h} \int_0^l M^n \frac{\partial M}{\partial Q} \, dx. \quad (3\text{-}99)$$

But when $0 < x_1 < a_1$, $M = Qa_2x_1/l$, $\partial M/\partial Q = a_2x_1/l$, and when $0 < x_2 < a_2$, $M = Qa_1x_2/l$, $\partial M/\partial Q = a_1x_2/l$; hence,

$$y = \left(\frac{Q}{M_0 l}\right)^n \frac{1}{hl} \left(a_2^{n+1} \int_0^{a_1} x_1^{n+1} \, dx_1 + a_1^{n+1} \int_0^{a_2} x_2^{n+1} \, dx_2\right),$$

giving for the deflection y under the point of application of the load Q the value

$$y = \left(\frac{Qa_1a_2}{M_0 l}\right)^n \cdot \frac{a_1a_2}{(n+2)h}. \quad (3\text{-}100)$$

If σ_{1m} denotes the maximum bending stress in the beam occurring under the load Q, since Qa_1a_2/l represents the maximum bending moment, after Eqs. (3-92),

$$\frac{\sigma_{1m}}{\sigma_0} = \frac{Qa_1a_2}{M_0 l}, \quad (3\text{-}101)$$

and y is found also equal to

$$y = \frac{\left(\dfrac{\sigma_{1m}}{\sigma_0}\right)^n a_1a_2}{(n+2)h}. \quad (3\text{-}102)$$

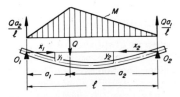

FIG. 3-10. Simply supported beam loaded by single load Q.

EXAMPLE 2.   Let us supplement this with the complete evaluation of the form of the deflected beam loaded by a single load Q, by integrating the differential equations for the deflections y_1 and y_2 in the left and right side of the span, using Eq. (3-93),

$$\frac{d^2 y_1}{d x_1^2} = -c_0 \left(\frac{x_1}{a_1}\right)^n, \qquad \frac{d^2 y_2}{d x_2^2} = -c_0 \left(\frac{x_2}{a_2}\right)^n, \qquad (3\text{-}103)$$

after denoting by c_0 the quantity

$$c_0 = \left(\frac{Q a_1 a_2}{M_0 l}\right)^n \frac{1}{h} = \left(\frac{\sigma_{1m}}{\sigma_0}\right)^n \frac{1}{h}. \qquad (3\text{-}104)$$

After integrating Eqs. (3-103) and properly fitting together their integrals at $x_1 = a_1$, $x_2 = a_2$, one obtains

$$y_1 = \frac{c_0 a_1^2}{(n+1)(n+2)} \left\{ \left[1 + (n+1)\frac{a_2}{a_1}\right]\frac{x_1}{a_1} - \left(\frac{x_1}{a_1}\right)^{n+2} \right\}, \qquad (0 \leq x_1 \leq a_1), \qquad (3\text{-}105)$$

and a similar expression for y_2 after interchanging x_1, a_1 with x_2, a_2.   Taking $x_1 = a_1$ in the preceding equation, one verifies indeed the former result computed in Eq. (3-100) from the variational work principle.[1]

A freely supported *beam carrying a concentrated load Q in the center $x = l/2$* of its span length l, according to Eq. (3-105) (after letting $x_1 = x$, $y_1 = y$, $a_1 = a_2 = a = l/2$), thus has the deflection

$$y = \frac{y_m}{n+1}\left[(n+2)\frac{x}{a} - \left(\frac{x}{a}\right)^{n+2} \right], \qquad (0 \leq x \leq a), \qquad (3\text{-}106)$$

where y_m denotes its maximum deflection:

$$y_m = \left(\frac{Ql}{4M_0}\right)^n \cdot \frac{l^2}{4(n+2)h} = \left(\frac{\sigma_{1m}}{\sigma_0}\right)^n \cdot \frac{l^2}{4(n+2)h}. \qquad (3\text{-}107)$$

Using $M = (\tfrac{1}{2})Qx$ for the bending moment, the bending strain ε_1 and stress σ_1 in the extreme fibers $z = h$ of the cross sections vary as

$$\varepsilon_1 = \left(\frac{M}{M_0}\right)^n = \left(\frac{Qx}{2M_0}\right)^n, \qquad \sigma_1 = \frac{\sigma_0 M}{M_0}. \qquad (3\text{-}108)$$

It may be of interest to compare the shapes of the deflected lines for the latter case when the exponent n in the deformation law $\varepsilon = (\sigma/\sigma_0)^n$ is increased. Curves representing the deflections y and the extreme fiber strain ε_1 (the ordinates ε_1 belong to what we called the "distorted" shape of the funicular polygon of the bending-moment line and are proportional to the curvatures $d^2 y/dx^2$ of the deflection line), corresponding to the exponent values $n = 1$, 2, 4, and 6, are reproduced in Figs. 3-11 and 3-12.   They were traced for the same values of y_m

[1] And if one lets the exponent in the power function $n = 1$ so that $\sigma = \sigma_0 \varepsilon = E\varepsilon$, the preceding formulas all coincide with the well-known ones of the elementary theory of an elastic beam having a constant modulus of elasticity E.

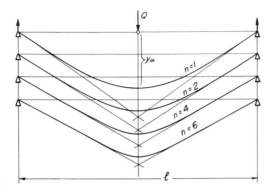

FIG. 3-11. Deflections of beam loaded in center of span by single force Q corresponding to deformation law $\varepsilon = (\sigma/\sigma_0)^n$, assuming exponent $n = 1, 2, 4,$ and 6.

and $\varepsilon_{1,\max}$ [corresponding to which the load Q and bending stress σ_{1m} may be evaluated from Eq. (3-107)]. One sees that *the greater the exponent n in the law $\varepsilon = (\sigma/\sigma_0)^n$ the more sharply the beam is permanently bent* nearest to the load Q and the more the plastic bending concentrates in the portion of the beam adjoining the load.[1]

EXAMPLE 3. Consider a beam of length l bent by two equal end moments M_1 and by a concentrated force P in the center, the two end supports acting as frictionless joints. Determine the curves representing the increase of the maximum deflection with the load P and moments M_1, that is, the character of those curves which were discussed in Figs. 3-6 and 3-7. Let two dimensionless parameters

$$m = \frac{M_1}{M_0}, \qquad p = \frac{Pa}{2M_0}$$

express the magnitudes of the end moments M_1 and of the center load P (Fig. 3-13) and let $a = l/2$. The differential equation for the deflection y is easily

[1] If n tends to approach infinity, both halves of the beam remain practically straight without having participated in a bending except in the closest vicinity of Q. Although the limiting case of the deformation law for $n \to \infty$ has a good meaning, since σ becomes $\sigma = \sigma_0 = \text{const}$ (which represents the ideally plastic substance deforming under a constant yield stress σ_0), as far as the plastic distortion and the distribution of the stresses in the beam are concerned near the center section, this approach toward $n \to \infty$ makes little sense, because it amounts finally to a concentration of the yielding of the material in a paper-thin layer on account of having excluded elastic portions in the strains. How the minimum principle of work just discussed may be extended to an ideally plasto-elastic substance, also permitting analysis of a plausible distribution of stress in the vicinity of the load Q, will be shown in the following section.

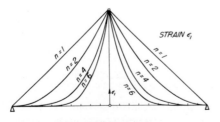

FIG. 3-12. Strains ε_1.

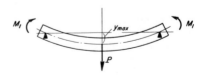

FIG. 3-13

integrated, using the bending moment when $0 \leq x \leq a$:

$$M = M_1 + (\tfrac{1}{2})Px = M_0\left(m + p\,\frac{x}{a}\right),$$

$$\frac{d^2y}{dx^2} = -\frac{\varepsilon_1}{h} = -\frac{1}{h}\left(\frac{M}{M_0}\right)^n = -\frac{1}{h}\left(m + p\,\frac{x}{a}\right)^n,$$

giving

$$y = \frac{a^2}{(n+1)(n+2)hp^2}\left[m^{n+2} + (n+2)(m+p)^{n+1}p\,\frac{x}{a} - \left(m + p\,\frac{x}{a}\right)^{n+2}\right],$$

showing that the maximum deflection of the beam, after letting $x = a$, is found equal to

$$y_{\max} = \frac{a^2}{(n+1)(n+2)hp^2}\{m^{n+2} + [(n+1)p - m](m+p)^{n+1}\}.$$

If the moment M_1 is taken equal to zero, $m = 0$, these last two equations coincide with Eqs. (3-106) and (3-107) of the preceding example, giving, for $m = 0$,

$$y_{\max} = \frac{p^n a^2}{(n+2)h},$$

but if the load P is taken equal to zero, $p = 0$, they appear in the indefinite form $0/0$ and converge to

$$y = \frac{m^n a^2}{2h}\left[2\,\frac{x}{a} - \left(\frac{x}{a}\right)^2\right], \qquad y_{\max} = \frac{m^n a^2}{2h},$$

indicating that when p or m acts solely the maximum deflection of the beam increases as the nth power of p or m, respectively, whereas when p and m act simultaneously this simple rule does not hold. $y_{\max}$ may be represented, however, by a surface $y_{\max} = F(m,p)$ on which a sequence of loading $m = m(\lambda)$, $p = p(\lambda)$ traces an ascending curve. In contrast to the cases when the strains grow to finite magnitudes which we treated in the previous chapter, it is noted here where we deal with infinitesimal strains that the deflections and the direct and complementary work of deformation W_i and W_i' done in the beam are uniquely determined by the final values of the load parameters m and p, independently of the path of loading. The differentials of work dW_i and dW_i' are complete differentials with respect to the load parameter variables m and p. Figure 3-14 illustrates the shape of the surface $y_{\max} = F(m,p)$ when the exponent $n = 2$, for the deformation law $\varepsilon = (\sigma/\sigma_0)^2$; when

$$y_{\max} = \frac{a^2}{12h}(6m^2 + 8mp + 3p^2) \qquad (a)$$

this surface is of second degree.[1]

[1] Equation (a) indicates how wrong it would be to add the deflections produced solely by m and by p, if the validity of the superposition principle were falsely postulated, amounting to disregarding the presence of the middle term in Eq. (a).

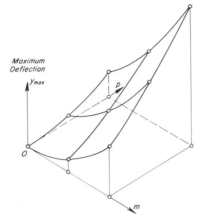

FIG. 3-14. Surface representing the maximum deflection $y_{\max}$ of a beam bent simultaneously by end moments M_1 and by a single load P in center of span. (The coordinates are $m = M_1/M_0$, $p = Pa/2M_0$ and $y_{\max}$.)

EXAMPLE 4. Find the maximum deflection in a simply supported beam loaded by a uniformly distributed load $p = $ const. In order to make use of the second work principle, suppose that a concentrated force Q is applied in addition to the distributed load p at the center of the span $x = l/2$, acting in the same sense as p. Since for $0 \leq x \leq l/2$

$$M = (\tfrac{1}{2})[(pl + Q)x - px^2], \qquad \frac{\partial M}{\partial Q} = \frac{x}{2},$$

from Eq. (3-99)

$$y_{\max} = \frac{2}{h} \int_0^{l/2} \left(\frac{M}{M_0}\right)^n \frac{\partial M}{\partial Q}\, dx$$

$$= \frac{1}{h} \cdot \left(\frac{pl}{2M_0}\right)^n \int_0^{l/2} x^{n+1} \left(1 + \frac{Q}{pl} - \frac{x}{l}\right)^n dx;$$

after letting $Q = 0$ and $u = x/l$ ($0 \leq u \leq \tfrac{1}{2}$), this gives

$$y_{\max} = \frac{pl}{2M_0 h}\, l^{n+2} \int_0^{\tfrac{1}{2}} u^{n+1}(1 - u)^n\, du,$$

where the integral may be evaluated after developing the integrand in a power series of u, which is not reproduced here. If n is an integer $n = 1, 2, \ldots$, the series breaks down and the integral can be easily computed numerically. Assuming $n = 1$, writing $\sigma = \sigma_0\varepsilon = E\varepsilon$ corresponding to the elastic material, one finds

$$y_{\max} = \frac{5}{384} \frac{pl^4}{IE},$$

in agreement with elementary elastic bending theory. When $n = 2$, one obtains

$$y_{\max} = \frac{55}{55,296} \left(\frac{pl^3}{I\sigma_0}\right)^2 h.$$

EXAMPLE 5. Consider the statically indeterminate case of bending of a beam resting on three supports and bent over two equal spans under a uniformly distributed load $p = $ const. If the beam were supported at the end points A and C (Fig. 3-15) and were loaded at its center B by a single force Q in the opposite direction to the load p, there would be a deflection y at point B under Q and p, according to Eqs. (3-77) and (3-98):

$$y = \frac{\partial W_i'}{\partial Q} = \frac{2M_0^{-n}}{(n + 1)h} \frac{\partial}{\partial Q} \int_0^{l/2} M^{n+1}\, dx.$$

Considering Q as the reaction exerted by the middle support B, the condition for its determination in order that y should vanish is therefore

$$\frac{\partial}{\partial Q} \int_0^{l/2} M^{n+1}\, dx = 0. \qquad (a)$$

After again writing $x/l = u$, we see that the bending moment for $0 \leq u \leq \frac{1}{2}$,

$$M = \frac{pl^2}{2}\left[\left(1 - \frac{Q}{pl}\right)u - u^2\right],$$

becomes zero when u takes the value $u_0 = x_0/l$,

$$u_0 = \frac{x_0}{l} = 1 - \frac{Q}{pl},$$

and M becomes negative when $u_0 < u \leq \frac{1}{2}$. Thus, the integral in Eq. (a) must be split in two parts as follows:

$$\frac{\partial}{\partial Q}\left[\int_0^{u_0} M^{n+1}\,du + \int_{u_0}^{\frac{1}{2}} (-M)^{n+1}\,du\right]$$

$$= (n + 1)\left[\int_0^{u_0} M^n \frac{\partial M}{\partial Q}\,du - \int_{u_0}^{\frac{1}{2}} (-M)^n \frac{\partial M}{\partial Q}\,du\right] = 0.$$

Substituting here

$$M = \frac{pl^2}{2}(u_0 u - u^2), \qquad \frac{\partial M}{\partial Q} = -\frac{1}{pl}\frac{\partial M}{\partial u_0} = -\frac{lu}{2},$$

the condition of Eq. (a) takes the form

$$\int_0^{u_0} (u_0 - u)^n u^{n+1}\,du = \int_{u_0}^{\frac{1}{2}} (u - u_0)^n u^{n+1}\,du, \qquad (b)$$

defining the unknown u_0 or reaction force $Q = pl(1 - u_0)$. If n is irrational, the integrals might be developed in series of powers of u_0 which we shall not discuss further. But to illustrate this with a simple case, suppose that n were equal to 2. We obtain then from the preceding condition

$$\frac{u_0^6}{60} = -\frac{u_0^6}{60} + \frac{1}{16}\left(\frac{u_0^2}{4} - \frac{u_0}{5} + \frac{1}{24}\right),$$

or an equation of sixth degree for u_0,

$$64u_0^6 - 30u_0^2 + 24u_0 - 5 = 0,$$

which by the method of trial and error was found to be satisfied by the approximate root

$$u_0 = 0.386, \qquad Q = 0.614pl,$$

showing that the center support B corresponding to a stress-strain law $\sigma = \sigma_0\sqrt{\varepsilon}$ carries 61 per cent of the total load pl, deflecting both spans of the continuous plastic beam resting on three supports. If we had chosen $n = 1$, corresponding to the perfectly elastic material $\sigma = \sigma_0\varepsilon = E\varepsilon$, we would have found from Eq. (b) the values $u_0 = \frac{3}{8} = 0.375$ and $Q = (\frac{5}{8})pl = 0.625pl$

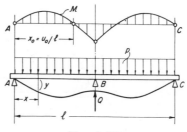

FIG. 3-15

in agreement with the theory of elastic beams; we may note that both afore-mentioned numerical results appear surprisingly close.

In conclusion, it may be said that the preceding formulas and expressions for the inelastic deflections in related cases of the bending of beams and bars *derived from the minimum complementary work principle may perhaps have further useful new applications for predicting the slow rates of sagging of metal beams loaded at elevated temperatures, by basing their theory of creep on the deformation law of Eq. (3-83).* The developments for evaluating the rates of slow sagging under the influence of creep in the bending of bars are obtained simply by writing a dot above the deflections, after replacing σ_0 by the constant $c = \sigma_0/\dot{\varepsilon}_0^{1/n}$ of Eqs. (3-84). A very analogous theory of the creep in bending probably deserving some attention could also be based, instead of on the power function law Eq. (3-83), *on the hyperbolic sine creep law* $\dot{\gamma}_0 = \dot{\gamma}^* \sinh (\tau_0/\tau^*)$ ($\dot{\gamma}^*, \tau^*$ are material constants).

3-4. Minimum-work Principles for Elastic–Ideally Plastic Substance. Let us treat now the case of an ideally plastic substance in which we wish, however, to consider also the elastic portions of the strains by postulating for the deformation law [Eqs. (3-65)] $\tau_0 = f(\gamma_0)$, a broken line having a steeply inclined straight portion $\tau_0 = \tau_y\gamma_0/\gamma_y$ when $-\gamma_y \leqq \gamma_0 \leqq \gamma_y$ ($\gamma_y = \tau_y/G$ denoting the unit shear at the yield point, τ_y the yield stress) over the elastic range of strains, and two horizontal straight branches $\tau_0 = \pm\tau_y = $ const in the plastic regions (Fig. 3-16). At sufficiently high loads there will be an elastic and a plastic region or several permanently strained regions in the body.

The principle of virtual displacements may be applied to such a system, assuming that the components of displacement are varied by the small amounts $\delta u, \delta v, \delta w$. The total internal work W_i done by the stresses in the body will consist of two parts, of the work that may be stored in the form of recoverable, elastic strain energy $W_{i,e}$ and of the work lost in producing the permanent distortions $W_{i,p}$ in the yielded elements of material. If, furthermore, W_e denotes the work done by the external forces (loads) and by the boundary stresses in the surface of the body, the principle of virtual displacements is expressed by

$$\delta W_{i,e} + \delta W_{i,p} - \delta W_e = 0. \quad (3\text{-}109)$$

The internal work may be computed from the volume integral

$$\int \omega \, dV,$$

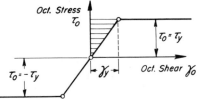

FIG. 3-16. Stress-strain law.

noting that the elastic strain energy per unit of volume ω_e, after Eqs. (2-18), equals

$$\omega_e = \frac{(\tfrac{3}{2})E\varepsilon^2}{1 - 2\nu} + (\tfrac{3}{4})G\gamma_0^2 \qquad (3\text{-}110)$$

and that the second term in this expression, representing the unit strain energy of distortion *in the yielded regions*, has a stationary value equal to $(\tfrac{3}{4})G\gamma_y^2 = \text{const}$ since the elastic octahedral unit shear γ_0 at the yield point $\tau_0 = \tau_y = \text{const}$ has the constant value $\gamma_0 = \gamma_y = \tau_y/G$ throughout the yielded portions of the body, while the unit work ω_p lost in producing the permanent portions of the strains equals

$$\omega_p = (\tfrac{3}{2})\int \tau_0 \, d\gamma_0 = \frac{3\tau_y}{2}(\gamma_0 - \gamma_y). \qquad (3\text{-}111)$$

The internal work is therefore computed from the volume integrals,

$$W_{i,e} = \int \omega_e \, dV, \qquad W_{i,p} = \int \omega_p \, dV, \qquad (3\text{-}112)$$

where the left integral has to be taken over the whole volume of the body with the stipulation just mentioned and the right integral only over the yielded parts of the volume.

The elastic complementary unit energy $\omega_e' = \omega_e$ being equal to ω_e throughout the entire body, provided that in the plasticized regions γ_0^2 in Eq. (3-110) is taken equal to $\gamma_y^2 = \text{const}$, we see, on the other hand, that the total complementary work W_i' to deform a body of an elastic–ideally plastic substance (having elastic and partially yielded portions) is simply equal to the total elastic strain energy $W_{i,e}$ stored in the body:[1]

$$W_i' = W_{i,e} = \int \omega_e \, dV. \qquad (3\text{-}113)$$

The reasoning which led to Eq. (3-77) of Sec. 3-3 may equally be applied to the material considered here. If single forces Q_i act, we see that the displacements q_i of their points of application in their directions are determined by

$$q_i = \frac{\partial W_{i,e}}{\partial Q_i} \qquad (3\text{-}114)$$

---

[1] The complementary unit work of distortion ω_d' is indeed represented in the broken-line stress-strain diagram of Fig. 3-16 *while the substance yields* under the octahedral shearing stress $\tau_0 = +\tau_y = \text{const}$, or for any point which is situated on the upper horizontal branch of the $\tau_0 = f(\gamma_0)$ curve, by the horizontally shaded triangular area $\tau_y\gamma_y/2$ times the factor $\tfrac{3}{4}$ or by $\omega_d' = (\tfrac{3}{4})G\gamma_y^2$, whereas all relations concerning the elastic volumetric strain ε, the mean stress, and the part of elastic energy of volume dilatation are unaffected by the plastic flow.

and that, in those cases of the variation of the state of internal stress in which the boundary stresses are not varied, the true stresses of the solution in an elastic–ideally plastic substance are those which make

$$\delta W_{i,e} = 0 \qquad (3\text{-}115)$$

or for which the elastic strain energy stored in the body is a minimum. This is the counterpart of the theorem of least energy which was expressed in Sec. 3-1, Eq. (3-41), for an elastic material.[1] We have tacitly assumed that the permanent parts of the strains do not cause a change of volume and that the variations are such that the process of yielding is nowhere interrupted.

Let us solve some *examples taken from the bending theory of beams* by postulating now the stress-strain law of an elastic–ideally plastic substance $\sigma = \sigma_0 f(\varepsilon)$ in accordance with Fig. 3-16 for uniaxial stress:

$$\varepsilon \leqq -\varepsilon_0, \qquad \sigma = -\sigma_0,$$

$$-\varepsilon_0 \leqq \varepsilon \leqq \varepsilon_0, \qquad \sigma = \frac{\sigma_0 \varepsilon}{\varepsilon_0}, \qquad (3\text{-}116)$$

$$\varepsilon_0 \leqq \varepsilon, \qquad \sigma = \sigma_0,$$

---

[1] ALFRED HAAR and THEODOR VON KÁRMÁN (Zur Theorie der Spannungs-zustände in plastischen und sandartigen Medien, Nachr. Ges. Wiss. Göttingen, pp. 204–218, 1909) discussed this variational principle first in its relation to a plastic substance in which, however, they assumed the criterion of maximum shearing stress by TRESCA and DE ST. VENANT to be valid and to the problems of the equilibria of loose materials (sand, earth), postulating in both types of sub-stances the presence of elastic strains. In following the ideas expressed in the courses of the mathematician FELIX KLEIN, they showed in this paper that for an elastic substance the linear stress-strain relations (Hooke's law) as well as the three conditions of compatibility of the strain components might be derived from the minimum condition of the strain energy, when treating this type of *conditioned* extremum problem of the definite integral expressing the strain energy, subject to the three conditions of the equilibrium of the stresses, according to the rules of classical calculus of variations. This latter method they attempted to extend to the two aforementioned types of solids.

In their footsteps HEINRICH HENCKY (Zur Theorie plastischer Deformationen und der hierdurch im Material hervorgerufenen Nachspannungen, Z. angew. Mathem. u. Mech., vol. 4, pp. 323–334, 1924) has shown that the stress-strain relations in a certain restricted form [see Vol. I, Eq. (24-21), $D_\varepsilon = (\frac{1}{2})\psi D_\sigma$, page 386, in what we termed a synthesis of small elastic and permanent strains] might be derived for the elastic–ideally plastic substance, namely, in the form applicable to those cases of flow when the principal directions of the tensors of stress and of elastic and permanent strain remain in coincidence during the yielding, from the condition of the minimum of the elastic strain energy $\delta W_i = 0$, subject to the three conditions of equilibrium of the stresses and to the condition of plasticity $\tau_0 = $ const. In treating again this "conditioned" extremum problem according to the rules of calculus of variations, after ingeniously having defined as the four Lagrangian multiplicators the displacement components u, v, w and a variable modulus of plasticity, Hencky succeeded in deriving the elastic-plastic stress-strain relations $D_\varepsilon = (\frac{1}{2})\psi D_\sigma$ of Eq. (24-21).

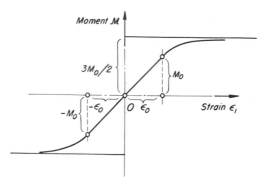

FIG. 3-17. Bending moment M in dependence on strain ε_1.

where ε represents the total (elastic plus permanent) strain, σ_0 is the yield stress in tension, and $\varepsilon_0 = \sigma_0/E$ is the elastic strain at the yield point. Using the designations explained in Sec. 3-3 and assuming that the beam has a rectangular cross section $b \times 2h$, there will be a bending moment under which it just starts to yield in the extreme fibers $z = \pm h$ equal to

$$M_0 = \frac{\sigma_0 I}{h} ; \qquad (3\text{-}117)$$

if ε_1 and σ_1 again denote the strain and stress at $z = h$, the bending moment M that such a section can carry, according to Eqs. (3-85) and (3-86), is expressed as follows:

When $-\varepsilon_0 < \varepsilon_1 < \varepsilon_0$:

$$M = \frac{M_0 \varepsilon_1}{\varepsilon_0} , \qquad\qquad \sigma_1 = \frac{Mh}{I} < \sigma_0,$$

or when $\begin{array}{l} \varepsilon_1 > \varepsilon_0 \text{:} \\ -\varepsilon_0 > \varepsilon_1 \text{:} \end{array}$ $\qquad\qquad\qquad\qquad\qquad\qquad\qquad (3\text{-}118)$

$$M = \pm(\tfrac{3}{2})M_0\left(1 - \frac{\varepsilon_0^2}{3\varepsilon_1^2}\right), \qquad \sigma_1 = \pm\sigma_0,$$

depending on whether the section is strained only elastically or has partially yielded external portions $-h < z < -z_0$ and $z_0 < z < h$.[†] Furthermore, the elastic strain energy ω_e per unit of volume at a point x,z and the integral

$$\int_0^h \omega_e \, dz$$

taken over half of the height of the cross section being equal to

$$\omega_e = \frac{\sigma\varepsilon}{2} = \frac{\sigma_0\varepsilon^2}{2\varepsilon_0} , \qquad \int_0^h \omega_e \, dz = \frac{\sigma_0 h \varepsilon_1^2}{6\varepsilon_0} , \qquad 0 < \varepsilon_1 < \varepsilon_0,$$

$$\omega_e = \frac{\sigma_0\varepsilon_0}{2} = \text{const}, \qquad \int_0^h \omega_e \, dz = \frac{\sigma_0 h \varepsilon_0}{2}\left(1 - \frac{2\varepsilon_0}{3\varepsilon_1}\right), \qquad \varepsilon_0 < \varepsilon_1$$

$\qquad\qquad\qquad\qquad\qquad\qquad\qquad\qquad\qquad\qquad\qquad\qquad\qquad\qquad\qquad (3\text{-}119)$

† This defines a curve M in dependence on ε_1 of antisymmetric shape as indicated in Fig. 3-17, having two horizontal asymptotes $M = \pm(\tfrac{3}{2})M_0$ determining the maximum bending moment that the beam can carry when its cross section yields completely.

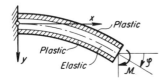

FIG. 3-18

we obtain with these values for the differential $dW_{i,e}$ of the elastic strain energy of bending stored in an element of the beam of the length dx

$$dW_{i,e} = 2b\,dx \int_0^h \omega_e\,dz \qquad (3\text{-}120)$$

for which, for brevity's sake, we shall write dW in what follows.

EXAMPLE 1.   Compute the angle of inclination φ of a section in a cantilever beam uniformly bent by a moment $M > M_0$ causing partial yielding in the beam (Fig. 3-18).   Using the second expression of the integral $\int_0^h \omega_e\,dz$, valid for $\varepsilon_1 > \varepsilon_0$ from Eqs. (3-119), since ε_1 and M are independent of x, from Eq. (3-120)

$$W = \sigma_0 bh\varepsilon_0 x\left(1 - \frac{2\varepsilon_0}{3\varepsilon_1}\right) = \frac{M_0\varepsilon_0 x}{h}\left(3 - \frac{\varepsilon_0}{\varepsilon_1}\right). \qquad (3\text{-}121)$$

After substituting here for the ratio $\varepsilon_0/\varepsilon_1$ its value computed from the second of the expressions for M given in Eqs. (3-118), namely,

$$\frac{\varepsilon_0}{\varepsilon_1} = \sqrt{3 - \frac{2M}{M_0}}, \qquad (3\text{-}122)$$

we obtain the elastic strain energy equal to

$$W = \frac{M_0\varepsilon_0 x}{h}\left(3 - \sqrt{3 - \frac{2M}{M_0}}\right) \qquad (3\text{-}123)$$

and therefore, according to the energy principle, the angle of inclination

$$\varphi = \frac{\partial W}{\partial M} = \frac{\varepsilon_0 x}{h\sqrt{3 - (2M/M_0)}} = \frac{\varepsilon_1 x}{h}, \qquad (3\text{-}124)$$

which is the same value that could have been computed from the differential equation of the deflections y of the partially yielded cantilever beam, namely,

$$\frac{d^2y}{dx^2} = \frac{\varepsilon_1}{h} = \text{const}, \qquad y = \frac{\varepsilon_1 x^2}{2h}, \qquad \varphi = \frac{dy}{dx} = \frac{\varepsilon_1 x}{h}.$$

EXAMPLE 2.   Find the maximum deflection y_m in a simply supported beam of length l carrying a single load Q in the center of its span after yielding has started.[1]   Let Q_0 and Q_m denote the loads at which yielding first starts and is completed in the center section $x = l/2$ of the beam, respectively.   The maximum bending moment in the beam being equal to $M = Ql/4$, we have, since $M_m = (\tfrac{3}{2})M_0$,

$$Q_0 = \frac{4M_0}{l}, \qquad Q_m = (\tfrac{3}{2})Q_0 = \frac{6M_0}{l}, \qquad (3\text{-}125)$$

[1] The two variational principles just mentioned were probably first discussed by JOSEF FRITSCHE in a paper, Arbeitsgesetze bei elastisch-plastischer Balkenbiegung, Z. angew. Math. u. Mech., vol. 11, no. 3, pp. 176–191, 1931, in their applications to the theory of bending of beams of an elastic–ideally plastic material.   In this remarkable paper Fritsche deserves credit for having extended the theorem by CASTIGLIANO to the case of bending of an elastic-plastic substance and has also worked out in slightly different manner the presently discussed example, among other cases of bending of beams.

the latter load Q_m defining the load-carrying capacity of the beam of ideally plastic material.[1] Observing the left side of the beam, yielding will spread from the center section while $Q_0 < Q < Q_m = (\tfrac{3}{2})Q_0$ toward the left to a point having the coordinate x_0, with the corresponding values $l/2 > x_0 > l/3$. Since in the section $x = x_0$, $M = Qx_0/2 = M_0$, in the equation

$$Qx_0 = 2M_0 = \frac{Q_0 l}{2} = \text{const} \tag{3-126}$$

the load Q and length of the unyielded portion of the beam x_0 are interdependent parameters, their product remaining constant during the spreading of the yielded zone. Furthermore, the ordinates $z_0 = h\varepsilon_0/\varepsilon_1$ of the boundary curve of the plastic zones in the beam lie in the region in which $\varepsilon_1 > \varepsilon_0$, and therefore, according to Eqs. (3-118), the bending moments must take on the values

$$M = (\tfrac{1}{2})Qx = (\tfrac{3}{2})M_0\left(1 - \frac{\varepsilon_0^2}{3\varepsilon_1^2}\right), \tag{3-127}$$

determining the ratios $\varepsilon_0/\varepsilon_1$ in their dependence on x, and hence

$$z_0 = \frac{h\varepsilon_0}{\varepsilon_1} = \pm h \cdot \sqrt{3 - \frac{Qx}{M_0}} = \pm h \cdot \sqrt{3 - \frac{2x}{x_0}} \tag{3-128}$$

defines $z_0 = f(x)$, namely, *the boundary curve of the plastic zones at a given load Q* for the corresponding value x_0 as an ordinary parabola for $x_0 \leq x \leq l/2$.

Let us compute now the elastic strain energy in the beam W consisting of the part W' in the elastically strained length $0 < x < x_0$ and of the part W'' in the partially yielded length $x_0 < x < l/2$ in the left half of the span. Using Eq. (3-120), taking $\omega_e = \sigma_0\varepsilon^2/2\varepsilon_0$, noting that $2hM_0/\varepsilon_0 = 2IE$, $M = (\tfrac{1}{2})Qx$, the part W' is equal to

$$W' = \frac{1}{2IE}\int_0^{x_0} M^2\, dx = \frac{Q^2 x_0^3}{24IE} = \frac{M_0^2 x_0}{6IE}, \tag{3-129}$$

whereas in the partially yielded portion $x_0 < x < l/2$, where $\varepsilon_1 > \varepsilon_0$, after Eqs. (3-119) and (3-128), the part of strain energy W'' is found equal to

$$W'' = \frac{M_0^2}{12IE}\left[9l - 22x_0 + 4x_0\left(3 - \frac{l}{x_0}\right)^{3/2}\right]. \tag{3-130}$$

The total strain energy stored in one-half of the length l of beam is therefore

$$W = W' + W'' = \frac{M_0^2}{12IE}\left[9l - 20x_0 + 4x_0\left(3 - \frac{l}{x_0}\right)^{3/2}\right]. \tag{3-131}$$

This energy for both halves of the beam being $2W$, the maximum deflection of the beam $y_m = 2\,\partial W/\partial Q$ or, after replacing Q by $Q = 2M_0/x_0$ and dQ by $dQ = -2M_0\, dx_0/x_0^2$, gives

$$y_m = -\frac{x_0^2}{M_0}\frac{\partial W}{\partial x_0}, \tag{3-132}$$

thus determining the maximum deflection in the partially yielded beam,

$$y_m = \frac{M_0 x_0^2}{6IE}\left[10 - \left(6 + \frac{l}{x_0}\right)\left(3 - \frac{l}{x_0}\right)^{1/2}\right], \tag{3-133}$$

[1] Cf. Vol. I, page 369.

or, in terms of the single load Q,

$$y_m = \frac{2M_0^3}{3IEQ^2}\left[10 - \left(6 + \frac{Ql}{2M_0}\right)\left(3 - \frac{Ql}{2M_0}\right)^{\frac{1}{2}}\right], \qquad (3\text{-}134)$$

valid unless $\frac{1}{2} \leq x_0 \leq \frac{1}{3}$ and $Q_0 \leq Q \leq (\frac{3}{2})Q_0$.

This gives at the instant when the beam just starts to yield at its center section under the load $Q_0 = 4M_0/l$ the deflection

$$y_{m0} = \frac{Q_0 l^3}{48IE}, \qquad (3\text{-}135)$$

in agreement with elementary bending theory of a fully elastic beam, and when $Q = Q_m = (\frac{3}{2})Q_0$ and the load-carrying capacity is just exhausted,

$$y_{mp} = (^{20}\!/_{9})y_{m0} = 2.22 y_{m0}. \qquad (3\text{-}136)$$

One verifies incidentally that the rate of increase of the load Q with the maximum deflection y_m, namely, $dQ/dy_m = 0$, just vanishes at the load-carrying capacity $Q = Q_m$ of the beam. Hereafter the beam deflects indefinitely under $Q_m = \text{const.}$

Several years ago the author computed the form of the deflected middle line of the beam for this case by integrating the differential equations for y:

$$\frac{d^2y}{dx^2} = -\frac{\varepsilon_1}{h} = -\frac{\varepsilon_0}{h\sqrt{3 - (2x/x_0)}}, \qquad x_0 \leq x \leq \frac{l}{2},$$
$$\qquad (3\text{-}137)$$
$$\frac{d^2y}{dx^2} = -\frac{\varepsilon_0 x}{hx_0}, \qquad 0 \leq x \leq x_0,$$

which gave, after fitting the two branches of the deflected line together, the following functions:

$$y = \frac{M_0 x_0^2}{3IE}\left[5 - \left(3 - \frac{2x}{x_0}\right)^{\frac{3}{2}} - \frac{3x}{x_0}\left(3 - \frac{l}{x_0}\right)^{\frac{1}{2}}\right], \qquad x_0 \leq x \leq \frac{l}{2},$$
$$\qquad (3\text{-}138)$$
$$y = \frac{M_0 x_0^2}{6IE}\cdot\frac{x}{x_0}\left[9 - \frac{x^2}{x_0^2} - \left(3 - \frac{l}{x_0}\right)^{\frac{1}{2}}\right], \qquad 0 \leq x \leq x_0,$$

within the plastic and the elastic branches of the left half of the beam, respectively. After letting $x = l/2$ in the former, one confirms that the resulting expression for the maximum deflection of the beam coincides with the one that we have derived for y_m from the energy principle in Eq. (3-133).

It may be instructive to compare the shapes of the curves representing in their ordinates the values of the strain ε_1 in the extreme fiber $z = h$ of the beam of an

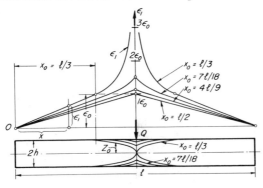

FIG. 3-19. Strain ε_1 in extreme fiber $z_1 = h$ in elastic and plastic zones of a bent bar.

elastic–ideally plastic substance plotted along the beam with the corresponding curves which illustrated the variation of ε_1 in beams whose material deforms according to a power function law which were reproduced in Figs. 3-11 and 3-12 in Sec. 3-3. Figure 3-19 reproduces four such curves, corresponding to the unyielded lengths $x_0/l = \frac{1}{2}, \frac{4}{5}, \frac{7}{18},$ and $\frac{1}{5}$; the last curve, corresponding to the complete yielding of the center cross section of the beam, rises indefinitely. The strain ε_1 being proportional to the curvature dy^2/dx^2 of the deflected line, these ε_1 curves, like the ones reproduced in Fig. 3-12, again bring out distinctly the fact of concentration of the plastic bending distortion near the point of application of the load Q as the latter approaches the load-carrying capacity $Q_m = (\frac{3}{2})Q_0$ of the beam, but in spite of the curvature tending to become infinitely great, the maximum deflection $y_{mp} = (\frac{20}{9})y_{m0}$ approaches this finite value. But since at this instant $dQ/dy_m = 0$, the beam enters the range of unstable equilibrium and would continue to deflect indefinitely.

BIBLIOGRAPHY

KACHANOV, L. M.: The Plastic-Elastic State of Solids, 1946.

KACHANOV, L. M.: Variational Principles of Elastic-Plastic Solids, 1946.

KACHANOV, L. M.: On the Mechanics of Plastic Solids, 1947. H. H. HAUSNER (ed.): "Plastic Deformation, Principles and Theories," 192 pp., a collection of papers by L. M. Kachanov, N. M. Beliaev, A. A. Ilyushin, W. Mostov, and A. N. Gleyzal, Mapleton House, Brooklyn, N.Y., 1948.

MARKOV, A. A.: On Variational Principles in the Theory of Plasticity, 1948.

ILYUSHIN, A. A.: Deformation of a Visco-plastic Solid, 149 pp., 1947.

HODGE, P., and W. PRAGER: A Variational Principle of Plastic Materials with Strain Hardening, 18 pp., 1947.

PRAGER, W.: Variational Principles in the Theory of Plasticity, 9 pp., 1948.

GREENBERG, H. J.: Complementary Minimum Principles for an Elastic-Plastic Material, 21 pp., 1948.

GREENBERG, H. J.: On the Variational Principles of Plasticity, 93 pp., 1949.

HODGE, P. G.: An Introduction to the Mathematical Theory of Perfectly Plastic Solids, 396 pp., 1950.[1]

[1] The above papers by Russian authors in these English translations and those by the American authors were published in typewritten form by the Graduate Division of Applied Mathematics, Brown University, Providence, R.I., with support of the Navy Department or the Office of Naval Research, Washington, D.C.

During the last 20 years there has developed a vast literature on the theory of plasticity by Russian authors, among whom particularly N. N. DAVIDENKOV, Y. B. FREEDMAN, A. A. ILYUSHIN, A. I. ISHLINSKI, and W. W. SOKOLOWSKY might be especially mentioned, several of whom published extensive monographs in Russian. A group of their papers is available in English translations prepared at Brown University and by the Pergamon Press Ltd., London.

The international literature on the mathematical theory of plasticity has been broadly surveyed in the book by J. N. GOODIER and P. G. HODGE cited below, at the end of which the reader can find the most extensive bibliography on this subject yet published, listing the titles of 155 non-Russian and 170 Russian papers and books devoted to this subject.

PRAGER, WILLIAM, and PHILIP G. HODGE: "Theory of Perfectly Plastic Solids,"
    264 pp., John Wiley & Sons, Inc., New York, 1951.
GOODIER, J. N., and P. G. HODGE: "Elasticity and Plasticity," 152 pp., John
    Wiley & Sons, Inc., New York, 1958 (containing a condensed survey over
    these fields).
HILL, R.: "The Mathematical Theory of Plasticity," 356 pp., Clarendon Press,
    Oxford, 1950.   See sections on plastic potential, p. 30, and on extremum
    and variational principles, p. 60.
HILL, R.: Mechanics of Quasi-static Plastic Deformation in Metals, article in
    G. I. Taylor 70th Anniversary Volume, p. 7, Cambridge University Press,
    London, 1956.
HILL, R.: Stability of Rigid-Plastic Solids, J. Mech. and Phys. Solids, vol. 6,
    p. 1, 1957.
SOKOLOWSKY, W. W.: "Theory of Plasticity" (in Russian), 306 pp., 1st ed., 1946;
    396 pp., 2d ed., 1950, Academy of Sciences of the U.S.S.R., Moscow.

Part II
ELASTICITY AND VISCOSITY

CHAPTER 4

ELASTICITY AND VISCOSITY

The most incomprehensive thing about the world is that it is comprehensive.   ALBERT EINSTEIN

Quoted from PHILIPP FRANK, "Einstein, His Life and Times," Alfred A. Knopf, Inc., New York, 1947.

4-1. Elasticity and Viscosity Combined in Their Simplest Manifestations in a Substance. A. INTRODUCTION. In an elastic solid the small components of strain are linear functions of the components of stress. The behavior of a substance is called *generally viscous* if the velocities with which its points are permanently displaced relative to each other increase with the stresses that deform it. A viscous substance thus deforms at faster rates of strain, the greater the stresses are, the simplest case being that of *a perfectly viscous substance* in which the components of the rates of strain increase permanently in proportion to the corresponding components of stress. The viscosity of solid substances becomes conspicuous when the temperature is raised, one of the commonest examples being a straight rod of glass held at a temperature approaching the softening range of glass and loaded in vertical position by a weight which is seen slowly to drop continuously, while the rod extends permanently at a rate of elongation (proportionally increasing with the weight) which is faster, the greater the weight is. In this section we shall review first a few cases of what might be termed simple, ideal, composite solids, namely, of substances in the concepts of which the ideal properties of the elasticity of a solid and of its viscosity manifest themselves simultaneously and in their simplest combination. Examples of this kind are considered also with the aim of a better understanding of the more general phenomena observed in the behavior of solid substances at elevated temperatures, such as the slow creep of ductile metals or of polycrystalline solids held under stress for a prolonged time, to be treated later under improved assumptions.

In the applications that we have in mind the velocities of motion are so small that the inertia terms containing the accelerations of the elements of material need not be considered, and static equilibrium of

157

the forces and internal stresses can be assumed. The displacements and strains are postulated small, and the material may be considered as compressible elastically while it is assumed to be permanently incompressible. In some cases the simplifying assumption may be made that the material is totally incompressible for both the elastic, reversible and for the permanent, irreversible parts of the strains.

The concepts of a few of these simple, ideal, composite solids may be clarified by describing first their behavior under tensile tests of the various types which have been already mentioned (Vol. I, Chap. 8), such as are represented for engineering materials in Figs. 4-1 through 4-4. Figure 4-1 reproduces the engineer's *long-time creep curves* which he records by plotting the extension (the total strain ε as the sum of the elastic and of the permanent strain) as a function of the time t when the stress $\sigma = $ const is held at a given, constant value at an elevated temperature. Figure 4-2 shows the observations in tensile tests run by stretching specimens *under constant rates of strain* $\dot{\varepsilon} = d\varepsilon/dt = $ const (by extending them under a given, relative velocity between the heads of the tensile bar). Figure 4-3, by increasing the stress σ in the test bar by equal amounts in equal times, i.e., at *a given constant rate of increase of stress* $d\sigma/dt = $ const, illustrates in the observed departure of the stress-strain curves from each other the effect of the speed of deformation. Figure 4-4 reproduces *relaxation tests* in which, after the application of an initial stress σ_1, the length of a tensile specimen is prevented from changing by holding both heads of it in fixed positions while the stress σ is seen to drop gradually after the time t elapses, in the manner indicated for a number of initial stresses σ_1.

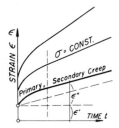

FIG. 4-1. Primary and secondary creep in creep curves.

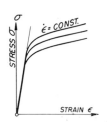

FIG. 4-2. Constant-strain-rate tests.

FIG. 4-3. Constant-rate-of-stress tests.

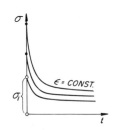

FIG. 4-4. Relaxation of stress.

B. VISCOELASTICITY. Consider a tensile rod subjected to a normal stress σ. Denote by ε' the elastic strain, by ε'' the permanent normal strain in the axial direction, by γ' and γ'' the elastic and the permanent unit shears in an oblique direction, and by placing a dot above ε, γ or the normal and shearing stress σ, τ, their derivatives with respect to the time t. In an *elastic* material,

$$\sigma = E\varepsilon', \tag{4-1}$$

and in a perfectly *viscous*, permanently *incompressible* substance, since the principal rates of normal strain under a simple extension are $\dot{\varepsilon}_1 = \dot{\varepsilon}''$ in the axial direction and $\dot{\varepsilon}_2 = \dot{\varepsilon}_3 = -\dot{\varepsilon}''/2$ in the lateral direction, the maximum rate of shear being equal to $\dot{\gamma}_{\max} = \dot{\varepsilon}_1 - \dot{\varepsilon}_2 = (\tfrac{3}{2})\dot{\varepsilon}''$ and the maximum shearing stress $\tau_{\max} = \sigma/2 = \mu\dot{\gamma}_{\max} = (\tfrac{3}{2})\mu\dot{\varepsilon}''$, we must have for viscous material

$$\sigma = 3\mu \frac{d\varepsilon''}{dt} = 3\mu\dot{\varepsilon}'', \tag{4-2}$$

where E is the modulus of elasticity and μ the coefficient of viscosity. Supposing that both types of strain figure additively in making up the total strain ε, we have

$$\varepsilon' = \frac{\sigma}{E}, \qquad \varepsilon = \varepsilon' + \varepsilon'' = \frac{\sigma}{E} + \varepsilon'',$$

$$\dot{\varepsilon}'' = \frac{\sigma}{3\mu}, \qquad \dot{\varepsilon} = \dot{\varepsilon}' + \dot{\varepsilon}'' = \dot{\varepsilon}' + \frac{E}{3\mu}\varepsilon' = \frac{\dot{\sigma}}{E} + \frac{\sigma}{3\mu}. \tag{4-3}$$

Such a substance is called *viscoelastic*.[1] If $G = E/2(1 + \nu)$ denotes the modulus of rigidity and ν denotes Poisson's ratio, we have, similarly, for viscoelastic behavior under shearing strains

$$\gamma' = \frac{\tau}{G}, \qquad \gamma = \gamma' + \gamma'' = \frac{\tau}{G} + \gamma'',$$

$$\dot{\gamma}'' = \frac{\tau}{\mu}, \qquad \dot{\gamma} = \dot{\gamma}' + \dot{\gamma}'' = \dot{\gamma}' + \frac{G}{\mu}\gamma' = \frac{\dot{\tau}}{G} + \frac{\tau}{\mu}. \tag{4-4}$$

If we use for the two ratios having the dimension of time the abbreviations

$$t_e = \frac{3\mu}{E}, \qquad t_s = \frac{\mu}{G} = \frac{2(1 + \nu)t_e}{3}, \tag{4-5}$$

called *the relaxation or adjustment times* of a normal and of a shearing stress, respectively, we may rewrite the preceding equations as

$$\dot{\varepsilon}' + \frac{\varepsilon'}{t_e} = \dot{\varepsilon}, \qquad \dot{\gamma}' + \frac{\gamma'}{t_s} = \dot{\gamma} \tag{4-6}$$

and express the elastic parts of the normal and shearing strains in terms of the total strains in the two equivalent forms:

$$\varepsilon' = \frac{\sigma}{E} = e^{-t/t_e}\left[\varepsilon(0) + \int_0^t \dot{\varepsilon}e^{t/t_e}\,dt\right],$$

$$\gamma' = \frac{\tau}{G} = e^{-t/t_s}\left[\gamma(0) + \int_0^t \dot{\gamma}e^{t/t_s}\,dt\right], \tag{4-7}$$

[1] It was first considered by J. CLERK MAXWELL in his paper, On the Dynamical Theory of Gases, Phil. Mag., vol. 35, pp. 129–145, 185–219, 1868 (see p. 133 of this paper).

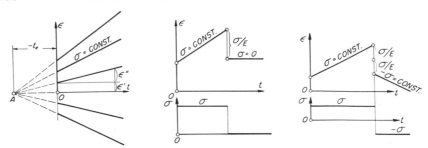

FIG. 4-5. Stress σ = const.   FIG. 4-6. Stress released.   FIG. 4-7. Stress reversed.

Viscoelasticity.

or, after applying partial integration, by

$$\varepsilon' = \frac{\sigma}{E} = \varepsilon - \frac{1}{t_e} e^{-t/t_e} \int_0^t \varepsilon e^{t/t_e} \, dt,$$

$$\gamma' = \frac{\tau}{G} = \gamma - \frac{1}{t_s} e^{-t/t_s} \int_0^t \gamma e^{t/t_s} \, dt,$$

(4-8)

where $\varepsilon(0)$, $\gamma(0)$ denote the values at time $t = 0$. The two material constants t_e and t_s are, in general, of slightly different magnitude but, for an incompressible elastic substance showing viscosity ($\nu = \frac{1}{2}$), $t_e = t_s$. The second terms on the right sides of Eqs. (4-8) obviously express the permanent parts ε'', γ'' of the strain times -1.

To imprint on our memory *viscoelastic behavior* in a substance, consider the following simplest types of tensile tests.

(1). *Stress held constant. Stress suddenly released.* While the stress is held invariable, σ = const, $\dot{\sigma} = \dot{\varepsilon}' = 0$,

$$\dot{\varepsilon} = \frac{\sigma}{3\mu} = \text{const},$$

$$\varepsilon = \frac{\sigma}{E}\left(1 + \frac{t}{t_e}\right).$$

(4-9)

The strain ε increases linearly with time t. For various values of σ = const, Eqs. (4-9) represent a pencil of rays emanating from point A (Fig. 4-5), the family of "creep curves" for a viscoelastic substance. On sudden release of the stress from the value σ to $\sigma = 0$, Fig. 4-6 is obtained, and when the stress is reversed from $+\sigma$ to $-\sigma$, we have Fig. 4-7.

(2). *Strain rate held constant.* $\varepsilon = ut$, $\dot{\varepsilon} = u$ = const, and from Eqs. (4-3) or (4-7),

$$E\dot{\varepsilon} = \dot{\sigma} + \frac{1}{t_e}\sigma = Eu = \text{const},$$

(4-10)

$$\sigma = \sigma_1(1 - e^{-t/t_e}),$$

(4-11)

denoting the stress at $t = \infty$ by $\sigma_1 = Eut_e = E\varepsilon_1$, $\varepsilon_1 = ut_e$. Since $t : t_e = \varepsilon : \varepsilon_1$, the stress may be expressed in terms of the total strain ε by

$$\sigma = \sigma_1(1 - e^{-\varepsilon/\varepsilon_1}). \qquad (4\text{-}12)$$

For different values of the strain rate $u = \varepsilon_1/t_e = \text{const}$ this family of geometrically similar exponential curves approaching horizontal asymptotes (Fig. 4-8) represents the stress-strain curves taken at constant rates of strain. After a sufficiently long time t has been allowed to elapse, the two types of test (1) and (2) are identical.

(3). *Stress rate held constant.* If the stress σ increases at a constant rate, $\dot{\sigma} = w = \text{const}$, $\sigma = wt$, and

$$\dot{\varepsilon} = \frac{w}{E}\left(1 + \frac{t}{t_e}\right), \qquad (4\text{-}13)$$

$$\varepsilon = \frac{w}{E}\left(t + \frac{1}{2t_e}t^2\right) = \frac{\sigma}{E}\left(1 + \frac{\sigma}{2t_ew}\right), \qquad (4\text{-}14)$$

the stress-strain curves consist of a family of ordinary parabolas starting with the same slope at the origin O (Fig. 4-9).

(4). *Relaxation.* After applying a normal stress σ_1, holding the strain invariable at value $\varepsilon = \sigma_1/E = \varepsilon_1 = \text{const}$, since $\dot{\varepsilon} = 0$,

$$t_e\dot{\sigma} + \sigma = 0, \qquad (4\text{-}15)$$

$$\sigma = \sigma_1 e^{-t/t_e}. \qquad (4\text{-}16)$$

Or similarly, if the substance is stressed by a shearing stress τ_1, holding the unit shear $\gamma = \tau_1/G = \gamma_1 = \text{const}$,

$$t_s\dot{\tau} + \tau = 0, \qquad (4\text{-}17)$$

$$\tau = \tau_1 e^{-t/t_s}, \qquad (4\text{-}18)$$

the originally elastic strain or unit shear is converted gradually into permanent strain or shear. The initial rate of decrease of stress at time $t = 0$, $\dot{\sigma} = -\sigma_1/t_e$, $\dot{\tau} = -\tau_1/t_s$, is proportional to the initial stress and inversely proportional to the time constants t_e or t_s, respectively.

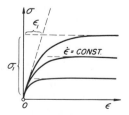

FIG. 4-8. Strain rate $\dot{\varepsilon} = \text{const}$.

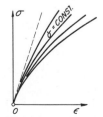

FIG. 4-9. Stress rate $\dot{\sigma} = \text{const}$.

Viscoelasticity.

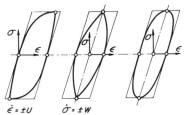

$\dot\varepsilon = \pm U$ $\qquad$ $\dot\sigma = \pm W$

FIG. 4-10   FIG. 4-11   FIG. 4-12

Viscoelasticity.
Hysteresis loops.

(5). *Hysteresis loops* might be produced in an infinite number of ways in periodic homogeneous stressing or straining operations. Assuming a rod stressed in the axial direction by normal stresses σ, three examples are reproduced in Figs. 4-10 through 4-12. Figure 4-10 represents the loop by deforming a rod back and forth with the constant rates of strain $\dot\varepsilon = \pm u = $ const; Fig. 4-11 shows the oscillations under constant rates of stressing $\dot\sigma = \pm w = $ const; and Fig. 4-12, under a sinusoidally varying stress $\sigma = \sigma_0 \sin \omega t$, producing the total strain

$$\varepsilon = \frac{1}{E} \left(\sigma \pm \frac{1}{\omega t_e} \sqrt{\sigma_0^2 - \sigma^2} \right), \tag{4-19}$$

All the loops are crossing the ε axis at $\sigma = 0$, $\varepsilon = \pm \sigma_0/\omega t_e$ under the slope $d\sigma/d\varepsilon = E$. The hysteresis loops consist in the first, second, and third types of cycles of two branches of exponential curves, of two parabolas and of ellipses, respectively, all of which cross the ε axis with the slope $d\sigma/d\varepsilon = E$ and become narrower at faster rates.[1]

C. FIRMOVISCOSITY. In a certain contrast to viscoelastic behavior, let us conceive a second type of composite solid by making the assumption that in it the stresses σ and τ are additively built up of two parts, of a stress σ' and τ' carried elastically and of a stress σ'' and τ'' necessary to overcome an internal resistance of a viscous nature in the substance opposing any change of strain and being proportional to the rate of change of strain $\dot\varepsilon$ and $\dot\gamma$, respectively[2]:

$$\sigma = \sigma' + \sigma'' = E\varepsilon + 3\mu \cdot \frac{d\varepsilon}{dt} = E(\varepsilon + t_r \dot\varepsilon),$$

$$\tau = \tau' + \tau'' = G\gamma + \mu \cdot \frac{d\gamma}{dt} = G(\gamma + t_g \dot\gamma), \tag{4-20}$$

$$t_r = \frac{3\mu}{E}, \qquad t_g = \frac{\mu}{G}. \tag{4-21}$$

[1] One may follow up the various kinds of sequences of stressing in a more complete manner by representing the three variables ε, $\dot\varepsilon$, and σ in a system of rectangular coordinates and by plotting the corresponding curves that they trace in the ε,σ, and the $\varepsilon,\dot\varepsilon$ planes, the latter depicting in geometric manner the *hodographs* (cf. J. Appl. Mechanics, vol. 55; Trans. ASME, no. 10, p. 61, 1933) of such motions.

[2] In this firmoviscous (nonconservative) system one can *not* separate an elastic from a permanent part in the strain ε, which tends to become $\varepsilon = \sigma/E$ as soon as $d\varepsilon/dt$ vanishes. An elastic, helical spring tied to a dashpot in parallel, the latter hindering the elastic extension of the former, represents a mechanical model of a firmoviscous substance (known as the *Kelvin model* of a solid).

This has been called *firmoviscosity*[1] although the corresponding basic phenomena are better known to engineers in bodies performing rapid oscillations as internal damping of a viscous nature, as one sees from

$$G\gamma = \tau - Gt_g \frac{d\gamma}{dt}, \qquad (4\text{-}22)$$

the second term on the right side expressing an internal damping force per unit of area and becoming significant at sufficiently large values of the rate of distortion $d\gamma/dt$.

This is contrasted with viscoelastic behavior after rewriting the corresponding relation for the latter from Eqs. (4-4) as follows:

$$\gamma = \gamma' + \gamma'' = \frac{1}{G}\left(\tau + \frac{1}{t_s}\int_0^t \tau\, dt\right) = \gamma' + \frac{1}{t_s}\int_0^t \gamma'\, dt, \qquad (4\text{-}23)$$

supposing that, at time $t = 0$, $\gamma'' = 0$, disclosing that, even though $t_s = \mu/G$ may be a constant time having a comparatively great value in very viscous material, the term $\gamma'' = (1/t_s)\int_0^t \gamma'\, dt$, representing the permanent distortion when τ invariably acts, grows continuously to values surpassing the elastic strain γ'. Thus, the adjustment-time constants t_r, t_g of firmoviscosity are supposed to have small values, while those of viscoelasticity t_e, t_s have great values.[2]

---

[1] For this imperfection in elastic behavior, HAROLD JEFFREYS proposed the name of firmoviscosity. See "The Earth, Its Origin, History and Physical Constitution," 3d ed., p. 10, Cambridge University Press, London, 1952; see also Proc. Roy. Soc. (London), Ser. A, vol. 138, p. 283, 1932.

[2] Although μ has the same dimension (kg cm^{-2} sec) in technical units for viscoelasticity and for firmoviscosity and the proportionality factor in $\tau = \mu\, d\gamma''/dt$ and in $\tau'' = \mu\, d\gamma/dt$, respectively, was denoted by the same symbol for convenience, it may be in order, to avoid some confusion, to give it a different name, calling μ in the first case (*elasticoviscosity*) *the coefficient of viscosity* and in the second case (*firmoviscosity*) *the coefficient of internal damping* of a substance. In the latter case, we do not favor calling μ the coefficient of "internal friction," as GUTENBERG proposed, in view of various, ideal solid substances possessing an internal resistance of the type of a Coulomb friction, in which the ratio of a shearing to a normal stress $\tau/\sigma = \mu$ is a constant, as in loose, granulated materials (sand). The reader should thus note that, with respect to geophysical applications, Eqs. (4-4) primarily serve to predict the extremely slow permanent deformation in the rocks constituting the upper strata in the earth's crust, produced in the phenomena of mountain-building or postglacial uplifts over formerly overglaciated regions of the continents during the prolonged epochs of time in geology, whereas Eqs. (4-20) may be useful for discussing the effects of internal damping on the laws of propagation and extenuation of earthquake waves in very rapid, elastic oscillations.

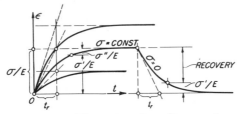

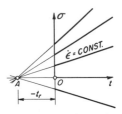

FIG. 4-13. Firmoviscosity. Stress rate
$\sigma = $ const.

FIG. 4-14. Firmovis-
cosity. Strain rate
$\dot{\varepsilon} = $ const.

(1). *Assuming firmoviscosity, after a stress σ is applied and held constant,* from Eqs. (4-20) and (4-21),

$$t_r\dot{\varepsilon} + \varepsilon = \frac{\sigma}{E} = \text{const}, \qquad \varepsilon = \frac{\sigma}{E}(1 - e^{-t/t_r}), \qquad (4\text{-}24)$$

and upon *sudden release of stress σ,*

$$t_r\dot{\varepsilon} + \varepsilon = 0, \qquad \varepsilon = \frac{\sigma}{E}e^{-t/t_r}, \qquad (4\text{-}25)$$

the strain ε responds with a time lag and assumes its final value equal to the elastic strain σ/E after a certain time elapses and similarly, after a sudden release of stress, recovers gradually. This *recovery* is just equal to the elastic strain (Fig. 4-13) at $t = \infty$ after unloading.

(2). *Under a constant rate of stretching $\dot{\varepsilon} = u = $ const, $\varepsilon = ut$,* the stress σ increases uniformly with time t or strain ε (Fig. 4-14):

$$\sigma = E(ut_r + \varepsilon) = Eu(t_r + t). \qquad (4\text{-}26)$$

(3). *If the rate of stress is constant, $\dot{\sigma} = w = $ const, $\sigma = wt$,* the strain ε responds with

$$\varepsilon = \frac{w}{E}[t - t_r(1 - e^{-t/t_r})] \qquad (4\text{-}27)$$

in a family of curves tangent in the origin $t = 0$ to the time axis and asymptotically approaching a pencil of rays emanating from a point $A(t = t_r)$ (Fig. 4-15).

(4). *Relaxation.* Suppose that after stress $\sigma_0 = $ const acted for a certain time t_1, while the strain ε increased to a value $\varepsilon_1 = \sigma_1/E < \sigma_0/E$, a further development of the strain *is stopped* and the substance not allowed to stretch further. Then, after this time, when $t > t_1$, the strain $\varepsilon = \varepsilon_1 = $ const and $\dot{\varepsilon} = 0$. But in a firmoviscous material, the stress σ needed to deform it being equal to the sum $\sigma = \sigma' + \sigma''$ of the part $\sigma' = E\varepsilon$ causing the strain ε and the part $\sigma'' = 3\mu\dot{\varepsilon}$ which is required for overcoming its viscous resistance, since the latter part *vanishes* when $t > t_1$, we see that the stress σ at time $t = t_1$ must drop suddenly from its original value σ_0 to its last, *elastically* carried value,

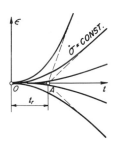

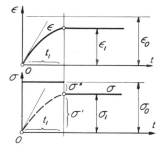

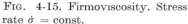

FIG. 4-15. Firmoviscosity. Stress rate $\dot\sigma = $ const.

FIG. 4-16. Firmoviscosity. Relaxation for $t > t_1$.

namely, according to Eqs. (4-24) to

$$\sigma = E\varepsilon_1 = \sigma_1 = \sigma_0(1 - e^{-t_1/t_r}) = \text{const.} \qquad (4\text{-}28)$$

We note that, in *a firmoviscous substance, relaxation of stress occurs instantaneously, provided that it is initiated within the adjustment period of the strains of the former application of stress*, as illustrated in Fig. 4-16. The earlier the relaxation is initiated after the application of a stress $\sigma = \sigma_0$, the greater will be the drop $\sigma_0 - \sigma = \sigma_0 e^{-t_1/t_r}$. For large values of t_1, obviously $\sigma = \sigma_0$, and no drop in stress occurs at all.

It should be borne in mind, however, that while the diagrams reproducing these kinds of changes in stress and strain are meant to illustrate comparatively slow processes of distortion under viscoelastic behavior, they refer in the case of a firmoviscous substance to rapid processes. The features in the behavior of these two substances may be seen at a cursory glance in Table 4-1.

TABLE 4-1

Test	Viscoelastic substance	Firmoviscous substance
Constant stress	Creep-time curves are straight lines. No creep limit exists. Creep never stops.	Strain-time curves become asymptotic to horizontal lines. Strain stops.
Constant strain rate	The stress-time or stress-strain curves approach horizontal asymptotes.	They are convergent straight lines.
Constant stress rate	The stress-strain curves are parabolas.	Exponential curves, asymptotic to convergent straight lines.
Relaxation	Gradual evanescence of stress.	Sudden drop of stress (conditionally).
Recovery	None.	Equal to elastic strain.

Although it is scarcely necessary to state that the phenomena of the slow creep of metals and of polycrystalline solids at elevated temperatures cannot be represented by the simple means that we are here discussing, for two important reasons, namely, because (1) the dependence of stress on rate of flow is certainly nonlinear for them and (2) plastic strains also occur in them and strain hardening and softening (recrystallization) with time at moderately high temperatures influence creep and relaxation, it is perhaps worthwhile to point here to the fact that, by a proper combination of the two superposition principles which were utilized in Eqs. (4-3) and (4-4) and Eqs. (4-20), defining viscoelastic and firmoviscous behavior, respectively, a few characteristic details in the creep of polycrystalline solids and in related phenomena might, to a certain extent, be qualitatively reproduced.

D. COMPOSITE, VISCOELASTIC SUBSTANCE DISCLOSING RECOVERY STRAINS. This leads us then to propose a *third, ideal, composite, viscoelastic, recovery-sensitive substance*, by postulating a principle of superposition in it for three distinct types of strain ε', ε'', ε''' and two types of stress σ', σ'' as follows:

$$\varepsilon = \varepsilon' + \varepsilon'' + \varepsilon''', \qquad \sigma = \sigma' + \sigma'', \tag{4-29}$$

supposing that the strain ε has an *elastic* part $\varepsilon' = \sigma/E$ instantaneously carried with the action of a stress σ, a *permanent* strain ε'' of a viscous nature proportional to $(\frac{1}{3}\mu)\int \sigma \, dt$ developing slowly when a stress causes a rate of strain $\dot{\varepsilon}'' = \sigma/3\mu$ proportional to stress, and a third part of strain ε''' of semipermanent character, which may be slowly recoverable under the interaction of the two additive fractions of stress σ' and σ'' that were postulated.   The latter are assumed equal to

$$\sigma' = E_r \varepsilon''', \qquad \sigma'' = 3\mu_r \dot{\varepsilon}''' \tag{4-30}$$

and offer consideration of prescribable "offsets" and "recovery strains" accompanying changes of stress or strain through the third type of strain ε''' if one reserves the right of choosing the constants E_r, μ_r governing the recoverable parts of the permanent strains independently of E, μ.

For this *third, composite solid*, assuming the validity of the relations based on Eqs. (4-29) and (4-30),

$$\varepsilon' = \frac{\sigma}{E}, \qquad \dot{\varepsilon}'' = \frac{\sigma}{3\mu}, \qquad t_e = \frac{3\mu}{E}, \tag{4-31}$$

$$\sigma = \sigma' + \sigma'' = E_r(\varepsilon''' + t_r\dot{\varepsilon}'''), \qquad t_r = \frac{3\mu_r}{E_r}, \tag{4-32}$$

$$\dot{\varepsilon} = \dot{\varepsilon}' + \dot{\varepsilon}'' + \dot{\varepsilon}''' = \frac{\dot{\sigma}}{E} + \frac{\sigma}{3\mu} + \frac{\sigma''}{3\mu_r}, \tag{4-33}$$

let us now again consider the following situations.

(1). *A sudden application of a stress σ* = const.   From the preceding equations we see that

$$\varepsilon' = \frac{\sigma}{E}, \qquad \dot{\varepsilon}'' = \frac{\sigma}{3\mu} = \text{const}, \qquad \varepsilon'' = \frac{\sigma}{3\mu} t$$

and from Eqs. (4-32),

$$t_r\dot{\varepsilon}''' + \varepsilon''' = \frac{\sigma}{E_r} = \text{const}, \qquad \varepsilon''' = \frac{\sigma}{E_r}(1 - e^{-t/t_r}),$$

showing that the strain ε will steadily increase according to

$$\varepsilon = \varepsilon' + \varepsilon'' + \varepsilon''' = \frac{\sigma}{E}\left(1 + \frac{t}{t_e}\right) + \frac{\sigma}{E_r}(1 - e^{-t/t_r}) \qquad (4\text{-}34)$$

along a curve approaching an inclined straight line, as can be seen in Fig. 4-17.   The creep curves $\varepsilon = f(t)$ for constant stress disclose a curved portion first, corresponding to a *primary* creep period.   Conversely, if a stress σ = const acted for a sufficient time while the strain reached a value ε_1, indicated at point A (Fig. 4-17), the strain ε on a sudden release of stress takes the values

$$\varepsilon = \varepsilon_1 - \frac{\sigma}{E} - \frac{\sigma}{E_r}(1 - e^{-t/t_r}) \qquad (4\text{-}35)$$

[the time t in Eq. (4-35) being counted from point A], the last term on the right representing the *recovery*.

(2). *Strain rate constant, $\varepsilon = ut$, $\dot{\varepsilon} = u$* = const.   From Eq. (4-33),

$$\dot{\sigma} + \frac{\sigma}{t_e} + E\dot{\varepsilon}''' = Eu = \text{const}, \qquad (4\text{-}36)$$

and from Eqs. (4-32),

$$\sigma = E_r(\varepsilon''' + t_r\dot{\varepsilon}'''). \qquad (4\text{-}37)$$

After substituting σ from Eq. (4-37) in Eq. (4-36) a differential equation for the recoverable strain ε''',

$$\ddot{\varepsilon}''' + \left[\frac{1}{t_e} + \frac{1}{t_r}\left(1 + \frac{E}{E_r}\right)\right]\dot{\varepsilon}''' + \frac{\varepsilon'''}{t_e t_r} = \frac{Eu}{E_r t_r} = \text{const}, \qquad (4\text{-}38)$$

is obtained.   The solution of it, ε''', when used in Eq. (4-37) furnishes also the stress σ but is not reproduced here explicitly for the initial

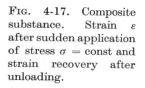

Fig. 4-17.   Composite substance.   Strain ε after sudden application of stress σ = const and strain recovery after unloading.

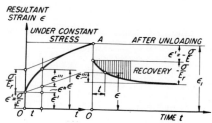

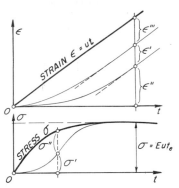

FIG. 4-18. Composite substance. Constant-strain-rate test.

conditions $t = 0$, $\varepsilon''' = \dot{\varepsilon}''' = 0$, which it has to satisfy. The trend of the three part strains ε', ε'', ε''' can be seen in Fig. 4-18. The stress soon reaches the asymptotic value $\sigma = Eut_e$, which is exactly the same as that of the visco-elastic case in Sec. 4-1B(2). The strain ε''' for $t = \infty$ approaches the constant value $\varepsilon''' = Eut_e/E_r$, as can be seen from Eq. (4-38).

(3). *Relaxation of stress.* If the strain is held constant and the strain rate $\dot{\varepsilon}$ vanishes, we can utilize the preceding equations (4-36) and (4-37). After letting $u = 0$ and eliminating from them the variable ε''', we find that the stress σ must satisfy the differential equation

$$\ddot{\sigma} + \left[\frac{1}{t_e} + \frac{1}{t_r}\left(1 + \frac{E}{E_r}\right)\right]\dot{\sigma} + \frac{\sigma}{t_e t_r} = 0. \tag{4-39}$$

Furthermore, Eq. (4-38) retains its validity, after letting $u = 0$, and we note that both differential equations (4-38) and (4-39) have exactly the same form, having the same constant factors. The integral of Eq. (4-39) has the form

$$\sigma = Ae^{\lambda_1 t} + Be^{\lambda_2 t}; \tag{4-40}$$

A, B are integration constants and λ_1, λ_2 are the two roots of a quadratic equation[1]

$$\lambda_1 = -\lambda_0 + \lambda,$$
$$\lambda_2 = -\lambda_0 - \lambda, \tag{4-41}$$

using the abbreviations

$$\frac{1}{T} = \frac{1}{t_r}\left(1 + \frac{E}{E_r}\right), \qquad \lambda_0 = \frac{1}{2}\left(\frac{1}{t_e} + \frac{1}{T}\right), \qquad \lambda = \sqrt{\frac{1}{4}\left(\frac{1}{t_e} + \frac{1}{T}\right)^2 - \frac{1}{t_e t_r}}. \tag{4-42}$$

A recoverable strain of the type ε''', that may have been formed during a distortion preceding the initiation of a state of relaxation under $\varepsilon = $ const, has an influence on the rate $\dot{\sigma}$ with which the stress σ starts to

[1] Obtained from Eq. (4-39) by letting $\sigma = e^{vt}$, giving $v^2 + 2bv + c = 0$, $v = -b \pm \sqrt{b^2 - c}$, where

$$b = \frac{1}{2}\left(\frac{1}{t_e} + \frac{1}{T}\right) = \lambda_0, \qquad c = \frac{1}{t_e t_r}.$$

The discriminant is always positive; both roots v (denoted in the text above by λ_1, λ_2) turn out to be always negative since $\lambda < \lambda_0$.

drop. It may be instructive, therefore, to consider two cases of the initial conditions for relaxation.

In the *first case*, let us assume that the initial stress $\sigma = \sigma_1$ acted only during an instant after which the specimen is left under $\varepsilon = \varepsilon_1 = \sigma_1/E = $ const to relax. This is expressed by the initial conditions $t = 0$, $\sigma = \sigma_1$, $\varepsilon'' = \varepsilon''' = 0$. The constants of integration are found equal to

$$A = \frac{\sigma_1}{2}\left[1 - \frac{\lambda_0 - (1/t_r)}{\lambda}\right], \qquad B = \frac{\sigma_1}{2}\left[1 + \frac{\lambda_0 - (1/t_r)}{\lambda}\right], \qquad (4\text{-}43)$$

and one computes for the initial rate of drop of stress

$$t = 0, \qquad \frac{d\sigma}{dt} = -\sigma_1\left(\frac{1}{t_e} + \frac{1}{t_r}\right). \qquad (4\text{-}44)$$

But the first term $-\sigma_1/t_e$ represents this rate for a viscoelastic substance. Thus we note that in a *recovery-sensitive solid the stress drops initially much faster* than in a solid not having recoverable strains ε''' if t_r is of the same order of magnitude or smaller than t_e.

In the *second case*, on the contrary, let us first hold the specimen loaded under the stress $\sigma_1 = $ const for such a long time that the strain ε''' has had time to increase to its maximum value $\varepsilon''' = \sigma_1/E_r$ (see Fig. 4-17, point A). If the specimen is then allowed to relax, the initial conditions are $t = 0$, $\sigma = \sigma_1$, $\varepsilon''' = \sigma_1/E_r$, and the constants of integration take the values

$$A = \frac{\sigma_1}{2}\left[1 - \frac{\lambda_0 - (1/T)}{\lambda}\right], \qquad B = \frac{\sigma_1}{2}\left[1 + \frac{\lambda_0 - (1/T)}{\lambda}\right], \qquad (4\text{-}45)$$

corresponding to which an initial rate of drop of stress is found:

$$t = 0, \qquad \frac{d\sigma}{dt} = -\frac{\sigma_1}{t_e}, \qquad (4\text{-}46)$$

equal to the initial relaxation rate of the viscoelastic substance.

Since $|\lambda_2| > |\lambda_1|$ in both cases, after a considerable time has elapsed, the term $Be^{\lambda_2 t}$ decreases much faster than the term $Ae^{\lambda_1 t}$ in Eq. (4-40) so that the stress will vary later as

$$\sigma = Ae^{\lambda_1 t}. \qquad (4\text{-}47)$$

In spite of A being smaller than $\sigma_1/2$, after a sufficient time, the stress σ will have greater ordinates and will decrease (since $|\lambda_1| < 1/t_e$) at a slower rate than the stress relaxes in a viscoelastic substance according to the function

$$\sigma = \sigma_1 e^{-t/t_e}. \qquad (4\text{-}48)$$

Thus we see that *the stress σ in a relaxation test of a substance having active recovery strains ε'''* (Fig. 4-19) *finally decreases under higher values*

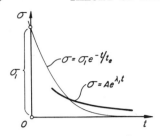

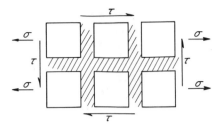

FIG. 4-19. Composite substance. Relaxation.

FIG. 4-20. Elastic blocks embedded in viscous substance.

and at slower rates than in a viscoelastic material of the same viscosity μ (and adjustment time t_e).   This is further illustrated in the following numerical examples of the curves toward which the relaxing stress σ asymptotically converges at large values of the time t:

E_r/E	μ/μ_r	σ/σ_1
⅓	³⁄₂	$0.122e^{-0.177(t/t_e)}$
1	1	$0.277e^{-0.382(t/t_e)}$
3	½	$0.500e^{-0.634(t/t_e)}$
Viscoelastic substance		e^{-t/t_e}

In summing up, we may state that this third type of ideal, composite, viscoelastic, recovery-sensitive substance ($\varepsilon = \varepsilon' + \varepsilon'' + \varepsilon'''$, $\sigma = \sigma' + \sigma''$) possesses properties through which certain phases in the inelastic behavior of actual polycrystalline solids or of certain organic materials ("plastics") might be expressible at least qualitatively and be reproduced.

One may phenomenologically attempt to explain the behavior of certain actual materials showing stress or strain-time relations on loading or unloading similar to those which were described for the substance defined by Eqs. (4-29) to (4-32) by postulating in their structure elemental particles responding either in an elastic or in a viscous way and construct artificial models of such materials.[1] If we assumed, for example, that the blocks of material in Fig. 4-20 are

[1] Cf. "First and Second Report on Viscosity and Plasticity," prepared by a Committee of the Academy of Sciences at Amsterdam, vol. 1, 265 pp., 1935; vol. 2, 287 pp., 1938. See a chapter in vol. 1, pp. 5–73, by J. M. BURGERS in which he analyzes a great number of mechanical models, made up of combinations of "elastic springs" and "dashpots," connected in units in pairs, in series or parallel, for illustrating the same phenomena which were discussed above in the text. An elastic spring and a dashpot, connected in series, in a *Maxwell unit*, represent viscoelasticity and in parallel, in a *Kelvin unit*, firmoviscosity, while a combination of both of these units, coupled in series, demonstrates our composite substance, having the three types of strain ε', ε'', ε''', etc.

elastic while the layers which separate them are viscous, a shearing stress indicated by τ would distort this anisotropic composite structure according to the rules of viscoelasticity, while if a normal stress acted in the direction indicated by σ, the structure would react partially according to firmoviscosity and partially to viscoelasticity.[1]

4-2. Theory of Elastic and of Purely Viscous Substance. With the intention of evaluating a number of useful solutions in some detail, we recapitulate briefly, with reference to Vol. I, Chaps. 25 and 26, the equations:

A. FOR A COMPRESSIBLE, ISOTROPIC, ELASTIC SOLID. Denoting the modulus of elasticity and rigidity by E and G; Poisson's ratio by ν; the components of infinitesimal, elastic strain by $\varepsilon_x, \varepsilon_y, \varepsilon_z, \gamma_{yz}, \gamma_{zx}, \gamma_{xy}$; of stress by $\sigma_x, \sigma_y, \sigma_z, \tau_{yz}, \tau_{zx}, \tau_{xy}$; and the components of displacement by u, v, w, the law of elasticity is expressed by the six stress-strain relations

$$\varepsilon_x = \frac{1}{E}\left[\sigma_x - \nu(\sigma_y + \sigma_z)\right], \ldots, \qquad \gamma_{yz} = \frac{\tau_{yz}}{G}, \ldots \qquad (4\text{-}49)$$

Denoting by ε the small, elastic dilatation of volume,

$$\varepsilon = \varepsilon_x + \varepsilon_y + \varepsilon_z, \qquad (4\text{-}50)$$

and by ε' and by σ the mean normal strain and stress,

$$\varepsilon' = \frac{\varepsilon}{3} = \frac{\varepsilon_x + \varepsilon_y + \varepsilon_z}{3}, \qquad \sigma = \frac{\sigma_x + \sigma_y + \sigma_z}{3}, \qquad (4\text{-}51)$$

by adding the first three stress-strain relations we have

$$\varepsilon' = \frac{\varepsilon}{3} = \frac{(1 - 2\nu)\sigma}{E}, \qquad (4\text{-}52)$$

---

[1] References to mechanical systems made up of elastic and viscous elements may be found in J. M. BURGERS, *op. cit.*, p. 21. A substance composed of elastic, solid grains embedded in a viscous mass was considered by M. BRILLOUIN, Ann. de chimie physique, 1898.

Certain plastics, after a rapid loading in compression to finite strains, may almost completely recover their former initial strain after sufficient time. Models of certain filamentous organic substances have frequently been proposed in which elastic strings are thought to be embedded in a viscous matrix. The phenomena of recovery and of creep have been investigated by HERBERT LEADERMAN, both theoretically and experimentally, for certain natural and artificial fibrous substances (silk, rayon, nylon) in "Elastic and Creep Properties of Filamentous Materials and Other High Polymers," 251 pp., The Textile Foundation, Washington, D.C., 1943.

See also R. HOUWINK, "Elasticity, Plasticity and Structure of Matter," 376 pp., Cambridge University Press, London, 1937, and MARKUS REINER, "Deformation and Flow, an Elementary Introduction to Theoretical Rheology," 346 pp., H. K. Lewis & Co., London, 1949.

and the former relations in their deviatoral form may also be expressed as follows:

$$\sigma_x - \sigma = 2G(\varepsilon_x - \varepsilon'), \dots, \qquad \tau_{yz} = G\gamma_{yz}, \dots . \qquad (4\text{-}53)$$

After introducing here the expressions for the components of strain in terms of the derivatives of the three rectangular components of displacement u, v, w,

$$\varepsilon_x = \frac{\partial u}{\partial x}, \qquad\qquad \varepsilon_y = \frac{\partial v}{\partial y}, \qquad\qquad \varepsilon_z = \frac{\partial w}{\partial z},$$

$$\gamma_{yz} = \frac{\partial w}{\partial y} + \frac{\partial v}{\partial z}, \qquad \gamma_{zx} = \frac{\partial u}{\partial z} + \frac{\partial w}{\partial x}, \qquad \gamma_{xy} = \frac{\partial v}{\partial x} + \frac{\partial u}{\partial y},$$

$$(4\text{-}54)$$

and after substituting the expressions for the six components of stress in the following three conditions of equilibrium, in the absence of body forces,

$$\frac{\partial \sigma_x}{\partial x} + \frac{\partial \tau_{xy}}{\partial y} + \frac{\partial \tau_{xz}}{\partial z} = 0,$$

$$\frac{\partial \sigma_y}{\partial y} + \frac{\partial \tau_{yz}}{\partial z} + \frac{\partial \tau_{yx}}{\partial x} = 0, \qquad (4\text{-}55)$$

$$\frac{\partial \sigma_z}{\partial z} + \frac{\partial \tau_{zx}}{\partial x} + \frac{\partial \tau_{zy}}{\partial y} = 0,$$

one obtains the differential equations by NAVIER for the three displacement components u, v, w:

$$(1 - 2\nu)\,\Delta u + \frac{\partial \varepsilon}{\partial x} = 0,$$

$$(1 - 2\nu)\,\Delta v + \frac{\partial \varepsilon}{\partial y} = 0, \qquad (4\text{-}56)$$

$$(1 - 2\nu)\,\Delta w + \frac{\partial \varepsilon}{\partial z} = 0.$$

The latter, using Eq. (4-52), may also be written in the seldom-used form

$$\frac{E}{3}\,\Delta u + \frac{\partial \sigma}{\partial x} = 0,$$

$$\frac{E}{3}\,\Delta v + \frac{\partial \sigma}{\partial y} = 0, \qquad (4\text{-}57)$$

$$\frac{E}{3}\,\Delta w + \frac{\partial \sigma}{\partial z} = 0,$$

where $\Delta = \partial^2/\partial x^2 + \partial^2/\partial y^2 + \partial^2/\partial z^2$ denotes Laplace's operator. By taking the derivatives of the preceding two groups of equations with respect to x, y, z, respectively, and adding, one sees that the dilatation of volume ε and the mean normal stress σ must satisfy *Laplace's equation:*

$$\Delta\varepsilon = 0, \qquad \Delta\sigma = 0. \tag{4-58}$$

B. For Isotropic, Incompressible, Elastic Material. If we take Poisson's ratio $\nu = \frac{1}{2}$, $E = 3G$, the dilatation of volume ε vanishes:

$$\varepsilon = \varepsilon_x + \varepsilon_y + \varepsilon_z = \frac{\partial u}{\partial x} + \frac{\partial v}{\partial y} + \frac{\partial w}{\partial z} = \operatorname{div} \mathbf{w} = 0, \tag{4-59}$$

where $\mathbf{w}$ denotes the small displacement vector $\mathbf{w} = \mathbf{i}u + \mathbf{j}v + \mathbf{k}w$. The stress-strain relations, according to Eqs. (4-53), are expressed by

$$\sigma_x = \sigma + 2G\varepsilon_x, \ldots, \qquad \tau_{yz} = G\gamma_{yz}, \ldots, \tag{4-60}$$

and Eqs. (4-57) by

$$G\,\Delta u + \frac{\partial\sigma}{\partial x} = 0,$$

$$G\,\Delta v + \frac{\partial\sigma}{\partial y} = 0, \tag{4-61}$$

$$G\,\Delta w + \frac{\partial\sigma}{\partial z} = 0,$$

$$\Delta\,\sigma = 0.$$

If in an elastic solid, however, *Poisson's ratio should vanish,* $\nu = 0$, $E = 2G$, Eqs. (4-57) take the form

$$\operatorname{div} \mathbf{w} = \frac{\sigma}{3E}$$

$$\frac{2G}{3}\,\Delta u + \frac{\partial\sigma}{\partial x} = 0,$$

$$\frac{2G}{3}\,\Delta v + \frac{\partial\sigma}{\partial y} = 0, \tag{4-62}$$

$$\frac{2G}{3}\,\Delta w + \frac{\partial\sigma}{\partial z} = 0.$$

C. Purely Viscous Substance. Postulating insignificantly small elastic parts of strain to be neglected, we assume that in this substance the rates of permanent unit shear increase proportionally with the corresponding shearing stresses. If we now denote by u, v, w the small components of the velocity vector $\mathbf{w} = \mathbf{i}u + \mathbf{j}v + \mathbf{k}w$ and postulate furthermore incompressibility and that the substance flows at very small velocities, we may neglect the accelerations in it and assume that the stresses remain in static equilibrium. In *a purely viscous, incompressible substance,* denoting the very small rates of strain by inserting a dot above the symbols of ε and γ, the stress–rate-of-strain relations are expressed by

$$\sigma_x = \sigma + 2\mu\dot{\varepsilon}_x, \qquad \tau_{yz} = \mu\dot{\gamma}_{yz},$$
$$\sigma_y = \sigma + 2\mu\dot{\varepsilon}_y, \qquad \tau_{zx} = \mu\dot{\gamma}_{zx}, \qquad (4\text{-}63)$$
$$\sigma_z = \sigma + 2\mu\dot{\varepsilon}_z, \qquad \tau_{xy} = \mu\dot{\gamma}_{xy},$$

where μ designates the coefficient of viscosity. The rates of strain are equal to

$$\dot{\varepsilon}_x = \frac{\partial u}{\partial x}, \qquad \dot{\varepsilon}_y = \frac{\partial v}{\partial y}, \qquad \dot{\varepsilon}_z = \frac{\partial w}{\partial z},$$

$$\dot{\gamma}_{yz} = \frac{\partial w}{\partial y} + \frac{\partial v}{\partial z}, \qquad \dot{\gamma}_{zx} = \frac{\partial u}{\partial z} + \frac{\partial w}{\partial x}, \qquad \dot{\gamma}_{xy} = \frac{\partial v}{\partial x} + \frac{\partial u}{\partial y} \qquad (4\text{-}64)$$

and

$$\dot{\varepsilon} = \dot{\varepsilon}_x + \dot{\varepsilon}_y + \dot{\varepsilon}_z = \frac{\partial u}{\partial x} + \frac{\partial v}{\partial y} + \frac{\partial w}{\partial z} = \text{div } \mathbf{w} = 0. \qquad (4\text{-}65)$$

We see that these expressions and the stress–rate-of-strain relations [Eqs. (4-63)] in a viscous solid have a form similar to the corresponding equations, (4-54) and (4-60), valid in an incompressible elastic solid, the coefficient of viscosity μ now replacing the modulus of rigidity G. Hence, *in a viscous, incompressible solid* in static equilibrium, u, v, w must satisfy the differential equations

$$\mu\,\Delta u + \frac{\partial\sigma}{\partial x} = 0, \qquad \mu\,\Delta v + \frac{\partial\sigma}{\partial y} = 0, \qquad \mu\,\Delta w + \frac{\partial\sigma}{\partial z} = 0, \qquad (4\text{-}66)$$

$$\Delta\sigma = 0,$$

disclosing that the latter equations in reference to the *velocity components* u, v, w are of the same form as Eqs. (4-61) in reference to the *displacement components* u, v, w in an elastic, incompressible solid after replacing G by μ.

Consequently, exact solutions are readily available for the slow flow of a purely viscous substance in static equilibrium in those which have been developed in the mathematical theory of elasticity and new ones may be derived by the classical means which have served to establish the solutions in the theory of elasticity.[1] In the following chapters we shall consider a number of exact solutions for incompressible elastic or purely viscous solids, frequently not drawing a line of demarcation between these two types of solids.

[1] It has been noted already in Vol. I (page 397) that in the above statement there might also be included those solutions which were derived for a *compressible* elastic solid, in which $v \neq \frac{1}{2}$, if Poisson's ratio v is not involved in them (or does not enter at least in certain essential components of stress or strain), for example, in certain expressions for deflected beams or slabs or under forces that act through a single boundary curve, etc.

CHAPTER 5

PLANE STRAIN AND PLANE STRESS

For this reason I state that the task of Mechanics consists in *describing* in the completest and in the simplest way the observable movements in nature.   Herewith I wish to say that what we are concerned with, is to state the phenomena occurring, but not to determine their *causes*.

Gustav Kirchhoff, Berlin, January, 1876, from the preface to the first edition of his collected lectures on mechanics.   From W. Wien (ed.), "Vorlesungen über mathematische Physik," vol. 1, "Mechanik," 4th ed., Verlag von B. G. Teubner, Leipzig, 1897.

5-1.   Planar Displacement or Velocity Field.   In a thin plate stretched in its plane through forces or in an extended body whose points are constrained to move in parallel planes, the components of displacement or of the velocities are essentially functions of two coordinates.   If the x,y plane is taken in the middle plane of the disk or in one of the parallel planes in the extended body and u,v denote the components of displacement or velocity in the directions of the x and y axes, they define a planar field of vectors.   Consider two adjoining points $P(x,y)$ and $Q(x + dx, y + dy)$ an infinitesimal distance $d\mathbf{r} = \mathbf{i}\,dx + \mathbf{j}\,dy$ apart, and let two axes intersecting at P in positions parallel with the x and y axes be carried by the body during the motion.   A small element $dx \times dy$ of material will suffer a small distortion and a small rotation relative to the x, y, and z axes supposed to be fixed in space.   The components of displacement u,v increase from P to Q by

$$du = \frac{\partial u}{\partial x}\,dx + \frac{\partial u}{\partial y}\,dy,$$

$$dv = \frac{\partial v}{\partial x}\,dx + \frac{\partial v}{\partial y}\,dy. \tag{5-1}$$

This may also be written

$$du = \frac{\partial u}{\partial x}\,dx + \frac{1}{2}\left(\frac{\partial u}{\partial y} + \frac{\partial v}{\partial x}\right)dy - \frac{1}{2}\left(\frac{\partial v}{\partial x} - \frac{\partial u}{\partial y}\right)dy,$$

$$dv = \frac{\partial v}{\partial y}\,dy + \frac{1}{2}\left(\frac{\partial u}{\partial y} + \frac{\partial v}{\partial x}\right)dx + \frac{1}{2}\left(\frac{\partial v}{\partial x} - \frac{\partial u}{\partial y}\right)dx. \tag{5-2}$$

The first two terms on the right sides of these equations contain the components of strain and unit shear

$$\frac{\partial u}{\partial x} = \varepsilon_x, \qquad \frac{\partial v}{\partial y} = \varepsilon_y, \qquad \frac{\partial v}{\partial x} + \frac{\partial u}{\partial y} = \gamma_{xy}, \qquad (5\text{-}3)$$

under which the element $dx\,dy$ distorts, and the third terms define a small rotation of it around an axis parallel to the z axis by an amount (angle)

$$\omega = \frac{1}{2}\left(\frac{\partial v}{\partial x} - \frac{\partial u}{\partial y}\right). \qquad (5\text{-}4)$$

Equations (5-1) may also be expressed by

$$du = \varepsilon_x\,dx + \frac{\gamma_{xy}}{2}\,dy - \omega\,dy,$$
$$dv = \varepsilon_y\,dy + \frac{\gamma_{xy}}{2}\,dx + \omega\,dx. \qquad (5\text{-}5)$$

If, however, u and v denote the components of velocity, we use a dot in $\dot\varepsilon_x$, $\dot\varepsilon_y$, $\dot\gamma_{xy}$, to denote the rates of strain, and $\dot\omega$ defines the angular velocity with which the element $dx\,dy$ rotates. We then have

$$\frac{\partial u}{\partial x} = \dot\varepsilon_x, \qquad \frac{\partial v}{\partial y} = \dot\varepsilon_y, \qquad \frac{\partial v}{\partial x} + \frac{\partial u}{\partial y} = \dot\gamma_{xy}, \qquad \frac{1}{2}\left(\frac{\partial v}{\partial x} - \frac{\partial u}{\partial y}\right) = \dot\omega, \quad (5\text{-}6)$$

and may write

$$du = \dot\varepsilon_x\,dx + \frac{\dot\gamma_{xy}}{2}\,dy - \dot\omega\,dy,$$
$$dv = \dot\varepsilon_y\,dy + \frac{\dot\gamma_{xy}}{2}\,dx + \dot\omega\,dx. \qquad (5\text{-}7)$$

The preceding relations indicate that the material element $dx\,dy$ is distorted under a planar tensor of pure strain or a planar tensor of rates of strain, respectively,

$$\begin{bmatrix} \varepsilon_x & \dfrac{\gamma_{xy}}{2} \\[2ex] \dfrac{\gamma_{xy}}{2} & \varepsilon_y \end{bmatrix} \quad \text{or} \quad \begin{bmatrix} \dot\varepsilon_x & \dfrac{\dot\gamma_{xy}}{2} \\[2ex] \dfrac{\dot\gamma_{xy}}{2} & \dot\varepsilon_y \end{bmatrix} \qquad (5\text{-}8)$$

while it is turned by an infinitesimal rotation[1] ω, $\dot\omega$.

[1] Or in vector notation, with reference to Vol. I, Chap. 14, after letting

$$d\mathbf{r} = \mathbf{i}\,dx + \mathbf{j}\,dy, \qquad \mathbf{w} = \mathbf{i}u + \mathbf{j}v,$$

$$d\mathbf{w} = \frac{\partial \mathbf{w}}{\partial x}\,dx + \frac{\partial \mathbf{w}}{\partial y}\,dy = \frac{\partial \mathbf{w}}{\partial x}\,(d\mathbf{r}\cdot\mathbf{i}) + \frac{\partial \mathbf{w}}{\partial y}\,(d\mathbf{r}\cdot\mathbf{j})$$

$$= d\mathbf{r}\cdot\left(\mathbf{i}\frac{\partial}{\partial x} + \mathbf{j}\frac{\partial}{\partial y}\right)\mathbf{w} = d\mathbf{r}\cdot\nabla\mathbf{w},$$

If, instead of rectangular coordinates x, y, planar polar coordinates r, α are used, vector $\mathbf{w}$ may be resolved in its radial and tangential components. Suppose that we again denote the latter in radial and tangential directions by the symbols u and v, respectively; by ε_r and ε_t, the unit strains in radial and tangential directions, and by γ_{rt}, the unit shear. These may be evaluated in terms of u and v at a cursory glance from Fig. 5-1 in which $ABCD$ represents a small

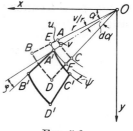

FIG. 5-1

element of material $r\, dr\, d\alpha$ in its unstrained condition and $A'B'C'D'$, in its slightly strained condition. The normal strains ε_r and ε_t are found equal to

$$\varepsilon_r = \frac{\overline{A'B'} - \overline{AB}}{\overline{AB}} = \frac{dr + [u + (\partial u/\partial r)\, dr] - u - dr}{dr} = \frac{\partial u}{\partial r},$$

$$\varepsilon_t = \frac{\overline{A'C'} - \overline{AC}}{\overline{AC}} = \frac{\overline{EF} + (\partial v/\partial \alpha)\, d\alpha - r\, d\alpha}{r\, d\alpha} \tag{5-9}$$

$$= \frac{(1 + u/r)r\, d\alpha + (\partial v/\partial \alpha)\, d\alpha - r\, d\alpha}{r\, d\alpha} = \frac{1}{r}\left(u + \frac{\partial v}{\partial \alpha}\right),$$

and the unit shear γ_{rt} is computed from the small change that the right

---

if the dyadic

$$\nabla \mathbf{w} = \mathbf{i}\,\frac{\partial \mathbf{w}}{\partial x} + \mathbf{j}\,\frac{\partial \mathbf{w}}{\partial y}$$

in its symmetric part represents the planar tensor of rate of pure strain [Eqs. (5-8)]

$$(\tfrac{1}{2})(\nabla \mathbf{w} + \mathbf{w}\nabla) = \begin{bmatrix} \dot{\varepsilon}_x & \dfrac{\dot{\gamma}_{xy}}{2} \\[2mm] \dfrac{\dot{\gamma}_{xy}}{2} & \dot{\varepsilon}_y \end{bmatrix},$$

and in its antisymmetric part

$$(\tfrac{1}{2})(\nabla \mathbf{w} - \mathbf{w}\nabla) = \begin{bmatrix} 0 & \dot{\omega} \\ -\dot{\omega} & 0 \end{bmatrix}$$

expresses the dyadic corresponding to an infinitesimal rotation around the axis, the latter might also be computed by evaluating

$$\operatorname{rot}\mathbf{w} = \nabla \times \mathbf{w} = \mathbf{k}\left(\frac{\partial v}{\partial x} - \frac{\partial u}{\partial y}\right) = 2\mathbf{k}\dot{\omega}.$$

angle $\measuredangle\, CAB$ suffered through the distortion, from the sum of two small angles:

$$\varphi = \frac{v + (\partial v/\partial r)\, dr - v}{dr} - \frac{v}{r} = \frac{\partial v}{\partial r} - \frac{v}{r},$$

$$\psi = \frac{u + (\partial u/\partial \alpha)\, d\alpha - u}{r\, d\alpha} = \frac{1}{r} \cdot \frac{\partial u}{\partial \alpha}, \qquad (5\text{-}10)$$

$$\gamma_{rt} = \varphi + \psi = \frac{\partial u}{r\, \partial \alpha} + \frac{\partial v}{\partial r} - \frac{v}{r}.$$

We need, furthermore, the expression for the small rotation ω which is derived by expressing STOKES' theorem for the small element of area $ABCD$ in Fig. 5-2, according to which the circulation around it (the line integral of the vector components pointing in the tangential directions taken around $ABCD$ in the positive sense of rotation) must be equal to twice the rotation of vector $\mathbf{w}$, namely, 2ω times the area $r\, dr\, d\alpha$ circumnavigated $2\omega r\, dr\, d\alpha$. But the circulation is equal to

$$u\, dr + \left(v + \frac{\partial v}{\partial r}\, dr\right)(r + dr)\, d\alpha - \left(u + \frac{\partial u}{\partial \alpha}\, d\alpha\right) dr - vr\, d\alpha = 2\omega r\, dr\, d\alpha;$$

hence

$$2\omega = \frac{1}{r} \frac{\partial}{\partial r}\, (rv) - \frac{1}{r} \frac{\partial u}{\partial \alpha}. \qquad (5\text{-}11)$$

Thus the components of strain $\varepsilon_r,\ \varepsilon_t,\ \gamma_{rt}$ are expressed in polar coordinates by

$$\varepsilon_r = \frac{\partial u}{\partial r}, \qquad \varepsilon_t = \frac{1}{r}\left(u + \frac{\partial v}{\partial \alpha}\right), \qquad \gamma_{rt} = \frac{\partial u}{r\, \partial \alpha} + \frac{\partial v}{\partial r} - \frac{v}{r}. \qquad (5\text{-}12)$$

The rates of strain and shear $\dot{\varepsilon}_r,\ \dot{\varepsilon}_t,\ \dot{\gamma}_{rt}$ are defined by the same right-hand expressions, respectively, when u, v represent the polar velocity components.

In many applications one is interested only in an evaluation of the strains or rates of strain and of the stresses. Since Eqs. (5-3) or (5-12) represent three relations for the components u and v, the latter may be eliminated from them by the process of differentiation. This leads to *the condition of compatibility* for the components of strain or of rates of strain, in rectangular coordinates,

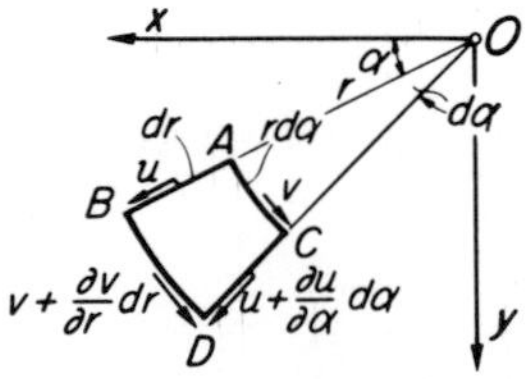

$$\frac{\partial^2 \varepsilon_x}{\partial y^2} + \frac{\partial^2 \varepsilon_y}{\partial x^2} = \frac{\partial^2 \gamma_{xy}}{\partial x\, \partial y}, \qquad (5\text{-}13)$$

and in polar coordinates,

$$\frac{1}{r} \frac{\partial^2 \varepsilon_r}{\partial \alpha^2} + \frac{\partial}{\partial r}\left[\frac{\partial}{\partial r}\, (r\varepsilon_t) - \varepsilon_r\right] = \frac{1}{r} \frac{\partial^2 (r\gamma_{rt})}{\partial r\, \partial \alpha}, \qquad (5\text{-}14)$$

FIG. 5-2

or the corresponding relations after inserting

the dots above the strain components, respectively. These conditions must always be satisfied in order that there shall exist a continuous system of components u and v in a distorted body.

5-2. Plane Strain. A solid in which the points are displaced in parallel planes, while the displacement and normal strain in the perpendicular direction to these planes vanish, is said to be in a state of plane strain. Using rectangular coordinates, choosing the x,y plane in one of these planes, in a state of plane strain

$$w = \varepsilon_z = \gamma_{xz} = \gamma_{yz} = \tau_{xz} = \tau_{yz} = 0.$$

A. ELASTIC SOLID. From the third of Eqs. (4-49), letting $\varepsilon_z = 0$, the normal stress σ_z must be equal to

$$\sigma_z = \nu(\sigma_x + \sigma_y) \tag{5-15}$$

and the mean stress σ equal to

$$\sigma = \frac{\sigma_x + \sigma_y + \sigma_z}{3} = \frac{(1 + \nu)(\sigma_x + \sigma_y)}{3}. \tag{5-16}$$

The stress-strain relations [Eqs. (4-49)] are

$$\varepsilon_x = \frac{\partial u}{\partial x} = \frac{1}{2G} [(1 - \nu)\sigma_x - \nu\sigma_y],$$

$$\varepsilon_y = \frac{\partial v}{\partial y} = \frac{1}{2G} [(1 - \nu)\sigma_y - \nu\sigma_x], \tag{5-17}$$

$$\gamma_{xy} = \frac{\partial v}{\partial x} + \frac{\partial u}{\partial y} = \frac{\tau_{xy}}{G},$$

from which

$$\sigma_x = \frac{2G}{1 - 2\nu} [(1 - \nu)\varepsilon_x + \nu\varepsilon_y],$$

$$\sigma_y = \frac{2G}{1 - 2\nu} [(1 - \nu)\varepsilon_y + \nu\varepsilon_x], \tag{5-18}$$

showing that the dilatation of volume is

$$\varepsilon = \varepsilon_x + \varepsilon_y = \frac{(1 - 2\nu)(\sigma_x + \sigma_y)}{2G} = \frac{3(1 - 2\nu)\sigma}{E}. \tag{5-19}$$

The two conditions of equilibrium,

$$\frac{\partial \sigma_x}{\partial x} + \frac{\partial \tau_{xy}}{\partial y} = 0, \qquad \frac{\partial \sigma_y}{\partial y} + \frac{\partial \tau_{xy}}{\partial x} = 0, \tag{5-20}$$

are satisfied by letting the components of stress σ_x, σ_y, τ_{xy} equal the second derivatives of an *Airy stress function* $F(x,y)$:

$$\sigma_x = \frac{\partial^2 F}{\partial y^2}, \qquad \sigma_y = \frac{\partial^2 F}{\partial x^2}, \qquad \tau_{xy} = -\frac{\partial^2 F}{\partial x \, \partial y}. \tag{5-21}$$

The condition of compatibility [Eq. (5-13)] of the components of strain ε_x, ε_y, γ_{xy}, when expressed in terms of the components of stress, using Eqs. (5-17),

$$(1 - \nu)\left(\frac{\partial^2 \sigma_x}{\partial y^2} + \frac{\partial^2 \sigma_y}{\partial x^2}\right) - \nu\left(\frac{\partial^2 \sigma_x}{\partial x^2} + \frac{\partial^2 \sigma_y}{\partial y^2}\right) = 2\frac{\partial^2 \tau_{xy}}{\partial x\, \partial y} \qquad (5\text{-}22)$$

shows that σ_x, σ_y, τ_{xy} may be determined from $F(x,y)$, for which, according to the preceding equation, the partial, linear differential equation of fourth order

$$\frac{\partial^4 F}{\partial x^4} + 2\frac{\partial^4 F}{\partial x^2\, \partial y^2} + \frac{\partial^4 F}{\partial y^4} = \Delta\Delta F = 0, \qquad (5\text{-}23)$$

known as *the biharmonic differential equation*, is obtained. If the boundary values of the stresses are prescribed, this amounts essentially, as one sees from Eqs. (5-17), to finding the function $F(x,y)$ from Eq. (5-23), having on the boundary edge prescribed ordinates F and normal derivatives $\partial F/\partial n$ (n outward normal to boundary cylinder of the body).[1]

After the stresses are evaluated one may determine the corresponding components of displacement u and v by integrating partially with respect to x and to y, respectively, the expressions for the unit strains ε_x and ε_y [Eqs. (5-17)] and by substituting the resulting values for u and v in the third stress-strain relation $\gamma_{xy} = \tau_{xy}/G$. These must satisfy it identically. This permits, from the three aforementioned relations, determination of the arbitrary functions accompanying these partial integrations and results also in a set of terms

$$u = c_1 - c_3 y, \qquad v = c_2 + c_3 x, \qquad (5\text{-}24)$$

representing a small translation and rotation of a rigid body. Obviously, this determination of u and v takes care of the compatibility condition for the strains, since it is based on the stress function $F(x,y)$ already complying with it.

[1] If, for example, an edge $x = $ const is free of stress, i.e., on it $\sigma_x = \tau_{xy} = 0$, the stress function $F(x,y)$ in a narrow strip along the boundary $x = $ const must be tangent to a certain plane $F = a + bx + cy$ so that for $x = $ const $\partial F/\partial x = b = $ const, $\partial F/\partial y = c = $ const. The equation $\Delta\Delta F = 0$ coincides in its form with the differential equation $\Delta\Delta w = 0$ of the small deflections w of a flat, elastic plate bent slightly under moments and shearing forces distributed along its boundary curve (see Sec. 8-1). Solving a problem of plane strain when the boundary stresses are prescribed thus amounts to finding the elastic surface of a flat plate for which the deflections w and normal slopes $\partial w/\partial n$ along its boundary curve (coinciding with the bounding cylinder of the body under the state of plane strain) are prescribed. This analogy was first utilized by K. WIEGHART (Mitt. Forschungsarb. Ver. deut. Ing., no. 49, 1908).

When, on the other hand, the components u and v are prescribed on the boundary of the body, these may be determined from the differential equations of NAVIER [Eqs. (4-56)] in their two-dimensional form, in which the Laplacian operator is taken $\Delta = \partial^2/\partial x^2 + \partial^2/\partial y^2$, from either of the two groups of equations

$$(1 - 2\nu)\Delta u + \frac{\partial \varepsilon}{\partial x} = 0,$$

$$(1 - 2\nu)\Delta v + \frac{\partial \varepsilon}{\partial y} = 0, \tag{5-25a}$$

$$\Delta \varepsilon = 0,$$

$$\frac{E}{3}\Delta u + \frac{\partial \sigma}{\partial x} = 0,$$

$$\frac{E}{3}\Delta v + \frac{\partial \sigma}{\partial y} = 0, \tag{5-25b}$$

$$\Delta \sigma = 0.$$

We may note a useful transformation of the group of Eqs. (5-25b) by means of the two identities

$$\Delta u = \frac{\partial}{\partial x}\left(\frac{\partial u}{\partial x} + \frac{\partial v}{\partial y}\right) - \frac{\partial}{\partial y}\left(\frac{\partial v}{\partial x} - \frac{\partial u}{\partial y}\right),$$

$$\Delta v = \frac{\partial}{\partial y}\left(\frac{\partial u}{\partial x} + \frac{\partial v}{\partial y}\right) + \frac{\partial}{\partial x}\left(\frac{\partial v}{\partial x} - \frac{\partial u}{\partial y}\right), \tag{5-26}$$

noting that the expressions in the first parentheses represent the dilatation of volume ε and in the second parentheses 2ω, where ω is the rotation in the planar displacement field of vector $\mathbf{w} = \mathbf{i}u + \mathbf{j}v$,

$$\varepsilon = \frac{\partial u}{\partial x} + \frac{\partial v}{\partial y}, \qquad 2\omega = \frac{\partial v}{\partial x} - \frac{\partial u}{\partial y}, \tag{5-27}$$

so that

$$\Delta u = \frac{\partial \varepsilon}{\partial x} - 2\frac{\partial \omega}{\partial y} = \frac{3(1 - 2\nu)}{E} \cdot \frac{\partial \sigma}{\partial x} - 2\frac{\partial \omega}{\partial y},$$

$$\Delta v = \frac{\partial \varepsilon}{\partial y} + 2\frac{\partial \omega}{\partial x} = \frac{3(1 - 2\nu)}{E} \cdot \frac{\partial \sigma}{\partial y} + 2\frac{\partial \omega}{\partial x}. \tag{5-28}$$

After substituting these in the two Navier equations, (5-25b), we see that the latter in a state of plane strain in an elastic substance are equivalent to *Cauchy-Riemann equations*,

$$\frac{\partial \omega}{\partial y} = \frac{3(1 - \nu)}{E}\frac{\partial \sigma}{\partial x} = \frac{1 - \nu}{1 - 2\nu} \cdot \frac{\partial \varepsilon}{\partial x},$$

$$\frac{\partial \omega}{\partial x} = -\frac{3(1 - \nu)}{E}\frac{\partial \sigma}{\partial y} = -\frac{1 - \nu}{1 - 2\nu} \cdot \frac{\partial \varepsilon}{\partial y}, \tag{5-29}$$

disclosing that the quantities

$$\omega \quad\text{and}\quad -\frac{3(1-\nu)\sigma}{E} \qquad (5\text{-}30)$$

$$\left[\text{or}\quad \omega \quad\text{and}\quad -\frac{(1-\nu)\varepsilon}{1-2\nu}\right]$$

may be taken as the real and imaginary parts of a function

$$H(z) = \omega - i\cdot\frac{3(1-\nu)\sigma}{E} \qquad (5\text{-}31)$$

of the complex variable $z = x + iy$ and that the rotation ω and the mean stress σ satisfy Laplace's equation:

$$\Delta\omega = 0, \qquad \Delta\sigma = 0. \qquad (5\text{-}32)$$

Any set of conjugate potentials ω and $-3(1-\nu)\sigma/E$ defines a set of displacement components u and v in a state of plane strain in an elastic body.

When, instead of rectangular coordinates, *polar coordinates* r and α are used, we have a normal stress σ_r in the radial and σ_t in the tangential direction and a shearing stress τ_{rt}. The two conditions for their equilibrium are obtained by a glance at Fig. 5-3, by adding the components of force acting on a small element of material $r\,dr\,d\alpha$ in radial and tangential directions, giving

$$\frac{\partial}{\partial r}(r\sigma_r) - \sigma_t + \frac{\partial \tau_{rt}}{\partial \alpha} = 0,$$

$$\frac{\partial \sigma_t}{\partial \alpha} + \frac{\partial}{\partial r}(r\tau_{rt}) + \tau_{rt} = 0, \qquad (5\text{-}33)$$

which are satisfied if one assumes for

$$\sigma_r = \frac{1}{r}\frac{\partial F}{\partial r} + \frac{1}{r^2}\frac{\partial^2 F}{\partial \alpha^2}, \qquad \sigma_t = \frac{\partial^2 F}{\partial r^2}, \qquad \tau_{rt} = -\frac{\partial r}{\partial r}\left(\frac{1}{r}\frac{\partial F}{\partial \alpha}\right), \quad (5\text{-}34)$$

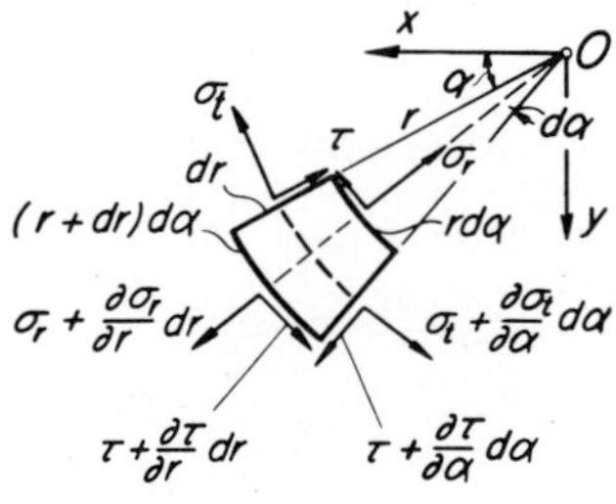

the sum of the normal stresses

$$\sigma_r + \sigma_t = \sigma_x + \sigma_y = \Delta F \qquad (5\text{-}35)$$

being an invariant, in a state of plane strain the quantity ΔF must also be an invariant and is expressed in polar coordinates, using Eqs. (5-34), by

FIG. 5-3

$$\sigma_r + \sigma_t = \Delta F = \frac{\partial^2 F}{\partial r^2} + \frac{1}{r}\frac{\partial F}{\partial r} + \frac{1}{r^2}\frac{\partial^2 F}{\partial \alpha^2}, \quad (5\text{-}36)$$

defining the Laplacian operator in them. The stress function $F(r,\alpha)$ satisfies Eq. (5-23), using (5-36) in terms of r and α. We have already evaluated the strains and the rotation in terms of the components of displacement in radial and tangential directions which we shall again denote by u and v, respectively, and have the stress-strain relations

$$\varepsilon_r = \frac{\partial u}{\partial r} = \frac{1}{2G}\left[(1 - v)\sigma_r - v\sigma_t\right],$$

$$\varepsilon_t = \frac{1}{r}\left(u + \frac{\partial v}{\partial \alpha}\right) = \frac{1}{2G}\left[(1 - v)\sigma_t - v\sigma_r\right], \qquad (5\text{-}37)$$

$$\gamma_{rt} = \frac{1}{r}\frac{\partial u}{\partial \alpha} + \frac{\partial v}{\partial r} - \frac{v}{r} = \frac{\tau_{rt}}{G},$$

from which the displacements u and v may be computed in a manner similar to that previously indicated, if the stress function is already known satisfying the boundary conditions for the stresses.

If the displacements u and v are prescribed along the boundary, one can substitute the expressions for the stresses,

$$\sigma_r = \frac{2G}{1 - 2v}\left[(1 - v)\varepsilon_r + v\varepsilon_t\right],$$

$$\sigma_t = \frac{2G}{1 - 2v}\left[(1 - v)\varepsilon_t + v\varepsilon_r\right], \qquad (5\text{-}38)$$

$$\tau_{rt} = G\gamma_{rt},$$

in the conditions of equilibrium [Eqs. (5-33)] and may obtain two partial differential equations for u and v which, however, in polar co-ordinates r, α become more involved than the corresponding equations, (5-25a) and (5-25b), were in rectangular coordinates. But their *second form*, based on the rotation ω and the mean stress σ, namely,

$$\frac{\partial \omega}{r\,\partial \alpha} = \frac{3(1 - v)}{E}\frac{\partial \sigma}{\partial r},$$

$$\frac{\partial \omega}{\partial r} = -\frac{3(1 - v)}{E}\frac{\partial \sigma}{r\,\partial \alpha}, \qquad (5\text{-}39)$$

remains preserved in these Cauchy-Riemann equations for the quantities

$$\omega \qquad \text{and} \qquad -\frac{3(1 - v)\sigma}{E}$$

representing a pair of conjugate potentials.

By making use of the expressions for ω and the dilatation of volume ε,

$$2\omega = \frac{v}{r} + \frac{\partial v}{\partial r} - \frac{\partial u}{r\,\partial \alpha}, \qquad \varepsilon = \frac{\partial u}{\partial r} + \frac{u}{r} + \frac{\partial v}{r\,\partial \alpha} = \frac{3(1 - 2v)\sigma}{E},$$

one verifies, since

$$\frac{\partial \varepsilon}{\partial r} - 2 \frac{\partial \omega}{r\, \partial \alpha} = \Delta u - \frac{u}{r^2} - \frac{2}{r^2}\frac{\partial v}{\partial \alpha},$$

$$\frac{\partial \varepsilon}{r\, \partial \alpha} + 2 \frac{\partial \omega}{\partial r} = \Delta v - \frac{v}{r^2} + \frac{2}{r^2}\frac{\partial u}{\partial \alpha},$$

that the NAVIER equations for the displacement components in radial and tangential directions u and v in polar coordinates r, α are expressed by the equations

$$\frac{E}{3}\left(\Delta u - \frac{u}{r^2} - \frac{2}{r^2}\frac{\partial v}{\partial \alpha}\right) + \frac{\partial \sigma}{\partial r} = 0,$$

$$\frac{E}{3}\left(\Delta v - \frac{v}{r^2} + \frac{2}{r^2}\frac{\partial u}{\partial \alpha}\right) + \frac{\partial \sigma}{r\, \partial \alpha} = 0.$$

B. An Incompressible Elastic Solid. We may briefly list the simplified forms of some of the preceding relations for plane strain for such a solid ($\nu = \frac{1}{2}$), in which the dilatation of volume ε,

$$\varepsilon = \varepsilon_x + \varepsilon_y = \frac{\partial u}{\partial x} + \frac{\partial v}{\partial y} = 0, \tag{5-40}$$

vanishes, the mean stress σ is

$$\sigma = \frac{\sigma_x + \sigma_y + \sigma_z}{3} = \frac{\sigma_x + \sigma_y}{2} = \sigma_z,$$

the stress-strain relations simplify to

$$\varepsilon_x = -\varepsilon_y = \frac{\sigma_x - \sigma_y}{4G} = \frac{\sigma_x - \sigma}{2G}, \qquad \gamma_{xy} = \frac{\tau_{xy}}{G},$$

the stresses σ_x and σ_y are equal to

$$\sigma_x = 2G\varepsilon_x + \sigma, \qquad \sigma_y = 2G\varepsilon_y + \sigma,$$

and u and v satisfy the two-dimensional equivalents of Eqs. (4-61):

$$G\,\Delta u + \frac{\partial \sigma}{\partial x} = 0, \qquad G\,\Delta v + \frac{\partial \sigma}{\partial y} = 0, \qquad \Delta \sigma = 0. \tag{5-41}$$

C. An Incompressible, Purely Viscous Substance. For this substance a similar set of equations is valid, remembering that u and v designate velocity components:

$$\dot{\varepsilon} = \frac{\partial u}{\partial x} + \frac{\partial v}{\partial y} = 0, \qquad \sigma = \frac{\sigma_x + \sigma_y}{2},$$

$$\dot{\varepsilon}_x = -\dot{\varepsilon}_y = \frac{\sigma_x - \sigma_y}{4\mu}, \qquad \sigma_x = 2\mu\dot{\varepsilon}_x + \sigma, \qquad \sigma_y = 2\mu\dot{\varepsilon}_y + \sigma, \tag{5-42}$$

$$\tau_{xy} = \mu\dot{\gamma}_{xy},$$

$$\mu\,\Delta u + \frac{\partial \sigma}{\partial x} = 0, \qquad \mu\,\Delta v + \frac{\partial \sigma}{\partial y} = 0, \qquad \Delta \sigma = 0. \tag{5-43}$$

For Secs. 5-2B and C, all relations in reference to the stress function $F(x,y)$ given under Sec. 5-2A remain valid.

Suppose that the velocity field u,v were to be determined for given boundary values of u and v in a viscous substance. u and v, on account of the continuity equation

$$\dot{\varepsilon} = \frac{\partial u}{\partial x} + \frac{\partial v}{\partial y} = 0, \tag{5-44}$$

may be derived from a stream function ψ, letting

$$u = \frac{\partial \psi}{\partial y}, \qquad v = -\frac{\partial \psi}{\partial x}. \tag{5-45}$$

Since the rotation gives

$$2\omega = \frac{\partial v}{\partial x} - \frac{\partial u}{\partial y} = -\Delta \psi, \tag{5-46}$$

on account of Eqs. (5-32), $\Delta\omega = 0$, the stream function ψ must be a biharmonic function satisfying

$$\underline{\underline{\Delta\Delta\psi = 0.}} \tag{5-47}$$

The velocity field u,v in a state of plane strain is thus determined in a viscous substance by the biharmonic function ψ supplying the boundary values ψ and normal slopes $\partial\psi/\partial n$ prescribed through the given distribution of the velocities on the boundary line. The corresponding components of stress may be evaluated, using the conjugate potential $-3\sigma/2E$ of the potential ω in terms of σ and ψ from

$$\sigma_x = \sigma + 2\mu \frac{\partial^2 \psi}{\partial x\, \partial y},$$

$$\sigma_y = \sigma - 2\mu \frac{\partial^2 \psi}{\partial x\, \partial y},$$

$$\tau_{xy} = \mu \left(\frac{\partial^2 \psi}{\partial y^2} - \frac{\partial^2 \psi}{\partial x^2} \right),$$

showing, incidentally, that the stream and the stress functions ψ and F are related to each other by either of the two equations

$$\mu \left(\frac{\partial^2 \psi}{\partial x^2} - \frac{\partial^2 \psi}{\partial y^2} \right) = \frac{\partial^2 F}{\partial x\, \partial y},$$

$$4\mu \frac{\partial^2 \psi}{\partial x\, \partial y} = \frac{\partial^2 F}{\partial y^2} - \frac{\partial^2 F}{\partial x^2}.$$

If polar coordinates are used, similarly, from

$$\dot{\varepsilon} = \frac{\partial(ru)}{\partial r} + \frac{\partial v}{\partial \alpha} = 0, \tag{5-48}$$

$$u = \frac{\partial \psi}{r\, \partial \alpha}, \qquad v = -\frac{\partial \psi}{\partial r}, \tag{5-49}$$

$$2\omega = \frac{1}{r}\frac{\partial}{\partial r}(rv) - \frac{1}{r}\frac{\partial u}{\partial \alpha} = -\Delta\psi = -\frac{\partial^2 \psi}{\partial r^2} - \frac{1}{r}\frac{\partial \psi}{\partial r} - \frac{1}{r^2}\frac{\partial^2 \psi}{\partial \alpha^2}, \tag{5-50}$$

$$\Delta\Delta\psi = 0, \tag{5-51}$$

and the procedure for establishing solutions in polar coordinates r,α is analogous to that explained for rectangular coordinates x,y.

5-3. Plane Stress. This state of stress exists in a thin disk of uniform thickness strained by forces in the direction of its middle plane. Choosing it for the x,y plane, the components of stress σ_z, τ_{xy}, τ_{yz} vanish throughout the plate, and the mean stress is $\sigma = (\sigma_x + \sigma_y)/3$.

Let us consider a state of plane stress in *a purely viscous* (incompressible) *material*. After the third of the stress–rate-of-strain relations [Eqs. (4-63)], since $\sigma_z = \sigma + 2\mu\dot{\varepsilon}_z = 0$, we have $\dot{\varepsilon}_z = -\sigma/2\mu$ and if $\dot{e}$ denotes the sum of the strain rates $\dot{\varepsilon}_x$ and $\dot{\varepsilon}_y$, representing the divergence of the velocity vector $\mathbf{w} = \mathbf{i}u + \mathbf{j}v$ in the planar field, we have

$$\dot{e} = \dot{\varepsilon}_x + \dot{\varepsilon}_y = \frac{\partial u}{\partial x} + \frac{\partial v}{\partial y} = \text{div } \mathbf{w} = -\dot{\varepsilon}_z = \frac{\sigma}{2\mu}, \tag{5-52}$$

the stress–rate-of-strain relations

$$\sigma_x = \sigma + 2\mu\dot{\varepsilon}_x, \qquad \sigma_y = \sigma + 2\mu\dot{\varepsilon}_y, \qquad \tau_{xy} = \mu\dot{\gamma}_{xy},$$

or

$$\dot{\varepsilon}_x = \frac{\partial u}{\partial x} = \frac{1}{3\mu}[\sigma_x - (\tfrac{1}{2})\sigma_y],$$

$$\dot{\varepsilon}_y = \frac{\partial v}{\partial y} = \frac{1}{3\mu}[\sigma_y - (\tfrac{1}{2})\sigma_x],$$

$$\dot{\gamma}_{xy} = \frac{\partial u}{\partial y} + \frac{\partial v}{\partial x} = \frac{\tau_{xy}}{\mu}.$$

After substituting the expressions for σ_x, σ_y, τ_{xy} in the equilibrium conditions [Eqs. (5-20)] we obtain

$$2\mu\,\Delta u + 3\frac{\partial\sigma}{\partial x} = 0,$$
$$2\mu\,\Delta v + 3\frac{\partial\sigma}{\partial y} = 0. \tag{5-53}$$

These two equations may likewise be transformed, after introducing in them the two-dimensional div $\mathbf{w} = \dot{e}$ and the rotation

$$\dot{\omega} = \tfrac{1}{2}(\partial v/\partial x - \partial u/\partial y),$$

in the Cauchy-Riemann equations for these variables:

$$\frac{\partial \dot{\omega}}{\partial y} = 2 \frac{\partial \dot{e}}{\partial x},$$

$$\frac{\partial \dot{\omega}}{\partial x} = -2 \frac{\partial \dot{e}}{\partial y}, \tag{5-54}$$

thus showing that the velocity field u,v in a state of plane stress is controlled by these equations, or, after substituting in them $\dot{e} = \sigma/2\mu$, by

$$\mu \frac{\partial \dot{\omega}}{\partial y} = \frac{\partial \sigma}{\partial x},$$

$$\mu \frac{\partial \dot{\omega}}{\partial x} = -\frac{\partial \sigma}{\partial y}, \tag{5-55}$$

disclosing that now $\mu \dot{\omega}$ and σ are conjugate harmonic functions.

The components of stress σ_x, σ_y, τ_{xy} may likewise be computed from a stress function F from $\Delta \Delta F = 0$.

For comparison, the corresponding equations *for plane stress* in an *elastic, compressible solid* are listed as follows:

Strains
$$\varepsilon_x = \frac{\partial u}{\partial x} = \frac{1}{E}(\sigma_x - \nu\sigma_y),$$

$$\varepsilon_y = \frac{\partial v}{\partial y} = \frac{1}{E}(\sigma_y - \nu\sigma_x), \tag{5-56}$$

$$\varepsilon_z = -\frac{\nu}{E}(\sigma_x + \sigma_y), \qquad \gamma_{xy} = \frac{1}{G}\tau_{xy},$$

$$e = \operatorname{div} \mathbf{w} = \frac{\partial u}{\partial x} + \frac{\partial v}{\partial y} = \frac{3(1-\nu)\sigma}{E}, \qquad \sigma = (\tfrac{1}{3})(\sigma_x + \sigma_y). \tag{5-57}$$

The displacements satisfy

$$2G \,\Delta u + 3 \frac{\partial \sigma}{\partial x} = 0,$$

$$2G \,\Delta v + 3 \frac{\partial \sigma}{\partial y} = 0. \tag{5-58}$$

$e = \operatorname{div} \mathbf{w}$, the rotation ω, and σ satisfy the equations

$$\frac{\partial e}{\partial x} = (1 - \nu)\frac{\partial \omega}{\partial y},$$

$$\frac{\partial e}{\partial y} = -(1 - \nu)\frac{\partial \omega}{\partial x}, \tag{5-59}$$

or

$$3 \frac{\partial \sigma}{\partial x} = E \frac{\partial \omega}{\partial y},$$

$$3 \frac{\partial \sigma}{\partial y} = -E \frac{\partial \omega}{\partial x} \tag{5-60}$$

5-4. Selected Solutions of the Biharmonic Differential Equation. The determination of the components of stress in states of plane strain in elastic or purely viscous material, of the components of velocity in a viscous substance, and of the deflections of a slightly bent flat elastic or viscous plate (see Chap. 9) centers around finding integrals of the biharmonic differential equation $\Delta\Delta f = 0$ for given boundary conditions. The function f may represent an AIRY stress function F, a stream function ψ, or the deflections of a flat plate w. Although it cannot be the purpose of this book to list and review in more detail the great number of valuable exact solutions developed by the elasticians during the past 50 to 60 years in this important field, it is felt some space should be devoted in this chapter to acquainting the reader briefly with the theory of deriving certain integrals of $\Delta\Delta f = 0$ in a selected group of two-dimensional problems, having a particular bearing on questions related to concentrated pressure in elastic and in viscous bodies and to some geophysical applications.

A. RADIAL SYMMETRY. When F represents a function of the radial distance r from an axis, with reference to Eq. (5-36),

$$\Delta\Delta F = \left(\frac{d^2}{dr^2} + \frac{1}{r}\frac{d}{dr}\right)\left(\frac{d^2F}{dr^2} + \frac{1}{r}\frac{dF}{dr}\right) = 0 \tag{5-61}$$

has the general solution

$$F = c_0 + c_1 r^2 + c_2 \ln r + c_3 r^2 \ln r. \tag{5-62}$$

If $F(r)$ is an Airy stress function, through it a radially symmetric state of stress is defined:

$$\sigma_r = \frac{dF}{r\,dr} = 2c_1 + \frac{c_2}{r^2} + c_3(2\ln r + 1),$$

$$\sigma_t = \frac{d^2F}{dr^2} = 2c_1 - \frac{c_2}{r^2} + c_3(2\ln r + 3). \tag{5-63}$$

Excluding first the part of the solution having the integration constant c_3, letting $c_3 = 0$, the terms containing c_1 and c_2 serve to express the state of stress in hollow cylinders stressed by internal or external pressure. For internal pressure, $r = a$, $\sigma_r = -p$; $r = b$, $\sigma_r = 0$, the well-known *Lamé formulas*

$$\sigma_r = -\frac{pa^2}{b^2 - a^2}\left(\frac{b^2}{r^2} - 1\right), \qquad \sigma_t = \frac{pa^2}{b^2 - a^2}\left(\frac{b^2}{r^2} + 1\right) \tag{5-64}$$

express the stresses either in an elastic or in a viscous hollow cylinder, and one obtains for the radial displacement of an elastic cylinder (since $v = 0$)

$$u = r\varepsilon_t = \frac{r}{2G}[\sigma_t - \nu(\sigma_r + \sigma_t)]$$

$$= \frac{pa^2}{2G(b^2 - a^2)}\left[\frac{b^2}{r} + (1 - 2\nu)r\right] \tag{5-65}$$

and for a purely viscous cylinder the radial velocity u with which it expands:

$$u = r\dot{\varepsilon}_t = \frac{r}{4\mu}(\sigma_t - \sigma_r) = \frac{pa^2b^2}{2\mu(b^2 - a^2)r}. \tag{5-66}$$

As to the part solution (letting $c_3 = c$),

$$F = cr^2 \ln r, \tag{5-67}$$

we may note that it has the interesting peculiarity that the tangential displacement component associated with it is a multiple-valued function of the coordinate α. Let us postulate an incompressible *elastic* material. If we substitute the corresponding components of stress,

$$\sigma_r = c(2 \ln r + 1),$$
$$\sigma_t = c(2 \ln r + 3), \tag{5-67a}$$
$$\tau_{rt} = 0,$$

in the stress-strain relations

$$\varepsilon_r = \frac{\partial u}{\partial r} = \frac{\sigma_r - \sigma_t}{4G} = -\frac{c}{2G},$$

$$\varepsilon_t = \frac{1}{r}\left(u + \frac{\partial v}{\partial \alpha}\right) = \frac{\sigma_t - \sigma_r}{4G} = \frac{c}{2G},$$

$$\gamma_{rt} = \frac{\partial u}{r \partial \alpha} + \frac{\partial v}{\partial r} - \frac{v}{r} = 0,$$

we may partially integrate the first two of them with respect to r and α, respectively, and determine the two arbitrary functions that this introduces, one dependent on α, the other on r, from the condition that γ_{rt} with the computed values of u and v must identically vanish. This gives

$$u = -\frac{cr}{2G} + a_1 \cos \alpha + a_2 \sin \alpha,$$

$$v = \frac{cr\alpha}{G} - a_1 \sin \alpha + a_2 \cos \alpha + a_3 r,$$

where the terms containing the integration constants a_1, a_2, a_3 obviously express a movement that would be possible in a rigid body. The presence of the multiple-valued term $cr\alpha/G$ in the expression for v (which after a full turn of the polar angle α by 2π increases by $2\pi r/G$) makes it possible, as ALOIS TIMPE[1] first remarked, to utilize the stress function $F = cr^2 \ln r$, in conjunction with the terms $c_1 r^2$ and $c_2 \ln r$, for expressing *a pure state of inherent elastic strain and stress in a closed ring with no external forces acting on it*. After evaluating c_1 and c_2 from the conditions $r = a$, $r = b$, $\sigma_r = 0$, indeed

$$\sigma_r = 2c\left[\frac{b^2 \ln (b/a)}{b^2 - a^2}\left(\frac{a^2}{r^2} - 1\right) + \ln \frac{r}{a}\right],$$

$$\sigma_t = 2c\left[-\frac{b^2 \ln (b/a)}{b^2 - a^2}\left(\frac{a^2}{r^2} + 1\right) + 1 + \ln \frac{r}{a}\right] \tag{5-67b}$$

[1] "Probleme der Spannungsverteilung in ebenen Systemen einfach gelöst mit Hilfe der Airyschen Spannungfunktion," 38 pp., Dissertation at University of Göttingen, Teubner, 1905.

describe a state of pure bending in a ring or hollow cylinder in which the resultant normal force

$$\int_a^b \sigma_t \, dr$$

across the radial plane sections also vanishes. In order to produce this state of stress, slice away a narrow sector β in the ring above the polar axis $\alpha = 0$ (Fig. 5-4), leaving a space empty,

$$\beta = \frac{v}{r} = \frac{2\pi c}{G},$$

apply the bending moment resulting from the distribution of the tangential stresses σ_t until the gap is just closed, and weld the two faces together. The moment is determined by the value to be attributed to the constant c in the previous equation. The cylindrical surfaces $r = a$ and $r = b$ being free, a state of pure, inherent bending then acts in the closed ring or cylinder. If the same state of stress is, however, produced instantaneously in a cylinder of viscoelastic material and the gap held closed, it will gradually evanesce because of relaxation.

B. SOME BIHARMONIC FUNCTIONS. SINGULARITIES OF STRESS. Let $H(z) = f + ig$ denote a function of the complex variable $z = x + iy = re^{i\alpha}$. Then the real and imaginary parts f and g of $H(z)$, since they satisfy the equations $\Delta f = 0$, $\Delta g = 0$, are harmonic functions (logarithmic potential functions), and the functions

$$F = f, g, r^2 f, r^2 g, xf, xg, yf, yg \qquad (5\text{-}67c)$$

are particular integrals of the biharmonic differential equation $\Delta\Delta F = 0$. These may be expressed in either rectangular or polar coordinates x, y or r, α and multiplied by indeterminate constants of integration, thus making it possible to express solutions of the biharmonic equation by means of finite or infinite sums in which the integration constants may be determined by the given boundary conditions. By choosing, for example, $z^n = (x + iy)^n$, after separating the real from the imaginary part of $H(z)$, if n is a positive integer, we obtain particular solutions in terms of polynomials,

$$x, y, x^2 - y^2, 2xy, x^3 - 3xy^2, 3x^2 y - y^3, \dots,$$

or, after letting

$$H(z) = z^n = r^n e^{in\alpha}, \qquad (5\text{-}67d)$$

we obtain the potentials expressed in polar coordinates r, α

$$r^n (\cos n\alpha, \sin n\alpha), \; r^{-n} (\cos n\alpha, \sin n\alpha)$$

$$[\sin (n \ln r), \cos (n \ln r)] \times [\sinh n\alpha, \cosh n\alpha],$$

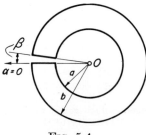

FIG. 5-4

depending on whether n is a positive, a negative, or an imaginary number, and one may multiply each of the preceding potential functions by r^2 and by an integration constant. The resulting trigonometric series developments may serve to express stress or stream functions F or ψ in cylinders or in ring- or sector-shaped bodies, etc.

Apart from these, certain biharmonic functions, such as

$$F = \ln r, \quad \alpha, \quad r^2 \ln r, \quad r^2 \alpha, \quad r \ln r \cdot \sin \alpha, \quad r \ln r \cdot \cos \alpha, \quad r\alpha \sin \alpha,$$

$$r\alpha \cos \alpha, \quad \sin 2\alpha, \quad \cos 2\alpha, \ldots,$$

occur, some of which represent useful states of stress under plane strain or stress.

If the components of stress corresponding to a stress function F tend to increase indefinitely around a point, one speaks of a singularity in the state of stress at that point. For example, the two conjugate stress functions derived from the complex function

$$H(z) = c \ln z = c(\ln r + i\alpha) = F_1 + iF_2$$

create two singularities of stress. The function $F_1 = c \ln r$ generates what may be called *a center of concentrated radial pull or compression* with the stresses

$$\sigma_r = -\sigma_t = \frac{c}{r^2}, \qquad \tau_{rt} = 0,$$

and velocities in radial and tangential directions

$$u = -\frac{c}{2\mu r}, \qquad v = 0,$$

also derivable from the stream function $\psi = -c\alpha/2\mu$; the second stress function $F_2 = c\alpha$ generates *a center of concentrated twist* with the stresses

$$\sigma_r = \sigma_t = 0, \qquad \tau_{rt} = -\frac{c}{r^2},$$

and velocities in radial and tangential directions

$$u = 0, \qquad v = \frac{c}{2\mu r},$$

representing a *vortex* around the origin $r = 0$, derivable from the stream function $\psi = (c/2\mu) \ln r$. The solutions derived from such singularities of stress are frequently needed, provided that they lie outside the region to be considered for expressing the states of stress in bodies having a hole or several cavities. In similar cases, namely, when a stress function has been introduced within doubly or multiply connected regions (as around a hole), some precautions must, however, be taken to ascertain whether one or both of the corresponding components of velocity (or displacement in the case of an elastic body) u and v are or are not expressed by multiple-valued functions of the coordinates x, y or r, α. If they generate multiple-valued velocities u, v, certain special states of stress are included in the stress function F, causing *an artificial distribution of "inherent stress"* (*Eigenspannungen*) around a cavity of the otherwise stressed body. We came across such a condition in the example of the stress function $F = cr^2 \ln r$ in Eqs. (5-67). As long as the location of the singularity is situated at a point of an external boundary curve circumscribing a singly connected region, this difficulty does not occur. It is a mathematically instructive task to investigate the nature of these singular solutions which may easily be constructed in series, by starting with a complex function $H(z)$ of the variable $z = x + iy$ having a singularity and deducing from it new ones through the process of subsequent differentiation or integration with respect to z.

Consider as a further example the stress function in an elastic body

$$F = cr \ln r \cdot \sin \alpha \qquad (5\text{-}68)$$

which generates the distribution of stress

$$\sigma_r = \sigma_t = \frac{c}{r} \sin \alpha, \qquad \tau_{rt} = -\frac{c}{r} \cos \alpha,$$

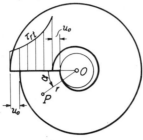

FIG. 5-5

and a displacement field in polar coordinates,

$$u = -\frac{c}{2G}(\sin \alpha + \alpha \cos \alpha),$$

$$v = \frac{c}{2G} \alpha \sin \alpha,$$

disregarding the additional terms of a rigid-body motion. Suppose that an infinite body (Fig. 5-5) is sliced by means of a plane normal to the x,y plane along the polar axis $\alpha = 0$ and a circular hole is cut into it around the origin $O(r = 0)$, having a radius $r = $ const. One ascertains that the stresses σ_r and τ_{rt} along the wall of the hole have neither a *resultant* force nor a moment so that no external load or moment is being transmitted through the hole to the body, and one sees that u and v in the straight plane cut, on the shore $\alpha = 0$, vanish, while after the polar angle α described a full turn, on the adjoining face,

$$\alpha = 2\pi, \qquad u = -\frac{c\pi}{G} = u_0 = \text{const}, \qquad v = 0.$$

The two shores of the plane cut have thus been displaced by an amount $u = u_0 = $ const relatively to each other in the direction of the polar axis. Since the shearing stress $\tau_{rt} = -c/r$ is equal on both shores $\alpha = 0$ and $\alpha = 2\pi$, we may weld the body together along them and again obtain a state of inherent stress in an infinite body without having applied external force resultants or moments to it. This state of stress served SIR GEOFFREY TAYLOR[1] in his theory of dislocations which was mentioned in Vol. I, page 60.

C. RADIAL STRESS FIELDS. (1). *Single normal force on a straight edge.* The stress function

$$F = \frac{P}{\pi} r\alpha \cos \alpha = \frac{P}{\pi} x\alpha \tag{5-69}$$

creates the well-known radial distribution of stress[2]

$$\sigma_r = -\frac{2P \sin \alpha}{\pi r}, \qquad \sigma_t = \tau_{rt} = 0, \tag{5-70}$$

with the associated field of radial and tangential velocity u_r, u_t in a viscous, incompressible substance:

$$u_r = -\frac{P}{2\pi\mu} \ln r \cdot \sin \alpha,$$

$$\tag{5-71}$$

$$u_t = -\frac{P}{2\pi\mu} (\ln r + 1) \cos \alpha,$$

omitting the rigid-body-motion terms. The components of velocity in the x and y directions u_x and u_y are expressed by

$$u_x = \frac{Pxy}{2\pi\mu r^2}, \qquad u_y = -\frac{P}{2\pi\mu}\left(\ln r + \frac{x^2}{r^2}\right). \tag{5-72}$$

The resultant of the single-acting radial stresses σ_r across a semicylinder $r = $ const extending from $\alpha = 0$ to $\alpha = \pi$, for a layer of material of unit thickness, is a force

[1] The Mechanism of Plastic Deformation of Crystals, Proc. Roy. Soc. (London), vol. 145, pp. 362, 388, 1934.
[2] First described by I. H. MICHELL (Proc. London Math. Soc., vol. 32, p. 35. 1900).

P in the direction of the y axis. Equations (5-70) define the state of stress in a semi-infinite body $y > 0$ bounded by the plane $y = 0$ which is loaded in the origin O (Fig. 5-6) by a single normal force P per unit of length along the z axis.

The maximum shearing stress in this radial stress field being equal to

$$\tau_{\max} = (\tfrac{1}{2})|\sigma_r| = \frac{P \sin \alpha}{\pi r},$$

the curves, along which $\tau_{\max} = \text{const}$, are circles (Fig. 5-7) tangent to the x axis, passing through the point of application of the single force P, since in them $r = 2a \sin \alpha$ (a = radius of such a circle). In a transparent elastic material subjected to a photoelastic test in white polarized light, the curves $\tau_{\max} = \text{const}$, known as the *isochromatics*, take on the uniform colors of the rainbow. The radial stress field therefore has these circles as isochromatics (Fig. 5-8 reproduces them in monochromatic light).

The expressions for the velocity components in a viscous substance and for the displacements in an elastic substance, in this two-dimensional state of stress and strain under a concentrated force (and in related applications in plane stress and strain), *do not tend to zero* at increasing distance from the point of application of a load resultant. It is therefore impossible to compute displacements relative to an infinitely distant point in the x,y plane.[1]

(2). *Single tangential force on a straight edge.* The formulas derived from the stress function,

$$F = \frac{P}{\pi} r\alpha \sin \alpha = \frac{P}{\pi} y\alpha,$$

$$\sigma_r = \frac{2P \cos \alpha}{\pi r}, \qquad \sigma_t = \tau_{rt} = 0, \tag{5-73}$$

$$u_r = \frac{P \ln r \cdot \cos \alpha}{2\pi\mu}, \qquad u_t = -\frac{P}{2\pi\mu}(\ln r + 1) \sin \alpha,$$

[1] Velocities or displacements can be evaluated only in limited regions of the body. One may prescribe, for example, that a certain point A ($r = a$, $\alpha = \pi/2$) in Fig. 5-6, chosen on the symmetry axis of the state of strain caused by the normal force P, shall remain at rest, by adding to Eqs. (5-71) the terms $u_r = c \sin \alpha$, $u_t = c \cos \alpha$ expressing a uniform velocity c in the direction of the y axis. One obtains as the resultant velocities

$$u_r = -\frac{P}{2\pi\mu} \sin \alpha \cdot \ln \frac{r}{a}, \qquad u_t = -\frac{P}{2\pi\mu} \cos \alpha \cdot \left(\ln \frac{r}{a} + 1\right)$$

and sees that the surface is depressed by the concentrated force P in its neighborhood and raised farther away from it, since the incompressible substance swallowed up under the load P must reappear elsewhere, as illustrated in Fig. 5-6.

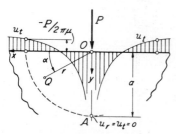

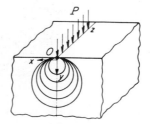

FIG. 5-6. Single normal force P.

FIG. 5-7. Single normal force P. The maximum shearing stress $\tau_{\max}$ is constant on the circles.

likewise describe the state of stress and the velocities in a semi-infinite body $y > 0$ loaded by a single force P acting in the direction of the negative x axis (Fig. 5-9) in the origin O. In both cases, (1) and (2), one may slice out of the infinite body a sector bounded by the straight lines $\alpha = (\pi/2) - \beta$ and $\alpha = (\pi/2) + \beta$ (since $\sigma_t = \tau_{rt} = 0$ on the pencil of rays $\alpha =$ const) and obtain the distributions of stress in a wedge loaded at its corner $r = 0$ by the part load Q carried on the circular arc $2r\beta$. When using Eqs. (5-73), one has the case of bending in a wedge-shaped cantilever beam loaded by a single force at the corner. In these states of radially distributed stress the curves $\tau_{\max} =$ const are circles, the direction of the force Q determining the axis of the system of circular iso-chromatics.[1] Since σ_r, u_r, u_t increase indefinitely when r approaches zero, the formulas should not be used within a certain region $0 < r < c$ around the point of application of the force P.

(3). *Concentrated moment.* The stress function F defining the stresses caused by a moment M concentrated at point O $(r = 0)$ of a free straight edge $y = 0$,

$$F = -\frac{M}{2\pi}(2\alpha - \sin 2\alpha), \qquad (5\text{-}74)$$

for which the stresses are equal to

$$\sigma_r = -\frac{2M \sin 2\alpha}{\pi r^2}, \qquad \sigma_t = 0, \qquad \tau_{rt} = -\frac{M(1 - \cos 2\alpha)}{\pi r^2}, \qquad (5\text{-}75)$$

[1] Nice examples of them are reproduced in MAX M. FROCHT, "Photoelasticity," vol. 2 chap. 2, John Wiley & Sons, Inc., New York, 1948.

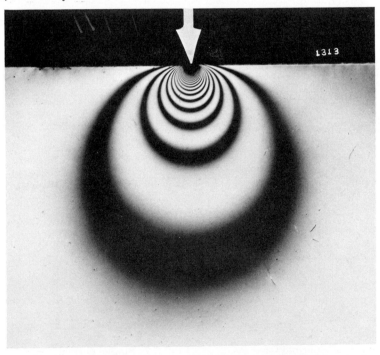

FIG. 5-8. Single normal force acting on a free edge in a state of plane strain. The isochromatic lines are circles. (*Courtesy of M. Frocht, Chicago, Ill.*)

may easily be constructed from the function F [Eq. (5-69)] for the single normal force P. Apply two equal forces P of opposite direction at two points O_1 and O_2 a small distance $2a$ apart, which have a couple $M = 2Pa$. By decreasing the lever arm $2a$ and increasing P while the moment M does not change, the singularity of a concentrated moment M at a point of a straight edge $y = 0$ is obtained.[1] The stress function

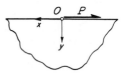

FIG. 5-9. Single tangential force P.

$$F = (\tfrac{1}{2})M \sin 2\alpha$$

defines the stresses

$$\sigma_r = -\frac{2M}{r^2} \sin 2\alpha, \qquad \sigma_t = 0, \qquad \tau_{rt} = \frac{M}{r^2} \cos 2\alpha$$

generated by a concentrated moment M which acts in the apex of a corner of a right angle bounded by the planes $\alpha = \pm\pi/4$.

D. PERIODIC STATES OF PLANE STRAIN. (1). *A group of periodic integrals* of the biharmonic equation is obtained by letting

$$F(x,y) = Y_n(y)\left(\sin \frac{n\pi x}{a} \quad \text{or} \quad \cos \frac{n\pi x}{a}\right), \tag{5-76}$$

where Y_n function of y

$\quad a$ const

$\quad n$ positive integer

After substituting F in the biharmonic equation $\Delta\Delta F = 0$, for Y_n the ordinary, linear differential equation of fourth order,

$$Y^{(4)} - 2\left(\frac{n\pi}{a}\right)^2 Y'' + \left(\frac{n\pi}{a}\right)^4 Y = 0, \tag{5-77}$$

is obtained, which is satisfied either by the integrals

$$Y_n = e^{n\pi y/a},\ e^{-n\pi y/a},\ ye^{n\pi y/a},\ ye^{-n\pi y/a} \tag{5-78a}$$

or by

$$Y_n = \sinh \frac{n\pi y}{a}, \quad \cosh \frac{n\pi y}{a}, \quad y \sinh \frac{n\pi y}{a}, \quad y \cosh \frac{n\pi y}{a}. \tag{5-78b}$$

[1] Choose the origin O of the coordinates x, y or r, α in the center of O_1O_2 and let

$$f = r\alpha \cos \alpha = x\alpha = x \arctan \frac{y}{x}.$$

Then we have the stress function

$$F(r,\alpha) = \frac{P}{\pi}(f_1 - f_2),$$

where

$$f_1 = x_1\alpha_1 = f(x - a, y) = -a\frac{\partial f}{\partial x},$$

$$f_2 = x_2\alpha_2 = f(x + a, y) = a\frac{\partial f}{\partial x},$$

but

$$\frac{\partial f}{\partial x} = \frac{\partial(x\alpha)}{\partial x} = \alpha - \frac{xy}{r^2},$$

and

$$F = -\frac{2Pa}{\pi} \cdot \frac{\partial f}{\partial x} = -\frac{M}{\pi}\left(\alpha - \frac{xy}{r^2}\right) = -\frac{M}{2\pi}(2\alpha - \sin 2\alpha).$$

These stress functions F can also serve to satisfy boundary conditions along the edges of a parallel strip $0 \leq x \leq a$, $-\infty < y < \infty$ or of a rectangle $0 \leq x \leq a$, $0 \leq y \leq b$.

Consider the trigonometric series built up of the groups of particular integrals:

$$F = \sum_{n=0}^{n} \left(a_n + b_n \frac{n\pi y}{a} \right) e^{-n\pi y/a} \left(\sin \frac{n\pi x}{a} \quad \text{or} \quad \cos \frac{n\pi x}{a} \right),$$

$$(n = 0, 1, 2, 3, \ldots), \quad (5\text{-}79)$$

where a_n and b_n are constants. One sees that this stress function may express a state of plane strain in a semi-infinite body $y \geq 0$ which is loaded by a periodic distribution of normal stresses $\sigma_y = f(x)$ or of shearing stresses $\tau_{xy} = g(x)$ or of both on the straight edge $y = 0$, giving vanishing values for σ_x, σ_y, τ_{xy} at $y = \infty$. If $a_n = b_n$, the shearing stresses τ_{xy} vanish, and if $a_n = 0$ the normal stresses σ_y vanish in the plane $y = 0$.

(2). *Estimating the pressures under parallel ranges of high mountains.* Suppose that, on the boundary plane $y = 0$ of a semi-infinite elastic or viscous body, the normal stresses

$$\sigma_y = -p\left(1 + \sin \frac{\pi x}{a} \right) \quad (5\text{-}80)$$

act, where p and a are constants and that for $y = 0$, $\tau_{xy} = 0$. A stress function F giving this distribution of pressures is

$$F = -(\tfrac{1}{2})px^2 + \frac{pa^2}{\pi^2}\left(1 + \frac{\pi y}{a} \right) e^{-\pi y/a} \sin \frac{\pi x}{a}. \quad (5\text{-}81)$$

Equation (5-80) in a first approximation could represent the distribution of the vertical normal stress on the horizontal level $y = 0$ drawn through the valley floors and caused by the weights of a regular chain of parallel ranges of high mountains, the crests of which (Fig. 5-10) are a distance $2a$ apart, and, if one lets $p = h\gamma/2$, of mountains of equal heights h having the specific weight of rocks equal to γ. In order to include also the hydrostatic pressures at greater depths $(y > 0)$ due to gravitation (Fig. 5-11), let us add two more terms in Eq. (5-81), by postulating below the level of the valley floors $y = 0$

$$F = -\frac{p}{2}(x^2 + y^2) - \frac{py^3}{3h} + \frac{pa^2}{\pi^2}\left(1 + \frac{\pi y}{a} \right) e^{-\pi y/a} \sin \frac{\pi x}{a}, \quad (5\text{-}82)$$

for which one computes the distribution of stress

$$\sigma_x = -p\left(1 + \frac{2y}{h} \right) - p\left(1 - \frac{\pi y}{a} \right) e^{-\pi y/a} \sin \frac{\pi x}{a},$$

$$\sigma_y = -p\left(1 + \frac{2y}{h} \right) - p\left(1 + \frac{\pi y}{a} \right) e^{-\pi y/a} \sin \frac{\pi x}{a}, \quad (5\text{-}83)$$

$$\tau_{xy} = \frac{p\pi y}{a} e^{-\pi y/a} \cos \frac{\pi x}{a},$$

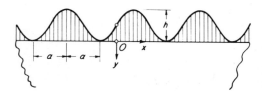

FIG. 5-10. Weight of mountain ranges.

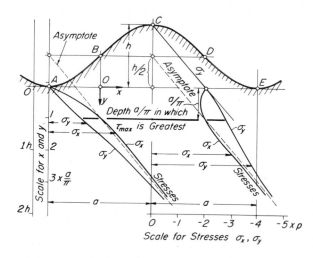

FIG. 5-11. Approximate distribution of stresses σ_x, σ_y under the weight of a mountain of the profile $ABCDE$.

where the constant $p = h\gamma/2$. At sufficiently great values of the depths y these formulas approach a distribution of hydrostatic pressures since the terms containing $e^{-\pi y/a}$ vanish.[1] From Eqs. (5-83) the values for σ_x and σ_y given in Table 5-1 were computed in the vertical cross sections of the ground, at $x = a/2$ under the crest of the mountain, and $x = -a/2$ under the valley, and reproduced by their curves in Fig. 5-11.[2]

This brings out in a first approximation the disturbance caused in the distribution of the underground pressures through the weight of a high mountain,

TABLE 5-1

Depth: $y\pi/a$	Under crest of mountain C, for $x = a/2$. Stresses		Under floor of valley A, for $x = -a/2$. Stresses	
	$-\sigma_x/p$	$-\sigma_y/p$	$-\sigma_x/p$	$-\sigma_y/p$
0	2	2	0	0
0.5	1.80	2.41	1.20	0.59
1	2	2.74	2	1.26
1.5	2.39	3.06	2.61	1.94
2	2.87	3.41	3.14	2.60
2.5	3.38	3.79	3.62	3.21
3	3.90	4.20	4.10	3.80
. . .	. . .	. . .	. . .	. . .

[1] It should be noted that the term $-2py/h$ in the expression of σ_y representing the action of gravity $\gamma = g\rho$ on this stress does not show up in the expression for the stress function F which satisfies $\Delta\Delta F = 0$ but is obtained by integrating $\partial\sigma_y/\partial y = -2p/h$.

[2] The height of the mountains was assumed equal to $h = 2a/\pi$ in Fig. 5-11, giving a steepest slope (at point B, $x = 0$) inclined at an angle of 45°. As one should expect, all curves for σ_x and σ_y will gradually approach the inclined asymptote $\sigma_x = \sigma_y = -p[1 + (2y/h)]$, but those for the pressures under the crest C start at the valley level $y = 0$ a distance p to the right and those under the valley floor A a distance $-p$ to the left of the asymptote.

which is of some interest to geologists.   Furthermore, if one computes from the three equations (5-83) the maximum shearing stress, one finds for it the value

$$\tau_{\max} = \sqrt{\frac{(\sigma_x - \sigma_y)^2}{4} + \tau_{xy}^2} = \frac{\pi p y}{a} e^{-\pi y/a}, \qquad (5\text{-}84)$$

i.e., that the maximum shearing stress $\tau_{\max}$ takes constant values in the horizontal planes $y = $ const in spite of the overtowering heights of parallel mountain ranges, and one sees that $\tau_{\max}$ reaches its maximum value in a horizontal plane, in the critical depth $y = a/\pi$ below the valley level, where

$$\tau_{\max} = e^{-1}p = 0.368p = 0.184h\gamma. \qquad (5\text{-}85)$$

The plane of greatest shear thus occurs at a constant depth $y = a/\pi$ (Fig. 5-11), *independently of the height h of the range, equal to approximately one-sixth of the distance 2a between crests or valleys, but the greatest shearing stress* $\tau_{\max}$ *under parallel ranges of high mountains is directly proportional to their heights h.*   It is well known to geologists that entire mountain ranges have been pushed together and shifted along horizontal thrust faults running under them, under the action of transcontinental movements of a geophysical nature persisting over certain geologic epochs.   We may conclude that even small, additional disturbances of this nature should be found concentrating their efforts along these layers in which the resistance against shear is first reached, namely, in the regions in which $\tau_{\max}$ has its greatest value, i.e., in this plane of greatest weakness $y = a/\pi$ below valley level. Isostatic considerations cannot change this fact since the weights of overtowering mountain ranges must be carried by the corresponding stresses under them in equilibrium states.

The rocks under a chain of mountains respond under their weight by displacements u, v of an elastic and of a viscous, permanent nature.   These may be judged by computing the elastic strain ε_x and rate of permanent strain $\dot{\varepsilon}_x$, respectively.   Supposing for simplicity an elastically incompressible material (assuming Poisson's ratio $\nu = \frac{1}{2}$), one sees from Eqs. (5-83), after integrating the expression for the strains

$$\varepsilon_x = \frac{\partial u}{\partial x} = -\varepsilon_y = -\frac{\partial v}{\partial y} = \frac{\sigma_x - \sigma_y}{4G} = \frac{\pi p}{2aG} y e^{-\pi y/a} \sin\frac{\pi x}{a},$$

that the *elastic components of the displacement* in horizontal and vertical direction, u and v, must be equal to

$$u = -\frac{py}{2G} e^{-\pi y/a} \cos\frac{\pi x}{a},$$

$$v = \frac{pa}{2\pi G}\left(1 + \frac{\pi y}{a}\right) e^{-\pi y/a} \sin\frac{\pi x}{a}, \qquad (5\text{-}86)$$

disclosing that in the horizontal plane at valley level $y = 0$

$$u = 0, \qquad v = \frac{pa}{2\pi G}\sin\frac{\pi x}{a}. \qquad (5\text{-}87)$$

The corresponding relations for *the small components of velocity u, v*, with which a point x,y underground *moves steadily owing to the viscosity of the rocks*, are given by replacing the modulus of rigidity G in the preceding expressions by the coefficient of viscosity μ.   We note that the ground sinks under the top of the mountains and is being raised in the valleys according to a sinusoidal wave.   It may be instructive to evaluate the vertical elastic displacement and permanent velocity

v across the valley floor level $y = 0$. Suppose
that the rocks have a modulus of rigidity of
a mean value equal to $G = 80,000$ kg/cm²,[†]
that the mountain has a height $h = 3,000$ m,
that $a = \pi h/2 = 4,713$ m, and the specific
weight of the rocks is $\gamma = 0.0027$ kg/cm³, so
that the pressure $p = h\gamma/2 = 405$ kg/cm².
This gives for the amplitude of sinusoidal
wave of *the elastic, vertical displacements*

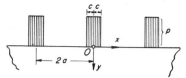

FIG. 5-12. Train of single normal
forces.

$$v_{\text{elas}} = \frac{pa}{2\pi G} = 363 \text{ cm} = 3.63 \text{ m}.$$

Similarly, assuming for the solid rocks in the uppermost regions of the earth's
crust a mean, comparatively high viscosity of the order, believed to be prevalent,[1]
of $\mu = 5 \times 10^{22}$ poises $= 5 \times 10^{16}$ [kg cm⁻² sec], the amplitude of the viscous
vertical velocity v with which the points of the horizontal plane $y = 0$ move is
found equal to

$$v_{\text{visc}} = \frac{pa}{2\pi\mu} = 6.02 \times 10^{-10} \text{ cm/sec} = 0.019 \text{ cm/year}$$

or approximately 2 cm per century. But the movements under high mountain
ranges caused by the viscosity of rocks may probably be much greater, because of
their imperfections.[2] If μ were a hundred times smaller, a velocity $v_{\text{visc}} = \sim 2$ m
per century might not be considered improbable. Movements of the latter order
of magnitude should become discernible, for example, in distortions of the axes
of the long railroad tunnels piercing the Saint Gotthard or the Simplon massifs
in the Swiss Alps, the first of which may soon look back on a century of existence.

(3). *Distribution of stress under a train of single normal forces.* Suppose that
on the straight edge $y = 0$ the normal stress σ_y is a periodic function of x, $\sigma_y = f(x)$,
of the period $2a$ having a constant value $\sigma_y = -p = \text{const}$ in the part of the
interval $-c < x < c$ and vanishing values beyond it, while $\tau_{xy} = 0$ on $y = 0$.
This discontinuous periodic function $\sigma_y = f(x)$ (Fig. 5-12) is expressed by the
cosine series:

$$\sigma_y = -\frac{2pc}{a}\left[(\tfrac{1}{2}) + \frac{a}{\pi c}\sum_{n=1}^{\infty}\frac{1}{n}\sin\frac{n\pi c}{a}\cos\frac{n\pi x}{a}\right] \qquad (n = 1, 2, 3, \ldots). \quad (5\text{-}88)$$

Let the width $2c$ of the loaded strips decrease while the pressure p is increased
in them, leaving the force $P = 2cp = \text{const}$, per unit length in the area $2c \times 1$.
The mathematician FEJÉR has shown that one may equate the limiting value of
the fractions appearing in the series to 1,

$$\lim_{c=0}\left(\sin\frac{n\pi c}{a} : \frac{n\pi c}{a}\right) = 1,$$

[†] A good sandstone has a modulus of elasticity $E = 240,000$ kg/cm² and, if $\nu = \frac{1}{2}$
is taken, $G = E/3$.

[1] Mentioned in BENO GUTENBERG (ed.), "Internal Constitution of the Earth," 2d ed.,
p. 389, Dover Publications, New York, 1951.

[2] The belts of the high mountains of the earth are known to be the loci of frequent
earth tremors and quakes.

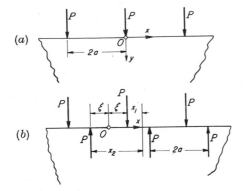

FIG. 5-13. Trains of single concentrated forces.

rewriting the *trigonometric series* in simpler form,

$$\sigma_y = -\frac{P}{a}\left(\frac{1}{2} + \sum_{n=1}^{\infty} \cos \frac{n\pi x}{a}\right), \qquad (n = 1, 2, 3, \ldots), \qquad (5\text{-}89)[1]$$

obtaining *the analytic expression of a train of equal single, concentrated compression loads P* in periodic intervals $2a$ (Fig. 5-13a).   By superposing two such infinite trains of loads $\pm P$, letting $x_1 = x - \xi$, $x_2 = x + \xi$,

$$\frac{P}{a}\sum\left(\cos \frac{n\pi x_1}{a} - \cos \frac{n\pi x_2}{a}\right) = \frac{2P}{a}\sum_{n=1}^{\infty} \sin \frac{n\pi \xi}{a} \sin \frac{n\pi x}{a}, \qquad (n = 1, 2, 3, \ldots),$$

(5-90)

this represents the train of alternating single forces shown in Fig. 5-13b.

Thus, if one postulates, for example, a stress function F:

$$F = -\frac{Px^2}{4a} + \sum_{n=1}^{\infty} a_n\left(1 + \frac{n\pi y}{a}\right)e^{-n\pi y/a}\cos \frac{n\pi x}{a}, \qquad (n = 1, 2, 3, \ldots), \quad (5\text{-}91)$$

one may determine the constants a_n in the latter series from the condition that on the edge $y = 0$ the normal stress σ_y,

$$\sigma_y = \frac{\partial^2 F}{\partial x^2} = -\frac{P}{2a} - \sum_n \frac{n^2\pi^2}{a^2} a_n \cos \frac{n\pi x}{a}, \qquad (5\text{-}92)$$

just represents the first train of loads P [Eq. (5-89)].   This gives for the constants a_n

$$a_n = \frac{Pa}{n^2\pi^2}.$$

Hence, *the stress function*

$$F = -\frac{Px^2}{4a} + \frac{Pa}{\pi^2}\sum_{n=1}^{\infty}\frac{1}{n^2}\left(1 + \frac{n\pi y}{a}\right)e^{-n\pi y/a}\cos \frac{n\pi x}{a}, \qquad (n = 1, 2, 3, \ldots)$$

(5-93)

---

[1] FEJÉR has shown that to a divergent series, such as is expressed in Eq. (5-89), a sense may be attributed if one determines its sum by the rule of the expanded arithmetic means of its finite part sums.   He proved that these arithmetic means of the first n terms converge toward the value zero in the *unloaded* parts of the interval when n is indefinitely increased. Cf. K. KNOPP, "Theorie der unendlichen Reihen," p. 455, Springer-Verlag, Berlin, 1922.

represents the state of stress in a semi-infinite body $y > 0$, namely,

$$\sigma_x = -\frac{P}{a} \sum_n^\infty \left(1 - \frac{n\pi y}{a}\right) e^{-n\pi y/a} \cos \frac{n\pi x}{a},$$

$$\sigma_y = -\frac{P}{2a} - \frac{P}{a} \sum_n^\infty \left(1 + \frac{n\pi y}{a}\right) e^{-n\pi y/a} \cos \frac{n\pi x}{a}, \qquad (5\text{-}94)$$

$$\tau_{xy} = -\frac{P}{a} \sum_n^\infty \frac{n\pi y}{a} e^{-n\pi y/a} \sin \frac{n\pi x}{a}, \qquad (n = 1, 2, 3, \ldots),$$

generated by a train of single compression forces P acting at equal distances $2a$ apart.

(4). *Fourier integral solution of semi-infinite body loaded on plane $y = 0$ by normal or shearing stresses.* Suppose that σ_y or τ_{xy} are given on the boundary $y = 0$ as single-valued functions of x which have finite (or have at single points integrably infinite) values in a certain interval of finite width and are equal to zero outside of it. In this case, we may assume a particular solution of the biharmonic equation in the form

$$\frac{1}{\alpha^2} (A + B\alpha y) e^{-\alpha y} \cos \alpha x \qquad (5\text{-}95)$$

and consider, instead of a sum, the definite *Fourier integral* taken between the limits zero and $\alpha = \infty$ for the stress function F.

If the surface $y = 0$ carries an even distribution of normal stress $\sigma_y = f(x)$, we take $A = B$ and may express the corresponding distribution of stress by

$$\sigma_x = -\int_0^\infty A(1 - \alpha y) e^{-\alpha y} \cos \alpha x \, d\alpha,$$

$$\sigma_y = -\int_0^\infty A(1 + \alpha y) e^{-\alpha y} \cos \alpha x \, d\alpha, \qquad (5\text{-}96)$$

$$\tau_{xy} = -y \int_0^\infty A\alpha e^{-\alpha y} \sin \alpha x \, d\alpha.$$

The variable parameter $A(\alpha)$, which is a function of the integration variable α, may be determined according to the rules for Fourier integrals[1] from the boundary condition which is prescribed for the normal stress $\sigma_y = f(x)$ on $y = 0$, namely,

$$\sigma_y = f(x) = -\int_0^\infty A(\alpha) \cos \alpha x \, d\alpha, \qquad y = 0,$$

from

$$A(\alpha) = -\frac{2}{\pi} \int_0^\infty f(\lambda) \cos \alpha\lambda \, d\lambda, \qquad (5\text{-}97)$$

supposing an *even* function $f(x)$.

In a similar way, using $C(\alpha)(y/\alpha)e^{-\alpha y} \cos \alpha x$, one may express the solution in terms of Fourier integrals representing the state of stress when an odd distribution of shearing stresses $\tau_{xy} = g(x)$ acts on $y = 0$. These general solutions have found interesting applications in the theory of concentrated pressures in two-dimensional distributions of stress.

---

[1] Cf. HEINRICH WEBER, "Die partiellen Differential Gleichungen der mathematischen Physik, nach Riemann's Vorlesungen," vol. 1, p. 48, Vieweg-Verlag, Brunswick, Germany, 1910.

5-5. Plane Strain in Viscoelastic Substance. One avoids the necessity for distinguishing between certain readjustment periods involving exponential factors e^{-t/t_r} dependent on the time t and certain time constants t_r, having various values, in the expressions for the stresses or strains, if one postulates incompressibility of the material both for the elastic and for the permanent parts of the strains, by assuming Poisson's ratio $\nu = \frac{1}{2}$ for both types of strain. Supposing $\nu = \frac{1}{2}$, the theory of plane strain becomes simpler and may be extended in what follows to viscoelastic behavior, with reference to Sec. 5-2B and C, denoting the elastic and permanent parts of strain and displacement with one and with two primes. When $\nu = \frac{1}{2}$, in a state of plane strain in which $\varepsilon_z = \varepsilon_z' + \varepsilon_z'' = 0$, both terms $\varepsilon_z' = 0$, $\varepsilon_z'' = 0$ vanish at any time t; furthermore also $\dot\varepsilon_z' = \dot\varepsilon_z'' = \dot\varepsilon_z = 0$. The mean stress σ being equal to

$$\sigma = \frac{\sigma_x + \sigma_y + \sigma_z}{3} = \frac{\sigma_x + \sigma_y}{2} = \sigma_z, \tag{5-98}$$

we have for the elastic and permanent parts of strain the stress-strain relations

$$\varepsilon_x' = -\varepsilon_y' = \frac{\sigma_x - \sigma_y}{4G}, \qquad \gamma_{xy}' = \frac{\tau_{xy}}{G},$$

$$\dot\varepsilon_x'' = -\dot\varepsilon_y'' = \frac{\sigma_x - \sigma_y}{4\mu}, \qquad \dot\gamma_{xy}'' = \frac{\tau_{xy}}{\mu}, \tag{5-99}$$

or

$$\sigma_x = \sigma + 2G\frac{\partial u'}{\partial x} = \sigma + 2\mu\frac{\partial \dot u''}{\partial x},$$

$$\sigma_y = \sigma + 2G\frac{\partial v'}{\partial y} = \sigma + 2\mu\frac{\partial \dot v''}{\partial y}, \tag{5-100}$$

$$\tau_{xy} = G\left(\frac{\partial v'}{\partial x} + \frac{\partial u'}{\partial y}\right) = \mu\left(\frac{\partial \dot v''}{\partial x''} + \frac{\partial \dot u''}{\partial y}\right);$$

after denoting the constant ratio $\mu/G = t_s$, since

$$u = u' + u'', \qquad v = v' + v'',$$

$$\dot u = \dot u' + \dot u'', \qquad \dot v = \dot v' + \dot v'',$$

the stress–rate-of-strain relations take the form

$$\dot\varepsilon_x = \frac{\partial \dot u}{\partial x} = \frac{1}{4G}\left[\dot\sigma_x - \dot\sigma_y + \frac{1}{t_s}(\sigma_x - \sigma_y)\right],$$

$$\dot\varepsilon_y = \frac{\partial \dot v}{\partial y} = \frac{1}{4G}\left[\dot\sigma_y - \dot\sigma_x + \frac{1}{t_s}(\sigma_y - \sigma_x)\right],$$

$$\dot\varepsilon_x + \dot\varepsilon_y = \frac{\partial \dot u}{\partial x} + \frac{\partial \dot v}{\partial y} = 0, \tag{5-101}$$

$$\dot\gamma_{xy} = \frac{\partial \dot v}{\partial x} + \frac{\partial \dot u}{\partial y} = \frac{1}{G}\left(\dot\tau_{xy} + \frac{1}{t_s}\tau_{xy}\right).$$

After solving these relations for the components of stress,

$$\dot{\sigma}_x + \frac{\sigma_x}{t_s} = 2G\frac{\partial \dot{u}}{\partial x} + \dot{\sigma} + \frac{\sigma}{t_s},$$

$$\dot{\sigma}_y + \frac{\sigma_y}{t_s} = 2G\frac{\partial \dot{v}}{\partial y} + \dot{\sigma} + \frac{\sigma}{t_s},$$

$$\dot{\tau}_{xy} + \frac{\tau_{xy}}{t_s} = G\left(\frac{\partial \dot{v}}{\partial x} + \frac{\partial \dot{u}}{\partial y}\right),$$

$$\sigma_z = \sigma,$$

$\qquad$ (5-102)

we may differentiate the equilibrium conditions [Eqs. (5-20)] with respect to the time t, add these to Eqs. (5-20), and substitute in their sums the preceding equations (5-102), thus obtaining for the displacement components u and v two partial differential equations of the independent variables x, y, and t *solving the problem of viscoelastic strain in incompressible material:*

$$G\,\Delta\dot{u} + \frac{\partial}{\partial x}\left(\dot{\sigma} + \frac{\sigma}{t_s}\right) = 0,$$

$$G\,\Delta\dot{v} + \frac{\partial}{\partial y}\left(\dot{\sigma} + \frac{\sigma}{t_s}\right) = 0,$$

$\qquad$ (5-103)

from which follows that

$$\Delta\dot{\sigma} + \frac{1}{t_s}\Delta\sigma = 0. \qquad (5\text{-}104)$$

Alternatively, by expressing the components of stress by means of an *Airy stress function* $F(x,y,t)$,

$$\sigma_x = \frac{\partial^2 F}{\partial y^2}, \qquad \sigma_y = \frac{\partial^2 F}{\partial x^2}, \qquad \tau_{xy} = -\frac{\partial^2 F}{\partial x\,\partial y}, \qquad (5\text{-}105)$$

using the condition of compatibility

$$\frac{\partial^2 \dot{\varepsilon}_x}{\partial y^2} + \frac{\partial^2 \dot{\varepsilon}_y}{\partial x^2} = \frac{\partial^2 \dot{\gamma}_{xy}}{\partial x\,\partial y}, \qquad (5\text{-}106)$$

one is led to the differential equation for the stress function $F(x,y,t)$,

$$\Delta\Delta\dot{F} + \frac{1}{t_s}\Delta\Delta F = 0, \qquad (5\text{-}107)$$

while the elastic parts of strain require that

$$\Delta\sigma = 0, \qquad \Delta\Delta F = 0. \qquad (5\text{-}108)$$

By letting $\sigma = \varphi(t)s(x,y)$ in Eq. (5-104),

$$\left(\dot{\varphi} + \frac{1}{t_s}\,\varphi\right)\Delta s(x,y) = 0, \qquad (5\text{-}109)$$

one may choose for $s(x,y)$ a solution of $\Delta s = 0$, conforming with Eqs. (5-108), and for $\varphi(t)$ an arbitrary function of time t; that is, one may multiply any potential function s by an arbitrary factor dependent on time, enabling one to express states of plane strain in which the boundary stresses (external loads) vary in some prescribed manner with the time t, or one may assume that

$$\dot{\varphi} + \frac{1}{t_s}\,\varphi = 0, \qquad \sigma = e^{-t/t_s}s(x,y), \qquad (5\text{-}110)$$

where $\Delta s = 0$. The same reasoning applies to the stress function F. After having established a set of solutions for u and v from Eqs. (5-103), the permanent and elastic parts of u and v are evaluated from

$$u'', v'' = \frac{1}{t_s}\,e^{-t/t_s}\int_0^t (u,v)e^{t/t_s}dt,$$

$$u' = u - u'', \qquad v' = v - v''. \qquad (5\text{-}111)$$

5-6. Relaxation of Pressure in a Long Cylinder Shrunk on a Rigid Shaft. As an example of a state of plane strain in viscoelastic material, let us consider the relaxation of the pressure p in the contact surface of a long cylindrical bushing that has been shrunk on a perfectly rigid shaft.

Suppose first that the material of the bushing were *fully incompressible* ($\nu = \frac{1}{2}$). Denoting by the subscript zero all values in the perfectly elastic material at time $t = 0$ upon loading, the radial, tangential, and axial normal stresses σ_r, σ_t, σ_z in a long, hollow cylinder of inner and outer radius a and b [see Eqs. (5-64) and (5-65)] are at time $t = 0$

$$\sigma_{r0} = -\frac{p_0 a^2}{b^2 - a^2}\left(\frac{b^2}{r^2} - 1\right), \qquad \sigma_{t0} = \frac{p_0 a^2}{b^2 - a^2}\left(\frac{b^2}{r^2} + 1\right),$$

$$\sigma_{z0} = (\tfrac{1}{2})(\sigma_{r0} + \sigma_{t0}) = \frac{p_0 a^2}{b^2 - a^2}, \qquad (5\text{-}112)$$

accompanied by the radial elastic displacement

$$u_0 = u_0' = \frac{p_0 a^2 b^2}{2G(b^2 - a^2)r}. \qquad (5\text{-}113)$$

In *incompressible* viscoelastic material, since the radial displacement at $r = a$ is held invariable, $u(a,t) = $ const, and the length of the cylinder does not change, obviously the three total rates of strain vanish everywhere, $\dot{\varepsilon}_r = \dot{\varepsilon}_t = \dot{\varepsilon}_z = 0$; also $\varepsilon_z' = \varepsilon_z'' = 0$ at all times, hence $\sigma_z = (\frac{1}{2})(\sigma_r + \sigma_t)$. Thus *the total radial displacement at any radius r must remain* $u(r,t) = u_0$, changing from the initially elastic to a finally permanent value, the part $u''(r,t)$ of u increasing after Eqs. (5-111) as

$$u''(r,t) = \frac{1}{t_s}u_0 e^{-t/t_s}\int_0^t e^{t/t_s}\,dt = u_0(1 - e^{-t/t_s}). \qquad (5\text{-}114)$$

From the formulas expressing the total rates of strain [Eqs. (5-101)] one sees, since $\dot{\varepsilon}_t$ and $\dot{\varepsilon}_r$ vanish as well as $\dot{\varepsilon}_z$ at all times t,

$$\dot{\varepsilon}_t = \frac{\dot{u}}{r} = -\dot{\varepsilon}_r = \frac{1}{4G}\left(\dot{\sigma}_t + \frac{\sigma_t}{t_s} - \dot{\sigma}_r - \frac{\sigma_r}{t_s}\right) = 0, \qquad (5\text{-}115)$$

that all three components of stress σ_r, σ_t, σ_z and also the contact pressure p will decay with the same time factor e^{-t/t_s}. Relaxation progresses as if the bushing were loaded by the pressure

$$p = p_0 e^{-t/t_s}, \tag{5-116}$$

and the stresses may be evaluated simply by placing p instead of p_0 in Eqs. (5-112).

Secondly, suppose that the material is *elastically compressible,* having a Poisson's ratio ν, the initial, elastic state in the shrunk-on cylinder at time $t = 0$ now being

$$\sigma_{r0} = -\frac{p_0 a^2}{b^2 - a^2}\left(\frac{b^2}{r^2} - 1\right),$$

$$\left.\sigma_{t0} = \frac{p_0 a^2}{b^2 - a^2}\left(\frac{b^2}{r^2} + 1\right), \right\} \tag{5-117}$$

$$\sigma_{z0} = \nu(\sigma_{r0} + \sigma_{t0}) = \frac{2\nu p_0 a^2}{b^2 - a^2},$$

$$u_0 = u_0' = \frac{p_0 a^2}{2G(b^2 - a^2)}\left[(1 - 2\nu)r + \frac{b^2}{r}\right]. \tag{5-118}$$

During the subsequent viscoelastic distortion, denoting by one and by two primes the elastic and the permanent parts of strain, we have

$$\varepsilon_r', \varepsilon_t', \varepsilon_z' = \frac{1}{2G}\left[(\sigma_r,\sigma_t,\sigma_z) - \frac{\nu}{1 + \nu}(\sigma_r + \sigma_t + \sigma_z)\right],$$

$$\dot{\varepsilon}_r'', \dot{\varepsilon}_t'', \dot{\varepsilon}_z'' = \frac{1}{2\mu}[(\sigma_r,\sigma_t,\sigma_z) - (\tfrac{1}{3})(\sigma_r + \sigma_t + \sigma_z)], \tag{5-119}$$

and the *condition of plane strain* $\varepsilon_z = \varepsilon_z' + \varepsilon_z''$, $\dot{\varepsilon}_z = \dot{\varepsilon}_z' + \dot{\varepsilon}_z''$ prescribes that

$$\dot{\sigma}_z + \frac{1}{t_r}\sigma_z = \nu(\dot{\sigma}_r + \dot{\sigma}_t) + \frac{1}{2t_r}(\sigma_r + \sigma_t), \tag{5-120}$$

where the time constant t_r stands for

$$t_r = \frac{3\mu}{E} = \frac{3\mu}{2(1 + \nu)G} = \frac{3t_s}{2(1 + \nu)}, \tag{5-121}$$

t_s denoting as previously $t_s = \mu/G$.

From Eqs. (5-119) and (5-120) one deduces for the total rates of strain

$$\dot{\varepsilon}_r = \frac{\partial \dot{u}}{\partial r} = \frac{1}{2G}\left[\dot{\sigma}_r - \dot{\sigma}_z + \frac{1}{t_s}(\sigma_r - \sigma_z)\right],$$

$$\dot{\varepsilon}_t = \frac{\dot{u}}{r} = \frac{1}{2G}\left[\dot{\sigma}_t - \dot{\sigma}_z + \frac{1}{t_s}(\sigma_t - \sigma_z)\right]. \tag{5-122}$$

When taken for $r = a$, the last equation supplies, at the bore of the bushing, *the condition of relaxation,* namely, that $(\dot{u})_{r=a} = 0$ for all times t or

$$\left[\dot{\sigma}_t - \dot{\sigma}_z + \frac{1}{t_s}(\sigma_t - \sigma_z)\right]_{r=a} = 0. \tag{5-123}$$

We note that the axial normal stress σ_z, and hence according to Eq. (5-120) also the sum $\sigma_r + \sigma_t$, cannot depend on the coordinate r but only on the time t and that the derivatives $\partial\sigma_z/\partial r$ or $\partial(\sigma_r + \sigma_t)/\partial r$ cancel out wherever they may appear.

The two normal stresses σ_r and σ_t may be evaluated from the condition of compatibility,

$$\frac{\partial(r\dot{\varepsilon}_t)}{\partial r} - \dot{\varepsilon}_r = 0, \tag{5-124}$$

and the condition of equilibrium, using Eqs. (5-122), from

$$\frac{\partial(r\dot{\sigma}_t)}{\partial r} - \dot{\sigma}_r + \frac{1}{t_s}\left[\frac{\partial(r\sigma_t)}{\partial r} - \sigma_r\right] = 0,$$

$$\frac{\partial(r\dot{\sigma}_r)}{\partial r} - \dot{\sigma}_t = 0, \qquad \frac{\partial(r\sigma_r)}{\partial r} - \sigma_t = 0, \tag{5-125}$$

by adding and respectively subtracting, after denoting by

$$s = \sigma_t + \sigma_r,$$
$$w = \sigma_t - \sigma_r, \tag{5-126}$$

giving for s and w the partial differential equations

$$\frac{\partial}{\partial r}\left(\dot{s} + \frac{s}{t_s}\right) = 0,$$

$$\frac{\partial}{\partial r}\, r^2\left(\dot{w} + \frac{w}{t_s}\right) = 0, \tag{5-127}$$

showing that

$$s = 2\psi_1(t), \qquad w = \frac{2}{r^2}\,\psi_2(t) \tag{5-128}$$

with $\psi_1(t)$, $\psi_2(t)$ as two arbitrary functions of the time t or that the normal stresses σ_r, σ_t are found equal to

$$\sigma_r = \psi_1 - \frac{1}{r^2}\,\psi_2,$$

$$\sigma_t = \psi_1 + \frac{1}{r^2}\,\psi_2. \tag{5-129}$$

The boundary conditions $r = a$, $\sigma_r = -p(t) = -p$ and $r = b$, $\sigma_r = 0$ are thus satisfied by

$$\sigma_r = -\frac{pa^2}{b^2 - a^2}\left(\frac{b^2}{r^2} - 1\right),$$

$$\sigma_t = \frac{pa^2}{b^2 - a^2}\left(\frac{b^2}{r^2} + 1\right), \qquad s = \frac{2pa^2}{b^2 - a^2}, \tag{5-130}$$

by functions of r identical with those in the initial elastic state at time $t = 0$, expressed in Eq. (5-118), except in the factor $p = p(t)$.

From the condition of plane strain [Eq. (5-120)] or

$$\dot{\sigma}_z + \frac{1}{t_r}\,\sigma_z = v\dot{s} + \frac{1}{2t_r}\,s, \tag{5-131}$$

after using the value of s just computed, one obtains, after carrying out the integration of the preceding differential equation, the first expression for the axial stress σ_z,

$$\sigma_z = \frac{2a^2}{b^2 - a^2}\left(vp + \frac{1 - 2v}{2t_r}e^{-t/t_r}\int_0^t pe^{t/t_r}\,dt\right),\qquad(5\text{-}132)$$

and from the condition of relaxation [Eq. (5-123)] likewise, by using the initial condition at time $t = 0$ for $r = a$,

$$[\sigma_t]_{\substack{r=a\\t=0}} = [\sigma_{t0}]_{r=a} = \frac{p_0a^2}{b^2 - a^2}\left(\frac{b^2}{a^2} + 1\right),\qquad [\sigma_z]_{\substack{r=a\\t=0}} = \frac{2vp_0a^2}{b^2 - a^2},\qquad(5\text{-}133)$$

the second expression for σ_z:

$$\sigma_z = \frac{a^2}{b^2 - a^2}\left[p\left(\frac{b^2}{a^2} + 1\right) - p_0\left(1 - 2v + \frac{b^2}{a^2}\right)e^{-t/t_s}\right].\qquad(5\text{-}134)$$

By equating both relations [Eqs. (5-132) and (5-134)] just obtained for σ_z, we see that the contact pressure $p(t)$ must satisfy the ordinary differential equation

$$\frac{dp}{dt} + \frac{p}{t_1} = -\frac{p_0e^{-t/t_s}}{\dfrac{1}{t_s} - \dfrac{1}{t_r}},\qquad(5\text{-}135)$$

where the constant t_1 stands for

$$t_1 = \left[1 + (1 - 2v)\frac{a^2}{b^2}\right]t_r,\qquad(5\text{-}135a)$$

supplying finally *the dependence of the contact pressure p on the time t,*

$$p = \frac{p_0b^2}{b^2 + 3a^2}\left\{\left[1 + (1 - 2v)\frac{a^2}{b^2}\right]e^{-t/t_s} + 2(1 + v)\frac{a^2}{b^2}e^{-t/t_1}\right\},\qquad(5\text{-}136)$$

whereas *the radial displacements u* [computed from the second of Eqs. (5-122)] vary with t and r as follows:

$$u = \frac{p_0a^2}{2G(b^2 - a^2)}\left\{\frac{b^2}{r} + (1 - 2v)\left[re^{-t/t_1} + (1 - e^{-t/t_1})\frac{a^2}{r}\right]\right\}.\qquad(5\text{-}137)$$

As time progresses the cylindrical bushing now shrinks inward except at $r = a$. The outer surface $r = b$ contracts by the amount radially:

$$u_{t=0} - u_{t=\infty} = \frac{(1 - 2v)p_0a^2}{2Gb}.\qquad(5\text{-}138)$$

If one takes Poisson's ratio $v = \frac{1}{2}$ in the preceding expressions, they coincide perfectly with those previously established for a fully incompressible material. In this second, exact theory of relaxation of stress in a viscoelastic cylinder of elastically compressible material, we may note [after substituting p taken from Eq. (5-136) in Eq. (5-134)] that the axial normal stress σ_z in the planes $z = \text{const}$ normal to the axis varies with the time t as

$$\sigma_z = \frac{p_0a^2b^2}{(a^2 + 3b^2)(b^2 - a^2)t_r}\left[\frac{3(a^2 + b^2)t_se^{-t/t_1}}{b^2} - 2t_1e^{-t/t_s}\right].\qquad(5\text{-}139)$$

Whereas in a fully incompressible substance, all three components of stress σ_r, σ_t, σ_z decreased with the same factor of decay e^{-t/t_s}, in an elastically compressible substance the pressure p together with both σ_r and σ_t decays along one time function but the axial normal stress σ_z decays along another more complex time function. While at all times t the condition of plane strain $\varepsilon_z = \varepsilon_z' + \varepsilon_z'' = 0$ has been precisely satisfied, in the second substance it does not follow that, at all times, $\varepsilon_z' = 0$ and $\varepsilon_z'' = 0$; on the contrary, one finds an exchange between the elastically and permanently carried parts of axial strain,

$$\varepsilon_z' = -\varepsilon_z'' = \frac{p_0 a^2 b^2 t_1}{G(b^2 + 3a^2)(b^2 - a^2)t_r}(e^{-t/t_1} - e^{-t/t_s}), \qquad (5\text{-}140)$$

and that, concurrently with the process of relaxation of stress in the radial directions, the axial normal stress σ_z relaxes along a time function that must be especially determined by cumbersome analysis. These complications of two incongruent relaxation processes, running simultaneously and influencing each other, are avoided in the first theory postulating $\nu = \frac{1}{2}$. It is hoped that these details may clarify the viscoelastic relaxation in states of plane strain.

Annex: Relaxation under combined stresses may affect the safety of machine parts. The high pressures holding press-fitted or thermally shrunk-on metal disks, wheels, tubes, or hubs tight on shafts may be lost under exposure to elevated temperatures. This has inspired EVAN A. DAVIS[1] to generalize the theory of rotationally symmetric states of plane strain of the viscoelastic substance by postulating, instead of the linear relation between the permanent rates of strain and the stresses, *a power function creep-speed law*, adapted and fitting to the behavior of many ductile metals and expressing the maximum shear stress $\tau_m = (\frac{1}{2})(\sigma_t - \sigma_r) = w/2$ in dependence on the maximum permanent rate of shear $\dot{\gamma}_m''$ by

$$\tau_m = \mu \dot{\gamma}_m'' = c(\dot{\gamma}_m'')^{1/(n+1)}, \qquad (0 < n), \qquad (5\text{-}141)$$

thus supposing for the metal *a variable viscosity* μ:

$$\mu = c^{n+1}\tau_m^{-n} = 2^n c^{n+1} w^{-n}. \qquad (5\text{-}142)$$

Since the total rates of strain, after Eq. (5-115),

$$\dot{\varepsilon}_t = -\dot{\varepsilon}_r = \frac{\dot{u}}{r} = \frac{1}{4}\left(\frac{\dot{w}}{G} + \frac{w}{\mu}\right) = (\frac{1}{2})\dot{\gamma}_m = 0, \qquad (5\text{-}143)$$

vanish everywhere, this now gives for $w = \sigma_t - \sigma_r$ the partial differential equation:

$$\frac{\dot{w}}{G} + \frac{w}{\mu} = \frac{1}{G} \cdot \frac{\partial w}{\partial t} + \frac{w^{n+1}}{2^n c^{n+1}} = 0. \qquad (5\text{-}144)$$

From this one obtains, after integration with the initial condition $t = 0$, $w_0 = \sigma_{t0} - \sigma_{r0} = 2p_0 a^2 b^2/(b^2 - a^2)r^2$, w in the form

$$w = \sigma_t - \sigma_r = \frac{1}{(k_1 t + k_2 r^{2n})^{1/n}} \qquad (5\text{-}145)$$

with the constants

$$k_1 = \frac{Gn}{2^n c^{n+1}}, \qquad k_2 = \left(\frac{b^2 - a^2}{2p_0 a^2 b^2}\right)^n, \qquad (5\text{-}145a)$$

[1] Relaxation of a Cylinder on a Rigid Shaft, J. Appl. Mechanics, March, 1960. See also his paper Relaxation of Stress in a Heat Exchanger Tube of Ideal Material, Trans. ASME, vol. 74, p. 381, 1952, in which he treated this case for a viscoelastic substance by means similar to those used in the first example (postulating $\nu = \frac{1}{2}$) described in the text above.

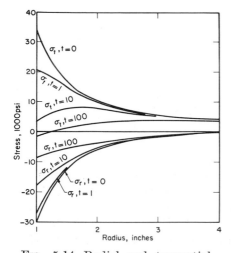

FIG. 5-14. Radial and tangential stresses for $n = 2$.

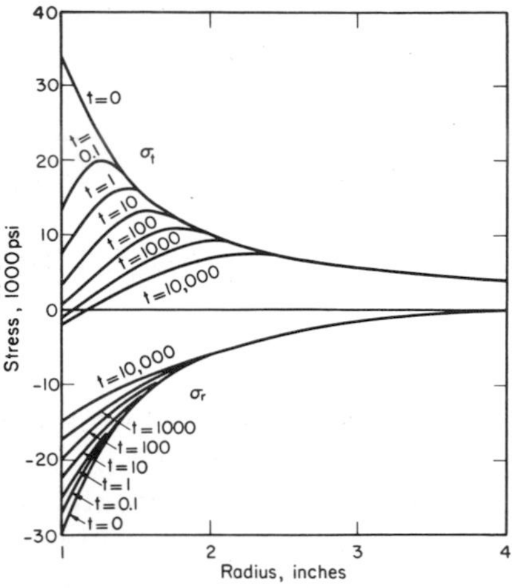

FIG. 5-15. Radial and tangential stresses for $n = 10$.

FIGS. 5-14 and 5-15. Relaxation of stresses σ_r, σ_t in a thick-walled metal cylinder shrunk on a rigid shaft, assuming the power-function creep speed law $\tau_m = c(\dot{\gamma}_m'')^{1/(n+1)}$: for $n = 2$ in Fig. 5-14, for $n = 10$ in Fig. 5-15. (After Evan A. Davis.)

whereas the sum of stresses $s = \sigma_t + \sigma_r$ may be computed (after substituting the just-found value of w in the condition of equilibrium) from

$$\frac{\partial s}{\partial r} = \frac{1}{r^2} \frac{\partial}{\partial r}(r^2 w) \qquad (5\text{-}146)$$

by a graphical integration with respect to r. The two integrals of Eqs. (5-144) and (5-146) thus determine s and w and the distribution of the radial and tangential stress $\sigma_r = (\frac{1}{2})(s - w)$, $\sigma_t = (\frac{1}{2})(s + w)$ in the metal cylinder at any time, allowing one to judge how the contact pressure $(\sigma_r)_{r=a} = -p(t)$ will decrease with the time t.

Figures 5-14 and 5-15 illustrate the distribution of stress σ_r, σ_t in a cylinder having the ratio of outer to inner radius $b/a = 4$ at the inscribed times $t = 0.1$, . . . , 10,000 hr, when the exponent n in the speed law [Eq. (5-142)] was assumed $n = 2$ and $n = 10$, respectively.[1] One sees the instructive fact that, for $n = 2$, relaxation of stress penetrates deeply into the wall of the cylinder (when $n = 0$, the case of viscoelasticity under an invariable viscosity, $\mu = $ const, is obtained with affine families of stress curves), while when $n = 10$ appreciable changes in σ_r, σ_t occur only in the inner third of the cylinder wall. The pressure p exerted through the bore $r = a$ relaxes more rapidly at the beginning and later at a less rapid rate than under uniaxial compression from the same initial values of $p = p_0$ at $t = 0$, which were chosen in both figures equal to $p_0 = 30,000$ lb/in.[2]

[1] In the quoted paper the modulus of rigidity $G = 7.77 \times 10^6$ lb/in.[2] and the viscosity μ, according to Eq. (5-142),

$$\mu = 2^n c^{n+1} w^{-n} = B w^{-n} \text{ [lb in.}^{-2} \text{ hr]}$$

were assumed, using for B:

When $n = 2$: $\qquad\qquad\qquad B = 7.92 \times 10^{16}$,

When $n = 10$: $\qquad\qquad\quad B = 9.80 \times 10^{52}$.

CHAPTER 6

CONCENTRATED PRESSURE

6-1. Expressing Components of Stress and Displacement in Semi-infinite Body in State of Plane Strain Generally by Means of Plane Harmonic Functions. The components of stress and displacement in a semi-infinite body of elastic, compressible or incompressible, or purely viscous material in a state of plane strain loaded either by a distribution of given normal stresses $\sigma_y = f^*(x)$ or of shearing stresses $\tau_{xy} = f^{**}(x)$ in the boundary plane, as the author has shown,[1] may be determined by *solving the first boundary-value problem of a plane harmonic function.* Although for the derivation of the expressions for the stresses we may make use of a stress function $F(x,y)$, we shall see that they may be evaluated in terms of plane harmonic functions without recourse to a biharmonic function $F(x,y)$.

Let us introduce, similarly as is done in the theory of steady, plane potential flow in hydrodynamics,[2] a function $Z(z)$ frequently designated there as "the complex stream function" of the complex variable $z = x + iy$, the real and imaginary parts $\varphi(x,y)$ and $\chi(x,y)$ of which define the orthogonal network of curves along which the velocity potential φ and the stream function χ have constant values:

$$Z(z) = \varphi + i\chi. \tag{6-1}$$

The components U and V in the direction of the x and y axes of the velocity vector $W = U + iV$ may then be constructed or evaluated from the derivative of the complex stream function,

$$\frac{dZ}{dz} = U - iV, \tag{6-2}$$

from the real and imaginary parts U and $-V$ of dZ/dz, the velocity vector being

$$W = U + iV, \tag{6-3}$$

---

[1] Darstellung ebener Spannungszustände mit Hilfe von winkeltreuen Abbildungen, Z. Physik, vol. 41, pp. 48–50, 1927.

[2] L. PRANDTL and O. TIETJENS, "Hydro and Aerodynamics," vol. 1, McGraw-Hill Book Company, Inc., New York, 1933.

the image of vector dZ/dz reflected on the x axis in the complex plane x, iy, and one has

$$U = \frac{\partial \varphi}{\partial x} = \frac{\partial \chi}{\partial y}, \qquad V = \frac{\partial \varphi}{\partial y} = -\frac{\partial \chi}{\partial x},$$

$$\frac{\partial U}{\partial x} = -\frac{\partial V}{\partial y}, \qquad \frac{\partial U}{\partial y} = \frac{\partial V}{\partial x}, \tag{6-4}$$

these potentials satisfying Laplace's equation $\partial^2 \varphi/\partial x^2 + \partial^2 \varphi/\partial y^2 = \Delta \varphi = 0$, etc. Suppose that we also introduce, temporarily, the integral of function $Z(z)$ by letting

$$\int Z \, dz = f(x,y) + ig(x,y). \tag{6-5}$$

We may then easily show that, in order to express the distribution of stress produced by a normal stress $\sigma_y = f^*(x)$ acting along the plane $y = 0$ of a semi-infinite body $y > 0$ while $\tau_{xy} = 0$ on $y = 0$, we may assume an AIRY stress function $F(x,y)$ of the form

$$F = y\varphi - g, \tag{6-6}$$

where φ and g represent the functions that we defined in the preceding equations. Let us express the stresses by affixing subscripts x and y to φ and g to denote the corresponding partial derivatives of φ and g,

$$\begin{aligned} \sigma_x = & \ F_{yy} = & 2\varphi_y - g_{yy} + y\varphi_{yy}, \\ \sigma_y = & \ F_{xx} = & - g_{xx} + y\varphi_{xx}, \\ \tau_{xy} = & -F_{xy} = & -\varphi_x + g_{xy} - y\varphi_{xy}, \end{aligned} \tag{6-7}$$

and let us apply the scheme of differentiations appearing in the group of Eqs. (6-4) with respect to Z and dZ/dz, namely,

$$\begin{aligned} Z &= \varphi + i\chi, & U &= \varphi_x = \chi_y, \\ \frac{dZ}{dz} &= U - iV, & V &= \varphi_y = -\chi_x, \end{aligned} \tag{6-8}$$

and also, in the second group, $\int Z \, dz$ and Z, namely,

$$\begin{aligned} \int Z \, dz &= f + ig, & \varphi &= f_x = g_y, \\ Z &= \varphi + i\chi, & -\chi &= f_y = -g_x. \end{aligned} \tag{6-9}$$

We may then express the derivatives appearing in Eqs. (6-7) as

$$\begin{aligned} g_{yy} &= \varphi_y = V, & 2\varphi_y - g_{yy} &= V, \\ g_{xx} &= -g_{yy} = -V, & -\varphi_x + g_{xy} &= -U + U = 0, \tag{6-10} \\ g_{xy} &= \varphi_x = U, \end{aligned}$$

and the *state of plane strain caused by a normal stress* $\sigma_y = f^*(x)$ acting as an external load on the plane $y = 0$ in the general, simple form

$$\sigma_x = V + y\frac{\partial V}{\partial y},$$

$$\sigma_y = V - y\frac{\partial V}{\partial y}, \tag{6-11}$$

$$\tau_{xy} = -y\frac{\partial V}{\partial x},$$

in which only one, single, plane harmonic function V appears together with its derivatives. We may note, since

$$V = (\tfrac{1}{2})(\sigma_x + \sigma_y) = \frac{3\sigma}{2(1 + \nu)}, \tag{6-12}$$

where σ denotes the mean stress $\sigma = (\tfrac{1}{3})(\sigma_x + \sigma_y + \sigma_z)$ [the axial normal stress σ_z for plane strain $\varepsilon_z = 0$ being equal to $\sigma_z = \nu(\sigma_x + \sigma_y)$], that since on the surface plane $y = 0$, $\sigma_y = f^*(x) = V$, *the problem of finding the state of stress caused by $\sigma_y = f^*(x)$ has thus been reduced to solving the first boundary-value problem for the plane harmonic (potential) function V for the boundary values $y = 0$, $V = \sigma_y = f^*(x)$.* Since on $y = 0$, $\sigma_x = \sigma_y$, on $y = 0$ the mean stress is $\sigma = (\tfrac{2}{3})(1 + \nu)\sigma_y$.

For an incompressible elastic body ($\nu = \tfrac{1}{2}$) the mean stress on the surface plane $y = 0$ is just equal to $\sigma = \sigma_y = f^*(x)$, and the same is true for a purely viscous, incompressible substance: $y = 0$, $\sigma = \sigma_y = f^*(x)$.

We may also compute at once the corresponding components of displacement ξ and η in an elastic, compressible body (we denote them here by ξ, η to avoid confusing the latter with the potential functions U, V) from Eqs. (5-18) and (6-11),

$$\varepsilon_x = \frac{\partial \xi}{\partial x} = \frac{1}{2G}\left[(1 - 2\nu)V + y\frac{\partial V}{\partial y}\right],$$

$$\varepsilon_y = \frac{\partial \eta}{\partial y} = \frac{1}{2G}\left[(1 - 2\nu)V - y\frac{\partial V}{\partial y}\right], \tag{6-13}$$

and may easily verify, after making use of Eqs. (6-8) and (6-9) and partial integration, that the displacements ξ and η are expressed by

$$\xi = -\frac{1}{2G}\left[(1 - 2\nu)\chi + y\frac{\partial \chi}{\partial y}\right] + c_1 + c_3 y,$$

$$\eta = \frac{1}{2G}\left[2(1 - \nu)\varphi - y\frac{\partial \varphi}{\partial y}\right] + c_2 - c_3 x, \tag{6-14}$$

these expressions identically satisfying also the third stress-strain relation $\tau_{xy} = G\gamma_{xy}$.

For an incompressible elastic solid ($v = \frac{1}{2}$), these last relations simplify to

$$\xi = -\frac{1}{2G}\, y\, \frac{\partial \varphi}{\partial x} = -\frac{1}{2G}\, yU,$$

$$\eta = \frac{1}{2G}\left(\varphi - y\, \frac{\partial \varphi}{\partial x}\right) = \frac{1}{2G}\,(\varphi - yV). \tag{6-15}$$

For a viscous substance we obtain the same relations for $\dot{\xi}$ and $\dot{\eta}$, after replacing G by μ (having omitted writing the rigid-body terms c_1, $c_2, \ldots$) and showing that, when $v = \frac{1}{2}$, ξ and η depend essentially on the single, potential function φ (real part of Z).

In a similar way, one proves that, if *a given distribution of shearing stresses* $\tau_{xy} = f^{**}(x)$ *acts on the surface* $y = 0$, while $\sigma_y = 0$ on $y = 0$, one has to assume for the stress function $F(x,y)$,

$$F = y\varphi, \tag{6-16}$$

that the stresses caused by $\tau_{xy} = f^{**}(x)$ are expressed by

$$\underline{\underline{\sigma_x = \quad 2V + y\, \frac{\partial V}{\partial y}}},$$

$$\underline{\underline{\sigma_y = \qquad -\, y\, \frac{\partial V}{\partial y}}}, \tag{6-17}$$

$$\underline{\underline{\tau_{xy} = -U - y\, \frac{\partial V}{\partial x}}},$$

and that the displacements are expressed by

$$\xi = -\frac{1}{2G}\left[2(1-v)\chi + y\, \frac{\partial \chi}{\partial y}\right] + c_1 + c_3 y,$$

$$\eta = \frac{1}{2G}\left[(1-2v)\varphi - y\, \frac{\partial \varphi}{\partial y}\right] + c_2 - c_3 x. \tag{6-18}$$

In the case of Eqs. (6-17) the function U solves the boundary-value problem for the shearing stresses $y = 0$, $\tau_{xy} = f^{**}(x) = -U$, but the state of stress depends now on both conjugate potentials U and V. Having shown in Eq. (5-31) that the rotation of vector $W = U + iV$, $\omega = (\frac{1}{2})(\partial \eta/\partial x - \partial \xi/\partial y)$, and $-3(1-v)\sigma/E$ represent the real and imaginary parts of a function,

$$H(z) = \omega - i\, \frac{3(1-v)\sigma}{E} = \omega - i\, \frac{3(1-v)\sigma}{2(1+v)G},$$

we see that

$$\frac{GH(z)}{1-v} = \frac{G\omega}{1-v} - i\, \frac{3\sigma}{2(1+v)} = U - iV = \frac{dZ}{dz}.$$

or that the two potential functions U and V used for expressing the states of stress in Eqs. (6-11) and (6-17) represent

$$U = \frac{G\omega}{1 - \nu}, \qquad V = \frac{3\sigma}{2(1 + \nu)}, \qquad (6\text{-}19)$$

U being proportional to the rotation ω and V to the mean stress σ in a state of plane strain. *For incompressible, elastic material* ($\nu = \frac{1}{2}$),

$$U = 2G\omega = G\left(\frac{\partial \eta}{\partial x} - \frac{\partial \xi}{\partial y}\right), \qquad V = \sigma = (\tfrac{1}{2})(\sigma_x + \sigma_y),$$

and *for a viscous substance,*

$$U = 2\mu\dot{\omega} = \mu\left(\frac{\partial \dot{\eta}}{\partial x} - \frac{\partial \dot{\xi}}{\partial y}\right), \qquad V = \sigma = (\tfrac{1}{2})(\sigma_x + \sigma_y),$$

the curves $V = \text{const}$ representing the isobars $\sigma = \text{const}$. We may add that the solution of the plane problem expressed in Sec. 5-4D in terms of Fourier integrals conforms precisely to the scheme of Eqs. (6-11) and (6-17).

In summing up, we can state that solving the problem of plane strain in a semi-infinite elastic or viscous body $y > 0$ for prescribed values of the normal stresses $\sigma_y = f^*(x)$ or of the shearing stresses $\tau_{xy} = f^{**}(x)$ along $y = 0$ amounts to constructing the field of the plane, conjugate harmonic functions:

$$V = \frac{3\sigma}{2(1 + \nu)} \qquad \text{or} \qquad U = \frac{G\omega}{1 - \nu}, \qquad (6\text{-}19a)$$

respectively, for their first boundary-value problems. This is facilitated and may be done by utilizing the methods of conformal mapping of one on another region for deriving the expressions[1] for U and V.

EXAMPLE 1. *One side of body loaded by uniform pressure.* Using polar coordinates r, α, the boundary conditions on the plane $y = 0$, $\alpha = 0$, $\sigma_t = \tau_{rt} = 0$ and $\alpha = \pi$, $\sigma_t = -p = \text{const}$, $\tau_{rt} = 0$ (Fig. 6-1) may be satisfied by assuming in Eq. (6-2)

$$\frac{dZ}{dz} = U - iV = C \ln z = C(\ln r + i\alpha), \qquad (6\text{-}20)$$

defining $U = C \ln r, \qquad V = -C\alpha, \qquad (6\text{-}21)$

where the real constant C is determined from the boundary condition using the expression for σ_y of Eqs. (6-11) that for $\alpha = \pi$, $\sigma_y = V = -C\pi = -p$, $C = p/\pi$.

---

[1] See also S. D. CAROTHER, Proc. Roy. Soc. (London), Ser. A, vol. 97, p. 110, 1920; A. E. H. LOVE, "Mathematical Theory of Elasticity," 2d ed., p. 201, Cambridge University Press, London, 1906; H. LAMB, "Hydrodynamics," 6th ed., p. 66, Dover Publications, New York, 1945; and L. PRANDTL and O. TIETJENS, page 210 (*loc. cit.*).

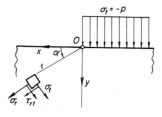

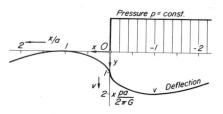

FIG. 6-1

FIG. 6-1a. Distortion of plane surface $y = 0$ of a semi-infinite elastic body $(y > 0)$ near the edge of a uniformly distributed pressure $p = $ const, acting on the side $x < 0$ on the plane $y = 0$.

The components of stress σ_x, σ_y, τ_{xy} are evaluated from Eqs. (6-11)[1]:

$$\sigma_x = -\frac{p}{2\pi}\left(2\alpha + \frac{2xy}{r^2}\right),$$

$$\sigma_y = -\frac{p}{2\pi}\left(2\alpha - \frac{2xy}{r^2}\right), \tag{6-22}$$

$$\tau_{xy} = -\frac{py^2}{\pi r^2}$$

or

$$\sigma_x = -\frac{p}{2\pi}(2\alpha + \sin 2\alpha),$$

$$\sigma_y = -\frac{p}{2\pi}(2\alpha - \sin 2\alpha), \tag{6-23}$$

$$\tau_{xy} = -\frac{p}{2\pi}(1 - \cos 2\alpha),$$

showing that the boundary conditions are satisfied. The components of displacement ξ, η in *an incompressible elastic solid* $(\nu = \frac{1}{2})$ may be computed from Eqs. (6-15):

$$\xi = -\frac{p}{2\pi G}y(\ln r + 1) + C_0 y + C_1,$$

$$\eta = \frac{p}{2\pi G}x\ln r \quad\quad - C_0 x + C_2. \tag{6-24}$$

If we specify, for example, that in a distant point $y = 0$, $x = a$ (on the unloaded side of the body) $\eta = 0$ and $\partial\eta/\partial x = 0$, we obtain the displacements

$$\xi = -\frac{p}{2\pi G}y\ln\frac{r}{a},$$

$$\eta = \frac{p}{2\pi G}\left[x\ln\left(\frac{r}{a}\right) - x + a\right]. \tag{6-25}$$

An elastic ground is thus depressed in the manner reproduced in Fig. 6-1a, the profile under the edge of the load $p = $ const becoming infinitely steep over a

[1] In differentiating the polar coordinates $r^2 = x^2 + y^2$, $\alpha = \arctan(y/x)$ with respect to x and y, we have $\partial r/\partial x = x/r$, $\partial r/\partial y = y/r$, $\partial\alpha/\partial x = -y/r^2$, $\partial\alpha/\partial y = x/r^2$.

very short length and the deflection at point $O(r = 0)$ becoming $\eta = pa/2\pi G$. The preceding formulas are valid for an incompressible elastic solid and may be applied as well to *a viscous ground* of incompressible material after replacing G by μ and inserting the dot in $\dot{\xi}$ and $\dot{\eta}$ to express the velocity components under which the ground will yield.

This state of stress is also derivable from the stress function

$$F = \frac{pr^2}{4\pi} (\sin 2\alpha - 2\alpha) \qquad (6\text{-}26)$$

and is expressed in terms of polar coordinates by the stress components σ_r, σ_t, and τ_{rt}:

$$\sigma_r = -\frac{p}{2\pi} (2\alpha + \sin 2\alpha),$$

$$\sigma_t = -\frac{p}{2\pi} (2\alpha - \sin 2\alpha), \qquad (6\text{-}27)$$

$$\tau_{rt} = \frac{p}{2\pi} (1 - \cos 2\alpha).$$

For the sake of completeness, we list the formulas expressing in polar coordinates r, α the components of displacement u, v for a *compressible* elastic solid having a Poisson's ratio ν:

$$u = -\frac{pr}{2\pi G} [(\tfrac{1}{2}) \sin 2\alpha + (1 - 2\nu)\alpha] + c_1 \cos \alpha + c_2 \sin \alpha,$$

$$\qquad (6\text{-}28)$$

$$v = \frac{pr}{2\pi G} [-(\tfrac{1}{2}) \sin 2\alpha + 2(1 - \nu) \ln r] - c_1 \sin \alpha + c_2 \cos \alpha + c_3 r.$$

We may note that the maximum shearing stress $\tau_{\max}$ for this state of stress,

$$\tau_{\max} = \sqrt{\frac{(\sigma_x - \sigma_y)^2}{4} + \tau_{xy}^2} = \frac{p}{\pi} \sin \alpha, \qquad (6\text{-}29)$$

becomes constant on the pencil of rays $\alpha = \text{const}$, assuming its greatest value

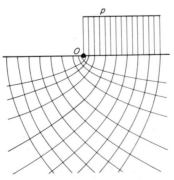

Fig. 6-2. Trajectories of principal stress.

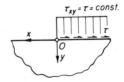

Fig. 6-3

on the ray $\alpha = \pi/2$; furthermore, if β denotes the angles under which the trajectories of principal stress intersect the pencil of rays $\alpha = $ const, since for them

$$\tan 2\beta = \frac{2\tau_{rt}}{\sigma_r - \sigma_t} = \frac{\cos 2\alpha - 1}{\sin 2\alpha} = -\tan \alpha,$$

β must be

$$\beta = -\frac{\alpha}{2} \quad \text{and} \quad \beta = \frac{\pi - \alpha}{2}.$$

This property prevails in a family of confocal orthogonal parabolas having the origin O for their common focus. The principal stress trajectories are a family of orthogonal parabolas (Fig. 6-2).

EXAMPLE 2. *Uniform shearing stress* $\tau_{xy} = \tau = $ const *on one side of body* (Fig. 6-3). We take

$$\frac{dZ}{dz} = U - iV = iC \ln z,$$

$$U = -C\alpha, \qquad V = -C \ln r, \qquad C = \frac{\tau}{\pi},$$

(6-30)

and, using these values, compute from Eqs. (6-17) the expressions for the stresses:

$$\sigma_x = -\frac{\tau}{\pi}\left[2 \ln r + \left(\frac{y}{r}\right)^2\right],$$

$$\sigma_y = \frac{\tau}{\pi}\left(\frac{y}{r}\right)^2,$$

(6-31)

$$\tau_{xy} = \frac{\tau}{\pi}\left(\alpha + \frac{xy}{r^2}\right),$$

which may also be deduced from a stress function

$$F = y\varphi = -\frac{\tau}{\pi}[y^2(\ln r - 1) + xy\alpha].$$

(6-32)

6-2. Parallel Strip in Plane Surface of a Body Loaded by Concentrated Uniform Pressure $p =$ const.

Let a uniform compression stress $\sigma_y = -p$ act on the right side of a point O_1 of a semi-infinite body, and superpose on this load a uniform tensile stress $\sigma_y = p$ to the right of a point O_2 (Fig. 6-4). The resulting load is then a uniform pressure $\sigma_y = -p = $ const, distributed over a strip of the width $O_1O_2 = 2c$, and one obtains, by superposing the two corresponding stress functions, with reference to Eq. (6-26),

$$F = -\frac{p}{2\pi}(r_1^2\alpha_1 - r_2^2\alpha_2),$$

(6-33)

where r_1, α_1 and r_2, α_2 denote the polar

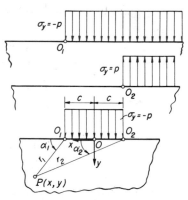

FIG. 6-4. By superposing the two distributions of load shown, the case of loading by a uniform pressure $p = $ const over a parallel strip $-c < x < c$ of the width $O_1O_2 = 2c$ is obtained.

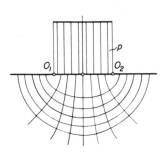

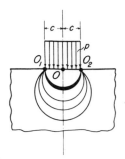

FIG. 6-5. Trajectories of principal stress.

FIG. 6-6. The maximum shear-
ing stress $\tau_{\max}$ is constant on
the circles passing through O_1
and O_2.

coordinates of a point P with respect to the origins O_1 and O_2, respectively.[1] The corresponding state of stress, using Eqs. (6-23), is expressed by

$$\sigma_x = -\frac{p}{2\pi}\,[2(\alpha_1 - \alpha_2) + \sin 2\alpha_1 - \sin 2\alpha_2],$$

$$\sigma_y = -\frac{p}{2\pi}\,[2(\alpha_1 - \alpha_2) - \sin 2\alpha_1 + \sin 2\alpha_2], \qquad (6\text{-}34)$$

$$\tau_{xy} = \frac{p}{2\pi}\,(\cos 2\alpha_1 - \cos 2\alpha_2).$$

The trajectories of principal stress for this state consist of confocal
orthogonal ellipses and hyperbolas with the points O_1 and O_2 as foci
(Fig. 6-5).[2]

[1] The terms containing $r_1{}^2 \sin 2\alpha_1 = 2x_1y_1$, $r_2{}^2 \sin 2\alpha_2 = 2x_2y_2$ cancel out in the
expression for F since they represent two equal states of pure shear of opposite
signs.

[2] With the help of the preceding expressions of the stresses at a point $P(x,y)$,
the angle of inclination φ of the trajectories with the x axis is found from

$$\tan 2\varphi = \frac{2\tau_{xy}}{\sigma_x - \sigma_y} = -\frac{\cos 2\alpha_1 - \cos 2\alpha_2}{\sin 2\alpha_1 - \sin 2\alpha_2} = \tan (\alpha_1 + \alpha_2)$$

to be $$\varphi = (\tfrac{1}{2})(\alpha_1 + \alpha_2), \qquad (\tfrac{1}{2})(\pi + \alpha_1 + \alpha_2),$$

which is a well-known property of an ellipse or hyperbola passing through point
P having O_1 and O_2 as the foci (the tangent and the normal of an ellipse or
hyperbola bisect the angles of the radii vectors O_1P and O_2P). We may add that
in this, as well as in the first example, the pattern of the principal stress trajectories coincides with the patterns of the stream and equipotential lines of a
plane flow of a perfect fluid passing through an orifice in a wall from one chamber
to an adjoining one or around a wall separating both chambers.

It is interesting to note that the maximum shearing stress τ_{max} computed with the help of Eqs. (6-34),

$$\tau_{max} = \sqrt{\frac{(\sigma_x - \sigma_y)^2}{4} + \tau_{xy}^2} = \frac{p}{\pi} \sin{(\alpha_1 - \alpha_2)}, \qquad (6\text{-}35)$$

has constant values on the circles drawn through the points O_1 and O_2 having their centers on the symmetry axis $x = 0$. The greatest value τ_{max} can take, namely, $\tau_{max} = p/\pi$, occurs on the semicircle having O for its center.

In a material which is comparatively weak in shear, the first shear fractures would be expected to occur under a uniform pressure p of sufficient magnitude in the crescent-shaped segment indicated in Fig. 6-6 along this semicircle of radius equal to c. The longitudinal cross section of a test specimen of an artificially darkened paraffin, which the author many years ago subjected to concentrated pressure (of a cylindrical punch) which was rapidly increased, very clearly disclosed the crescent-shaped region of destroyed structure which can be seen as a bright, semicircular band in the longitudinal section of the specimen reproduced in Fig. 6-7. At the author's suggestion, G. MESMER was able to produce *the circular isochromatics* in a photoelastic test for the two-dimensional case which was just discussed, by applying certain precautions in preparing a special stamp of celluloid, the sharp corners of which were carefully rounded off by grinding. The isochromatic lines thus obtained experimentally (see Fig. 6-8) were found to be very nearly circles passing through the corners of the punch, as predicted by Eq. (6-35).[1]

[1] Compare, in contrast to Fig. 6-8, the pattern of the isochromatic lines reproduced in Fig. 6-13, obtained under the impression of a rigid stamp having sharp corners.

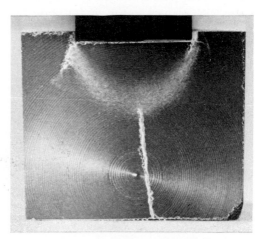

FIG. 6-7. Longitudinal section through a paraffin specimen compressed rapidly by a cylindrical punch. Note the bright, crescent-shaped region of destroyed structure.

FIG. 6-8. The isochromatics are circles passing through the corners of the punch if the contact surface of the latter has been properly fitted to produce a uniformly distributed pressure (case of a plane strain).

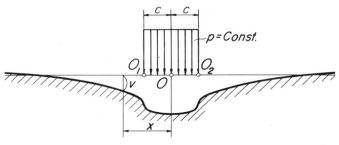

FIG. 6-9. Depression caused in surface of semi-infinite elastic or viscous body under a concentrated pressure $p =$ const in case of a plane strain.

By superposing the expressions [Eqs. (6-28)] for the two corresponding systems of displacement components, one sees that the surface of the body is depressed under the load $2pc$ according to the symmetric function with respect to the center point O of the loaded strip,

$$v = \frac{(1 - \nu)p}{\pi G} \left[(x - c) \ln (x - c)^2 - (x + c) \ln (x + c)^2 \right], \qquad (6\text{-}36)$$

apart from the rigid-body-motion terms. The distortion is seen in Fig. 6-9 and is reminiscent of the trace of an old carriage wheel in soft mud.

6-3. Impression of Rigid, Plane Plate on One Side of a Body. Solutions by M. Sadowsky for Rigid Plate of Finite Width and by H. Hertz for Contact of Parallel Cylinders. If one evaluates the expressions for the stresses and velocity components in polar coordinates for the stress function

$$F = r^n [a_n \sin n\alpha + b_n \sin (n - 2)\alpha] \qquad (6\text{-}37)$$

and the stream function ψ in incompressible viscous material associated with it,[1]

$$\psi = \frac{r^n}{2\mu} [a_n \cos n\alpha + b_n \cos (n - 2)\alpha] \qquad (6\text{-}38)$$

(a_n, b_n, n are constants), one sees that one may impose on the side $\alpha = \pi$ of the body the three conditions

$$u = \frac{\partial \psi}{r \, \partial \alpha} = 0, \qquad v = -\frac{\partial \psi}{\partial r} = 0, \qquad \tau_{rt} = -\frac{\partial}{\partial r}\left(\frac{\partial F}{r \, \partial \alpha}\right) = 0,$$

which give for

$$\begin{aligned} u &= 0, & [na_n + (n - 2)b_n] \sin n\pi &= 0, \\ v &= 0, & (a_n + b_n) \cos n\pi &= 0, & (6\text{-}39) \\ \tau_{rt} &= 0, & [na_n + (n - 2)b_n] \cos n\pi &= 0. \end{aligned}$$

Letting $\cos n\pi = 0$, n equal to one-half of an odd number, and

$$b_n = -\frac{na_n}{n - 2}, \qquad (6\text{-}39a)$$

they may be satisfied, and this secures also, on $\alpha = 0$, $\tau_{rt} = 0$. Thus, while the body side $\alpha = 0$ retains a stress-free surface ($\sigma_t = \tau_{rt} = 0$), the right side adheres smoothly to a plane: $\alpha = \pi$, $u = v = 0$; furthermore, there $\tau_{rt} = 0$ also vanishes. An infinite number of such states exists, but only one of them does not involve a true singularity around the origin when $n < \frac{3}{2}$, while, when $n > \frac{5}{2}$, the stresses increase with r, which is of little interest.

Considering $n = \frac{3}{2}$, we obtain $b_n = 3a_n$, $\sin (n - 2)\alpha = -\sin (\alpha/2)$, and after writing c for a_n, we have the stress function

$$F = cr^{\frac{3}{2}}\left(\sin \frac{3\alpha}{2} - 3 \sin \frac{\alpha}{2}\right) \qquad (6\text{-}40)$$

with the associated stream function ψ,

$$2\mu\psi = cr^{\frac{3}{2}}\left(\cos \frac{3\alpha}{2} + 3 \cos \frac{\alpha}{2}\right); \qquad (6\text{-}41)$$

the velocity components

$$u = -\frac{3cr^{\frac{1}{2}}}{4\mu}\left(\sin \frac{3\alpha}{2} + \sin \frac{\alpha}{2}\right),$$

$$v = -\frac{3cr^{\frac{1}{2}}}{4\mu}\left(\cos \frac{3\alpha}{2} + 3 \cos \frac{\alpha}{2}\right); \qquad (6\text{-}42)$$

[1] ψ may be computed from F by integrating:

$$4\mu \frac{\partial u}{\partial r} = \sigma_r - \sigma_t$$

or

$$4\mu \frac{\partial}{\partial r}\left(\frac{\partial \psi}{r \, \partial \alpha}\right) = \frac{1}{r}\frac{\partial F}{\partial r} + \frac{1}{r^2}\frac{\partial^2 F}{\partial \alpha^2} - \frac{\partial^2 F}{\partial r^2}.$$

and the components of stress

$$\sigma_r = -(\tfrac{3}{4})cr^{-\frac{1}{2}}\left(\sin\frac{3\alpha}{2} + 5\sin\frac{\alpha}{2}\right),$$

$$\sigma_t = -(\tfrac{3}{4})cr^{-\frac{1}{2}}\left(-\sin\frac{3\alpha}{2} + 3\sin\frac{\alpha}{2}\right), \qquad (6\text{-}43)$$

$$\tau_{rt} = -(\tfrac{3}{4})cr^{-\frac{1}{2}}\left(\cos\frac{3\alpha}{2} - \cos\frac{\alpha}{2}\right).$$

This shows that on the side remaining a plane, for $\alpha = \pi$, the normal stress $\sigma_t = -3cr^{-\frac{1}{2}}$ increases indefinitely toward its edge $r = 0$ and that, if this should represent a compression stress, we may, for example, prescribe, for $r = a$, $\sigma_t = -3ca^{-\frac{1}{2}} = -p$, so that the constant $c = (\tfrac{1}{3})pa^{\frac{1}{2}}$ is positive, while on the unloaded, free side, for $\alpha = 0$, $u = 0$, $v = -3cr^{\frac{1}{2}}/\mu$, the surface of the body becomes convex, ending with a vertical slope at the edge of the plate. After adding a vertical velocity, a point A ($r = x = a, y = 0$) may be taken at rest, and for the distorted profile (Fig. 6-10),

$$x > 0, \qquad v = \frac{3c}{\mu}(\sqrt{a} - \sqrt{x}), \qquad (6\text{-}44)$$

Equations (6-42) and (6-43) represent *the distribution of stress near the edge of a rigid plate pressed down on an incompressible solid.* The trajectories of principal stress are reproduced in Fig. 6-11. There is no tendency for slip of the material relative to the plate.

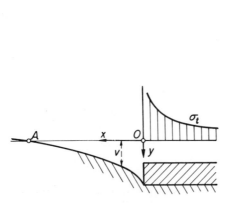

FIG. 6-10. Impression of a rigid plate.

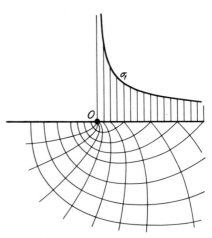

FIG. 6-11. Trajectories of principal stress under impression of a rigid stamp.

One finds similarly that the stress and stream functions

$$F_1 = c_1 r^{3/2}\left(\cos\frac{3\alpha}{2} - \cos\frac{\alpha}{2}\right),$$

$$2\mu\psi_1 = -c_1 r^{3/2}\left(\sin\frac{3\alpha}{2} + \sin\frac{\alpha}{2}\right),$$

(6-45)

define a state of stress,

$$\sigma_r = -(\tfrac{1}{4})c_1 r^{-1/2}\left(3\cos\frac{3\alpha}{2} + 5\cos\frac{\alpha}{2}\right),$$

$$\sigma_t = (\tfrac{1}{4})c_1 r^{-1/2}\left(3\cos\frac{3\alpha}{2} - 3\cos\frac{\alpha}{2}\right),$$

$$\tau_{rt} = (\tfrac{1}{4})c_1 r^{-1/2}\left(3\sin\frac{3\alpha}{2} - \sin\frac{\alpha}{2}\right),$$

(6-46)

and the velocities,

$$u_1 = -\frac{c_1 r^{1/2}}{4\mu}\left(3\cos\frac{3\alpha}{2} + \cos\frac{\alpha}{2}\right),$$

$$v_1 = -\frac{3c_1 r^{1/2}}{4\mu}\left(\sin\frac{3\alpha}{2} + \sin\frac{\alpha}{2}\right),$$

(6-47)

satisfying the boundary conditions $\alpha = 0$, $\sigma_t = \tau_{rt} = 0$ and $\alpha = \pi$, $u = v = 0$, $\sigma_t = 0$, $\tau_{rt} = -c_1 r^{-1/2}$. One sees that this represents *the distribution of pure shearing stresses exerted on the right side* $(x < 0, \alpha = \pi)$ *of a semi-infinite body* $\tau_{rt} = -c_1 r^{-1/2}$ *through a surface remaining a plane*, while the left side of the body $(x > 0, \alpha = 0)$ is free. This state of stress would not be disturbed by placing a rigid, plane plate above the right side of the body which would smoothly touch it, since, on this side of the body, both u and v vanish. Furthermore, suppose now, while we press the rigid plate down and produce the normal stress distribution $\sigma_t = -3cr^{-1/2}$ formerly described in Eqs. (6-42) and (6-43), that we start to move the plate with a small velocity $u = -u_0$ in the direction of the negative x axis above the body. If a Coulomb friction acts in the contact plane, in addition to the normal stresses $\sigma_t = -3cr^{-1/2}$, shearing stresses $\tau_{rt} = -\mu_0\sigma_t = 3\mu_0 cr^{-1/2}$ are produced ($\mu_0 =$ coefficient of solid friction). But, this system is exactly the distribution of shearing stresses $\tau_{rt} = -c_1 r^{-1/2}$ that we have just determined from F_1. We see, therefore, that, if we make $c_1 = -3\mu_0 c$, by superposing both states of stress derived from F and from F_1, we have determined *the exact state of stress in an incompressible, semi-infinite body on which a perfectly rigid, plane plate has been embedded under pressure while it is slowly pushed forward in the negative x direction against the resistance of Coulomb friction of the body*. We may note that, whereas the free, left side of the body $(\alpha = 0)$ sustains from the part of the stream function ψ the velocities $u = 0$, $v = -3cr^{1/2}$, the second part ψ_1 (due to the frictional forces) contributes the velocities $u_1 = -c_1 r^{1/2}/\mu = 3(\mu_0/\mu)cr^{1/2} = -\mu_0 v$ and $v_1 = 0$.

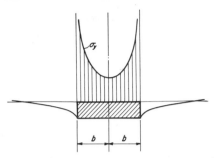

FIG. 6-12. Impression of rigid stamp of finite width.

We see that the action of the frictional forces extends the *free* side of the body with horizontal velocities equal to μ_0 times the vertical velocities with which the free surface bulges out laterally.

M. SADOWSKY[1] determined the distribution of pressure under *a rigid plate of finite width 2b* under plane strain for an elastic material. Assuming a plate of infinite length in the z direction, having the edges $x = \pm b$ (Fig. 6-12), he found that the normal stress σ_y under the plate is distributed according to the function

$$-b < x < b, \qquad \sigma_y = -\frac{Q}{\pi\sqrt{b^2 - x^2}}, \qquad (6\text{-}48)$$

where Q denotes the normal force in pounds per inch exerted by the plate in the area $2b \times 1$. The normal pressure σ_y was found to be inversely proportional to the ordinates of a circle $y = \sqrt{b^2 - x^2}$ of radius b. In order to derive Eq. (6-48), he expressed the displacement components ξ and η produced by a differential of a normal force $q(t)\, dt$, located at an arbitrary point t, $y = 0$ of the straight edge $y = 0$ of an elastic body. Using Eqs. (5-72) of Sec. 5-4C(1), for incompressible material, they are

$$d\xi = \frac{q(t)\, dt\, (x - t)y}{2\pi G[(x - t)^2 + y^2]},$$

$$d\eta = -\frac{q(t)\, dt}{2\pi G}\left[\ln\sqrt{(x - t)^2 + y^2} + \frac{(x - t)^2}{(x - t)^2 + y^2}\right].$$

Since under a rigid plate of width $2b$, $-b < t < b$, $\eta = \eta_0 = \text{const}$, after assuming $y = 0$ and integrating the latter expression of $d\eta$ with respect to t between the limits $-b$ and b, he was led to *the integral equation* for the determination of the unknown distribution of pressure $q(t)$ exerted by the plate,

$$\eta = -\frac{1}{2\pi G}\int_{t=-b}^{t=b} q(t)(\ln|x - t| + 1)\, dt = \eta_0 = \text{const},$$

which, according to Sadowsky, is solved by

$$b < x < b, \qquad q(x) = \frac{Q}{\pi\sqrt{b^2 - x^2}} = -\sigma_y,$$

[1] Zweidimensionale Probleme der Elastizitätstheorie, Z. angew. Math. u. Mech., vol. 8, p. 107, 1928. In this paper, Sadowsky treated a number of cases of concentrated pressure in two- and three-dimensional states of stress.

thus giving Eq. (6-48).   While he has not evaluated in detail the state
of stress, requiring, as one sees, partial integrations with respect to t of
the expressions for the stresses σ_x, σ_y, τ_{xy}, we may easily show that our
formulas for the stresses σ_r, σ_t, τ_{rt} [Eq. (6-43)] have determined completely the state of stress near one of the edges of the finite pressure
plate in its vicinity, which must correspond to Sadowsky's case.   If we
denote by r the distance of a point, say from the left corner of the pressure plate in its contact area, so that $r = b - x$, the ordinate y of the
circle $x^2 + y^2 = b^2$, when r is small compared with b, is

$$y^2 = b^2 - x^2 = b^2 - (b - r)^2 = \sim 2br,$$
$$y = \sqrt{2br},$$

and from Sadowsky's equation (6-48) the pressure is

$$\sigma_y = -\frac{Q}{\pi y} = -\frac{Q}{\pi\sqrt{2br}},$$

while we found the pressure distribution in Eqs. (6-43) for $\alpha = \pi$

$$\sigma_t = -3cr^{-\frac{1}{2}} = -3\frac{pa^{\frac{1}{2}}}{3}r^{-\frac{1}{2}} = -p \cdot \sqrt{\frac{a}{r}}, \qquad (6\text{-}49)$$

and both coincide by letting $p = Q/\pi\sqrt{2ab}$.

It is instructive to compare the pattern of the isochromatic lines
which have been observed in *a photoelastic test by G. Mesmer under the
impression of a rigid metal punch* with the pattern of the bicentric
family of circles corresponding to the case of a uniform pressure $p =$
const (Fig. 6-8).   The curves τ_{max} = const are reproduced in Fig. 6-13
for the rigid stamp with a plane surface and sharp corners, corresponding to the case treated by Sadowsky.   One sees clearly that the

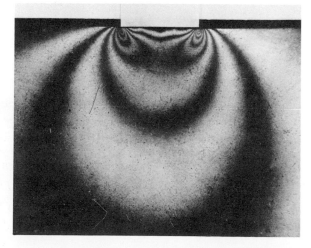

FIG. 6-13. Isochromatic
curves under the pres-
sure zone of a rigid
punch having a plane
contact surface with
sharp corners indicating
concentration of pres-
sure at the corners (case
of plane strain). (*After
G. Mesmer.*)

isochromatics in the vicinity of the contact plane are not circles; further-more, new, loop-shaped fringes of higher order radiate out from both sharp corners, thus confirming that the stresses must increase consider-ably toward the corners of the punch, where, according to Eqs. (6-43) and (6-48), σ_x and σ_y should increase indefinitely.

Let us consider a further example by taking

$$n = \tfrac{5}{2}, \qquad na_n + (n-2)b_n = 0$$

in Eqs. (6-39) so that $b_n = -5a_n$. This gives the stress function

$$F = cr^{\frac{5}{2}}\left(\sin\frac{5\alpha}{2} - 5\sin\frac{\alpha}{2}\right), \qquad (6\text{-}50)$$

the stream function

$$2\mu\psi = cr^{\frac{5}{2}}\left(\cos\frac{5\alpha}{2} - 5\cos\frac{\alpha}{2}\right), \qquad (6\text{-}51)$$

the velocities

$$u = -\frac{5cr^{\frac{3}{2}}}{4\mu}\left(\sin\frac{5\alpha}{2} - \sin\frac{\alpha}{2}\right),$$

$$v = -\frac{5cr^{\frac{3}{2}}}{4\mu}\left(\cos\frac{5\alpha}{2} - 5\cos\frac{\alpha}{2}\right), \qquad (6\text{-}52)$$

and the stresses

$$\sigma_r = -(\tfrac{15}{4})cr^{\frac{1}{2}}\left(\sin\frac{5\alpha}{2} + 3\sin\frac{\alpha}{2}\right),$$

$$\sigma_t = (\tfrac{15}{4})cr^{\frac{1}{2}}\left(\sin\frac{5\alpha}{2} - 5\sin\frac{\alpha}{2}\right), \qquad (6\text{-}53)$$

$$\tau_{rt} = -(\tfrac{15}{4})cr^{\frac{1}{2}}\left(\cos\frac{5\alpha}{2} - \cos\frac{\alpha}{2}\right),$$

satisfying the boundary values

$$\alpha = 0, \qquad \sigma_t = \tau_{rt} = 0, \qquad u = 0, \qquad v = \frac{5}{\mu}cr^{\frac{3}{2}},$$

$$\alpha = \pi, \qquad \sigma_t = -15cr^{\frac{1}{2}}, \qquad \tau_{rt} = 0, \qquad u = v = 0. \qquad (6\text{-}54)$$

If c is a positive constant, this gives on the right side $\alpha = \pi$ of a semi-infinite body *a normal pressure which increases as the ordinates of a parabola* with the distance r from the edge of the loaded area (Fig. 6-14, in which the trajectories of principal stress have also been traced) and a distribution of stress[1] as reproduced in Fig. 6-15. At the edge of the plate *the free surface of the body touches smoothly the compression plane.*

[1] The stresses σ_r, σ_t, τ_{rt} are plotted in Fig. 6-15 in a polar diagram with their positive values radially inward (except for τ_{rt}) to be measured from the circle shown in the figure, the radius of which was taken as the unit of length.

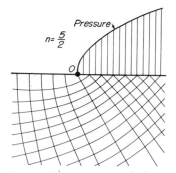

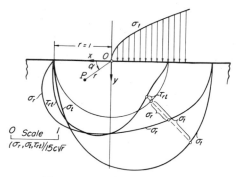

FIG. 6-14. Trajectories of principal stress under a state of plane strain in semi-infinite viscous body carrying on one side the pressures

$$\sigma_t = -15c\sqrt{r}.$$

FIG. 6-15. Stress distribution in semi-infinite body caused by surface pressures $\sigma_t = -15c\sqrt{r}$.

H. HERTZ[1] in his classical work on the contact pressures between convex elastic bodies found that the normal pressure in the contact area of two parallel cylinders of equal radii R and elastic material, pressed together under a normal force Q (in pounds per inch length), is expressed by

$$-b < x < b, \qquad \sigma_y = -\frac{p_0}{b}\sqrt{b^2 - x^2}, \qquad (6\text{-}55)$$

where the width of the parallel strip in which the two cylinders touch each other is denoted by $2b$ and p_0 is the maximum pressure in pounds per square inch for $x = 0$ (x is the distance of a point in the contact strip from its center line). Hertz found (assuming Poisson's ratio $\nu = 0.3$) that

$$b = 1.08 \cdot \sqrt{\frac{QR}{E}}. \qquad (6\text{-}56)$$

Since the pressures in the contact area σ_y are represented by the ordinates of *a semiellipse* traced above the width $2b$, the normal resultant force Q per unit length transmitted in the area $2b$ times 1 in. is equal to

$$Q = \frac{\pi}{2}bp_0. \qquad (6\text{-}57)$$

Suppose that we increase the radii R of both cylinders together with the contact width $2b$ but hold $(b - x)/b$ to small values. Then

$$\sigma_y = -\frac{p_0}{b}\sqrt{(b + x)(b - x)} \sim p_0\sqrt{\frac{2(b - x)}{b}}, \qquad (6\text{-}58)$$

[1] "Gesammelte Werke von Heinrich Hertz," vol. 1, Leipzig, 1895. For further references on elliptic distributions of pressure (also of shearing stresses) see J. O. SMITH and C. K. LIN, J. Appl. Mechanics, vol. 20, pp. 157–166, 1953. See also Sec. 7-2C.

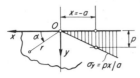

FIG. 6-16

we may replace the elliptic pressure distribution [Eqs. (6-55)] of Hertz in the contact area by our parabolic distribution [Eqs. (6-54)],

$$\sigma_t = -15c\sqrt{r}, \qquad (6\text{-}59)$$

by letting $p_0\sqrt{2/b} = 15c$ and $b - x = r$, and may note that the stress function $F(r,\alpha)$ that we introduced in Eq. (6-50) represents the distribution of stress in the vicinity of one of the edges $x = b$ of the Hertzian contact area of two comparatively large elastic cylinders.

6-4. The Elastic Tilting of a Continental Shore under a High Tide. The high ocean tides[1] periodically displace great quantities of water back and forth on the slopes of the continental shelves, changing the distribution of their loads and causing an elastic deflection of the surface of the earth of observable magnitude. Leaving out of our present consideration the elastic response of the earth's outer crust under the attractions of the sun and moon through the bodily tides in the solid earth itself, to which some references are made in another chapter, let us apply an exact solution of the problem of plane strain to this case with the intention of making an estimate of the elastic tilting of a shore under an advancing high ocean tide. For this purpose, let us consider the state of stress in an extended body under a pressure that increases linearly with the coordinate x on one side $(x < 0)$ of the body (Fig. 6-16). It may be derived in the simplest way from the imaginary part of the function

$$z \ln z = (x \ln r - y\alpha) + i(x\alpha + y \ln r), \qquad (6\text{-}60)$$

after amending the harmonic function in the second parentheses,

$$V = \frac{p}{a\pi}\left[x\alpha - y \ln\left(\frac{r}{a}\right) - \frac{y}{2}\right], \qquad (6\text{-}61)$$

postulating this to be the expression for the potential function V introduced in Sec. 6-1 in Eq. (6-2) and serving, according to Eqs. (6-11), for evaluating the components of stress,

$$\sigma_x = V + y\frac{\partial V}{\partial y} = \frac{p}{a\pi}\left[x\alpha + 2y \ln\left(\frac{r}{a}\right)\right],$$

$$\sigma_y = V - y\frac{\partial V}{\partial y} = \frac{p}{a\pi}(x\alpha - y), \qquad (6\text{-}62)$$

$$\tau_{xy} = -y\frac{\partial V}{\partial x} = -\frac{p}{a\pi}y\alpha.$$

---

[1] The unfamiliarity with their occurrence—it is reported in history—beyond the amazement they caused the warriors in ancient times who could witness them has influenced decisively the outcome of some historic events (for example, the annihilation of Alexander's assembled fleet through the tides of the Indian Ocean sweeping up the Indus River estuary).

These give for $\alpha = 0$ $(y = 0)$, $\sigma_y = \tau_{xy} = 0$ a stress-free surface and for $\alpha = \pi$ $(y = 0, x < 0)$, $\sigma_y = px/a$, $\tau_{xy} = 0$ a pressure increasing linearly with $-x$ and, for $x = -a$, $\sigma_y = -p$, explaining the constant p. The displacement components u, v are evaluated from

$$\varepsilon_x = \frac{\partial u}{\partial x} = \frac{\sigma_x - \sigma_y}{4G} = c\left[2y\ln\left(\frac{r}{a}\right) + y\right] = -\frac{\partial v}{\partial y} = -\varepsilon_y,$$

$$u = c\left[2xy\ln\left(\frac{r}{a}\right) - 2y^2\alpha - xy\right],$$

$$v = c\left[-r^2\ln\left(\frac{r}{a}\right) + x^2\right], \qquad\qquad (6\text{-}63)$$

$$c = \frac{p}{4\pi aG},$$

assuming incompressibility.

Referring to Fig. 6-17, superpose now on the load O_1B_1 linearly increasing with x_1, $\sigma_y = px_1/a$ $(x_1 < 0)$ a second, similar load O_2B_2, $\sigma_y = -px_2/a$ $(x_2 < 0)$, starting from point O_2. The differences between the ordinates of the two straight lines O_1B_1 and O_2B_2 in the shaded portion O_1AC may then represent the weights of an incoming high tide brought on a gently sloping ocean shore. For $y = 0$ the horizontal displacements u vanish and the ground is slightly tilted by vertical displacements

$$v = \frac{c}{2}\left[-x_1^2\ln\left(\frac{x_1}{a}\right)^2 + x_2^2\ln\left(\frac{x_2}{a}\right)^2 + 2(x_1^2 - x_2^2)\right], \qquad (6\text{-}64)$$

where we may write

$$x_1 = x - b, \qquad x_2 = x + b,$$

counting x from the new origin O in the center of the distance $O_1O_2 = 2b$. Or, after denoting

$$\xi = \frac{x}{a}, \qquad \beta = \frac{b}{a},$$

$$\xi_1 = \frac{x_1}{a} = \xi - \beta,$$

$$\xi_2 = \frac{x_2}{a} = \xi + \beta,$$

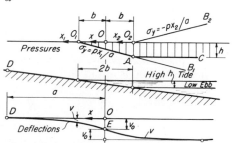

FIG. 6-17. Elastic deflection v of continental shelf under a spring tide.

we obtain for the deflection v of the surface of the ground, for $y = 0$,

$$v = ca^2 \left(-\frac{\xi_1^2}{2} \ln \xi_1^2 + \frac{\xi_2^2}{2} \ln \xi_2^2 + \xi_1^2 - \xi_2^2 + c_0 \xi + c_1 \right) \qquad (6\text{-}65)$$

after having amended this with the terms $c_0 \xi + c_1$ of rigid-body motion. Suppose that the width of wetted beach $2b$ is small compared with the length a, which we shall assume to be so great that the ground at $x = a$ at point D remains undisturbed and at rest, with a horizontal tangent when $x = a$, $y = 0$, $v = 0$, $\partial v/\partial x = 0$. Since $\beta = b/a$ is a small quantity compared with $\xi = 1$, one can express v in simpler form (excepting the region near the origin O, ξ small) after having computed $c_0 = -1$, $c_1 = 2$, giving

$$v = \frac{pb}{\pi G} (\xi \ln \xi - \xi + 1), \qquad (6\text{-}66)$$

limiting this to positive ξ, excepting the small values of ξ. [Because of the symmetry conditions expressed in Eq. (6-65) one sees that v is an *odd* function of ξ and we need not consider ξ to be negative.] Let us finally introduce the hydrostatic pressure $q = \gamma h$ corresponding to the greatest difference h between the levels at high and low tide, by replacing the constant p by (see Fig. 6-17)

$$p = \frac{qa}{2b}.$$

We may sum up the results concerning the elastic deflections v of a beach under the displaced weights of the water masses of a high tide of height h as follows:

$$v = \frac{qa^2}{16\pi bG} (-\xi_1^2 \ln \xi_1^2 + \xi_2^2 \ln \xi_2^2 - 12\beta\xi + 8\beta). \qquad (6\text{-}67)$$

This distorted surface has the slopes

$$\frac{dv}{dx} = \frac{qa}{4\pi bG} [(\xi + \beta) \ln |\xi + \beta| - (\xi - \beta) \ln |\xi - \beta| - 2\beta]; \qquad (6\text{-}68)$$

thus, *the vertical subsidence OE* (Fig. 6-17) *of the ocean shore* at the origin O ($x = \xi = 0$) is found equal to

$$\underline{v_{x=0} = \frac{qa}{2\pi G}}, \qquad (6\text{-}69)$$

and *the greatest slope under which the surface of the earth is tilted* toward the ocean is found equal to

$$\underline{\left(\frac{dv}{dx} \right)_{x=0} = \frac{q}{2\pi G} \left[\ln \left(\frac{b}{a} \right) - 1 \right]}, \qquad (6\text{-}70)$$

where $q = \gamma h$ (h = height of spring tide; $\gamma = 1,000$ kg/m³ weight of 1 m³ water) and $2b$ is the width of the wetted region of the beach.

Suppose that in a distance of $a = 100$ km $= 10^5$ m the ground level has not been disturbed further, that the height of a great tide is $h = 2\pi = 6.28$ m, that it covered a width on the beach $2b = 200$ m, and that the modulus of rigidity of the rocks is $G = 80,000$ kg/cm² (comparable figure for sandstone). This would give the vertical deflection at point O (Fig. 6-17)

$$v_{x=0} = 12.5 \text{ cm}$$

and a tilting of the ground by an angle

$$\left(\frac{dv}{dx}\right)_{x=0} = -9.9 \times 10^{-6}$$

or, since an arc second $1'' = 4.8481 \times 10^{-6}$, by approximately 2 arc seconds, a quantity which might be observable.[1]

[1] The reader is referred for further information on the elastic distortion of the earth's surface under extraneous forces to BENO GUTENBERG (ed.), "Internal Constitution of the Earth," 1st ed., 413 pp., McGraw-Hill Book Company, Inc., New York, 1939; also 2d ed., 439 pp., Dover Publications, New York, 1951.

CHAPTER 7

AXIALLY SYMMETRIC DISTRIBUTIONS OF STRESS

7-1. Equations in Cylindrical Coordinates. Under a rotationally symmetric state of stress and strain, refer a point P to cylindrical coordinates r and z through its distances from the axis and from a plane normal to it and resolve the small displacement vector of P into its radial (u) and axial (v) component. The edges of a small element of material (Fig. 7-1) limited by two cylinders r, $r + dr = $ const, two planes z, $z + dz = $ const, and two planes intersecting in the z axis inclined at a small angle with respect to each other suffer the normal strains ε_r, ε_t, and ε_z in the radial, tangential, and axial directions,

$$\varepsilon_r = \frac{\partial u}{\partial r}, \qquad \varepsilon_t = \frac{u}{r}, \qquad \varepsilon_z = \frac{\partial v}{\partial z}, \qquad (7\text{-}1)$$

and the right angle between the radius r and the generatrix of the cylinder passing through point P changes by the small angle expressing the unit shear

$$\gamma_{rz} = \gamma = \frac{\partial u}{\partial z} + \frac{\partial v}{\partial r} \qquad (7\text{-}2)$$

in the plane passing through the axis.[1]

If σ_r, σ_t, and σ_z denote the components of normal stress in radial, tangential, and axial directions, and $\tau_{rz} = \tau$ denotes the shearing stress in the two faces of the element intersecting in PQ, for *an elastic material* the stress-strain relations hold:

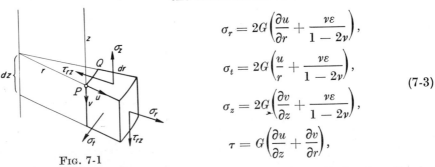

$$\sigma_r = 2G\left(\frac{\partial u}{\partial r} + \frac{\nu\varepsilon}{1 - 2\nu}\right),$$

$$\sigma_t = 2G\left(\frac{u}{r} + \frac{\nu\varepsilon}{1 - 2\nu}\right),$$

$$\sigma_z = 2G\left(\frac{\partial v}{\partial z} + \frac{\nu\varepsilon}{1 - 2\nu}\right), \qquad (7\text{-}3)$$

$$\tau = G\left(\frac{\partial u}{\partial z} + \frac{\partial v}{\partial r}\right),$$

FIG. 7-1

[1] Excluding consideration also of displacements of a vortical nature (torsion in the planes $z = $ const) associated with shearing stresses and unit shears τ_{tz} and γ_{tz}.

(G is modulus of rigidity; ν is Poisson's ratio), where ε denotes the dilatation of volume:

$$\varepsilon = \varepsilon_r + \varepsilon_t + \varepsilon_z = \frac{\partial u}{\partial r} + \frac{u}{r} + \frac{\partial v}{\partial z}. \tag{7-4}$$

The conditions of equilibrium of the stresses acting in the surface of the small element (Fig. 7-1) are expressed by the equations:

$$\frac{\partial \sigma_r}{\partial r} + \frac{\sigma_r - \sigma_t}{r} + \frac{\partial \tau}{\partial z} = 0,$$

$$\frac{\partial \sigma_z}{\partial z} + \frac{\partial \tau}{\partial r} + \frac{\tau}{r} = 0; \tag{7-5}$$

if one substitutes the preceding expressions for the components of stress in Eqs. (7-5), one obtains two differential equations for the displacement components u and v:

$$(1 - 2\nu)\left(\Delta u - \frac{u}{r^2}\right) + \frac{\partial \varepsilon}{\partial r} = 0,$$

$$(1 - 2\nu)\Delta v + \frac{\partial \varepsilon}{\partial z} = 0, \tag{7-6}$$

where Δ denotes the Laplacian operator,

$$\Delta = \frac{\partial^2}{\partial r^2} + \frac{\partial}{r \, \partial r} + \frac{\partial^2}{\partial z^2},$$

while the dilatation of volume

$$\varepsilon = \frac{(1 - 2\nu)}{2(1 + \nu)G}(\sigma_r + \sigma_t + \sigma_z) = \frac{1 - 2\nu}{E}(\sigma_r + \sigma_t + \sigma_z) \tag{7-7}$$

satisfies Laplace's equation

$$\Delta\varepsilon = \frac{\partial^2 \varepsilon}{\partial r^2} + \frac{\partial \varepsilon}{r \, \partial r} + \frac{\partial^2 \varepsilon}{\partial z^2} = 0. \tag{7-8}$$

One may convert Eqs. (7-6) using Eq. (7-8) in the differential equations for each of the displacement components u and v:

$$\left(\Delta - \frac{1}{r^2}\right)\left(\Delta u - \frac{u}{r^2}\right) = 0, \tag{7-9}$$

$$\Delta\Delta v = 0. \tag{7-10}$$

A. Timpe[1] has established a set of useful particular integrals of the latter equations by developing the expressions for the components of stress in series of polynomials containing the powers of the cylindrical coordinates r and z, by means of which he expressed certain exact solutions of radial symmetry in elastic bodies, for example, in a thick, elastic plate loaded on one plane by a uniform pressure.

[1] Achsensymmetrische Deformation von Undrehungskörpern, Z. angew. Math. u. Mech., vol. 4, p. 361, 1924.

In what follows, we shall discuss the problem of a *semi-infinite, elastic body* $z \geq 0$, by assuming that in the surface plane $z = 0$ either the normal stresses σ_z or the shearing stresses τ or the components of displacement u, v have prescribed values, conforming with the conditions of rotational symmetry.   While this group of problems of the theory of elasticity has been investigated by general methods based on the theory of potential functions, it is outside the scope of this book to review even briefly some of these general means of solving these questions,[1] and we shall discuss briefly only one special method of constructing certain solutions which utilizes certain particular integrals of Eqs. (7-9) and (7-10), with reference to a more general method treated in the RIEMANN-WEBER book cited in the footnote by postulating an important group of solutions in the form $Z(z) R(r)$.   One combination of integrals for u, satisfying Eq. (7-9), is then given by

$$u = e^{\pm \alpha z} J_1(\alpha r), \qquad z e^{\pm \alpha z} J_1(\alpha r), \qquad (7\text{-}11)$$

and a second group for v, satisfying Eq. (7-10), by

$$v = e^{\pm \beta z} J_0(\beta r), \qquad z e^{\pm \beta z} J_0(\beta r), \qquad (7\text{-}12)$$

where $J_0(\beta r)$ and $J_1(\alpha r)$ designate the Bessel's functions of zero and first order and first kind for a real variable and α, β are real constants. $J_0(x)$ and $J_1(x)$ each represent an integral of an oscillating nature, behaving regularly at the origin $x = 0$, of Bessel's differential equation,

$$x^2 \frac{d^2 y}{dx^2} + x \frac{dy}{dx} + (x^2 - n^2)y = 0, \qquad (7\text{-}13)$$

for the value of $n = 0$ and $n = 1$, respectively. $J_0(x)$ and $J_1(x)$ are expressed by the infinite series convergent for all values of x,

$$J_0(x) = 1 - \frac{(x/2)^2}{(1!)^2} + \frac{(x/2)^4}{(2!)^2} - \frac{(x/2)^6}{(3!)^2} + \cdots - \cdots \qquad (7\text{-}14)$$

$$J_1(x) = \frac{x}{2} - \frac{(x/2)^3}{1 \cdot 2} + \frac{(x/2)^5}{1 \cdot 2 \cdot 2 \cdot 3} - \frac{(x/2)^7}{1 \cdot 2 \cdot 3 \cdot 2 \cdot 3 \cdot 4} + \cdots - \cdots \qquad (7\text{-}15)$$

[1] BOUSSINESQ, "Applications des potentiels directes, inverses, logarithmics à l'étude de l'équilibre et du mouvement des solides élastiques," Paris, 1885; HEINRICH WEBER, "Die partiellen Differential Gleichungen der mathematischen Physik, nach Riemann's Vorlesungen," 5th ed., vol. 2, pp. 184–198, Vieweg-Verlag, Brunswick, Germany, 1910; A. E. H. LOVE, "Treatise on the Mathematical Theory of Elasticity," 2d ed., chap. 8, pp. 180–200, Cambridge University Press, London, 1906; and R. D. MINDLIN (Columbia University, New York) in a number of valuable papers (on contact between spheres and related questions), from which lack of space prohibits quotation.   E. STERNBERG and M. A. SADOWSKY have worked out the exact solution of the axially symmetric problem of an elastic body containing two spherical cavities by expressing it in terms of bipolar spherical coordinates (Office of Naval Research, Rept. NFonr-32906, 95 pp., 1951. See also J. Appl. Mechanics, 1951).   See also papers by E. STERNBERG, R. A. EUBANKS, and F. ROSENTHAL (Illinois Institute, Chicago, 1951–1953) on elastic spheres under concentrated· loads, etc.

asymptotically converging, when x tends to approach $x = \infty$, toward the functions[1]

$$J_0(x) = \sqrt{\frac{2}{\pi x}}\, \sin\left(x + \frac{\pi}{4}\right),$$

$$J_1(x) = \sqrt{\frac{2}{\pi x}}\, \sin\left(x - \frac{\pi}{4}\right),$$

(7-16)

and for which the rules hold:

$$\frac{dJ_0}{dx} = J_0' = -J_1, \qquad \frac{dJ_1}{dx} = J_1' = J_0 - \frac{J_1}{x},$$

$$\int J_1\, dx = -J_0, \qquad \int x J_0\, dx = x J_1,$$

(7-17)

$$\int_0^\infty J_0(x)\, dx = \int_0^\infty J_1(x)\, dx = 1, \qquad \int_0^\infty \frac{1}{x} J_1(x)\, dx = 1.$$

The functions $J_0(\alpha r)$ and $J_1(\alpha r)$ can serve in infinite sums or in definite integrals to express, in a way analogous to trigonometric series or Fourier's integrals, arbitrary functions of r and thus to satisfy prescribed boundary conditions along the plane $z = 0$ of a semi-infinite body $z > 0$.

7-2. Concentrated Pressure. The Surface Stresses in a Semi-infinite Body. Suppose that in the plane surface $z = 0$ of a semi-infinite body a distribution of normal stresses (Fig. 7-2) $\sigma_z = -p = f(r)$ is prescribed, p representing normal pressures while shearing stresses τ in this plane vanish. This includes the case when the normal pressures p act over the area of a circle of a radius $r = a$ and vanish beyond it for $r > a$. In these cases of concentrated pressure, the four components of stress σ_r, σ_t, σ_z, τ for large values of the coordinate z gradually evanesce when z tends to become infinite; therefore one will be mainly interested in their values near the boundary plane $z = 0$.

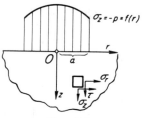

FIG. 7-2

We shall prove below that for $z = 0$ *the*

[1] See W. E. BYERLY, "Elementary Treatise on Fourier's Series and Spherical, Cylindrical and Ellipsoidal Harmonics," p. 219, Ginn & Company, Boston, 1893; A. GRAY, G. B. MATHEWS, and J. M. MACROBERT, "A Treatise on Bessel's Functions and Their Applications to Physics," Macmillan & Co., Ltd., London, 1931; E. JAHNKE and F. EMDE, "Funktionen Tafeln mit Formeln und Kurven," Teubner, Leipzig, 1909; PAUL SCHAFHEITLIN, "Die Theorie der Besselschen Funktionen," Teubner, Leipzig, 1908; THEODORE VON KÁRMÁN AND MAURICE A. BIOT, "Mathematical Methods in Engineering," p. 47, McGraw-Hill Book Company, Inc., New York, 505 pp., 1940.

normal stresses in the surface of the body reach the boundary values

$$\sigma_z = -p, \tag{7-18}$$

$$\sigma_r = -p + (\tfrac{1}{2})(1 - 2\nu)\bar{p},$$

$$\sigma_t = -2\nu p - (\tfrac{1}{2})(1 - 2\nu)\bar{p},$$

and that the radial displacement u is given by

$$z = 0, \qquad u = -\frac{(1 - 2\nu)\bar{p}r}{4G}, \tag{7-19}$$

so that these quantities in the surface plane $z = 0$ may at once be evaluated from these extremely simple general formulas.[1]   The symbol $\bar{p}$ with a bar represents *the mean value of pressure taken over the area of a circle of variable radius r,*

$$\bar{p} = \frac{2}{r^2} \int_0^r p(\lambda)\lambda\, d\lambda, \tag{7-20}$$

where, when the pressure $p(\lambda)$ vanishes, when $\lambda > a$, the upper limit of the integral is to be taken at the fixed value $r = a$.

Referring to Eqs. (7-11) and (7-12), let us introduce a system of the components of displacement in the body:

$$u = (A + B\alpha z)e^{-\alpha z}J_1(\alpha r),$$
$$v = (C + D\alpha z)e^{-\alpha z}J_0(\alpha r), \qquad (z \geq 0), \tag{7-21}$$

$A, \ldots, D$ being integration constants, u representing an integral of Eq. (7-9), and v an integral of Eq. (7-10).   The four constants $A, \ldots, D$ are not independent, because they are tied to each other through Eqs. (7-6) which must simultaneously be satisfied if we substitute the displacement components u and v in them.   This constitutes two conditions for them, and a third is prescribed through the requirement that the shearing stress $\tau = 0$ should vanish in the plane $z = 0$ or that for $z = 0$

$$\frac{\partial u}{\partial z} + \frac{\partial v}{\partial r} = 0,$$

which gives

$$C = -A + B,$$

---

[1] For an exercise the reader may attempt to prove the formulas for σ_r and σ_t by postulating that in the surface plane $z = 0$ the first condition of equilibrium [Eqs. (7-5)] takes the special form

$$\frac{d\sigma_r}{dr} + \frac{\sigma_r - \sigma_t}{r} = -\frac{\partial \tau}{\partial z} = \frac{d\sigma_z}{dr},$$

where $d\sigma_z/dr$ is a given function of r and the equation for u takes the form

$$z = 0, \qquad \frac{d^2u}{dr^2} + \frac{du}{r\, dr} - \frac{u}{r^2} = \frac{d}{dr}\left[\frac{1}{r} \cdot \frac{d(ru)}{dr}\right] = \frac{(1 - 2\nu)}{2G}\frac{d\sigma_z}{dr}.$$

as one can easily verify after computing the derivatives $\partial u/\partial z$ and $\partial v/\partial r$, using the differentiation rules of Eqs. (7-17). Similarly, after carrying out the elaborate process of differentiation prescribed in Eqs. (7-6)[1] on the expressions for u and v postulated in Eqs. (7-21), one finds that

$$B = D = -\frac{A}{1 - 2\nu}, \qquad C = -\frac{2(1 - \nu)A}{1 - 2\nu}.$$

Since A is still indefinite, we may write, instead of $A/(1 - 2\nu)$, a new constant A and can choose the displacement components subject to the condition $z = 0$, $\tau = 0$ in the form

$$u = A(1 - 2\nu - \alpha z)e^{-\alpha z}J_1(\alpha r),$$
$$v = -A[2(1 - \nu) + \alpha z]e^{-\alpha z}J_0(\alpha r). \tag{7-22}$$

The integration constant A is to be determined by prescribing in a second boundary condition, in the surface plane $z = 0$, either the distribution of the normal stresses σ_z or of the displacement vectors $\sqrt{u^2 + v^2}$, or, in the case of alternating conditions, in parts of the surface plane the latter may be prescribed as when a rigid body is impressed on it, while in the unloaded parts thereof the normal stresses σ_z must vanish. In order to satisfy the second boundary condition, we assume that the integration constant $A(\alpha)$ is a function of the parameter α, we multiply the right sides of Eqs (7-22) by $d\alpha$, and integrate them between the limits $\alpha = 0$ and $\alpha = \infty$, postulating the components of displacement u and v in terms of the definite integrals:

$$u = \int_0^\infty A(\alpha)(1 - 2\nu - \alpha z)e^{-\alpha z}J_1(\alpha r)\, d\alpha,$$
$$v = -\int_0^\infty A(\alpha)[2(1 - \nu) + \alpha z]e^{-\alpha z}J_0(\alpha r)\, d\alpha. \tag{7-23}$$

With these expressions the dilatation of volume ε may be computed from

$$\varepsilon = \frac{\partial u}{\partial r} + \frac{u}{r} + \frac{\partial v}{\partial z} = 2(1 - 2\nu)\int_0^\infty A(\alpha)e^{-\alpha z}J_0(\alpha r)\alpha\, d\alpha, \tag{7-24}$$

and one sees that in the surface plane $z = 0$

$$u = (1 - 2\nu)\int_0^\infty A(\alpha)J_1(\alpha r)\, d\alpha,$$

$$v = -2(1 - \nu)\int_0^\infty A(\alpha)J_0(\alpha r)\, d\alpha, \tag{7-25}$$

$$\varepsilon = 2(1 - 2\nu)\int_0^\infty A(\alpha)J_0(\alpha r)\alpha\, d\alpha.$$

[1] We note that the dilatation of volume ε, after Eq. (7-4), is expressed by
$$\varepsilon = \alpha^2[A + B\alpha z - C + D(1 - \alpha z)]e^{-\alpha z}J_0(\alpha r).$$

In order to evaluate $A(\alpha)$, consider the boundary condition that in the plane $z = 0$ the normal stress σ_z is a prescribed function of r.   After substituting in the following expression for the normal stress σ_z the values of $(\partial v/\partial z)_{z=0}$ computed from the second of Eqs. (7-23) and of ε from the last of Eqs. (7-25), this results in the boundary condition for $z = 0$

$$\sigma_z = 2G\left(\frac{\partial v}{\partial z} + \frac{\nu\varepsilon}{1 - 2\nu}\right),$$

$$\sigma_z = -p = f(r) = 2G\int_0^\infty A(\alpha)J_0(\alpha r)\alpha\, d\alpha. \tag{7-26}$$

Comparison of the expression of ε [Eqs. (7-25)] and of σ_z [Eq. (7-26)] shows that *the dilatation of volume ε in the boundary plane*

$$z = 0, \qquad \varepsilon = -\frac{(1 - 2\nu)p}{G}, \tag{7-27}$$

is proportional to the pressures p, and since ε satisfies Laplace's equation,

$$\Delta\varepsilon = 0, \tag{7-28}$$

ε is determined by this boundary-value problem of a potential function, assuming that ε declines toward zero at $z = \infty$.

In the theory of Bessel's functions one shows that an arbitrary function $f(r)$, subject to certain conditions which are usually satisfied in these practical applications,[1] may be expressed by the Fourier integral[2]

$$f(r) = \int_0^\infty J_0(\alpha r)\alpha\, d\alpha\int_0^\infty f(\lambda)J_0(\alpha\lambda)\lambda\, d\lambda. \tag{7-29}$$

Thus, by comparison of the right sides of Eqs. (7-26) and (7-29) the function $A(\alpha)$ is determined by the definite integral:

$$2GA(\alpha) = -\int_0^\infty p(\lambda)J_0(\alpha\lambda)\lambda\, d\lambda. \tag{7-30}$$

Consequently u and v, after Eqs. (7-25), in the plane $z = 0$ are found equal to

$$u = -\frac{1 - 2\nu}{2G}\int_0^\infty p(\lambda)\lambda\, d\lambda\int_0^\infty J_1(\alpha r)J_0(\alpha\lambda)\, d\alpha, \tag{7-31}$$

$$v = \frac{1 - \nu}{G}\int_0^\infty p(\lambda)\lambda\, d\lambda\int_0^\infty J_0(\alpha r)J_0(\alpha\lambda)\, d\alpha. \tag{7-32}$$

---

[1] $f(r)$ may change its value discontinuously in a finite number of places or may tend to become integrably infinite in certain points.

[2] See page 234 (RIEMANN-WEBER, *op. cit.*, vol. 1, p. 200).

According to a well-known formula[1] of integral calculus, the inner integral in Eq. (7-31) represents the *discontinuous function* of the variable λ,

$$\int_0^\infty J_1(\alpha r) J_0(\alpha\lambda)\, d\alpha = \frac{1}{r} \qquad \text{for} \qquad 0 < \lambda < r,$$

$$= 0 \qquad \text{for} \qquad r < \lambda < \infty, \tag{7-35}$$

and we may omit writing it in Eq. (7-31) by expressing u more simply as follows:

$$u = -\frac{1 - 2\nu}{2Gr} \int_0^r p(\lambda)\lambda\, d\lambda, \tag{7-36}$$

where we have placed r as the upper limit (instead of ∞) since the discontinuous factor in Eq. (7-35) vanishes when $\lambda > r$. But

$$2\int_0^r p(\lambda)\lambda\, d\lambda = \bar{p}r^2, \tag{7-37}$$

denoting by $\bar{p}$ the mean value of the pressures p in the circle of variable radius r $(0 < r < \infty)$.

Hence, the radial displacement u in the boundary plane is found equal to

$$z = 0, \qquad u = -\frac{(1 - 2\nu)\bar{p}r}{4G}, \tag{7-38}$$

proving Eqs. (7-19).

---

[1] The integral [Eq. (7-35)] may be evaluated by substituting in the double integral of Eq. (7-29) the discontinuous function $f(r) = 1$ when $0 < r < a$ and $f(r) = 0$ when $a < r < \infty$. By letting $f(\lambda) = 1$, the inner integral gives, after writing $\lambda = a$ in its upper limit,

$$\int_0^a J_0(\alpha\lambda)\lambda\, d\lambda = \frac{1}{\alpha^2}\Big[\alpha\lambda J_1(\alpha\lambda)\Big]_{\lambda=0}^{\lambda=a} = \frac{aJ_1(\alpha a)}{\alpha}. \tag{7-33}$$

Thus, provided that $0 < r < a$,

$$f(r) = 1 = a\int_0^\infty J_1(\alpha a) J_0(\alpha r)\, d\alpha, \tag{7-34}$$

where r represents the independent variable and a a constant value of it. Hence, noting that in Eq. (7-35) λ represents the independent variable and r a constant value of λ, we see that the integral Eq. (7-35) represents

$$\int_0^\infty J_1(\alpha r) J_0(\alpha\lambda)\, d\alpha = \frac{1}{r} \qquad \text{when} \qquad 0 < \lambda < r,$$

$$= 0 \qquad \text{when} \qquad r < \lambda < \infty.$$

The last integral is reminiscent of DIRICHLET's integral representing the function of λ,

$$\int_0^\infty \frac{1}{\alpha} \sin \alpha \cos \alpha\lambda\, d\alpha = \frac{\pi}{2} \qquad \text{when} \qquad 0 < \lambda < 1,$$

$$= 0 \qquad \text{when} \qquad 1 < \lambda < \infty,$$

and both might be termed "discontinuous factors."

The displacement v in Eq. (7-32) cannot be evaluated as simply, but we may at least compute the value of v in the axis of the specimen,

$$r = z = 0, \qquad v_0 = \frac{1-v}{G} \int_0^\infty p(\lambda)\lambda\, d\lambda \int_0^\infty J_0(\alpha\lambda)\, d\alpha,$$

which gives, since

$$\int_0^\infty J_0(\alpha\lambda)\, d\alpha = \frac{1}{\lambda},$$

the value

$$v_0 = \frac{1-v}{G} \int_0^\infty p(\lambda)\, d\lambda. \qquad (7\text{-}39)^1$$

Having now at our disposal the values of u and ε in the plane $z = 0$, we can evaluate the normal stresses from Eqs. (7-3) in the boundary plane $z = 0$, finding them expressed generally by the formulas

$$\sigma_z = -p,$$
$$\sigma_r = -p + (\tfrac{1}{2})(1 - 2v)\bar{p}, \qquad (7\text{-}40)$$
$$\sigma_t = -2vp - (\tfrac{1}{2})(1 - 2v)\bar{p},$$

which hold over the entire surface plane, provided that $\bar{p}$ is computed from Eq. (7-37).　At the axis of the specimen,

$$z = r = 0, \qquad \sigma_z = -p_{r=0},$$
$$\sigma_r = \sigma_t = -(\tfrac{1}{2})(1 + 2v)p_{r=0}. \qquad (7\text{-}41)$$

In the case of concentrated pressures p prescribed over the area of a circle of radius a having a resultant normal force

$$P = 2\pi \int_0^a pr\, dr, \qquad (7\text{-}42)$$

[1] If the function $f(r)$, defining the normal stress $\sigma_z = -p = f(r)$ in the surface plane $z = 0$, changes abruptly at some value $r = a$, as in the case of a concentrated pressure which is distributed over a circle of radius a, and if σ_z or $f(r)$ has a finite value $-p_a$ when r increases toward $r = a$ and both vanish when $r > a$, *the circle* $r = a$ *is the locus of a certain singularity of the state of stress.*　The nature of this singularity has been fully discussed for a state of plane strain in Sec. 6-1 in Example 1 [see Eqs. (6-22) and (6-25), page 215].　The radial component of displacement u suffers in this case a sudden change of the slope $\partial u/\partial r$.　It is noteworthy that the curve representing *the axial displacement* v *obtains a vertical tangent* $\partial v/\partial r = \infty$ over a very short interval when r passes through the value a so that the profile of the body takes the shape indicated by the curves representing u and v in Fig. 7-3.

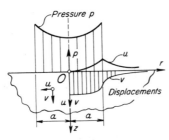

FIG. 7-3. Displacements u and v under concentrated pressures p.

since, when r is greater than a, p vanishes and the mean pressure is equal to $\bar{p} = P:\pi r^2$ for $r > a$, we note that, under the free surface of the body,

$$\sigma_r = -\sigma_t = \frac{(1 - 2\nu)P}{2\pi r^2}, \qquad r > a, \qquad z = 0, \qquad (7\text{-}43)$$

i.e., that these normal stresses are the same as if the force P were concentrated in the center of the circle $r = a$ as a single, concentrated normal force. Our integral expressions for the stress components which we omit here must, when z and r increase indefinitely, converge toward *Boussinesq's solution* for the distribution of stress caused by a single, normal force P acting in the origin (Fig. 7-4),[1] namely:

$$\sigma_r = \frac{P}{2\pi}\left[\frac{1 - 2\nu}{R(R + z)} - \frac{3zr^2}{R^5}\right],$$

$$\sigma_t = \frac{P}{2\pi}\left[-\frac{1 - 2\nu}{R(R + z)} + \frac{z}{R^3}\right],$$

$$\sigma_z = -\frac{3P}{2\pi}\cdot\frac{z^3}{R^5}, \qquad\qquad (7\text{-}44)$$

$$\tau = -\frac{3P}{2\pi}\cdot\frac{z^2r}{R^5},$$

where
$$R^2 = r^2 + z^2,$$

which solution has the displacements

$$u = \frac{P}{4\pi G}\left[\frac{rz}{R^3} - \frac{(1 - 2\nu)r}{R(R + z)}\right],$$

$$v = \frac{P}{4\pi G}\left[\frac{2(1 - \nu)}{R} + \frac{z^2}{R^3}\right], \qquad (7\text{-}45)$$

giving in the boundary plane $z = 0$,

$$u = -\frac{(1 - 2\nu)P}{4\pi Gr}, \qquad v = \frac{(1 - \nu)P}{2\pi Gr}, \qquad (7\text{-}46)$$

and one verifies, indeed, when $z = 0$, $r > a$, that the expressions for u [Eqs. (7-38)] taking $\bar{p} = P/\pi r^2$ and for σ_r and σ_t [Eq. (7-43)] coincide with the corresponding ones in Boussinesq's solution.

7-3. A. Uniform Pressure Distributed over a Circle. Consider, for example, the case when the pressure p (Fig. 7-5) is constant over the

---

[1] A. and L. Föppl, "Drang und Zwang," vol. 2, p. 225, R. Oldenbourg-Verlag, Munich, 1920, or S. Timoshenko and J. N. Goodier, "Theory of Elasticity," 2d ed., p. 364, McGraw-Hill Book Company, Inc., New York, 1951.

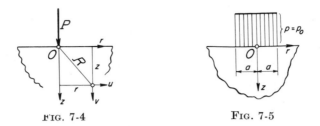

FIG. 7-4   FIG. 7-5

area of a circle of radius a and vanishes beyond it: $p = p_0 = $ const for $0 < r < a$, $p = 0$ for $a < r < \infty$.   Equation (7-30) gives then for $A(\alpha)$ the value

$$2GA(\alpha) = -p_0 \int_0^a \lambda J_0(\alpha\lambda)\, d\lambda = -p_0 \frac{a}{\alpha} J_1(\alpha a), \qquad (7\text{-}47)$$

and one obtains for the complete expressions for the displacements u and v and for the dilatation of volume ε from Eqs. (7-23)

$$u = -\frac{p_0 a}{2G} \int_0^\infty (1 - 2\nu - \alpha z) \frac{e^{-\alpha z}}{\alpha} J_1(\alpha a) J_1(\alpha r)\, d\alpha,$$

$$v = \frac{p_0 a}{2G} \int_0^\infty [2(1-\nu) + \alpha z] \frac{e^{-\alpha z}}{\alpha} J_1(\alpha a) J_0(\alpha r)\, d\alpha, \qquad (7\text{-}48)$$

$$\varepsilon = -\frac{(1-2\nu)p_0 a}{G} \int_0^\infty e^{-\alpha z} J_1(\alpha a) J_0(\alpha r)\, d\alpha.$$

These give, in the surface plane $z = 0$,

$$u = -\frac{(1-2\nu)p_0 a}{2G} \int_0^\infty \frac{1}{\alpha} J_1(\alpha a) J_1(\alpha r)\, d\alpha,$$

$$v = \frac{(1-\nu)p_0 a}{G} \int_0^\infty \frac{1}{\alpha} J_1(\alpha a) J_0(\alpha r)\, d\alpha, \qquad (7\text{-}49)$$

$$\varepsilon = -\frac{(1-2\nu)p_0 a}{G} \int_0^\infty J_1(\alpha a) J_0(\alpha r)\, d\alpha.$$

The displacement component u and the dilatation of volume ε in the plane $z = 0$ may be expressed from these integrals, after making use of Eqs. (7-38) and (7-27), letting $\bar{p} = p$ for $0 < r < a$, $\bar{p} = p_0 a^2/r^2$ for for $r > a$, explicitly by the formulas

$$u = -\frac{(1-2\nu)p_0 r}{4G}, \qquad 0 < r < a,$$

$$u = -\frac{(1-2\nu)p_0 a^2}{4Gr}, \qquad a < r < \infty, \qquad (7\text{-}50)$$

$$\varepsilon = -\frac{(1-2\nu)p_0}{G}, \qquad 0 < r < a,$$

$$\varepsilon = 0, \qquad a < r < \infty. \qquad (7\text{-}51)$$

The vertical component of displacement v cannot be evaluated as easily but we may at least compute from the integral [Eq. (7-49)] two important values of v, namely, in the surface plane $z = 0$ at the axis $r = 0$ and just under the edge of the compressed zone $r = a$ by remarking that one obtains, when taking $r = 0$ and $r = a$ in Eq. (7-49), the integrals

$$\int_0^\infty \frac{1}{\alpha} J_1(\alpha a) \, d\alpha = 1, \qquad \int_0^\infty \frac{1}{\alpha} J_1(\alpha a) J_0(\alpha a) \, d\alpha = \frac{2}{\pi}, \qquad (7\text{-}52)$$

respectively.[1]   Therefore the displacement component v is found equal

at $\quad z = r = 0$: $\qquad$ to $\quad v = v_0 = \dfrac{(1 - v)p_0 a}{G}$,

$$(7\text{-}53)$$

at $\quad z = 0$, $\qquad r = a$: $\qquad$ to $\quad v_a = \dfrac{2}{\pi} v_0$,

and we may note that, under a uniform concentrated pressure $p = p_0 = $ const, a cup-shaped indentation is produced, the deflection v dropping from its maximum value $v = v_0$ at the axis and center $r = 0$ of the circle $r = a$ to $v_a = (2/\pi)v_0$ or approximately two-thirds of its value at the rim $r = a$ of the compressed area.

The boundary values of the stresses, after Eqs. (7-40), are in the surface plane $z = 0$,[2]

$$\sigma_z = -p_0, \qquad \sigma_r = \sigma_t = -\frac{(1 + 2v)p_0}{2}, \qquad 0 < r < a,$$

$$(7\text{-}54)$$

$$\sigma_z = 0, \qquad \sigma_r = -\sigma_t = \frac{(1 - 2v)p_0 a^2}{2r^2}, \qquad a < r < \infty,$$

and we may evaluate the normal stresses on the axis $r = 0$ of the semi-infinite body from Eqs. (7-48) by computing ε and the strains $\varepsilon_r = \varepsilon_t = u/r$† as follows:

$$\varepsilon = -\frac{(1 - 2v)p_0 a}{G} \int_0^\infty e^{-\alpha z} J_1(\alpha a) \, d\alpha,$$

$r = 0$,

$$(7\text{-}55)$$

$$\varepsilon_t = -\frac{p_0 a}{4G} \int_0^\infty (1 - 2v - \alpha z) e^{-\alpha z} J_1(\alpha a) \, d\alpha.$$

See page 235 (SCHAFHEITLIN, *op. cit.*, p. 65).

[2] The reader will note that at the edge of the compressed area $r = a$ all three normal stresses change their values abruptly when r passes from $r < a$ to $r > a$; the axial stress σ_z changes from $\sigma_z = -p_0$ to $\sigma_z = 0$, the radial stress σ_r from $\sigma_r = -(1 + 2v)p_0/2$ to $\sigma_r = +(1 - 2v)p_0/2$, and the tangential stress σ_t from $\sigma_t = -(1 + 2v)p_0/2$ to $\sigma_t = -(1 - 2v)p_0/2$. This is in line with the character of the *singularity* occurring on the edge $r = a$, described in Sec. 6-1, Eqs. (6-22).

† Noting that in the integrant of the integral expressing the ratio u/r by Eqs. (7-48) the term

$$\left[\frac{J_1(\alpha r)}{\alpha r} \right]_{r=0} = \frac{\alpha r/2}{\alpha r} = \frac{1}{2} .$$

These integrals[1] may be expressed in finite terms, and we find

$$\varepsilon = -\frac{(1 - 2\nu)p_0}{G} [1 - z(a^2 + z^2)^{-\frac{1}{2}}],$$

$$\varepsilon_t = -\frac{p_0}{4G} [1 - 2\nu - 2(1 - \nu)z(a^2 + z^2)^{-\frac{1}{2}} + z^3(a^2 + z^2)^{-\frac{3}{2}}].$$

(7-56)

The distribution of the normal stresses along the axis $r = 0$ in the semi-infinite body under a uniform pressure p_0, distributed over a circle of radius a, is herewith found to be (since for $r = 0$, $\varepsilon_r = \varepsilon_t$, $\varepsilon_z = \partial v / \partial z = \varepsilon - 2\varepsilon_t$)

$$\sigma_z = 2G\left(\frac{\partial v}{\partial z} + \frac{\nu\varepsilon}{1 - 2\nu}\right) = 2G\left[\frac{(1 - \nu)\varepsilon}{1 - 2\nu} - 2\varepsilon_t\right],$$

$$\sigma_r = \sigma_t = 2G\left(\varepsilon_t + \frac{\nu\varepsilon}{1 - 2\nu}\right),$$

(7-57)[2]

$$\underline{r = 0, \qquad \sigma_z = -p_0[1 - z^3(a^2 + z^2)^{-\frac{3}{2}}],}$$

$$\sigma_r = \sigma_t = -\frac{p_0}{2}[1 + 2\nu - 2(1 + \nu)z(a^2 + z^2)^{-\frac{1}{2}} + z^3(a^2 + z^2)^{-\frac{3}{2}}].$$

---

[1] By partial integration,

$$I = \int_0^\infty e^{-\alpha z}J_1(\alpha a)\, d\alpha = -\frac{1}{a}\int_0^\infty e^{-\alpha z}d[J_0(\alpha a)]$$

$$= -\frac{1}{a}\left[e^{-\alpha z}J_0(\alpha a)\right]_0^\infty - \frac{z}{a}\int_0^\infty e^{-\alpha z}J_0(\alpha a)\, d\alpha$$

$$= \frac{1}{a}[1 - z(a^2 + z^2)^{-\frac{1}{2}}],$$

where the integral

$$\int_0^\infty e^{-\alpha z}J_0(\alpha a)\, d\alpha = (a^2 + z^2)^{-\frac{1}{2}}$$

is one which was evaluated in RIEMANN-WEBER; see page 234 (*op. cit.*, vol. 1, p. 194). Furthermore,

$$\int_0^\infty e^{-\alpha z}\alpha J_1(\alpha a)\, d\alpha = -\frac{\partial I}{\partial z} = \frac{1}{a}\frac{\partial}{\partial z}[z(a^2 + z^2)^{-\frac{1}{2}}].$$

[2] A check on the correctness of these polynomials is that, when z tends to become infinite, they converge toward the Boussinesq expressions given in Eqs. (7-44). For example,

$$\sigma_z = -p_0\left[1 - \left(1 + \frac{a^2}{z^2}\right)^{-\frac{3}{2}}\right] = -p_0\left(1 - 1 + \frac{3a^2}{2z^2}\right) = -\frac{3P}{2\pi z^2}.$$

We may also compute the maximum shearing stress

$$\tau_{\max} = (\tfrac{1}{2})(\sigma_z - \sigma_t)$$

along the z axis, $r = 0$:

$$\tau_{\max} = (\tfrac{1}{4})p_0[-1 + 2\nu - 2(1 + \nu)z(a^2 + z^2)^{-\frac{1}{2}} + 3z^3(a^2 + z^2)^{-\frac{3}{2}}], \quad (7\text{-}58)$$

and may note that it increases first with z and subsequently decreases, reaching a maximum value at the depth

$$z_m = a\sqrt{\frac{2(1 + \nu)}{7 - 2\nu}}. \tag{7-59}$$

Thus we find in the axis $r = 0$ of the body under the compressed area an isolated spot at this depth [for Poisson's ratio $\nu = 0.3$ at $z_m = 0.637a$ and in an incompressible elastic solid, $\nu = \tfrac{1}{2}$ at $z_m = (1/\sqrt{2})a = 0.707a$], at which the absolute value of the maximum shearing stress becomes an analytic maximum,

$$|\tau_{\max}|_{\max} = \begin{cases} 0.33p_0 & \text{when} \quad \nu = 0.3, \\ 0.29p_0 & \text{when} \quad \nu = \tfrac{1}{2}. \end{cases} \tag{7-60}$$

One may expect that under increasing pressures p_0 the first yielding will start around this isolated point $r = 0$, $z = z_m$, but in view of the combined discontinuities (occurring along the edge of the compressed area $r = a$ in the surface plane $z = 0$) in the values of the three normal stresses, in view of the fact that the radial stress σ_r just outside of the circle $r = a$ becomes a *tensile stress*, and in view of the peculiar, singular behavior of the shearing stress τ_{rt} (having the vanishing value $\tau_{rt} = 0$ in the plane $z = 0$, but a *finite* value in the cylinder normal to it, $r = a = $ const) *the first shear fractures will soon overtake the isolated yielding, initiating at the edge $r = a$ of the compressed area and developing normally to the surface plane $z = 0$ inward in the body.*

In an *incompressible elastic solid,* $\nu = \tfrac{1}{2}$, the stresses in the surface plane $z = 0$ take the values

$$\begin{aligned} 0 < r < a, \qquad & \sigma_z = \sigma_r = \sigma_t = -p_0, \\ r > a, \qquad & \sigma_z = \sigma_r = \sigma_t = 0, \end{aligned} \tag{7-61}$$

and along the axis $r = 0$

$$\sigma_z = -p_0\left[1 - \left(1 + \frac{a^2}{z^2}\right)^{-\frac{3}{2}}\right],$$

$$\sigma_r = \sigma_t = -\frac{p_0}{2}\left[2 - 3\left(1 + \frac{a^2}{z^2}\right)^{-\frac{1}{2}} + \left(1 + \frac{a^2}{z^2}\right)^{-\frac{3}{2}}\right]. \tag{7-62}$$

The center $r = z = 0$ of the compressed area is deflected by the amount

$$v_0 = \frac{p_0 a}{2G}. \tag{7-63}$$

A purely viscous substance under a uniform pressure $p_0 = $ const distributed over a circle of radius a will distort continuously under the stresses which were just listed while the center of the compressed area is displaced with the vertical velocity

$$v_0 = \frac{p_0 a}{2\mu} . \tag{7-64}$$

B. Rigid Plate Impression. A perfectly rigid cylindrical punch of radius a having a plane base produces in a semi-infinite, elastic body under a resultant normal force P, according to Boussinesq, a distribution of normal stresses in the plane impression:

$$0 < r < a, \qquad \sigma_z = -p = - \frac{P}{2\pi a \sqrt{a^2 - r^2}} , \tag{7-65}$$

and the vertical displacement

$$0 < r < a, \qquad v = \frac{(1 - \nu)P}{4aG} . \tag{7-66}$$

Since the contact pressures p along the sharp edge $r = a$ of the punch in elastic material tend to become infinite, it is unavoidable that the material under the edge of a rigid impression plate is strained beyond the yield point or, if it is brittle, starts to crack along a cylinder $r = a = $ const normal to the surface plane $z = 0$.

C. Hertzian Distribution of Stress. Suppose that in the plane $z = 0$ of a semi-infinite body $z > 0$ a normal pressure

$$\sigma_z = -p = -p_0 \sqrt{1 - \frac{r^2}{a^2}} \tag{7-67}$$

acts within a circle of radius a and that p vanishes for $r > a$. The ordinates of the normal stress σ_z plotted above the radii r in the plane $z = 0$ are represented by one half of an ellipsoid of revolution, and under the resultant normal force

$$P = \frac{2\pi}{3} p_0 a^2 \tag{7-68}$$

the distribution of the normal stresses σ_r and σ_t in the surface plane $z = 0$ may easily be evaluated from Eqs. (7-40) after computing the value of the mean pressure $\bar{p}$,

$$\bar{p} = \frac{2}{r^2} \int_0^r pr \, dr, \tag{7-69}$$

giving

When $0 \leq r \leq a$: $\bar{p} = \frac{2p_0 a^2}{3r^2} \left[1 - \left(1 - \frac{r^2}{a^2}\right)^{3/2} \right],$

When $r \geq a$· $\bar{p} = \frac{2p_0 a^2}{3r^2} .$

$$\tag{7-70}$$

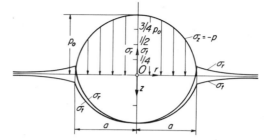

Fig. 7-6. Hertzian distribution of stress under pressure

$$p = p_0 \sqrt{1 - \frac{r^2}{a^2}}$$

on semi-infinite body.

In the center of the circle the stresses are

$$r = 0, \qquad \sigma_z = -p_0, \qquad \sigma_r = \sigma_t = -(\tfrac{1}{2})(1 + 2\nu)p_0. \qquad (7\text{-}71)$$

Figure 7-6 reproduces the curves for σ_r, σ_t, σ_z in the surface plane of the body (taking $\nu = 0.3$). The deflection v_0 of the saucer-shaped depression under the normal force P in the center $r = z = 0$, after Eq. (7-39), is equal to

$$v_0 = \frac{1 - \nu}{G} \int_0^a p \, dr = \frac{(1 - \nu)p_0}{Ga} \int_0^a \sqrt{a^2 - r^2} \, dr = \frac{(1 - \nu)\pi p_0 a}{4G}. \qquad (7\text{-}72)$$

D. Conchoidal Fracture. In view of what has been stated about the initiation of a circular fracture under uniformly distributed concentrated pressures and under a rigid-plate impression and in conjunction with the presence of a relative maximum of the maximum shearing stress $\tau_{\max}$ some distance away from the loaded surface plane, one will expect that the brittle fracture tends to bend inward and will assume a cup-shaped form. The evidence from observations on fractures under concentrated pressures in brittle materials supports these conclusions. Under a gentle blow of a hammer having a flattened head with a sharp edge, porcelain, glass, cold asphalt, etc., are seen to chip off in a concave, cup-shaped "conchoidal" fracture starting normally to the plane surface that was hit and frequently having many small ripple markings (reminiscent of the appearance of a sea shell) probably caused by acoustical wave phenomena. The destruction through "pitting" of hardened steel bodies is another evidence of the presence of an isolated maximum of $\tau_{\max}$ at some distance under the center of a circular compression area: when hardened steel rolls (or wheels) travel continuously over a hardened steel base (the rails), the small chunks of abrased material compressed between the rolls and the base will act as areas of concentrated pressures with the result that small pits will be chipped off under them from the bodies in contact. We have mentioned[1] some related observations of the isochromatics in photoelastic tests under concentrated pressures under states of plane strain in which

[1] Cf. Sec. 6-2, Fig. 6-8.

the isochromatics took a circular shape.   It is conjectured that the celebrated *meteor craters* in Arizona and in northern Canada (Chubb's Crater Lake) owe their sharp edge with its steeply inclined, near-vertical slopes and their cup-shaped form to the cutting action of a dense swarm of meteors that hit the earth in a nearly vertical direction and dug out the interior of the huge hole.[1]

G. K. GILBERT,[2] ALFRED WEGENER, H. C. UREY, and others have attributed the formation of *the craters on the surface of the moon to the impacts of meteors*.   Observers have noticed that the numerous craters of smaller size (estimated to have diameters of an order of magnitude from barely visible to tens of kilometers) all appear as regular, comparatively shallow, round, cup-shaped pits which are frequently surrounded by a perfectly circular, slightly elevated regular rim.   A few of them have a distinctly elliptical contour; obviously those were hit under an inclined direction with respect to the moon's surface.

Since stony meteors reaching the earth abound in number, with 35 of them to one metallic, iron-nickel (disclosing the *Widmannstädten* crystalline structure) meteor,[3] it appears probable that the small, circular craters were dug out on the moon through stony meteors or their denser swarms.   Considering the extremely low temperature believed to prevail in the light type of rocks of brittle nature which make up the surface of the moon, the absence of an atmosphere on it, and the fact that solid bodies falling on the moon from outer space must possess a low temperature near the absolute zero of the temperature scale, one sees that the cutting action through the impacts of stony meteors hitting the rocks with cosmic end velocities on the moon must be tremendous.   The former and the latter in their extremely brittle condition would be shattered instantaneously through brittle fractures

---

[1] The meteor crater in Arizona (between Flagstaff and Winslow) is ¾ mile, Chubb Crater east of the Hudson Bay 2 miles wide; the former has been mapped by H. H. NININGER, director of the meteorite museum at Sedona, Arizona, the latter described by C. S. BEALS, Dominion astronomer, who reported before the 1957 meeting of the International Union of Geodesy and Geophysics in Toronto, Canada, the discovery of several similar *holes caused by meteoric impacts*, one on the eastern shores of the Hudson Bay being about 400 miles in diameter, comparable with the *Mare Imbrium*, the largest visible dark area on the moon.

[2] In his paper "The Moon's Face," Bull. Phil. Soc., Washington, vol. 12, p. 24, 1893.   Cf. also H. C. UREY's instructive paper "The Origin and Nature of the Moon," Endeavor, vol. 19, no. 74, pp. 87–99, April, 1960, with several photographs of the moon.

[3] According to BENO GUTENBERG (ed.), "Internal Constitution of the Earth," 1st ed., p. 114, McGraw-Hill Book Company, Inc., New York, 1939.   The author had occasion in 1932 to subject a small prism cut out from an iron-nickel meteor to a compression test under axial stress; it behaved at normal temperature in a very ductile manner (see Vol. I, Figs. 18-13, and 18-14, page 281), showing pronounced Lüders' flow layers.

in the contact area, disintegrating into a powder, or even volatilized through the conversion of the kinetic energy into heat, so that in the chipped-off cup no residual matter would remain, nor much around it.[1] As far as one can judge, the average, small, circular moon craters conform to the stated rules of conchoidal fractures in a glassy, brittle material caused by a highly concentrated pressure. Since large stony meteors are comparatively rare, it is probable that the regular, circular craters of intermediate size, having diameters of a few tens of kilometers, were not chiseled out by single, larger bodies but rather by single, dense swarms of stony meteors which crossed the moon's path. The genesis of the irregular scarps and of the large dark areas named *maria* seems less plausibly understandable and must be left unexplained here. Whereas very small meteorites are known to enter the earth's atmosphere in tremendous numbers daily and to burn up in it through the friction of the air, it is conjectured that they act as a dissipated gentle "sand blasting" on our terrestrial, atmosphereless companion's surface.

In closing, it might be incidentally mentioned that steel plates have been cut by directing high-speed jets of water normally on them.

---

[1] The rare iron-nickel meteors of ductile metal, on the other hand, may sustain some plastic distortion and possibly embed themselves in the hole.

CHAPTER 8

THEORY OF BENDING OF FLAT, THIN PLATES

8-1. Bending of Plates. Let the x,y plane coincide with the middle plane of a flat plate of uniform thickness h, considered small compared with the dimensions of the plate, denoting by w the deflection of the plate at point x, y, $z = 0$, small compared with the thickness h. The planes $z = \pm h/2$ may be free, or the plate may carry a distributed transversal pressure load $p = f(x,y)$ on the plane $z = -h/2$. In a *thin* plate subjected to slight bending, straight lines perpendicular to the middle plane $z = 0$ remain straight lines normal to the deflected middle surface $w(x,y)$; the elastic bending strains ε_x, ε_y, γ_{xy} at a point $P(x,y,z)$ are expressed by

$$\varepsilon_x = -z\frac{\partial^2 w}{\partial x^2}, \qquad \varepsilon_y = -z\frac{\partial^2 w}{\partial y^2}, \qquad \gamma_{xy} = -2z\frac{\partial^2 w}{\partial x\,\partial y}\ ; \qquad (8\text{-}1)$$

and since the normal stress σ_z can only be small compared with the bending stresses σ_x, σ_y, τ_{xy}, after letting $\sigma_z = 0$, in *a thin plate of compressible, elastic material* the normal and shearing stresses σ_x, σ_y, τ_{xy}, according to the elasticity law, are expressed by

$$\sigma_x = \frac{E}{1-\nu^2}(\varepsilon_x + \nu\varepsilon_y) = -\frac{Ez}{1-\nu^2}\left(\frac{\partial^2 w}{\partial x^2} + \nu\frac{\partial^2 w}{\partial y^2}\right),$$

$$\sigma_y = \frac{E}{1-\nu^2}(\varepsilon_y + \nu\varepsilon_x) = -\frac{Ez}{1-\nu^2}\left(\frac{\partial^2 w}{\partial y^2} + \nu\frac{\partial^2 w}{\partial x^2}\right), \qquad (8\text{-}2)$$

$$\tau_{xy} = G\gamma_{xy} = -2Gz\frac{\partial^2 w}{\partial x\,\partial y}\ ,$$

being proportional to the distance z. These stresses exert through the normal sections $x = \text{const}$, $y = \text{const}$ two bending moments m_x and m_y and a twisting moment m_{xy} per unit width:

$$m_x = \int_{-h/2}^{h/2} \sigma_x z\,dz = -N\left(\frac{\partial^2 w}{\partial x^2} + \nu\frac{\partial^2 w}{\partial y^2}\right),$$

$$m_y = \int_{-h/2}^{h/2} \sigma_y z\,dz = -N\left(\frac{\partial^2 w}{\partial y^2} + \nu\frac{\partial^2 w}{\partial x^2}\right), \qquad (8\text{-}3)$$

$$m_{xy} = \int_{-h/2}^{h/2} \tau_{xy} z\,dz = -(1-\nu)N\frac{\partial^2 w}{\partial x\,\partial y}\ ,$$

where the constant

$$N = \frac{Eh^3}{12(1 - \nu^2)} \tag{8-4}$$

denotes the plate modulus or rigidity.

Furthermore, if

$$p_x = \int_{-h/2}^{h/2} \tau_{xz}\, dz, \qquad p_y = \int_{-h/2}^{h/2} \tau_{yz}\, dz \tag{8-5}$$

designate the shearing forces per unit width in the direction normal to the deflected surface $w(x,y)$, the conditions of equilibrium of these forces in the transverse direction and of the moments require that

$$p_x = \frac{\partial m_x}{\partial x} + \frac{\partial m_{xy}}{\partial y}, \qquad p_y = \frac{\partial m_y}{\partial y} + \frac{\partial m_{xy}}{\partial x}, \qquad \frac{\partial p_x}{\partial x} + \frac{\partial p_y}{\partial y} + p = 0, \tag{8-6}$$

assuming that the plate is not stressed by forces parallel to its middle plane. After substituting m_x, m_y, m_{xy} from Eqs. (8-3) in Eqs. (8-6), one obtains for the shearing forces

$$p_x = -N\frac{\partial \Delta w}{\partial x}, \qquad p_y = -N\frac{\partial \Delta w}{\partial y}, \tag{8-7}$$

and for the deflection w LAGRANGE's partial differential equation of fourth order ($\Delta = \partial^2/\partial x^2 + \partial^2/\partial y^2$):

$$\Delta\Delta w = \frac{\partial^4 w}{\partial x^4} + 2\frac{\partial^4 w}{\partial x^2\, \partial y^2} + \frac{\partial^4 w}{\partial y^4} = \frac{p}{N}. \tag{8-8}$$

The elastic surface w must satisfy this equation and two boundary conditions in every element of the boundary curve of the plate. If the latter refer to the components of normal and shearing stress, transmitted through the cylinder bounding the plate normally to it and n denotes the outward direction normal to and s tangential to the boundary curve of the plate, as has been mentioned in Sec. 3-1, page 106, these are expressed by the two boundary conditions of GUSTAV KIRCHHOFF as follows:

$$m_n = -N\left(\frac{\partial^2 w}{\partial n^2} + \nu\frac{\partial^2 w}{\partial s^2}\right),$$

$$p'_n = -N\left[\frac{\partial^3 w}{\partial n^3} + (2 - \nu)\frac{\partial^3 w}{\partial n\, \partial s^2}\right], \tag{8-9}$$

where m_n represents the external bending moment whose axis coincides with s, and p_n' is the *amended shearing force* perpendicular to the elastic surface of the plate, both taken per unit width in the cylinder circumscribing the edge of the plate. The amended shearing forces p_n' are hereby defined, according to a theorem by LORD KELVIN and P. G. TAIT, as the sum[1]

$$p'_n = p_n + \frac{\partial m_{ns}}{\partial s}, \tag{8-10}$$

p_n expressing the normal-shearing-force stress resultant and m_{ns} the twisting moment transmitted in the element $ds \times h$ per unit width, namely,

$$p_n = -N \frac{\partial \Delta w}{\partial n}, \qquad m_{ns} = -(1 - \nu)N \frac{\partial^2 w}{\partial n\, \partial s}, \tag{8-11}$$

the normal shearing force p_n being thus supplemented by the additional shearing force $\partial m_{ns}/\partial s$, so that their sum supplies the expression for the *amended shearing force* p_n' in Eqs. (8-9).   There remains the task of dealing subsequently only with the latter force resultants p_n' and disregarding entirely the twisting moments m_{ns} along the boundary curve of the plate.   We may note that, in terms of rectangular co-ordinates, this amounts to prescribing along an edge $x = $ const the moment m_x and the amended shearing force

$$p'_x = p_x + \frac{\partial m_{xy}}{\partial y} = -N\left[\frac{\partial^3 w}{\partial x^3} + (2 - \nu)\frac{\partial^3 w}{\partial x\, \partial y^2}\right] \tag{8-12}$$

and that in those cases when *the twisting moment m_{xy} in a sharp, rectangular corner of a plate*, say at $x = a$, $y = b$, *does not vanish*—this is the case, for example, when along these two edges the boundary conditions $w = 0$ and $\Delta w = 0$ are prescribed and when such edges in the usual engineering terminology are designated as "simply supported edges," because along them the bending moments m_x and m_y also vanish—there results in the amended shearing forces p_x' and p_y' *a single, concentrated force of the amount* $Q = 2(m_{xy})_{x=a,y=b}$, *equal to twice the value of the twisting moment at the corner.*   Thus, the term "simply supported" for a straight edge, along which $w = \Delta w = 0$, seems inappropriate. This condition should rather be expressed as follows: The edges $x = a$, $y = b$ are forced to remain straight near the corner, requiring a downward, concentrated force Q, preventing the uplifting of the corner which would otherwise (in the absence of Q) occur, provided that m_{xy} does not vanish in the corner.

[1] Equation (8-10) expresses, according to Kelvin and Tait, the simple kinematic fact that in a *thin* plate the actual distribution of twisting moments m_{ns}, as computed by Eqs. (8-11) along the boundary cylinder, may be replaced by an equivalent distribution of normal shearing forces $\partial m_{ns}/\partial s$ without altering essentially the form of the elastic surface w and the herewith prescribed state of stress in the plate (except in a narrow band running along the boundary curve, in accordance with St. Venant's principle).   Cf. page 115 (*loc. cit.*).

In *elastic, incompressible material*, when $v = \frac{1}{2}$, we obtain with $N = Eh^3/9 = Gh^3/3$, which we may denote by $N_e = (\frac{1}{3})Gh^3$,

$$m_x = -N_e\left[\frac{\partial^2 w}{\partial x^2} + (\tfrac{1}{2})\frac{\partial^2 w}{\partial y^2}\right],$$

$$m_y = -N_e\left[\frac{\partial^2 w}{\partial y^2} + (\tfrac{1}{2})\frac{\partial^2 w}{\partial x^2}\right],$$

$$m_{xy} = -(\tfrac{1}{2})N_e\frac{\partial^2 w}{\partial x\,\partial y},$$

$$p_x = -N_e\frac{\partial \Delta w}{\partial x}, \qquad p_y = -N_e\frac{\partial \Delta w}{\partial y}$$

(8-13)

$$N_e\Delta\Delta w = p.$$

(8-14)

In a plate of purely viscous material, on the other hand, after writing μ instead of G and for the plate modulus $N_v = (\frac{1}{3})\mu h^3$, we have to insert dots above ε_x, ε_y, γ_{xy} and w, in order to obtain rates of strain and the velocity of sagging $\dot{w} = \partial w/\partial t$ (t the time) and obtain

$$m_x = -N_v\left[\frac{\partial^2 \dot{w}}{\partial x^2} + (\tfrac{1}{2})\frac{\partial^2 \dot{w}}{\partial y^2}\right], \ldots,$$

$$p_x = -N_v\frac{\partial \Delta \dot{w}}{\partial x}, \ldots,$$

(8-15)

and for the deflection, the differential equation

$$N_v\Delta\Delta\dot{w} = (\tfrac{1}{3})\mu h^3\Delta\Delta\dot{w} = p,$$

(8-16)

where p may or may not depend on the time t. Since the groups of equations (8-15) and (8-16) have similar forms to Eqs. (8-13) and (8-14), an abundance of exact solutions for viscous plates is readily on hand among the ones which were derived for elastic plates. The maximum bending stresses in the plate may be computed (taking $z = h/2$) from

$$\sigma_x, \sigma_y, \tau_{xy} = \frac{6}{h^2}(m_x, m_y, m_{xy}).$$

(8-17)

8-2. Circular, Viscous Plates under Rotationally Symmetric Loading.
When the distributed load $p = p_0 f(r)$ and the deflections w are functions of the radial distance r from the center of a circular plate, since the Laplacian operator $\Delta = d^2/dr^2 + d/r\,dr = (1/r)d/dr(rd/dr)$, Eq. (8-16) for a plate of viscous material becomes

$$\left(\frac{d^2}{dr^2} + \frac{d}{r\,dr}\right)\left(\frac{d^2\dot{w}}{dr^2} + \frac{d\dot{w}}{r\,dr}\right) = \frac{p}{N_v} = \frac{3p_0 f(r)}{\mu h^3}$$

(8-18)

having the general integral

$$\dot{w} = \dot{w}_0 + c_1 + c_2 r^2 + c_3 \ln r + c_4 r^2 \ln r,$$

(8-19)

where $\dot{w}_0$ is a particular solution corresponding to the right-hand term in Eq. (8-18).   This may always be computed by subsequent quadratures after letting

$$\frac{d}{r\,dr}\left(r\frac{d\dot{w}_0}{dr}\right) = \dot{u}, \qquad \frac{d}{r\,dr}\left(r\frac{d\dot{u}}{dr}\right) = \frac{p_0}{N_v}f(r),$$

$$\dot{u} = \frac{p_0}{N_v}\int\frac{dr}{r}\int rf(r)\,dr, \qquad \dot{w}_0 = \int\frac{dr}{r}\int r\dot{u}\,dr. \qquad (8\text{-}20)$$

If the parameter of load p_0 depends on the time t, these equations require a further integration with respect to the time t.

For example, if *a circular viscous plate* of radius a is subjected *to an invariable uniform pressure* $p = $ const, not dependent on the time t, when the edge $r = a$ is firmly clamped ($r = a$, $w = dw/dr = 0$) the deflections w increase with time t as

$$w = \frac{pt}{64N_v}(a^2 - r^2)^2, \qquad (8\text{-}21)$$

and if the plate is simply supported on its rim, when for $r = a$, $w = 0$ and $m_r = -N_v[d^2\dot{w}/dr^2 + (\frac{1}{2})d\dot{w}/r\,dr] = 0$,

$$w = \frac{pt}{64N_v}\left[\frac{14}{3}a^2(a^2 - r^2) + r^4 - a^4\right]. \qquad (8\text{-}22)$$

Similarly, when the plate carries a single, invariable, concentrated force P at the center, when the edge $r = a$ is firmly clamped,

$$w = \frac{Pt}{16\pi N_v}\left(a^2 - r^2 - 2r^2\ln\frac{a}{r}\right), \qquad (8\text{-}23)$$

and when the edge is simply supported,

$$w = \frac{Pt}{16\pi N_v}\left[\frac{7}{3}(a^2 - r^2) - 2r^2\ln\frac{a}{r}\right]. \qquad (8\text{-}24)$$

In the two latter cases, the bending moments m_r, m_t increase toward the center $r = 0$ of the plate indefinitely, because of the presence of the terms containing $\ln(a/r)$, for the plate having a clamped circumference as

$$m_r = \frac{P}{8\pi}\left(3\ln\frac{a}{r} - 2\right), \qquad m_t = \frac{P}{8\pi}\left(3\ln\frac{a}{r} - 1\right) \qquad (8\text{-}25)$$

and for the simply supported plate as

$$m_r = \frac{3P}{8\pi}\ln\frac{a}{r}, \qquad m_t = \frac{P}{8\pi}\left(3\ln\frac{a}{r} + 1\right); \qquad (8\text{-}26)$$

but finite expressions for m_r, m_t and for the maximum bending stresses might be established also in the center $r = 0$ of the plate,

$$r = 0, \qquad \sigma_r = \sigma_t = \frac{6}{h^2}(m_r)_{r=0},$$

after assuming that the single force $P = \pi c^2 p$ is being distributed as a finite pressure p over a small circle of the radius c in the manner shown in the theory of elastic plates.[1]   One sees that the shearing force p_r in the circular sections

---

[1] The corresponding expressions may be found in the author's, "Die elastischen Platten," pp. 58–67, J. Springer, Berlin, 1925, from which Eqs. (8-21) to (8-24) were taken.

$r =$ const, when a concentrated force P acts at the center $r = 0$ of the plate, tends also to become infinite as

$$p_r = -N_v \frac{d\Delta \dot{w}}{dr} = -\frac{P}{2\pi r} . \qquad (8\text{-}27)$$

8-3. The Theory of the Bending of Rectangular, Elastic Plates. This theory has been developed for more than 130 years through many exact solutions, and the reader must be referred to an extensive literature on this subject. The elastic surfaces of rectangular plates and the distributions of stress in them have been expressed either by means of double periodic functions in double series or by means of periodic functions in the form of single, trigonometric series. In a rectangle having the sides $x = 0, x = a, y = 0$, and $y = b$, the double trigonometric series

$$w = \frac{16p}{\pi^6 N} \sum_{m=1}^{\infty} \sum_{n=1}^{\infty} \frac{\sin (m\pi x/a) \sin (n\pi y/b)}{mn(m^2/a^2 + n^2/b^2)^2} , \qquad (m, n = 1, 3, 5, \ldots), \quad (8\text{-}28)$$

expresses the elastic surface of a plate bent laterally by a uniform pressure $p =$ const, and the series

$$w = \frac{4P}{\pi^4 abN} \sum_{m=1}^{\infty} \sum_{n=1}^{\infty} \frac{\sin (m\pi \xi/a) \sin (n\pi \eta/b) \sin (m\pi x/a) \sin (n\pi y/b)}{(m^2/a^2 + n^2/b^2)^2} ,$$

$$(m, n = 1, 2, 3, \ldots), \quad (8\text{-}29)$$

expresses the elastic surface of such a plate loaded by a single, concentrated force P at a point having the coordinates ξ, η (Fig. 8-1). Both these solutions are due to NAVIER, the founder of the theory of elasticity (1821), and satisfy the boundary conditions $w = 0, \Delta w = 0$ on the sides of the rectangle.

Suppose that a rectangular plate $a \times b$ carries as external load a four-sided pyramid piled up above it (Fig. 8-2) so that the lateral pressure p within a quarter of the plate in the triangle OAB is expressed by

$$p = \frac{2p_0 x}{a} ,$$

p_0 denoting the pressure exerted at the center $x = a/2, y = b/2$ of the

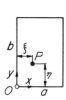

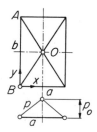

FIG. 8-1. Rectangular plate loaded by a single force P.   FIG. 8-2. Pyramidal load.

base rectangle.   W. ORNSTEIN,[1] by evaluating through a trigonometric series this distribution of pressure, could prove that the corresponding *elastic surface* of the rectangular plate satisfying the conditions $w = 0$ and $\Delta w = 0$ on the four sides of the rectangle may be expressed by *the single trigonometric series*

$$w = \frac{4p_0 a^4 b^4}{3\pi^6 N (a^2 + b^2)^2} \sum_1^\infty \frac{1}{n^6} \sin \frac{n\pi x}{a} \sin \frac{n\pi y}{b}, \qquad (n = 1, 3, 5, \ldots). \qquad (8\text{-}30)$$

In order to satisfy the boundary conditions $w = \Delta w = 0$ in an actual experiment of a rectangular plate, bent according to one of the preceding three elastic surfaces, a downward concentrated force Q equal to twice the value of the twisting moment m_{xy} in each of the four corners of the rectangle is required.   In its absence the preceding solutions do not represent correctly the shape of the bent plate, since its corners will be uplifted[2] if $Q = 0$.

In 1900, ESTANAVE[3] developed a solution corresponding to Eq. (8-28) *for the rectangular plate under a uniform pressure p* by expressing it, however, through a *single*, trigonometric series as the sum of the two elastic surfaces w_1 and w_2:

$$w = w_1 + w_2,$$

$$w_1 = \frac{pa^4}{24N} \left(\frac{x^4}{a^4} - 2\frac{x^3}{a^3} + \frac{x}{a} \right) = \frac{4pa^4}{\pi^5 N} \sum_{n=1}^\infty \frac{1}{n^5} \sin \frac{n\pi x}{a}, \qquad (8\text{-}31)$$

$$w_2 = \frac{pa^4}{N} \sum_{n=1}^\infty \left(a_n \cosh \frac{n\pi y}{a} + b_n \frac{n\pi y}{a} \sinh \frac{n\pi y}{a} \right) \sin \frac{n\pi x}{a}, \qquad (n = 1, 3, 5, \ldots).$$

The constants satisfying the boundary conditions $w = \Delta w = 0$ on the rim of the rectangle are[4]

$$a_n = -\frac{2(2 + \alpha_n \tanh \alpha_n)}{n^5 \pi^5 \cosh \alpha_n}, \qquad b_n = \frac{2}{n^5 \pi^5 \cosh \alpha_n},$$

$$\alpha_n = \frac{n\pi b}{2a}, \qquad (n = 1, 3, 5, \ldots). \qquad (8\text{-}32)$$

---

[1] WILHELM ORNSTEIN, Note on Rectangular Plates: Deflection under Pyramidal Load, Quart. Appl. Math., vol. 11, no. 3, pp. 339–341, October, 1953.

[2] The uplifting of the corners of simply supported rectangular plates loaded by a uniform pressure or a single force has long ago been observed in the early plate tests by C. VON BACH ("Das Ingenieurlaboratorium und die Materialprüfungsanstalt der Technischen Hochschule Stuttgart," K. Wittwer, Stuttgart, 5; 191 also, "Elastizität und Festigkeit," 9th ed., Springer, Berlin, 1924).   The phenomenon of the uplifting of plate corners has been studied in careful tests by M. BERGSTRÄSSER with rectangular plates of mirror glass on the suggestion of the author in Göttingen.   See his "Versuche mit freiaufliegenden rechteckigen Platten unter Einzelkraft-Belastung," Forschungsarb., Ver. deut. Ing., vol. 302, 25 pp. V.D.I. Verlag, Berlin, 1928.

[3] Contribution à l'étude de l'équilibre d'une plaque rectangulaire mince, Thèses, Paris, 1900.

[4] The deflections w are referred to an origin chosen at the center point of one of the longer sides b.

One chooses for the side a the shorter of the two sides of the rectangle $a \times b$ in which case the series also converges excellently for the bending moments.[1] The maximum deflection w_0 in the center $x = a/2, y = 0$, is equal to

$$b/a = \qquad 1 \qquad\qquad 2.04 \qquad\quad 3.82 \qquad\qquad \infty$$

$$w_0 = 0.00406 \quad 0.01026 \quad 0.01276 \quad 0.01302 \times \frac{pa^4}{N} .$$

8-4. Parallel Plate Strip Loaded by Single Force P.

The equation for the deflection w for an infinite plate carrying a train of single, concentrated forces P along the x axis of the type discussed in Eq. (5-90) (Fig. 5-13b) may be established by means of the particular integrals of $\Delta\Delta w = 0$, listed as biharmonic functions in Sec. 5-4D(1), Eq. (5-79), in the form of a trigonometric series

$$w = \frac{Pa^2}{2\pi^3 N} \sum_{n=1}^{\infty} \frac{e^{-(n\pi y/a)}}{n^3} \left(1 + \frac{n\pi y}{a}\right) \sin\frac{n\pi\xi}{a} \sin\frac{n\pi x}{a} , \qquad (8\text{-}33)$$

valid for $y \geqq 0$ ($n = 1, 2, 3, \ldots$), which subdivides the plate in an infinite number of parallel strips of width a, each carrying one single load (Fig. 8-3), and expresses *the elastic surface of an infinitely long plate strip, freely supported on the two parallel straight edges $x = 0$ and $x = a$ and loaded by a single force P at point $x = \xi, y = 0$*.

If the force P acts, for example, in the center $\xi = a/2$ of the plate strip,

$$w = \frac{Pa^2}{2\pi^3 N} \sum_{n=1}^{\infty} \frac{(-1)^{(n-1)/2}}{n^3} e^{-(n\pi y/a)} \left(1 + \frac{n\pi y}{a}\right) \sin\frac{n\pi x}{a} , \qquad (n = 1, 3, 5, \ldots),$$

$$(8\text{-}34)$$

its maximum deflection is found equal to

$$w = \left(1 + \frac{1}{3^3} + \frac{1}{5^3} + \cdots\right) \frac{Pa^2}{2\pi^3 N} = 0.01695 \frac{Pa^2}{N} . \qquad (8\text{-}35)$$

The second derivatives of the elastic surface [Eq. (8-33)] can be expressed as follows:

$$2N\frac{\partial^2 w}{\partial x^2} = \varphi - y\frac{\partial\varphi}{\partial y} ,$$

$$2N\frac{\partial^2 w}{\partial y^2} = \varphi + y\frac{\partial\varphi}{\partial y} , \qquad (8\text{-}36)$$

$$2N\frac{\partial^2 w}{\partial x \, \partial y} = y\frac{\partial\varphi}{\partial x} ,$$

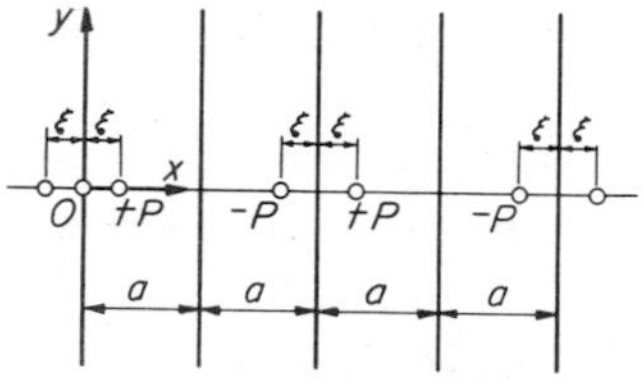

FIG. 8-3

[1] For many details and numerical values for the bending moments, shear forces, etc., cf. *op. cit.*, page 254 (also ESTANAVE, *loc. cit.*).

where the function $\varphi(x,y)$,

$$\varphi = N\Delta w = -\frac{P}{\pi} \sum_{n=1}^{\infty} \frac{e^{-(n\pi y/a)}}{n} \sin \frac{n\pi\xi}{a} \sin \frac{n\pi x}{a}, \qquad (8\text{-}37)$$

valid for $y \geqq 0$ $(n = 1, 2, 3, \ldots)$, obviously represents the mean curvature $\partial^2 w/\partial x^2 + \partial^2 w/\partial y^2 = \Delta w$ times the plate modulus N of the deflected plate. Since along the parallel edges $x = 0$ and $x = a$, $\varphi = 0$ and since in the neighborhood of the point of application of a concentrated, single force P, as we have seen in Sec. 8-2, Eq. (8-27), the shearing forces in a circle of small radius r increase indefinitely as

$$p_r = -N\frac{d\Delta w}{dr} = -\frac{P}{2\pi r}, \qquad (8\text{-}38)$$

the surface φ must have a singularity at point $x = \xi$, $y = 0$ $(r = 0)$ behaving like

$$\varphi = \frac{P}{2\pi} \ln r. \qquad (8\text{-}39)$$

We see that this function φ *represents Green's function* satisfying $\Delta\varphi = 0$, having vanishing values on the sides of the plate $x = 0$ and $x = a$ and becoming infinite as the $\ln r$ at point $x = \xi$, $y = 0$. The function φ would be represented by a thin membrane fastened on the edges of the plate and deflected by a needle at one point (Fig. 8-4).

Green's function for which we obtained the series (8-37) may be expressed in finite form as follows:[1]

$$\varphi = N\Delta w = \frac{P}{4\pi} \ln \frac{\cosh(\pi y/a) - \cos[\pi(x - \xi)/a]}{\cosh(\pi y/a) - \cos[\pi(x + \xi)/a]}. \qquad (8\text{-}40)$$

The right sides of Eqs. (8-36) and thus the bending and twisting moments m_x, m_y, m_{xy} may be evaluated in finite terms and the distribution of the shearing forces p_x which support the infinite plate along the two edges $x = 0$ and $x = a$ be computed. One finds, for example, on the symmetry line $y = 0$ (Fig. 8-5) the bending moments in finite form,

$$m_x = m_y = \frac{(1 + \nu)P}{8\pi} \ln \frac{1 - \cos[\pi(x + \xi)/a]}{1 - \cos[\pi(x - \xi)/a]}, \qquad m_{xy} = 0, \quad (8\text{-}41)$$

and when the single force P acts in the center of the span $(\xi = a/2)$,

$$m_x = m_y = \frac{(1 + \nu)P}{8\pi} \ln \frac{1 + \sin(\pi x/a)}{1 - \sin(\pi x/a)} = \frac{(1 + \nu)P}{8\pi} \ln \cot^2 \frac{\pi}{2}\left(\frac{1}{2} - \frac{x}{a}\right). \tag{8-42}$$

By computing $p_x = -N\partial\Delta w/\partial x$, using Eq. (8-40), one finds that the

[1] Green's function may be constructed by the conformal mapping of the parallel strip $0 \leqq x \leqq a$ on the unit circle, as was shown in author's book on elastic plates (*op. cit.*, p. 99).

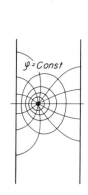

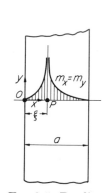

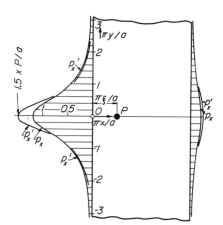

FIG. 8-4. Green's function φ.

FIG. 8-5. Bending moments.

FIG. 8-6. Distribution of shearing forces p_x and of amended shearing forces $p_x' = p_x + \partial m_{xy}/\partial y$ along edges $x = 0$ and $x = a$.

FIGS. 8-4, 8-5, and 8-6. Infinite plate strip loaded by single force P.

shearing force is expressed by

$$p_x = -\frac{P}{2a} \cdot \frac{\sin(\pi\xi/a)[\cos(\pi\xi/a) - \cosh(\pi y/a)\cos(\pi x/a)]}{\{\cosh(\pi y/a) - \cos[\pi(x-\xi)/a]\}\{\cosh(\pi y/a) - \cos[\pi(x+\xi)/a]\}},\tag{8-43}$$

giving along the two edges of the plate strip the simple formulas for the distribution of the shearing forces:

$$x = 0, a, \qquad p_x = \pm\frac{P}{2a} \cdot \frac{\sin(\pi\xi/a)}{\cosh(\pi y/a) \mp \cos(\pi\xi/a)},\tag{8-44}$$

the upper and lower signs referring to $x = 0$ and $x = a$, respectively. Although along these edges twisting moments m_{xy} also act, equal to

$$m_{xy} = -(1-\nu)N\frac{\partial^2 w}{\partial x\,\partial y} = -\frac{(1-\nu)y}{2}\frac{\partial\varphi}{\partial x} = \frac{(1-\nu)yp_x}{2},\tag{8-45}$$

after what has just been stated, we may disregard their presence and evaluate *the true distribution of shearing forces* through *the amended shearing forces* required to balance the single force P along both plate edges $x = 0, x = a$

$$p_x' = p_x + \frac{\partial m_{xy}}{\partial y} = \frac{3-\nu}{2}p_x + \frac{1-\nu}{2}y\frac{\partial p_x}{\partial y}$$

and find that p_x' is expressed by

$$p_x' = \frac{p_x}{2}\left[3 - \nu - (1-\nu)\frac{(\pi y/a)\sinh(\pi y/a)}{\cosh(\pi y/a) \mp \cos(\pi\xi/a)}\right],\tag{8-46}$$

($\pm$ in the second term referring to $x = 0, a$). An example is shown in Fig. 8-6.

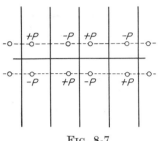

FIG. 8-7

By superposing two parallel rows of single forces $\pm P$ (Fig. 8-7) on an infinite plate one may describe, by using the results obtained for the plate strip, the state of stress in a long rectangular plate bent by a single force P, applied at a point near one of the short sides for the edge conditions $w = \Delta w = 0$. An infinite number of trains of single forces superposed in pairs of parallel lines gives the solution by Navier [Eq. (8-29)].

8-5. Infinite Plate Supported on a Substratum and Loaded by a Transversal, Single Force. The great German physicist HEINRICH HERTZ[1] determined in 1884 the elastic deflections of an extended slab of ice floating on water, on which a single weight is placed. He thus established the solution of the differential equation for the deflections of an infinite, elastic plate bent under a single, transversal force which depresses it in a downward bulged form into a fluid on which it floats against the buoyancy pressures of the latter. Hertz's solution has been applied by engineers to a related problem concerning elastic plates used in the foundations of buildings, transmitting their weights to the ground, and in the design of reinforced-concrete slabs in highway construction.[2] Apart from these and related applications in engineering problems of plates supported on elastic foundations, it is thought that the case of an infinite plate of an elastic or of a viscous substance, carrying a transversal load and lying on a substratum that reacts with buoyancy pressures or resilient resistances of a viscous nature or with both, is encountered in several interesting problems of the bending and *warping of the earth's solid crust* under extraneous forces. Examples in geomechanics which might be mentioned here are the bending distortions of the earth's crust, evidenced in the gradual, slow subsidence of the ground levels under the weights of the great glaciers that formerly covered vast regions of the continents, and in the slow rebound and uplift of the ground during the postglacial epochs of geologic history (the last ice age, after which extended glaciers melted away). Numerous evidences of the changes of ground

---

[1] Wiedemann's Ann. Physik u. Chemie, vol. 22, p. 449, 1884; also published in "Gesammelte Werke von Heinrich Hertz," vol. 1, p. 288, Leipzig, 1895.

[2] H. M. WESTERGAARD has discussed in a remarkable paper (Om Beregning af Plader paa elastisk Underlag med saerligt Heublik paa Sporgsmaalet om Spaendinger i Betonveji, Ingeniøren, vol. 32, no. 42, 1923) the deflections and the stresses in an infinite plate supported on an elastic ground, caused by a train of loads spaced at equal intervals, endeavoring to supply design information for the case of concrete slabs of highways, subjected to stressing through the concentrated loads of the wheels of vehicles.

levels over extended regions of the earth's crust, caused by the changes of ice loads or by the weights of accumulating sediments, are well known in geology, and the extremely small vertical velocities with which the ground levels in certain regions have sunk or risen are estimable in measurable magnitudes.[1]

A plate of gravitating material of the specific weight γ_p and thickness h, the boundaries of which may be indefinite, resting on a semifluid substratum of slightly greater specific weight γ_s, exerts in its plane condition a uniform pressure $\gamma_p h$ on the substratum. A single, concentrated, transversal force P brought on the plate causes it to deflect in a surface of revolution with a deflection w. Disregarding its weight as an external load by assuming that it is still carried by the uniform pressure $\gamma_p h$, we note that a gravitating substratum reacts on the plate with buoyancy pressures $q = -\gamma_s w$ when the plate deflects. The radially symmetrical deflections depending on the radial distance r of a point from the point of attack of the single force, *in elastic material*, with reference to Eq. (8-8), must satisfy the differential equation

$$\Delta\Delta w = \left(\frac{d^2}{dr^2} + \frac{d}{r\,dr}\right)\left(\frac{d^2w}{dr^2} + \frac{dw}{r\,dr}\right) = \frac{q}{N} = -\frac{\gamma_s}{N}w. \qquad (8\text{-}47)$$

For plates supported on a solid, elastically responding soil, engineers assume that this exerts a bending or reaction pressure that is proportional to the deflections w of the plate, $q = -kw$, where k is considered an empirically given constant (of the dimension kg/cm³). They compute the deflections and the state of stress in bending in *elastic plates resting on elastic foundation* from an equation

$$\Delta\Delta w = -\frac{k}{N}w \qquad (8\text{-}48)$$

having an identical form with Eq. (8-47).

If, on the other hand, the plate is of *viscoelastic material* and is supported on a solid, elastic foundation ($q = -kw$) or floats on a fluid substratum ($k = \gamma_s$), we have to insert a dot above w on the left side and to write on the right side of the equation

$$\frac{\dot{q} + (q/t_e)}{N} = -\frac{k}{N}\left(\dot{w} + \frac{w}{t_e}\right),[†]$$

where the constant of the dimension of time is $t_e = 3\mu/E$ (the viscosity μ and E refer to the material of the plate), and we obtain the deflections w from the equation

$$\Delta\Delta\dot{w} = -\frac{k}{N}\left(\dot{w} + \frac{w}{t_e}\right). \qquad (8\text{-}49)$$

[1] Cf. also Sec. 10-1.

[†] See Sec. 10-2, Eqs. (10-3).

When *the permanent strains become predominant*, we may disregard the elastic parts of the strain [this amounts to assuming incompressibility $\nu = \frac{1}{2}, E = \infty, t_e = 0$, but $N t_e = (Eh^3/9)(3\mu/E) = (\frac{1}{3})\mu h^3 = N_v$, using N_v as plate modulus] and obtain for *the deflections w of a purely viscous plate on substratum*

$$\Delta\Delta\dot{w} = -\frac{k}{N_v}\,w. \tag{8-50}$$

In geomechanical applications one might also consider the case of a *purely viscous plate floating on a gravitating and heavily viscous substratum* (such as certain thick layers of clays or consolidated muds) which would conform with an equation of the form

$$\Delta\Delta\dot{w} = -\frac{\gamma_s}{N_v}\,w - \frac{k_s}{N_v}\,\dot{w} \tag{8-51}$$

analogous to that of Eq. (8-49) where the constant k_s depends on the viscosity of the substratum.[1]

In what follows, we shall be concerned with integrating H. HERTZ's equation (8-47). Denoting by a an arbitrary length, by x and y the independent and the dependent variable, and by α a constant parameter in dimensionless form, defined by

$$x = \frac{\alpha r}{a}, \qquad y = \frac{w}{a}, \qquad \alpha^4 = \frac{\gamma_s a^4}{N}, \qquad N = \frac{Eh^3}{12(1-\nu^2)}, \tag{8-52}$$

Eq. (8-47) or[2]

$$\left(\frac{d^2}{dx^2} + \frac{d}{x\,dx}\right)\left(\frac{d^2y}{dx^2} + \frac{dy}{x\,dx}\right) = -y \tag{8-53}$$

may be split in the two simultaneous differential equations:

$$\frac{d^2y}{dx^2} + \frac{dy}{x\,dx} = z,$$

$$\frac{d^2z}{dx^2} + \frac{dz}{x\,dx} = -y. \tag{8-54}$$

---

[1] If k_s is large compared with γ_s, Eq. (8-51) has the same form for $\dot{w}$ as Eq. (8-47) for w, and the integrals of the latter may be used to express $\dot{w}$.

[2] Some authors in their textbooks prefer to deal with the fourth-order equation for y [Eq. (8-53)] which explicitly is

$$x^3 y^{(4)} + 2x^2 y''' - xy'' + y' - x^3 y = 0$$

and attempt to express its four integrals through series developments, including certain logarithmic terms, without regard to the simultaneous equations for the *two* dependent complex variables y and z defined in Eqs. (8-54), thereby destroying the beauty of symmetry inherent in these latter equations, establishing the relation to the Bessel's functions $J_0(u)$, $Y_0(u)$, corresponding to the complex arguments $u = x\sqrt{i}$ and $u = x\sqrt{-i}$.

If one substitutes in both of them either for $z = iy$ or for $z = -iy$ ($i = \sqrt{-1}$), *both* preceding equations take the *same* form, either with the upper or with the lower sign:

$$xy'' + y' \mp ixy = 0, \tag{8-55}$$

respectively, which are represented in BESSEL's general differential equation

$$x^2 y'' + xy' + (\mp ix^2 - n^2)y = 0 \tag{8-56}$$

having in the usual designation the two integrals $J_n(x\sqrt{\mp i})$ and $Y_n(x\sqrt{\mp i})$, corresponding to either the upper or the lower sign in Eq. (8-56). Since in Eq. (8-55) $n = 0$, we obtain for its two signs the pairs of Bessel's functions of zero order and of first and second type,

$$J_0(x\sqrt{\mp i}), \qquad Y_0(x\sqrt{\mp i}),$$

and see that the complete integral of Eq. (8-53) must be

$$y = AJ_0(x\sqrt{i}) + BJ_0(x\sqrt{-i}) + CY_0(x\sqrt{i}) + DY_0(x\sqrt{-i}), \tag{8-57}$$

where $A, \ldots, D$ are complex integration constants.

These four integrals having the complex arguments[1] $u = x\sqrt{i}$ or $u = x\sqrt{-i}$ are to be evaluated from

$$J_0(u) = 1 - \frac{(u/2)^2}{1!^2} + \frac{(u/2)^4}{2!^2} - \frac{(u/2)^6}{3!^2} + \cdots - \cdots \tag{8-58}$$

$$\frac{\pi}{2} Y_0(u) = (0.11593 - \ln u)J_0(u)$$

$$- \frac{(u/2)^2}{1!^2} + \frac{(1 + \frac{1}{2})(u/2)^4}{2!^2} - \frac{(1 + \frac{1}{2} + \frac{1}{3})(u/2)^6}{3!^2} + \cdots - \cdots, \tag{8-59}$$

---

[1] In the text above we use the function of zero order of second type $Y_0(u)$, introduced by PAUL SCHAFHEITLIN in his book "Die Theorie der Besselschen Funktionen," 129 pp., Verlag von B. G. Teubner, Leipzig and Berlin, 1908 (see p. 106 in his book), which behaves at $u = \infty$ as referred to below in our Eqs. (8-70), quoted from Schafheitlin [*op. cit.*, p. 42, eq. (2)]. The attention of the reader is called to the fact that the function designated by the same symbol $Y_0(u)$ in E. JAHNKE and F. EMDE's well-known Mathematical Tables and Formulas of Functions ("Funktionentafeln mit Formeln und Kurven," Verlag von B. G. Teubner, Leipzig and Berlin, 1909, also available in an English edition; see p. 94 in their book) is not the same as Schafheitlin's and that $Y_0(u)$ in the text above, or

$$[Y_0(u)]_{\text{Schafh.}} = \frac{2}{\pi} \{0.11593 J_0(u) - [Y_0(u)]_{\text{Jahnke}}\}, \tag{8-57a}$$

where $0.11593 = \ln 2 - C = \ln 2 - 0.57722$, C being Euler's constant $C = \lim_{n=\infty} \left(1 + \frac{1}{2} + \frac{1}{3} + \cdots + \frac{1}{n} - \ln n\right)$ (see JAHNKE and EMDE, *op. cit.*, p. 27).

taking for the multiple-valued, complex arguments u and for the logarithms of u the following principal values:

Either
$$u = x\sqrt{i} = xe^{i\pi/4} = \frac{1}{\sqrt{2}}(1+i)x,$$

$$\ln u = \ln(x\sqrt{i}) = \ln x + \frac{\pi}{4}i,$$

or
$$u = x\sqrt{-i} = xe^{-i\pi/4} = \frac{1}{\sqrt{2}}(1-i)x,$$

(8-60)

$$\ln u = \ln(x\sqrt{-i}) = \ln x - \frac{\pi}{4}i,$$

corresponding to which the four functions in Eq. (8-57) appear as two pairs of conjugate, complex functions; thus, after separating the real (Re) and imaginary (Im) parts,

$$J_0(x\sqrt{\pm i}) = \operatorname{Re} J_0 + i \operatorname{Im} J_0 = S_1(x) \pm iS_2(x), \qquad (8\text{-}61)$$

where $S_1(x)$ and $S_2(x)$ represent the infinite series

$$S_1(x) = 1 - \frac{(x/2)^4}{2!^2} + \frac{(x/2)^8}{4!^2} - \frac{(x/2)^{12}}{6!^2} + \cdots - \cdots, \qquad (8\text{-}62)$$

$$S_2(x) = \quad - \frac{(x/2)^2}{1!^2} + \frac{(x/2)^6}{3!^2} - \frac{(x/2)^{10}}{5!^2} + \cdots - \cdots. \qquad (8\text{-}63)$$

Similarly,

$$\frac{\pi}{2} Y_0(x\sqrt{\pm i}) = \left(0.11593 - \ln x \mp \frac{\pi i}{4}\right)(S_1 \pm iS_2) - S_3 \mp iS_4, \qquad (8\text{-}64)$$

where $S_3(x)$ and $S_4(x)$ represent the infinite series

$$S_3(x) = \left(1 + \frac{1}{2}\right)\frac{(x/2)^4}{2!^2} - \left(1 + \frac{1}{2} + \frac{1}{3} + \frac{1}{4}\right)\frac{(x/2)^8}{4!^2}$$

$$+ \left(1 + \frac{1}{2} + \frac{1}{3} + \frac{1}{4} + \frac{1}{5} + \frac{1}{6}\right)\frac{(x/2)^{12}}{6!^2} - \cdots + \cdots, \qquad (8\text{-}65)$$

$$S_4(x) = \frac{(x/2)^2}{1!^2} - \left(1 + \frac{1}{2} + \frac{1}{3}\right)\frac{(x/2)^6}{3!^2}$$

$$+ \left(1 + \frac{1}{2} + \frac{1}{3} + \frac{1}{4} + \frac{1}{5}\right)\frac{(x/2)^{10}}{5!^2} - \cdots + \cdots, \qquad (8\text{-}66)$$

and, after separating the real from the imaginary parts,

$$Y_0(x\sqrt{i}) = R_1(x) + iR_2(x),$$
$$Y_0(x\sqrt{-i}) = R_1(x) - iR_2(x),$$

(8-67)

with
$$R_1(x) = \frac{2}{\pi}\left(0.11593 S_1 - S_1 \ln x + \frac{\pi}{4}S_2 - S_3\right),$$

$$R_2(x) = \frac{2}{\pi}\left(0.11593 S_2 - S_2 \ln x - \frac{\pi}{4}S_1 - S_4\right).$$

(8-68)

Thus we see, since each pair of the functions J_0 and Y_0 is a pair of conjugate complex functions, that we may express *the complete integral* Eq. (8-53) *in real form* as follows:

$$y = a_1 S_1(x) + a_2 S_2(x) + c_1 R_1(x) + c_2 R_2(x), \qquad (8\text{-}69)$$

where a_1, a_2, c_1, c_2 are real constants of integration. For their determination, we have two boundary conditions for the plate available at the origin $r = x = 0$ and two conditions when x approaches infinity. To see the behavior of y when x increases indefinitely toward $x = \infty$, we make use of the well-known asymptotic expressions in the theory of Bessel's functions [writing for the principal values of $(\pm i)^{-\frac{1}{4}} = e^{\mp i\pi/8}$]:

$$J_0(x\sqrt{\pm i}) = J_0(u) = \sqrt{\frac{2}{\pi u}} \sin\left(u + \frac{\pi}{4}\right)$$

$$= \frac{e^{x/\sqrt{2}}}{\sqrt{2\pi x}} \cdot e^{\mp i\left(\frac{x}{\sqrt{2}} - \frac{\pi}{8}\right)}, \qquad (8\text{-}70a)$$

$$Y_0(x\sqrt{\pm i}) = Y_0(u) = \sqrt{\frac{2}{\pi u}} \cos\left(u + \frac{\pi}{4}\right)$$

$$= \frac{e^{x/\sqrt{2}}}{\sqrt{2\pi x}} \cdot (\mp i) \cdot e^{\mp i\left(\frac{x}{\sqrt{2}} - \frac{\pi}{8}\right)}. \qquad (8\text{-}70b)$$

By abbreviating,

$$\cos\left(\frac{x}{\sqrt{2}} - \frac{\pi}{8}\right) = c, \qquad \sin\left(\frac{x}{\sqrt{2}} - \frac{\pi}{8}\right) = s,$$

$$e^{\pm i\left(\frac{x}{\sqrt{2}} - \frac{\pi}{8}\right)} = c \pm is, \qquad (8\text{-}71)$$

we see that the complete integral of Eq. (8-69), when x tends to become infinite, approaches asymptotically the function in *real* form,

$$x = \infty, \qquad y = \frac{e^{x/\sqrt{2}}}{\sqrt{2\pi x}} \cdot (a_1 c - a_2 s - c_1 s + c_2 c), \qquad (8\text{-}72)$$

and that, in order that the boundary condition $x = \infty$, $y = 0$ in an infinite plate be satisfied, we have obviously to choose

$$c_1 = -a_2, \qquad c_2 = a_1. \qquad (8\text{-}73)$$

Furthermore, since in the third term containing the function $R_1(x)$ in Eq. (8-69) a term $S_1(x) \ln x$ appears and in the center of the plate $x = 0$, $S_1(0) = 1$, $\ln (0) = -\infty$, in order to obtain a finite deflection w at $x = 0$, we have to take the integration constant $c_1 = 0$ and thus also $a_2 = 0$. The complete integral therefore reduces to

$$y = a_1 [S_1(x) + R_2(x)]. \qquad (8\text{-}74)$$

The first term in the brackets being the real part of $J_0(u)$ and the second the imaginary part of $Y_0(u)$ for the complex argument $u = x\sqrt{i}$, the complete integral may also be written as

$$y = a_1[\operatorname{Re} J_0(u) + \operatorname{Im} Y_0(u)], \qquad u = x\sqrt{i}. \qquad (8\text{-}75)$$

The last unknown constant of integration a_1 is finally determined from the boundary condition that the shearing forces p_r in the plate in the vicinity of its center $r = x = 0$ must have a resultant equal to the single, concentrated force P or that p_r, in a circle of small radius r (x), according to the theory of circular plates [Sec. 8-2, Eq. (8-27)] must become equal to

$$p_r = -N \frac{d\,\Delta w}{dr} = -N \frac{d}{dr}\left(\frac{d^2w}{dr^2} + \frac{dw}{r\,dr}\right) = -\frac{P}{2\pi r}. \qquad (8\text{-}76)$$

In terms of the variables x and y [using $r = ax/\alpha = (N/\gamma_s)^{1/4} \cdot x$, $w = ay$], this gives

$$\left[x \frac{d}{dx}\left(\frac{d^2y}{dx^2} + \frac{dy}{x\,dx}\right)\right]_{x=0} = \frac{P}{2\pi a\sqrt{\gamma_s N}}. \qquad (8\text{-}77)$$

Interpreting, in a transitory way, y as a complex function of $u = x\sqrt{i}$, a glance at Eqs. (8-54) shows that the differential expression may also be written, using $z = -iy$, as

$$x \frac{dz}{dx} = -ix \frac{dy}{dx} = -\left(iu \frac{dy}{du}\right)_{u=0}. \qquad (8\text{-}78)$$

But, if the first term of $y = a_1 J_0(u)$ from Eqs. (8-75) is herein substituted, it does not contribute to it, and if the second term $y = a_1 Y_0(u)$ in complex form is taken, using the complete expression for $Y_0(u)$ given in Eq. (8-59), after differentiating it with respect to u in the vicinity of $u \sim 0$, one obtains $dY_0/du = -2/\pi u$ and

$$-\left(iu \frac{dy}{du}\right)_{u=0} = \frac{2ia_1}{\pi}. \qquad (8\text{-}79)$$

The second term of Eqs. (8-75), as the imaginary part of $Y_0(u)$, with $u = x\sqrt{i}$ in this preceding expression contributes therefore $+2a_1/\pi$, and the integration constant a_1 obtains the value[1]

$$a_1 = \frac{P}{4a \cdot \sqrt{\gamma_s N}}. \qquad (8\text{-}80)$$

---

[1] This value might also have been computed by making use of the expanded expressions in real form for $S_1(x)$ and $R_2(x)$ in Eq. (8-74), noting that only a single term in them, namely, $S_2(x) \ln x$, contributes for $x = 0$ to the differential expression Eq. (8-77).

The elastic surface of the deflected plate under a single force P and supported by the buoyancy pressures $-\gamma_s w$ *of the substratum is thus expressed by*

$$w = \frac{P}{4 \cdot \sqrt{\gamma_s N}} [S_1(x) + R_2(x)], \qquad x = \sqrt[4]{\frac{\gamma_s}{N}} \cdot r, \qquad (8\text{-}81)$$

$$w = \frac{P}{4\sqrt{\gamma_s N}} \left\{ \frac{S_1(x)}{2} + \frac{2}{\pi} [0.11593 S_2(x) - S_2(x) \ln x - S_4(x)] \right\}, \quad (8\text{-}82)$$

giving for *the maximum deflection* $w_{\max}$ under the load P at $x = r = 0$ $[S_1(0) = 1, S_2(0) = S_4(0) = 0]$ the value

$$w_{\max} = \frac{P}{8 \cdot \sqrt{\gamma_s N}}, \qquad (8\text{-}83)$$

agreeing with the one computed by HERTZ.   An extended plate resting on a solid, elastic foundation under the pressures $q = -kw$ has the same deflections, provided that γ_s is replaced by the bending constant k. The bending moments might be evaluated from

$$m_r = -N \left(\frac{d^2 w}{dr^2} + v \frac{dw}{r \, dr} \right),$$

$$m_t = -N \left(v \frac{d^2 w}{dr^2} + \frac{dw}{r \, dr} \right), \qquad (8\text{-}84)$$

but we shall refrain from listing their rather complex expressions tending to increase indefinitely around a concentrated force[1] P.

---

[1] Equation (8-83) overestimates the deflection and bending stresses if the load P is distributed over a comparatively greater area as a uniform pressure $p = $ const, for example, over a circle of a radius a which is a large multiple of the plate thickness h.   In this case the deflections are to be evaluated from two differential equations, namely:

When $0 \leq r \leq a$: $N\Delta\Delta w_1 = p - \gamma_s w_1,$

and when $r \geq a$: $N\Delta\Delta w_2 = -\gamma_s w_2.$ (8-85)

The eight integration constants, associated with the deflections w_1 and w_2, are to be evaluated from two conditions at $r = 0$, four conditions of continuity at $r = a$, and two conditions prescribed at $r = \infty$, this involving a considerable amount of computation.   One may establish a simpler approximate solution by replacing w_1 on the right side of the first equation [Eqs. (8-85)] through its mean value $\overline{w}_1$ over the interval $0 < r < a$, so that the first equation is expressed by

$$N\Delta\Delta w_1 = p - \gamma_s \overline{w}_1 = \text{const},$$

which has the same form as the equation for a circular plate under uniform pressure $p - \gamma_s \overline{w}_1 = $ const, and associating it with the second equation valid when $r > a$.

A purely viscous plate loaded by a single weight P will be *depressed into a resilient substratum against pressures of a viscous nature* $q = -k_s\dot{w}$ with which it resists (neglecting the part due to buoyancy $-\gamma_s w$) according to Eq. (8-51),

$$N_v \Delta\Delta\dot{w} = -k_s\dot{w}, \qquad (8\text{-}86)$$

with rates $\dot{w}$ which are determined by the preceding formulas (8-82) and (8-83), after writing in them, instead of the deflection w, γ_s, N, the rate of deflection $\dot{w}, k_s, N_v = (\tfrac{1}{3})\mu h^3$.

A group of rock strata supported by such a resilient substratum would thus slowly sink over a prolonged period of time under the weight of a massive pile of ice with the maximum velocity under the hump of ice:

$$\left(\frac{dw}{dt}\right)_{\max} = \frac{P}{8\cdot\sqrt{(\tfrac{1}{3})k_s\mu h^3}}. \qquad (8\text{-}87)$$

If the earth's outer crust, considered as *a purely viscous plate*, is supposed to reach to such great depths at which the substratum underlaying it, because of its high temperatures, reacts more or less as a fluid ($q = -\gamma_s w$), the deflections, on the other hand, will vary according to

$$N_v \Delta\Delta\dot{w} = -\gamma_s w. \qquad (8\text{-}88)$$

A solution of this equation under a single force P that increases exponentially with the time t as

$$P = P_0 e^{t/t_0} \qquad (8\text{-}89)$$

is found, using the previous formulas, to be

$$w = \frac{P_0 e^{t/t_0}}{4\cdot\sqrt{\gamma_s N_v}}\left[S_1\left(\frac{\alpha r}{a}\right) + R_2\left(\frac{\alpha r}{a}\right)\right], \qquad (8\text{-}90)$$

producing an affine sequence of deflections w. The time constant

$$t_0 = \frac{N_v \alpha^4}{\gamma_s a^4} \qquad (8\text{-}91)$$

controls the rate of sinking of the plate, and one may, for example, postulate that the heretofore arbitrary length a defines the radius at which the *first* zero value of the transcendental function in the brackets occurs, thus determining the unknown parameter α from

$$S_1(\alpha) + R_2(\alpha) = 0 \qquad (8\text{-}92)$$

and prescribing for the chosen a a vanishing deflection w. Since the greater a is, the smaller the time constant t_0 becomes, we note that, *the faster the plate deflects, the greater the area of it to be submerged in the principal trough under the load within the radius a.*

For an infinite plate supported by buoyancy pressures, the isostatic equilibrium requires that the resultant of these pressures $q = -\gamma_s w$ be equal and opposite to the single force P carried by the plate:

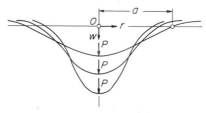

$$P = 2\pi\gamma_s \int_0^\infty rw\, dr. \qquad (8\text{-}93)$$

FIG. 8-8. Deflections of viscous plate on substratum under invariable single force P.

If P were held invariable with time t, since the deflections w within the principal trough in *a viscous plate* must continuously increase with t, one sees that *the radius a under an invariable load P* = const *must decrease* and there will develop a hinge along a circle, around which the deflected line instantaneously turns relative to its previous position, this circular hinge changing its location and moving inward toward the apex of the trough. In other words, while the principal depression deepens continuously, it becomes narrower, and a ring-shaped elevation forms around it that is raised above the former profiles of the deflected plate (see a few consecutive profiles in Fig. 8-8).[1]

[1] The distortion of a viscoelastic, infinite slab under an invariable transversal load will be treated in Sec. 10-4.

CHAPTER 9

BENDING OF VISCOELASTIC BEAMS

9-1. Beams of Uniform Cross Sections Bent by Transversal Forces. Consider a slender, prismatic beam or rod of uniform cross sections bent by transversal forces in one of the planes of principal inertia moment, choosing the x axis passing through the centers of gravity of the cross sections, and assuming that the planes of normal sections in a slender beam remain planes normal to the deflected elastic line. The fibers in the distance z from the neutral axis nn [in which the bending strains ε and the normal stresses of bending σ vanish (Fig. 9-1)] are extended in the direction of the x axis proportionally to z. If we denote the elastic and the permanent part of strain ε by ε' and ε'' and if we likewise define an elastic (w') and permanent (w'') part of the deflection w,

$$\varepsilon = \varepsilon' + \varepsilon'', \qquad w = w' + w'', \tag{9-1}$$

since the bending strains are proportional to the respective curvatures of the distorted axis of the beam, in viscoelastic material (E = Young's modulus, μ = viscosity coefficient), after placing a dot above a quantity whenever it is differentiated with respect to the time t, we have

$$\varepsilon' = -z\frac{\partial^2 w'}{\partial x^2} = \frac{\sigma}{E}, \qquad \varepsilon'' = -z\frac{\partial^2 w''}{\partial x^2}, \qquad \varepsilon = -z\frac{\partial^2 w}{\partial x^2}, \tag{9-2}$$

$$\dot{\varepsilon}' = -z\frac{\partial^2 \dot{w}'}{\partial x^2} = \frac{\dot{\sigma}}{E}, \qquad \dot{\varepsilon}'' = -z\frac{\partial^2 \dot{w}''}{\partial x^2} = \frac{\sigma}{3\mu}, \tag{9-3}$$

$$\dot{\varepsilon} = \dot{\varepsilon}' + \dot{\varepsilon}'' = -z\frac{\partial^2 \dot{w}}{\partial x^2} = \frac{1}{E}\left(\dot{\sigma} + \frac{\sigma}{t_e}\right), \qquad t_e = \frac{3\mu}{E}. \tag{9-4}$$

After multiplying each of the three relations of the first column of these equations by $z\,dA$ (dA denoting an element of the area A of the

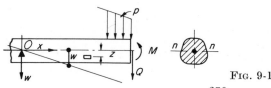

Fig. 9-1

270

cross sections in the distance z from the neutral axis nn) and integrating them with respect to the coordinate z over the area A, noting that

$$\int z^2 \, dA = I, \qquad \int \sigma z \, dz = M, \qquad \int \dot{\sigma} z \, dz = \dot{M} \qquad (9\text{-}5)$$

represent the planar moment of inertia I of the cross sections, the bending moment M, and its time derivative $\dot{M}$ in a section $x = \text{const}$ of the beam, if furthermore we denote the shearing force in a section $x = \text{const}$ by Q and the distributed load per unit length that the beam may carry by $p = f(x,t)$, we obtain

$$M = -IE \frac{\partial^2 w'}{\partial x^2} = -3I\mu \frac{\partial^2 \dot{w}''}{\partial x^2}, \qquad (9\text{-}6)$$

$$IE \frac{\partial^2 \dot{w}}{\partial x^2} = -\dot{M} - \frac{M}{t_e}, \qquad (9\text{-}7)$$

$$IE \frac{\partial^3 \dot{w}}{\partial x^3} = -\frac{\partial}{\partial x}\left(\dot{M} + \frac{M}{t_e}\right) = -\dot{Q} - \frac{Q}{t_e}, \qquad (9\text{-}8)$$

$$IE \frac{\partial^4 \dot{w}}{\partial x^4} = -\frac{\partial}{\partial x}\left(\dot{Q} + \frac{Q}{t_e}\right) = \dot{p} + \frac{p}{t_e}. \qquad (9\text{-}9)$$

Equations (9-7) and (9-9) represent two forms of the differential equation of the deflected elastic line w of a viscoelastic beam, while Eq. (9-6) helps to compute the elastic and permanent parts w' and w'' of the deflection w.

From Eq. (9-4), which we may write in the form

$$\dot{\varepsilon}' + \frac{\varepsilon'}{t_e} = \dot{\varepsilon}, \qquad (9\text{-}10)$$

the elastic strain ε' is expressed in terms of the total strain ε by [1]

$$\varepsilon'(t) = e^{-t/t_e}\left[\varepsilon(0) + \int_0^t \dot{\varepsilon} e^{t/t_e} \, dt\right] = \varepsilon(t) - \frac{e^{-t/t_e}}{t_e} \cdot \int_0^t \varepsilon e^{t/t_e} \, dt, \qquad (9\text{-}11)$$

where $\varepsilon(0)$ is the total bending strain ε at time $t = 0$. If at $t = 0$ no permanent strain $\varepsilon''(0)$ existed, $\varepsilon(0)$ equals the elastic strain $\varepsilon'(0)$. Looking upon Eq. (9-7) as on a first-order differential equation with respect to the time t of the bending moment M, we may compute M from it after the scheme of Eq. (9-11) as follows:

$$M(t) = -IE\left(\frac{\partial^2 w}{\partial x^2} - \frac{e^{-t/t_e}}{t_e} \cdot \int_0^t \frac{\partial^2 w}{\partial x^2} \cdot e^{t/t_e} \, dt\right) = -IE \frac{\partial^2 w'}{\partial x^2}, \qquad (9\text{-}12)$$

where we equated this with the second expression for M taken from Eq. (9-6). This last equation may now be integrated twice with respect to

[1] Cf. Sec. 4-1, Eqs. (4-7) and (4-8).

the variable x, disclosing that the elastic part of the deflection w' in terms of the total deflection w is expressed at any time t by

$$w' = w - \frac{e^{-t/t_e}}{t_e} \cdot \int_0^t we^{t/t_e}\, dt = -\frac{1}{IE}\int dx \int M\, dx + c_1 x + c_2, \qquad (9\text{-}13)$$

where the integration constants c_1 and c_2 depend on t, and that the permanent part of deflection w'', being $w'' = w - w'$, is

$$w'' = \frac{e^{-t/t_e}}{t_e}\int_0^t we^{t/t_e}\, dt. \qquad (9\text{-}14)$$

After differentiating this with respect to the time t, one obtains $\dot{w}'' = w'/t_e$ and for w'' the second, equivalent expression:

$$w''(t) = w''(0) + \frac{1}{t_e}\int_0^t w'\, dt. \qquad (9\text{-}15)$$

The differential equation of the elastic line for a viscoelastic beam [Eq. (9-9)] simplifies in the case of a *purely elastic solid* to

$$IE\,\frac{d^4 w}{dx^4} = p \qquad (9\text{-}16)$$

and for a *purely viscous solid* to[1]

$$3I\mu\,\frac{\partial^4 \dot{w}}{\partial x^4} = p, \qquad (9\text{-}17)$$

disclosing the simple rule which has already been mentioned that a viscous beam under a steady (time-independent) load p sags with uniform rates $\dot{w}$ proportionally to the deflections w of a beam of elastic material bent by the same load under the same boundary conditions. This is also true for a viscoelastic beam carrying only steady loads if they are placed simultaneously on it, the beam deflecting with steady velocities $\dot{w}$ proportionally to its initial, elastic deflections w'.

If the beam starts to deflect from an unloaded condition (the initial values of all loads being zero), the deflection w may be computed after integrating Eq. (9-7) or (9-9) with respect to t either from

$$IE\,\frac{\partial^2 w}{\partial x^2} = -M - \frac{1}{t_e}\int_0^t M\, dt,$$

or

$$IE\,\frac{\partial^4 w}{\partial x^4} = p + \frac{1}{t_e}\int_0^t p\, dt. \qquad (9\text{-}18)$$

[1] If the permanent parts of strain $\varepsilon'' = (\frac{1}{3}\mu)\int \sigma\, dt$ due to long-time action become predominant, the elastic parts ε' may be neglected besides the former. This type of purely viscous solid is characterized by a small value of the time constant $t_e = 3\mu/E$, and after multiplying Eq. (9-9) by t_e, neglecting the term $t_e\dot{p}$ besides p, and writing $Et_e = 3\mu$, Eq. (9-17) is obtained.

Suppose, on the other hand, that after suddenly loading a beam by single forces applied at several points, the latter are held in their elastically deflected positions fixed in space for an indefinite time. Then $\dot{w} = 0$, and from Eq. (9-7)

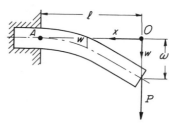

$$t_e \dot{M} + M = 0, \qquad M = M_1 e^{-t/t_e}, \text{ (9-19)}$$

the internal bending moments M and con-

FIG. 9-2

sequently the bending stresses σ in the beam gradually evanesce. After a sufficiently long time has elapsed, the beam will remain in its deflected position after it is liberated, its deflections having been converted through *relaxation* into permanent ones.

EXAMPLE 1. *For a viscoelastic cantilever* of length l built in at one end A and loaded by a single force $P = F(t)$ at the other end O (Fig. 9-2) with the bending moments $M = -Px$ from

$$\frac{\partial^2 \dot{w}}{\partial x^2} = \frac{\partial^3 w}{\partial x^2 \, \partial t} = \left(\dot{P} + \frac{P}{t_e} \right) \frac{x}{IE} \tag{9-20}$$

after integrating twice with respect to x and once with respect to t,

$$w = \left(P + \frac{1}{t_e} \int_0^t P \, dt \right) \frac{x^3}{6IE} + \varphi_1 + \varphi_2 x, \tag{9-21}$$

assuming that, for $t = 0$, $P = 0$, $w = 0$, φ_1 and φ_2 denote two arbitrary functions of t. Abbreviating the expression within the parentheses which is a known function of time by

$$P^* = P + \frac{1}{t_e} \int_0^t P \, dt \tag{9-22}$$

and denoting the maximum deflection under point O by ω, from the end conditions, $x = 0$, $w = \omega = \varphi_1$, and $x = l$, $w = 0$, $\partial w / \partial x = 0$,

$$\varphi_1 = \omega = \frac{P^* l^3}{3IE}, \qquad \varphi_2 = -\frac{P^* l^2}{2IE}, \tag{9-23}$$

the deflections of the cantilever are found equal to

$$w = \omega f(x) = \omega \left(\frac{x^3}{2l^3} - \frac{3x}{l} + 1 \right) = (\omega' + \omega'') f(x) \tag{9-24}$$

having the elastic and permanent parts

$$w' = \omega' f(x), \qquad \omega' = \frac{P l^3}{3IE},$$

$$w'' = \omega'' f(x), \qquad \omega'' = \frac{P l^3}{3IE t_e} \int_0^t P \, dt \tag{9-25}$$

If, for example, the single force P increases linearly with the time t, $P = Pt/t_0$, we have

$$\omega' = \frac{P_0 l^3}{3IE} \cdot \frac{t}{t_0}, \qquad \omega'' = \frac{P_0 l^3}{6IE} \cdot \frac{t^2}{t_0 t_e}.$$

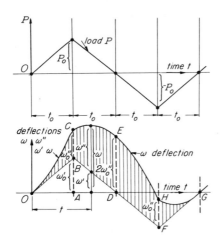

FIG. 9-3. Load P and deflections ω, ω', ω'' in dependence on time t for oscillating viscoelastic cantilever beam.

After a time period $t = t_0$ elapses,

$$P = P_0, \qquad \omega_0' = \frac{2t_e}{t_0}\,\omega_0'' = \frac{P_0 l^3}{3IE}.$$

EXAMPLE 2. *Oscillating cantilever.* With reference to the previous example, suppose that the single force P deflecting the cantilever changes periodically, as indicated in the upper half of Fig. 9-3, increasing and decreasing linearly with time between the limits $\pm P_0$, the full period of an oscillation amounting to $4t_0$. Then, using the relations just explained in Example 1, the maximum deflections ω and their elastic and permanent parts ω' and ω'' at the end of the cantilever $x = 0$ trace the easily understandable curves $OCEHG$, consisting of parabolas and the broken line $OBDFG$, respectively, the shaded ordinates representing the permanent parts ω'' of the deflection at various times t,

the deflection at time $2t_0$ being equal to

$$2\omega_0'' = \frac{P_0 l^3}{3IE} \cdot \frac{t_0}{t_e}$$

and of permanent nature, etc. The curve $P = f(\omega)$ of the load P in dependence on the maximum deflection ω that it produces is a hysteresis loop, consisting of two parabolic arcs of the type described in Sec. 1-1 [$B(e)$ in Fig. 4-11], confirming what has been said there in regard to hysteresis loops described under a constant rate of increase of stress

$$\dot{\sigma} = \frac{\partial \sigma}{\partial t} = \frac{\dot{M}}{S} = \frac{\dot{P}x}{S} = \frac{P_0 x}{t_0 S} = \text{const}$$

(S = section modulus of the beam).

9-2. Viscoelastic Beam Bent by Axial Compression Force Causing Buckling.

Let us investigate the motion of the points of a beam of viscoelastic material of length l, measuring its deflections w from the straight line in which two equal and opposite compression forces P in its ends are transferred to it. Since the bending moment M in a section x and its time derivative $\dot{M}$ are

$$M = Pw, \qquad \dot{M} = \dot{P}w + P\dot{w}, \tag{9-26}$$

with reference to Eq. (9-7) the deflection w satisfies the differential equation

$$\frac{\partial^2 \dot{w}}{\partial x^2} = -\frac{1}{IE}\left(\dot{M} + \frac{M}{t_e}\right) = -\frac{1}{IE}\left(\dot{P}w + P\dot{w} + \frac{P}{t_e}w\right) \tag{9-27}$$

or, after letting

$$\beta^2 = \frac{P}{IE}, \qquad (9\text{-}28)$$

$$\frac{\partial^2 \dot{w}}{\partial x^2} + \beta^2 \dot{w} = -\left(2\beta\dot{\beta} + \frac{\beta^2}{t_e}\right)w. \quad (9\text{-}29)$$

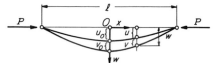

FIG. 9-4. Beam having initial deflection $u = u_0 \cos \dfrac{\pi x}{l}$.

If the beam is subjected to an *invariable* compression load P (held at value $P = $ const, independent of time t) $\dot{P} = 0$, the deflections are determined by

$$\frac{\partial^2 \dot{w}}{\partial x^2} + \beta^2 \dot{w} + \frac{\beta^2}{t_e} w = 0. \qquad (9\text{-}30)$$

A. Beam Supported in Hinges at Both Ends and Initially Not Perfectly Straight. Suppose that we have a beam as shown in Fig. 9-4, having a slightly curved axis in its unstressed, original form for which we may postulate the function

$$u = u_0 \cos \frac{\pi x}{l}. \qquad (9\text{-}31)$$

When a load P is suddenly imposed on the beam, it will deflect first elastically and u will increase by a small, elastic deflection v to the total deflection

$$w = u + v, \qquad (9\text{-}32)$$

the additional elastic deflection v, according to elementary theory of elastic bending, being determined by the differential equation:[1]

$$IE \frac{d^2 v}{dx^2} = -Pw = -P\left(v + u_0 \cos \frac{\pi x}{l}\right). \qquad (9\text{-}33)$$

After letting

$$v = v_0 \cos \frac{\pi x}{l} \qquad (9\text{-}34)$$

the constant v_0,

$$v_0 = \frac{u_0}{(\pi^2/\beta^2 l^2) - 1} = \frac{u_0}{(P_e/P) - 1}, \qquad (9\text{-}35)$$

is found to increase with the load P, becoming infinite when P equals the *Euler load*,

$$P_e = \frac{IE\pi^2}{l^2}, \qquad (9\text{-}36)$$

---

[1] In the left-hand term of Eq. (9-33) we must write $d^2 w/dx^2 = d^2 v/dx^2$ in order to take account of the fact that strains are caused only by v (not by u).

under which the elastic beam buckles. If we denote the constant quantity by α,

$$\alpha = \frac{1}{(\pi^2/\beta^2 l^2) - 1} = \frac{P}{P_e - P} \tag{9-37}$$

the initial elastic deflection of the beam may be expressed by

$$w = u + v = (1 + \alpha)u_0 \cos \frac{\pi x}{l} , \tag{9-38}$$

and we may assume for *the deflection w of the viscoelastic beam* at a time t

$$w = w_0 e^{\alpha t/t_e} \cos \frac{\pi x}{l} \tag{9-39}$$

which satisfies Eq. (9-33) and the initial condition that, at $t = 0$,

$$w = w_0 \cos \frac{\pi x}{l} = (1 + \alpha)u_0 \cos \frac{\pi x}{l} ,$$

provided that one chooses

$$w_0 = (1 + \alpha)u_0. \tag{9-40}$$

The maximum deflection of the viscoelastic beam at $x = 0$,

$$w_{\max} = (1 + \alpha)u_0 \, e^{\alpha t/t_e}, \tag{9-41}$$

thus increases with time t at a rate

$$\dot{w}_{\max} = \frac{\alpha(1 + \alpha)u_0}{t_e} \cdot e^{\alpha t/t_e}, \tag{9-42}$$

the center of the beam starting to deflect at time $t = 0$ at the rate

$$\dot{w}_{\max} = \frac{\alpha(1 + \alpha)u_0}{t_e} = \frac{P_e P u_0}{(P_e - P)^2 t_e} \cdot \tag{9-43}$$

$\dot{w}_{\max}$ becomes greater, the more the load P approaches the *Euler buckling load P_e*, and it becomes infinite when $P = P_e$. As time progresses, the greater the axial load P is, the more accelerated are the rates, beyond the initial rates, with which the beam deflects; for example, if $\alpha = 1$, under a compression force P equal to one-half of the Euler buckling load P_e at the rates of deflection,

$$\dot{w} = 2 \frac{u_0}{t_e} e^{t/t_e} \cos \frac{\pi x}{l} ,$$

whereas, if $\alpha = 9$, at nine-tenths of the buckling force,

$$\dot{w} = 90 \frac{u_0}{t_e} e^{9t/t_e} \cos \frac{\pi x}{l} ,$$

and we note that after a sufficiently long time t has elapsed the deflections w increase indefinitely at all loads P.

B. Buckling of Viscoelastic Beam under Invariable Compression Force Having Initial Eccentricity c. When a load P is imposed on the beam having an eccentricity c (Fig. 9-5), the *initial, elastic* deflection that it sustains equals

$$w = c \frac{\cos \beta x}{\cos \beta l/2} , \qquad \beta^2 = \frac{P}{IE} . \qquad (9\text{-}44)$$

The deflection w in a viscoelastic beam satisfying Eq. (9-30) and having at time $t = 0$ this prescribed form may be expressed by a series

$$w = \sum_n A_n e^{\beta^2 t / n^2 t_e} \cos \left(\sqrt{n^2 + \beta^2} \cdot x \right), \qquad (9\text{-}45)$$

where the constants n and A_n have to be determined. The initial condition at time $t = 0$ requires that, apart from the constants, we express the function $f(x) = \cos \beta x$ in the internal $-l/2 < x < l/2$ in terms of an infinite cosine series, supposing that $f(x)$ beyond the fundamental interval is extended as a periodic function of period $2l$, as indicated in Fig. 9-6. This is the case for the series

$$f(x) = \cos \beta x = \sum_{m=1}^{\infty} a_m \cos \frac{m\pi x}{l} , \qquad (m = 1, 3, 5, \ldots), \qquad (9\text{-}46)$$

where the constants a_m, after evaluating the integral,

$$a_m = \frac{2}{l} \int_0^l f(x) \cos \frac{m\pi x}{l} \cdot dx,$$

are found equal to

$$a_m = \frac{\sin (m + \alpha)\pi}{(m + \alpha)\pi} + \frac{\sin (m - \alpha)\pi}{(m - \alpha)\pi} ,$$

where α now denotes

$$\alpha = \frac{\beta l}{\pi} = \sqrt{\frac{P}{P_e}} .$$

Hence, the constants are

$$A_n = \frac{c a_m}{\cos \alpha \pi/2} , \qquad n^2 = \frac{(m^2 - \alpha^2)\pi^2}{l^2} ,$$

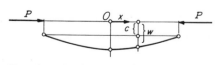

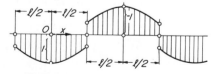

FIG. 9-5. Compression force P having eccentricity c.

FIG. 9-6. $f(x) = \cos \beta x$.

and this results in the expression for the deflection w of the viscoelastic beam:

$$w = \frac{c}{\cos \alpha \pi/2} \sum_{m=1}^{\infty} a_m e^{\alpha^2 t/(m^2 - \alpha^2)t_e} \cdot \cos \frac{m\pi x}{l}, \qquad (m = 1, 3, 5, \ldots). \quad (9\text{-}47)$$

The deflections w increase indefinitely at all loads after a sufficient time has elapsed and again with faster and more accelerated rates $\dot{w}$, the closer the axial force P approaches the critical Euler buckling load P_e under which the beam buckles instantaneously.

C. BENDING OF A PURELY VISCOUS BEAM UNDER INVARIABLE AXIAL COMPRESSION FORCE P HAVING AN ECCENTRICITY c. Let us consider the case of a purely viscous beam in which no elastic strains are present, by assuming $E = \infty, t_e = 3\mu/E = 0, Et_e = 3\mu$, the deflections of which are to be determined from the differential equation

$$\frac{\partial^2 \dot{w}}{\partial x^2} = -\frac{P}{3\mu I} \cdot w$$

or, after now denoting $\beta^2 = P/3\mu I$, from

$$\frac{\partial^2 \dot{w}}{\partial x^2} = -\beta^2 w. \qquad (9\text{-}48)$$

Under an invariable compression force P having an eccentricity c the bending moment M is distributed uniformly after the load is suddenly imposed at time $t = 0$ and is equal to $M = M_0 = Pc = \text{const.}$ Expanding this in a periodic function of x of period $2l$ (see Fig. 9-7), the initial condition for the beam at $t = 0$ is expressed by

$$M = \frac{4Pc}{\pi} \sum_{m=1}^{\infty} \frac{(-1)^{(m-1)/2}}{m} \cos \frac{m\pi x}{l}, \qquad (m = 1, 3, 5, \ldots), \quad (9\text{-}49)$$

and the solution satisfying Eq. (9-48) with the preceding condition is found in a manner analogous to that in Sec. 9-2B:

$$w = \frac{4c}{\pi} \sum_{m=1}^{\infty} \frac{(-1)^{(m-1)/2}}{m} \cdot e^{\beta^2 l^2 t/m^2 \pi^2} \cos \frac{m\pi x}{l}, \qquad (m = 1, 3, 5, \ldots). \quad (9\text{-}50)$$

For a *purely viscous bar no critical load exists*, but its deflections will increase indefinitely under any invariable axial compression force P and at faster rates, the greater this force is. If we denote a time constant t_0 by making it equal to

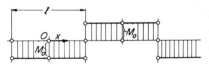

FIG. 9-7. $M = \pm M_0 = \pm Pc.$

$$t_0 = \left(\frac{\pi}{\beta l}\right)^2 = \frac{3\pi^2 \mu I}{Pl^2}, \qquad (9\text{-}51)$$

the maximum deflection in the center $x = 0$ of the span l may be expressed by the simple series of the time t,

$$w_{\max} = \frac{4c}{\pi}\left(e^{t/t_0} - \frac{1}{3}e^{t/9t_0} + \frac{1}{5}e^{t/25t_0} - \cdots + \cdots\right), \qquad (9\text{-}52)$$

showing that the greater P or the smaller the time t_0 is, the faster the deflection $w_{\max}$ will increase with the time t.

Part III

SUBSIDENCE AND POSTGLACIAL UPLIFT OF GROUND. FLOW OF SUBSTANCES DEFORMING UNDER GENERAL SPEED LAWS. THERMAL STRESSES AND THERMAL SHOCKS. RESIDUAL STRESSES

CHAPTER 10

THE BENDING OF A VISCOELASTIC SLAB
RESTING ON A SUBSTRATUM THAT RESPONDS
WITH BUOYANCY PRESSURES

Naturalist, a person well versed in Natural Philosophy—Johnson's Dictionary. Armed with this authority, chemists, electricians, astronomers and mathematicians may surely claim to be admitted along with merely descriptive investigators of nature to the honourable and convenient title of Naturalist, and refuse to accept so un-English, unpleasing and meaningless a variation from old usage as "physicist."

Footnote in a paper by Lord Kelvin, Effect of Earth's Elastic Yielding on the Tides, sec. 16. In his "Mathematical and Physical Papers," vol. 3, "Elasticity, Heat, Electromagnetism," sec. 8-20, p. 318, Cambridge University Press, London, 1890.

10-1. Subsidence and Uplift of Ground Levels. From geologic evidence, it is known that extended tracts of land were periodically and temporarily, over comparatively shorter periods of time, covered by ice, by huge glaciers, and that these ice ages subsided to epochs of a general recession during which the ice sheets gradually melted away as, for example, during the last ice age, preceding historic times, when vast parts of the northern hemisphere (Canada and the northern parts of the United States and of Europe) were covered with ice sheets of a few kilometers thickness that subsequently disappeared. The consequences of their gradual accumulation and subsequent recession have been described as subsidences of the ground levels under the weights of the masses of ice, often surrounded by uplifted regions, and as a slow rebound or uplift of the areas that have lost their cover of ice during the postglacial period of time, respectively, which caused many changes in the drainage areas of river systems, the temporary existence of glacial inland lakes, etc.[1]

The weight of a sheet of ice of thickness h_i and specific weight rounded off to $\gamma_i = 1,000$ kg/m³, deposited on the earth's slab, assumed to have

[1] Outstanding examples are the uplift of vast regions of northwest America and the Fennoscandian uplift, to which some references are made in later sections.

the mean specific weight $\gamma_e = 3,000$ kg/m³, floating supposedly on substratum of this same density, in isostatic equilibrium, would depress the slab by

$$\frac{\gamma_i h_i}{\gamma_e} = (\tfrac{1}{3})h_i.$$

An extended glacier of 3 km thickness resting on a portion of continental tableland submerges it by 1 km, and after it has melted, the ground rises by the same amount. Changes of the levels of the affected land masses of this or even much smaller order of magnitude occurring over several thousand years must be easily detectable and have been recorded in numerous observations.

A mathematical treatment of these interesting phenomena of the gradual, slow warping of the outer layers of the earth's crust caused by the changes of the ice loads leads into the theory of the bending of viscoelastic plates which has been very little developed as yet. It is felt, however, that some light may be thrown on it in this chapter and on related problems which may occur in engineering practice, in foundations resting on resilient ground, by considering the simplest cases of this type, namely, those of *the distortion of an infinite slab of uniform thickness of viscoelastic material slightly bent to a cylindrical surface*, the deflections w of which are functions of only one coordinate, x, and of the time t, after assuming that the infinite slab is loaded by extraneous forces while it rests (floats) in a deflected shape on substratum of slightly greater density behaving as a fluid.

A mathematically, closely related problem, namely, that of the bending of slender beams of purely elastic material resting on an elastic foundation, has been treated by engineers.[1] Their deflections are computed when the beam rests on an elastic ground by assuming that the contact pressure q between the beam and the ground is proportional to the deflection w of the beam: $q = -kw$, k being an empirically determined bedding constant of the dimension of kilograms per square centimeter if q is expressed as a load per unit length. This hypothesis is, strictly speaking, an approximate expression of the facts, since the displacement w normal to the free, plane surface $z = 0$ of an *extended, semi-infinite elastic body* $(z > 0)$ at a given point x,y does not depend only on the local pressure q exerted at this point but on an integral of all the contact forces q which act in the vicinity of the point. In the case under consideration, however, when the pressures q are created by pressure heads $q = -\gamma_s w$ of a gravitating fluid substratum, the contact pressures $q = -kw$ $(k = \gamma_s)$ supporting the slab are precisely expressed.

---

[1] M. HETÉNYI, "Beams on Elastic Foundation," 255 pp. University of Michigan Press, Ann Arbor, Mich.; also Oxford University Press, London, 1946. This book covers not only the theory of elastically supported beams but a number of related problems in the theory of elastic shells.

10-2. Viscoelastic Slab Resting on Substratum. Consider *an infinite slab* of viscoelastic material and uniform thickness h in a horizontal position. Assume the x,y plane in the middle plane of the slab, the positive z coordinate and deflection w pointing downward. The slab is slightly bent to a cylindrical surface, the deflection ordinates w of which are a function of the coordinate x and of the time t under a system of extraneous forces that includes a distributed load $p = f(x,t)$ and the contact pressures $q = -kw$ exerted by the substratum. This case of one-dimensional bending of a *slab* may be tied to the theory of bending of *a slender viscoelastic beam* developed in Chap. 9, supposing that the beam is deflected by the sum of a distributed pressure load p and the contact pressures $q = -kw$ of the substratum. The differential equation of the deflections w of such a beam, with reference to Eq. (9-9), is

$$IE \frac{\partial^4 \dot{w}}{\partial x^4} = -k\left(\dot{w} + \frac{w}{t_e}\right) + \dot{p} + \frac{p}{t_e}, \tag{10-1}$$

where I inertia moment of cross sections of beam
       E modulus of elasticity
       t_e $3\mu/E$
       μ coefficient of viscosity

and where the dots denote the derivatives with respect to the time t.

For *an infinite viscoelastic slab* of uniform thickness h resting on a substratum the corresponding equation is obtained after writing, instead of the bending rigidity of the beam IE in Eq. (10-1), *the slab modulus N* defined in the theory of bending of flat, elastic plates [Sec. 8-1, Eq. (8-4)]:

$$N = \frac{Eh^3}{12(1 - \nu^2)}, \tag{10-2}$$

ν denoting Poisson's ratio. The deflection w of a viscoelastic slab is determined from the differential equation[1]

$$N \frac{\partial^4 \dot{w}}{\partial x^4} = -k\left(\dot{w} + \frac{w}{t_e}\right) + \dot{p} + \frac{p}{t_e}, \qquad t_e = \frac{3\mu}{E}. \tag{10-3}$$

On account of the vanishing bending strains $\varepsilon_y = 0$ and rates of strain $\dot{\varepsilon}_y = 0$, apart from the bending stresses σ_x and bending moments $m_x = \int \sigma_x z\, dz$ per unit width, the infinite slab, bent according to a cylindrical surface, carries normal stresses σ_y and bending moments $m_y = \int \sigma_y z\, dz$ across the sections normal to the y axis. Since in a purely

[1] The dimensions of the constants appearing in Eqs. (10-1) and (10-3) are:

Bending rigidity of beam IE, [kg cm²]   Distributed load p:
Slab modulus N, [kg cm]   In beam, [kg/cm]
Bedding constant for beam k, [kg/cm²]   In slab, [kg/cm²]
Bedding constant for slab k, [kg/cm³]

elastic slab $m_y = \nu m_x$ but in a purely viscous slab $m_y = (\tfrac{1}{2})m_x$, in a viscoelastic slab, for example, on sudden loading the first relation holds; after a sufficient time has elapsed, while the load remained at the same value, after the permanent strains have become predominant, the second relation holds, and one sees that in such a plate a readjustment of the bending stresses σ_x, σ_y (and moments m_x, m_y) must gradually take place.   One avoids the necessity of dealing with these readjustment periods, which complicate the computations, *by postulating Poisson's ratio ν for the elastic parts of strain to be equal to $\tfrac{1}{2}$,* the value valid for the permanent parts of strain.[1]   In the following developments of the bending theory of viscoelastic slabs resting on a substratum, we shall, therefore, *assume $\nu = \tfrac{1}{2}$, that is, incompressibility also for the elastic parts of the strains,* and for the slab modulus N the value

$$N = \frac{Eh^3}{12(1-\nu^2)} = \frac{Eh^3}{9}.$$ (10-4)

[1] Consider, for example, the case of pure bending in the slab.   Suppose that, at time $t = 0$, a moment $m_x = m_0 = \text{const}$ is applied and maintained at this value.   Using the theory of plates, one easily shows that the bending moment m_y must gradually increase from the value $m_y = \nu m_0$ to the value $m_y = (\tfrac{1}{2})m_0$ according to the function

$$m_y = (\tfrac{1}{2})m_0[1 - (1 - 2\nu)e^{-t/t_e}],$$

while the deflections of the slab increase with time as

$$w = -\frac{m_0 x^2}{6N}\left[4(1-\nu)^2 + \frac{3t}{t_e} + (1-2\nu)^2(1 - e^{-t/t_e})\right]$$

with the velocities

$$\dot{w} = \frac{\partial w}{\partial t} = -\frac{m_0 x^2}{6Nt_e}[3 + (1 - 2\nu)^2 e^{-t/t_e}],$$

and the elastic part of the deflection varies as

$$w' = -\frac{m_0 x^2}{6N}\left\{3 + \left[1 - 4\nu^2 + (1-2\nu)^2\frac{t}{t_e}\right]e^{-t/t_e}\right\}.$$

But, if we let $\nu = \tfrac{1}{2}$ the preceding expressions simplify to

$$m_y = (\tfrac{1}{2})m_0, \qquad w = -\frac{m_0 x^2}{2N}\left(1 + \frac{t}{t_e}\right),$$

$$\dot{w} = -\frac{m_0 x^2}{2Nt_e}, \qquad w' = -\frac{m_0 x^2}{2N},$$

confirming the value of postulating incompressibility.   In fact, in these cases of cylindrical bending in infinite slabs, similarly as in the theory of plane strain, in viscoelastic material [Cf. Sec. 5-6, Eqs. (5-120) and (5-121)] because of the condition of plane strain $\varepsilon_y = \varepsilon_y' + \varepsilon_y'' = 0$ imposed on the slab, a relaxation process runs concurrently for the component of stress σ_y with the variation of the stresses σ_x with time t which is more simply handled if $\nu = \tfrac{1}{2}$ is assumed.

From Eq. (10-3) an important conclusion may
be drawn at once.   If the external pressures p
do not depend on the time t or tend to approach
steady values with time, when $\dot{p} = 0$, the rate
of deflection $\dot{w} = \partial w/\partial t$ gradually evanesces at
every point of the slab because the sum of the
extraneous pressures p and the reaction pres-

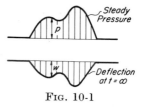

FIG. 10-1

sures $q = -kw$ approaches the value zero at every point when, after
some time, both become equal: $kw = p$.

A steady distribution of the extraneous pressures $p = f(x)$ *thus finally
leaves a precise imprint in the permanently bent form of the slab* in the
curve of its deflections in which a state of perfect, isostatic equilibrium
between p and $-kw$ *in an entirely unstressed, permanently bent position
of the slab comes to exist* (Fig. 10-1).   Mathematically, we may add, this
must be true for functions $p = f(x)$ even containing sudden kinks in
their slopes or finite discontinuities in the values of p which should
reappear in the shape of the deflected middle surface of the slab.   This
consequence of theory of isostasy of the earth's crust appears logical if
a massive slab were able to sustain in a stress-free condition similar
discontinuities in its bent form.   Actually, however, it will respond
with other types of distortion; for example, near abrupt changes of
pressure through the formation of steeply inclined faults (surfaces of
disruption through slip) or in the vicinity of a gradually increasing sharp
curvature of the deflected middle surface, the bending stresses will
reach the limit of fracture or the yield point in the material, precluding
application of regular bending theory long before the more advanced
stages of bending can in reality develop.

For *a slab of elastic material*, not having viscosity ($\mu = 0$, $t_e = 0$,
$w'' = 0$, $w = w'$) the deflections w for the slab resting on an elastic
foundation ($q = -kw$), loaded by a pressure p, are found from

$$N \frac{d^4 w}{dx^4} = -kw + p, \qquad (10\text{-}5)$$

and for *a purely viscous slab*, after neglecting the elastic strains and
deflections ($w' = 0$, $w = w''$), with a slab modulus

$$N_0 = \frac{\mu h^3}{3}, \qquad (10\text{-}6)$$

the deflection w is determined by the equation

$$N_0 \frac{\partial^4 \dot{w}}{\partial x^4} = -kw + p. \qquad (10\text{-}7)$$

10-3. Infinite Viscoelastic Slab Bent by a Single Force.

A. THE DEFLECTION CHANGES EXPONENTIALLY WITH TIME.   Suppose that $p = 0$, no external distributed load acts on the slab, the deflections are determined from Eq. (10-3), after putting $p = 0$ in it, from

$$N \frac{\partial^4 \dot{w}}{\partial x^4} = -k\left(\dot{w} + \frac{w}{t_e}\right), \qquad (10\text{-}8)$$

and a group of integrals may be obtained by letting the deflection w equal

$$w = w_0 X(x) \varphi(t), \qquad (10\text{-}9)$$

where w_0 is a constant deflection.   Substituting this in the preceding equation,

$$\frac{X^{(4)}}{X} = -\left(\dot{\varphi} + \frac{\varphi}{t_e}\right) \frac{k}{N\dot{\varphi}}, \qquad (10\text{-}10)$$

let these two expressions dependent either on x or on t equal a negative constant $-c$ $(c > 0)$ and suppose that we write, instead of c,

$$c = \frac{4\lambda^4}{a^4}, \qquad (10\text{-}11)$$

where a denotes an arbitrarily chosen length and λ is a dimensionless quantity.   Then, the left part of Eq. (10-10) gives

$$\frac{d^4 X}{dx} = -\frac{4\lambda^4}{a^4} X \qquad (10\text{-}12)$$

showing that the four integrals satisfying this linear, fourth-order differential equation prescribing the function $X(x)$ must have the form[1]

$$X(x) = e^{\sqrt[4]{-4}(\lambda x/a)} = e^{\pm(1 \pm i)(\lambda x/a)}$$

or, in real form

$$X(x) = (e^{\lambda x/a} \quad \text{or} \quad e^{-\lambda x/a})\left(\cos \frac{\lambda x}{a} \quad \text{or} \quad \sin \frac{\lambda x}{a}\right). \qquad (10\text{-}13)$$

Furthermore, the right part of Eq. (10-10), using (10-11), gives for the function $\varphi(t)$

$$\left(\frac{4\lambda^4 N}{ka^4} - 1\right) t_e \cdot \frac{d\varphi}{dt} = \varphi \qquad (10\text{-}14)$$

or, if we abbreviate by:

$$\beta = \frac{4\lambda^4 N}{ka^4}, \qquad t_0 = (\beta - 1)t_e,$$

$$t_0 \dot{\varphi} = \varphi, \qquad \varphi = e^{t/t_0}, \qquad (10\text{-}15)$$

---

[1] Using the four roots: $\sqrt[4]{-1} = \pm(1 \pm i)/\sqrt{2}$.

and we note that the constant t_0 having the dimension of a time can be either positive or negative, depending on whether

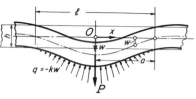

$$1 < \beta, \qquad t_0 > 0,$$

or
$$(10\text{-}16)$$

$$0 < \beta < 1, \qquad -t_e = -\frac{3\mu}{E} < t_0 < 0.$$

FIG. 10-2

The deflections of the viscoelastic slab,

$$w = w_0 e^{t/t_0} X\left(\frac{\lambda x}{a}\right), \tag{10-17}$$

in the first case ($\beta > 1$) will increase and in the second case ($0 < \beta < 1$) will decrease with the time t, describing a loading or unloading process, respectively, in the slab.

Restricting the *application to an infinitely long slab loaded by a single, concentrated force P per unit of length*, uniformly distributed along the y axis ($x = 0$) (Fig. 10-2), we need the combination of two particular integrals for the positive values of x:

$$X\left(\frac{\lambda x}{a}\right) = e^{-\lambda x/a}\left(\cos\frac{\lambda x}{a} + \sin\frac{\lambda x}{a}\right), \tag{10-18}$$

giving, for $x = 0$, $\partial w/\partial x = 0$ and vanishing deflections w when x tends to increase to $x = \infty$. This represents, apart from the exponential time factor e^{t/t_0}, the well-known curve of rapidly declining oscillations akin to the deflected elastic line of a long beam or slab of perfectly elastic material, supported on an elastic foundation, whose deflections, when $p = 0$, satisfy

$$\frac{d^4 w^*}{dx^4} = -\frac{k}{N} w^* \tag{10-19}$$

[see Eq. (10-5)]. The latter equation gives, if we define a parameter λ_0 by

$$\lambda_0^4 = \frac{k a^4}{4N} \tag{10-20}$$

(a denoting the same arbitrary length as before) for the case of a single, concentrated force at $x = 0$, the solution for *the elastic slab* for $x > 0$,

$$w^* = w_0^* X_0\left(\frac{\lambda_0 x}{a}\right) = w_0^* e^{-\lambda_0 x/a}\left(\cos\frac{\lambda_0 x}{a} + \sin\frac{\lambda_0 x}{a}\right), \tag{10-21}$$

where w_0* is the maximum deflection at $x = 0$, whereas *the viscoelastic slab* at time $t = 0$ has the deflection curve

$$w = w_0 X\left(\frac{\lambda x}{a}\right) = w_0 e^{-\lambda x/a}\left(\cos\frac{\lambda x}{a} + \sin\frac{\lambda x}{a}\right). \qquad (10\text{-}22)$$

The functions $X(\lambda x/a)$ and $X_0(\lambda_0 x/a)$ differ in the value of the parameters λ and λ_0. Suppose that we understand under the arbitrary length a the distance of the first zero of the function $X(\lambda x/a)$ from the origin $x = 0$ and denote by l and l_0 the width of the principal troughs between the nearest zeros of X and X_0 on both sides of the single force. Then, $l = 2a$ and w and w* vanish at $x = a = (\frac{1}{2})l$ and $x = (\frac{1}{2})l_0$, respectively, when

$$\sin\lambda = -\cos\lambda, \qquad \lambda = (\tfrac{3}{4})\pi,$$

and

$$\sin\frac{\lambda_0 l_0}{l} = -\cos\frac{\lambda_0 l_0}{l}, \qquad \lambda_0 = \frac{3\pi l}{4 l_0} = \frac{\lambda l}{l_0}.$$

Since, according to the definition equation for the constant β [Eqs. (10-15)],

$$\beta = \left(\frac{\lambda}{\lambda_0}\right)^4 = \left(\frac{l_0}{l}\right)^4, \qquad (10\text{-}23)$$

we see that the ratio of the two wavelengths is

$$\frac{l_0}{l} = \sqrt[4]{\beta} \qquad (10\text{-}24)$$

and that the width l of *the principal trough in the deflection curve under the single force of a viscoelastic slab is shorter on loading* (when $\beta > 1$) and *is longer on unloading* (when $0 < \beta < 1$) *than the length l_0 of an elastic slab* having the same values k and N.

The elastic part w' of the deflection w is evaluated from Eq. (9-13),

$$\dot{w}' + \frac{w'}{t_e} = \dot{w} = \frac{w_0}{t_0} X\left(\frac{\lambda x}{a}\right) e^{t/t_0}, \qquad (10\text{-}25)$$

and the permanent part w'' from Eq. (9-14),

$$\dot{w}'' = \frac{w'}{t_e}. \qquad (10\text{-}26)$$

By letting

$$w' = w_0 X\left(\frac{\lambda x}{a}\right) T(t),$$

from Eq. (10-25),

$$T(t) = Ce^{-t/t_e} + e^{t/t_0} \cdot \frac{t_e}{t_0 + t_e}, \qquad (10\text{-}27)$$

where C is an integration constant.

B. AFFINE SEQUENCE OF DEFLECTIONS FOR LOADING BY SINGLE FORCE P.
Supposing that $\beta > 1$, a special sequence of deflections of a viscoelastic slab is
obtained by taking the integration constant $C = 0$,

$$T(t) = e^{t/t_0} \cdot \frac{t_e}{t_0 + t_e} = \frac{1}{\beta} e^{t/t_0}, \tag{10-28}$$

corresponding to which the elastic w', permanent w'', and total deflections w of
the slab are equal to

$$w' = \frac{w t_e}{t_0 + t_e} = \frac{w}{\beta},$$

$$w'' = \frac{w t_0}{t_0 + t_e} = \frac{w(\beta - 1)}{\beta}, \tag{10-29}$$

$$w = w' + w'' = w_0 X\left(\frac{\lambda x}{a}\right) e^{t/t_0},$$

which all vanish at $t = \infty$. We may call this the sequence of affine deflections
of the slab, characterized by the property that the ratios $w':w'':w$ remain
unchanged during the distortion. If, for example, $\beta = 2$, $t_0 = t_e$, $w' = w'' = $
$(\frac{1}{2})w$, the wavelength is $l = (2)^{-1/6}l_0 = 0.84l_0$.

At time $t = 0$,

$$w' = \frac{w_0 X}{\beta}, \qquad w'' = \frac{(\beta - 1)w_0 X}{\beta}, \qquad w = w_0 X, \tag{10-30}$$

and we may alternatively consider this to be the initial condition for the distortion for subsequent times $t > 0$.

If P denotes the single, concentrated force per unit width which acts at point
$x = 0$ deflecting the slab, since this force must equal the weight of the displaced
volume of the substratum, we have for an infinite slab

$$P = 2k \int_{x=0}^{x=\infty} w \, dx. \tag{10-31}$$

But

$$\int_0^\infty w \, dx = w_0 e^{t/t_0} \int_0^\infty X\left(\frac{\lambda x}{a}\right) dx = \frac{w_0 a}{\lambda} e^{t/t_0}$$

and the single force P is

$$P = \frac{2kaw_0}{\lambda} e^{t/t_0} = P_0 e^{t/t_0}. \tag{10-32}$$

Here

$$P_0 = \frac{2kaw_0}{\lambda} \tag{10-32a}$$

denotes the value of P at time $t = 0$ and P_0 thus determines the value of the
maximum deflection w_0 at $t = 0$.†

† The rate of loading

$$\frac{dP}{dt} = \dot{P} = \frac{P_0}{t_0} e^{t/t_0}$$

at time $t = 0$, $\dot{P} = P_0/t_0$ increases inversely with the value of the time constant t_0:

$$t_0 = (\beta - 1)t_e = \frac{3\mu(\beta - 1)}{E},$$

i.e., with the viscosity μ. If β approaches the critical value $\beta = 1$, the rate of loading
becomes infinite, since t_0 vanishes and $\lambda = \lambda_0$, a case in which the solution of Eq. (10-8)

For a slab of perfectly elastic material, we would have similarly found for the single force

$$P_0^* = \frac{2kaw_0^*}{\lambda_0}. \tag{10-33}$$

C. SUDDEN UNLOADING. Let a slab, after it has passed through an affine sequence of deflections, at some time t, have the deflection

$$w_1 = c_1 X\left(\frac{\lambda x}{a}\right) = c_1 e^{-\lambda x/a}\left(\cos\frac{\lambda x}{a} + \sin\frac{\lambda x}{a}\right) \tag{10-34}$$

[where we have written c_1 instead of $w_0 e^{t/t_0}$, with reference to Eqs. (10-29)] under the single force

$$P_1 = \frac{2kac_1}{\lambda} \tag{10-35}$$

and suddenly release this force. The slab will rebound purely elastically, according to Eqs. (10-21) and (10-33), with the deflections

$$w_2 = -c_2 X_0\left(\frac{\lambda_0 x}{a}\right) = -c_2 e^{-\lambda_0 x/a}\left(\cos\frac{\lambda_0 x}{a} + \sin\frac{\lambda_0 x}{a}\right) \tag{10-36}$$

and with a force

$$P_2 = -\frac{2kac_2}{\lambda_0} = -P_1; \tag{10-37}$$

since

$$c_2 = \frac{c_1 \lambda_0}{\lambda}$$

the slab takes the new deflected form

$$w = w_1 + w_2 = c_1 X - c_2 X_0 = \frac{P_1}{2ka}(\lambda X - \lambda_0 X_0), \tag{10-38}$$

its maximum deflection at $x = 0$ having been reduced to

$$w_0 = c_1 - c_2 = \frac{P_1}{2ka}(\lambda - \lambda_0). \tag{10-39}$$

The form of the unloaded slab is reproduced in the lower figure in Fig. 10-3 obtained from the shaded differences of the ordinates drawn between the curves w_1 and $-w_2$ in the upper figure (assuming that $\lambda = 2\lambda_0$). It is perhaps noteworthy that through the sudden release of the single force P_1, *two symmetrically oriented gentle bulges have been raised above the horizontal level $w = 0$.*

---

would appear to fail. The case $\beta = 1$ obviously corresponds to a perfectly elastic slab having vanishing viscosity, in which case the deflections may be applied suddenly or with any rate, since they are independent of time. But, suppose that the quantity $\beta - 1$ became extremely small, say, for example, $\beta - 1 = 10^{-12}$, and that the relaxation time constant t_e dependent on the viscosity μ were extremely large, say, for example, $t_e = 10^{12}$. This would make $t_0 = 1$ sec, and although $\beta = 1 + 10^{-12}$ is very near to its critical value $\beta = 1$, we would obtain a finite exponential factor e^{t/t_0}. Thus, a time-dependent solution $w = w_0 X(x) e^{t/t_0}$ exists as long as

$$\lim_{\beta=1, t_e=\infty} [(\beta - 1)t_e] = t_0$$

remains finite.

FIG. 10-3. Infinitely long slab resting on buoyant substratum. Upper figure, w_1, initial (partially elastic and partially permanent) deflections of infinite viscoelastic slab under a single force P_1; $-w_2$, deflections of elastic rebound. Lower figure, $w = w_1 + w_2$, deflected line after sudden release of force P_1.

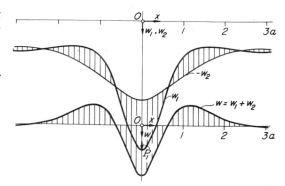

This may represent an extremely simplified picture of an example of a very rapid postglacial uplift, having some bearing on what might be expected if, for example, the load of a long glacial tongue spread over a longitudinal trough having gently rising slopes quickly melts away. The upper parts of the slopes of the valley, under which the ground under the weight of the ice tongue was formerly depressed, are raised above the horizontal plane and become two parallel elevations or gently curved ridges—at least for a certain period of time.[1]

If $0 < \beta < 1$, one may treat in a similar way a continuous regression of deflections under a gradually diminished single force $P = P_0 e^{-t/t_1}$ by letting $t_0 = -t_1, t_1 = (1 - \beta)t_e$.

10-4. The Deflection Progresses under an Invariable Single Force P.

We make use of the solution of the differential equation (10-8) in Eqs. (10-29) and (10-32) expressing the deflection w and single force P:

$$w = c_0 e^{t/t_0} X\left(\frac{\lambda x}{a}\right) = c X\left(\frac{\lambda x}{a}\right),$$
$$P = P_0 e^{t/t_0}, \tag{10-40}$$

where we have denoted the maximum deflection of the slab at $x = 0$ by

$$c = c_0 e^{t/t_0} \tag{10-41}$$

and where the constants t_0 and P_0 are given by

$$t_0 = t_e\left[\left(\frac{\lambda}{\lambda_0}\right)^4 - 1\right], \qquad t_e = \frac{3\mu}{E}, \qquad P_0 = \frac{2kac_0}{\lambda}, \tag{10-42}$$

[1] The profile illustrated in the lower figure in Fig. 10-3 and expressed by Eq. (10-38) is characterized by the temporary balance of the upward- and downward-directed buoyancy pressures $q = -kw$, but this is an intermediate form of the earth's distorted slab, since these pressures remain active and under their action, as time further progresses, all waves will be gradually smoothed out to the horizontal plane. That the buoyancy pressures $q = -kw$ beneath the elevated portions of the slab take on positive values (became tensile stresses) need not be considered objectionable in view of the superposed hydrostatic pressures due to the weights of all layers constituting the viscoelastic slab which, being irrelevant for the bending distortion, need not be considered but the presence of which prevents the true contact pressure beneath the slab from taking on the sign of tensile normal stresses q.

c_0 and P_0 being the values of c and P at time $t = 0$.   In this sequence of increasing deflections w and single force P exponentially with the time t, while the parameter λ is held constant,

$$\frac{c}{P} = \frac{c_0}{P_0} = \frac{\lambda}{2ka} = \text{const,} \tag{10-43}$$

the maximum deflection c and the single force P are represented by two exponential curves in their dependence on the time t, whereas P versus c is a straight line, as illustrated in Figs. 10-4 through 10-6, in which the points A, B, and C belong to the same time t.

While $\lambda = $ const, suppose that the load P and deflection c during a differential of time dt have increased by the differentials dP and dc (the corresponding points in Figs. 10-4 and 10-6 are represented by A', B', C'):

$$dP = \frac{P_0}{t_0} e^{t/t_0}\, dt, \qquad dc = \frac{c_0}{t_0} e^{t/t_0}\, dt. \tag{10-44}$$

After using Eq. (10-43) we have for the change of the deflections during the time dt

$$dw = dc X\left(\frac{\lambda x}{a}\right), \qquad dc = \frac{\lambda}{2ka}\, dP. \tag{10-45}$$

After this infinitesimal change, suppose that *the slab is suddenly unloaded by just* dP.   This causes a purely elastic rebound for which, according to Eqs. (10-36) and (10-37), the deflections of the slab decrease by the differentials

$$dw' = dc' X_0\left(\frac{\lambda_0 x}{a}\right), \qquad dc' = \frac{\lambda_0}{2ka}\, dP. \tag{10-46}$$

If dC and dW denote the deflections at $x = 0$ and x after this infinitesimal unloading (the new state in the slab being represented by the points A'', B'', C''), these will be expressed by

$$dC = dc - dc' = dP \cdot \frac{\lambda - \lambda_0}{2ka},$$
$$dW = dw - dw' = X\, dc - X_0\, dc'. \tag{10-47}$$

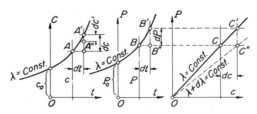

FIG. 10-4   FIG. 10-5   FIG. 10-6

FIGS. 10-4, 10-5, and 10-6. Increments of maximum deflection c and force P.

But, to point C'' (Fig. 10-6) corresponds a new value $\lambda + d\lambda$ along the straight line OC'' which is obtained by holding constant in Eqs. (10-42) not λ but P, so that after differentiating it, we see that $dc = \overline{CC''}$ must also be equal to

$$dc = \frac{P \, d\lambda}{2ka} . \tag{10-48}$$

Since this dc is the same value as that expressed in Eqs. (10-44) and (10-45), we have

$$dP : P = d\lambda : \lambda = dt : t_0 \tag{10-49}$$

and can express dC and dW in Eqs. (10-47) in terms of λ as follows:

$$dC = \frac{P \cdot [1 - (\lambda_0/\lambda)] \, d\lambda}{2ka} ,$$

$$dW = \frac{P \cdot [X - (\lambda_0/\lambda)X_0] \, d\lambda}{2ka} . \tag{10-50}$$

Denote by t_1 the time when the increment dP was added and by λ_1 the value of λ while the load increased to the value $P = P_0 e^{t_1/t_0}$; now suppose that, after the load has been restored to this value, similar, infinitesimal loading and unloading steps as described are repeated an infinite number of times, restoring in each cycle the force to its value $P = P_0 e^{t_1 t_0} = \text{const.}$ Then, the new deflections C and W will accrue:

$$C = \frac{P}{2ka} \int_{\lambda_1}^{\lambda} \left(1 - \frac{\lambda_0}{\lambda}\right) d\lambda = \frac{P\lambda_0}{2ka}\left(\frac{\lambda - \lambda_1}{\lambda_0} - \ln\frac{\lambda}{\lambda_1}\right), \tag{10-51}$$

$$W = \frac{P}{2ku}\left[\int_{\lambda_1}^{\lambda} X\left(\frac{\lambda x}{a}\right) d\lambda - \lambda_0 X\left(\frac{\lambda_0 x}{a}\right)\int_{\lambda_1}^{\lambda} \frac{d\lambda}{\lambda}\right]. \tag{10-52}$$

But

$$\int_{\lambda_1}^{\lambda} X\left(\frac{\lambda x}{a}\right) d\lambda = \int_{\lambda_1}^{\lambda} e^{-\lambda x/a}\left(\cos\frac{\lambda x}{a} + \sin\frac{\lambda x}{a}\right) d\lambda$$

$$= \frac{a}{x}\left(e^{-\lambda_1 x/a}\cos\frac{\lambda_1 x}{a} - e^{-\lambda x/a}\cos\frac{\lambda x}{a}\right)$$

and

$$W = \frac{P}{2ka}\left[\frac{a}{x}\left(e^{-\lambda_1 x/a}\cos\frac{\lambda_1 x}{a} - e^{-\lambda x/a}\cos\frac{\lambda x}{a}\right) - \lambda_0 X_0\left(\frac{\lambda_0 x}{a}\right) \cdot \ln\frac{\lambda}{\lambda_1}\right]^{\dagger}. \tag{10-53}$$

In summing up, then, we note that first, during the time period $0 < t < t_1$, the viscoelastic slab bends with deflections w that increase

† The first term in this expression, when x is taken equal to zero, appears in the form 0/0, but from Eq. (10-52) one sees that its true value equals $\lambda - \lambda_1$, confirming the value of $W_{x=0} = C$.

exponentially with the time,

$$w = c_0 e^{t/t_0} X_1\left(\frac{\lambda_1 x}{a}\right), \tag{10-54}$$

under a similarly growing force

$$P = P_0 e^{t/t_0}, \qquad P_0 = \frac{2kac_0}{\lambda_1}, \tag{10-55}$$

while the parameter λ is held at the value $\lambda = \lambda_1 = \text{const}$ and the time constant t_0 at the value

$$t_0 = t_e\left[\left(\frac{\lambda_1}{\lambda_0}\right)^4 - 1\right] = \text{const.} \tag{10-56}$$

This produces at time $t = t_1$ the deflection

$$w_1 = c_1 X_1\left(\frac{\lambda_1 x}{a}\right), \qquad c_1 = c_0 e^{t_1/t_0}, \tag{10-57}$$

under the force

$$P_0 e^{t_1/t_0} = P. \tag{10-58}$$

Secondly, if we consider the latter values as the initial values for a second series of distortions W and C, when subsequently the force is held at $P = \text{const}$ and $t > t_1$, $\lambda > \lambda_1$, the viscoelastic slab will sustain the additional deflections W and C that we have evaluated in Eqs. (10-53) and (10-51). The total deflection at a time $t > t_1$ is therefore

$$w = w_1 + W, \qquad c = c_1 + C. \tag{10-59}$$

Finally, while P is held constant, we wish to establish the relation between the parameter λ and the time t. But from Eq. (10-49),

$$\frac{d\lambda}{\lambda} = \frac{dt}{t_0}, \tag{10-60}$$

since the value of t_0 depends on the variable λ,

$$t_0 = t_e\left[\left(\frac{\lambda}{\lambda_0}\right)^4 - 1\right], \tag{10-61}$$

the preceding relation, after substituting t_0 in it, defines a differential equation connecting λ and t:

$$\left[1 - \left(\frac{\lambda_0}{\lambda}\right)^4\right] d\left(\frac{\lambda}{\lambda_0}\right)^4 = \frac{4}{t_e} dt. \tag{10-62}$$

With the initial condition $t = t_1$, $\lambda = \lambda_1$ this is satisfied by

$$\frac{4(t - t_1)}{t_e} = \left(\frac{\lambda}{\lambda_0}\right)^4 - \left(\frac{\lambda_1}{\lambda_0}\right)^4 - \ln\left(\frac{\lambda}{\lambda_1}\right)^4. \tag{10-63}$$

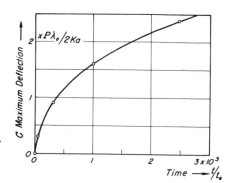

FIG. 10-7. Variation of maximum deflection C with time when $\lambda_1 = \lambda_0$.

The function $\lambda = F(t - t_1)$ is represented by a concave curve that rises continuously with decreasing rate. An example can be seen in Fig. 10-7.

An interesting special case results if the initial value λ_1 is chosen equal to $\lambda_1 = \lambda_0$. This case occurs when *the slab is originally loaded rapidly, purely elastically,* at the time $t_1 = 0$ under a single force P, causing *an initially elastic deflection*

$$w_1 = c_1 X_0 \left(\frac{\lambda_0 x}{a}\right), \qquad c_1 = \frac{P\lambda_0}{2ka}. \qquad (10\text{-}64)$$

The expressions given in Eqs. (10-51), (10-53), and (10-63) simplify in this case, and while P is subsequently held constant, the maximum deflection C at $x = 0$ increases with λ as

$$C = \frac{P\lambda_0}{2ka}\left(\frac{\lambda}{\lambda_0} - 1 - \ln\frac{\lambda}{\lambda_0}\right) \qquad (10\text{-}65)$$

while the time t progresses as

$$t = (\tfrac{1}{4})t_e \cdot (u - 1 - \ln u), \qquad (10\text{-}66)$$

where the symbol u abbreviates $u = (\lambda/\lambda_0)^4$. These last two equations define in parametric form the variation of the maximum deflection $C = W_{x=0}$ with the time t for the values $\lambda > \lambda_0$. The curve of the deflections W is given by

$$W = \frac{P}{2ka}\left[\frac{a}{x}\left(e^{-\lambda_0 x/a}\cos\frac{\lambda_0 x}{a} - e^{-\lambda x/a}\cos\frac{\lambda x}{a}\right) - \lambda_0 X_0\left(\frac{\lambda_0 x}{a}\right)\ln\frac{\lambda}{\lambda_0}\right], \qquad (10\text{-}67)$$

and the total deflection is

$$w = w_1 + W. \qquad (10\text{-}68)$$

Tables 10-1 and 10-2 and Fig. 10-8 disclose that the wavelength $l = 2a$ of the principal trough in which an infinite viscoelastic slab under an invariable single force $P = \text{const}$ progressively deflects decreases

TABLE 10-1. DEFLECTIONS $w_1 = (P\lambda_0/2ka)X_0(\lambda_0 x/a)$, W, AND TOTAL DEFLECTIONS $w = w_1 + W$ FOR INFINITE, VISCOELASTIC SLAB UNDER A SINGLE FORCE P WHICH IS MAINTAINED AT A CONSTANT VALUE

$\lambda_0 x/a =$	0	0.25	0.50	0.75	1.00	1.25	1.50	2.00	2.50	3.00
$X_0(\lambda_0 x/a) = \dfrac{2ka}{P\lambda_0} w_1 =$	1	0.946	0.824	0.668	0.509	0.363	0.234	+0.067	−0.017	−0.042
$\lambda/\lambda_0 = 2$ $W = \dfrac{P\lambda_0}{2ka} \times$	+0.307	0.229	+0.097	−0.022	−0.098	−0.128	−0.118	−0.068	+0.015	+0.012
$\lambda/\lambda_0 = 2$ $w =$	+1.307	1.175	0.921	0.646	0.411	0.235	+0.116	−0.001	−0.002	−0.030
$\lambda/\lambda_0 = 3$ $W = \dfrac{P\lambda_0}{2ka} \times$	+0.901	0.593	+0.129	—	−0.31	—	—	−0.10	—	—
$\lambda/\lambda_0 = 3$ $w =$	+1.901	1.539	0.953	—	+0.20	—	—	−0.03	—	—

TABLE 10-2. MAXIMUM DEFLECTIONS C AT $x = 0$ AT VARIOUS TIMES t

$\lambda/\lambda_0 =$	1	2	3	4	5
$u = (\lambda/\lambda_0)^4 =$	1	16	81	256	625
Time $t/t_e =$	0	48.92	302.4	996.0	2,470.4
Maximum deflection $C = P\lambda_0/2ka \times$	0	0.31	0.90	1.61	2.39

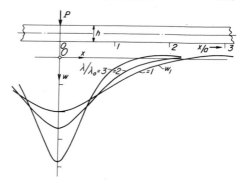

FIG. 10-8. Successive forms of line of deflections w of a viscoelastic slab under a single, concentrated force P held invariable.

continuously with the time t. The trend of $w_1 = c_1 X_0(\lambda_0 x/a)$ representing the initial elastic deflection of the slab at the time $t = 0$, the deflection curve W, and the total deflection $w = w_1 + W$ have been recorded corresponding to the stages $\lambda/\lambda_0 = 1, 2$, and 3 in Tables 10-1 and 10-2, where the maximum deflections $W_{x=0} = C$ are also tabulated for a few values of the ratio λ/λ_0 and the corresponding ratios of time t/t_e. Figure 10-8 illustrates in three curves the deflected form of the viscoelastic slab bent under a constant single force P for the stages $\lambda/\lambda_0 = 1, t/t_e = 0$ (initial, elastic deflection); $\lambda/\lambda_0 = 2, t/t_e = 0.31$; and $\lambda/\lambda_0 = 3, t/t_e = 0.90$. It is instructive to note in Fig. 10-8 that, *while the central trough and depression under an invariable load deepen and become narrower, two adjoining regions on its flanks are raised and bulge up in two gently elevated hills.*

Figure 10-7 reproduces the variation of the maximum deflection C of the slab with time t for the special case $\lambda_1 = \lambda_0$, and we may note that an originally elastically deflected viscoelastic slab starts to bend permanently with an infinite rate of increase of the deflection $dC/dt = \dot{C} = \infty$ (a vertical slope at the origin $t = 0$). When, however, $\lambda_1 > \lambda_0$, the initial rate of deflection $\dot{C}$ at the instant $t = t_1$ when the load becomes constant is finite and jumps by a certain amount.

Obviously, all three curves (w, w_1, W) at any time t comply with the requirement of isostatic equilibrium,

$$\int_0^\infty w \, dx = \int_0^\infty w_1 \, dx = \text{const}, \qquad \int_0^\infty W \, dx = 0,$$

expressing that the displaced volume (weight) of substratum when the external load on the slab is held constant remains unchanged. This verifies what has been already mentioned, namely, that the deeper the sharply bent bottom of the central trough under the force $P = \text{const}$ is being submerged into the substratum, the higher the two adjoining regions are raised relatively above the initial deflection line w_1. Also the sharper will be the peak accompanying the slab distortion in the curve representing the distribution of the bending moments m_x at $x = 0$ which might be evaluated, after integrating Eq. (9-7),

$$\dot{m}_x + \frac{m_x}{t_e} = -N \frac{\partial^2 \dot{w}}{\partial x^2}$$

with respect to the time t.

10-5. Purely Viscous Slab.   When permanent strains predominate, one may neglect the elastic strains and compute the deflections from Eq. (10-7), assuming $p = 0$:

$$\frac{d^4 \dot{w}}{dx^4} = - \frac{kw}{N_0}, \qquad N_0 = (\tfrac{1}{3})\mu h^3. \qquad (10\text{-}69)$$

By letting

$$w = w_0 e^{t/t_0} X\left(\frac{\lambda x}{a}\right), \qquad t_0 = \frac{4\lambda^4 N_0}{ka^4}, \qquad (10\text{-}70)$$

one obtains for $X(\lambda x/a)$ the integrals quoted in Eq. (10-13); for example, if one takes

$$X\left(\frac{\lambda x}{a}\right) = e^{-\lambda x/a}\left(\cos \frac{\lambda x}{a} + \sin \frac{\lambda x}{a}\right), \qquad (10\text{-}71)$$

there results the solution for the infinite viscous slab on substratum deflected under a single force P acting at point $x = 0$:

$$P = 2k \int_0^\infty w \, dx = 2kw_0 e^{t/t_0} \int_0^\infty X\left(\frac{\lambda x}{a}\right) dx = \frac{2kw_0 a e^{t/t_0}}{\lambda}, \qquad (10\text{-}72)$$

which increases exponentially with the time t.

If one assumes, on the other hand,

$$w = w_0 e^{-t/t_0} X\left(\frac{\lambda x}{a}\right), \qquad t_0 = \frac{\lambda^4 N_0}{ka^4}, \qquad (10\text{-}73)$$

Eq. (10-69) is satisfied with either of the four functions,

$$X\left(\frac{\lambda x}{a}\right) = e^{\lambda x/a}, \; e^{-\lambda x/a}, \; \cos \frac{\lambda x}{a}, \; \sin \frac{\lambda x}{a},$$

and one can consider a recession of the deflections from an initially deformed state of a slab.   For example, in a slab of finite length a having simply supported ends $x = 0$ and $x = a$, and taking $\lambda = n\pi$ ($n = 1, 2, 3, \dots$), whose deflections may be expressed by the trigonometric series

$$w = \sum_{n=1}^\infty c_n e^{-t/t_n} \sin \frac{n\pi x}{a}, \qquad t_n = \frac{n^4 \pi^4 N_0}{ka^4}, \qquad (10\text{-}74)$$

the constants c_n of which may be computed from the condition that at the time $t = 0$

$$w = \sum_{n=1}^\infty c_n \sin \frac{n\pi x}{a} = f(x), \qquad (10\text{-}75)$$

the slab has an arbitrarily prescribed deflected form plunged into the substratum. Since the time constants t_n increase with the fourth power of n, we may note a peculiarity in the law of recession of the deflections of a viscous slab, namely, the higher the order of the harmonics is, the more slowly they disappear. If some prominent wrinkles were present in the initial form of the slab, they will prevail after the lower harmonics prescribing the original form have long disappeared—a fact which may have some bearing in geologic applications.[1]

10-6. The Bending of Slabs under Distributed Pressure. A variety of integrals of the complete differential equation (10-3),

$$N\frac{\partial^4 \dot{w}}{\partial x^4} = -k\left(\dot{w} + \frac{w}{t_e}\right) + \dot{p} + \frac{p}{t_e}, \tag{10-76}$$

may be established for infinite slabs bent under distributed pressures $p = f(x,t)$.

A. STEADY DISTRIBUTED PRESSURE

$$p = p_0\left(1 + \cos\frac{\pi x}{a}\right). \tag{10-77}$$

We may omit the mean value $p = p_0 = \text{const}$ in this and similar periodic functions to be treated, remembering that a uniform pressure load p_0 deposited on the earth's slab depresses it as a solid plate vertically downward by the amount p_0/k. Bearing in mind that this displacement p_0/k has to be added to the deflections to be considered if the function $p = f(x)$ has a mean value $p_0 = \text{const}$, we may disregard the latter part of the distributed load and write for p

$$p = p_0 \cos\frac{\pi x}{a}; \tag{10-77a}$$

after substituting this, $\dot{p} = 0$, and for the deflection,

$$w = \frac{p_0}{k}\varphi(t)\cos\frac{\pi x}{a}, \tag{10-78}$$

in Eq. (10-76), denoting by

$$\lambda_0^4 = \frac{ka^4}{4N}, \quad t_0 = \left(1 + \frac{\pi^4}{4\lambda_0^4}\right)t_e = \left(1 + \frac{\pi^4 N}{ka^4}\right)t_e, \quad t_e = \frac{3\mu}{E}, \tag{10-79}$$

we obtain for $\varphi(t)$

$$t_0\dot{\varphi} + \varphi = 1, \qquad \varphi = 1 + Ce^{-t/t_0}. \tag{10-80}$$

Postulating, for example, a sudden application of the pressure load p at time $t = 0$, the slab initially deflects elastically according to the equation

$$N\frac{d^4 w}{dx^4} = -kw + p = -kw + p_0\cos\frac{\pi x}{a} \tag{10-81}$$

with a deflection

$$w_{el} = w_0\cos\frac{\pi x}{a}, \tag{10-82}$$

[1] See Sec. 10-8, page 330.

where the constant w_0 is to be taken equal to

$$w_0 = \frac{p_0/k}{1 + (\pi^4/4\lambda_0^4)} = \frac{p_0 t_e}{k t_0} . \tag{10-83}$$

The deflection w in Eq. (10-78) satisfying this initial condition $t = 0$, $w = w_{\text{el}}$ or $\varphi(0) = t_e/t_0 = C + 1$ is

$$w = \frac{p_0}{k}\left[\left(\frac{t_e}{t_0} - 1\right)e^{-t/t_0} + 1\right]\cos\frac{\pi x}{a} . \tag{10-84}$$

The elastic w' and permanent w'' parts of the deflection $w = w' + w''$ may be computed from

$$\dot{w}' + \frac{w'}{t_e} = \dot{w}, \qquad \dot{w}'' = \frac{w'}{t_e} ,$$

giving

$$w' = \frac{p_0}{k}\left[\left(\frac{t_e}{t_0} + 1\right)e^{-t/t_e} - e^{-t/t_0}\right]\cos\frac{\pi x}{a} ,$$

$$w'' = \frac{p_0}{k}\left[1 - \left(\frac{t_e}{t_0} + 1\right)e^{-t/t_e} + \frac{t_e}{t_0}e^{-t/t_0}\right]\cos\frac{\pi x}{a} . \tag{10-85}$$

The deflection amplitude thus increases from its initial, elastic value $w_0 = p_0 t_e/k t_0$ to the final, permanent value $w'' = p_0/k$ at $t = \infty$, with the heights of the crests of the waves formed equaling the depths of their troughs (Figs. 10-9 and 10-10). The rise of ground in the crests of these waves, however, is compensated by the uniform vertical displacement p_0/k due to the mean pressure p_0 of the load as expressed by Eq. (10-77), the slab having only positive deflections deforming along troughs below the original level $w = 0$.

B. The Pressure Is a Periodic Function of x. *If the pressure load p were an arbitrary periodic, for example, an even function of x*

$$p = f(x) = p_0 \sum_1^\infty c_n \cos\frac{n\pi x}{a} \tag{10-86}$$

(having omitted for the reason previously stated the term c_0), letting the deflection of the slab equal

$$w = \frac{p_0}{k} \sum_1^\infty \varphi_n(t) \cos\frac{n\pi x}{a} , \tag{10-87}$$

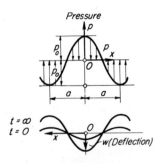

Fig. 10-9. Deflections under steady pressure $p = p_0\left(1 + \cos\dfrac{\pi x}{a}\right).$

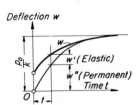

Fig. 10-10

the coefficients $\varphi_n(t)$ are determined by the series of first-order differential equations of time t:

$$t_n \dot{\varphi}_n + \varphi_n = c_n, \qquad t_n = \left(1 + \frac{n^4 \pi^4}{4\lambda_0^4}\right) t_e,$$

$$\varphi_n(t) = c_n + C_n e^{-t/t_n}.$$

(10-88)

Considering again a sudden application of the distributed load p at time $t = 0$ causing an elastic deflection

$$w_{\rm el} = \frac{p_0}{k} \sum_1^{\infty} \frac{c_n t_e}{t_n} \cos \frac{n\pi x}{a},$$

(10-89)

the initial condition $t = 0$, $w = w_{\rm el}$ is satisfied by choosing $C_n = [(t_e/t_n) - 1]c_n$, supplying the time-dependent factors in the trigonometric series of Eq. (10-87):

$$\varphi_n(t) = c_n \left[\left(\frac{t_e}{t_n} - 1\right)e^{-t/t_n} + 1\right].$$

(10-90)

EXAMPLE 1. If an infinite viscoelastic slab is loaded by a uniform pressure $p = p_0 = $ const distributed over periodic intervals of the width $2c$ (Fig. 10-11) and the mean pressure $p_0 c/a$ is being disregarded, $p = f(x)$ is represented by the series

$$p = \frac{2p_0}{\pi} \sum_n \frac{1}{n} \sin \frac{n\pi c}{a} \cos \frac{n\pi x}{a}, \qquad (n = 1, 2, 3, \ldots),$$

(10-91)

and the resulting deflection of the slab by the series

$$w = \frac{2p_0}{\pi k} \sum_n \left[\frac{e^{-t/t_n}}{1 + (n^4 \pi^4 / 4\lambda_0^4)} + 1 - e^{-t/t_n}\right] \frac{\sin(n\pi c/a) \cos(n\pi x/a)}{n}.$$

(10-92)

On application of the pressure load, the slab deflects at time $t = 0$ with a smooth wavy curve:

$$w = \frac{2p_0}{\pi k} \sum_{n=1}^{\infty} \frac{\sin(n\pi c/a) \cos(n\pi x/a)}{n[1 + (n^4 \pi^4 / 4\lambda_0^4)]}.$$

(10-93)

When the time tends to approach infinity, however, the terms e^{-t/t_n} in Eq. (10-92) cancel out, and in the remaining infinite series we recognize $1/k$ times the original series [Eq. (10-91)] representing the pressure $p = f(x)$, so that, for $t = \infty$, $w = p/k$. In view of the finite discontinuities of the pressure curve $p = f(x)$ we are led to the paradoxical result that the deflections w, when t approaches infinity, tend to disclose similar finite discontinuities, confirming what has been stated about the final equilibrium form of a viscoelastic slab (see page 287) in which an imprint of the original steady pressure curve $p = f(x)$ is left in the function $w(x)$. We must conclude that it does not make sense to consider the series (10-92) when this advanced stage of distortion is due to occur, because, long before this stage can develop, the bending stresses in the slab will become excessively great, causing local plastic flow or disruption.

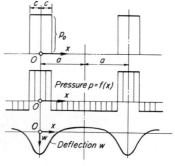

FIG. 10-11

If the width $2c$ of the strips in which the pressure p_0 acts is decreased but the resultant loads $2cp_0 = P$ are held constant, the deflection converges toward the series

$$w = \frac{P}{ka} \sum_1^\infty \left[\left(\frac{t_e}{t_n} - 1 \right) e^{-t/t_n} + 1 \right] \cos \frac{n\pi x}{a} \qquad (10\text{-}94)$$

representing the wavy distortion of a slab under a train of concentrated forces P equally spaced in the distances $2a$, this series becoming divergent when t approaches infinity.

C. ARBITRARY, STEADY DISTRIBUTION OF PRESSURES. If the period $2a$ of the periodic pressure function is increased indefinitely, we are led to the most general solution for the deflections of an infinite slab under a steady distributed load which is expressible by a FOURIER integral. Suppose that we consider an *even* function $f(x)$ which is expressible by the definite integral

$$f(x) = \int_0^\infty c(\lambda) \cos \lambda x \, d\lambda,$$

$$c(\lambda) = \frac{2}{\pi} \int_0^\infty f(\alpha) \cos \lambda \alpha \, d\alpha. \qquad (10\text{-}95)$$

We may postulate a given, arbitrary, steady, even distribution of pressures $p = p_0 f(x)$ by an integral

$$p = p_0 f(x) = p_0 \int_0^\infty c(\lambda) \cos \lambda x \, d\lambda, \qquad (10\text{-}96)$$

and the corresponding deflections w of the infinite slab generally, at the time t, in the form

$$w = \frac{p_0}{k} \int_0^\infty \varphi(\lambda,t) \cos \lambda x \, d\lambda, \qquad (10\text{-}97)$$

where the prefacing constant factors p_0 and p_0/k have the dimension of a pressure and a length, respectively. The function $\varphi(\lambda,t)$ may be determined in a perfectly analogous manner to the way in which a similar function was found for the terms of the trigonometric developments in Sec. 10-6B after substituting Eq. (10-97) in the differential equation (10-76), assuming for a steady load $\dot{p} = 0$, which gives for $\varphi(\lambda,t)$

$$t_\lambda \dot{\varphi} + \varphi = c(\lambda), \qquad \varphi = Ce^{-t/t_\lambda} + c(\lambda),$$

$$t_\lambda = \left(1 + \frac{\lambda^4 a^4}{4\lambda_0^4} \right) t_e, \qquad \lambda_0^4 = \frac{ka^4}{4N}, \qquad t_e = \frac{3\mu}{E}. \qquad (10\text{-}98)$$

Similarly, on sudden application of $p = p_0 f(x)$ at the time $t = 0$, an elastic deflection w_{el} occurs equal to

$$w_{el} = t_e \int_0^\infty \frac{c(\lambda) \cos \lambda x \, d\lambda}{t_\lambda}, \qquad (10\text{-}99)$$

and the initial condition, $t = 0$, $w = w_{el}$, is satisfied by

$$\varphi(\lambda,t) = c(\lambda) \left[\left(\frac{t_e}{t_\lambda} - 1 \right) e^{-t/t_\lambda} + 1 \right]; \qquad (10\text{-}100)$$

thus, Eq. (10-97) or the *general solution for the deflections w of an infinite, visco-elastic slab under the steady pressure $p = p_0 f(x)$* is expressed by

$$w = \frac{p_0}{k} \int_0^\infty c(\lambda) \left[\left(\frac{t_e}{t_\lambda} - 1 \right) e^{-t/t_\lambda} + 1 \right] \cos \lambda x \, d\lambda. \qquad (10\text{-}101)$$

EXAMPLE 2. If the pressure $p = p_0 f(x)$ were given through the discontinuous function of x indicated in Fig. 10-12, by letting

$$f(x) = 1 \qquad \text{when} \qquad 0 \leqq x < c,$$

$$f(x) = 0 \qquad \text{when} \qquad c < x,$$

one has for $c(\lambda)$

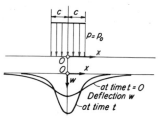

$$c(\lambda) = \frac{2}{\pi} \int_0^C \cos \lambda \alpha \, d\alpha = \frac{2}{\pi\lambda} \sin \lambda c; \quad (10\text{-}102)$$

FIG. 10-12

the pressure p is expressed by the well-known, so-called discontinuous DIRICHLET factor[1]

$$p = \frac{2p_0}{\pi} \int_0^\infty \frac{1}{\lambda} \sin \lambda c \cos \lambda x \, d\lambda, \qquad (10\text{-}103)$$

and the deflection is expressed by Eq. (10-101) using Eq. (10-102). The maximum deflection at time $t = 0$, $x = 0$ is

$$w = \frac{2p_0}{\pi k} \int_0^\infty \frac{\sin \lambda c \, d\lambda}{\lambda[1 + (a^4\lambda^4/4\lambda_0^4)]}. \qquad (10\text{-}104)$$

Suppose that we decrease the width $2c$ of the loaded zone in Fig. 10-12 and increase the pressure p_0, holding $2cp_0 = P = \text{const.}$ The preceding formulas must then express the case of the bending of an infinite viscoelastic slab, resting on substratum and *loaded* by an invariable, concentrated force P, which was treated in Sec. 10-4 in the special case covered by Eqs. (10-64) to (10-68) for which explicit expressions for the deflected slab in finite terms were developed. Thus, the definite integrals Eqs. (10-101) using (10-102) must converge, when $(\sin \lambda c)/\lambda c$ is replaced by unity, toward the corresponding functions listed in Sec. 10-4. Equation (10-104) converges by letting in the integrand $\lim [\sin (\lambda c)/\lambda c] = 1$ toward

$$w = \frac{P}{\pi k} \int_0^\infty \frac{d\lambda}{1 + (a^4\lambda^4/4\lambda_0^4)} = \frac{\sqrt{2}\, P\lambda_0}{\pi k a} \int_0^\infty \frac{du}{1 + u^4}, \qquad (10\text{-}105)$$

but the indefinite integral may be computed by

$$\int \frac{du}{1 + u^4} = \frac{1}{4\sqrt{2}} \left(\ln \frac{1 + \sqrt{2} \cdot u + u^2}{1 - \sqrt{2} \cdot u + u^2} + 2 \arctan \frac{\sqrt{2} \cdot u}{1 - u^2} \right),$$

giving for the definite integral Eq. (10-105) and for the initial, maximum, elastic deflection of the infinite beam at $x = 0$ and time $t = 0$

$$\int_0^\infty \frac{du}{1 + u^4} = \frac{\pi}{2\sqrt{2}}, \qquad w = \frac{P\lambda_0}{2ka}, \qquad (10\text{-}106)$$

confirming, indeed, the value that we previously obtained for sudden, elastic loading under a single force P in Eq. (10-64).

[1] HEINRICH WEBER, "Die partiellen Differential Gleichungen der mathematischen Physik, nach Riemann's Vorlesungen," 5th ed., vol. 1, p. 50, Friedr. Vieweg und Sohn, Brunswick, Germany, 1910.

EXAMPLE 3. Suppose that a steady pressure p were distributed over an infinite, viscoelastic slab in a symmetrical hill having gently declining slopes according to the function of x:

$$p = p_0 f(x) = \frac{p_0 a^2}{a^2 + x^2} \tag{10-107}$$

(a is a constant length). Then, from Eqs. (10-95),[1]

$$c(\lambda) = \frac{2}{\pi} \int_0^\infty \frac{\cos \lambda \alpha \, d\alpha}{1 + (\alpha/a)^2} = ae^{-\lambda a}, \tag{10-108}$$

and the slab deflections w at time t are expressed, using Eq. (10-101), by

$$w = \frac{p_0 a}{k} \int_0^\infty e^{-\lambda a}\left[\left(\frac{t_e}{t_\lambda} - 1\right)e^{-t/t_\lambda} + 1\right] \cos \lambda x \, d\lambda. \tag{10-109}$$

This gives, on sudden application of the load [Eq. (10-107)], the *elastic* deflection

$$t = 0, \qquad w = \frac{p_0 a}{k} \int_0^\infty \frac{e^{-\lambda a} \cos \lambda x \, d\lambda}{1 + (\lambda^4 a^4/4\lambda_0^4)}, \tag{10-110}$$

and as time progresses, this form changes until, at $t = \infty$, the deflections become *permanent* in the final shape of the slab:

$$w = \frac{p_0 a^2}{k(a^2 + x^2)}. \tag{10-111}$$

D. DISTRIBUTED PRESSURE VARYING WITH TIME t. The preceding developments may easily be extended to the treatment of distributed pressures varying with time, either increasing or decreasing with t, to loading or unloading processes in the infinite slab. Referring to Sec. 10-6B, for example, we may distinguish two important cases:

Case a. A given (arbitrary) periodic distribution of pressure may vary with the time t as

$$p = p_0\psi(t)f(x) = p_0\psi(t)\sum_1^\infty c_n \cos\frac{n\pi x}{a}, \qquad (n = 1, 2, 3, \ldots), \tag{10-112}$$

in which case the pressure curves for subsequent times are a family of affine curves.

Case b. Or, an originally arbitrary, periodic distribution of pressure may vary according to a law

$$p = p_0 f(x,t) = p_0 \sum_n c_n\psi_n(t) \cos\frac{n\pi x}{a}, \tag{10-113}$$

assuming that the time factors $\psi_n(t)$ in the terms of the series are prescribed in a reasonable manner.

---

[1] The definite integral of Eq. (10-108) was evaluated by HEINRICH WEBER, *op. cit.*, p. 50.

Consider, for a comparison of modes of deflection in viscoelastic slabs, with reference to Eq. (10-112), the following laws of variation of distributed loads of some geophysical interest:

Case 1: $\psi(t) = 1$
        Loading
Case 2: $\psi(t) = 1 - e^{-t/t_p}$

Case 3: $\psi(t) = e^{-t/t_p}$ (10-114)
        Unloading
Case 4: $\psi(t) = \dfrac{t_1 e^{-t/t_1} - t_2 e^{-t/t_2}}{t_1 - t_2}$

(t_p, t_1, t_2 are given constants).

Case 1 reverts back to steady pressure, covered in Sec. 10-6B; case 2 would permit describing the distortion in a slab under a gradually increasing, arbitrary distributed load p, first growing fast and later tending to become a steady distribution; case 3, a gradual evanescence of load under decreasing rates; and case 4, unloading of a slab carrying pressures p which start to decrease with a vanishing rate $dp/dt = 0$.

Assuming for the pressure load p [Eq. (10-112)] and for the deflection w a series,

$$w = \frac{p_0}{k} \sum_n \varphi_n(t) \cos \frac{n\pi x}{a},$$ (10-115)

after substituting w in Eq. (10-76), the time-dependent coefficients φ_n are determined by the series of differential equations

$$t_n \dot{\varphi}_n + \varphi_n = c_n(\dot{\psi} t_e + \psi), \qquad t_n = \left(1 + \frac{n^4 \pi^4}{4\lambda_0^4}\right) t_e,$$ (10-116)

from which, after a partial integration with respect to the time t,

$$\int \dot{\psi} e^{t/t_n} \, dt = \psi \cdot e^{t/t_n} - \frac{1}{t_n} \int \psi e^{t/t_n} \, dt,$$

the functions φ_n are found equal to

$$\varphi_n = C_n e^{-t/t_n} + \frac{c_n}{t_n}\left[t_e \psi + \left(1 - \frac{t_e}{t_n}\right) e^{-t/t_n} \cdot \int \psi e^{t/t_n} \, dt\right].$$ (10-117)

The integration constants C_n are determined from the initial condition to be satisfied by the functions φ_n:

Case 2: $t = 0,$ $\varphi_n = 0,$

Case 3, 4: $t = 0,$ $\varphi_n = c_n,$

resulting in the following functions $\varphi_n(t)$:

Case 2: $\varphi_n = \dfrac{c_n}{t_p - t_n} [(t_p - t_e)(1 - e^{-t/t_p}) - (t_n - t_e)(1 - e^{-t/t_n})]$,   (10-118)

Case 3: $\varphi_n = \dfrac{c_n}{t_p - t_n} [(t_p - t_e)e^{-t/t_p} - (t_n - t_e)e^{-t/t_n}]$.   (10-119)

For Case 4 we list the formulas for unloading by assuming only the first term in the series (10-112) to be present, writing $c_1 = 1$, corresponding to a declining pressure load,

$$p = p_0\psi(t)\cos\frac{\pi x}{a} = \frac{p_0}{t_1 - t_2}(t_1 e^{-t/t_1} - t_2 e^{-t/t_2})\cos\frac{\pi x}{a}, \qquad (10\text{-}120)$$

decreasing at the rate

$$\dot{p} = -\frac{p_0}{t_1 - t_2}(e^{-t/t_1} - e^{-t/t_2})\cos\frac{\pi x}{a},$$

$\dot{p}$ vanishing at time $t = 0$.   Letting the deflection

$$w = \frac{p_0}{k}\,\varphi(t)\cos\frac{\pi x}{a}, \qquad (10\text{-}121)$$

$\varphi(t)$ is to be determined, using Eq. (10-116), after writing for $t_n = t_0$ from

$$t_0\dot{\varphi} + \varphi = \frac{(t_1 - t_e)e^{-t/t_1} - (t_2 - t_e)e^{-t/t_2}}{t_1 - t_2}, \qquad t_0 = \left(1 + \frac{\pi^4 N}{ka^4}\right)t_e. \quad (10\text{-}122)$$

Suppose, alternatively, that this unloading of the viscoelastic slab floating on substratum were to start from an entirely permanently bent position that it had assumed under a previously steady pressure load,

$$p = p_0\cos\frac{\pi x}{a},$$

after it reached its isostatic equilibrium configuration:

$$w = \frac{p_0}{k}\cos\frac{\pi x}{a}. \qquad (10\text{-}123)$$

If we consider the latter form as the initial deflection for the unloading cycle starting at time $t = 0$, comparing Eqs. (10-121) and (10-123), this requires that the initial condition $t = 0$, $\varphi(0) = 1$ be satisfied, with the result that $\varphi(t)$ from Eq. (10-122) is expressed by

$$\varphi(t) = e^{-t/t_0} + A_1(e^{-t/t_1} - e^{-t/t_0}) - A_2(e^{-t/t_2} - e^{-t/t_0}),$$

$$A_1 = \frac{t_1(t_1 - t_e)}{(t_1 - t_0)(t_1 - t_2)}, \qquad A_2 = \frac{t_2(t_2 - t_e)}{(t_2 - t_0)(t_1 - t_2)}, \qquad (10\text{-}124)$$

where the time constants t_1 and t_2 may be chosen arbitrarily to fit a physically prescribed time period of evanescence of the extraneous pressure load p [Eq. (10-120)].

If these two time constants are equal to each other, $t_1 = t_2$, the function $\psi(t)$ in Eq. (10-120) converges toward

$$\psi(t) = \lim_{t_2 = t_1}\frac{t_1 e^{-t/t_1} - t_2 e^{-t/t_2}}{t_1 - t_2} = \left(1 + \frac{t}{t_1}\right)e^{-t/t_1}, \qquad (10\text{-}125)$$

the pressure p varies as

$$p = p_0\left(1 + \frac{t}{t_1}\right) e^{-t/t_1} \cos \frac{\pi x}{a}, \qquad (10\text{-}126)$$

and $\varphi(t)$ as

$$\varphi(t) = e^{-t/t_0} + \left[1 - \frac{t_1 - t_e}{t_1}\left(\frac{t_0}{t_1 - t_0} - \frac{t}{t_1}\right)\right] \frac{t_1(e^{-t/t_1} - e^{-t/t_0})}{t_1 - t_0}.$$

$$(10\text{-}127)$$

If $t_1 = t_2$ were chosen equal to $t_e = 3\mu/E$, the ground would yield according to the symmetric time function

$$\varphi(t) = \frac{t_e e^{-t/t_e} - t_0 e^{-t/t_0}}{t_e - t_0}, \qquad \text{where} \qquad t_0 = \left(1 + \frac{\pi^4 N}{ka^4}\right)t_e,$$

$$(10\text{-}128)$$

illustrating simple laws for ground-level changes,

$$w = \frac{p_0}{k} \varphi(t) \cos \frac{\pi x}{a},$$

accompanying gradual evanescence of load.

10-7. Postglacial Warping of Earth's Crust, Illustrated with Examples. Two extended regions of mainland presently covered by massive ice sheets are Antarctica and Greenland, the latter's glacial conditions having been carefully studied and mapped by ALFRED WEGENER's expedition of 1930–1931 on which its valiant leader perished.[1] The surveys of this expedition disclosed that the rock base of Greenland may be compared to a pan with an elevated rim, consisting of the rugged mountains surrounding the peninsula, the flat dish being filled with a lens-shaped cake of ice rising to an elevation of 3,000 m,

---

[1] ELSE WEGENER and FRITZ LOEWE, "Alfred Wegeners letzte Grönlandfahrt," 304 pp., F. A. Brockhaus, Leipzig, 1932; JOHANNES GEORGI, "Im Eis vergraben," 224 pp., Paul Müller, Munich, 1933. Considering the major, northern part of Greenland as a rectangle of a width of 800 km and length of 1,800 km, covered with a layer of ice 2.0 km thick, the volume of this mass of ice of approximately 3 million km³, if it were to melt, would raise the level of the oceans in their present extension by 8 meters.

Lack of space prohibits quoting from the extensive bibliography devoted to individual papers on postglacial uplifts. The reader is, however, referred to BENO GUTENBERG (ed.), "Internal Constitution of the Earth," 439 pp., 2d ed., Dover Publications, Inc., New York, 1951 (see Chap. 15, p. 386, of this book) and especially to the papers by BENO GUTENBERG, Tilting Due to Glacial Melting, J. Geol., vol. 41, pp. 449–467, 1933; Changes in Sea Level, Postglacial Uplift and Mobility of the Earth's Interior, Bull. Geol. Soc. Am., vol. 52, pp. 721–772, 1941; Is the Land Around Hudson Bay at Present Rising? Am. J. Sci., vol. 240, pp. 147–149, 1942; and Postglacial Uplift in the Great Lakes Region, Arch. Meteorol., Geophys. u. Bioklimatol., Ser. A, vol. 7, pp. 243–251, 1954. (In this latter paper, 26 references to articles may be found.)

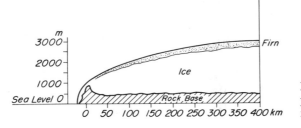

FIG. 10-13. F. Loewe's profile through inland ice of half of Greenland.

the thickness of which increases from 500 to 1,000 m from the borders to 2,700 m toward the center, as illustrated in the profile reproduced in Fig. 10-13, with the shape of the downward-bent rock base of a hypothetic thickness of the earth's slab[1] of 50 km in Fig. 10-14.

A. A DISTRIBUTED GLACIAL LOAD DECREASES PROPORTIONALLY AT ALL POINTS ACCORDING TO A TIME FUNCTION. Influenced by these and related observations of the melting of glacial sheets of comparable extension and thickness that have blanketed other regions of the earth during the last ice age and subsequently disappeared, let us consider examples of the motion and bending distortion of the earth's slab under a locally decreasing glacial load after steady glaciation has come to an end. Being interested in long-time effects, let us assume that the earth's crust reacted as *a purely viscous body* by neglecting its elastic deformation and responding with the differential equation for its deflections w [see Eq. (10-7)]:

$$N_0 \frac{\partial^4 \dot{w}}{\partial x^4} = -kw + p, \qquad N_0 = (\frac{1}{3})\mu h_0^3 \qquad (10\text{-}129)$$

(h_0 = thickness, μ = viscosity of earth slab), supposing that a tract of land was blanketed over a period of time by the weights of parallel ranges of glaciers of the heights

$$h = h_i\left(1 + \cos\frac{\pi x}{a}\right) \qquad (10\text{-}130)$$

---

[1] B. BROCKAMP, E. SORGE, and K. WÖLCKEN, "Wissenschaftliche Ergebnisse der deutschen Grönland-Expedition von A. Wegener, 1929 und 1930/31," vol. 2, Leipzig, 1933. One of the purposes of Wegener's expedition was to determine the profile of the rock base under the ice of the peninsula of Greenland by using echo soundings through the ice, in order to ascertain whether or not the earth's crust, according to the rules of isostasy, is bent downward by the glacial load. The measurements actually indicated a trough in the central parts but were not sufficiently completed. Subsequent seismic soundings carried out by a French expedition: "Campagne au Grönland 1950" (A. JOSEF, Expédition Polaire Francaise de Paul-Émile Victor, Rappts. prélim., vol. 15, 43–56, 1952), according to Gutenberg's paper of 1954 left no doubts that the rock base under the center of Greenland has the form of a flat, saucer-shaped, concave pan.

under the pressures

$$p = p_0\left(1 + \cos\frac{\pi x}{a}\right), \qquad \text{(10-131)}$$

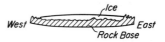

FIG. 10-14. Exaggerated hypothetic profile through earth's slab under Greenland. (*After F. Loewe and T. Georgi.*)

depressing the land in parallel valleys having the depths

$$w = \frac{p_0}{k}\left(1 + \cos\frac{\pi x}{a}\right), \qquad \text{(10-132)}$$

p_0 being equal to $p_0 = h_i\gamma_i$ and $k = \gamma_e$ [$\gamma_i = 1{,}000$ kg/m³ and $\gamma_e = 3{,}000$ kg/m³ are specific weights of the ice and of the rocks in the substratum of the slab, so that $2p_0/k = (\frac{2}{3})h_i$ represents the greatest depths of the valleys below the level $w = 0$ in isostatic slab equilibrium]. *After defrosting sets in, the pressure p may vary with time t as*

$$p = p_0\psi(t)\left(1 + \cos\frac{\pi x}{a}\right) \qquad \text{(10-133)}$$

under decreasing values of $\psi(t) < 1$. Letting

$$p = p_0\psi + p^*, \qquad p^* = p_0\psi\cos\frac{\pi x}{a}, \qquad \text{(10-134)}$$

and the corresponding deflection

$$w = \frac{p_0}{k}\psi + w^*, \qquad w^* = \frac{p_0}{k}\phi(t)\cos\frac{\pi x}{a}, \qquad \text{(10-135)}$$

from Eq. (10-129),

$$N_0\frac{\partial^4\dot{w}^*}{\partial x^4} = -kw^* + p^*, \qquad \text{(10-136)}$$

one has for $\phi(t)$

$$t_0\dot{\phi} + \phi = \psi, \qquad t_0 = \frac{N_0\pi^4}{ka^4} = \frac{\pi^4\mu h_0^3}{3ka^4}, \qquad \text{(10-137)}$$

$$\phi(t) = e^{-t/t_0}\left(C + \frac{1}{t_0}\int \psi e^{t/t_0}\,dt\right), \qquad \text{(10-138)}$$

and for the deflection w at times $t > 0$ during deglaciation

$$w = \frac{p_0}{k}\left(\psi + \phi\cos\frac{\pi x}{a}\right),$$

$$w = \frac{p_0}{k}\left[\psi - \phi + \phi\left(1 + \cos\frac{\pi x}{a}\right)\right]. \qquad \text{(10-139)}$$

Since at time $t = 0$, $\psi = 1$ and $w = (p_0/k)[1 + \cos(\pi x/a)]$, the initial condition to be satisfied by the function $\phi(t)$ in Eq. (10-139) is $t = 0$, $\phi = 1$.

EXAMPLE 1. Suppose that at time $t = 0$ the pressure p [Eq. (10-131)] were reduced to zero. Then, on reduction of the mean pressure p_0 to zero, the slab must rise uniformly by the amount $-p_0/k$ from its initially bent position ABC to the position $A_1B_1C_1$ (Fig. 10-15),

$$t = 0, \qquad w^* = \frac{p_0}{k} \cos \frac{\pi x}{a}, \qquad (10\text{-}140)$$

in which parallel ridges of an amplitude height $p_0/k = (\tfrac{1}{3})h_i$ have risen above the equilibrium level $w = 0$ (Fig. 10-15).

These waves are subsequently wiped out according to the solution of Eq. (10-136), letting $p^* = 0$:

$$w^* = \frac{p_0}{k} e^{-t/t_0} \cdot \cos \frac{\pi x}{a}. \qquad (10\text{-}141)$$

Consider glaciers of a height $2h_i = 3{,}000$ m similar to the maximum thickness of the ice cap covering present-day Greenland and a width $2a = 600$ km, initially causing valleys $2p_0/k = (\tfrac{2}{3})h_i = 1{,}000$ m deep and that the earth's slab is $h_0 = 50$ km thick and has a viscosity $\mu = 5 \times 10^{22}$ poises $= 5 \times 10^{16}$ kg/cm^2 sec, $k = \gamma_e = 0.003$ kg/cm^3. Then, the time constant t_0 in Eq. (10-137) is found equal to

$$t_0 = \frac{\pi^4 \mu h_0^3}{3\gamma_e a^4} = 8.35 \times 10^{10} \text{ sec.} \qquad (10\text{-}142)$$

But one sidereal year (the time of one revolution of the earth around the sun with respect to the stars) being equal to $T_s = 365.256$ solar days (of 24 hr or 86,400 sec) or $T_s = 3.1558 \times 10^7$ sec, we obtain for the time constant

$$t_0 = 2{,}650 \text{ sidereal years.}$$

The amplitude of the waves risen up to their position $A_1B_1C_1$ at time $t = 0$, after defrosting set in suddenly, is initially $w_m = p_0/k = (\tfrac{1}{3})h_i = 500$ m, and these amplitudes will decrease subsequently at the rate

$$\dot{w}_m = -\frac{p_0}{kt_0} e^{-t/t_0}.$$

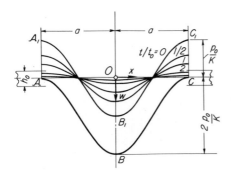

FIG. 10-15. Sequence of deflections w following rapid deglaciation.

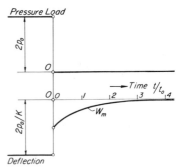

FIG. 10-16. Variation of deflection w_m.

The initial velocity of subsidence at the wave crests and of uplifting in the troughs has the comparatively high value

$$t = 0, \qquad \dot{w}_m = \mp \frac{p_0}{kt_0} = \mp 18.94 \text{ cm/year},$$

and one obtains for the motion of the ground during the postglacial period (Fig. 10-16) the figures in Table 10-3.

TABLE 10-3. POSTGLACIAL UPLIFT AND SUBSIDENCE OF GROUND LEVEL

Time ratio t/t_0 ...	0	½	1	2	3	4	5
e^{-t/t_0}	1	0.607	0.368	0.1353	0.0498	0.01832	0.00674
Time t, years	0	1,325	2,650	5,300	7,950	10,600	13,250
Amplitude of deflection of earth's slab w_m, meters	500	304	184	67.7	24.9	9.16	3.37
Maximum rate of uplift or subsidence $\dot{w}_m$, cm/year	18.94	11.5	6.97	2.55	0.94	0.35	0.13

After defrosting, the ground in the wave troughs or crests rises or sinks, in a century of time, by:

6.97 m after 2,650 years
2.55 m after 5,300 years
0.35 m after 10,600 years

Whereas, because of the exaggerated assumption of a sudden deglaciation, unduly high rates of uplift or subsidence during its early times resulted, let us consider in the following examples modes of gradual deglaciation.

EXAMPLE 2. Suppose that we choose, with reference to Sec. 10-6D, Case 4, the time function factor $\psi(t)$ in the expression for the pressure [Eq. (10-133)]

$$\psi(t) = p_0 \cdot \frac{t_1 e^{-t/t_1} - t_2 e^{-t/t_2}}{t_1 - t_2} \qquad (10\text{-}143)$$

representing curves for various ratios $m = t_2/t_1$, as traced for $m = \frac{1}{2}$, 1, 2 in Fig. 10-17. The deflections w during the postglacial retreat of ice loads vary as

$$w = \frac{p_0}{k}\left(\psi + \phi \cos\frac{\pi x}{a}\right) \qquad (10\text{-}144)$$

FIG. 10-17. Maximum pressure

$$p = 2p_0\psi =$$

$$2p_0 \cdot \frac{t_1 e^{-t/t_1} - t_2 e^{-t/t_2}}{t_1 - t_2}$$

caused by weight of ice during period of declining glaciation.

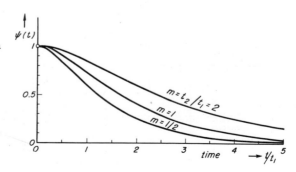

with the time function $\phi(t)$ computed from Eq. (10-138):

$$\phi(t) = e^{-t/t_0} + \frac{t_1^2(e^{-t/t_1} - e^{-t/t_0}) - t_2^2(e^{-t/t_2} - e^{-t/t_0})}{(t_1 - t_2)(t_1 - t_0)}. \qquad (10\text{-}145)$$

Incidentally, this, as other expressions for ϕ for a purely viscous slab, may be obtained from those which were developed for a viscoelastic slab in Sec. 10-6 by neglecting the elastic parts of strain, by letting the time constant $t_e = 3\mu/E = 0$ in the former formulas but replacing the former value of $t_0 = [1 + (\pi^4 N/ka^4)]t_e$ by the new value $t_0 = \pi^4 N_0/ka^4$ now valid for the purely viscous slab. Thus, by choosing the ratio $m = t_2/t_1$ and t_1, one may fit the curve [Eq. (10-143)] controlling the law of deglaciation to suit actual observations of a gradual retreat of glaciation.

EXAMPLE 3. A special law of deglaciation is obtained by assuming $t_2 = t_1$, $m = 1$, for which $\psi(t)$, as we have seen in Eq. (10-125), converges toward the function

$$\psi = \left(1 + \frac{t}{t_1}\right)e^{-t/t_1}, \qquad (10\text{-}146)$$

ϕ becoming

$$\phi = \frac{(t_1 + t)e^{-t/t_1}}{t_1 - t_0} - \frac{t_0(t_1 e^{-t/t_1} - t_0 e^{-t/t_0})}{(t_1 - t_0)^2}, \qquad (10\text{-}147)$$

the second term of which represents a comparatively minor part of the value of ϕ.

EXAMPLE 4. By postulating that $t_2 = t_1 = t_0 = \pi^4 N_e/ka^4$, we obtain *the interesting case of this special law of deglaciation* for which

$$\phi = \psi = \left(1 + \frac{t}{t_0}\right)e^{-t/t_0}, \qquad (10\text{-}148)$$

the deflection of the viscous slab w recedes with the same time factor in

$$w = \frac{p_0}{k}\left(1 + \frac{t}{t_0}\right)e^{-t/t_0} \cdot \left(1 + \cos\frac{\pi x}{a}\right) \qquad (10\text{-}149)$$

as the ice load,

$$p = p_0\left(1 + \frac{t}{t_0}\right)e^{-t/t_0} \cdot \left(1 + \cos\frac{\pi x}{a}\right), \qquad (10\text{-}150)$$

and the deflections of the slab $w = p/k$ at all times t and everywhere recede proportionally to the ice loads p.

Suppose that we choose for $t_0 = 2,650$ years the value that we found in Example 1. We would then obtain for the motion of the ground during the postglacial period $t > 0$ the figures in Table 10-4.

TABLE 10-4. POSTGLACIAL UPLIFT, ASSUMING $\psi = [1 + (t/t_0)]e^{-t/t_0}$

Time ratio t/t_0	0	½	1	2	3	4	5
ψ	1	0.911	0.736	0.406	0.1992	0.0916	0.0404
Time t, years	0	1,325	2,650	5,300	7,950	10,600	13,250
Maximum deflection of earth's slab w_m, meters	1,000	911	736	406	199	92	40
Maximum rate of uplift $\dot{w}_m$, cm/year	0	−11.5	−13.9	−10.2	−5.3	−2.8	−1.3

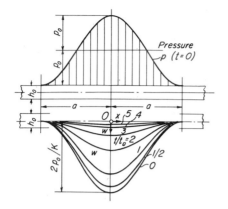

FIG. 10-18. Postglacial uplift. Sequence of deflections w for deglaciation law

$$p = p_0\left(1 + \frac{t}{t_0}\right)e^{-t/t_0} \cdot \left(1 + \cos\frac{\pi x}{a}\right).$$

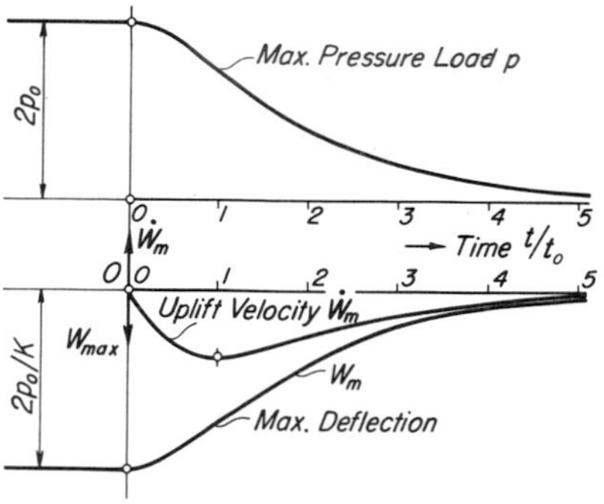

FIG. 10-19. Postglacial uplift.

Excepting the crests of waves, the ground rises everywhere (Figs. 10-18 and 10-19) with the velocities

$$\dot{w} = -\frac{p_0 t}{kt_0^2}e^{-t/t_0}\left(1 + \cos\frac{\pi x}{a}\right), \qquad (10\text{-}151)$$

increasing from zero to the rate of maximum uplift with respect to time,

$$t = t_0, \qquad \dot{w}_{\max} = -\frac{p_0}{kt_0}e^{-1}\left(1 + \cos\frac{\pi x}{a}\right),$$

after the time $t = t_0 = 2{,}650$ years, when the valley floors ($x = 0$) rise at the maximum rate

$$x = 0, \qquad t = t_0, \qquad \dot{w}_{\max} = -0.736\frac{p_0}{kt_0}$$

$$= -13.9 \text{ cm/year} = -13.9 \text{ m/century},$$

this rate becoming subsequently, per century of time,

10.2 m after   5,300 years
2.8 m after 10,600 years
1.3 m after 13,250 years

B. RECORDS OF POSTGLACIAL UPLIFTS OF GROUND LEVELS. According to B. GUTENBERG,[1] the postglacial *uplift in Fennoscandia* under which the Scandinavian peninsula emerged from its formerly submerged position (at the height of

---

[1] Page 309, *loc. cit.* An instructive map showing the contour lines of equal rate of uplift for Fennoscandia, attributed to SAURAMO, which was probably constructed from the observations of the rise of old seashore lines during a century of time, is reproduced in the second edition of Gutenberg's book on p. 387. For an improved version of this map, see Gutenberg's paper of 1954.

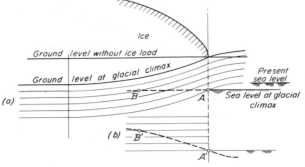

FIG. 10-20. (a) Bending of earth's crust at glacial climax. (b) $A'B'$, present, uptilted position of old seashore line AB after completed postglacial rebound of crust.

the last, Pleistocene glaciation) centers with its maximum rate of uplift around the northernmost corner of the Bottnic Gulf of the Baltic Sea, while an elliptic area around the center of maximum uprising velocity emerges with rates decreasing with the distances from it. According to data attributed to SAURAMO, the present rate of uplift at this center amounts to just *one meter per century*, a figure that compares favorably with the rate of uplift of 1.3 m/century which was computed in Table 10-4 after 13,250 years elapsed since the beginning of deglaciation. If the other assumptions made in Example 4 seem acceptable relative to the circumstances of the Fennoscandian uplift, the above figures would support the mean value of the viscosity of the earth's slab $\mu = 5 \times 10^{22}$ poises on which the computation was based and which has been also claimed by Gutenberg.

Attention has likewise been devoted to the postglacial uplifts of the ground levels in the northeastern part of the United States and in eastern Canada by American geologists. RICHARD J. LOUGEE,[1] in 1928, discovered evidence indicating the catastrophic draining of "Glacial Lake Hitchcock" which existed for 4,000 years and was suddenly drained through crustal movements, giving birth to the Connecticut River. The southern edge of the great continental ice sheet that covered the northeastern states had, at the climax of the last ice age, advanced to a line which, according to LOUGEE,[2] runs through the New England States in a direction parallel to the Atlantic East Coast, transgressing seaward beyond it farther north. This edge receded backward, as the ice melted away, in spasmodic time intervals, stagnating along four or five, more or less parallel, distinctly recognizable, intermediate lines. Around the latter the ground was tilted in planes sloping upward in the direction in which the ice front retreated. These uplifts around certain "hinges"—according to LOUGEE—are very clearly evidenced through the tilted positions of many, old, former, ocean beaches and

---

[1] Proc. Natl. Acad. Sci. U.S., vol. 21, p. 36, 1935.

[2] RICHARD J. LOUGEE, A Chronology of Postglacial Time in Eastern North America, Sci. Monthly, May, 1953, pp. 259–276, with 17 sketches. He writes in this paper: "Raised (former) marine shorelines extend to elevations hundreds of feet above sea level around the borders of glaciated North America, but it is not generally known that they preserve a record of uplift of the earth's crust which amounts to a history of postglacial time." He estimates the vertical movement of ground in the Hudsonian ice center since the glacial climax at 914 m or 3,000 ft and found a rise of ground in the northwestern direction across some of the New England States amounting to 18 to 24 ft/mile (3.41 to 4.55 m/km) produced during one single spasmodic, tilting motion of the ground. See also, on recoil of glaciated tracts of land, REGINALD ALDWORTH DALY, "Strength and Structure of the Earth," 434 pp., Prentice-Hall, Inc., Englewood Cliffs, N.J., 1940 (see p. 326).

FIG. 10-21. Postglacial upwarp after LOUGEE.

glacial-lake shorelines found by geologists, which rise landward with slopes that gradually decrease with the distances from the east coast toward the Hudson Bay as the center of the glaciated region.   Figure 10-20 illustrates the uptilted position $A'B'$ that a formerly horizontal line (old seashore) AB would take after a postglacial warping upward of the earth's crust were completed, and Fig. 10-21 shows the decrease of such slopes in a vertical profile of the continent in a northwestern section, described by Lougee, as one proceeds landward.   The parallel curves in Fig. 10-20a represent earth strata under a full ice load; in Fig. 10-20b, these curves have again become straight lines after the ice load disappeared.

GUTENBERG likewise describes the ground-level changes *in the Great Lakes region* of North America as consisting of an upward tilting of the ground around a "hinge," with presently practically vanishing uplifts, along a straight line that runs in a northwestern direction passing a little north of the cities of Milwaukee and Cleveland.   While the changes in elevation along this line are negligible, the levels along a straight-line tangent to the northern tips of Lake Superior and Lake Ontario *rise* at present at a rate equal to about 40 cm per century, the ground within this band of land being tilted upward in northeasterly directions 7 to 9 cm per 100 km distance per century.

C. THE BENDING DISTORTION OF EARTH'S VISCOUS SLAB TRAILS AN EXTENDED, STRAIGHT GLACIAL FRONT THAT RETREATS WITH A STEADY VELOCITY.   In the preceding examples we treated the distortion of the earth's slab by assuming that an ice load above a given locality would decrease with time.   Let us now consider the bending distortion which *trails* an extended, straight glacial front that retreats with a small velocity c continuously in a manner comparable with the just-mentioned observations.

EXAMPLE 5. Consider as an intermediate example, serving only to clarify a simple case of *a moving pressure wave*, the following distribution of pressure along the surface of a slab:

$$p = p_0 \cos \frac{\pi(x - ct)}{a} \qquad (10\text{-}152)$$

representing a load which moves with uniform velocity $c = $ const above an infinite slab (if a mean value p_0 were added to it, not unlike the weights of parallel sand dunes drifting under wind action on a beach).   Writing for p

$$p = p_1 + p_2,$$

$$p_1 = p_0 \psi_1(t) \cos \frac{\pi x}{a}, \qquad \qquad \psi_1 = \cos \frac{\pi ct}{a},$$

$$\qquad\qquad\qquad\qquad\qquad\qquad\qquad\qquad\qquad\qquad (10\text{-}153)$$

$$p_2 = p_0 \psi_2(t) \sin \frac{\pi x}{a}, \qquad \qquad \psi_2 = \sin \frac{\pi ct}{a},$$

then, as previously, the deflection of a viscous slab resting on substratum, satisfying Eq. (10-129), is found equal to

$$w = w_1 + w_2, \qquad t_0 = \frac{N_0 \pi^4}{ka^4},$$

$$w_1 = \frac{p_0}{k} \phi_1(t) \cos \frac{\pi x}{a}, \qquad \phi_1 = \frac{-e^{-t/t_0} + \cos(\pi ct/a) + (\pi ct_0/a) \sin(\pi ct/a)}{1 + (\pi ct_0/a)^2},$$
$$\text{(10-154)}$$

$$w_2 = \frac{p_0}{k} \phi_2(t) \sin \frac{\pi x}{a}, \qquad \phi_2 = \frac{(\pi ct_0/a)[e^{-t/t_0} - \cos(\pi ct/a)] + \sin(\pi ct/a)}{1 + (\pi ct_0/a)^2},$$

this giving, at time $t = 0$, $w = 0$. As time progresses, the deflection w,

$$w = \frac{p_0}{k[1 + (\pi ct_0/a)^2]} \left[e^{-t/t_0} \left(\sin \frac{\pi x}{a} - \cos \frac{\pi x}{a} \right) \right.$$
$$\left. + \cos \frac{\pi(x - ct)}{a} - \frac{\pi ct_0}{a} \sin \frac{\pi(x - ct)}{a} \right], \qquad \text{(10-155)}$$

establishes itself after t has become a considerable multiple of t_0 in the form

$$t = \infty, \qquad w = \frac{(p_0/k)[\cos \pi(x - ct)/a - (\pi ct_0/a) \sin \pi(x - ct)/a]}{1 + (\pi ct_0/a)^2}, \qquad \text{(10-156)}$$

or, if one introduces a phase angle ω defined by

$$\tan \omega = \frac{\pi ct_0}{a} = \frac{cN_0 \pi^5}{ka^5}, \qquad \omega = \arctan \frac{\pi ct_0}{a}, \qquad \text{(10-157)}$$

the deflection w becomes, when $t = \infty$,

$$w = \frac{p_0 \cos[\omega + (\pi/a)(x - ct)]}{k\sqrt{1 + \tan^2 \omega}}, \qquad \text{(10-158)}$$

a wave trailing the pressure load p with the phase ω, both waves moving to the right with velocity c (Fig. 10-22). The amplitude of these deflections

$$\frac{p_0}{k\sqrt{1 + \tan^2 \omega}} = \frac{p_0}{k} \cos \omega \qquad \text{(10-159)}$$

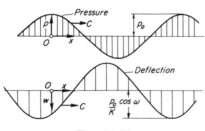

FIG. 10-22

under a moving load is smaller than its isostatic value p_0/k under an unmoving similar load.

EXAMPLE 6. *Earth's slab covered on one side by uniform glacial load which melts away at its edge at a uniform rate. Wave of deflections in slab.* Let us apply this elementary solution to two cases of a slowly retreating, straight, glacial front, having the form of either Fig. 10-23 or 10-24, by supposing that the earth's slab is being loaded by the weights of an extended sheet of ice as illustrated in these figures, the edge A of which melts away at the rate c m/sec. If the ice front has a vertical edge, we may express the pressure p by the *Fourier integral*

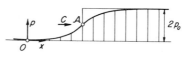

FIG. 10-23

$$x > ct, \qquad p = p_0$$

$$+ \frac{2}{\pi} p_0 \int_0^\infty \frac{1}{\lambda} \sin \lambda(x - ct) \cdot d\lambda, \qquad (10\text{-}160)$$

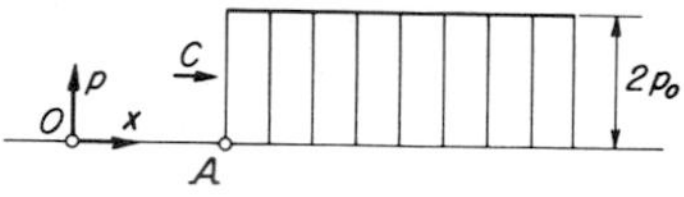

and if the ice front slopes down gradually as in Fig. 10-24, supposing that

FIG. 10-24

$$p = p_0[2 - e^{-\beta(x-ct)}], \qquad \text{when} \qquad x > ct,$$

$$p = p_0 e^{\beta(x-ct)} \qquad \text{where} \qquad x < ct,$$

FIGS. 10-23 and 10-24. Pressure distributions moving with horizontal velocity c.

by the integral

$$x > ct, \qquad p = p_0 + \frac{2}{\pi} \beta^2 p_0 \int_0^\infty \frac{\sin \lambda(x - ct) \, d\lambda}{\lambda(\lambda^2 + \beta^2)}, \qquad (10\text{-}161)$$

where β is a given constant.

Bearing in mind that a slab is depressed under the mean value of pressure $p = p_0 = $ const by an amount $w = p_0/k = $ const, we may omit these terms in the following and evaluate the deflections w of a viscous slab from Eq. (10-129):

$$N_0 \frac{\partial^4 \dot{w}}{\partial x^4} = -kw + p \qquad (10\text{-}162)$$

using for p the integral

$$p = p_1 + p_2 = p_0 \int_0^\infty c_0(\lambda) \sin \lambda(x - ct) \, d\lambda,$$

split in the parts

$$p_1 = p_0 \int_0^\infty \psi_1(t) \sin \lambda x \, d\lambda, \qquad \psi_1(t) = c_0(\lambda) \cos (\lambda ct),$$

$$\qquad\qquad\qquad\qquad\qquad\qquad\qquad\qquad\qquad\qquad\qquad (10\text{-}163)$$

$$p_2 = p_0 \int_0^\infty \psi_2(t) \cos \lambda x \, d\lambda, \qquad \psi_2(t) = -c_0(\lambda) \sin (\lambda ct),$$

where $c_0(\lambda)$ abbreviates either of the two expressions

$$c_0(\lambda) = \frac{2}{\pi\lambda} \qquad \text{or} \qquad c_0(\lambda) = \frac{2\beta^2}{\pi\lambda(\lambda^2 + \beta^2)}, \qquad (10\text{-}164)$$

corresponding to the vertical or the gently sloping glacial front [Eqs. (10-160) and (10-161), respectively]. By following the procedure applied in the simple, preceding example relative to Eq. (10-152)[1] we set up the deflection w satisfying

[1] In order to obtain the expressions for the time functions $\phi_1(t)$, $\phi_2(t)$ in the integrands in Eqs. (10-165) from the corresponding expressions found in Eqs. (10-154), we have to write instead of π/a the integration variable λ and instead of $t_0 = N_0\pi^4/ka^4$ the new value

$$t_0 = \frac{N_0\lambda^4}{k}, \qquad (10\text{-}166)$$

our new functions ϕ_1 and ϕ_2 satisfying the following equations with this latter value of t_0:

$$t_0\dot{\phi}_1 + \phi_1 = \psi_1 = c_0 \cos (\lambda ct), \qquad t_0\dot{\phi}_2 + \phi_2 = \psi_2 = -c_0 \sin (\lambda ct),$$

with the initial condition $t = 0$, $\phi_1 = 0$, $\phi_2 = 0$.

Eq. (10-162) as the sum of the two parts:

$$w_1 = \frac{p_0}{k} \int_0^\infty \phi_1 \sin \lambda x \, d\lambda, \qquad \phi_1 = \frac{-e^{-t/t_0} + \cos(\lambda ct) + \lambda ct_0 \sin(\lambda ct)}{1 + (\lambda ct_0)^2},$$

$$w_2 = \frac{p_0}{k} \int_0^\infty \phi_2 \cos \lambda x \, d\lambda, \qquad \phi_2 = \frac{\lambda ct_0[-e^{-t/t_0} + \cos(\lambda ct)] - \sin(\lambda ct)}{1 + (\lambda ct_0)^2},$$

$$(10\text{-}165)$$

w vanishing at time $t = 0$.

If the time increases indefinitely, the deflected *viscous earth slab* tends to *approach a certain definite form*, namely (after striking out the exponential term e^{-t/t_0} in the expressions for ϕ_1 and ϕ_2 and rearranging terms),

$$w = \frac{p_0}{k} \int_0^\infty c_0(\lambda) \frac{\sin \lambda(x - ct) + \lambda ct_0 \cos \lambda(x - ct)}{1 + (\lambda ct_0)^2} \, d\lambda, \qquad (x > ct). \quad (10\text{-}167)$$

This, being a function of the variable $x - ct$, *represents a wave of deflected form which moves along the slab in the direction of the positive x with the velocity c and trails the similarly retreating glacial pressure load p.* One value of the deflection w may easily be evaluated, namely, the one for which $x - ct = 0$, that is, if we choose for $x = 0$, $t = 0$, *the deflection under the front of the glacial load*, under point A in Figs. 10-23 and 10-24, is found equal to

$$w_0 = \frac{p_0}{k} \int_0^\infty \frac{\lambda ct_0 c_0(\lambda) \, d\lambda}{1 + (\lambda ct_0)^2}. \qquad (10\text{-}168)$$

If we substitute herein for $c_0(\lambda)$ the first value, $c_0(\lambda) = 2/\pi\lambda$, corresponding to the abrupt, vertical glacial front (Fig. 10-23) and the value of t_0 from Eq. (10-166), we obtain, with the abbreviating constant $a = N_0 c/k$, the deflection w_0 of the slab *under point A,*

$$w_0 = \frac{2p_0}{5\pi k} \int_0^\infty \frac{d(a\lambda^5)}{1 + a^2\lambda^{10}} = \frac{2p_0}{5\pi k} \int_0^\infty \frac{du}{1 + u^2} = \frac{2p_0}{5\pi k} \left. \arctan u \right|_0^\infty,$$

$$w_0 = \frac{p_0}{5k}, \qquad (10\text{-}169)$$

and if we take for $c_0(\lambda)$ the second value given in Eqs. (10-164), corresponding to a sloping glacial front (Fig. 10-24), we obtain this deflection equal to

$$w_0 = \frac{2p_0 a}{\pi k} \int_0^\infty \frac{\lambda^4 \, d\lambda}{[1 + (\lambda/\beta)^2](1 + a^2\lambda^{10})}, \qquad (10\text{-}170)$$

which must be smaller than the former value $p_0/5k$.

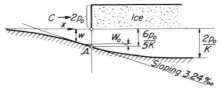

FIG. 10-25. Deflection of earth's slab under uniform glacial load covering one half of ground which melts away at its edge with rate c.

We may compute the angle of tilting of the ground under the moving vertical front of ice load at point A ($x - ct = 0$), using $c_0(\lambda) = 2/\pi\lambda$, after differentiating Eq. (10-167) with respect to x, finding *the earth's slab inclined under the slope* $\partial w/\partial x$ *at* $x = ct$:

$$\frac{\partial w}{\partial x} = \frac{2p_0}{\pi k} \int_0^\infty \frac{d\lambda}{1 + a^2\lambda^{10}} = \frac{2p_0}{\pi k a^{1/5}} \int_0^\infty \frac{dz}{1 + z^{10}} = 0.647\,\frac{p_0}{k a^{1/5}}. \quad (10\text{-}171)[1]$$

Whereas the deflection $w_0 = p_0/5k$ in the profile of the ground under a retreating, vertical ice front is independent of the velocity c, the slope $(\partial w/\partial x)_{x=ct}$, under which the ground is tilted, is inversely proportional to $a^{1/5} = (N_0c/k)^{1/5}$ or to the fifth root of the velocity c with which the front retreats.

Again using some of the values for the constants assumed in Example 1 for an earth's slab of thickness $h_0 = 50$ km $= 5 \times 10^6$ cm, having the viscosity $\mu = 5 \times 10^{22}$ poises $= 5 \times 10^{16}$ kg cm^{-2} sec, floating on a substratum of the specific weight $\gamma_e = k = 0.003$ kg/cm^3 and covered on one side of the ground by an ice sheet $2h_i = 3$ km $= 3 \times 10^5$ cm thick which melts away at its edge with a rate c cm/sec (Fig. 10-25), the ground is uniformly depressed under the mean pressure $p_0 = h_i\gamma_i = 150$ kg/cm^2 by the amount $p_0/k = 500$ m $= 5 \times 10^4$ cm, so that *the total deflection that the slab suffers under the edge, at point A of the ice front*, using Eq. (10-169), amounts to

$$\left(1 + \frac{1}{5}\right)\frac{p_0}{k} = \frac{6p_0}{5k} = 600 \text{ m},$$

while its maximum deflection is $2p_0/k = 1000$ m farther away. With the slab modulus $N_0 = (1/3)\mu h_0^3 = 2.083 \times 10^{36}$ kg cm sec, $N_0/k = 6.94 \times 10^{38}$ cm^4 sec, suppose that we assume for the constant

$$a = \frac{N_0c}{k} = 1 \times 10^{35} \text{ cm}^5.$$

Then, the velocity c with which the glacial edge melts away amounts to

$$c = \frac{ak}{N_0} = 1.44 \times 10^{-4} \text{ cm/sec}$$

$$= 1.44 \times 3.156 \times 10^3 \text{ cm/year} = 45.4 \text{ m/year};$$

i.e., the glacial front moves back by 45.4 km in 1,000 years. With the preceding

---

[1] After splitting this last definite integral in the two parts,

$$\int_0^\infty = \int_0^1 + \int_1^\infty,$$

and developing the integrands in series, we have

$$\int_0^\infty \frac{dz}{1 + z^{10}} = \left(1 - \frac{1}{11} + \frac{1}{21} - \frac{1}{31} + \cdots\right) + \left(\frac{1}{9} - \frac{1}{19} + \frac{1}{29} - \cdots\right)$$

$$= 1 + 2\left(\frac{1}{99} - \frac{1}{399} + \frac{1}{899} - \frac{1}{1,599} + \cdots\right)$$

$$= 1 + 2\left[\sum_1^\infty \frac{(-1)^{n-1}}{(10n)^2} + \sum_1^\infty \frac{(-1)^{n-1}}{(10n)^4} + \sum_1^\infty \frac{(-1)^{n-1}}{(10n)^6} + \cdots\right]$$

$$= 1.017, \qquad (n = 1, 2, 3, \cdots).$$

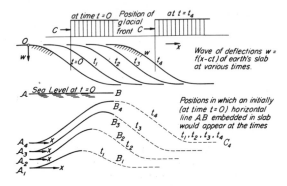

FIG. 10-26. Subsequent form of curves in which an initially horizontal straight line AB embedded in the ground appears after a deflection wave $w = f(x - ct)$, as indicated above, swept over the ground.

values we find that the ground under the vertical edge of ice (at point A of Fig. 10-25) must be tilted under a slope, using Eq. (10-171),

$$\left(\frac{\partial w}{\partial x}\right)_{x=ct} = \frac{0.647 p_0 a^{-\frac{1}{3}}}{k} = 0.00324$$

rising 3.24 m/km toward the area that has lost its ice load. The depression caused under and behind the retreating glacial sheet is indicated in Fig. 10-25. The angle of tilting would change little if the rate of melting c were, for example, one-half or twice as great:[1]

Rate of melting: $c = 22.7$ m/year   Slope: $\partial w / \partial x = 3.72\%_{0}$

$c = 45.4$ m/year $\partial w / \partial x = 3.24\%_{0}$

$c = 90.8$ m/year $\partial w / \partial x = 2.82\%_{0}$

If a deflection wave $w = f(x - ct)$ of the tentatively assumed shape illustrated in Fig. 10-26 swept over the ground, *a horizontal line such as AB embedded at time $t = 0$ in the ground* (representing an old seashore at $t = 0$) would, at equally spaced times t_1, t_2, t_3, t_4, take the positions A_1B_1, ..., A_4B_4 shown in the lower part of Fig. 10-26, corresponding to the positions of the deflection wave indicated (the curves A_1B_1, ... were traced in displaced positions, to avoid confusing them, but their left, starting points A_1, ..., A_4 have to coincide with point A). They represent the differences in ordinates $w_n - w_0 = f(x - ct_n) - f(x)$ plotted above the coordinate x, the uppermost line $A_4B_4C_4$ being exactly an inverted picture in its left half A_4B_4 of any of the w curves. In the field, the rising halves traced by full lines could be observed; the dropping halves (dashed lines) would be buried under ice and not be observable. The rising halves of these curves conform with the general trends of uptilted old seashore lines in northeastern America as described by LOUGEE.

While the rule was formerly stated (see Sec. 10-2) that a *steady* distribution of pressure p leaves a precise imprint in the deflection line of a viscous slab after a sufficiently long time has elapsed, and thus a steady pressure function having a finite discontinuity, such as the one represented in Fig. 10-23, does not permit consideration of the final, sharply bent slab deflection line, *it is noteworthy that*

---

[1] If, hypothetically, a uniform rate of melting c were assumed during the deglaciation of North America, the distance between the most advanced position of the ice along the Atlantic Coast (at the time of glacial climax) and the Hudson Bay being about 2,000 km = 1,240 miles, to the three rates just compared would correspond times of deglaciation of 88, 44, and 22 thousand years, respectively.

this difficulty does not arise when a pressure wave
of the same form sweeps slowly along the slab,
because under the critical region of pressure
new and new-material elements are involved
which thus prevent the gradual building up
of a sharp corner in the deflection line. The
asymptotic shape of this line at $t = \infty$ remains
the smooth curve derived in Eq. (10-167) or
illustrated in Fig. 10-25.

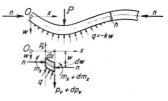

FIG. 10-27

**10-8. Viscous Slab Resting on Substratum, Bent by Axial
Compression Force n.** Let us consider the case of one-dimensional
bending of an infinite, horizontal slab on a substratum, loaded by
single, transversal forces and by a uniform axial compression force n
per unit width acting in the direction of its middle plane parallel to the
x axis. If Poisson's ratio is taken equal to one-half, there will also be a
uniform compression $n/2$ present in the direction of the y axis. In the
absence of extraneous distributed pressures ($p = 0$), the equilibrium
conditions of the vertical shearing forces[1] p_v and of the bending moments
m_x (Fig. 10-27)

$$\frac{\partial p_v}{\partial x} = kw,$$

$$p_v = \frac{\partial m_x}{\partial x} - n\frac{\partial w}{\partial x},$$

give

$$\frac{\partial^2 m_x}{\partial x^2} = \frac{\partial p_v}{\partial x} + n\frac{\partial^2 w}{\partial x^2} = kw + n\frac{\partial^2 w}{\partial x^2}. \tag{10-172}$$

Supposing first, generally, a slab of viscoelastic material, we have,
with reference to Chap. 9, Eq. (9-7),

$$N\frac{\partial^2 \dot{w}}{\partial x^2} = -\left(\dot{m}_x + \frac{m_x}{t_e}\right), \qquad t_e = \frac{3\mu}{E},$$

$$N\frac{\partial^4 \dot{w}}{\partial x^4} = -\frac{\partial^2}{\partial x^2}\left(\dot{m}_x + \frac{m_x}{t_e}\right). \tag{10-173}$$

After differentiating Eq. (10-172) with respect to the time t and
substituting the second derivatives $\partial^2 m_x/\partial x^2$ and $\partial^2 \dot{m}_x/\partial x^2$ in the
preceding equation, we see that *the deflections w of a viscoelastic slab also*

[1] Following the practice suggested by M. HETÉNYI, page 284, *op. cit.* (in his book
see chap. 6, p. 127), the shearing force p_v and bending moment m_x per unit width
are expressed in the *vertical* planes $x = $ const, while previously they were defined
in the plane sections *normal* to the deflected surface of the slab.

carrying an axial compression force n acting in the *x* direction may be determined from the differential equation

$$N \frac{\partial^4 \dot{w}}{\partial x^4} + n \frac{\partial^2 \dot{w}}{\partial x^2} + \left(\dot{n} + \frac{n}{t_e} \right) \frac{\partial^2 w}{\partial x^2} + k \left(\dot{w} + \frac{w}{t_e} \right) = 0. \qquad (10\text{-}174)$$

In the following we shall consider the special case of *a purely viscous slab subjected to an invariable axial force n* (not dependent on time *t*). After multiplying Eq. (10-174) by t_e and disregarding those terms which obtain the factor t_e (since it is supposed to be small), but using the modulus for the viscous slab,

$$N_0 = N t_e = \frac{Eh^3}{9} \frac{3\mu}{E} = (\tfrac{1}{3}) \mu h^3,$$

this equation simplifies to

$$N_0 \frac{\partial^4 \dot{w}}{\partial x^4} + n \frac{\partial^2 w}{\partial x^2} + kw = 0. \qquad (10\text{-}175)$$

We may note that the corresponding equation for *an elastic slab* (not having viscosity) supported on an elastic foundation loaded by an axial compression force *n*,

$$N \frac{d^4 w}{dx^4} + n \frac{d^2 w}{dx^2} + kw = 0, \qquad (10\text{-}176)$$

has a very similar form. The latter equation has been investigated by engineers[1] in connection with the buckling problem of elastic instability for the corresponding case of slender beams.

Returning to Eq. (10-175) and letting

$$w = X(x) \varphi(t),$$

we obtain

$$\frac{X^{(4)}}{(n/N_0) X'' + (k/N_0) X} = -\frac{\varphi}{\dot{\varphi}} = c = \text{const} \qquad (10\text{-}177)$$

and may distinguish two cases, depending on whether the constant *c* having the dimension of a time is negative or positive:

Case 1: $c = -t_a$,

Case 2: $c = t_b$,

t_a, t_b representing essentially *positive* constant times.
Case 1: Assuming $c = -t_a$, let

$$\beta^2 = \frac{n t_a l^2}{2 N_0}, \qquad \lambda_a^4 = \frac{k t_a l^4}{N_0}, \qquad (10\text{-}178)$$

[1] See page 284 [cf. HETÉNYI, *op. cit.*, eq. (115), p. 135].

where l is an indeterminate length.   Then,

$$t_a = \frac{2\beta^2 N_0}{nl^2} = \frac{N_0 \lambda_a^4}{kl^4},$$
(10-179)

and the compression force n in terms of the dimensionless parameters β and λ_a is expressed by

$$n = \frac{2k\beta^2 l^2}{\lambda_a^4}.$$
(10-180)

The second part of Eq. (10-177), assuming $c = -t_a$, gives $\varphi = e^{t/t_a}$, and the first part, assuming $X = $ constant $\times e^{\lambda x/l}$ for the determination of λ, the characteristic equation of fourth order

$$\lambda^4 + 2\beta^2 \lambda^2 + \lambda_a^4 = 0,$$
(10-181)

having the four roots:

$$\lambda_1 = -\lambda_3 = \beta \cdot \sqrt{-1 + \sqrt{1 - \left(\frac{\lambda_a}{\beta}\right)^4}},$$

$$\lambda_2 = -\lambda_4 = \beta \cdot \sqrt{-1 - \sqrt{1 - \left(\frac{\lambda_a}{\beta}\right)^4}}.$$
(10-182)

The corresponding four particular integrals have different forms, depending on whether

Case 1A: $\lambda_a < \beta$,
Case 1B: $\lambda_a = \beta$,
Case 1C: $\lambda_a > \beta$,

the inner, small square-root expression represents a real number, is equal to zero, or to an imaginary number.   The axial force n is, respectively,

$$n \gtreqless 2 \cdot \sqrt{\frac{kN_0}{t_a}}.$$
(10-183)

Case 1A: $\lambda_a < \beta$.   If we denote

$$\alpha_a = \sqrt{1 - \left(\frac{\lambda_a}{\beta}\right)^4},$$
(10-184)

since α_a is a real fraction, $\alpha_a < 1$, the four roots of Eq. (10-181) are the imaginary numbers

$$\lambda_1 = -\lambda_3 = i\beta\sqrt{1 - \alpha_a}, \qquad \lambda_2 = -\lambda_4 = i\beta\sqrt{1 + \alpha_a}, \quad (10\text{-}185)$$

and Eq. (10-175) has the four, particular integrals in real form:

$$e^{t/t_a}\left(\sin\frac{\sqrt{1 - \alpha_a}\,\beta x}{l}, \cos\frac{\sqrt{1 - \alpha_a}\,\beta x}{l}\right),$$

$$e^{t/t_a}\left(\sin\frac{\sqrt{1 + \alpha_a}\,\beta x}{l}, \cos\frac{\sqrt{1 + \alpha_a}\,\beta x}{l}\right).$$
(10-186)

Case 1B: $\lambda_a = \beta$.   This gives in the preceding expressions, by taking $\alpha_a = 0$, two pairs of equal roots $\lambda_1 = \lambda_2$, $\lambda_3 = \lambda_4$ in which case the particular solutions

$$e^{t/t_a}\left(\sin\frac{\beta x}{l}\,,\ \cos\frac{\beta x}{l}\,,\ x\sin\frac{\beta x}{l}\,,\ x\cos\frac{\beta x}{l}\right) \tag{10-187}$$

are obtained.   The compression force n is equal to

$$n = 2\cdot\sqrt{\frac{kN_0}{t_a}}\,. \tag{10-188}$$

Case 2: It may be in order to inject here the formulas corresponding to Case 2, when the constant $c = t_b$ introduced in Eq. (10-177) is positive. Again letting

$$\beta^2 = \frac{nt_b l^2}{2N_0}\,, \qquad \lambda_b^4 = \frac{kt_b l^4}{N_0}\,, $$
$$n = \frac{2\beta^2 k l^2}{\lambda_b^4}\,, \tag{10-189}$$

we obtain $\varphi = e^{-t/t_b}$ and the characteristic equation

$$\lambda^4 - 2\beta^2\lambda^2 - \lambda_b^4 = 0 \tag{10-190}$$

having for all values of λ_b and β two real and two imaginary roots

$$\lambda_1 = -\lambda_2 = \beta\cdot\sqrt{\alpha_b + 1}, \qquad \lambda_3 = -\lambda_4 = i\beta\cdot\sqrt{\alpha_b - 1}, \tag{10-191}$$

where α_b, denoting

$$\alpha_b = \sqrt{1 + \left(\frac{\lambda_b}{\beta}\right)^4}\,, \tag{10-192}$$

now is a number greater than 1.   In this case, we are led to the group of four particular integrals in real form:

$$e^{-t/t_b}\!\left(e^{\sqrt{1+\alpha_b}\cdot\beta x/l},\ e^{-\sqrt{1+\alpha_b}\cdot\beta x/l}\right),$$
$$e^{-t/t_b}\!\left(\cos\frac{\sqrt{\alpha_b - 1}\cdot\beta x}{l}\,,\ \sin\frac{\sqrt{\alpha_b - 1}\cdot\beta x}{l}\right). \tag{10-193}$$

While in Cases 1, 1A, and 1B, the deflection w increases, in Case 2 it will decrease with time t.

In each of these three groups of particular integrals, solutions of simple, periodic, oscillating form occur.   If the slab initially possessed deflections of this form, the preceding formulas enable us *to consider the growth or the decay of the permanent undulations of an infinite viscous slab carried by buoyancy pressures and subjected to an axial, uniform, compression force n* perpendicularly to the crests of the initial waves.

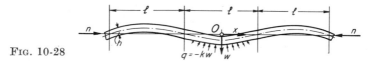

FIG. 10-28

Suppose that it possessed at the time $t = 0$, for example, the small, permanent deflections of an arbitrarily chosen wavelength $2l$ and, amplitude w_0 (Fig. 10-28):

$$w = w_0 \cos \frac{\pi x}{l}. \qquad (10\text{-}194)$$

When $\lambda_a = \beta$ (Case 1B), the slab bends with the deflections

$$w = w_0 e^{t/t_a} \cos \frac{\beta x}{l}, \qquad (10\text{-}195)$$

and w at $t = 0$ coincides with the former form if $\beta = \lambda_a = \pi$. Denoting the corresponding value of the time constant t_a by t_0 and of the compression force n by n_0 in this particular case, we obtain from Eq. (10-179)

$$t_0 = \frac{\pi^4 N_0}{kl^4} \qquad (10\text{-}196)$$

and from Eq. (10-180) for the compression force the value[1]

$$n_0 = \frac{2}{\pi^2} kl^2. \qquad (10\text{-}197)$$

Similarly, considering Case 1A, when $\lambda_a < \beta$ and when the particular solution has the first form

$$w = w_0 e^{t/t_a} \cos \frac{\sqrt{1 - \alpha_a} \cdot \beta x}{l}, \qquad (10\text{-}198)$$

this coincides at $t = 0$ with Eq. (10-194) if $\beta \sqrt{1 - \alpha_a} = \pi$, and we find in terms of α_a $(\alpha_a < 1)$:

$$\beta^2 = \frac{\pi^2}{1 - \alpha_a}, \qquad t_a = \frac{(1 + \alpha_a)t_0}{1 - \alpha_a}, \qquad n = \frac{n_0}{1 + \alpha_a}. \qquad (10\text{-}199)$$

If we use the second particular solution developed in Case 1A,

$$w = w_0 e^{t/t_a} \cos \frac{\sqrt{1 + \alpha_a} \cdot \beta x}{l}, \qquad (10\text{-}200)$$

[1] We might have assumed, instead of Eq. (10-194), for the same fundamental length l a deflection

$$w = w_m \cos \frac{m\pi x}{l}$$

(m is an integer) to which correspond the series of values of the compression forces n and time constants t_a,

$$n = \frac{2kl^2}{m^2 \pi^2}, \qquad t_a = \frac{m^4 \pi^4 N_0}{kl^4}$$

and similarly when considering Case 1A. See Eq. (10-208) below.

letting $\beta \sqrt{1 + \alpha_a} = \pi$, we likewise obtain

$$\beta^2 = \frac{\pi^2}{1 + \alpha_a}, \qquad t_a = \frac{(1 - \alpha_a)t_0}{1 + \alpha_a}, \qquad n = \frac{n_0}{1 - \alpha_a}. \tag{10-201}$$

By attributing to the characteristic ratio λ_a/β fixed values within the permissible interval

$$1 \geq \frac{\lambda_a}{\beta} \geq 0$$

or by letting α_a run through the values

$$0 \leq \alpha_a \leq 1,$$

the compression force n and the time constant t_a will vary in the ranges

and
$$\begin{aligned} n_0 \geq n \geq (\tfrac{1}{2})n_0, & \qquad t_0 \leq t_a < \infty, \\ n_0 \leq n < \infty, & \qquad t_0 \geq t_a \geq 0, \end{aligned} \tag{10-202}$$

in the first and second group, respectively, and the time constant t_a covers the entire range between zero and infinity in the preceding two groups of solutions which also include Case 1B if we let $\alpha_a = 0$. The deflections w increase with time t, except when α_a becomes exactly equal to 1. When, in Eqs. (10-199), $\alpha_a = 1$, $\beta = \infty$, $t_a = \infty$, we may still postulate that the $\lim \beta \sqrt{1 - \alpha_a} = \pi$ maintains its finite value π. The case $\alpha_a = 1$ leads to the remarkable observation that *there exists a certain compression force, namely,*

$$n = (\tfrac{1}{2})n_0 = \frac{kl^2}{\pi^2}, \tag{10-203}$$

which prevents the initially present waves from evanescing or growing (they would certainly disappear in a viscous slab if the force n should vanish). Under this force $n = kl^2/\pi^2$ the originally present undulations of the viscous slab,

$$w = w_0 \cos \frac{\pi x}{l}, \tag{10-204}$$

remain preserved since t_a in Eqs. (10-199) becomes infinite.[1]

---

[1] One verifies easily indeed, by going back to the differential equation, Eq. (10-175), that, when the axial force n has *this value of indifference* $n = (\tfrac{1}{2})n_0$, the sum of the second and third terms in Eq. (10-175) cancels out and that consequently the rates of deflection $\dot{w}$ vanish; also that, when the compression force takes on this special value $n_0/2$, *the bending moments m_x vanish along the entire length of the slab* at any amplitude w_0 of a deflection curve $w = w_0 \cos (\pi x/l)$ because the moments m_x caused by n just balance those due to the buoyancy pressures and to the vertical shearing forces p_v at every point. A force equal to $n_0/2$ is unable to produce further deflections.

We may add that Case 2, which was considered above, supplies the missing range for the compression force $0 < n < n_0/2$. If we choose among the integrals of Eq. (10-193) as solution

$$w = w_0 e^{-t/t_b} \cos \frac{\sqrt{\alpha_b - 1} \cdot \beta x}{l}, \qquad (10\text{-}205)$$

this coincides at $t = 0$ with

$$w = w_0 \cos \frac{\pi x}{l}$$

if we make $\beta \sqrt{\alpha_b - 1} = \pi$, where for all values of λ_b, β

$$\alpha_b = \sqrt{1 + \left(\frac{\lambda_b}{\beta}\right)^4}. \qquad (10\text{-}206)$$

Thus we find for Case 2

$$\beta^2 = \frac{\pi^2}{\alpha_b - 1}, \qquad t_b = \frac{(\alpha_b + 1)t_0}{\alpha_b - 1}, \qquad n = \frac{n_0}{\alpha_b + 1}, \qquad (10\text{-}207)$$

showing, since $\alpha_b > 1$, that the time constant t_b varies within the range $\infty > t_b \geq t_0$ and the force n within the range $(\frac{1}{2})n_0 \geq n \geq 0$. *Under a force that is smaller than $n_0/2$ the undulations which were originally present will gradually evanesce, the slab will straighten out with time,* and this is also true when the slab is left unloaded ($n = 0$), when α_b becomes infinite, because of the active buoyancy pressures exerted by the substratum at rates corresponding to the minimum time constant $t_b = t_0$.

The preceding results could have been obtained at once by substituting in the differential equation (10-175)

$$\frac{\partial^4 w}{\partial x^4} + \frac{n}{N_0} \cdot \frac{\partial^2 w}{\partial x^2} + \frac{k}{N_0} \cdot w = 0,$$

$$w = a_m e^{c_m t} \cos \frac{m \pi x}{l}, \qquad (10\text{-}208)$$

where m is an integer, satisfying it if the constant c_m is chosen equal to

$$c_m = \frac{(n/N_0) \cdot (m^2 \pi^2/l^2) - k/N_0}{m^4 \pi^4/l^4}. \qquad (10\text{-}209)$$

The constant c_m takes on either a positive or a negative value, depending on whether the compression force

$$n \gtreqless \frac{kl^2}{m^2 \pi^2}, \qquad c_m \gtreqless 0, \qquad (10\text{-}210)$$

and if $m = 1$, c_1 coincides with $c_1 = 1/t_a$ or $c_1 = -1/t_b$, respectively, in the former notation.

A series of terms of this form permits consideration of the deflections in an infinite viscous slab on substratum under an axial compression force n, for example, in the case that the initial undulations of the slab at time $t = 0$ are prescribed as an even, arbitrary, periodic function of x,

$$t = 0, \qquad w = f(x) = \sum_1^\infty a_m \cos \frac{m\pi x}{l}, \qquad (m = 1, 3, 5, \ldots). \qquad \text{(10-211)}$$

We may note some strange occurrences in the terms of the corresponding series expressing the deflections of the slab at time t:

$$w = \sum_m a_m e^{c_m t} \cos \frac{m\pi x}{l} \qquad \text{(10-212)}$$

if the compression force n takes on one of the values of indifference,

$$n_m = \frac{kl^2}{m^2 \pi^2}, \qquad \text{(10-213)}$$

for which in the corresponding term the factor c_m in the exponent of $e^{c_m t}$ [see Eq. (10-209)] vanishes. The corresponding harmonic in the series (10-212) remains, all harmonics lower than the stationary one evanesce, and all higher harmonics grow with time t.

Consider, for example, *a viscous slab possessing originally a fundamental mode of gentle undulations of a great wavelength $2l$ on which small wrinkles of a higher order are superposed* (Fig. 10-29):

$$w = w_1 \cos \frac{\pi x}{l} + w_m \cos \frac{m\pi x}{l}. \qquad \text{(10-214)}$$

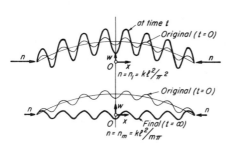

FIG. 10-29. Bending distortion of viscous slabs under axial compression n. Above, wrinkles grow when $n = n_1$. Below, wrinkles remain unchanged when $n = n_m$ but fundamental mode disappears.

We may observe the following strange occurrences. Under a compression force n equal to

$$n = n_1 = \frac{kl^2}{\pi^2} \qquad \text{(10-215)}$$

the small wrinkles will grow at a very slow rate indefinitely, while the amplitude of the fundamental mode remains unchanged. If the axial force n had the much smaller value

$$n = n_m = \frac{kl^2}{m^2 \pi^2}, \qquad \text{(10-216)}$$

the fundamental mode will disappear at a comparatively fast rate, but the small wrinkles stay preserved in the slab. If the axial force n has a value between

$$n_m < n < n_1,$$

one will see the wrinkles growing indefinitely while the long undulation straightens out.[1]

This, then, completes a discussion of the growth or the decay of simple undulations in an infinite, purely viscous slab, lying on substratum under the action of an invariable axial thrust n, in which the questions of the instability of the viscoelastic equilibria could not be investigated since the elastic parts of the bending strains were neglected a priori. An investigation of the conditions of instability and of the buckling of slabs would have required the more elaborate integration of the complete differential equation (10-174). But the preceding remarks have perhaps illustrated certain circumstances that might have been at work in the upper layers of the earth's crust, after the instabilities occurred and simple undulations took on the character of permanent distortions producing flat geosynclines and anticlines. We may add that geologic evidence has disclosed striking *examples of the formation of parallel wrinkles of comparatively short wavelengths* in deformed bundles of strata (folds) in mountain chains. Classical examples that might be mentioned here are the *Jura Mountain folds* in northwestern Switzerland with their partially, intensely folded layers of Jurassic limestones (Fig. 10-30) so thoroughly studied by Swiss geologists and described in the monumental book by the great geologist ALBERT HEIM[2] and the regular, parallel folds of the *Appalachian Mountains* in the eastern United States, the structure of which with their fan-shaped cleavage

[1] In a soft clay of the required degree of wetness, one may possibly be able to produce these modes of selective distortions.

[2] ALBERT HEIM, "Geologie der Schweiz," 2 vols., 1018 pp., Chr. Herm. Tauchnitz, Leipzig, 1919. Figure 10-30 reproduces four vertical profiles through the Jura Mountain chains of western Switzerland, published in figure sheet no. XXIII on page 583 in the first volume of Albert Heim's book. The layer shown in a thick black line is Lias, the next layers overlying it consist of Jurassic formations, those underlying it are Trias, the base under the latter (left white in the profiles) is marked grey, saltish clay (*Salzton*). As far as the author is aware, geologists assume that the folded Jura chains seen in the profiles in Fig. 10-30 are underlain by a sequence of rocks (layers of clay or rocksalt?) which behaved much more plastically under the prevailing conditions of a horizontal thrust in the depths below these chains of mountains than the overlying, deformed strata did, while the latter were pushed together and relatively displaced above the plastic base layers. The two upper profiles of Fig. 10-30 disclose partially intense folding, over-thrusted folds and local disruptions, and the elevated parts of the ground forming the present tops of the mountains in all profiles coincide frequently with the crests of waves or tops of the folds in the underlying strata.

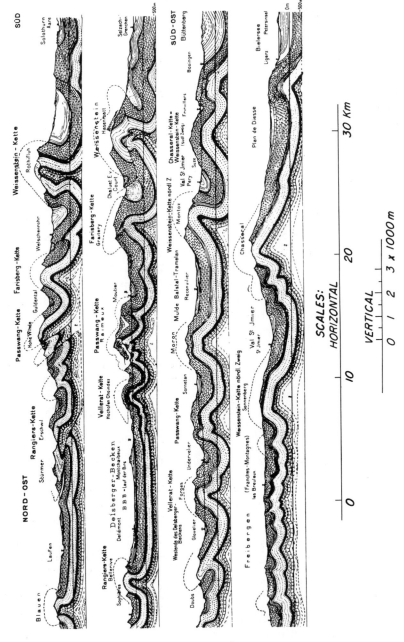

FIG. 10-30. Four profiles through the Jura Mountains, Switzerland. *(Reproduced from Albert Heim, "Geologie der Schweiz," vol. 1, p. 583, Chr. Herm. Tauchnitz, Leipzig, 1919.)*

planes and slaty lineation was so carefully studied by ERNST CLOOS.[1] One may conjecture that the frequently regular, wavy form of their strata of rocks originated once from quite gentle, regular sinusoidal undulations.

Case (1C) $\lambda_a > \beta$.   Denoting as before by

$$\beta^2 = \frac{nt_a l^2}{2N_0}, \qquad \lambda_a^4 = \frac{kt_a l^4}{N_0},$$

the time constant t_a

$$t_a = \frac{2N_0 \beta^2}{nl^2} = \frac{N_0 \lambda_a^4}{kl^4}, \tag{10-217}$$

and the axial, compression force n

$$n = \frac{2\beta^2 kl^2}{\lambda_a^4}, \tag{10-218}$$

if we now let

$$1 + \alpha^2 = \left(\frac{\lambda_a}{\beta}\right)^4, \qquad (\alpha > 0), \tag{10-219}$$

the roots of the characteristic equation (10-181) become two pairs of complex, conjugate numbers:

$$\lambda_1 = -\lambda_3 = \beta \cdot \sqrt{-1 + i\alpha} = \alpha_1 + i\alpha_2,$$

$$\lambda_2 = -\lambda_4 = \beta \cdot \sqrt{-1 - i\alpha} = -\alpha_1 + i\alpha_2, \tag{10-220}$$

having the same absolute value λ_a and with their radii vectors symmetrically inclined with respect to the imaginary axis i.

---

[1] ERNST CLOOS, Oölite Deformation in the South Mountain Fold, Maryland, Bull. Geol. Soc. Am., vol. 58, pp. 843–918, 1947; also Johns Hopkins Univ. Studies in Geology, no. 16, pt. 1, 1950; "The Physical Features of Washington County," 330 pp., Dept. Geology of Maryland, Baltimore, 1951 (several articles by E. Cloos, pp. 1–97); Appalachenprofil in Maryland, Geol. Rundschau, vol. 41, pp. 145–160, 1953.   E. Cloos analyzed with particular care the various phases of the plastic distortion of material elements within the folds, attempting to reconstruct their shapes for various former states through which they have passed during their evolutions in geologic history, and described in various localities regular, fan-shaped systems of the cleavage surfaces in their relative positions within the folds.   The distorted forms of small, formerly, initially, spherical inclusions (pebbles, mud pellets, and fossils) served him also for a quantitative determination of the principal, permanent strains in the deformed rock strata, finding surprisingly great values for the major and minor principal strains of 20 to 25 per cent, but essentially plane states of finite, permanent strain with the third strain at vanishing values.

This determines the numerical values of the real and the imaginary parts in the four roots λ_n as follows:

$$\alpha_1 = \sqrt{\frac{\lambda_a^2 - \beta^2}{2}} = l \cdot \sqrt{\sqrt{\frac{kt_a}{4N_0}} - \frac{nt_a}{4N_0}} \,,$$

$$\alpha_2 = \sqrt{\frac{\lambda_a^2 + \beta^2}{2}} = l \cdot \sqrt{\sqrt{\frac{kt_a}{4N_0}} + \frac{nt_a}{4N_0}} \,,$$

showing that

$$\alpha_2^2 + \alpha_1^2 = \lambda_a^2,$$

$$\alpha_2^2 - \alpha_1^2 = \frac{n\lambda_a^4}{2kl^2} \,,$$

(10-221)

$$\alpha_1 = \frac{\lambda_a}{\sqrt{2}} \sqrt{1 - \frac{n\lambda_a^2}{2kl^2}} \,,$$

$$\alpha_2 = \frac{\lambda_a}{\sqrt{2}} \sqrt{1 + \frac{n\lambda_a^2}{2kl^2}} \,,$$

(10-222)

and that the four, corresponding, particular integrals of Eq. (10-175) in their real form are

$$e^{t/t_a}(e^{\alpha_1 x/l}, e^{-\alpha_1 x/l})\left(\cos\frac{\alpha_2 x}{l}, \sin\frac{\alpha_2 x}{l}\right)$$

subject to the condition $\beta < \lambda_a$ or provided that the compression force is

$$n < 2 \cdot \sqrt{\frac{kN_0}{t_a}} = 2k\left(\frac{l}{\lambda_a}\right)^2 .$$

As an example, using two of these particular integrals, we may express *the deflections w of an infinite viscous slab on substratum, carrying at the origin $x = 0$ a single, transversal load $P = P_0 e^{t/t_a}$ that increases with time while the slab is subjected to an invariable compression force n in the direction of the x axis*, after having taken care of the boundary condition $x = 0$, $\partial w/\partial x = 0$ and for $x \geqq 0$, by

$$w = w_0 e^{(t/t_a) - (\alpha_1 x/l)}\left(\cos\frac{\alpha_2 x}{l} + \frac{\alpha_1}{\alpha_2}\sin\frac{\alpha_2 x}{l}\right).$$

(10-223)

We may determine the constant w_0, representing the maximum deflection of the slab under the load P at $x = 0$ and the time $t = 0$ from the condition that the shearing force p_v be equal to $-P_0/2$ or

$$p_v = -\left[N_0\frac{\partial^3 w}{\partial x^3} + n\frac{\partial w}{\partial x}\right]_{\substack{x=0 \\ t=0}} = -\frac{2(\alpha_2^1 + \alpha_2^2)\alpha_1 N_0 w_0}{t_a l^3} = -\frac{P_0}{2} .$$

(10-224)

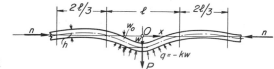

FIG. 10-31

After using Eqs. (10-221) and (10-222) this simplifies to the equivalent expressions for w_0:

$$w_0 = \frac{P_0 l}{4\alpha_1} \sqrt{\frac{t_a}{kN_0}} = \frac{P_0 \lambda_a^2}{4kl\alpha_1}$$

or

$$w_0 = \frac{P_0 \lambda_a}{2\sqrt{2kl}} \sqrt{1 - \frac{n\lambda_a^2}{2kl^2}}, \qquad (10\text{-}225)$$

where P_0 is the value of P at time $t = 0$.

We have to determine now the two dimensionless quantities α_1 and α_2. For one condition for them, we choose the first of Eqs. (10-221):

$$\alpha_1^2 + \alpha_2^2 = \lambda_a^2;$$

for the second we choose a geometric condition by prescribing the length of the span of the principal trough in the deflection line of the slab nearest to the single force P. In order that the following formulas conform with the designations used in discussing Cases 1, 1A, and 1B, we specify that we shall understand under the indeterminate length l the length of this span, by making $x = l/2$ the distance of the first zero $w = 0$ of the deflection w from the origin $x = 0$ (Fig. 10-31). This condition, after we substitute $x = l/2$, $w = 0$ in Eq. (10-223), gives

$$\alpha_1 = \alpha_2 \cot \frac{\alpha_2}{2} = -\alpha_2 \cdot \frac{1 + \cos \alpha_2}{\sin \alpha_2}. \qquad (10\text{-}226)$$

Since $\pm\alpha_1$ and $\pm\alpha_2$ were the rectangular coordinates in the complex plane of four points representing the four complex roots λ_n of the characteristic equation (10-181), the two conditions set up for α_1 and α_2 may be interpreted as requiring that in a plane of rectangular coordinates α_1, α_2 a family of concentric circles having λ_a for their radii be intersected by the curve prescribed in Eq. (10-226). This latter curve[1] is symmetrical with respect to the α_1 axis, has an apex at the point $\alpha_1 = -2$, $\alpha_2 = 0$, and approaches the two horizontal lines $\alpha_2 = \pm 2\pi$ as asymptotes (Fig. 10-32). For an infinite slab, the deflections w should vanish at $x = \infty$, requiring α_1 to be positive in Eq. (10-226). One sees that only the branch of the curve shown by a heavy line has to be considered between the points B and C.

We disregard further branches of the curve beyond the ranges $-2\pi > \alpha_2 > 2\pi$, confining the discussion only to the fundamental mode.

To point B corresponds the limiting case 1B, when $\lambda_a = \beta = \pi$, and consequently, since

$$\alpha_1^2 + \alpha_2^2 = \lambda_a^2, \qquad \alpha_2^2 - \alpha_1^2 = \beta^2, \qquad (10\text{-}227)$$

the values α_1 and α_2 are $\alpha_1 = 0$, $\alpha_2 = \pi$. From Case 1B we know that the slab did not carry a transversal force and hence $P = 0$. This is confirmed by Eq. (10-224), when assuming in it $\alpha_1 = 0$; the shearing force p_v at the origin $x = 0$ and with it the force P vanish. The slab is subjected only to an axial compression equal to

$$n = n_0 = \frac{2kl^2}{\pi^2} \qquad (10\text{-}228)$$

corresponding to which

$$t_a = t_0 = \frac{\pi^4 N_0}{kl^4}. \qquad (10\text{-}229)$$

To point C corresponds the other limiting case when the axial force in the slab vanishes, $n = 0$. We have $\beta = 0$, Eqs. (10-227) show that $\alpha_1 = \alpha_2 = \lambda_a/\sqrt{2}$, and Eq. (10-226) that

$$\cotan \frac{\lambda_a}{2\sqrt{2}} = -1, \qquad \lambda_a = \frac{3\pi}{\sqrt{2}};$$

hence

$$\alpha_1 = \alpha_2 = (\tfrac{3}{2})\pi,$$
$$t_a = \frac{81\pi^4 N_0}{4kl^4} = (81\tfrac{1}{4})t_0, \qquad (10\text{-}230)$$

and the maximum deflection w_0 of the slab at $t = 0$, when $n = 0$ [see Eq. (10-225)], becomes equal to

$$w_0 = \frac{P_0 \lambda_a}{2\sqrt{2kl}} = \frac{3\pi P_0}{4kl}. \qquad (10\text{-}231)$$

One verifies easily in this latter case, when the viscous slab carries only a concentrated, single force $P = P_0 e^{t/t_a}$ at the origin $x = 0$, that the deflections w satisfying the differential equation

$$N_0 \frac{\partial^4 w}{\partial x^4} + kw = 0$$

are equal to

$$w = w_0 e^{(t/t_a) - (3\pi x/2l)} \left(\cos \frac{3\pi x}{2l} + \sin \frac{3\pi x}{2l} \right),$$

$$w = \sqrt{2} w_0 e^{(t/t_a) - (3\pi x/2l)} \cos \left(\frac{3\pi x}{2l} - \frac{\pi}{4} \right),$$

$$(10\text{-}232)$$

where the constants w_0 and t_a have the just-determined values, and that

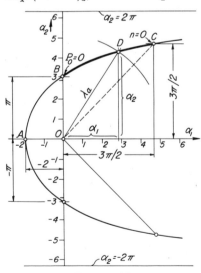

FIG. 10-32.
Curve $\alpha_1 = -\alpha_2 \cotan (\alpha_2/2)$.

the preceding function coincides with Eq. (10-223) when no axial force n acts.

In looking over case 1C, one sees by varying α_1 within the limits $0 \leq \alpha_1 \leq (\frac{3}{2})\pi$, corresponding to points B and C in Fig. 10-32, that α_2 and λ_a as the ordinates and the radii vectors OD of a point D of the curve branch BC vary within the ranges

$$\pi \leq \alpha_2 \leq (\tfrac{3}{2})\pi \qquad \text{and} \qquad \pi \leq \lambda_a \leq 3\pi/\sqrt{2}.$$

This brings about a variation of the axial compression force n (β varies between the limits $\pi \geq \beta \geq 0$), using for $n = 2kl^2\beta^2/\lambda_a{}^4$

$$\frac{2kl^2}{\pi^2} = n_0 \geq n \geq 0, \tag{10-233}$$

and of the time constant $t_a = N_0\lambda_a{}^4/kl^4$, using $t_0 = \pi^4 N_0/kl^4$,

$$(8\tfrac{1}{4})t_0 \geq t_a \geq t_0.$$

In order to compare the modes of bending described by case 1C let us assume that we hold invariable the wavelength l of the principal trough in the deflection line of the slab and the initial maximum deflection w_0 in its center $x = 0$ at time $t = 0$.   As α_1, α_2 vary, the deflection line between the fixed points $x = 0$, $w = w_0$ and $x = l/2$, $w = 0$ will naturally have slightly different forms.   The values of the single force P_0 may be computed from Eq. (10-225).   This has been illustrated in the curve P_0 versus the compression force n reproduced in Fig. 10-33, showing a short hump but beyond it a continuous drop of the single load P_0 with increasing n.   Let us state also the value of the maximum rate of deflection with which the slab responds at time $t = 0$ at point $x = 0$ to the action of loads P_0 and n. It is found from Eq. (10-223) equal to

$$(\dot{w}_{\max})_{t=0} = \frac{w_0}{t_a} = \frac{kw_0l^4}{N_0\lambda_a{}^4} \tag{10-234}$$

inversely proportional to the fourth power of $\lambda_a = \overline{OD}$ of radius vector $\overline{OD}$ in Fig. 10-32.   If, for comparison, we hold k, N_0, w_0, l invariably fixed and increase the values of the compression force n from zero toward n_0, since point D in Fig. 10-32 moves from C toward B, radius vector $\overline{OD} = \lambda_a$ becomes continuously shorter, and we note then that

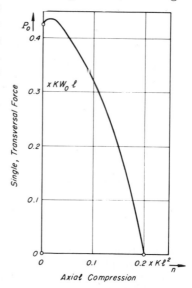

FIG. 10-33. Viscous slab. P_0 versus n.

the single load P_0 in Fig. 10-33 diminishes while *the slab not only will start to deflect at continuously, rapidly increasing rates but that, the greater we have chosen the compression force n, the faster these rates* $\dot{w}_{max} = (\dot{w}_{max})_{t=0} \cdot e^{t/t_a}$ *must also increase with the time t.*

10-9. Variation of Elasticity and Viscosity in the Earth's Outer Crust Due to Increase of Temperature with Depth. In the preceding determinations of states of plane strain and of bending in viscoelastic substances, we regarded the moduli of elasticity and rigidity E and G and the coefficient of viscosity μ as material constants throughout the bodies. In Secs. 1-5 to 1-7, where equations of state in solids were discussed in some detail, we have seen that the elastic properties of solids depend on two important variables of state, namely, the absolute temperature T and the mean stress σ; the same must be conjectured concerning the property of viscosity. Bearing in mind that the temperature θ and the mean stress $\sigma = -p$ greatly increase with the depths under the surface of the earth's shell, certain general modes of the warping of the upper strata and of the viscoelastic distortion of the outer solid crust under given extraneous forces which we have treated in previous sections may now be revised by taking some account of the variability of the material constants E, G, ν, and μ entering in the stress-strain and stress–rate-of-strain relations with the depths underground. Let us briefly list a few suggestions as to how this could be done without arriving at too involved statements.

We assume the earth's outermost shell of a thickness h of 60 to 100 km to be composed of *homogeneous rock material* of uniform density[1] and a limited region may be referred to rectangular coordinates x, y, z, choosing the x,y plane to coincide with the plane of the horizon, the z coordinate measuring the depth under the earth's surface pointing downward. While both variables of state θ and p increase with z toward the center of the earth at gradually decreasing rates, it suffices entirely to assume that *within the crust* $0 < z < h$ *the geothermal gradient*[2] $d\theta/dz$ *and the pressure gradient dp/dz have constant values. For*

---

[1] Disregarding here the claims derived from earthquake records that the outer crust probably consists of a few layers having distinct elasticity values increasing slightly in certain planes of discontinuity with their densities (the differentiation of certain basaltic layers, etc.) at comparatively shallow depths.

[2] Data on the increase of the temperature in the earth's crust with depth were gathered in deep mines, during the piercing of long railroad tunnels through high mountain ranges, but particularly through the measurements of the temperatures in deep petroleum wells. For observation records on the geothermal gradient, see BENO GUTENBERG (ed.), "Internal Constitution of the Earth," McGraw-Hill Book Company, Inc., New York, 1939; pp. 132–141, see also 2d ed., pp. 150–166, Dover Publications, New York, 1951; and DORSEY HAGER, "Practical Oil Geology," 5th ed., 466 pp., McGraw-Hill Book Company Inc., New York, 1938, (records on oil-well temperatures on pp. 271–272). See also R. W. FRENCH,

the geothermal gradient an average figure of $d\theta/dz = 0.0300°C/m$ (of 3 °C increase in temperature with every 100-m increase in depth) and *for the pressure gradient dp/dz* = 0.300 atm (kg/cm²) per meter may be assumed, postulating the mean specific weight of the denser types of rocks prevailing at greater depths, approaching the base of the outer crust,

---

Geothermal Gradients in California Oil Wells (presented at Spring Meeting of the Pacific Coast Division of Production, American Petroleum Institute, April, 1939, p. 653). *The deepest oil wells* in the United States were drilled by the Superior Oil Company, Los Angeles, Calif., in which the following temperatures were observed:

Limoneira Well No. 1, Ventura County, California		Pacific Creek No. 1 Well, Sublette County, Wyoming	
Depth, ft	Temperature, °F	Depth, ft	Temperature, °F
8,501	160	12,316	195
12,027	200	15,258	233
16,729	240	20,521	310
18,742	250		

and by *the Ohio Oil Company, Bakersfield, Calif.: oil well no. 72-4 in Kern County near Bakersfield, Calif., holding at present the record of the deepest bore drilled on the earth, having reached the depth of* 21,482 *ft* = 6,548 *m* at which, by extrapolation, a temperature of 340°F = 171°C was recorded. (For drilling data on this well, see WILLIAM T. RINTOUL, Petrol. Engr., October, 1953, pp. 420–442.)

After subtracting 21 °C as atmospheric temperature, the average geothermal gradient $d\theta/dz$ computed from the observations at the greatest depth in the oil wells amounted to:

In Sublette County, Wyoming: $\qquad$ $d\theta/dz \begin{cases} = 2.13°C/100 \text{ m} \\ = 2.29°C/100 \text{ m} \end{cases}$

In Kern County, Calif:

The author acknowledges the great kindness of having supplied him with the above observation data to DONALD E. KOCH, Chief Engineer, The Superior Oil Company, Los Angeles, Calif., and to W. B. EMERY II, District Engineer, The Ohio Oil Company, Bakersfield, Calif., and to DR. J. M. HOLMQUIST, Director of Research, Spang Chalfant Company, Ambridge, Pa.

The above data on $d\theta/dz$ obtained from the deepest oil wells seem to be rather on the conservative side, because the conditions encountered in them due to drilling-fluid circulation seldom permit the time necessary for reestablishment of the undisturbed thermal equilibrium which existed in the rocks underground previous to drilling. But, the general data, as recorded by Gutenberg and others, indicate certain variations of the geothermal gradient with the locality, which may perhaps have a greater significance than has heretofore been attributed to them in the effects which they must have on the mean slow creep of the substrata below the high mountain ranges of the earth, in view of the fact that the creep rates under which solids in general and the rocks in particular must creep under small differences between the principal stresses are greatly influenced by the smallest differences in temperature.

to be around $\gamma = 3{,}000$ kg/m³. The two variables of state, namely, the temperature θ and the mean (hydrostatic) pressure p (both are taken equal to zero at the surface $z = 0$) then have the following values:

Depth z, km	Temperature, °C	Pressure, kg/cm²
0.1	3	30
1	30	300
10	300	3,000
50	1500	15,000
100	3000	30,000

Most of the sedimentary and igneous rocks known from the surface of the earth would, under atmospheric pressure ($p \sim 0$), be molten around 1500°C. Allowing for a certain increase of their melting temperature under the high all-sided hydrostatic pressures[1] of the order indicated above, prevalent at the lower levels of the earth's shell, the question whether the rocks at these depths and the substratum on which the upper solid crust rests are considered to be in the fluid state or not seems irrelevant for the purpose of judging some trends in the probable variation of the elasticity within the major parts of the earth's outer solid shell. After what has been tentatively considered in Chap. 1 concerning the form of the isothermal curves $\theta = $ const in a plot of the mean normal stress $\sigma = -p$ versus the elastic dilatation of volume e in a *homogeneous* shell of rocks (Cf. Secs. 1-5 and 1-6, Figs. 1-9 and 1-10), one must generally expect a substantial decrease of the moduli of elasticity and rigidity E and G and likewise of the viscosity μ, due to the combined effects of an increase of θ and of p with depth z in homogeneous material.

Suppose that $E, \nu,$ and μ *were known functions of depth* z.   Consider an earth slab of great width subjected to a horizontal pull or push by a force $n_x = \int_0^h \sigma_x \, dz$ in the direction of the x axis while $\varepsilon_y = 0$.   *An elastic slab* is subjected to a distribution of normal stresses σ_x and σ_y ($\tau_{xy} = 0$):

$$\sigma_x = \frac{E\varepsilon_x}{1 - \nu^2}, \qquad \sigma_y = \nu\sigma_x = \frac{\nu E\varepsilon_x}{1 - \nu^2}. \qquad (10\text{-}235)$$

The normal stress resultants per unit width n_x, n_y across the perpendicular planes $x = $ const, $y = $ const may be computed after integrating

---

[1] According to JOHN JOLY, "The Surface History of the Earth," page 41, Clarendon Press, Oxford, 1930, basalts melt around 1170°C under atmospheric pressure. Concerning the increase of the melting temperature of rocks with pressure, the reader is referred to Joly's book and geological treatises.

these expressions with respect to the coordinate z,

$$n_x = \int \sigma_x \, dz = \varepsilon_x \int \frac{E \, dz}{1 - \nu^2}, \qquad n_y = \int \sigma_y \, dz = \varepsilon_x \int \frac{\nu E \, dz}{1 - \nu^2}, \quad (10\text{-}236)$$

and their lines of action are situated at the depths

$$z'_x = \frac{1}{n_x} \int \sigma_x z \, dz, \qquad z'_y = \frac{1}{n_y} \int \sigma_y z \, dz, \qquad\qquad (10\text{-}237)$$

respectively, where the integrals are taken between the limits $z = 0$ and $z = h$.

Likewise in *a purely viscous slab* stretched under a prescribed rate of strain $\dot{\varepsilon}_x$, in incompressible material, under an invariable force n_x, while $\dot{\varepsilon}_y = 0$,

$$\sigma_x = 2\sigma_y = 4\dot{\varepsilon}_x \mu,$$

$$n_x = 2n_y = 4\dot{\varepsilon}_x \int \mu \, dz, \qquad\qquad (10\text{-}238)$$

these forces n_x, n_y attacking at

$$z''_x = z''_y = \frac{\int \mu z \, dz}{\int \mu \, dz}. \qquad\qquad (10\text{-}239)$$

Suppose that *a viscoelastic earth slab* were subjected to a horizontal pull or push while the rate of strain is maintained $\dot{\varepsilon}_x = \dot{\varepsilon}_0 = \text{const}$ and $\dot{\varepsilon}_y = 0$. If $t_e = 3\mu/E$ now denotes a parameter of time which varies with depth z, we may express the rates of strain as follows:

$$E\dot{\varepsilon}_x = \dot{\sigma}_x + \frac{1}{t_e} \sigma_x - \nu\dot{\sigma}_y - \frac{1}{2t_e} \sigma_y = E\dot{\varepsilon}_0,$$

$$E\dot{\varepsilon}_y = -\nu\dot{\sigma}_x - \frac{1}{2t_e} \sigma_x + \dot{\sigma}_y + \frac{1}{t_e} \sigma_y = 0. \qquad (10\text{-}240)$$

After adding or subtracting these equations, integrating the sum $\sigma_x + \sigma_y$ or difference $\sigma_x - \sigma_y$ with respect to time t, if the slab, for example, at time $t = 0$ was entirely unstressed and unstrained, we obtain for the stresses σ_x and σ_y the expressions

$$\sigma_x = 4\dot{\varepsilon}_0 \mu - \dot{\varepsilon}_0 \mu (3e^{-t/t_a} + e^{-t/t_b}),$$

$$\sigma_y = 2\dot{\varepsilon}_0 \mu - \dot{\varepsilon}_0 \mu (3e^{-t/t_a} - e^{-t/t_b}), \qquad (10\text{-}241)$$

where we denoted by

$$t_a = 2(1 - \nu)t_e, \qquad t_b = (\tfrac{2}{3})(1 + \nu)t_e \qquad\qquad (10\text{-}242)$$

two parameters of the dimension of time varying with z. Or we may, alternatively, postulate that, at time $t = 0$, a force had been imposed on the slab producing an initial, elastic extension $\varepsilon_x = \varepsilon_0' = $ const (independent of x) and that the strain rate subsequently was held at $\dot{\varepsilon}_x = \dot{\varepsilon}_0 = $ const. Apart from the terms already appearing in Eqs. (10-241), this adds two more terms,

$$(\tfrac{1}{2})E\varepsilon_0' \left(\frac{e^{-t/t_a}}{1-\nu} + \frac{e^{-t/t_b}}{1+\nu} \right),$$

$$(\tfrac{1}{2})E\varepsilon_0' \left(\frac{e^{-t/t_a}}{1-\nu} - \frac{e^{-t/t_b}}{1+\nu} \right),$$

(10-243)

on the right sides of Eqs. (10-241) for σ_x and σ_y, respectively.

The preceding and subsequent expressions are greatly simplified by assuming for Poisson's ratio invariability with depth z and the value[1] $\nu = \tfrac{1}{2}$ for which, namely,

$$t_a = t_b = t_e = \frac{3\mu}{E}.$$

(10-244)

After denoting the mean values of E and of μ across the slab by

$$E_m = \frac{1}{h} \int_0^h E \, dz, \qquad \mu_m = \frac{1}{h} \int_0^h \mu \, dz,$$

(10-245)

this gives in the first example, when the viscoelastic slab is extended at uniform rate $\dot{\varepsilon}_0 = $ const from the unstrained state,

$$\sigma_x = 2\sigma_y = 4\dot{\varepsilon}_0\mu(1 - e^{-t/t_e}),$$

$$n_x = 2n_y = 4\dot{\varepsilon}_0 \int_0^h \mu(1 - e^{-t/t_e}) \, dz$$

(10-246)

In the second example, when it is initially pulled out to the elastic strain ε_0' and subsequently elongated permanently at the rate of strain $\dot{\varepsilon}_0 = $ const under which it will, at $t = \infty$, attain the same stress resultant $n_x = n_0$ under which it started to yield at $t = 0$, namely,

$$n_x = n_0 = \int_0^h \sigma_x \, dz = (\tfrac{4}{3})\varepsilon_0' h E_m = 4\dot{\varepsilon}_0 h \mu_m,$$

(10-247)

requiring that $\dot{\varepsilon}_0$ be chosen equal to

$$\dot{\varepsilon}_0 = \varepsilon_0' \frac{E_m}{3\mu_m} = \frac{\varepsilon_0'}{t_m},$$

(10-248)

[1] While postulating $\nu = \tfrac{1}{2} = $ const throughout the shell eliminates burdensome differentiation between various adjustments taking place between the stresses, as we have already pointed out on previous occasions, the reader is aware that, after assuming incompressibility for the elastic distortions, no finite value is attributed to the bulk modulus K. This assumption would be senseless if phenomena in geophysics such as dilatational earthquake waves were to be treated.

the distribution of normal stress across the viscoelastic slab is

$$\sigma_x = 2\sigma_y = \frac{n_0}{h}\left[\frac{\mu}{\mu_m} + \left(\frac{E}{E_m} - \frac{\mu}{\mu_m}\right)e^{-t/t_e}\right], \qquad (10\text{-}249)$$

where E, μ, $t_e = 3\mu/E$ are given functions of z. We note that in the latter case, at time $t = 0$, the slab starts to deform with *the elastic distribution*

$$\sigma_x = 2\sigma_y = \frac{n_0 E}{E_m h}, \qquad (10\text{-}250)$$

this changing over, at time $t = \infty$, to a *viscous distribution*

$$\sigma_x = 2\sigma_y = \frac{n_0 \mu}{\mu_m h}. \qquad (10\text{-}251)$$

The stresses are originally proportional to the values of E and finally become proportional to those of μ, while the resultant force n_x gradually shifts its line of action from z_e to z_μ:

$$z_e = \frac{1}{E_m h}\int_0^h Ez\,dz, \qquad z_\mu = \frac{1}{\mu_m h}\int_0^h \mu z\,dz, \qquad (10\text{-}252)$$

z_e and z_μ measuring the distances of the centers of gravity C_e and C_μ (Fig. 10-34) of the areas under the E and μ curve.

If one may be inclined to hypothesize that the curve for E may be concave (see Fig. 1-10 in Chap. 1) and the one for μ convex and ascending toward a sharp peak near the surface $z = 0$ (in the coldest, upper range of the earth slab), this would lead to the consequence that the major (destructive) effects of a long-range push or pull would be localized essentially within the uppermost layers of rock nearest the earth's surface, toward the end of the viscous distortion engaging them to the major stresses, for the reason that the line of attack of the horizontal force n_x is gradually being raised, as illustrated in Fig. 10-34. In view of the lack of dependable laboratory data covering the variation of E and μ for rocks under simultaneous exposure to greatly increasing temperatures and pressures, one may be further inclined to illustrate these conditions in the earth's massive slab by drawing in first approximation two straight, inclined lines, equalizing somewhat the plausible

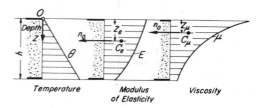

FIG. 10-34. Elasticity and viscosity in earth's slab.

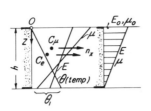
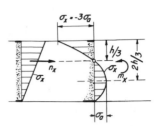

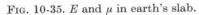

FIG. 10-35. E and μ in earth's slab.   FIG. 10-36. Stresses due to:
Normal   Bending
force n_x moment m_x

curvatures of the actual distribution curves for E and μ (see Figs. 10-35 and 10-36). The first would assume that E and μ attain finite values at the bottom $z = h$ of the shell, whereas in the second figure (Fig. 10-36) E and μ are supposed, hypothetically, to vanish at depth $z = h$.

It is an elementary supposition to draw or evaluate the corresponding distributions of stress through the slab, the stress ordinates at $t = 0$ and $t = \infty$ becoming proportional to the values of E and μ, with their resultants passing through the centers of gravity in the trapezoids or triangles in Figs. 10-35 and 10-36. For example, corresponding to Fig. 10-36, the modulus of elasticity, the coefficient of viscosity, and the temperature across the slab are represented by the linear functions

$$E = E_0\left(1 - \frac{z}{h}\right), \qquad \mu = \mu_0\left(1 - \frac{z}{h}\right), \qquad \theta = \frac{\theta_1 z}{h}, \qquad (10\text{-}253)$$

E_0 and μ_0 defining the values at the earth's surface $z = 0$, and θ_1 representing a general melting temperature reached at the base of the shell $z = h$. An invariable axial horizontal force n_x stresses the slab with the time-independent normal stress distribution

$$\sigma_x = 2\sigma_y = \frac{2n_x}{h}\left(1 - \frac{z}{h}\right) \qquad (10\text{-}254)$$

at uniform, permanent rate of strain $\dot{\varepsilon}_x = \sigma_x/4\mu = n_x/2\mu_0 h$ in the direction of the x axis, the load n_x attacking at the depth $z = h/3$.†

† It is scarcely necessary to point out that one need not consider in these states of distortion in a massive earth slab the stresses caused by the nonuniform thermal expansion (in spite of the extremely high values of the temperature $\theta = \theta_1 z/h$ approaching the melting point underground). If the slab were free, it would have to curl up, being severely heated from below, but its free thermal expansion being inhibited, a state of increasing compression stresses σ_x, σ_y will force the cup to stay plane. But these thermal stresses cannot come into existence, because they are annihilated through relaxation, owing to the low viscosity μ at high temperatures. Differences between the two principal stresses σ_x, σ_y in horizontal direction and the normal stress σ_z in vertical direction, also in an infinite elastic body

Likewise, *in an infinite, elastic slab subjected to cylindrical bending* $(\varepsilon_y = 0)$ in which the modulus of elasticity E varies linearly with z according to

$$E = E_0\left(1 - \frac{z}{h}\right),$$

by elementary supposition[1] the bending strain

$$\varepsilon_x = \varepsilon_a\left(\frac{3z}{h} - 1\right) \tag{10-255}$$

generates the bending stress [see Eqs. (10-235)], assuming $\nu = \frac{1}{2}$,

$$\sigma_x = 2\sigma_y = \frac{4E\varepsilon_x}{3} = \frac{4E_0\varepsilon_a}{3}\left(1 - \frac{z}{h}\right)\left(\frac{3z}{h} - 1\right); \tag{10-256}$$

if we denote at $z = (\frac{2}{3})h$, $\varepsilon_x = \varepsilon_a$, $\sigma_x = \sigma_a$ (see Fig. 10-36), taking for σ_a,

$$\sigma_a = \frac{4E_0\varepsilon_a}{9},$$

$$\sigma_x = \frac{3\sigma_a}{h^2}\left(-3z^2 + 4hz - h^2\right), \tag{10-257}$$

this distribution of the bending stresses σ_x is expressed by *a parabola*, while the bending moments become equal to

$$m_x = 2m_y = \int_0^h \sigma_x z\, dz = (\frac{1}{4})\sigma_a h^2. \tag{10-258}$$

The absolute value of *the greatest bending stress* σ_x occurring in the plane $z = 0$ being $\sigma_{\max} = 3\sigma_a = 12m_x/h^2$, this is *just twice the maximum value* $6m_x/h^2$ *of the stress in a slab of uniform, invariable elasticity.* Since, furthermore, the curvature of the elastic deflection line w is

$$\frac{d^2w}{dx^2} = -\frac{\varepsilon_x}{z - (h/3)} = -\frac{3\varepsilon_a}{h} = -\frac{(\frac{3}{2})m_x}{N}, \tag{10-259}$$

where $N = (\frac{1}{9})E_m h^3$ may denote the slab modulus of the equivalent slab of uniform elasticity $E_m = (\frac{1}{2})E_0$, it is seen that *the slab having variable elasticity deflects* $\frac{3}{2}$ *times as much as one of invariable elasticity.*

---

settled under its own weight, are wiped out through relaxation. The horizontal normal stresses $\sigma_x - \sigma$, $\sigma_y - \sigma$ exist only on a hypothetical, sudden application of horizontal force resultants or bending moments or when the earth slab is being continuously deformed with small, finite rates of strain $\dot{\varepsilon}_x$, $\dot{\varepsilon}_y$, as under a steady push or pull or by steady bending moments originating in the adjoining masses of the continental block, such extraneous forces being active over the long geologic periods of time.

[1] The neutral axis of bending is situated at the depth $z = h/3$ (Fig. 10-36) and we let the bending strain ε_x at $z = 0$ equal $\varepsilon_x = -\varepsilon_a$.

The corresponding statements apply to a *purely viscous slab having the variable* viscosity

$$\mu = \mu_0\left(1 - \frac{z}{h}\right). \tag{10-260}$$

One sees that computations are the least involved when the E and the μ curve at all values of z differ by a constant factor in their ordinates. This leads us to propose, for describing *the interaction between the elastic and the permanent parts of strain* in their dependence on the time t in an approximate way, instead of operating with two empirical functions prescribing the values of E and μ as traced in Fig. 10-34,

$$E = E_m f(\zeta), \qquad \mu = \mu_m g(\zeta), \tag{10-261}$$

(E_m, μ_m being the average values of E, μ over the earth's slab, and denoting $\zeta = z/h$), to construct *the arithmetic means* of the two actual ratios,

$$\frac{E}{E_m} = f(\zeta), \qquad \frac{\mu}{\mu_m} = g(\zeta),$$

as a new, averaging function

$$F(\zeta) = \frac{f(\zeta) + g(\zeta)}{2} = \frac{1}{2}\left(\frac{E}{E_m} + \frac{\mu}{\mu_m}\right) = \frac{1}{2}\left(\frac{G}{G_m} + \frac{\mu}{\mu_m}\right) \tag{10-262}$$

and to use this distribution function $F(\zeta)$. In other words, this amounts to assuming (Poisson's ratio invariable and equal to $\nu = \frac{1}{2}$) that the modulus of elasticity E, of rigidity G, and the viscosity μ in the slab (Fig. 10-37) vary with depth $z = h\zeta$ as

$$\underline{E : E_m = G : G_m = \mu : \mu_m = F(\zeta),} \tag{10-263}$$

making the parameter of time t_e,

$$t_e = \frac{3\mu}{E} = \frac{\mu}{G} = \frac{\mu_m}{G_m}, \tag{10-264}$$

a constant (independent of $\zeta = z/h$). Then, for the sake of completing *the case of the bending of such a viscoelastic slab*,

$$\int_0^1 F(\zeta)\, d\zeta = 1,$$

$$\zeta_n = \frac{z_n}{h} = \int_0^1 F(\zeta)\zeta\, d\zeta, \tag{10-265}$$

$$\zeta_i^2 = \left(\frac{z_i}{h}\right)^2 = \int_0^1 F(\zeta)\zeta^2\, d\zeta,$$

FIG. 10-37. Hypotheti-
cal elasticity and vis-
cosity distribution in
earth's shell $E/E_m =$
$\mu/\mu_m = F(\zeta)$.

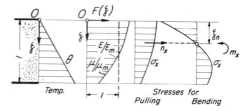

ζ_n defining the location of the neutral axis[1] and ζ_i the radius of gyration of the area under the curve $F(\zeta)$ or $E = E_m F(\zeta)$, if the subscripts 0 and 1 refer to the upper and lower boundary plane $\zeta = 0$ and $\zeta = 1$, with the elastic bending strains

$$\varepsilon_x' = \varepsilon_1' \frac{\zeta - \zeta_n}{1 - \zeta_n} = -(\zeta - \zeta_n)h\frac{\partial^2 w'}{\partial x^2},$$

the stresses are [using $\nu = \frac{1}{2}$ in Eqs. (10-235)]

$$\sigma_x = 2\sigma_y = (\tfrac{4}{3})E\varepsilon_x' = -(\tfrac{4}{3})Eh(\zeta - \zeta_n)\frac{\partial^2 w'}{\partial x^2}, \qquad (10\text{-}266)$$

and the bending moments are

$$m_x = 2m_y = h^2\int_0^1 \sigma_x\zeta\,d\zeta = -(\tfrac{4}{3})h^3\frac{\partial^2 w'}{\partial x^2}\int_0^1 E(\zeta - \zeta_n)\zeta\,d\zeta,$$

$$\underline{m_x = 2m_y = -[(\tfrac{4}{3})E_m h^3(\zeta_i^2 - \zeta_n^2)]\frac{\partial^2 w'}{\partial x^2}} = -N_v\frac{\partial^2 w'}{\partial x^2}. \qquad (10\text{-}267)$$

The quantity enclosed in brackets obviously represents *the slab modulus of the slab of variable viscoelasticity*, namely, generally

$$\underline{N_v = (\tfrac{4}{3})E_m h^3(\zeta_i^2 - \zeta_n^2) = 12(\zeta_i^2 - \zeta_n^2)N_c,} \qquad (10\text{-}268)$$

where $N_c = (\tfrac{1}{9})E_m h^3$ would express the slab modulus for invariable viscoelasticity (Fig. 10-37).

We may conclude that *the theory of bending of the earth's viscoelastic slab as developed in Secs. 10-2 to 10-7 in which a uniform elasticity and viscosity were postulated* (E, μ being assumed as material constants throughout the slab) *may now be extended to and amended for covering the bending of the earth's slab in which the moduli E, G and the viscosity μ vary with the depth $z = h\zeta$ along the averaging distribution $F(\zeta)$* [Eq. (10-263)] and under the provision that for the slab modulus the new value N_v

---

[1] Strictly, in a slab having generally variable elasticity and viscosity one should carefully distinguish *three distinct neutral axes*, in which at a given time t either the total strain ε_x or rate of strain $\dot{\varepsilon}_x$ or the bending stress σ_x vanishes. The momentary axis of rotation of the plane of a cross section (in which $\dot{\varepsilon}_x = 0$) need not coincide with the axis $\varepsilon_x = 0$, etc. By imposing the aforementioned restrictions on the E and μ curves [Eqs. (10-263)] these difficulties are eliminated.

computed in Eq. (10-268) is used instead of N_c, taking herewith, in a justifiable, approximating way, account of the variations of the mechanical properties in the solid crust due to the gradual increase of the temperatures $\theta = \theta_1 \zeta$ with depths z.

Thus, in the absence of axial normal force resultants n_x, when $n_x = 0$, the deflections w of the earth's slab having variable visco-elasticity, resting on buoyant substratum, and carrying a prescribed, distributed, transversal pressure load p dependent on the coordinate x and on the time t, could be determined according to Eq. (10-3) through the linear, partial differential equation

$$N_v \frac{\partial^4 \dot{w}}{\partial x^4} = \dot{p} + \frac{p}{t_e} - k\left(\dot{w} + \frac{w}{t_e}\right) \qquad (10\text{-}269)$$

in which N_v, t_e, k are constants, by utilizing the conclusions formerly arrived at, excepting the final expressions for the bending stresses σ_x and σ_y.

The stresses σ_x and σ_y do not follow the usual proportionality law with z, but their values $\sigma_x = 2\sigma_y = 4E\varepsilon_x'/3$ have to be computed from the products of $E = E_m F(\zeta)$ times the *elastic* parts ε_x' of the bending strains ε_x, while the former are related to the latter through the standard transformation formulas:

$$\dot{\varepsilon}_x' + \frac{\varepsilon_x'}{t_e} = \dot{\varepsilon}_x, \qquad \varepsilon_x' = \varepsilon_x - \frac{e^{-t/t_e}}{t_e} \int_0^t \varepsilon_x e^{t/t_e}\, dt. \qquad (10\text{-}270)$$

Since from Eq. (10-266),

$$\sigma_x = 2\sigma_y = -\frac{4E_m h(\zeta - \zeta_n)}{3} F(\zeta) \frac{\partial^2 w'}{\partial x^2}, \qquad (10\text{-}271)$$

and therein for the elastic part w' of the slab deflection w the same transformation formulas hold [see Eq. (10-25)],

$$\dot{w}' + \frac{w'}{t_e} = \dot{w}, \qquad w' = w - \frac{e^{-t/t_e}}{t_e} \int_0^t w e^{t/t_e}\, dt, \qquad (10\text{-}272)$$

after substituting the expression for the total deflection w in terms of x and t obtained from differential equation (10-269), after integration, this then also solves the evaluation of the bending stresses σ_x and σ_y across any vertical section of the earth's slab $x = $ const or $y = $ const from Eq. (10-271) and completes the theory of bending of the earth's slab having a variable viscoelasticity and resting on substratum in one-dimensional bending under lateral loads.

CHAPTER 11

THE DISTRIBUTION OF PRESSURE IN THIN LAYERS OF VISCOUS MATERIAL UNDER COMPRESSION

11-1. Steady Extrusion through a Narrow, Rectangular Orifice. The velocity u with which a viscous substance flows when extruded under pressure from a container through a narrow channel between two parallel walls $y = \pm h$ is parallel to the walls. Assuming the x axis parallel to the walls in the direction of flow, since the hydrostatic pressure p is constant in the cross sections, $x = $ const (Fig. 11-1) and the rates of strain $\dot{\varepsilon}_x = \dot{\varepsilon}_y = 0$, the normal stresses $\sigma_x = \sigma_y = -p$ depend only on x, and the rate of shear is $\dot{\gamma}_{xy} = \partial u/\partial y = \tau_{xy}/\mu$. From the condition of equilibrium,

$$\frac{\partial \tau_{xy}}{\partial y} = -\frac{\partial \sigma_x}{\partial x} = \frac{\partial p}{\partial x} = \text{const},$$

$$\tau_{xy} = \frac{\partial p}{\partial x} \cdot y = \mu \frac{\partial u}{\partial y},$$

$$(11\text{-}1)$$

the velocity of flow u is obtained:

$$u = u_0\left(1 - \frac{y^2}{h^2}\right) = -\frac{h^2}{2\mu} \cdot \frac{\partial p}{\partial x} \cdot \left(1 - \frac{y^2}{h^2}\right) \qquad (11\text{-}2)$$

which has a parabolic distribution, with the mean velocity $\bar{u} = (\tfrac{2}{3})u_0$, denoting by $u_0 = -(h^2/2\mu) \cdot \partial p/\partial x$ the maximum of velocity u. Since the efflux per unit of width of the channel and per unit of time is

$$Q = 2h\bar{u} = (\tfrac{4}{3})hu_0, \qquad (11\text{-}3)$$

the pressure gradient $\partial p/\partial x$ required for extruding a volume of the viscous substance Q through a narrow channel is found equal to

$$\frac{\partial p}{\partial x} = -\frac{3\mu Q}{2h^3}. \qquad (11\text{-}4)$$

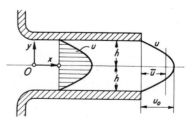

Fig. 11-1

349

11-2.   Viscous Substance Compressed between Two Long, Rectangular, Parallel Plates.   If the width $2a$ of the compressed material is small compared with the length $2b$, taking the z axis parallel to the latter direction, the substance will not flow in the direction parallel to the z axis, $w = 0$, and we have a case of plane flow with the velocities u and v parallel to the x and y axes (Fig. 11-2).   If we assume that the layer of viscous material squeezed between the parallel pressure plates adheres to the latter while they approach each other, the velocities imposed on the planes $y = \pm h$ are

$$y = h, \qquad u = 0, \qquad v = -v_0 = \text{const},$$
$$y = -h, \qquad u = 0, \qquad v = v_0 \quad = \text{const}.$$

In this state of plane flow,

$$u = \frac{\partial \psi}{\partial y}, \qquad v = -\frac{\partial \psi}{\partial x},$$

the stream function ψ complying with the boundary conditions

$$y = h, \qquad \psi = v_0 x, \qquad \frac{\partial \psi}{\partial y} = 0,$$

$$y = -h, \qquad \psi = -v_0 x, \qquad \frac{\partial \psi}{\partial y} = 0,$$

is the biharmonic [see Sec. 5-2, Eq. (5-47)],

$$\psi = \frac{v_0 x}{2h^3} (3h^2 y - y^3), \tag{11-5}$$

furnishing the velocities

$$u = \frac{3v_0 x}{2h} \left(1 - \frac{y^2}{h^2}\right),$$
$$v = -\frac{v_0}{2} \left(\frac{3y}{h} - \frac{y^3}{h^3}\right). \tag{11-6}$$

We may note that the velocity components u in the direction of the pressure plates are again distributed according to parabolas.

The mean stress σ or pressure $p = -\sigma$ is computed from its gradients, using Eqs. (5-43),

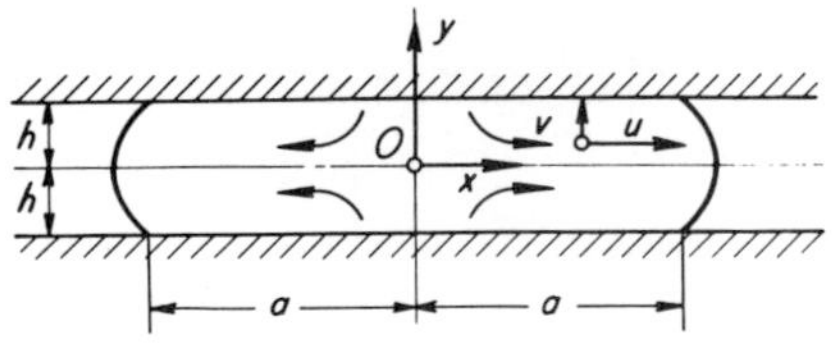

FIG. 11-2

$$\frac{\partial p}{\partial x} = \mu \, \Delta u = -\frac{3\mu v_0 x}{h^3},$$

$$\frac{\partial p}{\partial y} = \mu \, \Delta v = \frac{3\mu v_0 y}{h^3},$$

$$p = p_0 + \frac{3\mu v_0}{2h^3} (y^2 - x^2), \tag{11-7}$$

denoting by p_0 the pressure p at the origin $x = y = 0$. p_0 is determined by imposing on this last equation the approximate condition that, for $x = \pm a, y = 0, p = 0$, giving

$$p_0 = \frac{3\mu v_0 a^2}{2h^3},\tag{11-8}$$

$$p = \frac{p_0}{a^2}(a^2 + y^2 - x^2),\tag{11-9}$$

while the three components of stress σ_x, σ_y, τ_{xy} are found from Eqs. (5-42):

$$\sigma_x = -p + 2\mu\dot{\varepsilon}_x = \frac{p_0}{a^2}(x^2 - 3y^2 - a^2 + 2h^2),$$

$$\sigma_y = -p + 2\mu\dot{\varepsilon}_y = \frac{p_0}{a^2}(x^2 + y^2 - a^2 - 2h^2),\tag{11-10}$$

$$\tau_{xy} = \mu\dot{\gamma}_{xy} = -\frac{2p_0 xy}{a^2}.$$

The pattern of the streamlines $\psi = \text{const}$ and the distribution of the velocities u parallel to the plates in one-half of the layer of viscous material compressed between the plates $y = \pm h$ are reproduced in Figs. 11-3 and 11-4. The streamlines start in a direction perpendicular to the pressure plates but soon bend very sharply in the direction of main flow parallel to the plates. Figure 11-5 shows the distribution of the stresses σ_x, σ_y, τ_{xy} and of the pressure $p = -\sigma$ in the axis $x = 0$ and along the edge $x = a$ of the layer of viscous material. Figure 11-5

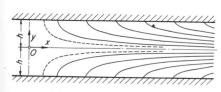

FIG. 11-3. Streamlines.

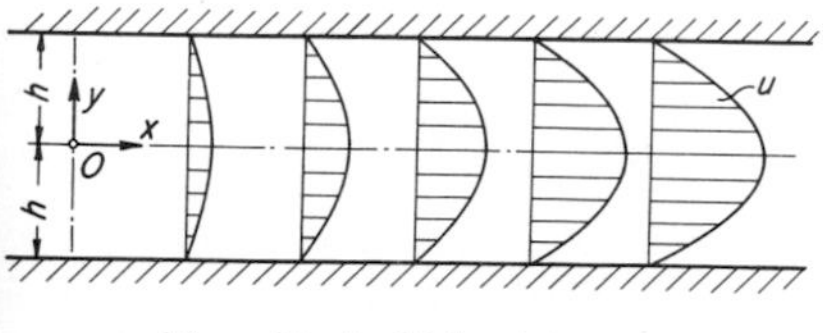

FIG. 11-4. Velocities u.

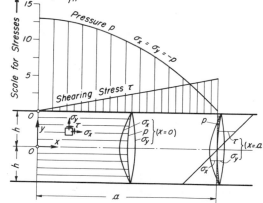

FIG. 11-5. Stress distribution.

FIGS. 11-3, 11-4, and 11-5. Plane flow of a viscous substance compressed between two parallel plates.

indicates that neither the normal nor the shearing stresses σ_x and τ_{xy} vanish along the edge $x = a$, as would strictly be required in an exact solution along a free edge. The boundary condition for τ_{xy} of a free edge is satisfied only at point $x = a$, $y = 0$. But one sees that the values of σ_x and p along $x = a$ are small when compared with the maximum pressure p_0 in the axis $x = 0$ of the specimen, so that the solution may be considered satisfactory. The shearing stresses τ_{xy} along $x = a$ are not necessarily small; however, they consist of an equilibrium system of forces distributed on a narrow edge, so that their local influence at $x = a$ is not important. The maximum pressure p_0 required to squeeze a comparatively thin layer of viscous material between parallel plates is proportional to the velocity v_0 with which each plate is moved, to the square of the width $2a$, and inversely proportional to the third power of the thickness $2h$ of the layer. *The total resultant compression load P for a rectangular pressure area of length 2b and width 2a*, using the value of p in Eq. (11-9) for $y = 0$, is approximately

$$P = 4b \int_0^a (p)_{y=0}\, dx = (\tfrac{8}{3})p_0 ab = \underline{\underline{\frac{4\mu a^3 b v_0}{h^3}}}, \qquad (11\text{-}11)$$

a formula which can serve for an experimental determination of the coefficient of viscosity μ of a substance by compressing it in a thin layer between parallel plates, provided that h is small and b is large compared with a.

11-3. Axially Symmetric Flow of a Viscous Substance. Circular Layer of Viscous Material Compressed between Parallel Plates. Using cylindrical coordinates r and z, denoting by u the radial and by v the axial velocity components for a cylinder of radius a of viscous material, compressed between the planes $z = \pm h$ moving with the absolute velocities $\mp v_0$ toward each other, we may express the rates of strain in the radial, tangential, and axial directions and the rate of shear in terms of the components of stress σ_r, σ_t, σ_z, τ_{rz} (Fig. 11-6) by

$$\dot{\varepsilon}_r = \frac{\partial u}{\partial r} = \frac{1}{3\mu}[\sigma_r - (\tfrac{1}{2})(\sigma_t + \sigma_z)],$$

$$\dot{\varepsilon}_t = \frac{u}{r} = \frac{1}{3\mu}[\sigma_t - (\tfrac{1}{2})(\sigma_z + \sigma_r)],$$

$$\dot{\varepsilon}_z = \frac{\partial v}{\partial z} = \frac{1}{3\mu}[\sigma_z - (\tfrac{1}{2})(\sigma_r + \sigma_t)], \qquad (11\text{-}12)$$

$$\dot{\gamma}_{rz} = \frac{\partial u}{\partial z} + \frac{\partial v}{\partial r} = \frac{1}{\mu}\tau_{rz}.$$

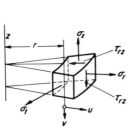

FIG. 11-6

After introducing the pressure

$$p = -(\tfrac{1}{3})(\sigma_r + \sigma_t + \sigma_z) \tag{11-13}$$

and solving for the stresses

$$\sigma_r = 2\mu \frac{\partial u}{\partial r} - p,$$

$$\sigma_t = 2\mu \frac{u}{r} - p, \tag{11-14}$$

$$\sigma_z = 2\mu \frac{\partial v}{\partial z} - p,$$

these relations have to be combined with the two conditions of equilibrium [see Sec. 7-1, Eqs. (7-5)],

$$\frac{\partial (r\sigma_r)}{\partial r} - \sigma_t + r\frac{\partial \tau_{rz}}{\partial z} = 0,$$

$$r\frac{\partial \sigma_z}{\partial z} + \frac{\partial}{\partial r}(r\tau_{rz}) = 0, \tag{11-15}$$

and the condition of continuity

$$\frac{\partial u}{\partial r} + \frac{u}{r} + \frac{\partial v}{\partial z} = \frac{1}{r}\frac{\partial (ru)}{\partial r} + \frac{\partial v}{\partial z} = 0, \tag{11-16}$$

showing that for this radial and axial flow the velocities u and v may be derived from a stream function ψ:

$$u = \frac{1}{r}\cdot\frac{\partial \psi}{\partial z}, \qquad v = -\frac{1}{r}\cdot\frac{\partial \psi}{\partial r}. \tag{11-17}$$

After substituting the expressions for the stresses [Eqs. (11-14)] in Eqs. (11-15) for the gradients of pressure,

$$\frac{\partial p}{\partial r} = \mu\left(\Delta u - \frac{u}{r^2}\right),$$

$$\frac{\partial p}{\partial z} = \mu \cdot \Delta v \tag{11-18}$$

is obtained, where Δ denotes the Laplacian operator:

$$\Delta = \frac{\partial^2}{\partial r^2} + \frac{\partial}{r\,\partial r} + \frac{\partial^2}{\partial z^2}. \tag{11-19}$$

In order to eliminate the pressure p from Eqs. (11-18), the rotation of the velocity field $\omega = (\tfrac{1}{2})(\partial u/\partial z - \partial v/\partial r)$ is computed in terms of the stream function ψ:

$$2r\omega = \frac{\partial^2 \psi}{\partial r^2} - \frac{\partial \psi}{r\,\partial r} + \frac{\partial^2 \psi}{\partial z^2} = \Delta'\psi, \tag{11-20}$$

where the sum of the preceding three differential quotients has been denoted by the sign of the operator:

$$\Delta' = \frac{\partial^2}{\partial r^2} - \frac{\partial}{r\,\partial r} + \frac{\partial^2}{\partial z^2}. \tag{11-21}$$

But from Eqs. (11-18),

$$\frac{\partial}{\partial z}\left(\Delta u - \frac{u}{r^2}\right) - \frac{\partial}{\partial r}\Delta v = 0, \tag{11-22}$$

and this last equation, with $2\omega = \partial u/\partial z - \partial v/\partial r$, gives

$$\Delta\omega = \frac{\omega}{r^2}. \tag{11-23}$$

Noting that $\Delta = \Delta' + (2/r)(\partial/\partial r)$, after substituting here the expression for ω taken from Eq. (11-20), one finds that the stream function ψ in the case of a rotationally symmetric flow must satisfy the fourth-order partial differential equation

$$\Delta'\Delta'\psi = 0 \tag{11-24}$$

first given by STOKES,[1] under the boundary conditions

$$z = h, \qquad u = 0, \qquad v = -v_0 = \text{const},$$
$$z = -h, \qquad u = 0, \qquad v = v_0 = \text{const}.$$

One verifies that this is the case for a function $\psi = c_1 r^2 z + c_2 r^2 z^3$ by assuming

$$\psi = \frac{v_0 r^2}{4h^3}(3h^2 z - z^3), \tag{11-25}$$

giving the velocities

$$u = \frac{\partial\psi}{r\,\partial z} = \frac{3v_0 r}{4h^3}(h^2 - z^2),$$
$$v = -\frac{\partial\psi}{r\,\partial r} = -\frac{v_0}{2h^3}(3h^2 z - z^3); \tag{11-26}$$

gradients of pressure

$$\frac{\partial p}{\partial r} = -\frac{3\mu v_0 r}{2h^3}, \qquad \frac{\partial p}{\partial z} = \frac{3\mu v_0 z}{h^3}; \tag{11-27}$$

and for the pressure,

$$p = \frac{3\mu v_0}{4h^3}(a^2 - r^2 + 2z^2), \tag{11-28}$$

[1] See HORACE LAMB, "Hydrodynamics," p. 591, Dover Publications, New York, 1945.

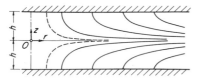

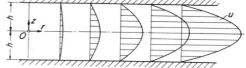

FIG. 11-7. Radial flow of a viscous substance compressed between two circular plates. Streamlines.

FIG. 11-8. Radial flow of a viscous substance compressed between two circular plates. Radial velocity components u.

satisfying the condition that, for $r = a, z = 0, p = 0$, corresponding to which the stress components are found equal to:

$$\sigma_r = \sigma_t = \frac{3\mu v_0}{4h^3}\left(r^2 - a^2 - 4z^2 + 2h^2\right),$$

$$\sigma_z = \frac{3\mu v_0}{4h^3}\left(r^2 - a^2 + 2z^2 - 4h^2\right),\qquad (11\text{-}29)$$

$$\tau_{rz} = -\frac{3\mu v_0}{2h^3}\cdot rz.$$

The maximum pressure $p_{\max}$ at the center of the cylinder $r = z = 0$ is equal to

$$p_{\max} = \frac{3\mu v_0 a^2}{4h^3},\qquad (11\text{-}30)$$

and in the middle plane $z = 0$ the pressure is distributed according to a paraboloid of revolution,

$$p = p_{\max}\left(1 - \frac{r^2}{a^2}\right);\qquad (11\text{-}31)$$

hence *the total axial compression load P required to squeeze a cylindrical viscous layer of radius a* between two planes a distance $2h$ apart is equal to:

$$P = (\tfrac{1}{2})\pi a^2 p_{\max} = \frac{3\pi\mu v_0 a^4}{8h^3},\qquad (11\text{-}32)$$

an equation which again may well serve for an experimental determination of the viscosity μ of a material through a compression test. The compression force P is proportional to the fourth power of the radius a of the test specimen. The pattern of the streamlines of flow and the distribution of the radial velocities u are reproduced in Figs. 11-7 and 11-8.[1]

---

[1] Concerning the boundary values of the stresses on the cylindrical surface $r = a$ remarks similar to those made in Sec. 11-2 hold.

Use of the preceding relations was made in compression tests carried out at the Westinghouse Research Laboratories with certain plastics deformed at slightly elevated temperatures, by measuring the thickness $2h$ of the layer of material and the velocity $v_0 = -dh/dt$ of the upper compression plate. The formulas are based on the assumption that the displacements are small compared with the smallest dimension, i.e., the thickness $2h$ of the cylindrical layer. But suppose that $v_0 = -dh/dt$ and h are measured from time to time t, while the load P is held constant and h and a vary according to $ha^2 = h_0a_0{}^2 = $ const, h_0 and a_0 being the values of h and a at time $t = 0$. Then from Eq. (11-32), after writing for $v_0 = -dh/dt$,

$$-\frac{dh}{h^5\,dt} = \frac{8P}{3\pi\mu a_0^4 h_0^2} = \text{const},$$

$$\frac{1}{h^4} - \frac{1}{h_0^4} = \frac{32Pt}{3\pi\mu a_0^4 h_0^2}, \qquad (11\text{-}33)$$

the thickness $2h$ should decrease with the time t as the ordinates of this higher-order hyperbola, provided that the viscosity μ has remained unaltered. If, on the other hand, indications are that the substance underwent structural changes, one may plot h above the time t, draw the tangents to $h = f(t)$, determine the velocity $v_0 = -dh/dt$, and compute the instantaneous mean viscosity μ of the substance.

CHAPTER 12

THE FLOW OF A GENERALLY VISCOUS SUBSTANCE THROUGH A CYLINDRICAL TUBE

12-1. Steady Flow of Generally Viscous Substance through a Tube. In the previous chapters, the validity of linear stress-strain or stress–rate-of-strain relations was postulated for the treatment of equilibrium states in incompressible, elastic or viscous bodies, respectively. Consider now the speed-dependent flow of substances under the more general condition that the rate of shear is a known function of the shearing stress. Let us choose as an example the steady, smooth flow of such a *generally viscous substance* through a straight, cylindrical tube and determine the distribution of the velocities in a cross section of the tube and the gradient of the pressure under which a prescribed discharge can be obtained through a tube.[1]

Under steady, smooth (nonturbulent) flow of a substance through a cylindrical tube, the velocities are parallel to the tube's axis. Denote by u the velocity in the radial distance r from the axis and, for the sake of convenience, by the letter v the rate of shear (instead of using the previous symbol $\dot\gamma = d\gamma/dt$) which is equal to $v = -du/dr$.

Under these rates of shear v, shearing stresses τ are produced in the coaxial cylinders $r = $ const of length l in the fluid, having a resultant

---

[1] Much has been written about the flow of semifluid materials through tubes by the investigators calling themselves rheologists, interested in many of the physical, chemical, and structural aspects of the flow of softer grades of substances, pastes, suspensions of solid particles in fluids (paints), high polymers, plastics, etc., through capillary tubes. In this book, we cannot enter into this subject, and the reader is referred to the books by EUGENE C. BINGHAM, "Fluidity and Plasticity," 440 pp., McGraw-Hill Book Company, Inc., New York, 1922; R. HOUWINK, "Elasticity, Plasticity and Structure of Matter," 376 pp., Cambridge University Press, London, 1937; MARKUS REINER, "Ten Lectures on Theoretical Rheology," Rubin Mass, Jerusalem, 1943; and "Deformation and Flow, an Elementary Introduction to Theoretical Rheology," 346 pp., H. K. Lewis, London, 1949 (see extensive bibliography in this book). We shall also refrain from using certain names to designate special types of solids or fluids which the rheologists have introduced, because some of these terms do not fit well with most of the important solid materials used in engineering constructions. See also footnote in Vol. I, page 421.

$2\pi r l\tau$, opposing the difference of the pressure $p\pi r^2$, and if v_a, τ_a, and a denote the values of v, τ, and r on the inner surface of the tube, we have

$$\tau = \frac{pr}{2l} = \frac{\tau_a r}{a}, \qquad \tau_a = \frac{pa}{2l}. \tag{12-1}$$

Assuming a given law of deformation in shear,

$$v = f(\tau), \tag{12-2}$$

$v_a = f(\tau_a)$, we have

$$\frac{du}{dr} = -v = -f(\tau) = -f\left(\frac{pr}{2l}\right) \tag{12-3}$$

for the velocity of flow; assuming that the fluid sticks to the tube wall, $r = a$, $u = 0$, u is

$$u = \frac{2l}{p}\int_\tau^{\tau_a} f(\tau)\,d\tau = \int_r^a f\left(\frac{pr}{2l}\right)dr, \tag{12-4}$$

and the transported volume of material per unit of time or discharge Q is

$$Q = 2\pi \int_0^a ur\,dr = \pi a^2 \bar{u}, \tag{12-5}$$

$\bar{u}$ denoting the mean velocity in the tube sections.

12-2. Poisseuille's Flow. For a fluid in which the rate of shear increases linearly with the shearing stress $v = f(\tau) = \tau/\mu$ (Fig. 12-1),

$$v = -\frac{du}{dr} = \frac{pr}{2\mu l}, \qquad u = \frac{pa^2}{4\mu l}\left(1 - \frac{r^2}{a^2}\right), \tag{12-6}$$

the volume of fluid passing per unit of time is equal to

$$Q = \frac{\pi p a^4}{8\mu l}, \qquad \bar{u} = \frac{pa^2}{8\mu l}, \tag{12-7}$$

expressing *Poisseuille's law* for the efflux in laminary flow through a capillary tube for a perfectly viscous fluid.[1]

---

[1] JEAN LEONARD MARIE POISSEUILLE, Recherches expérimentales sur le mouvement des liquides dans les tubes de très petits diamètres, Mém. par divers savants acad. roy. sci., tome 9, pp. 433–545, Paris, 1846. This classical paper has been reprinted in an English translation prepared by WINSLOW H. HERSCHEL in EUGENE C. BINGHAM (ed.), Rheological Memoirs, vol. 1, no. 1, p. 101, January, 1940. Poisseuille, as a physician, traced the passage of blood corpuscles through the capillary arteries in living organisms, measuring the fluctuations of the pressure of blood, which led him to his later, most careful experimental determinations of his efflux formula: $Q = \text{const } pa^4/l$ for distilled water flowing through thin capillary glass tubes at 10°C, which he established purely empirically. In his paper the term *viscosity* was not mentioned a single time; it was defined shortly after its publication by MAXWELL.

12-3. Bingham's Fluid. EUGENE C. BINGHAM,[1] when experimenting with suspensions of solid particles in a fluid, found that Poisseuille's formula would not fit the observations unless the viscosity law was assumed to become valid after a finite limit of plasticity (Bingham called it the *yield value*) τ_0 was reached in the substance in simple shear:

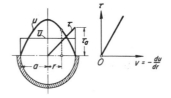

$$\tau = \tau_0 + \mu v. \qquad (12\text{-}8)$$

FIG. 12-1. Flow of viscous fluid.

The substance starts to flow unless $\tau > \tau_0$ near the walls of the tube in the region $c \leqq r \leqq a$, where $\tau_0 \leqq \tau \leqq \tau_a$, exhibiting there unit shears $v = -du/dr$, while the interior portion of fluid within a cylinder $0 \leqq r \leqq c$ is carried with a uniform velocity $u = u_c = \text{const}$, like a solid plug

[1] *Op. cit.*, p. 223. M. REINER (*op. cit.*, p. 36) and the rheologists called a substance for which the shear-rate law [Eq. (12-8)] holds a *Bingham body*.

FIG. 12-2. JEAN LEONARD MARIE POISSEUILLE. (Born April 23, 1797; died Dec. 26, 1869.) Details on his life may be found in Rheological Memoirs, vol. 1, no. 1, January, 1940. Easton, Pa.

FIG. 12-3. EUGENE COOK BINGHAM, Professor of Chemistry, Lafayette College, Easton, Pa. (Born Dec. 8, 1878, in Cornwall, Vt.; died Nov. 6, 1945.) Details on his life may be found in the Journal of Colloid Science, vol. 2, no. 1, February, 1947. (*Photo, Blackstone Studios, New York.*)

with the fluid (Fig. 12-4; Fig. 12-5a reproduces this speed law). A toothpaste ejected from the nozzle of its tube may illustrate the velocity profile of Fig. 12-4. Thus,

when $0 \leqq r \leqq c$:　　$v = 0,$　　　$u = u_c,$

when $c \leqq r \leqq a$:　　$v = -\dfrac{du}{dr} = \dfrac{\tau - \tau_0}{\mu},$　　　$\tau = \dfrac{pr}{2l},$

and for $r = c, \tau = \tau_0 = pc/2l; r = a, \tau = \tau_a = pa/2l.$

After integrating,

$$\frac{du}{dr} = \frac{\tau_0}{\mu} - \frac{pr}{2\mu l} = \frac{\tau_0}{\mu}\left(1 - \frac{r}{c}\right), \qquad (12\text{-}9)$$

the velocity of flow when $c \leqq r \leqq a$ is obtained equal to

$$u = \frac{p}{4\mu l}[a^2 - r^2 - 2c(a - r)]. \qquad (12\text{-}10)$$

In order to express this velocity profile and the discharge Q of a tube in their dependence on the pressure drop p/l, we introduce for the latter the dimensionless quantity

$$\beta = \frac{pa}{2\tau_0 l} = \frac{\tau_a}{\tau_0} \qquad (12\text{-}11)$$

and denote the ratio of plug to tube radius by $\alpha = c/a$. Since then $c = 2\tau_0 l/p$, also $\beta = 1/\alpha$, for this fluid the velocity for $r \geqq c$,

$$u = \frac{\tau_0 a}{2\mu}\left[\beta\left(1 + \frac{r}{a}\right) - 2\right]\left(1 - \frac{r}{a}\right), \qquad (12\text{-}12)$$

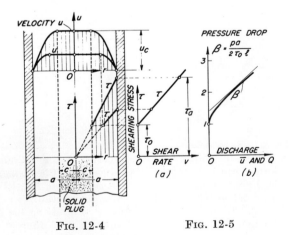

FIG. 12-4　　　　　FIG. 12-5

FIGS. 12-4 and 12-5. Flow of Bingham fluid through tube for speed law $\tau = \tau_0 + \mu v.$

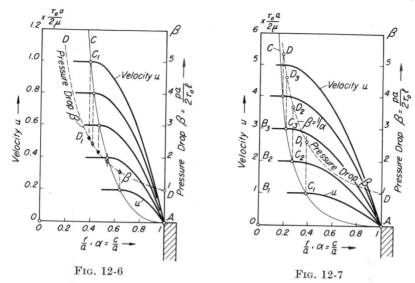

FIG. 12-6   FIG. 12-7

FIGS. 12-6 and 12-7. Distribution of velocities in tube for Bingham fluid.

having its maximum at $r = c$, is equal to

$$u_c = \frac{\tau_0 a}{2\mu}\left(\frac{1}{\alpha} - 2 + \alpha\right) = \frac{\tau_0 a}{2\mu}\left(\beta - 2 + \frac{1}{\beta}\right). \qquad (12\text{-}13)$$

This shows that the maxima in the velocity profile u occur $(du/dr = 0)$ at points having the coordinates $r = \alpha a$, $u = u_c$ on a certain hyperbola given by the preceding equation and facilitates the plotting of the velocity profiles[1] (Figs. 12-6 and 12-7) while the variation of the discharge Q of the tube with the pressure drop β is expressed by

$$Q = \pi c^2 u_c + 2\pi \int_c^a ur\,dr = \frac{\pi \tau_0 a^3}{12\mu}\left(3\beta - 4 + \frac{1}{\beta^3}\right) = \pi a^2 \bar{u} \qquad (12\text{-}14)$$

or by a curve which starts at a point $\beta = 1$, $Q = 0$ with a horizontal tangent (Fig. 12-8) and very rapidly approaches an inclined straight-line asymptote having the equation

$$Q = \frac{\pi \tau_0 a^3}{12\mu}(3\beta - 4), \qquad (12\text{-}15)$$

the initial value of $\beta = 1 = pa/2\tau_0 l$ representing the minimum drop of pressure p/l required to *initiate the flow* of a Bingham fluid. When β

---

[1] This hyperbola [Eq. (12-13)] AC, traced in Figs. 12-6 and 12-7 by a thin line, embraces the points $C_1, C_2, C_3, \ldots$ at which the velocity curves u reach their horizontal tangents; the radii $B_1C_1, B_2C_2, \ldots$ define the radius $c = \alpha a$ of the solid plug of fluid moved with the fluid. The thin, dashed line DD represents $\beta = 1/\alpha$, and by projecting the points $C_1, C_2, \ldots$ vertically on the hyperbola $\beta = 1/\alpha$ one obtains in the ordinates read on DD the corresponding pressure drop β.

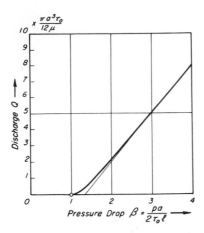

FIG. 12-8. Discharge Q as dependent on pressure drop β for Bingham fluid.

takes on large values, one sees that the velocity profiles in Fig. 12-7 approach more and more the Poiseuille parabolas [Eqs. (12-6)] and that the discharge Q converges finally toward the Poiseuille expression:

$$ Q \doteq \frac{\pi \tau_0 a^3}{4\mu} \beta = \frac{\pi p a^4}{8\mu l} . \quad (12\text{-}16) $$

If this last formula were applied to this flow, irrespective of the geometry of flow just discussed, an *apparent viscosity* μ_a would be computed for it equal to

$$ \mu_a = \frac{3\beta^4 \mu}{1 - 4\beta^3 + 3\beta^4} , \quad (12\text{-}17) $$

where $\beta = pa/2\tau_0 l$, and $\mu_a = \infty$ would be found when $\beta = 1$.

This theory of the late Bingham has nicely explained the deviations from the Poiseuille flow that he observed in certain fluids and that a certain minimum pressure ($\beta = 1$) is necessary to make them flow.[1]

12-4. Biviscous Substance. Suppose that a substance has two distinct ranges of viscosity, that it requires a greater increase of stress to make it flow at low than at higher rates of shear, which may be due to a sudden change in its structure at a critical rate of shear. Suppose that the shear diagram consists of two inclined lines (Fig. 12-10a):

$$ \begin{aligned} \tau &= \mu_1 v, \quad \tau_1 = \mu_1 v_1, & 0 < v < v_1, \\ \tau &= \tau_1 + \mu(v - v_1), & v_1 < v, \end{aligned} \quad (12\text{-}18) $$

assuming that $\mu_1 > \mu$. The steep range of viscosity (μ_1) will be encountered around the axis of the tube in the region $0 \leqq r \leqq c$, but the shearing stress τ in the tube will remain a continuous function of the radius r: $\tau = pr/2l$.

---

[1] HENRY E. MAHNCKE and WILLIAM TABOR in their paper "A Simple Demonstration of Flow Type in Greases" (Lubrication Eng., vol. 11, no. 1, pp. 22–28, 1955) found that the laminar flow of certain greases through cylindrical tubes conforms pretty well to the postulate of the shearing-stress–rate-of-shear diagram of a Bingham fluid illustrated in Fig. 12-5a. They found, however, that the velocity profile within the so-called "plug" (when $0 \leqq r \leqq c$ in the tube) disclosed a slight curvature, similar to the conditions to be treated in Sec. 12-4 for what we term a *biviscous substance*. The reader may also find various references to related cases of more generally viscous fluids in this paper.

At small pressures $p < p_1 = 2\tau_1 l/a$ simple Poisseuille flow prevails,

$$u = \frac{p}{4\mu_1 l}(a^2 - r^2), \qquad Q = \frac{\pi p a^4}{8\mu_1 l}, \qquad (12\text{-}19)$$

unless $0 < \beta < 1$, if again β denotes the quantity measuring the drop in pressure:

$$\beta = \frac{pa}{2\tau_1 l} = \frac{p}{p_1}.$$

When $\beta > 1$, two concentric regions having the viscosities μ_1 and μ develop in the flow, and the velocity distribution becomes

$$u = \frac{v_1 a}{2}\left[\frac{\mu_1}{\mu}\beta - \left(\frac{\mu_1}{\mu} - 1\right)\left(2 - \frac{1}{\beta}\right) - \beta\frac{r^2}{a^2}\right], \qquad 0 \leqq r \leqq c,$$

$$u = \frac{v_1 a}{2}\left[\frac{\mu_1}{\mu}\beta - 2\left(\frac{\mu_1}{\mu} - 1\right)\left(1 - \frac{r}{a}\right) - \frac{\mu_1}{\mu}\beta\frac{r^2}{a^2}\right], \qquad c \leqq r \leqq a,$$

$$(12\text{-}20)$$

where, as previously, $\beta = 1/\alpha = a/c$. Figure 12-9 reproduces a velocity profile, the dashed curve ACD separating the two branches of u curves. When $\beta > 1$, a volume per unit of time

$$Q = \frac{\pi \tau_1 a^3}{12\mu}\left[\left(1 - \frac{\mu}{\mu_1}\right)\left(\frac{1}{\beta^2} - 4\right) + 3\beta\right] \qquad (12\text{-}21)$$

passes through the tube. With this consideration of a stiffer range of viscosity μ_1 in the portion near the axis in the substance, this represents a further generalization of Bingham's assumption. Instead of the perfectly rigid portion not yielding below the critical value τ_0, we have assumed that the portion $0 \leqq r \leqq c$ also suffers unit shears even though the shearing stresses in it have not yet reached the point of discontinuity τ_1 at which the viscosity drops from the value μ_1 to μ.

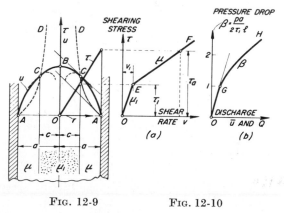

FIG. 12-9   FIG. 12-10

FIGS. 12-9 and 12-10. Flow of fluid through tube having two viscosity ranges.

In the extrusion of solids, lubricating greases are used to reduce the friction at the walls and the wear of the dies. *In the case of a lubricated surface*, the velocity u at the walls vanishes only in the lubricant, but *the extruded solid piece slips with a finite velocity u_c along the walls*. If a stiff, viscous solid is extruded through a cylindrical die, the working surface of which is kept lubricated, the velocity in the thin layer of thickness δ of the lubricant is $u = u_c(a - r)/\delta$, the rate of shear $v = -du/dr = u_c/\delta = $ const, and since the shearing stress, at $r = a$, is $\tau = \tau_a = pa/2l$, if μ denotes the viscosity of the lubricant assumed to be quite small compared with that of the solid μ_1, we must have a velocity of slip

$$u_c = \frac{\tau_a \delta}{\mu} = \frac{pa\delta}{2\mu l},$$

while the piece to be extruded is being deformed with the velocities

$$u = u_c + \frac{pa^2}{4l\mu_1}\left(1 - \frac{r^2}{a^2}\right),$$

the displaced volume of material per second being

$$Q = \pi a^2 u_c + \frac{\pi pa^4}{8\mu_1 l} = \frac{\pi pa^4}{8\mu_1 l}\left(1 + \frac{4\mu_1 \delta}{\mu a}\right).$$

The greater the thickness δ of the lubricating agent and the smaller its viscosity μ can be kept, compared with that of the work piece μ_1, the more of the solid can be extruded and the faster its velocity through a die.

12-5.   Flow, Assuming Power Function for Shear Diagram. The flow of certain softer solids through a cylindrical tube may be treated by postulating a power function for the shear diagram $v = f(\tau)$. While this has been proposed in the form $v = c\tau^n$, we shall, however, suppose that the shear law is expressed by

$$v = v_0 \frac{\tau}{\tau_1} + v_1\left(\frac{\tau}{\tau_1}\right)^n, \qquad (n > 1), \qquad (12\text{-}22)$$

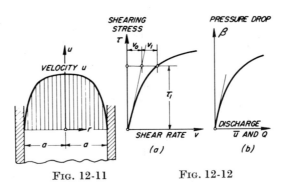

FIG. 12-11   FIG. 12-12

FIGS. 12-11 and 12-12. Flow of fluid through tube for speed law

$$v = v_0 \cdot \frac{\tau}{\tau_1} + v_1\left(\frac{\tau}{\tau_1}\right)^n.$$

by including a linear term in this function in order to obtain a finite viscosity

$$\left(\frac{d\tau}{dv}\right)_{\tau=0} = \frac{\tau_1}{v_0}$$

at vanishing stress and rate of shear (Fig. 12-12a).   The material constants v_0 and v_1 have the dimensions of rates of shear and τ_1 is a shearing stress.

Some of the softer, nonferrous metals may be extruded in the form of round rods from a pressure vessel through an opening in a hard die in a range of temperatures in which they become workable.   Although these nozzles usually have a slightly tapered conical orifice, we may, for a first, simple treatment, assume that the rod is formed in a short cylindrical tube of length l and radius a.   Using $v = -du/dr, \tau = pr/2l$, and after substituting these in Eq. (12-22), denoting again a dimensionless constant by β defined by

$$\beta = \frac{pa}{2\tau_1 l},$$

after integrating,

$$\frac{du}{dr} = -v_0\beta\frac{r}{a} - v_1\left(\frac{\beta r}{a}\right)^n,\qquad(12\text{-}23)$$

we find that the velocity u with which the material passes through the tube is equal to

$$u = \frac{v_0 a\beta}{2}\left(1 - \frac{r^2}{a^2}\right) + \frac{v_1 a\beta^n}{n+1}\left[1 - \left(\frac{r}{a}\right)^{n+1}\right],\qquad(12\text{-}24)$$

while a volume of material per unit of time

$$Q = 2\pi\int_0^a ur\,dr = \pi a^2\bar{u} = \pi a^3\left(\frac{v_0\beta}{4} + \frac{v_1\beta^n}{n+3}\right)\qquad(12\text{-}25)$$

is extruded.   It may, perhaps, be noted that the greatest velocity in the axis $(r = 0)$ of the tube u_{max} and the mean velocity $\bar{u}$,

$$u_{max} = \frac{v_0 a}{2}\beta + \frac{v_1 a}{n+1}\beta^n,$$

$$\bar{u} = \frac{v_0 a}{4}\beta + \frac{v_1 a}{n+3}\beta^n,\qquad(12\text{-}26)$$

are expressed by polynomials having the same powers of β as the speed law [Eq. (12-22)] has in the powers of τ/τ_1.   The higher the values of the exponent n, the flatter the velocity profiles become in their center portion.   Figure 12-13 illustrates an example for $n = 3$, $v_1 = 2v_0$ at three different pressures corresponding to $\beta = 1, 2$, and 3.

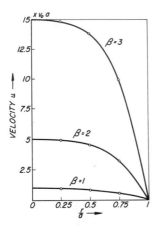

FIG. 12-13. Velocities u for speed law

$$v = v_0 \left[\frac{\tau}{\tau_1} + 2\left(\frac{\tau}{\tau_1}\right)^3 \right],$$

$(n = 3)$.

The part of the rate of work done during the passage of material through the extrusion tube[1] is

$$\dot{W} = \pi a^2 p \bar{u} = 2\pi \tau_1 l a^2 \left(\frac{v_0 \beta^2}{4} + \frac{v_1 \beta^{n+1}}{n+3} \right). \quad (12\text{-}27)$$

12-6. Flow under Hyperbolic Sine Speed Law in a Tube. Experiments with ductile metals in which the rates of shear were varied over a very wide range from the slowest rates encountered in long-time creep tests to the fastest ones which produced in high-speed (impact) tensile tests[2] have indicated that at elevated temperatures the dependence of the rate of shear v on the shearing stress τ can be expressed by the hyperbolic sine law

$$v = v_1 \sinh \frac{\tau}{\tau_1} \quad (12\text{-}28)$$

first proposed in 1928 by L. PRANDTL (v_1 and τ_1 are material constants, at a given temperature, of the dimensions of a rate of shear and of a shearing stress).

In recent papers PRANDTL[3] remarked that this speed law expressing

[1] A piston in an extrusion cylinder forcing the material to flow out through the orifice must, in addition, supply the kinetic energy $\pi a^2 \rho \bar{u} \cdot (\bar{u})^2/2$ of the moving masses and the work for deforming the substance enclosed in the pressure container before it has reached the extrusion nozzle. The latter may be estimated roughly as the work of compression $\dot{W}_1$ required to transform a cylindrical chunk (the content of the pressure vessel) of material into a cylindrical rod of radius a. Supposing that this is done in radial compression $\sigma_r = \sigma_t = -p_0$, $\sigma_z = 0$ under the natural rates of strain $\dot{\varepsilon}_r = \dot{\varepsilon}_t = -\dot{\varepsilon}_z/2 = \dot{r}/r$, since the radially displaced volume per unit of time $2\pi r h \dot{r}$ reappears in the extruded rod as $\pi a^2 \bar{u}$, one sees that

$$\dot{\varepsilon}_r = \frac{\dot{r}}{r} = \frac{\pi a^2 \bar{u}}{2\pi r^2 h} = \frac{A \bar{u}}{2V},$$

where $A = \pi a^2$ and V is the content of the pressure cylinder $V = \pi r^2 h$. But the average maximum rate of shear v for this radial compression is $v = \dot{\varepsilon}_r - \dot{\varepsilon}_z = 3\dot{\varepsilon}_r = 3A\bar{u}/2V$. If the shear-rate diagram (Fig. 12-12) is known, this then determines its mean maximum-shearing-stress ordinate $\tau = \tau_{\max} = p_0/2$, that is, the pressure p_0 required, and thus the additional rate of work

$$\dot{W}_1 = A\bar{u}p_0.$$

[2] See Vol. I, page 417; see also Chap. 16.

[3] Fliessgrenze normal zäher Stoffe im Rohr, Z. angew. Math. u. Mech., vol. 30, no. 5–6, pp. 169–174, May, 1950. See also a very illustrative short paper by PRANDTL, Betrachtungen zur Rheologie, Physik. Bl., vol. 5, no. 4, pp. 161–172, 1950.

generally the dependence of the rates of strain on stress in solids and fluids may well describe the flow through a cylindrical tube of substances which he called *normally viscous*, in distinction from the ones for which $\tau = \mu v$. The hyperbolic sine law unifies in one single function several well-established facts known from the observations of the general behavior of solids and fluids over a wide range of temperatures; it satisfies the logical requirement for a shear law that it be expressed by an odd function between the two variables v and τ, that solids are known to deform at extremely small rates of shear proportionally with the stresses and at high rates according to an exponential function. Equation (12-28) when solved in terms of τ is expressed by

$$\frac{\tau}{\tau_1} = \ln \left(\frac{v}{v_1} + \sqrt{1 + \frac{v^2}{v_1^2}} \right)$$

(12-29)

and defines the viscosity of a substance,

$$\frac{d\tau}{dv} = \frac{\tau_1}{v_1 \cosh (\tau/\tau_1)} \, ,$$

(12-30)

which decreases with the shearing stress τ, whether negative or positive, and indicates that, for example, the ductile metals have a comparatively narrow, perfectly viscous range when the stresses and shear rates are quite small,

$$\mu = \frac{\tau_1}{v_1} = \text{const},$$

(12-31)

whereas, at comparatively high rates of shear, the yield stresses τ,

$$\frac{\tau}{\tau_1} = \ln \frac{2v}{v_1} \, ,$$

(12-32)

increase as the logarithms of the rates of shear v, a law that was originally proposed and already verified for metals by P. Ludwik[1] in 1908.

Let us compute the distribution of the velocities u in a cylindrical tube and the volume per unit of time Q discharged through it for a substance for which the hyperbolic sine speed law [Eq. (12-28)] is valid. After denoting again by β the dimensionless constant,

$$\beta = \frac{pa}{2\tau_1 l} = \frac{\tau_a}{\tau_1} \, ,$$

(12-33)

the shearing stresses

$$\tau = \frac{pr}{2l} \, , \qquad \tau_a = \frac{pa}{2l}$$

(12-34)

will cause the rates of shear

$$v = -\frac{du}{dr} = v_1 \sinh \frac{\beta r}{a} \, ,$$

(12-35)

[1] Cf. Vol. I, page 21.

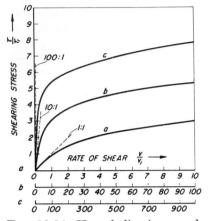

FIG. 12-14. Hyperbolic sine speed law $v = v_1 \sinh \dfrac{\tau}{\tau_1}$.

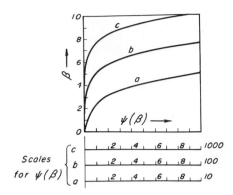

FIG. 12-15. Curves representing function $\psi(\beta)$ defining efflux Q of fluid.

from which equation, after integrating, the velocity distribution

$$u = \frac{v_1 a}{\beta}\left(\cosh \beta - \cosh \frac{\beta r}{a}\right) \tag{12-36}$$

is obtained, with the greatest velocity at the tube axis, $r = 0$,

$$u_{\max} = \frac{v_1 a}{\beta}(\cosh \beta - 1). \tag{12-37}$$

After also computing the mean velocity $\bar{u}$ in the tube, the fluid volume discharged per unit of time is found equal to

$$Q = \pi a^2 \bar{u} = 2\pi v_1 a^3 \left(\frac{\cosh \beta}{2\beta} - \frac{\sinh \beta}{\beta^2} + \frac{\cosh \beta - 1}{\beta^3}\right), \tag{12-38}$$

where the constant β, according to Eq. (12-33), measures the drop of pressure p/l.

The function of β in the parentheses may be expressed by a power series as follows[1]:

$$Q = \frac{2\pi v_1 a^3}{\beta} \sum_{n=1}^{\infty} \frac{n(2n + 1)\beta^{2n}}{(2n + 2)!}, \qquad (n = 1, 2, 3, \ldots); \tag{12-39}$$

both of these expressions for the volume Q discharged through the tube have the form

$$Q = \pi a^2 \bar{u} = \pi a^3 v_1 \psi(\beta), \tag{12-40}$$

thus defining Q or the mean velocity $\bar{u}$ of efflux in terms of the dimensionless parameter β serving as a measure for the pressure drop p/l.

---

[1] In PRANDTL's paper, this series is attributed to FR. VANDREY. It serves well for evaluating Q at small pressure drops p/l (small values of β) and even when β becomes several units large.

The function $\psi(\beta)$ is thus defined by

$$\psi(\beta) = 2(\cdots),\tag{12-40a}$$

using the expression within the parentheses in Eq. (12-38).

In summing up, we may then reproduce in the manner suggested by PRANDTL in two figures, by means of three curves having a similar trend, the hyperbolic sine speed law and the function $\psi(\beta)$ controlling the efflux Q of fluid of a tube (Figs. 12-14 and 12-15).

By transforming slightly the term before the series in order to have it correspond with Poisseuille's law, we may rewrite this series as follows, after letting $\mu = (d\tau/dv)_{\tau=0} = \tau_1/v_1$,

$$Q = \frac{\pi p a^4}{8\mu l} \cdot \varphi(\beta), \qquad \varphi(\beta) = 1 + \frac{\beta^2}{9} + \frac{\beta^4}{240} + \frac{\beta^6}{12,600} + \cdots.\tag{12-41}$$

When β is small or for small pressure heads p/l, this approaches Poisseuille's formula of efflux [Eqs. (12-7)] while the velocity u takes on the parabolic distribution [since $\cosh(\beta r/a) - 1 \cong \beta^2 r^2/2a^2$]

$$u = \frac{p a^2}{4\mu l}\left(1 - \frac{r^2}{a^2}\right)\tag{12-42}$$

of the flow of a simple, viscous fluid. As the pressure head increases with β, the steady distribution of the flow velocities u changes in its relative shape: The velocity curves straighten out more and more over their interval, taking steeper and steeper slopes nearer the tube wall. This becomes particularly conspicuous if one plots the ratios of the velocities u to their mean value $\bar{u}$ at various values of β. Figures 12-16 and 12-17 reproduce several velocity profiles in two different scales for

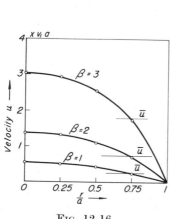

FIG. 12-16

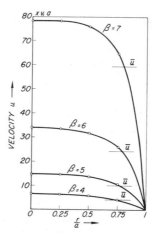

FIG. 12-17

FIGS. 12-16 and 12-17. Distribution of velocities u in tube for hyperbolic sine speed law.

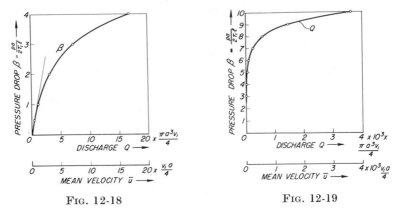

$$\text{F{\scriptsize IG}. 12-18} \qquad\qquad\qquad \text{F{\scriptsize IG}. 12-19}$$

F{\scriptsize IGS}. 12-18 and 12-19. Dependence of mean velocity $\bar{u}$ and discharge Q on pressure drop for hyperbolic sine speed law.

different assumed values of β, while Figs. 12-18 and 12-19 show how the pressure drop β varies with the discharge of volume of material Q.

We may note here that the special shear-rate functions $v = f(\tau)$ that we have previously mentioned, some of which were independently proposed by investigators, may be more or less related to the function $v = v_1 \sinh (\tau/\tau_1)$ or be interpreted as approximate expressions of the latter function covering a limited range of the variables τ and v.   This may equally be asserted for the Bingham shear-rate law, the biviscous and the power-function-shear diagrams that we have considered.   Suppose that we denote the two material constants entering the shear diagram of Bingham in Eq. (12-8) by attaching the subscripts zero to them in

$$\tau = \tau_0 + \mu_0 v \tag{12-43}$$

while the subscripts 1 refer to the hyperbolic sine function

$$v = v_1 \sinh \left(\frac{\tau}{\tau_1}\right) \tag{12-44}$$

and we distinguish the corresponding dimensionless constants,

$$\beta_0 = \frac{pa}{2\tau_0 l} = \frac{\tau_a}{\tau_0}, \qquad \beta_1 = \frac{pa}{2\tau_1 l} = \frac{\tau_a}{\tau_1}, \tag{12-45}$$

as applied to the former and to the latter functions, respectively.   Suppose that we have also evaluated the velocity curves u for these two cases,

$$u = \frac{\tau_0 a}{2\mu_0}\left(1 - \frac{r}{a}\right)\left[\beta_0\left(1 + \frac{r}{a}\right) - 2\right] \tag{12-46}$$

and

$$u = \frac{v_1 a}{\beta_1}\left(\cosh \beta_1 - \cosh \frac{\beta_1 r}{a}\right), \tag{12-47}$$

by using Eqs. (12-12) and (12-36) and the corresponding effluxes Q, assuming, for example, a certain pressure head p/l which determines a certain value of the maximum shearing stress $\tau = \tau_a$ at the tube wall $r = a$, namely,

$$\tau_a = \frac{pa}{2l} = \tau_1 \beta_1 = \tau_0 \beta_0, \tag{12-48}$$

and through which a certain rate of shear $v_a = v_1 \sinh(\tau_a/\tau_1)$ is defined at the tube wall.

Referring to Fig. 12-20 representing the shear diagram $v = v_1 \sinh(\tau/\tau_1)$, now draw the tangent $\overline{PQ}$ to it at point $P(v_a, \tau_a)$ and consider the ordinate $\overline{OQ} = \tau_0$ as the "yield value" and $\overline{QP}$ as defining the straight line [Eq. (12-8)] of a BINGHAM fluid having the slope μ_0. Then, at the prescribed pressure p, furnishing the same shearing stress τ_a and rate of shear v_a, we may compare the velocity profiles in Eqs. (12-46) and (12-47) for these two types of substances and may find them similar in shape. In fact, we may compute the values of the two material constants μ_0 and τ_0 entering Eq. (12-46) from the condition that $\overline{QP}$ in Fig. 12-20 be the tangent to the curve $v = v_1 \sinh(\tau/\tau_1)$ at point $P(v_a, \tau_a)$.†

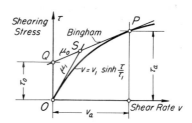

FIG. 12-20. Three speed laws compared:

OP, $v = v_1 \sinh \dfrac{\tau}{\tau_1}$

OQP, Bingham fluid

OSP, biviscous fluid

Similarly, by tracing the broken line OSP in Fig. 12-20 tangent at the origin O and at point $P(v_a, \tau_a)$ to $v = v_1 \sinh(\tau/\tau_1)$, one may construct a shear diagram representing *a biviscous fluid* approaching the former function, finding for it the two viscosities [using Eqs. (12-48a) and (12-48b)]

$$\mu_1 = \frac{\tau_a}{v_a} \cdot \frac{\sinh \xi}{\xi}, \qquad \mu_0 = \frac{\tau_a}{v_a} \cdot \frac{\tanh \xi}{\xi} \qquad (12\text{-}49)$$

with the critical shearing stress under point S

$$\tau_s = \tau_a \frac{\cosh \xi - (\sinh \xi)/\xi}{\cosh \xi - 1}. \qquad (12\text{-}50)$$

Or one may consider a function of the type introduced in Sec. 12-5, Eq. (12-22), and, after adjusting its three available material constants including the exponent n of the power term, one may make it osculate even at a much closer range to the hyperbolic sine curve than the former approximate functions permitted. Some of

---

† If we abbreviate by

$$\xi = \frac{\tau_a}{\tau_1}, \qquad \eta = \frac{v_a}{v_1}, \qquad (12\text{-}48a)$$

we then have

$$\eta = \sinh \xi \qquad (12\text{-}48b)$$

and find that the two material constants of the BINGHAM fluid, if this were substituted for the PRANDTL substance (in the neighborhood of the preceding chosen values of ξ and η), are given by

$$\frac{\tau_0}{\tau_a} = 1 - \frac{\tanh \xi}{\xi}, \qquad \mu_0 = \frac{\tau_a}{v_a} \cdot \frac{\tanh \xi}{\xi}, \qquad (12\text{-}48c)$$

while, according to Eq. (12-48),

$$\beta_0 = \frac{\tau_a}{\tau_0} = \frac{\tau_1}{\tau_0} \beta_1. \qquad (12\text{-}48d)$$

These expressions could be further simplified, depending on whether a substitution of one for the other shear diagram is desired in the range of small or of great values of ξ and η. *Thus, the formulas that were derived for a Bingham fluid appear or may now be interpreted as approximate expressions valid in a limited range of the $v = v_1 \sinh(\tau/\tau_1)$ law.*

these details may seem, perhaps, useful in judging many former attempts that have been made to introduce new flow functions. We may state that, from this viewpoint, *the hyperbolic sine law of flow embraces in the most general way many special laws of flow that have been independently proposed by investigators for interpreting the efflux of substances of a generally viscous character through tubes.*

12-7. Measuring High Viscosities. Among the many methods for measuring viscosity, some of which require simple and some more elaborate procedures, only a few might be mentioned here among those which lend themselves to a determination of higher degrees of viscosity in absolute units.[1] For an absolute determination of viscosity, it is indispensable that the test permit control of the shearing stresses τ and rates of shear $v = d\gamma/dt$ based on quantitatively measurable values of τ and v; in general, the determination of

$$\mu = \frac{d\tau}{dv}$$

from a reliably established function $\tau = f(v)$ from the tests. The coefficient of viscosity μ as a shearing stress divided by a rate of unit shear, when expressed in engineering units of the *technical system* (T.S.) [kg(weight) for the unit of force, cm for length, and sec for time], has the dimensions [kg cm^{-2} sec] (T.S.).   A substance has unit viscosity,

$$\underline{\underline{1 \text{ [kg cm}^{-2} \text{ sec]} \quad (\text{T.S.})}}$$

when a shearing stress of 1 kg/cm^2 causes two parallel planes 1 cm apart to move in tangential direction by 1 cm in 1 sec.   This unit has not yet received a name (in dynamics of fluids and gases one prefers to define it by 1 [kg m^{-2} sec].

Expressed in the *physical system* of cgs units, based on gram for unit of mass, cm, sec, the dimensions of unit viscosity are obtained by dividing a shearing stress equaling the unit force of 1 dyne [gram (mass) cm sec^{-2}] per 1 cm^2 area: 1 dyne/cm^2 by the rate of unit shear of 1 per sec.   This unit has received the name *one poise* (after Poisseuille):

$$\underline{\underline{1 \text{ poise} = 1 \text{ (dyne/cm}^2)(\text{sec}) = 1 \text{ [gr cm}^{-1} \text{ sec}^{-1}] \quad (\text{cgs})}}$$

Since 1 kg (weight) in engineering units (T.S.) equals the product of 1,000 gram (mass) (cgs) times the gravity acceleration $g = 981$ cm/sec^2, 1 kg (weight)(T.S.) = 981,000 [grams (mass) cm sec^{-2}] = 981,000 dyne (cgs), we see that the *engineer's unit viscosity equals*

$$1 \text{ [kg cm}^{-2} \text{ sec](T.S.)} = 981,000 \text{ [dyne cm}^{-2} \text{ sec]} = 981,000 \text{ poise (cgs)}$$

or approximately one million poises.

[1] See the books on ASTM Standards describing methods and their specifications for testing viscosity.

The viscosity μ of a few substances may be illustrated through the following figures:

Water at temperature, °C	0	20	100
Viscosity μ: (kg/cm²)(sec) (T.S.) .	1.83×10^{-8}	1.03×10^{-8}	2.89×10^{-9}
centipoise (cgs) . .	1.83	1.03	0.289

(One centipoise equals one-hundredth poise.)

	Viscosity μ, poise
Glass (in annealing range).	10^{13}
Asphalts (greatly variable)	10^{10}–10^{12}
Copper (at 200°C under a tensile stress of 450 kg/cm²) . .	9×10^{17}
0.35% C steel (at 454°C under a tensile stress of 527 kg/cm²)	10^{18}
50-60-km-thick upper earth's crust	5×10^{22}

In a perfectly viscous substance ($\tau = \mu v$) STOKES' falling-sphere formula serves for an absolute determination of the viscosity according to which the viscous drag D caused by a sphere of radius r falling with a uniform velocity u,

$$D = 6\pi\mu r u,$$

is equal to the difference of its weight in the vacuum and the buoyancy of the viscous fluid, or

$$D - (\tfrac{4}{3})\pi r^3 g(\rho - \rho')$$

where ρ is the density of the falling sphere, ρ' density of fluid, and $g = 981$ cm/sec².

For measuring higher viscosities, such as those of solid tars, asphalts, etc., *a falling- or rotating-cylinder viscometer* may be used. The former, attributed to POCHETTINO,[1] utilizes the slow motion of a long, heavy cylinder, embedded in vertical position in the viscous semisolid material to be tested, either under its own weight or under a difference of pressures (p_1 above and p_2 below the metal plunger and the viscous substance) (Fig. 12-21) or under the action of both. If γ_0 designates the specific weight of the substance, γ_1 that of the plunger, and p is the pressure in the substance in the horizontal planes at the depth x, the equilibrium of a ring-shaped element of the substance requires that

$$\frac{\partial}{\partial r}(r\tau) = \left(\frac{\partial p}{\partial x} - \gamma_0\right)r, \qquad (12\text{-}51)$$

where τ is the shearing stress at r, x. When the heavy plunger is falling in the manner indicated in Fig. 12-21, its vertical velocity u_1 is found equal to

$$u_1 = \left(\frac{p_1 - p_2}{l} + \gamma_0\right)\frac{b^2 - a^2}{4\mu} + \frac{(\gamma_1 - \gamma_0)a^2}{2\mu}\ln\frac{b}{a} \qquad (12\text{-}52)$$

(b and a are the outer and inner radius of the space filled with the substance to be tested). In a very viscous substance, one may let $p_1 = p_2 = 0$, letting the plunger drop under its weight alone, and evaluate μ. The method furnishes a convenient means for testing viscosities of the order of 10^6 to 10^9 poises.

[1] See EMIL HATCHECK, "The Viscosity of Liquids," p. 182, D. Van Nostrand Company, Inc., Princeton, N.J., 1928.

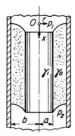

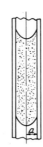

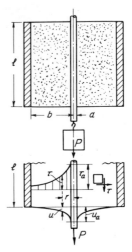

FIG. 12-21. Falling cylinder.

FIG. 12-22. Bulging meniscus.

FIG. 12-23. Dragging a pin through a viscous substance.

A variation of the method, known as *the bulging meniscus test* or viscometer (Fig. 12-22), consists of letting a column of height l of viscous material in a glass tube held in vertical position sag slowly under its own weight or under an additional pressure difference $p_1 - p_2$. The lower surface of the substance bulges gradually in a paraboloid of revolution, and one observes the meniscus through a cathetometer. If the tube has a radius a, the substance a specific weight γ_0, the shearing stress τ is

$$\tau = -\left(\frac{p_1 - p_2}{l} + \gamma_0\right)\frac{r}{2}, \tag{12-53}$$

and from $\partial u/\partial r = \tau/\mu$ one computes the form of the meniscus of velocity distribution u:

$$u = \left(\frac{p_1 - p_2}{l} + \gamma_0\right)\frac{a^2 - r^2}{4\mu}; \tag{12-54}$$

by observing the sinking of the meniscus at $r = 0$ with velocity u_0, one has for the viscosity

$$\mu = \left(\frac{p_1 - p_2}{l} + \gamma_0\right)\frac{a^2}{4u_0}. \tag{12-55}$$

Lack of space prohibits quoting the numerous variations in the methods of timing the flow through capillary tubes that have served to build various viscosimeters utilizing gravity in descending or also in ascending columns.[1]

[1] See E. O. RHODES, E. W. VOLKMANN, and C. T. BARKER, New Viscosimeter for Bitumens Has Extended Range; Koppers Products Company, Pittsburgh, Pa. (Eng. News-Record, no. 21, 1935). An ascending air bubble is used by these authors, a method also attributed to POCHETTINO (Nuovo cimento, ser. 6, 8, and 77, 1914).

On the other hand, one may utilize *a revolving plug* embedded in a ring-shaped viscous material, turned by a constant torque M around its axis, *creating a steady vortex of viscous flow,* and compute the viscosity from

$$\mu = \frac{M}{4\pi a l u_1}\left(1 - \frac{a^2}{b^2}\right), \tag{12-56}$$

where a radius of plug
  b radius of tube filled with substance over length l
  u_1 peripheral velocity of turning plug
  M constant torque

A slender cylindrical rod that has been cast into a substance filling a tube of radius b along its axis may be kept loaded in the axial direction by a constant force P (Fig. 12-23). Under its action, the rod is displaced with a uniform velocity u_a under a shearing stress τ_a, and the viscosity of the substance is determined from

$$\mu = \frac{P \ln (b/a)}{2\pi l u_a} \tag{12-57}[1]$$

where a radius
  l cast-in length of rod
  P $2\pi a l \tau_a$

If this formula is applied to a slender, cylindrical needle which is permitted to penetrate gradually under a weight W into the viscous substance and one substitutes for l the variable depth z to which the needle has penetrated and for the velocity $u_a = dz/dt$, one sees from Eq. (12-57) that the submerged length z of the needle in a perfectly viscous substance should increase as the square root of the time t:

$$z = \sqrt{\frac{W \ln (b/a) \cdot t}{\pi \mu}}. \tag{12-58}$$

In a substance in which the rate of shear v is a power function of the shearing stress τ, on the other hand,

$$v = v_1\left(\frac{\tau}{\tau_1}\right)^n, \qquad (n > 1), \tag{12-59}$$

using for $|\tau| = \tau_a a/r$, $v = -du/dr$, from

$$\frac{du}{dr} = -v_1\left(\frac{\tau_a a}{\tau_1 r}\right)^n, \tag{12-60}$$

the velocity u_a with which the needle penetrates is found equal to

$$u_a = \frac{v_1 a}{n - 1}\left(\frac{\tau_a}{\tau_1}\right)^n \cdot \left[1 - \left(\frac{a}{b}\right)^{n-1}\right]; \tag{12-61}$$

[1] Referring to Fig. 12-23, we have $(\partial/\partial r)(r\tau) = 0$, $\tau = \mu(\partial u/\partial r) = -\tau_a(a/r)$, $u = (\tau_a a/\mu) \cdot \ln (b/r)$, $u_a = (\tau_a a/\mu) \cdot \ln (b/a)$, and $u = u_a \cdot [\ln (b/r)/\ln (b/a)]$; hence,

$$\left(\frac{\partial u}{\partial r}\right)_{r=a} = -\frac{u_a}{a \ln (b/a)}$$

and

$$\tau_a = \mu\left(\frac{\partial u}{\partial r}\right)_{r=a} = -\frac{\mu u_a}{a \ln (b/a)} = -\frac{P}{2\pi a l},$$

giving Eq. (12-57).

if one substitutes again for $u_a = dz/dt$ and for $\tau_a = W/2\pi az$, *this penetrometer test should give the result that*

$$\left(\frac{z}{a}\right)^{n+1} = \frac{(n+1)v_1 t}{n-1}\left(\frac{W}{2\pi a^2 \tau_1}\right)^n \cdot \left[1 - \left(\frac{a}{b}\right)^{n-1}\right] \qquad (12\text{-}62)$$

or that the penetration depth z under a constant weight W should increase as the $1/(n+1)$th power of the time t and at equal times as the $n/(n+1)$th power of the loads W.†

The schemes of viscosity tests given above may similarly be based on other (than the linear) speed laws after a slightly more elaborate analysis.

12-8. Torsion of Round Bar, Assuming Hyperbolic Sine Speed Law.

The deformation laws of solids at elevated temperatures can be investigated by making torsion or bending tests on slender bars at various rates of twisting or bending.   As a last example, let us consider *the torsion of a round bar* at various rates of twisting, after *assuming the hyperbolic sine law* as valid for the material.   Denote the angle of twist by θ for two cross sections a unit of length apart and by $\dot\theta$ the rate of twisting.   The rate of shear v in the distance r from the axis is then

$$v = r\dot\theta = \frac{v_a r}{a} = v_1 \sinh\frac{\tau}{\tau_1}, \qquad (12\text{-}63)$$

and the shearing stress τ is equal to

$$\tau = \tau_1 \ln\left(\frac{v}{v_1} + \sqrt{1 + \frac{v^2}{v_1^2}}\right), \qquad (12\text{-}64)$$

defining the distribution of stress τ in a round bar:

$$\tau = \tau_1 \ln\left[\frac{v_a r}{v_1 a} + \sqrt{1 + \left(\frac{v_a r}{v_1 a}\right)^2}\right]. \qquad (12\text{-}65)$$

Since the rates of shear v in a section are proportional to r, the function $\tau = f(r)$ is represented by the inverse hyperbolic sine

$$\tau = \tau_1 \sinh^{-1}(v_a r/v_1 a).$$

The torque $M = 2\pi\int_0^a \tau r\,dr$, which stays constant at a given rate of twisting or for a constant maximum rate of shear at $r = a$, $v = v_a = a\dot\theta = $ const, when the abbreviations

$$\xi = \frac{\tau_a}{\tau_1}, \qquad \eta = \frac{v_a}{v_1} = \sinh\xi \qquad (12\text{-}66)$$

† Equivalent expressions were given by C. MACK, Rheology of Bituminous Mixtures Relative to the Properties of Asphalts, Proc. Assoc. Asphalt Paving Technologists, vol. 13, pp. 194–255, 1942.   When the exponent $n = 1$, Eq. (12-62) appears in the form 0/0, but after computing the true value, one finds that $z = $ const $\cdot \sqrt{t}$ in agreement with Eq. (12-58).

are used, is expressed either in terms of ξ by

$$M = \frac{2\pi\tau_1 a^3}{9 \sinh^3 \xi} [3\xi \sinh^3 \xi - \cosh^3 \xi + 3 \cosh \xi - 2] \qquad (12\text{-}67)$$

or in terms of η by

$$M = \frac{2\pi\tau_1 a^3}{9} \left[3 \ln (\eta + \sqrt{1 + \eta^2}) + \frac{(2 - \eta^2)\sqrt{1 + \eta^2}}{\eta^3} - 2 \right].$$
$$(12\text{-}68)$$

When ξ and η are both small and $\eta = \xi$, we obtain the torque equal to

$$M = (\tfrac{1}{2})\pi\tau_1 a^3 \xi = (\tfrac{1}{2})\pi\tau_a a^3 \qquad (12\text{-}69)$$

in *a viscous rod*, the material of which deforms according to *the linear law* $\tau = \mu v$, $\mu = \tau_1/v_1 = \tau_a/v_a = $ const, and when ξ and η both have large values, it is equal to

$$M = (\tfrac{2}{3})\pi\tau_a a^3 \qquad (12\text{-}70)$$

because the shearing stress $\tau = f(r)$ approaches more and more the distribution that it would have *in an ideally plastic substance in torsion*, namely, $\tau = \tau_a = $ const (independent of r).   *The deformation law of Eq. (12-63) thus bridges the interval between these two simple cases of torsion in which either the shearing stress is equal to $\tau = \tau_a r/a$ or equal to $\tau = \tau_a = $ const.*

CHAPTER 13

THERMAL STRAIN AND STRESS

13-1. Theory of Thermal Strain and Stress. Machine parts stressed under external loads may be further exposed to thermal stresses if they operate under elevated temperatures. With the increase of the working temperatures in steam plants, in steam and gas turbines, in the containers of the chemical industry, and in petroleum stills, it has become necessary to evaluate the thermal stresses induced in the walls of spindles, casings, the steel tubes conducting hot fluids, etc. Their determination may require different methods of attack, depending on whether the strains due to thermal expansion of the material remain purely elastic and of reversible nature or become permanent in the stressed bodies or parts thereof. Being aware that the specific volume of metals may change because of (1) elastic strain, (2) thermal expansion, (3) sudden allotropic transformation in the crystal structure, or (4) gradual permanent changes in the structure through plastic cold or hot work and that the mechanical constants of solids—the moduli of elasticity, the coefficient of thermal expansion, of viscosity, and the yield stress—vary with temperature in a manner by no means simple, one will realize that the evaluation of thermal stresses if the temperature varies widely in a body raises involved questions,[1] particularly if the temperature field is of a transient nature, i.e., may change very rapidly with time, in good heat conductors, as in metals. If the thermal stresses last for a short time and have comparatively high values, one is led to cases of thermal shocks, when parts of the surface of a body are spontaneously exposed to intense heating for a short while in a comparatively thin layer. Whereas the thermal stresses in such cases might be evaluated also in plastic substances, having a yield stress

[1] With reference to Sec. 1-7, it may be instructive to recall the general trend of variation of modulus of elasticity E, of coefficient of linear, thermal expansion α, and of the product $E\alpha$ with the homologous temperature (ratio of absolute temperature T to melting temperature T_m), as illustrated for aluminum and for iron in Figs. 13-1 and 13-2, and to recall the variation of the stress-strain curve covering the transition from the elastic to the plastic range of strains and the variation of the yield stress with temperature in the example for a nickel steel reproduced in Figs. 13-3 and 13-4.

378

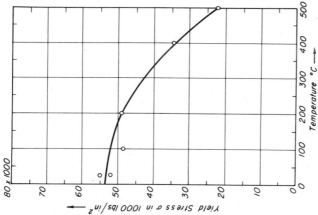

Fig. 13-4. Yield stress of nickel steel at various temperatures. (*After P. G. McVetty.*)

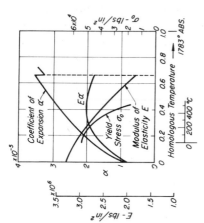

Fig. 13-2. Variation of E, α, Eα, and σ₀ with temperature for iron.

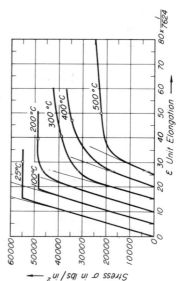

Fig. 13-3. Stress-strain diagrams of nickel steel at various temperatures. (*After P. G. McVetty.*)

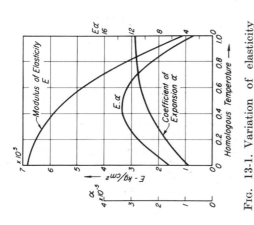

Fig. 13-1. Variation of elasticity modulus E and expansion coefficient α of aluminum with temperature.

decreasing with temperature, on the other hand, in a hot body loaded continuously over a long period of time, the viscous parts of the strains become important and permanent distortion due to creep or relaxation of stress has to be considered. The effects of a discontinuous change of specific volume associated with an allotropic transformation in the crystal structure when the temperature passes through a characteristic range (frequently causing inherent residual stresses upon rapid cooling or quenching) are difficult to predict.[1]

Excluding the phenomena associated with permanent strain or permanent volume changes, a general theory of thermal strain and stress in isotropic, elastic substances if the temperatures vary over a wider range must be more involved than the linear theory of purely elastic strains, because it would have to be based on a general equation of state, assuming that the thermal unit dilatation of volume and the moduli of elasticity and rigidity are nonlinear functions of the temperature θ (and of the mean stress σ). A workable theory has been evolved by confining it to a comparatively narrow range of variation of temperature, by postulating mean constant values of the expansion coefficient and the moduli of elasticity independent of θ. Denoting by α the coefficient of linear, thermal expansion, supposing that the thermal volume expansion is small, of the order of the elastic dilatation of volume, and that the temperature is expressed by $\theta = f(x,y,z,t)$ (t is the time), measuring it for convenience above an ambient value

---

[1] The most important example is the transformation of the α into the γ iron in steel around 900°C, causing a volume change the magnitude of which is dependent also on the speed with which the temperature is changed. Commercial Armco iron, when heated up to and passing through 900°C, discloses a sudden decrease of specific volume of 0.004 and, when cooled and passing through 905°C, an increase of 0.006, or nearly ½ per cent. Sudden changes in volume of this order of magnitude during the cooling must be considered as great, even when they are compared with the shrinkage of volume due to the total thermal contraction of the steel when the temperature drops from 900°C to room temperature (20°C), which amounts to 0.0375, i.e., the γ–α volume increase is one-sixth of the latter. The average change in volume due to thermal expansion per degree centigrade is about 0.0375 : 880 = 0.000043 or only ¹⁄₁₄₀ of the discontinuous volume change due to the γ–α transformation. Since this sudden increase of volume on cooling (quenching) passes as a wave through the body in which the temperature decreases rapidly toward its cooled surface, one may visualize the complex effects caused in the thermal stresses that will accrue in a body during the cooling cycle and finally in the residual stresses, in view also of the fact that the purely elastic volume change in the outer parts of a compact body (a sphere) which have cooled down to room temperature is of the order of 0.001 [a stress $\sigma = 75{,}000$ lb/in.² in uniaxial tension in steel having a modulus of elasticity $E = 3.10^7$ lb/in.² and Poisson's ratio $\nu = 0.3$ would produce a dilatation of volume $(1 - 2\nu)\sigma/E$ just equal to 0.001], whereas the volume in the innermost still hot parts of the body, because of the γ–α transformation, increases by 0.006, thus putting the cold parts under high tensile stresses.

taken equal to zero, using rectangular coordinates x, y, z, the thermal increase in volume being proportional to the increase in temperature $3\alpha\theta$, if an element of material is subjected simultaneously to a state of stress σ_x, σ_y, σ_z, τ_{yz}, $\ldots$, the strains are expressed by

$$\varepsilon_x = \frac{\partial \xi}{\partial x} = \frac{1}{E}(\sigma_x - \nu\sigma_y - \nu\sigma_z) + \alpha\theta, \ldots,$$

$$\gamma_{yz} = \frac{\partial \zeta}{\partial y} + \frac{\partial \eta}{\partial z} = \frac{\tau_{yz}}{G}, \ldots,$$

(13-1)

and the dilatation of volume by

$$\varepsilon = \varepsilon_x + \varepsilon_y + \varepsilon_z = \frac{1 - 2\nu}{E}(\sigma_x + \sigma_y + \sigma_z) + 3\alpha\theta,$$

(13-2)

ξ, η, ζ denoting the components of displacement. Solving for the stresses,

$$\sigma_x, \sigma_y, \sigma_z = 2G\left[\frac{\partial \xi}{\partial x}, \frac{\partial \eta}{\partial y}, \frac{\partial \zeta}{\partial z} + \frac{\nu\varepsilon - (1 + \nu)\alpha\theta}{1 - 2\nu}\right],$$

$$\tau_{yz} = G\left(\frac{\partial \zeta}{\partial y} + \frac{\partial \eta}{\partial z}\right), \ldots.$$

(13-3)

if these are substituted in the conditions of equilibrium [Eqs. (4-55)] of the components of stress, one obtains three differential equations for the components of displacement ξ, η, ζ of the form, supposing static equilibrium,

$$(1 - 2\nu)\,\Delta\xi + \frac{\partial \varepsilon}{\partial x} = 2(1 + \nu)\alpha\frac{\partial \theta}{\partial x}.$$

$$(1 - 2\nu)\,\Delta\eta + \frac{\partial \varepsilon}{\partial y} = 2(1 + \nu)\alpha\frac{\partial \theta}{\partial y},$$

(13-4)

$$(1 - 2\nu)\,\Delta\zeta + \frac{\partial \varepsilon}{\partial z} = 2(1 + \nu)\alpha\frac{\partial \theta}{\partial z},$$

whereas the dilatation of volume ε must satisfy the equation

$$\Delta\varepsilon = \frac{(1 + \nu)\alpha}{1 - \nu} \cdot \Delta\theta.$$

(13-5)

By applying once more the operator $\Delta = \partial^2/\partial x^2 + \partial^2/\partial y^2 + \partial^2/z^2$ on Eqs. (13-4), one may eliminate ε from them, obtaining

$$\Delta\Delta(\xi,\eta,\zeta) = \frac{\alpha}{1 - \nu}\left(\frac{\partial \Delta\theta}{\partial x}, \frac{\partial \Delta\theta}{\partial y}, \frac{\partial \Delta\theta}{\partial z}\right).$$

(13-6)

A second form of Eqs. (13-4) corresponding to Eqs. (4-57) is

$$\Delta\xi + \frac{3}{E}\frac{\partial\sigma}{\partial x} = -\alpha\frac{\partial\theta}{\partial x},$$

$$\Delta\eta + \frac{3}{E}\frac{\partial\sigma}{\partial y} = -\alpha\frac{\partial\theta}{\partial y}, \qquad (13\text{-}7)$$

$$\Delta\zeta + \frac{3}{E}\frac{\partial\sigma}{\partial z} = -\alpha\frac{\partial\theta}{\partial z},$$

whereas the mean normal stress $\sigma = (\frac{1}{3})(\sigma_x + \sigma_y + \sigma_z)$ satisfies the equation

$$\Delta\sigma = -\frac{2E\alpha}{3(1-\nu)}\Delta\theta. \qquad (13\text{-}8)$$

Professor ERNST MELAN[1] in Vienna has recently published an elegant solution of the preceding differential equations in terms of what he calls *a thermal displacement potential*, by expressing the displacement components as the derivatives of a function $\psi(x,y,z)$:

$$\xi = \frac{\partial\psi}{\partial x}, \qquad \eta = \frac{\partial\psi}{\partial y}, \qquad \zeta = \frac{\partial\psi}{\partial z}, \qquad (13\text{-}9)$$

giving for the dilatation of volume

$$\varepsilon = \frac{\partial\xi}{\partial x} + \frac{\partial\eta}{\partial y} + \frac{\partial\zeta}{\partial z} = \Delta\psi. \qquad (13\text{-}10)$$

After substituting these expressions in the three differential equations (13-4) one obtains

$$\Delta\left(\frac{\partial\psi}{\partial x}, \frac{\partial\psi}{\partial y}, \frac{\partial\psi}{\partial z}\right) = \frac{(1+\nu)\alpha}{1-\nu}\left(\frac{\partial\theta}{\partial x}, \frac{\partial\theta}{\partial y}, \frac{\partial\theta}{\partial z}\right),$$

respectively, and one sees that the displacement potential ψ must satisfy the equation

$$\Delta\psi = \frac{(1+\nu)\alpha}{1-\nu}\cdot\theta, \qquad (13\text{-}11)$$

where the integration constant necessarily vanishes. Once a solution of this equation is established, Eqs. (13-1) and (13-3) for the components of stress and strain take the symmetric form

$$\sigma_x = 2G\left(\frac{\partial^2\psi}{\partial x^2} - \Delta\psi\right), \qquad \tau_{yz} = 2G\frac{\partial^2\psi}{\partial y\,\partial z},$$

$$\sigma_y = 2G\left(\frac{\partial^2\psi}{\partial y^2} - \Delta\psi\right), \qquad \tau_{zx} = 2G\frac{\partial^2\psi}{\partial z\,\partial x}, \qquad (13\text{-}12)$$

$$\sigma_z = 2G\left(\frac{\partial^2\psi}{\partial z^2} - \Delta\psi\right). \qquad \tau_{xy} = 2G\frac{\partial^2\psi}{\partial x\,\partial y},$$

[1] Wärmespannungen in Scheiben, Österr. Ing. Arch., vol. 4. no. 2, p. 153, 1950; also Österr. Akad. Wiss. Math.-naturw. Kl., Anz., no. 14, p. 285, 1949.

and the strains,

$$\varepsilon_x = \frac{\partial^2 \psi}{\partial x^2}, \qquad \varepsilon_y = \frac{\partial^2 \psi}{\partial y^2}, \qquad \varepsilon_z = \frac{\partial^2 \psi}{\partial z^2},$$

$$\gamma_{yz} = 2\frac{\partial^2 \psi}{\partial y\,\partial z}, \qquad \gamma_{zx} = 2\frac{\partial^2 \psi}{\partial z\,\partial x}, \qquad \gamma_{xy} = 2\frac{\partial^2 \psi}{\partial x\,\partial y}. \qquad (13\text{-}13)$$

In an incompressible, elastic solid $(\nu = \frac{1}{2})$ the dilatation of volume is purely thermal:

$$\varepsilon = 3\alpha\theta; \qquad (13\text{-}14)$$

the stresses are

$$\sigma_x = \sigma + 2G(\varepsilon_x - \alpha\theta), \ldots, \qquad \tau_{yz} = G\gamma_{yz}, \ldots; \qquad (13\text{-}15)$$

and the components of displacement are obtained from the differential equations

$$\Delta\xi + \frac{1}{G}\frac{\partial\sigma}{\partial x} = -\alpha\frac{\partial\theta}{\partial x},$$

$$\Delta\eta + \frac{1}{G}\frac{\partial\sigma}{\partial y} = -\alpha\frac{\partial\theta}{\partial y}, \qquad (13\text{-}16)$$

$$\Delta\zeta + \frac{1}{G}\frac{\partial\sigma}{\partial z} = -\alpha\frac{\partial\theta}{\partial z},$$

whereas

$$\Delta\sigma = -4G\alpha\,\Delta\theta.$$

The temperature in these equations is considered an a priori known function $\theta = f(x,y,z)$. In massive bodies in which the temperatures are to be raised or lowered by gradual heating or cooling through their surface or in metallic parts of machines representing good conductors of heat in which the temperatures may vary rapidly with time, however, the first step in the evaluation of thermal stresses under these transient states of heat flow may require the determination of that unknown, most unfavorable, instantaneous distribution of temperature $\theta = f(x,y,z,t)$ under which *the maximum values of the thermal stresses will occur.*[1] In other words, this demands expression of the space and time-dependent distribution of the temperature θ analytically by attempting to solve the partial differential equation of the conduction of heat (*Fourier's equation*) first,

$$\frac{\partial\theta}{\partial t} = \frac{k}{c_0\gamma_0}\cdot\Delta\theta, \qquad (13\text{-}17)$$

under the prescribed boundary conditions for the heat flow (k denotes the thermal conductivity; c_0 and γ_0, the specific heat and weight of material). Supposing that the hot body is surrounded by a medium of

[1] An example in engineering practice is encountered in the massive, solid or hollow cylinders of the rotors of large steam turbines during their heating-up period preceding their running under power, when they have to be warmed up gradually in order to prevent undesirable thermal distortions and also too high thermal stresses in them (see Sec. 13-4B below).

more or less uniform temperature and that the latter is measured from this ambient value, one assumes usually as a thermal boundary condition along the surface of the body that the amount of heat lost through heat transfer in a unit area of the surface per unit of time $-k\ \partial\theta/\partial n$ is proportional to the drop of temperature θ between the emitting body and the surrounding medium, or that

$$-k\frac{\partial\theta}{\partial n} = \lambda\theta$$

in the surface, n denoting the direction of the outward normal to it and λ the constant of emissivity or heat transfer.[1]

Under a *steady*, time-independent distribution of the temperature in a body, since

$$\Delta\theta = \frac{\partial^2\theta}{\partial x^2} + \frac{\partial^2\theta}{\partial y^2} + \frac{\partial^2\theta}{\partial z^2} = 0,$$

the dilatation of volume ε and the mean stress $\sigma = (\frac{1}{3})(\sigma_x + \sigma_y + \sigma_z)$ in an elastic substance again satisfy LAPLACE's equation,

$$\Delta\varepsilon = 0, \qquad \Delta\sigma = 0,$$

as in a body under uniform temperature.[2]

If
$$\sigma_z = \nu(\sigma_x + \sigma_y) - E\alpha\theta, \tag{13-18}$$

the stress-strain relations simplify to their two-dimensional form,

$$\varepsilon_x = \frac{1}{2G}\left[(1-\nu)\sigma_x - \nu\sigma_y\right] + (1+\nu)\alpha\theta,$$

$$\varepsilon_y = \frac{1}{2G}\left[(1-\nu)\sigma_y - \nu\sigma_x\right] + (1+\nu)\alpha\theta, \tag{13-19}$$

$$\gamma_{xy} = \frac{\tau_{xy}}{G},$$

[1] On problems of heat conduction in solids see H. GRÖBER, "Grundgesetze der Wärmeleitung und des Wärmeüberganges," Springer-Verlag, Berlin, 1921; M. BOSCH, "Die Wärmeübertragung," 2d ed., Springer-Verlag, Berlin, 1927; H. S. CARLSLAW, "Introduction to the Mathematical Theory of the Conduction of Heat in Solids," Macmillan & Co., Ltd., London, 1921; and books on partial differential equations.

[2] The problems of thermal stresses caused by *steady*, time-independent distributions of temperature have been treated in the book by ERNST MELAN and HEINZ PARKUS, "Wärmespannungen infolge stationärer Temperaturfelder," 114 pp., Springer-Verlag, Vienna, 1953, containing a broad survey of theory based on the classical postulates of linear stress-strain relations with invariable values of the elastic and thermal material constants and describing the thermal stresses in two- and three-dimensional cases, in disks, plates, bodies of revolution, etc. A continuation of this book (HEINZ PARKUS, "Instationäre Wärmespannungen," 165 pp., Springer-Verlag, Vienna, 1959, deals with thermal stresses in *transient* temperature fields, including a limited survey of thermal stresses in viscoelastic and plastoelastic substances.

or, using the mean stress $\sigma = (\frac{1}{3})(\sigma_x + \sigma_y + \sigma_z)$, to

$$\sigma = \frac{E(\varepsilon - 3\alpha\theta)}{3(1 - 2\nu)},$$

$$\varepsilon_x = \frac{1}{E}[(1 + \nu)\sigma_x - 3\nu\sigma] + \alpha\theta,$$

$$\varepsilon_y = \frac{1}{E}[(1 + \nu)\sigma_y - 3\nu\sigma] + \alpha\theta, \qquad (13\text{-}20)$$

$$\varepsilon = \varepsilon_x + \varepsilon_y = \frac{3(1 - 2\nu)\sigma}{E} + 3\alpha\theta,$$

giving for the stresses

$$\sigma_x = 2G(\varepsilon_x - \alpha\theta) + \frac{3\nu\sigma}{1 + \nu} = 2G\varepsilon_x + \sigma_z,$$

$$\sigma_y = 2G(\varepsilon_y - \alpha\theta) + \frac{3\nu\sigma}{1 + \nu} = 2G\varepsilon_y + \sigma_z, \qquad (13\text{-}21)$$

$$\sigma_z = -2G\alpha\theta + \frac{3\nu\sigma}{1 + \nu} = \frac{2G}{1 - 2\nu}[\nu\varepsilon - (1 + \nu)\alpha\theta].$$

The displacements ξ and η satisfy the equations

$$(1 - 2\nu)\,\Delta\xi + \frac{\partial\varepsilon}{\partial x} = 2(1 + \nu)\alpha\,\frac{\partial\theta}{\partial x},$$

$$(1 - 2\nu)\,\Delta\eta + \frac{\partial\varepsilon}{\partial y} = 2(1 + \nu)\alpha\,\frac{\partial\theta}{\partial y}, \qquad (13\text{-}22)$$

$$\Delta\varepsilon = \frac{1 + \nu}{1 - \nu}\cdot\alpha\,\Delta\theta,$$

or

$$\Delta\xi + \frac{3}{E}\frac{\partial\sigma}{\partial x} = -\alpha\,\frac{\partial\theta}{\partial x},$$

$$\Delta\eta + \frac{3}{E}\frac{\partial\sigma}{\partial y} = -\alpha\,\frac{\partial\theta}{\partial y}, \qquad (13\text{-}23)$$

$$\Delta\sigma = -\frac{2E\alpha}{3(1 - \nu)}\,\Delta\theta,$$

where

$$\Delta = \frac{\partial^2}{\partial x^2} + \frac{\partial^2}{\partial y^2}.$$

The stresses σ_x, σ_y, τ_{xy} may also be computed using a stress function $F(x,y)$ satisfying, when thermal strains are present, the equation

$$\Delta\Delta F = -\frac{E\alpha\,\Delta\theta}{1 - \nu}, \qquad (13\text{-}24)$$

together with the boundary conditions to be prescribed for $F(x,y)$.

If the temperature $\theta = f(x,y)$ is *steady*, $\Delta\theta = 0$, under a state of plane strain, according to Eqs. (13-11) and (13-24), both the stress function $F(x,y)$ and Melan's function $\psi(x,y)$ are biharmonic:

$$\Delta\Delta F = 0, \quad \Delta\Delta\psi = 0; \tag{13-25}$$

since the stresses are expressed by

$$\sigma_x = \frac{\partial^2 F}{\partial y^2} = -2G\frac{\partial^2 \psi}{\partial y^2},$$

$$\sigma_y = \frac{\partial^2 F}{\partial x^2} = -2G\frac{\partial^2 \psi}{\partial x^2},$$

$$\sigma_z = \nu\,\Delta F - E\alpha\theta = -2G\,\Delta\psi, \tag{13-26}$$

$$\tau_{xy} = -\frac{\partial^2 F}{\partial x\,\partial y} = 2G\frac{\partial^2 \psi}{\partial x\,\partial y}$$

for plane strain under steady temperatures,

$$\Delta F = -\frac{E\alpha\theta}{1-\nu}, \qquad F = -2G\psi. \tag{13-27}$$

13-2. Stress-free States of Thermal Plane Strain.

An elastic body in which thermal strains are present owing to nonuniform temperatures may remain unstressed, as, for example, a flat strip that curls up when one side is exposed to radiating heat. A body under a state of plane strain $\varepsilon_z = 0$ may remain entirely stress-free in the planes parallel to the x,y plane ($\sigma_x = \sigma_y = \tau_{xy} = 0$), while constrained not to expand in the direction of the z axis, requiring, according to Eq. (13-18), the normal stress $\sigma_z = -E\alpha\theta$ under the thermal strains

$$\varepsilon_x = \varepsilon_y = (1+\nu)\alpha\theta,$$

$$\gamma_{xy} = \frac{\partial\xi}{\partial y} + \frac{\partial\eta}{\partial x} = 0. \tag{13-28}$$

From their condition of compatibility,

$$\frac{\partial^2\varepsilon_x}{\partial y^2} + \frac{\partial^2\varepsilon_y}{\partial x^2} = \frac{\partial^2\gamma_{xy}}{\partial x\,\partial y} = 0, \tag{13-29}$$

one sees that one necessary condition for such a stress-free state is that the temperature θ be in a steady state,

$$\Delta\theta = 0, \tag{13-30}$$

and furthermore, from Eqs. (13-19), that the displacements ξ and η satisfy the equations

$$\frac{\partial\xi}{\partial x} = \frac{\partial\eta}{\partial y} = (1+\nu)\alpha\theta, \qquad \frac{\partial\xi}{\partial y} = -\frac{\partial\eta}{\partial x} \tag{13-31}$$

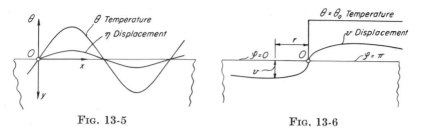

FIG. 13-5   FIG. 13-6

or be *a pair of conjugate plane harmonic functions,* satisfying[1]

$$\Delta\xi = 0, \qquad \Delta\eta = 0. \tag{13-32}$$

This may be illustrated by examples.

EXAMPLE 1. Suppose that in a semi-infinite body a steady field of temperatures θ for $y > 0$ prevails:

$$\theta = \theta_0 e^{-\beta y}\sin\beta x. \tag{13-33}$$

The corresponding thermal displacements

$$\xi = -(1 + \nu)\alpha\theta_0\,\frac{1}{\beta}\,e^{-\beta y}\cos\beta x,$$

$$\eta = -(1 + \nu)\alpha\theta_0\,\frac{1}{\beta}\,e^{-\beta y}\sin\beta x \tag{13-34}$$

will not create any stress (except σ_z), and we may note that the body surface $y = 0$ under the heated portions bulges upward and under the cooled ones is depressed downward (Fig. 13-5).

EXAMPLE 2. Similarly, if a steady stream of heat passes through a semi-infinite body whose right half $\varphi = \pi$ is kept at a uniform temperature $\theta = \theta_0 = $ const, while in its left half $\varphi = 0$, $\theta = 0$ (Fig. 13-6), the temperature will be

$$\theta = \frac{\theta_0\varphi}{\pi}\,; \tag{13-35}$$

the isotherms $\theta = $ const in this temperature field are represented by the pencil of rays emanating from the origin O.

Using polar coordinates r, φ and denoting the displacements in radial and tangential directions by u and v, we have

$$\varepsilon_r = \varepsilon_t = (1 + \nu)\alpha\theta, \qquad \gamma_{rt} = 0,$$

or

$$\frac{\partial u}{\partial r} = \frac{u}{r} + \frac{\partial v}{r\,\partial\varphi} = \frac{(1 + \nu)\alpha\theta_0\varphi}{\pi},$$

$$\frac{\partial u}{r\,\partial\varphi} + \frac{\partial v}{\partial r} - \frac{v}{r} = 0. \tag{13-36}$$

[1] Cf. E. MELAN, Temperaturverteilungen ohne Wärmspannungen, Österr. Ing. Arch., vol. 4, no. 1, 1951. Apart from the conditions of Eqs. (13-30) and (13-31), he states that, in the general, three-dimensional case of thermal strains, the stresses will vanish in a free body which can adjust its shape without external constraints when the temperature is expressible by a function of the form

$$\theta(x,y,z) = \sum a_{ikl}x^iy^kz^l, \qquad (i,k,l = 0,1,2,\ldots),$$

the a_{ikl} representing arbitrary constants.

Again u and v satisfy these Cauchy-Riemann equations, and we find by partial integration

$$u = \frac{(1 + \nu)\alpha\theta_0}{\pi} \cdot r\varphi,$$

$$v = \frac{(1 + \nu)\alpha\theta_0}{\pi} \cdot r \ln \frac{a}{r},$$ (13-37)

where we have omitted the terms of rigid-body motion and a may denote a fairly large constant length.   The surface of the body bulges upward on the heated side $\varphi = \pi, 0 < r < a$, and is depressed on the cold side $\varphi = 0, 0 < r < a$, no stresses accompanying this distortion.

EXAMPLE 3.   If the surface temperature is held at the value $\theta = -\theta_0 = \text{const}$ on the left side ($\varphi = 0$) and $\theta = \theta_0 = \text{const}$ on the right side ($\varphi = \pi$) of the body, the transversal displacements v in the surface are twice as great as in Example 2.

EXAMPLE 4.   By superposing two temperature fields of the type

$$\theta_1 = \frac{\theta_0\varphi_1}{\pi}, \qquad \theta_2 = -\frac{\theta_0\varphi_2}{\pi}$$

with their origins O_1 and O_2 displaced, from which the polar systems r_1, φ_1 and r_2, φ_2 originate (Fig. 13-7), one obtains the temperature distribution for steady heat flow:

$$\theta = \frac{\theta_0(\varphi_1 - \varphi_2)}{\pi}$$ (13-38)

in which a parallel strip of the width $O_1O_2 = 2c$ in the surface of a semi-infinite body is held at the value $\theta = \theta_0 = \text{const}$, while θ vanishes on both sides of the strip.   The isotherms and flow lines of heat for this temperature field consist of the familiar system of orthogonal bicentric circles [we found the system of the family of circles emanating from the origins O_1 and O_2 as the isochromatics $\tau_{\max} = \text{const}$ under a concentrated pressure $p = \text{const}$ in a state of plane strain (see Sec. 6-2, Figs. 6-6 and 6-8)].

The surface of the body under the corresponding thermal strains warps according to (see Fig. 13-7)

$$v = \frac{(1 + \nu)\alpha\theta_0}{2\pi}[(x + c) \ln (x + c)^2$$
$$- (x - c) \ln (x - c)^2]$$ (13-39)

and bulges up in a flat ridge having sharply rounded edges under the heated strip.

In Sec. 6-2, Eq. (6-36), we found a similar function representing the transversal displacement v of the surface of a semi-infinite body under a concentrated pressure $p = \text{const}$, distributed over a parallel strip of the width $2c$, namely,

$$v = \frac{(1 - \nu)p}{\pi G}[(x - c) \ln (x - c)^2$$
$$- (x + c) \ln (x + c)^2],$$ (13-40)

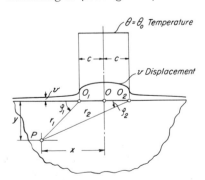

FIG. 13-7. Bulging of a locally heated surface.

causing a depression under the load (Fig. 6-9), and we may note that by choosing the temperature θ_0 equal to

$$\theta_0 = \frac{2(1-\nu)p}{(1+\nu)\alpha G} \qquad (13\text{-}41)$$

the two profiles, one convex, the other concave, of the distorted surface of a semi-infinite body are congruent curves and will fit into each other. If we assign to the temperature θ_0 the negative sign, both profiles of the distorted surface perfectly coincide; thus *we may produce the same distortion by cooling locally to* $-\theta_0 = $ *const a strip of width 2c in the surface of a semi-infinite body as is produced by a concentrated pressure p = const, while the region under the load is highly stressed*.[1]

13-3. Thermal Stresses in Cylinders.

Assuming that the temperature θ is a function of the radial distance r of a point from the axis in a long cylinder, permitted to expand freely in the axial direction under a constant axial strain $\varepsilon_z = \varepsilon_0 = $ const, a state of plane strain prevails in which, the axial, normal stress being equal to

$$\sigma_z = E\varepsilon_0 + \nu(\sigma_r + \sigma_t) - E\alpha\theta, \qquad (13\text{-}42)$$

the normal strains ε_r and ε_t in the radial and tangential directions will be

$$\varepsilon_r = \frac{d\rho}{dr} = \frac{1+\nu}{E}\left[(1-\nu)\sigma_r - \nu\sigma_t\right] - \nu\varepsilon_0 + (1+\nu)\alpha\theta,$$

$$\varepsilon_t = \frac{\rho}{r} = \frac{1+\nu}{E}\left[(1-\nu)\sigma_t - \nu\sigma_r\right] - \nu\varepsilon_0 + (1+\nu)\alpha\theta, \qquad (13\text{-}43)$$

which must satisfy the compatibility condition

$$\frac{d(r\varepsilon_t)}{dr} - \varepsilon_r = 0, \qquad (13\text{-}43a)$$

where ρ denotes the radial displacement of a point and the conditions of compatibility of the strains and of equilibrium of the stresses require that

$$\frac{d}{dr}(r\sigma_t) - \sigma_r = -\frac{E\alpha r}{1-\nu}\cdot\frac{d\theta}{dr}, \qquad (13\text{-}44)$$

$$\frac{d}{dr}(r\sigma_r) - \sigma_t = 0. \qquad (13\text{-}45)$$

---

[1] We note the close analogy of the preceding states of plane, thermal distortion with the states caused by concentrated pressures, for similar distributions of the boundary values of the temperature θ and of the normal stresses σ_y in the surface of a semi-infinite body, incidentally remarking that in these examples of stress-free cases of pure thermal strains just considered the elasticity moduli of the substance do not appear in the systems of the displacement components.

By adding and by subtracting these two equations and integrating, the normal stresses are found equal to

$$\sigma_r = c_1 - \frac{c_2}{r^2} - \frac{E\alpha}{1-\nu} \cdot \frac{1}{r^2} \int \theta r \, dr,$$

$$\sigma_t = c_1 + \frac{c_2}{r^2} - \frac{E\alpha}{1-\nu} \left(\theta - \frac{1}{r^2} \int \theta r \, dr \right), \qquad (13\text{-}46)$$

$$\sigma_z = 2\nu c_1 + E\varepsilon_0 - \frac{E\alpha\theta}{1-\nu}.$$

To these we may add the condition that the cylinder is allowed to expand or to contract freely in the axial direction, requiring that no axial resultant force shall act or that the integral taken over the cross section of the cylinder,

$$\int \sigma_z r \, dr = 0, \qquad (13\text{-}47)$$

shall vanish.[1]

A. IN A SOLID CYLINDER, of radius a, the boundary conditions $r = 0$, $\sigma_r = \sigma_t$; $r = a$, $\sigma_r = 0$ and Eq. (13-47) are satisfied with

$$c_1 = \frac{E\alpha\theta_m}{2(1-\nu)}, \qquad c_2 = 0, \qquad \varepsilon_0 = \frac{2(1-\nu)c_1}{E} = \alpha\theta_m,$$

denoting the mean temperature in the cylinder by

$$\theta_m = \frac{2}{a^2} \int_0^a \theta r \, dr. \qquad (13\text{-}48)$$

The thermal stresses in it are expressed by

$$\sigma_r = \frac{E\alpha}{2(1-\nu)} \left[\theta_m - \frac{2}{r^2} \int_0^r \theta r \, dr \right],$$

$$\sigma_t = \frac{E\alpha}{2(1-\nu)} \left[\theta_m - 2\theta + \frac{2}{r^2} \int_0^r \theta r \, dr \right], \qquad (13\text{-}49)$$

$$\sigma_z = \frac{E\alpha}{1-\nu} (\theta_m - \theta),$$

[1] Or leaving aside Eq. (13-44), using only Eq. (13-45), one obtains for the radial displacement ρ

$$\rho'' + \frac{\rho'}{r} - \frac{\rho}{r^2} = \frac{d}{dr}\left[\frac{d(r\rho)}{r \, dr} \right] = \frac{(1+\nu)\alpha}{1-\nu} \cdot \frac{d\theta}{dr}$$

from which ρ and the stresses may also be evaluated.

which may be written in the symmetrical form

$$\sigma_r = -\frac{E\alpha}{2(1-\nu)}\left[\theta - \theta_m - \left(\theta - \frac{2}{r^2}\int_0^r \theta r\, dr\right)\right],$$

$$\sigma = -\frac{E\alpha}{2(1-\nu)}\left[\theta - \theta_m + \left(\theta - \frac{2}{r^2}\int_0^r \theta r\, dr\right)\right], \qquad (13\text{-}50)$$

$$\sigma_z = -\frac{E\alpha}{1-\nu}(\theta - \theta_m)$$

or, after denoting by the symbols ψ and ψ' two functions of the variable radius r and by σ a constant quantity, defined as follows:

$$\psi = \frac{\theta - \theta_m}{\theta^*}, \qquad \psi' = \frac{1}{\theta^*}\left(\theta - \frac{2}{r^2}\int_0^r \theta r\, dr\right) = \psi - \frac{2}{r^2}\int_0^r \psi r\, dr, \quad (13\text{-}51)$$

$$\sigma = \frac{E\alpha\theta^*}{2(1-\nu)},$$

the thermal stresses in a solid cylinder may be expressed simply in the form

$$\sigma_r = -\sigma(\psi - \psi'),$$

$$\sigma_t = -\sigma(\psi + \psi'), \qquad (13\text{-}52)$$

$$\sigma_z = -2\sigma\psi.$$

The variables ψ and ψ' may be interpreted *as two dimensionless temperatures*, dependent on radius r, ψ being measured above the mean temperature θ_m over the cross section of the cylinder and ψ' being measured above the mean temperature in the circle of variable radius r, both divided by an arbitrarily chosen constant temperature θ^*. The mean value of ψ vanishes:

$$\int^a \psi\, \theta r\, dr = 0. \qquad (13\text{-}53)$$

If the subscripts 0 and a refer to $r = 0$ and $r = a$, we obtain the thermal stresses (noting that, for $r = 0$, $\psi_0' = 0$):

At the center, $r = 0$:

$$\sigma_r = \sigma_t = \frac{\sigma_z}{2} = -\sigma\psi_0 = \frac{E\alpha(\theta_m - \theta_0)}{2(1-\nu)}, \qquad (13\text{-}54)$$

At the surface, $r = a$:

$$\sigma_r = 0, \qquad \sigma_t = \sigma_z = -2\sigma\psi_a = -\frac{E\alpha(\theta_a - \theta_m)}{1-\nu},$$

supplying their maximum values if θ increases or decreases monotonously with r in the second line. The cylinder expands radially in its surface $r = a$ by

$$\rho_a = \alpha a \theta_m \qquad (13\text{-}55)$$

or by the same amount as if it were heated or cooled uniformly to the mean temperature θ_m.

Suppose, for example, that the temperature θ in the cylinder would increase with r proportionally with a power of r or of the ratio $u = r/a$:

$$\theta = \theta_a \left(\frac{r}{a}\right)^n = \theta_a u^n \qquad (n > 1). \qquad (13\text{-}56)$$

The average temperature θ_m is

$$\theta_m = \frac{2}{a^2} \int_0^a \theta r \, dr = \frac{2\theta_a}{n+2}, \qquad (13\text{-}57)$$

and by letting $\theta^* = \theta_a$ we have for

$$\psi = u^n - \frac{2}{n+2}, \qquad \psi' = \frac{nu^n}{n+2}, \qquad \sigma = \frac{\alpha E\theta_a}{2(1-\nu)}, \qquad (13\text{-}58)$$

and the thermal stresses are:

$$\sigma_r = -\sigma(\psi - \psi') = \frac{2\sigma}{n+2}(1 - u^n),$$

$$\sigma_t = -\sigma(\psi + \psi') = \frac{2\sigma}{n+2}[1 - (n+1)u^n], \qquad (13\text{-}59)$$

$$\sigma_z = -2\sigma\psi = \frac{2\sigma}{n+2}[2 - (n+2)u^n].$$

The outer portion, being hotter, is stressed in compression in peripheral and axial directions and the inner portion in tension (Fig. 13-8, assuming $n = 2$).

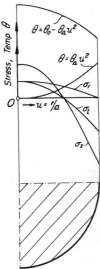

Theorem: Since the thermal stresses in an unrestrained body do not change by adding to or subtracting from the given distribution of the temperatures θ a uniform temperature $\theta_0 = $ const we could as well have assumed in the cylinder

$$\theta = -(\theta_0 - \theta_a u^n)$$

and note, if we reverse the sign and suppose that the cylinder has the temperatures (see the upper curve in Fig. 13-8)

$$\theta = \theta_0 - \theta_a u^n, \qquad (13\text{-}60)$$

i.e., is colder in its outer than in its inner portion, that it is strained by the temperatures of Eq. (13-60) by the same thermal stresses, but of opposite signs, as the cylinder having the temperatures of Eq. (13-56). We shall make use of this theorem for evaluating the maximum values of thermal stresses during the transient states of heat flow developing, for example, in cylinders or spheres which have initially a uniform

Fig. 13-8. Thermal stresses in a cylinder for
$$\theta = \theta_a u^2.$$

temperature and which are brought suddenly into a much warmer or a much colder surrounding medium (see Sec. 13-4).

B. FOR A LONG, HOLLOW CYLINDER,[1] in which the temperature is a function of r, one may similarly show that the thermal stresses may be evaluated from a corresponding set of symmetrical expressions:

$$\sigma_r = -\sigma\left[\psi - \psi' + \frac{r_1^2}{r^2}(\psi' - \psi)\right],$$

$$\sigma_t = -\sigma\left[\psi + \psi' - \frac{r_1^2}{r^2}(\psi' - \psi)\right], \qquad (13\text{-}61)$$

$$\sigma_z = -2\sigma\psi,$$

in which σ denotes the same constant as for the solid cylinder and it is assumed that the hollow cylinder is not constrained to expand or to contract in the axial direction. If r_1 and r_2 denote the inner and outer radii and θ_m the mean temperature, we have

$$\theta_m = \frac{2}{r_2^2 - r_1^2}\int_{r_1}^{r_2}\theta r\,dr,$$

$$\psi = \frac{\theta - \theta_m}{\theta^*}, \qquad \sigma = \frac{E\alpha\theta^*}{2(1 - \nu)}, \qquad (13\text{-}62)$$

$$\psi' = \frac{1}{\theta^*}\left(\theta - \frac{2}{r^2 - r_1^2}\int_{r_1}^{r}\theta r\,dr\right) = \psi - \frac{2}{r^2 - r_1^2}\int_{r_1}^{r}\psi r\,dr,$$

and we may easily show that the values of ψ' on the inner and outer surfaces of the hollow cylinder are equal to[2]

$$r = r_1, \qquad \psi_1' = 0; \qquad r = r_2, \qquad \psi_2' = \psi_2,$$

thus giving the thermal stresses

At $r = r_1$,

$$\sigma_r = 0, \qquad \sigma_t = \sigma_z = -2\sigma\psi_1 = -\frac{E\alpha(\theta_1 - \theta_m)}{1 - \nu},$$

At $r = r_2$,

$$\sigma_r = 0, \qquad \sigma_t = \sigma_z = -2\sigma\psi_2 = -\frac{E\alpha(\theta_2 - \theta_m)}{1 - \nu}. \qquad (13\text{-}63)$$

[1] On thermal stresses in hollow cylinders, see RUDOLF LORENZ, Temperaturspannungen in Hohlzylindern, Z. Ver. deut. Ingr., vol. 51, p. 743, 1907 (for rotationally symmetric distributions of the temperature), and C. H. KENT, Thermal Stresses in Thin-Walled Cylinders, Applied Mechanics Meeting, ASME, June, 1931 (radial temperature gradient constant, but θ may vary with z in the axial direction). For circular disks, see I. MALKIN, J. Franklin Inst., vol. 232, p. 129, 1941.

[2] The integral in the second term of the expression for ψ' in Eqs. (13-62), when the upper limit r approaches the value of the inner radius r_1, may be taken:

$$\int_{r_1}^{r}\psi r\,dr = \psi_1\int_{r_1}^{r}r\,dr = (\tfrac{1}{2})\psi_1(r^2 - r_1^2);$$

hence for $r = r_1$, from Eqs. (13-62), $\psi_1' = 0$, whereas when $r = r_2$ the integral vanishes, since the mean value of ψ taken over the section of the tube equals zero and consequently, for $r = r_2$, $\psi_2' = \psi_2$.

In these last formulas neither of the two radii r_1 and r_2 nor the thickness of the hollow cylinder appears. If we compare two tubes of the same material having inner radii r_1 and r_1' and thicknesses $h = r_2 - r_1$ and $h' = r_2' - r_1'$ and erect the same ordinates of the temperatures θ over their corresponding radii r and r', having the proportions

$$r - r_1 : r' - r_1' = h : h',$$

the thermal stresses are the same at corresponding points.

C. IN A THIN, SOLID, CIRCULAR DISK OR IN A FLAT RING, in which $\theta = f(r)$, the thermal stresses may be computed from the preceding expressions using, however, for the constant stress σ the new value

$$\sigma = \frac{E\alpha\theta^*}{2} \tag{13-64}$$

which corresponds to a vanishing value of the axial stress, $\sigma_z = 0$.

In a solid disk:

$$\text{At } r = 0: \qquad \sigma_r = \sigma_t = -(\tfrac{1}{2})E\alpha(\theta_0 - \theta_m),$$
$$\text{At } r = a: \qquad \sigma_t = -(\tfrac{1}{2})E\alpha(\theta_a - \theta_m), \tag{13-65}$$

and in a flat ring in which $\theta = \theta_1, \theta_2$ for $r = r_1, r_2$:

$$\text{At } r = r_1: \qquad \sigma_t = -E\alpha(\theta_1 - \theta_m),$$
$$\text{At } r = r_2: \qquad \sigma_t = -E\alpha(\theta_2 - \theta_m). \tag{13-66}$$

Consider, for example, a flat ring of inner and outer radii r_1 and r_2 which conducts heat radially outward when the distribution of the temperature in it has become *steady*, the temperature being kept at the value $\theta = \theta_1$ at $r = r_1$ and at the value $\theta_2 = 0$ at $r = r_2$. The flat sides of the ring are supposed to be covered with a perfect heat-insulating material. Then the temperature in the ring is given by

$$\theta = \theta_1 \frac{\ln (r/r_2)}{\ln (r_1/r_2)}, \tag{13-67}$$

and the mean temperature θ_m amounts to

$$\theta_m = \frac{2}{r_2^2 - r_1^2} \int_{r_1}^{r_2} \theta r \, dr = \theta_1 \left[\frac{1}{\ln (r_2/r_1)^2} - \frac{r_1^2}{r_2^2 - r_1^2} \right]. \tag{13-68}$$

Using Eqs. (13-66), the ring will be stressed as follows:

$$\text{At } r = r_1: \qquad \sigma_t = -E\alpha\theta_1 \left[\frac{r_2^2}{r_2^2 - r_1^2} - \frac{1}{\ln (r_2/r_1)^2} \right],$$
$$\text{At } r = r_2: \qquad \sigma_t = -E\alpha\theta_1 \left[\frac{r_1^2}{r_2^2 - r_1^2} - \frac{1}{\ln (r_2/r_1)^2} \right] = E\alpha\theta_m. \tag{13-69}$$

13-4. Transient States of Thermal Stress in Cylinders.

A. RADIAL TRANSIENT HEAT FLOW. Let us consider now the problem of thermal stresses in a long, solid cylinder which had an initially uniform temperature by assuming, as may frequently occur in machines, that the surface $r = a$ of the cylinder is brought in good thermal contact with a much colder or a warmer medium. Realizing that it takes time until the material just below the surface of the cylinder is chilled or is warmed up and that it requires further time until the cold or the heat wave can penetrate into the interior of the cylinder, we may represent the exchange of heat through conduction by a family of temperature curves $\theta = f(r,t)$ plotted over the radius r for times $t = t_1, t_2, \ldots$, as illustrated in Figs. 13-9 and 13-10. Denoting in the first case the initially uniform temperature in the cylinder at time $t = 0$ by $\theta = \theta_c =$ const and assuming the temperature in the medium to be $\theta = 0$, we may contrast this with the second case by taking for the initial temperature in the cylinder $\theta = 0$ and $\theta = \theta_c > 0$ in the medium. From these distributions of $\theta = f(r,t)$ we can construct, for example, the curves representing the temperature θ_0 at the center $r = 0$, θ_a at the surface $r = a$, and θ_m, the mean temperature in the cylinder at various times t, obtaining Fig. 13-11, corresponding to Fig. 13-9 for the gradual cooling of the cylinder. Since the thermal stresses at $r = 0$ and $r = a$ are proportional to $\theta_0 - \theta_m$ and $\theta_a - \theta_m$ [see Eqs. (13-54)], the ordinates representing these differences in Fig. 13-11 illustrate the growth and subsequent decay of the thermal stresses induced at $r = 0$ and $r = a$ in the cylinder with time, and we may read their maximum values occurring at some time t_0 and t_a in Fig. 13-11.

The problems of determining the temperature curves $\theta = f(r,t)$ in a solid cylinder cooled or heated from its surface being the same, the thermal stresses corresponding to Fig. 13-10 are, in their absolute values, the same as those corresponding to Fig. 13-9, and only their signs have to be reversed. Their determination hinges on the solution of the equation of heat conduction in a cylinder for radial heat flow, namely,

$$\frac{\partial \theta}{\partial t} = \frac{k}{c_0 \gamma_0} \left(\frac{\partial \theta}{r \, \partial r} + \frac{\partial^2 \theta}{\partial r^2} \right) \tag{13-70}$$

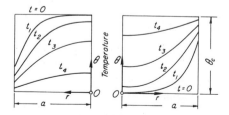

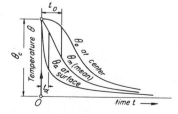

FIG. 13-9. For cooling.   FIG. 13-10. For heating.

FIGS. 13-9 and 13-10. Distributions of temperature θ in solid cylinder.

FIG. 13-11. Decay of temperatures θ_0, θ_m, θ_a in solid cylinder during cooling.

where the constants denote the heat conductivity k, kcal/(m hr °C); the specific heat c_0, kcal/(kg °C), the specific weight γ_0, kg/m^3. Assuming for the initial condition that, at time $t = 0$, $\theta = \theta_c = $ const in the cylinder and that subsequently the heat emitted by the cylinder through its surface $r = a$ is proportional to the drop of temperature θ between it and the surrounding medium or that, for $r = a$,

$$\frac{\partial \theta}{\partial r} + \frac{\lambda \theta}{k} = 0, \tag{13-71}$$

where λ denotes the constant of emissivity in kcal/(m^2 hr °C), the solution of Eq. (13-70) satisfying the preceding thermal boundary condition is well known in the theory of heat conduction and has been expressed by an infinite series

$$\theta = 2\theta_c c \sum_n \frac{e^{-\beta_n t} J_0(\alpha_n r/a)}{(c^2 + \alpha_n^2) J_0(\alpha_n)}, \tag{13-72}$$

where c represents the dimensionless constant of relative emissivity,

$$c = \frac{\lambda a}{k}, \tag{13-73}$$

and the series of also dimensionless parameters $\alpha_n = \alpha_1, \alpha_2, \ldots$ is to be computed from the roots of the transcendental equation [expressing the boundary condition, Eq. (13-71)]

$$\alpha J_1(\alpha) - c J_0(\alpha) = 0 \tag{13-74}$$

and the constants β_n are proportional to $\alpha_n{}^2$:

$$\beta_n = \frac{k\alpha_n^2}{c_0 \gamma_0 a^2}, \tag{13-75}$$

$J_0(\alpha_n r/a)$, $J_1(\alpha_n r/a)$ being the Bessel's functions of zero and of first order.[1] The mean temperature θ_m may easily be evaluated by computing the integral

$$\theta_m = \frac{2}{a^2} \int_0^a \theta r \, dr = 4\theta_c c^2 \sum_n \frac{e^{-\beta_n t}}{\alpha_n^2 (c^2 + \alpha_n^2)}, \tag{13-76}$$

so that the two temperature differences $\theta_0 - \theta_m$ and $\theta_a - \theta_m$ defining the thermal stresses at the center $r = 0$ and surface $r = a$ of a cylinder at any time t are found equal to

$$r = 0, \qquad \theta_0 - \theta_m = 2\theta_c c \sum_n \frac{e^{-\beta_n t}}{c^2 + \alpha_n^2} \left[\frac{1}{J_0(\alpha_n)} - \frac{2c}{\alpha_n^2} \right],$$

$$r = a, \qquad \theta_a - \theta_m = 2\theta_c c \sum_n \frac{e^{-\beta_n t}}{c^2 + \alpha_n^2} \left(1 - \frac{2c}{\alpha_n^2} \right), \tag{13-77}$$

supplying the values for the thermal stresses according to Eqs. (13-54) during the cooling process of a cylinder:

$$\text{At } r = 0: \qquad \sigma_r = \sigma_t = \frac{\sigma_z}{2} = -\frac{E\alpha_0(\theta_0 - \theta_m)}{2(1 - \nu)},$$

$$\text{At } r = a: \qquad \sigma_r = 0, \qquad \sigma_t = \sigma_z = -\frac{E\alpha_0(\theta_a - \theta_m)}{1 - \nu}, \tag{13-78}$$

[1] The reader may find a derivation of Eq. (13-72) in H. GRÖBER (see page 384; *op. cit.*, p. 53) or in W. E. BYERLY, "Fourier's Series and Spherical, Cylindrical and Ellipsoidal Harmonics," p. 229, Ginn & Company, Boston, 1893.

with α_0 denoting the expansion coefficient. By plotting the temperature differences $\theta_0 - \theta_m$, $\theta_m - \theta_a$ at various times t one may determine from their maximum values those of the thermal stresses occurring during the transient cooling period in a solid cylinder.[1]

The preceding formulas include as a limiting case the fastest cooling process in a cylinder, when the emissivity constants λ and $c = a\lambda/k$ become infinite. This case of a theoretically infinitely efficient cooling medium has only academic value because no such medium exists. From the boundary condition [Eq. (13-74)], $\lim_{c=\infty} [cJ_0(\alpha)] = \alpha J_1(\alpha)$, showing that $J_0(\alpha) = 0$, i.e., that the parameters α_n when $\lambda = \infty$ are the roots of $J_0(\alpha)$, one sees that the temperature in the cylinder varies as

$$\theta = 2\theta_c \sum_n \frac{e^{-\beta_n t}J_0(\alpha_n r/a)}{\alpha_n J_1(\alpha_n)} \tag{13-79}$$

and that, by letting $c = \infty$ in Eq. (13-76), the mean temperature θ_m is now given by

$$\theta_m = 4\theta_c \sum_n \frac{e^{-\beta_n t}}{\alpha_n^2}. \tag{13-80}$$

At time $t = 0$ the temperature θ_a at the surface $r = a$ of the cylinder drops immediately to zero, and $\theta_a = 0$ at all times t; the mean temperature at time $t = 0$ is $\theta_m = \theta_c$;[†] hence when $\lambda = \infty$, the maximum thermal stresses in the surface of the cylinder reach their greatest value at $t = 0$, $r = a$,

$$\sigma_t = \sigma_z = \frac{E\alpha_0\theta_c}{2(1 - \nu)}, \tag{13-81}$$

at the instant the cold shock is applied.[2]

B. EXPERIMENTAL EVIDENCE. Leaving aside the mathematically oversimplified limiting case $\lambda = \infty$, some experimental information concerning the practical validity of the thermal boundary condition [Eq. (13-71)] may seem in

† Incidentally, it is noted, after substituting $t = 0$, $\theta_m = \theta_c$ in Eq. (13-80), that a theorem concerning the Bessel's function of zero order is obtained, namely,

$$\sum_n^\infty \frac{1}{\alpha_n^2} = \frac{1}{4},$$

i.e., that the sum of the reciprocal squares of the roots α_n of $J_0(\alpha) = 0$ equals $\frac{1}{4}$.

[1] Or by letting $d(\theta_0 - \theta_m)/dt = d(\theta_a - \theta_m)/dt = 0$, after differentiating the two series in Eqs. (13-77) with respect to t, one may evaluate the corresponding times t_0 and t_a, respectively, at which the maxima occur.

[2] *The latter values greatly overestimate the thermal stresses* which may be expected to occur, even under the severest cooling conditions that one may be able to impose in a test. It seems physically improbable that a cold shock would have an effect without allowing for a finite time for its development. A. STODOLA ("Steam and Gas Turbines," 5th German ed., p. 961, 1922, or English ed., McGraw-Hill Book Company, Inc., New York, 1927), when considering the warming-up period of a cold turbine shaft, after superheated steam was allowed to circulate around it (thus treating the opposite case of a heat shock to the one mentioned in the text above), made use of Eq. (13-79) for plotting the consecutive distributions of the temperature $\theta = f(r, t)$ in the shaft but, as just indicated, they greatly exaggerate the speed with which a heat wave is truly able to penetrate into a steel body. See also S. TIMOSHENKO and J. N. GOODIER, "Theory of Elasticity," 2d ed., p. 411, McGraw-Hill Book Company, Inc., New York, 1951, quoting the same improbable family of temperature curves.

order on which the preceding computation of thermal stresses was based, at least for the transfer of heat from an atmosphere of superheated steam to a cold steel body. The process of transfer of heat under these circumstances is by no means so simple that one may attribute to it during its duration a constant value of the relative emissivity $c = \lambda a/k$, because λ is known to vary considerably with the temperature of the surface layers of the solid, particularly during the first period of transfer of heat.[1] When superheated steam of 250° to 350°C is allowed to flow around cold steel, first it is condensed in a thin film of water covering the steel. This water film enhances the transfer of heat to the body, and one may count on a value of λ of the order of perhaps 4,000 kcal/(m^2 hr °C) at a steam temperature of 320°C, 1 atm pressure. If we take $k = $ kcal/(m hr °C) for the heat conductivity in steel and for the radius of the cylinder $a = 0.45$ m, this gives for $c = \lambda a/k$ the value $c = 40$. A short time later, when the surface temperature of the cylinder increased to 100°C, the water film evaporated, the emissivity constant for steam drops to the low value of $\lambda = 80$ kcal/(m^2 hr °C) and thus $c = \lambda a/k$ becomes equal to $c = 0.80$, only one fiftieth of its original, high value, these figures also depending considerably on the velocity with which the steam strikes along the solid. Thus the warming-up process of a cold shaft or of a massive, solid, cylindrical rotor of a steam turbine, by means of letting superheated steam circulate around them, progresses during the major part of heating under the comparatively low value of the relative emissivity constant of perhaps $c = \lambda a/k = 0.8$ to 1.0 and one sees how wrong it would be to assume $c = \infty$ for similar cases in steel bodies and to use the temperatures expressed by Eq. (13-79).

The variation of the temperature with the radius r and time t may be illustrated by some tests made by T. C. RATHBONE at the South Philadelphia Works of the Westinghouse Electric Corporation in 1929 with a steel disk of $a = 25\frac{3}{4}$ in. outside radius and 8 in. thickness (having a hole of 4-in. diameter) which was heated on its outer cylindrical surface by superheated steam. The disk was perfectly insulated on its flat sides so that a radial heat flow passed through it. Figure 13-12 reproduces the temperature observations $\theta = f(r,t)$ for various times t across the disk after steam was allowed to circulate around its periphery. From the observed curves the constant β_1 in the first term of the series (13-72) was computed and, since the other constants were known, the value of λ was evaluated in three of the curves:

After a heating period	Average steam temperature, °F	Emissivity constant λ, kcal/(m^2 hr °C)
1 hr to 2 hr 47 min	620	81.2
2 hr 47 min to 4 hr 4 min	655	72.1
4 hr 4 min to 6 hr	660	63.9

Assuming for λ a mean value of $\lambda = 70$ kcal/(m^2 hr °C), the curves in Fig. 13-13 were plotted, indicating that in a first approximation the temperatures θ at the corresponding times fitted well to the observed points, thus verifying the validity of the thermal boundary condition [Eq. (13-71)] over a certain range of temperatures.

[1] The constant of heat transfer λ from a fluid to a solid depends on a number of physical parameters (the velocity of the fluid, its own heat conductivity, density, specific heat at constant pressure, viscosity, etc.) and on whether the flow within the boundary layer adhering to the solid is laminar or turbulent.

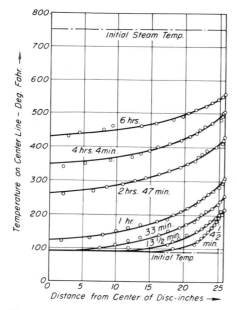

FIG. 13-12. Temperature distribution in steel disk heated by steam for several periods of heating. (*Plotted from tests by T. C. Rathbone, South Philadelphia.*)

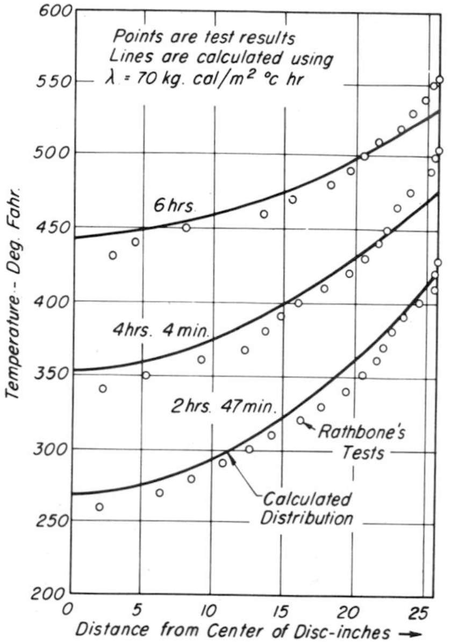

FIG. 13-13. Three temperature distribution curves observed by Rathbone in a steel disk heated on its periphery.

C. CHARTING OF TEMPERATURE DISTRIBUTIONS IN CYLINDERS.

Returning to Eq. (13-72) and the associated formulas with it, one recognizes easily that one controls the entire range of the characteristic distributions of the temperatures $\theta = \theta_c f(r,t)$ during the cooling of a solid cylinder if one plots the curves $\theta/\theta_c = f(r,t)$ for successive times and corresponding to a few chosen values of the characteristic, dimensionless constant of relative emissivity,

$$ c = \frac{\lambda a}{k}, $$

by using the ratio r/a and the temperature ratio θ/θ_c as the abscissas and ordinates in the family of curves traced for different times $t = t_1$, t_2, ...[1] The form of these curves in charts made up for a constant value of c is thus made independent of the initial temperature θ_c and outside radius a, and the same curves also represent the cases of the heating of cylinders after inverting the figures. The combination of constants $k/c_0\gamma_0 a^2$ appearing in the expression defining the constants β_n [Eq. (13-75)] and thus in the exponents of the exponential terms $e^{-\beta_n t}$,

[1] One sees that the characteristic roots α_n of Eq. (13-74) depend only on c and similarly all terms making up the series of Eq. (13-72) except the exponential terms $e^{-\beta_n t}$ containing the time t and the constants β_n.

having the dimension of the reciprocal value of a time which we may denote by t_c, letting

$$\frac{1}{t_c} = \frac{k}{c_0 \gamma_0 a^2},\qquad (13\text{-}82)$$

is irrelevant, since if one has constructed a family of curves for fixed values of c and t_c, one may obtain the same family by retaining c but changing the constant t_c, say to a new value $t_c{'}$, for a new succession of times $t' = (t_c{'}/t_c)t = (t_c{'}/t_c)(t_1, t_2, \dots)$, that is, by stretching the time scale from t to t'. Thus one may plot the first family, for example, by taking $t_c = 1$ hr. Two cylinders of the same material, exchanging heat with the same medium, will disclose the same family of curves $\theta/\theta_c = f(r/a, t/t_c)$ if one compares these curves at the times $t'/t = (a'/a)^2$. This has been illustrated by two families of temperature curves θ/θ_c in Figs. 13-14 and 13-15 reproducing the distributions of temperatures corresponding to the values of relative emissivity $c = 1$ and $c = 10$, the latter representing a much more rapid cooling of a cylinder.

D. THERMAL SHOCKS. When a hot or cold wave has not had sufficient time to penetrate deeply into the interior of a cylinder[1] or a body, one may assume that the temperature θ in the surface layers varies with the depths as in a semi-infinite body according to

$$\frac{\partial \theta}{\partial t} = \frac{k}{c_0 \gamma_0} \cdot \frac{\partial^2 \theta}{\partial x^2}\qquad (13\text{-}83)$$

and one may utilize the solution of this equation under the initial condition $t = 0$, $\theta = \theta_c = $ const and the boundary condition at $x = 0$, $\partial \theta/\partial x + c\theta/a = 0$:[†]

$$\theta = \theta_c\left\{\Phi\left(\frac{u}{2v}\right) + \left[1 - \Phi\left(\frac{u}{2v} + cv\right)\right]e^{cu + c^2 v^2}\right\},\qquad (13\text{-}84)$$

[†] See P. FRANK and R. VON MISES, "Die Differential- und Integralgleichungen der Mechanik und Physik," vol. 2, p. 236, Friedr. Vieweg und Sohn, Brunswick, Germany, 1927.

[1] The series (13-72) does not converge too well after the first instants of exposing the outside walls of a cylinder to a much cooler or warmer medium. If the difference between temperatures is comparatively great, the first instants of heat exchange may be termed a cold or heat shock, the treatment of which is given above.

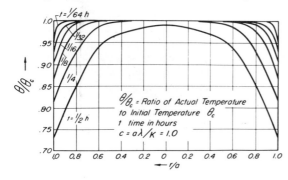

FIG. 13-14. Temperature distribution curves in a cylinder, $c = \lambda a/k = 1$.

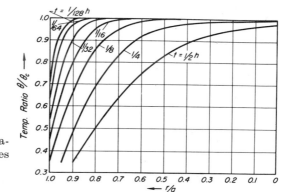

FIG. 13-15. Temperature distribution curves in a solid cylinder,

$$c = \lambda a / k = 10.$$

where the function $\Phi(z)$ represents the *Gaussian* error integral

$$\Phi(z) = \frac{2}{\sqrt{\pi}} \int_0^z e^{-z^2} dz, \qquad (13\text{-}85)$$

the values of which may be found tabulated;[1] the two independent variables u and v denote the ratios

$$u = \frac{x}{a}, \qquad v = \sqrt{\frac{t}{t_c}} ; \qquad (13\text{-}86)$$

and the constants c and t_c denote, as formerly, the combinations of constants:

$$c = \frac{\lambda a}{k}, \qquad t_c = \frac{c_0 \gamma_0 a^2}{k}, \qquad (13\text{-}87)$$

where a may now represent an arbitrarily chosen constant length. Equation (13-84) was used by W. THOMSON (LORD KELVIN) in his early investigations on the cooling of the earth's outer solid shell.

It may be of interest to record the temperature θ_0 in the surface of a solid body which has been exposed to a cold shock. Taking $x = u = 0$ in Eq. (13-84), one sees that the temperature θ_0 must decrease with the time as

$$\theta_0 = \theta_c e^{c^2 v^2} [1 - \Phi(cv)]$$
$$= \theta_c e^{c^2 t/t_c} \left[1 - \Phi\left(c \cdot \sqrt{\frac{t}{t_c}} \right) \right], \qquad (13\text{-}88)$$

the term within the brackets decreasing much faster as the exponential term increases with the argument cv. For large values of the latter, this function may be expressed by the semiconvergent series

$$\theta_0 = \frac{\theta_c}{\sqrt{\pi} \cdot cv} \left[1 - \frac{1}{2(cv)^2} + \frac{1 \cdot 3}{2^2(cv)^4} - \frac{1 \cdot 3 \cdot 5}{2^3(cv)^6} + \cdots \right], \qquad (13\text{-}89)$$

[1] E. JAHNKE and F. EMDE, "Funktionentafeln," p. 33, Teubner, Leipzig, 1909.

approaching, when cv tends toward infinity,

$$\theta_0 = \frac{\theta_c}{\sqrt{\pi \cdot cv}} = \frac{1}{c}\sqrt{\frac{t_c}{\pi t}}, \tag{13-90}$$

showing that the surface temperature, after some time has elapsed, decreases as the reciprocal square root of time. At $t = 0$ the rate of decrease of θ_0 is infinite. The drop of the surface temperature for the value $c = 1$ may be seen in Figs. 13-16 and 13-17 in which θ_0/θ_c is plotted above v and t, respectively. The drop of the surface temperature corresponding to a fixed value of the relative emissivity $c = \lambda a/k$ is obtained by plotting the ordinates θ_0/θ_c represented in Figs. 13-16 and 13-17 above the abscissas $v' = v/c$, $t' = t/c$ after condensing or stretching the horizontal scales in the former figures.

The thermal stresses in the interior of a semi-infinite body induced by this cold shock, if we assume that the body does not sustain strains in the direction parallel to the surface plane $x = 0$ ($\varepsilon_y = \varepsilon_z = 0$), are equal to

$$\sigma_x = 0, \qquad \sigma_y = \sigma_z = \frac{E\alpha(\theta_c - \theta)}{1 - \nu}. \tag{13-91}$$

σ_y and σ_z vary with the depth x proportionally with the temperature differences $\theta_c - \theta$ as represented in Fig. 13-18 and the stresses in the surface $x = 0$ as $\theta_c - \theta_0$ (Fig. 13-19). They increase as time progresses and would reach their greatest value after an infinitely long time. But it has to be borne in mind that in a body of *finite* dimensions the mean temperature θ_m (which in the infinite body was taken equal to θ_c) would also start to decrease as time progresses and thus the curve θ_0/θ_c in Figs. 13-17 and 13-19 has a physical meaning only in its first, steeply dropping portion, if it is to be utilized for predicting the thermal stresses within the surface layers of a body having *finite* dimensions. In a cold (hot) shock, the surface layers are stressed in tension (compression).

Whereas the preceding treatment of a thermal shock induced on the

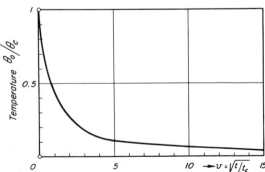

FIG. 13-16. Surface temperature in a semi-infinite body.

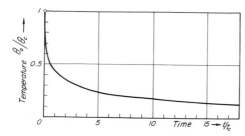

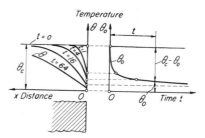

FIG. 13-17. Variation of surface temperature θ_0 with time t in a semi-infinite body exposed to a cold shock.

FIG. 13-18. Temperatures in interior of body at various times t.

FIG. 13-19. Surface temperature θ_0. The thermal stresses in the surface $x = 0$ are

$$\sigma_y = \sigma_z$$
$$= \frac{E\alpha(\theta_c - \theta_0)}{1 - \nu}$$

FIGS. 13-18 and 13-19. Cold shock in a semi-infinite body.

surface of a semi-infinite elastic block $x \geqq 0$ was based on the supposition that the massive, solid block of material was suddenly immersed along its surface plane $x = 0$ in a medium (a fluid) having a different ambious temperature substantially higher or lower than the initial temperature $\theta_c = $ const that the block originally possessed, M. A. SADOWSKY[1] investigated the effect of a thermal shock of a different type. He assumed that the plane surface $x = 0$ of a semi-infinite elastic body $x \geqq 0$ was exposed to localized, spontaneous heating inside the area of a circle $r = a$ in the plane $x = 0$, causing a sudden finite rise of temperature within a very thin layer and during an infinitely short time, not unlike that which a blowtorch would produce if directed toward the circle $r = a$, and he raised the question of the static stresses instantaneously produced in the body. This does not require solving a transient problem of heat conduction but rather an analysis of a static distribution of elastic strain and stress of rotational symmetry which SADOWSKY evaluated elegantly in terms of *Jacobian* elliptic functions.

E. YIELDING OF MATERIAL UNDER THERMAL STRESSES. A thermal wave entering a body on sudden heating may strain the surface layers beyond the plastic limit under biaxial equal stresses σ_0. Assuming for a short time of plastic overstraining that the yield limit σ_0 is represented by a curve depending on the temperature $\theta = T - 273° - t_0$

[1] Thermal Shock on a Circular Surface of Exposure of an Elastic Halfspace, 20 pp., Office of Naval Research, Rept. NR-064-405, issued by Rensselaer Polytechnic Institute, Troy, N.Y., January, 1954.

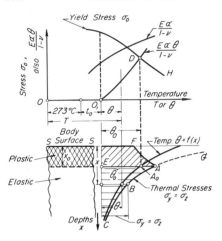

FIG. 13-20. Thermal surface stresses including plastic flow.

(T is the absolute and t_0 the initial temperature of the body, in degrees centigrade) (Fig. 13-20) and that E, α, ν are known functions of T, one may also trace the curves for the product $E\alpha/(1 - \nu)$ and for $E\alpha\theta/(1 - \nu)$ above θ within the elastic range of strains, as shown in the upper part of Fig. 13-20. Their ordinates then define, within the range $0 < \theta < \theta_0$, the elastic stresses $\sigma = E\alpha\theta/(1 - \nu)$ and for $\theta > \theta_0$ the yield stresses σ_0 in the two branches of curves $O_1 D$ and DH, respectively. Suppose that at some time t the heat wave has taken the position in the body corresponding to the curve $\theta = f(x)$ shown in the lower part of Fig. 13-20. One may then read at the values of θ the ordinates $E\alpha\theta/(1 - \nu)$ or σ_0 in the upper curves and transfer them to the corresponding depths x horizontally in the lower part of Fig. 13-20, *thus obtaining the broken line CBAF which represents the thermal stresses under the surface of the body $x = 0$, defining in the doubly shaded layer $0 < x < x_0$ the plastically strained portion and below it the elastically strained portion in the body, together with their thermal stresses.* The high values of the elastically carried stresses under the dotted portion AG of the curve CAG are thus seen to have been reduced to those corresponding to the branch AF owing to the enhanced ductility of the material, where the temperatures were $\theta > \theta_0$ and the material yielded. Since these stresses are compressive, even under sudden exposure to comparatively high surface temperatures, not much damage may be expected to occur; the case is different, however, when on sudden cooling the material is stressed in tension, as the yield point is raised in the coldest region near the surface, the material is made more brittle, and tensile fractures may result (cracks accompanying sudden chilling).

13-5. Sphere. In a sphere in which the temperature θ is a function of the radial distance r of a point from its center and of the time t, $\theta = f(r,t)$, the strains $\varepsilon_r = du/dr$ and $\varepsilon_t = u/r$ are equal to

$$\varepsilon_r = \frac{1}{E}(\sigma_r - 2\nu\sigma_t) + \alpha\theta,$$

$$\varepsilon_t = \frac{1}{E}[(1 - \nu)\sigma_t - \nu\sigma_r] + \alpha\theta,$$

(13-92)

and the conditions of equilibrium of the stresses σ_r, σ_t and of compatibility of the strains ε_r, ε_t,

$$\frac{d\sigma_r}{dr} - \frac{2(\sigma_t - \sigma_r)}{r} = 0,$$

$$\frac{d\sigma_t}{dr} + \frac{\sigma_t - \sigma_r}{r} = -\frac{E\alpha}{1 - \nu} \cdot \frac{d\theta}{dr}, \qquad (13\text{-}93)$$

are satisfied by

$$\sigma_r = -\frac{2c_1}{r^3} + c_2 - \frac{2E\alpha}{(1 - \nu)r^3} \int \theta r^2 \, dr,$$

$$\sigma_t = \frac{c_1}{r^3} + c_2 - \frac{E\alpha}{1 - \nu} \left(\theta - \frac{1}{r^3} \int \theta r^2 \, dr \right). \qquad (13\text{-}94)$$

In *a solid sphere* of radius a, $c_1 = 0$, $c_2 = 2E\alpha\theta_m/3(1 - \nu) = \sigma$, θ_m denoting its mean temperature,

$$\theta_m = \frac{3}{a^3} \int_0^a \theta r^2 \, dr, \qquad (13\text{-}95)$$

the thermal stresses are equal to

$$\sigma_r = \frac{\sigma}{\theta_m} \left(\theta_m - \frac{3}{r^3} \int_0^r \theta r^2 \, dr \right) \qquad = -\sigma(\psi - \psi'),$$

$$\sigma_t = -\frac{\sigma}{\theta_m} \left(-\theta_m + \frac{3}{2}\theta - \frac{3}{2r^3} \int_0^r \theta r^2 \, dr \right) = -\sigma\left(\psi + \frac{\psi'}{2} \right), \qquad (13\text{-}96)$$

where the functions ψ and ψ' defined by

$$\psi = \frac{\theta - \theta_m}{\theta_m}, \qquad \psi' = \frac{1}{\theta_m} \left(\theta - \frac{3}{r^3} \int_0^r \theta r^2 \, dr \right) = \psi - \frac{3}{r^3} \int_0^r \psi r^2 \, dr \qquad (13\text{-}97)$$

represent variables analogous to those introduced in Sec. 13-3A for a cylinder. For $r = 0$, $\psi_0' = 0$ and for $r = a$, $\psi_a' = \psi_a$, and the thermal stresses are:

In center of sphere, $r = 0$:

$$\sigma_r = \sigma_t = -\sigma\psi_0 = -\frac{\sigma(\theta_0 - \theta_m)}{\theta_m},$$

In surface of sphere, $r = a$:

$$\sigma_r = 0, \qquad \sigma_t = -\frac{3\sigma\psi_a}{2} = \frac{3\sigma(\theta_m - \theta_a)}{2\theta_m}. \qquad (13\text{-}98)$$

The temperature θ in a transient radial state of cooling in a sphere that had initially, at time $t = 0$, the uniform temperature $\theta = \theta_c = \text{const}$ and emits heat to a medium of zero temperature is expressed by the series

$$\theta = \frac{a}{r} \sum_n B_n e^{-\alpha_n^2 t/t_c} \frac{\sin(\alpha_n r/a)}{\sin \alpha_n}, \qquad (13\text{-}99)$$

where

$$B_n = \frac{2c\theta_c}{c^2 - c + \alpha_n^2}, \qquad c = \frac{\lambda a}{k}, \qquad t_c = \frac{c_0\gamma_0 a^2}{k}, \qquad (13\text{-}100)$$

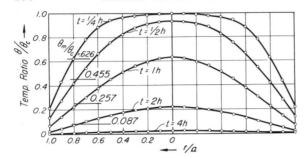

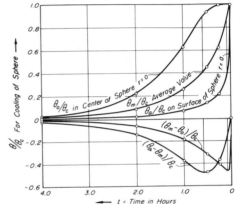

Fig. 13-21. Temperature distributions in a solid sphere for

$$c = \lambda a/k = 10.$$

Temperature curves for cooling of sphere.

Fig. 13-22. Temperature ratios θ/θ_c for $\theta = \theta_0, \theta_m, \theta_a$ plotted as a function of time t when $c = \lambda a/k = 10$.

and the constant parameters $\alpha_n = \alpha_1, \alpha_2, \ldots$ are the positive series of roots of the transcendental equation of α,

$$(1 - c) \tan \alpha = \alpha, \qquad (13\text{-}101)$$

the symbols $k, \lambda, c_0, \gamma_0$ denoting the same quantities as in Sec. 13-4A.[1]

The mean temperature θ_m in the sphere being equal to

$$\theta_m = \frac{3}{a^3} \int_0^a \theta r^2 \, dr = 3c \sum_n \frac{B_n}{\alpha_n^2} \cdot e^{-\alpha_n^2 t/t_c}, \qquad (13\text{-}102)$$

the temperature differences appearing in Eqs. (13-98) for the thermal stresses may be computed from the series

$$r = 0, \qquad \theta_0 - \theta_m = \sum_n B_n \left(\frac{\alpha_n}{\sin \alpha_n} - \frac{3c}{\alpha_n^2} \right) e^{-\alpha_n^2 t/t_c},$$

$$\qquad\qquad\qquad\qquad\qquad\qquad\qquad\qquad\qquad (13\text{-}103)$$

$$r = a, \qquad \theta_a - \theta_m = \sum_n B_n \left(1 - \frac{3c}{\alpha_n^2} \right) e^{-\alpha_n^2 t/t_c}.$$

[1] Equation (13-99) is the well-known solution of the differential equation for the conduction of heat in a sphere:

$$\frac{\partial \theta}{\partial t} = \frac{k}{c_0 \gamma_0} \left(\frac{2}{r} \frac{\partial \theta}{\partial r} + \frac{\partial^2 \theta}{\partial r^2} \right)$$

under the initial condition $t = 0$, $\theta = \theta_c = \text{const}$ and satisfying the boundary condition for $r = a$:

$$\frac{\partial \theta}{\partial r} + \frac{\lambda}{k} \theta = 0.$$

In the special case of infinite emissivity $\lambda = \infty$, $c = \infty$, causing the temperature in the surface $r = a$ of the sphere θ_a to drop to zero, from Eq. (13-101), since $\tan \alpha = 0$, the roots of which are $\alpha_n = n\pi$, the temperatures θ and θ_m are expressed by the series

$$\theta = \frac{2\theta_c a}{\pi r} \sum_n \frac{(-1)^{n+1}}{n} \cdot e^{-n^2\pi^2 t/t_c} \sin \frac{n\pi r}{a},$$

$$\theta_m = \frac{6\theta_c}{\pi^2} \sum_n \frac{e^{-n^2\pi^2 t/t_c}}{n^2}, \qquad (n = 1, 2, 3, \ldots).$$

(13-104)

A nonuniformly heated sphere expands radially in its surface $r = a$ by an amount $u_a = \alpha a \theta_m$ equal to that of a sphere having the uniform temperature $\theta_m = \text{const.}$[1]

One may represent the transient cooling or heating of spneres in charts by plotting the ratio of the temperatures θ/θ_c above the ratios $u = r/a$ at various times $t = (\frac{1}{4},\frac{1}{2},1,2, \ldots)t_c$, the character of such families of curves depending essentially on the value of the constant of relative emissivity $c = \lambda a/k$ that one has chosen. Two examples are shown in Figs. 13-21 and 13-23 for $c = 10$ and $c = 1$, and one may

[1] The radial, thermal displacements $u = r\varepsilon_t$ in a nonuniformly heated sphere in which the temperature is $\theta = f(r)$ are equal to

$$u = \frac{\alpha \cdot}{3(1 - \nu)} \left[2(1 - 2\nu)\theta_m r + \frac{3(1 + \nu)}{r^2} \int_0^r \theta r^2 \, dr \right].$$

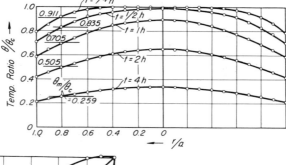

FIG. 13-23. Temperature distributions in a solid sphere for

$c = \lambda a/k = 1.0.$

Temperature curves for cooling of sphere.

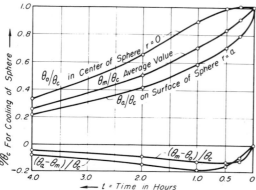

FIG. 13-24. Temperature ratios θ/θ_c for $\theta = \theta_0, \theta_m, \theta_a$ plotted as a function of time t for $c = \lambda a/k = 1.0.$

construct from them three curves indicating the decline of θ_0/θ_c, θ_a/θ_c at $r = 0$ and $r = a$ and of the mean temperature ratio θ_m/θ_c with time t (Figs. 13-22 and 13-24), thus obtaining in the differences of their ordinates the trend for the variation of the thermal stresses with the time t at the center $r = 0$ and the surface $r = a$ of spheres. The maxima of these differences are indicated in Figs. 13-22 and 13-24, which define the maximum values of the corresponding thermal stresses induced during the transient cooling or heating of spheres.

13-6. Thermal Stresses during Transient Heating and Relaxation of Stress in Thin Circular Disk of Viscoelastic Material. Let us consider the inherent thermal stresses straining a thin, solid, circular disk of constant thickness of viscoelastic material, in the absence of any external forces, under a radially symmetric distribution of the temperature $\theta = f(r,t)$ which may change as time t progresses. The thermal stresses will follow with a certain lag the prescribed variation of θ. As a special case we may assume that this temperature distribution tends to become steady, $\theta = f(r)$, with the consequence that a *process of slow self-relaxation of the thermal stresses results* in the disk until they gradually lapse and evanesce, owing to the viscosity of the substance.

Denoting by one and two primes the elastic and permanent parts of the strains ε_r, ε_t, ε_z in the radial, tangential, and axial directions and by σ_r, σ_t, $\sigma_z = 0$ the normal stresses in a thin disk, we have

$$\varepsilon_r' = \frac{\partial \rho'}{\partial r} = \frac{1}{E}(\sigma_r - \nu\sigma_t) + \alpha\theta, \qquad \dot{\varepsilon}_r'' = \frac{1}{3\mu}\left(\sigma_r - \frac{\sigma_t}{2}\right),$$

$$\varepsilon_t' = \frac{\rho'}{r} = \frac{1}{E}(\sigma_t - \nu\sigma_r) + \alpha\theta, \qquad \dot{\varepsilon}_t'' = \frac{1}{3\mu}\left(\sigma_t - \frac{\sigma_r}{2}\right), \qquad (13\text{-}105)$$

$$\varepsilon_z' = -\frac{\nu}{E}(\sigma_r + \sigma_t) + \alpha\theta, \qquad \dot{\varepsilon}_z'' = -\frac{1}{6\mu}(\sigma_r + \sigma_t),$$

$$\varepsilon_r' + \varepsilon_t' + \varepsilon_z' = \frac{(1 - 2\nu)(\sigma_r + \sigma_t)}{E} + 3\alpha\theta, \qquad \varepsilon_r'' + \varepsilon_t'' + \varepsilon_z'' = 0;$$

the radial displacement ρ and velocity $u = \partial\rho/\partial t$,

$$\rho = \rho' + \rho'', \qquad u = \frac{\partial\rho}{\partial t} = u' + u''; \qquad (13\text{-}106)$$

and the total rates of strain

$$\dot{\varepsilon}_r = \frac{\partial u}{\partial r} = \frac{1}{E}\left(\dot{\sigma}_r + \frac{\sigma_r}{t_e} - \nu\dot{\sigma}_t - \frac{\sigma_t}{2t_e} + \alpha E\dot{\theta}\right),$$

$$\dot{\varepsilon}_t = \frac{u}{r} = \frac{1}{E}\left(\dot{\sigma}_t + \frac{\sigma_t}{t_e} - \nu\dot{\sigma}_r - \frac{\sigma_r}{2t_e} + \alpha E\dot{\theta}\right), \qquad (13\text{-}107)$$

where the dots denote differentiation with respect to the time t and where

$$t_e = \frac{3\mu}{E} \qquad (13\text{-}108)$$

is a time constant and μ the coefficient of viscosity, assuming that E, ν, μ are constants (independent of the temperature θ).

The conditions of compatibility of the strain rates $\dot{\varepsilon}_r$, $\dot{\varepsilon}_t$ and of equilibrium of the stresses σ_r, σ_t,

$$\frac{\partial(r\dot{\varepsilon}_t)}{\partial r} - \dot{\varepsilon}_r = 0, \qquad \frac{\partial(r\sigma_r)}{\partial r} - \sigma_t = 0, \qquad (13\text{-}109)$$

if we let

$$s = \sigma_t + \sigma_r,$$
$$w = \sigma_t - \sigma_r, \qquad (13\text{-}110)$$

in terms of the latter variables are then expressed by the differential equations

$$\frac{\partial}{\partial r}(r\dot{s}) - \dot{s} + \frac{1}{t_e}\left[\frac{\partial}{\partial r}(rs) - s\right] + \alpha E r\frac{\partial\dot{\theta}}{\partial r} = 0,$$

$$\frac{\partial}{\partial r}(r\dot{w}) + \dot{w} + \frac{1}{t_e}\left[\frac{\partial}{\partial r}(rw) + w\right] + \alpha E r\frac{\partial\dot{\theta}}{\partial r} = 0; \qquad (13\text{-}111)$$

if we use the abbreviations

$$S = \frac{\partial(rs)}{\partial r} - s = r\frac{\partial s}{\partial r}, \qquad (13\text{-}112)$$

$$W = \frac{\partial(rw)}{\partial r} + w = \frac{1}{r}\frac{\partial}{\partial r}(r^2 w),$$

we have

$$\dot{S} + \frac{S}{t_e} = -\alpha E r\frac{\partial\dot{\theta}}{\partial r},$$

$$\dot{W} + \frac{W}{t_e} = -\alpha E r\frac{\partial\dot{\theta}}{\partial r}, \qquad (13\text{-}113)$$

and, after integrating these equations with respect to the time t between the limits $t = 0$ and t,

$$S(t) = r\frac{\partial s}{\partial r} = e^{-t/t_e}\left[S(0) - E\alpha r\int_0^t \frac{\partial\dot{\theta}}{\partial r}e^{t/t_e}\,dt\right],$$

$$W(t) = \frac{\partial(r^2 w)}{r\partial r} = e^{-t/t_e}\left[W(0) - E\alpha r\int_0^t \frac{\partial\dot{\theta}}{\partial r}e^{t/t_e}\,dt\right]. \qquad (13\text{-}114)$$

Instead of $S(0)$ and $W(0)$ representing the values of S and W at time $t = 0$, that is, essentially two arbitrary functions of the variable r, we may write

$$S(0) = E\alpha \cdot \frac{r\,d\varphi_1(r)}{dr}, \qquad W(0) = E\alpha\frac{d[r^2\varphi_2(r)]}{r\,dr}, \qquad (13\text{-}115)$$

denoting by $\varphi_1(r)$, $\varphi_2(r)$ such functions of r and for the integral appearing in the brackets, by partial integration,

$$\int_0^t \frac{\partial \theta}{\partial r} e^{t/t_e} \, dt = e^{t/t_e} \cdot \frac{\partial \theta}{\partial r} - \left(\frac{\partial \theta}{\partial r}\right)_{t=0} - \frac{1}{t_e} \int_0^t \frac{\partial \theta}{\partial r} e^{t/t_e} \, dt. \qquad (13\text{-}116)$$

Thus from Eqs. (13-114)

$$\frac{1}{E\alpha} \cdot \frac{\partial s}{\partial r} = e^{-t/t_e} \left[\frac{d\varphi_1}{dr} + \left(\frac{\partial \theta}{\partial r}\right)_{t=0} + \frac{1}{t_e} \int_0^t \frac{\partial \theta}{\partial r} e^{t/t_e} \, dt\right] - \frac{\partial \theta}{\partial r}, \qquad (13\text{-}117)$$

$$\frac{1}{E\alpha} \cdot \frac{\partial (r^2 w)}{\partial r} = e^{-t/t_e} \left[\frac{d(r^2 \varphi_2)}{dr} + r^2 \left(\frac{\partial \theta}{\partial r}\right)_{t=0} + \frac{r^2}{t_e} \int_0^t \frac{\partial \theta}{\partial r} e^{t/t_e} \, dt\right] - r^2 \frac{\partial \theta}{\partial r},$$

and these two equations for the unknowns s and w can once more be integrated with respect to r between the limits $r = 0$ and r, using

$$\int_0^r r^2 \frac{\partial \theta}{\partial r} \, dr = r^2 \theta - 2 \int_0^r \theta r \, dr,$$

whereby on the left side of the first of Eqs. (13-117), from

$$\int_0^r \frac{\partial s}{\partial r} \, dr = s - s_0,$$

a third, arbitrary function s_0 of the time t is introduced which represents the value of s in the center of the disk $r = 0$ at time t. If we likewise denote by θ_0 the temperature at $r = 0$ and by

$$\theta_m = \frac{2}{a^2} \int_0^a \theta r \, dr$$

the mean temperature of the disk (at any time), the two arbitrary functions $\varphi_1(r)$, $\varphi_2(r)$ are determined from the initial state of thermal stress in the disk at time $t = 0$, for which we know that[1] at time $t = 0$

$$s = \sigma_t + \sigma_r = E\alpha(\theta_m - \theta)_{t=0},$$

$$w = \sigma_t - \sigma_r = E\alpha\left(-\theta + \frac{2}{r^2} \int_0^r \theta r \, dr\right)_{t=0}, \qquad (13\text{-}118)$$

$$s_0 = E\alpha(\theta_m - \theta_0)_{t=0};$$

[1] See Sec. 13-3A, Eqs. (13-50), which were, however, valid for a long cylinder under a state of plane strain $\varepsilon_z = \text{const}$ and in which, for the combination of constants $E\alpha/2(1 - \nu)$ in the expressions for σ_r, σ_t, in order that these may apply to a thin, circular disk, under a state of plane stress, $\sigma_z = 0$, the combination of constants $E\alpha/2$ has to be substituted, giving Eqs. (13-118). [See also Sec. 13-3C, Eqs. (13-64) and (13-65).]

one finds thereby that

$$\varphi_1(r) - \varphi_1(0) = (\theta_0 - \theta)_{t=0}, \qquad \varphi_2(r) = \left(-\theta + \frac{2}{r^2}\int_0^r \theta r\, dr\right)_{t=0}. \quad (13\text{-}119)$$

The third, arbitrary function s_0, representing the value of $s = \sigma_t + \sigma_r$ for $r = 0$, is determined from the boundary condition that on the circumference of the disk $r = a$ the radial stress σ_r has to vanish or that at any time t, $r = a$, $\sigma_r = (\tfrac{1}{2})(s - w) = 0$, $s = w$, which defines the unknown value of s_0:

$$s_0 = E\alpha\left[\theta_m - \theta_0 - \frac{e^{-t/t_e}}{t_e}\cdot\int_0^t (\theta_m - \theta_0)e^{t/t_e}\, dt\right], \qquad (13\text{-}120)$$

with the final result that *the distribution of thermal stresses in a thin disk of viscoelastic material at any time t is found expressed by*

$$s = \sigma_t + \sigma_r = E\alpha\left[\theta_m - \theta_0 - \frac{e^{-t/t_e}}{t_e}\cdot\int_0^t (\theta_m - \theta_0)e^{t/t_e}\, dt\right],$$
$$w = \sigma_t - \sigma_r = E\alpha\left[-\theta + \frac{2}{r^2}\int_0^r \theta r\, dr + \frac{e^{-t/t_e}}{t_e}\cdot\int_0^t\left(\theta - \frac{2}{r^2}\int_0^r \theta r\, dr\right)e^{t/t_e} dt\right], \qquad (13\text{-}121)$$

defining the thermal stresses $\sigma_r = (\tfrac{1}{2})(s - w)$, $\sigma_t = (\tfrac{1}{2})(s + w)$ *following transient states of the temperatures* $\theta = f(r,t)$.

Suppose that θ beginning from a time $t = t_1$ were *steady*.[1] Then, counting t from $t = t_1$, the values of θ appearing within the time integrals in Eqs. (13-121) can be placed before the integral signs and, after inserting

$$\int_0^t e^{t/t_e}\, dt = t_e(e^{t/t_e} - 1),$$

s and w are expressed by

$$s = E\alpha(\theta_m - \theta)e^{-t/t_e},$$
$$w = E\alpha\left(-\theta + \frac{2}{r^2}\int_0^r \theta r\, dr\right)e^{-t/t_e}, \qquad (13\text{-}122)$$

and the stresses σ_r and σ_t by

$$\sigma_r = (\tfrac{1}{2})(s - w) = (\tfrac{1}{2})E\alpha\left(\theta_m - \frac{2}{r^2}\int_0^r \theta r\, dr\right)e^{-t/t_e},$$
$$\sigma_t = (\tfrac{1}{2})(s + w) = (\tfrac{1}{2})E\alpha\left(\theta_m - 2\theta + \frac{2}{r^2}\int_0^r \theta r\, dr\right)e^{-t/t_e}, \qquad (13\text{-}123)$$

[1] It is understood that any steady distribution of temperature $\theta = f(r)$, not being a solution of $\Delta\theta = 0$, requires that in a thin disk heat be conducted through the flat sides to or from the disk.

where the expressions before the exponential time factor e^{-t/t_e} represent the initial state of stress at time $t = 0$ [in which we recognize the expressions $\sigma(\psi \mp \psi')$ introduced in Sec. 13-3A, Eqs. (13-51)]. *An inherent state of thermal stress in a viscoelastic disk held at the steady temperatures $\theta = f(r)$ thus gradually evanesces through self-relaxation* while the initially elastic strains change to permanent strains.

During this relaxation, points of the disk move with the radial velocity u,

$$u = \frac{\partial \rho}{\partial t} = r\dot{\varepsilon}_t = - \frac{(1 - 2\nu)\alpha}{4t_e}\left(\theta_m r - \frac{2}{r}\int_0^r \theta r\, dr\right)e^{-t/t_e}, \quad (13\text{-}124)$$

from which the radial displacements ρ are computed:

$$\rho = \frac{\alpha\theta_m r}{4}[1 + (1 - 2\nu)e^{-t/t_e}] + \frac{\alpha}{2r}[3 - (1 - 2\nu)e^{-t/t_e}] \cdot \int_0^r \theta r\, dr. \quad (13\text{-}125)$$

This gives for $r = a$, at the periphery of the disk at any time ,

$$\rho_a = \alpha a\theta_m = \text{const}, \quad (13\text{-}126)$$

the interesting result that, while the thermal stresses in *a solid, viscoelastic disk*, under a steady temperature field $\theta = f(r)$ *relax, its periphery will neither contract nor expand beyond the radial displacement $\rho_a = \alpha a\theta_m$* that the disk would have obtained had it been kept under the uniform temperature $\theta_m = \text{const}$. In the interior of the disk there will occur, however, small readjustments in the positions of the points toward the radial displacements $[\rho(r)]_{t=\infty}$ finally assumed.

After the thermal stresses σ_r, σ_t have completely disappeared, suppose that the disk is rapidly cooled and its temperature $\theta = f(r)$ reduced to $\theta = 0$.   While the disk in its hot, relaxed condition was entirely stress-free, in its cold condition it must become stressed again because of the thermal volume contractions $-3\alpha\theta$ suffered by its elements.   Since this amounts to superposing a temperature field $-\theta$ on the field $\theta = f(r)$, obviously *when it is cold, the disk will be subjected to a system of residual thermal stresses* just equal and of opposite signs to those expressed in Eqs. (13-123) (after letting $t = 0$ in them).

13-7.   Thermal Shock in Suddenly Plasticized Flow Layer at Extremely Low Temperatures in Ductile Metals.   The metals having a face-centered-cubic (f.c.c.) or the close-packed-hexagonal (c.p.h.) lattice structure possess, when the absolute temperature T approaches $T = 0$, a surprisingly high ductility in tensile tests.   Pure nickel (f.c.c.) and zirconium (c.p.h.), for example, at normal temperature, $T = 300°K$ ($\theta = 27°C$) and at the extremely low temperature of $T = 4.2°K$ (the boiling temperature of liquid helium at atmospheric pressure) have the tensile strength $\sigma_{l,\max}$ and elongation ε shown in the accompanying table.[1]

Metal	T = 300°K		T = 4.2°K	
	Tensile strength $\sigma_{l,\max}$, kg/cm²	Elongation ε	Tensile strength $\sigma_{l,\max}$, kg/cm²	Elongation ε
Nickel	3,860	0.54	7,180	0.62
Zirconium	2,460	0.35	6,470	0.47

The mechanical work of deformation ω to stretch them to the fracture point [appearing as the area under the tensile stress-strain curve $\sigma_l = f(\varepsilon)$] expressed as work expended in kilogram-meters per cubic centimeter unit volume is as follows:

When the metal is tested at:	Specific mechanical work	
	Nickel	Zirconium
300°K	$\omega = 16$	$\omega = 8$ kg-m/cm³
4°K	$\omega = 34$	$\omega = 26$ kg-m/cm³

According to the principle of conservation of energy, this mechanical work ω is converted into thermal energy, and the equivalent heat

$$H = \omega/J = 0.00234\omega \qquad (J = 427 \text{ kg-m/kcal, Joule's number})$$

generated per cubic centimeter of deformed metal is, respectively,

At $T = 300°K$: $H = 0.0374$ kcal/cm³   for nickel;
                                $H = 0.0187$ kcal/cm³   for zirconium;
At $T = 4°K$: $H = 0.0795$ kcal/cm³   for nickel;
                                $H = 0.0608$ kcal/cm³   for zirconium

which will alter the aforementioned temperatures.

The tensile tests made with these (and other structurally similar) metals at the extremely low temperature of 4° absolute showed a very strange, unexpected phenomenon, discovered by E. T. WESSEL, to which special attention is called here.   While even at $78°K = -195°C$ smooth stress-strain diagrams were recorded, at 4.2°K *very regular, fine*

---

[1] See the tensile stress-strain curves in Sec. 16-8, page 600, on which the data above were based.

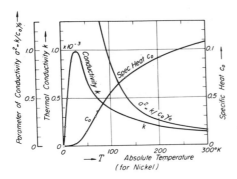

FIG. 13-25. Thermal properties of nickel at very low temperatures: specific heat c_0, (kcal/kg °K); thermal conductivity k, kcal/(cm sec °K); conductivity parameter $a^2 = k/c_0\gamma_0$, cm²/sec.

serrations became evident[1] in dense succession, the amplitudes of which increased with the total, plastic extension ε, clearly disclosing the fact that the yielding at 4°K ceased to progress uniformly over the gauge length and that in the tensile bars numerous, discrete shear layers had formed with each abrupt change in the stress-strain curve. It seems to us probable that the finely jagged curves in the diagrams are a consequence of the peculiar conditions of the conduction of heat through metals that prevail under very low temperatures and control the evanescence of heat generated in the layers of shear. To depict these conditions, in Fig. 13-25 three curves are plotted for the metal nickel, representing the specific heat c_0 in kcal/(kg °K); the thermal conductivity k in kcal/(cm sec °K); and the conductivity parameter $a^2 = k/c_0\gamma_0$ cm²/sec occurring in FOURIER's equation of heat conduction [Eq. (13-17)]:

$$\frac{\partial \theta}{\partial t} = a^2 \Delta\theta, \qquad a^2 = \frac{k}{c_0\gamma_0}, \tag{13-127}$$

in their dependence on the absolute temperature T (γ_0 kg/cm³ denotes the specific weight, taken invariable) over the range from zero absolute to $T = 300°K = 27°C$.[2]

One sees that in the lower range the specific heat c_0 decreases very rapidly toward zero absolute, while the thermal conductivity k increases to a sharp maximum and then drops very rapidly with decreasing

[1] The jagged curves may be seen in Sec. 16-8 in Figs. 16-64 through 16-66.
[2] Values of the thermal conductivity k in terms of watts/(cm °K) for metals are tabulated in comprehensive form in the pamphlet by ROBERT L. POWELL and WILLIAM A. BLANPIED, Thermal Conductivity of Metals and Alloys at Low Temperatures (a review of literature), 68 pp., Natl. Bur. Standards (U.S.) Circ. 556, Sept. 1, 1954. In order to express k in the technical system of units, kg weight, cm, sec, one converts

$$1 \text{ watt}/(\text{cm °K}) = 0.000239 \text{ kcal}/(\text{cm sec °K}).$$

The values of the specific heat c_0 at low temperatures may be found in LANDOLT and BÖRNSTEIN, "Physikalisch-Chemische Tabellen," 5th ed., 2 vols., 1923, and supplementary vol. 2 (Pt. 2, 1931) and 3 (Pt. 3, 1936), Julius Springer, Berlin.

absolute temperature,[1] both c_0 and k vanishing at $T = 0$. One also sees that the parameter $a^2 = k/c_0\gamma_0$ tends to increase enormously toward $T = 0$. These facts show that if FOURIER's equation (13-127) were to be precisely rewritten over a wider range of temperatures, this would require considering c_0 and k as pure functions of θ, leading to insurmountable difficulties in solving problems in heat conduction. But a few interesting conclusions may be drawn from Fig. 13-25. Furthermore, it is conjectured that the conductivity parameter a^2 decreases with the cold work and the more a metal is stretched at these low temperatures, because of the increase of the number of the small cleavage facets in the crystal grains.

These circumstances make it probable, when the critical stage of discontinuous yielding in discrete shear layers has been reached, that the heat evolved within the thin flow layers temporarily cannot escape fast enough into the adjoining cold parts of the metal and that the temperature rises to a marked degree in the slip layers, causing the corresponding rapid drop of yield stress and load in each serration, until the temperature difference is canceled out through heat conduction.

Let us first evaluate the *rise of temperature* $\Delta\theta$ in the tensile bars from the amounts of heat H previously given, supposing tentatively that it is not dissipated by conduction. In the tests at room temperature we may assume that $H = \gamma_0 c_0 \Delta\theta$, using the invariable mean value of the specific heat c_0 corresponding to $T = 300°$K, namely, for nickel $c_0 = 0.108$ and for zirconium $c_0 = 0.066$ cal/°K. With the specific weights $\gamma_0 = 0.0085$ and 0.0065 kg/cm³, respectively, we find that *the temperature of the tensile bar rises* (at $T = 300°$K) *by*

$$\Delta\theta = 40.8°\text{C} \qquad in\ nickel,$$

$$\Delta\theta = 43.6°\text{C} \qquad in\ zirconium.$$

[1] In the range from $T = 0$ to $T = 40°$K, according to the Bureau of Standards tables, the thermal conductivity k in terms of watts/(cm °K) varies as

$$\frac{1}{k} = \alpha T^2 + \beta T^{-1} \qquad (13\text{-}128)$$

with the constants α and β for:

Nickel:	$\alpha \times 10^5 = 10.4$,	$\beta = 4.6$
Zirconium:	$= 125$	$= 34$
Iron:	$= 10.2$	$= 9.6$
Copper:	$= 2.5$	$= 0.35$

The analytic maximum of k, after Eq. (13-128), occurs at $T_m = (\beta/2\alpha)^{1/3}$ with the value $k_{max} = (2/3)(2\alpha\beta^2)^{-1/3}$ and, in the close vicinity of $T = 0$, k may be approximated by

$$k = 2.39 \times 10^{-4}\left(\frac{T}{\beta}\right) \qquad \text{kcal/(cm sec °K)} \qquad (13\text{-}129)$$

giving for
Nickel:
$$k = 7.0 \times 10^{-6}T$$
Zirconium:
$$k = 5.2 \times 10^{-5}T.$$

In the tests made at 4°K the expected rise $\Delta\theta$ being much greater, we have to give consideration to the variation of the specific heat c_0 with the temperature by letting

$$H = \gamma_0 \int_{4°K}^{T} c_0(T)\, dT = \gamma_0 \bar{c}_0\, \Delta\theta. \qquad (13\text{-}130a)$$

In order to estimate the mean value $\bar{c}_0$ over the unknown interval from $T_1 = 4°K$ to T we have replaced the curve $c_0(T)$ shown in Fig. 13-25 by a parabola passing through $(T = 0, c_0 = 0)$ and $(T_2 = 300°K, c_{02})$, by letting $c_0 = c_{02}(T/T_2)^{1/2}$. This gives for the unknown upper limit T of the integral of Eq. (13-130a)

$$\left(\frac{T}{T_2}\right)^{3/2} = \left(\frac{T_1}{T_2}\right)^{3/2} + \frac{3H}{2\gamma_0 c_{02} T_2} \qquad (13\text{-}130b)$$

and for *the rise in temperature in the tensile bar tested at* 4°K due to the heat H evolved from mechanical work ω, in first approximation, the values of $\Delta\theta$ at 4°K:

$$\underline{\Delta\theta = 172°C} \qquad \textit{for nickel,}$$

$$\underline{\Delta\theta = 239°C} \qquad \textit{for zirconium.}$$

This gives for nickel 4.2 and for zirconium 5.5 times the rise $\Delta\theta$ at room temperature.

We have to give consideration now to the discontinuous mode of yielding at 4°K and to the fact that single flow layers form. Suppose that in the tensile bar n thin, plane shear layers formed successively. Then in each layer a mechanical work ω/n was converted into heat H/n. But since yielding is instantaneously concentrated within a *single* layer of $(1/n)$th of the total bar volume, the density of specific work and heat evolved per unit volume flow layer are just ω and H, respectively. Thus suppose that a hot layer, having an average thickness $2h$, has at time $t = 0$ an initial, uniform temperature, say $\theta = \theta_0 = $ const, for $-h \leq x \leq h$ and is embedded on both sides in cold metal having the temperature $\theta = 0$ for $-\infty < x < -h$ and $h < x < +\infty$. It interests us to know *how fast the thermal shock* to which the layer is subjected by a sudden elevation of its temperature to θ_0 (to $\theta_0 = 172°C$ in nickel, $\theta_0 = 239°C$ in zirconium) will be dissipated by conduction of heat into the adjoining cold parts of the metal.

The solution of this classical problem of heat conduction is well known[1] for the case that $a^2 = k/\gamma_0 c_0 = $ const (independent of temperature θ) giving the symmetric curves for θ at later times t shown in Fig. 13-26 according to the equation

$$\theta = \frac{\theta_0}{2}\left[\psi\left(\frac{h-x}{2a\sqrt{t}}\right) + \psi\left(\frac{h+x}{2a\sqrt{t}}\right)\right], \qquad (13\text{-}131)$$

---

[1] See page 400 (FRANK and MISES, *op. cit.*, vol. 2, p. 191).

where the functions ψ denote the *Gaussian* error integral functions of the indicated arguments.

In the middle plane $x = 0$ of the flow layer the temperature θ decreases with the time t as

$$\theta = \theta_0 \psi(v) = \theta_0 \psi\left(\frac{h}{2a\sqrt{t}}\right) = \theta_0 \psi\left(\sqrt{\frac{t_0}{t}}\right),$$

where

$$v^2 = \frac{h^2}{4a^2 t} = \frac{t_0}{t}, \qquad (13\text{-}132)$$

$$t_0 = \frac{h^2}{4a^2} = \frac{h^2 \gamma_0 c_0}{4k},$$

the temperature θ for $x = 0$ having the following values:

$v =$	∞	3	2.5	2	1.5	1
$t/t_0 =$	0	0.111	0.160	0.250	0.444	1
$\theta/\theta_0 =$	1	1.000	1.000	0.995	0.966	0.843

$v =$	0.8	0.6	0.4	0.2	0.1	0.0316	0.01
$t/t_0 =$	1.563	2.778	6.250	25	100	1,000	10,000
$\theta/\theta_0 =$	0.742	0.604	0.428	0.223	0.112	0.035	0.0112

with the rate of decrease

$$\frac{d\theta}{dt} = \frac{2\theta_0}{\sqrt{\pi}} e^{-v^2} \frac{dv}{dt} = -\frac{\theta_0}{t_0 \sqrt{\pi}} v^3 e^{-v^2}, \qquad (13\text{-}133)$$

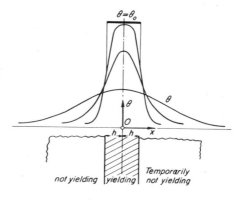

FIG. 13-26. Temperatures θ in and around a plasticized layer $2h$ of metal after sudden yielding.

giving for *the steepest rate* the beautifully symmetric expression

$$\left|\frac{d\theta}{dt}\right|_{\max} = \frac{\theta_0}{t_0\sqrt{\pi}}\,(3\!\!/\!\!_2)^{3\!\!/\!\!_2}\cdot e^{-3\!\!/\!\!_2}, \qquad (13\text{-}134)$$

defining the inflection point I of the temperature-time curve at (Fig. 13-27)

$$t_i = (2\!\!/\!\!_3)t_0, \qquad \theta_i = \theta_0\psi(1.225) = 0.9194\theta_0$$

and indicating that the temperature θ in the middle plane $x = 0$ of the flow layer drops faster with time t, the smaller t_0 and the greater $a^2 = k/\gamma_0 c_0$ are.

Since the preceding simple relations are based on fixed (temperature-independent) values of the thermal quantities c_0, k, and a^2, it requires a little thought to estimate their plausible values in the second case with which we are mainly concerned, namely, when the tensile test is run at the very low temperature of 4°K. Since the thermal shock heats up a thin flow layer suddenly in nickel by 172°C and the values of a^2, for nickel at 200°K, are $a^2 = 0.256$ and, at 100°K, $a^2 = 0.920$ cm²/sec, we shall not be too far wrong in assuming that, while T changes between 200° and 100°K, $a^2 = (2\!\!/\!\!_3)(0.920 - 0.256) = 0.440$ cm²/sec, and, hence, $t_0 = h^2/4a^2 = h^2/1.76$. Suppose that the thickness of the flow layers $2h$ were 1 mm, $h = 0.05$ cm. Then $t_0 = 1.42 \times 10^{-3}$ sec, and the absolute temperature T would reach the values (using the tabulated values on page 417) in the middle plane $x = 0$ of the layer upon cooling (Fig. 13-28, curve 22):

After time $t \times 10^3$ (sec) =	0	1.42	35.5	142	∞
Absolute temperature T (°K) =	176	149	42	24	4

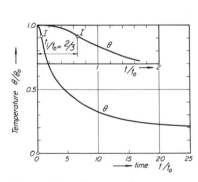

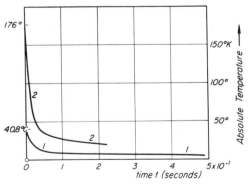

FIG. 13-27. Decay of temperature θ with time t in middle plane $x = 0$ of a suddenly plasticized flow layer.

FIG. 13-28. Dissipation of heat shock in a thin Lüders flow layer in nickel. Curve 1-1 in tensile test at room temperature. Curve 2-2 in tensile test run at 4°K.

The temperature in the flow layer would drop from 176° to 24°K in 0.142 sec. But it has been observed[1] that the ultimate strength of nickel varies approximately linearly near the absolute zero, decreasing with T over the range $0 < T < 200°$K as

$$\sigma_{l\,max} = 7,400 - 19T. \qquad (13\text{-}135)$$

Thus while the initial temperature of the heat shock $T = 176°$K stagnated at this high value only for a very short time, it would have reduced σ_{lmax} (and the flow stresses) very substantially, from 7,400 to $\sigma_{lmax} = 4,050$ kg/cm^2, had it lasted a trifle longer. But our rough estimates of the aftereffects of these thermal shocks, spreading in thin layers of metal, offer sufficient proof that the strange serrations in the stress-strain diagrams recorded at temperatures approaching the absolute zero $T = 0$ are caused by repeated drops of the yield stresses due to the short periods of intermittent concentration of thermal energy in the plasticized layers of flow. The oscillations of load become pronounced because at 4°K it requires in nickel more than twice and in zirconium even more than three times the work ω to deform these metals plastically than at room temperature and because the capacity for raising the temperature when heat is created through conversion of mechanical work increases enormously with the evanescent values of the specific heat c_0.

That the serrations are associated with brief thermal shocks is further supported by the observations made in the stress-strain curve for zirconium taken at 4°K, in which they started to show up right after the bend of the diagram and increased to much greater amplitudes than in nickel for the reasons that (1) the specific heat c_0 is roughly half as great, (2) the rise in temperature $\Delta\theta$ is 1.4 times greater, and (3) the ultimate strength near the absolute zero drops 1.5 times faster with an increase of temperature than for nickel, all three causes contributing toward enlarging the relative amplitudes of the load oscillations in zirconium compared with nickel. We may close these reflections on the plastic behavior of metals at very low temperatures by remarking that the concentration of thermal energy in the regions of minute weakness, from which the layers of shear originate and spread through a tensile bar, may create small transient fields of thermal stress around the clusters from which the ears of plastic distortion start to grow and— strange as it may appear—that thermal phenomena as yet little investigated may become significant for understanding the mechanical and plastic behavior of metals in this as yet little-explored lowest range of temperature.

[1] Cf. Sec. 16-8, Fig. 16-58, observed by E. T. WESSEL.

CHAPTER 14

INHERENT AND RESIDUAL STRESS

14-1. Introduction. By *inherent stresses* we understand a system of stresses which may exist in equilibrium in the interior of a body when neither normal nor shearing stresses are being transmitted in any element through its surface. In slender, prismatic, or cylindrical bars having their lateral faces free of stress, inherent stresses, however, may be present although tractions may act in their end sections, provided that the *resultant* forces and resultant moments of the latter vanish. Inherent stresses can be produced in a perfectly elastic substance. We have mentioned an example of them in Sec. 5-4A, in a closed elastic ring having the inner and outer cylindrical surface entirely free of stress, while in its interior a system of radial and tangential inherent stresses acts, and we noted that such systems are encountered whenever one of the components of elastic displacement is not a single-valued function of one of the coordinates. Several examples in elastic bodies were mentioned in the preceding chapter under nonuniform distributions of temperature, as in cylinders or disks, which may be strained by thermal stresses in the absence of any external loads.

Inherent stresses may, however, be generated in solids for a number of other reasons. If a part or several parts in a body have been *strained permanently* beyond the limit of plasticity and the external forces and moments are removed, the material in the overstrained region and around it will, in general, be subjected to inherent stresses which are then called *residual stresses*.[1] The yielding may be of a plastic nature, as in ductile metals, or because of the slow, permanent creep at elevated temperature under a prolonged action of stress or because of the viscous parts of the strains in viscoelastic substances which may accumulate when the bodies are kept under strain during longer time intervals.

If, for example, a hardened steel ball is pressed into a piece of ductile metal, the material around the yielded portion of the permanent

[1] German engineers call them *Eigenspannungen*, analogously to the word *Eigenfunktionen* introduced by mathematicians to designate the functions that belong to certain values of the parameters in a differential equation under given boundary conditions. The term *inherent stress* is proposed as a general term for this kind of internal stress created by the body itself, *residual stress* being reserved for the case where a permanent strain is its cause.

indentation cannot remain unstressed after the removal of the load, since the region under the ball has obtained normal compression stresses acting in a lateral direction. The plastically distorted part behaves like a hard wedge driven into a tree trunk. The residual stresses left in severely cold-rolled or drawn bars are familiar to steel men, particularly after such pieces have undergone successive reductions through repeated cold operations without annealing. Severely overdrawn wires or bars may contain in their interior even tension cracks at periodic intervals and may be entirely useless after having been overstrained permanently.

Residual stresses may be caused by structural changes in certain parts of a body in which the specific volume of the substance has been altered through an allotropic transformation of the crystal structure of the solid or the formation of a new phase in alloys due to heat treatment, normalization, hardening, quenching, the diffusion of carbon or of gas (nitrogen) through the surface into steel, etc. They are frequently the consequence of a combination of the effects induced by volume changes due to the formation of a new phase in the crystal structure and of the thermal stresses produced through unequal shrinkage when the temperatures are again equalized. A common example is the damage done to the wheels of railroad cars by repeated, severe braking operations, after which the circumference of the rims of the shrunk-on treads may become visibly red for a fraction of an inch thick through the friction-heat exerted by the brake shoes, while beyond the red-hot rim the material of the wheel remains cold, with the result that the severely overheated portion of the tread has to yield instantaneously under compression stresses (while it is still hot) and is immediately thereafter subjected to a rapid chilling by conduction of heat into the cool portions of the wheel. Although a volume increase due to the $\gamma - \alpha$ polymorphic transformation of steel accompanies quenching, during the thermal contraction which follows the general cooling of the rim, the permanent shrinkage exceeds the former extension in circumferential direction and makes the diameter of the outer portions of the tread too small to fit on the inner portions and the formerly red-hot parts of the tread will finally become severely strained in tension in the peripheral direction.[1]

---

[1] See CHARLES B. BRYANT, Mech. Eng., vol. 76, no. 3, p. 255, 1954. If such overstrained treads of railroad wheels are replaced and sawed through, they may open up and spring back violently and may break into several pieces, disclosing the high residual stresses that they contained. A related phenomenon in severely cold-drawn brass tubes (cartridges) is known as "season cracking" and may become conspicuous if such tubes are surrounded by a corrosive atmosphere (they may split open violently in the presence of minute amounts of mercury vapor in the air).

Whereas residual stresses of dangerous magnitude in important construction parts are the undesirable aftereffects of certain manufacturing processes and have to be eliminated by annealing, in a few cases they serve to advantage for the purpose of reducing the maximum values of the tensile stresses under service conditions in machine parts.

The Austrian artillery general UCHATIUS was one of the first to propose their utilization for prestressing the region around the bore of the early types of cast-bronze barrels of artillery guns in compression, by pulling a mandril with a slightly greater diameter than that of the barrel through the latter.   This led to the well-known process of *autofrettage* in the manufacture of heavy-walled gun barrels which is presently applied in arsenals by subjecting the steel barrels to high hydraulic pressures through which they are slightly expanded permanently for the purpose of setting up residual, circumferential, compression stresses around the bore, through which the peak stresses in tension at the bore during firing are substantially reduced.   A second example to be referred to is the overspeeding of steam-turbine disks. The disks of large steam turbines rotating at high angular velocities are essentially stressed in biaxial tension.[1]   In order to prevent unforeseen destruction of these disks by hidden flaws, it is a general practice to test them on the proving floors at angular speeds chosen for safety reasons 10 to 20 per cent higher than in service.   Solid disks or disks with a hub may thus be slightly expanded plastically around the center or near the hub; after overspeeding, residual compression stresses remain in them in the critical region which obtains the highest tensile stresses under operating conditions.[2]   As a further example, we may mention the surprisingly high bending strength of artificially chilled plate glass. When a red-hot plate of glass is subjected to rapid cooling by blowing cold air on both sides of it, a thin layer solidifies, while the temperature in the interior of the plate, which still behaves as a viscous material, at first remains unchanged.   In silica and glass, which have a low coefficient of thermal expansion (compared with metals), this at first sets up tensile stresses in the chilled surface layers which are comparatively not high.   When subsequently the soft interior cools slowly, the tensile surface stresses change to compression stresses upon the gradual, thermal contraction of the interior of the plate, but

---

[1] Vol. I, page 485.

[2] Cf. A. STODOLA, "Steam and Gas Turbines," English ed., vol. 2, p. 1080, McGraw-Hill Book Company, Inc., New York; also F. LÁSZLÓ, Geschleuderte Umdrehungskörper im Gebiet bleibender Deformation, Z. angew. Math. u. Mech., no. 5, p. 281, 1929.   Apart from the generation of a beneficial system of residual stresses, we may note that in ductile metals with pronounced strain hardening the strength has also been raised locally in the disks, provided that the Bauschinger effect does not obscure the advantages otherwise achieved.

glass, having a very high compression strength, withstands them well in the chilled surface layers, while under the low values of the viscosity in the warmer interior no damaging effects are produced by the small tensile stresses simultaneously produced there. The high, residual, compression stresses left in both surface layers raise the bending strength of chilled glass to its remarkably great value in the applications in which it may be subjected to tensile (bending) stress.

It did not escape the attention of EMIL HEYN, in his early work on residual stresses, that the latter have a significance also in the mechanism of the microstructure of metals and may be present in and around their crystal grains as *micro residual stresses* which he called "hidden elastic stresses."[1] Similarly, as we have recognized two types of surfaces of slip which accompany plastic deformation of metals, namely, the coarse layers of flow, the traces of which appear as LÜDERS' lines on polished specimens of mild steel, and the small packages of gliding surfaces (slip lines) inside the crystal grains, two types of inherent stresses may be distinguished, according to whether the regions in which they occur are comparable in size to those of a stressed body or whether they are of the order of the size of the crystal grains.

14-2. First Method of Calculating Residual Stresses Due to Yielding. In metals having a definite yield point, the residual stresses after unloading may, in a first approximation, be evaluated by assuming that after plastic deformation and subsequent removal of the

[1] In contrast to his *Reckspannungen* (inherent stresses). See E. HEYN, Festschr. Kaiser Wilhelm Ges., p. 121, 1921, and Stahl u. Eisen, 1917; also A. MARTENS and E. HEYN, "Materialienkunde," 2d ed., p. 280, J. Springer, Berlin, 1912. On residual stresses in drawn brass, compare G. MASING, Veröffentl. Siemenskonzern, Berlin, vol. 3, no. 1, 1923; no. 2, 1924; vol. 5, nos. 1 and 2, 1925; Z. Metallk., p. 257, 1924; Proc. First and Second Intern. Congr. Appl. Mechanics, Delft, 1924, and Zurich, 1926; also G. SACHS and G. ESPEY, Residual Stress in Cartridge-brass Tubing, Paper 1386, Metals Technol., and G. SACHS, Tightness of Expanded Tube Joints, ASME Applied Mechanics Meeting, 1947. On microresidual stresses, see a series of papers by F. LÁSZLÓ [Tessellated Stresses, Parts 1–5, J. Iron Steel Inst. (London), p. 173, 1943; p. 183, 1944; p. 207, 1945; p. 5, 1950] in which he considered the stress and strain systems set up in and around certain idealized elementary blocks of laminations of two phases of materials, embedded in random orientation in a common matrix, when the aggregate is subjected to a uniform stress or when the temperature is rapidly reduced, thus attempting to predict the microstresses which might be produced in the perlite of steel or in the structure of heterogeneous materials.

In regard to the subject of residual stresses, the reader is referred to an excellent short monograph by K. HEINDLHOFER, "Evaluation of Residual Stress," 186 pp., Metallurgy and Metallurgical Engineering Series, McGraw-Hill Book Company, Inc., New York, 1948, in which also the various methods of the experimental determination of these stresses are reviewed to which special reference is herewith made and to W. R. OSGOOD (ed.), "Residual Stresses in Metals and Metal Construction," 363 pp., Reinhold Publishing Corporation, New York, 1954.

load the metal behaves like a perfectly elastic material. Postulating an ideally plastic material which may represent a low-carbon steel having the familiar, idealized stress-strain diagram for a loading and unloading cycle reproduced in Fig. 14-1, in which the working stress has been reversed from its value at the yield point B to the stress for yielding in the opposite sense D, assuming small strains, suppose that we denote by

$$\sigma_x^*, \sigma_y^*, \sigma_z^*, \tau_{yz}^*, \tau_{zx}^*, \tau_{xy}^*$$

the stresses at the instant at which the yielding is just interrupted in a body (corresponding to point B in Fig. 14-1) and by

$$\sigma_x', \sigma_y', \sigma_z', \tau_{yz}', \tau_{zx}', \tau_{xy}'$$

a system of stresses assumed to act as if the body were perfectly elastic and chosen so that, when combined with the preceding system, the required values of the *resultant* forces and moments will result. For *complete unloading* the latter must vanish, but for partial unloading they would have specified values. The resulting differences in stress

$$\sigma_x = \sigma_x^* - \sigma_x', \dots, \qquad \tau_{yz} = \tau_{yz}^* - \tau_{yz}', \dots, \qquad (14\text{-}1)$$

then define the system of residual stresses.

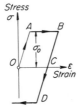

FIG. 14-1. Idealized stress-strain diagram for loading and unloading.

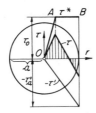

FIG. 14-2. Residual stress τ in permanently twisted round bar.

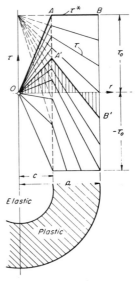

FIG. 14-3. Torsion. The broken lines represent the shearing stresses τ in bar during unloading after previous yielding. $OA'B'$ defines the residual stresses in bar after complete unloading.

EXAMPLE 1.   *Residual stresses in torsion.*   Suppose that a round bar of a mild steel has been twisted beyond the yield point in torsion and subsequently the torque is released.   The broken line OAB (Fig. 14-2) represents the shearing stress τ^* as a function of the variable radius r, τ_0 denoting the yield stress in simple shear, τ^*, γ^* the shearing stress and unit shear at r, and θ^* the specific angle of twist just when yielding is stopped.   If the bar is unloaded, it untwists through some angle θ', and the unit shear along a circle of radius r decreases an amount $\gamma' = r\theta'$ from its original value $\gamma^* = r\theta^*$ and becomes equal to

$$\gamma = \gamma^* - \gamma' = r(\theta^* - \theta'), \tag{14-2}$$

while the shearing stress decreases by the amount $\tau' = G\theta'r = \tau_a'r/a$.   By subtracting these values of τ' from those of τ^* represented by the broken line OAB, a set of broken lines is obtained, illustrating the distributions of the shearing stresses

$$\tau = \tau^* - \tau' \tag{14-3}$$

along the radius r during unloading (Fig. 14-3), corresponding to the angle of untwist θ', the line $OA'B'$ with shaded ordinates representing *the residual stresses τ for complete unloading*, when the external torque $M = M^* - M'$ vanishes or when

$$M' = (\tfrac{1}{2})\pi a^3 \tau_a' = (\tfrac{1}{2})\pi a^4 G\theta' = M^* = \pi\tau_0\left(\frac{2a^3}{3} - \frac{c^3}{6}\right), \tag{14-4}$$

giving

$$\tau_a' = \frac{\tau_0}{3}\left(4 - \frac{c^3}{a^3}\right), \tag{14-4a}$$

where c radius to which yielding progressed
      a outer radius of bar
     τ_a' elastic unloading stress at $r = a$

If the angle of untwisting θ' is further increased, the shearing stress τ at $r = a$ may reach the value $\tau = -\tau_0$ and the bar starts again to yield in the opposite sense.

The method indicated above may also be applied to strain-hardening metals in which the octahedral shearing stress of yielding increases monotonously with the octahedral unit shear according to a function $\tau_0 = f(\gamma_0)$.

EXAMPLE 2.   Considering again the torsion test in a round bar and referring to Vol. I, Chap. 21, we may obtain *the distribution of the residual shearing stresses τ for a strain-hardening metal* during unloading after computing the stresses τ^* from the stress-strain curve for shear $\tau^* = f(\gamma^*) = f(r\theta^*)$ for direct loading and subtracting from the ordinates of this curve the ordinates $\tau' = G\gamma' = \tau_a'r/a$ (Fig. 14-4) when the torque $M = M^* - M'$ vanishes.

EXAMPLE 3.   *The residual stresses in a hollow cylinder* strained permanently by internal pressure p may be obtained in a similar manner.   If, for example, the stress-strain curve for simple shear can be expressed by a power function[1]

$$\tau = \tau_0\gamma^{n/2}, \tag{14-5}$$

where τ_0 and $0 < n < 2$ are given constants, the radial and tangential stresses σ_r^* and σ_t^* in a thick-walled cylinder yielding under this law may be computed at the instant when the plastic flow is interrupted from

$$\sigma_r^* = -\frac{pa^n}{b^n - a^n}\left(\frac{b^n}{r^n} - 1\right),$$

$$\sigma_t^* = \frac{pa^n}{b^n - a^n}\left[(n - 1)\frac{b^n}{r^n} + 1\right], \tag{14-6}$$

[1] Cf. Vol. I, Sec. 31-2.

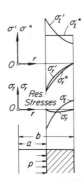

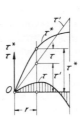

FIG. 14-4. Initial yield stresses τ^* and residual stresses τ in twisted round bar.

FIG. 14-5. Residual stresses σ_r, σ_t in cylinder which has been permanently deformed by internal pressure p.

a and b denoting the inner and outer radii of the cylinder, assuming that it has not changed its length. The residual stresses may be evaluated after release of the pressure p by subtracting from the preceding values of σ_r^* and σ_t^* those which would be present in a perfectly elastic cylinder (which may be obtained by taking $n = 2$ in the preceding expressions), namely,

$$\sigma_r' = -\frac{pa^2}{b^2 - a^2}\left(\frac{b^2}{r^2} - 1\right),$$

$$\sigma_t' = \frac{pa^2}{b^2 - a^2}\left(\frac{b^2}{r^2} + 1\right),$$

$$(14\text{-}7)$$

giving

$$\sigma_r = \sigma_r^* - \sigma_r', \qquad \sigma_t = \sigma_t^* - \sigma_t'. \qquad (14\text{-}8)$$

These differences remain valid as long as at no place within the cylinder the limit of plasticity is reached a second time during the removal of the pressure p. An example is shown in Fig. 14-5 for $n = 1$, $\tau = \tau_0 \gamma^{\frac{1}{2}}$.

EXAMPLE 4. *Residual stress in an overspeeded disk of uniform thickness.* Supposing the maximum-shearing-stress theory of yielding and that a disk of radius a was rotated at a peripheral velocity $u = a\omega$ at which the center portion has yielded, the velocity u at which the yielded portion extended to a radius $r = c$, according to Vol. I, Eq. (34-33), page 488, is determined by the equation

$$\frac{u^2}{u_0^2} = \frac{\sigma}{\sigma_0} = \frac{24a^4}{3(3 + \nu)a^4 - 2(1 + 3\nu)a^2c^2 + (1 + 3\nu)c^4}, \qquad (14\text{-}9)$$

where u_0 denotes for a thin free ring spinning in its plane the velocity at which the ring yields,

$$u_0 = a\omega_0 = \sqrt{\frac{\sigma_0 g}{\gamma_0}}, \qquad (14\text{-}10)$$

σ_0 being the yield stress in tension, γ_0 the specific weight of the disk material, g the gravity acceleration, and σ a characteristic constant stress as defined by Eq. (14-9). The velocity u in a partially yielding disk under the assumed law of yielding may be chosen between the limits

$$1.55u_0 \leq u \leq \sqrt{3}u_0 = 1.73u_0. \qquad (14\text{-}11)$$

The residual stresses after the disk is stopped may be computed by constructing the values of the radial and tangential stresses $\sigma_r{}^*$ and $\sigma_t{}^*$ corresponding to the peripheral velocity u given by Eq. (14-9), using Eqs. (34-31) and (34-32) of Vol. I, page 487, and subtracting from them the stresses $\sigma_r{}'$ and $\sigma_t{}'$ [Eqs. (34-27) and (34-29)], corresponding to an elastic disk run at the same angular velocity $\omega = u/a = \omega_0 \sqrt{\sigma/\sigma_0}$ at which the disk was spun when it yielded.

Two examples may illustrate this in Figs. 14-6 and 14-7 in which the curves representing stress systems $\sigma_r{}^*$, $\sigma_t{}^*$, $\sigma_r{}'$, $\sigma_t{}'$ and $\sigma_r = \sigma_r{}^* - \sigma_r{}'$, $\sigma_t = \sigma_t{}^* - \sigma_t{}'$ are reproduced for *the case of partial yielding*, when the yielded zone extended to $c = a/2$, corresponding to the value of characteristic stress $\sigma = 2.65\sigma_0$ and peripheral velocity $u = \sqrt{2.65}u_0 = 1.63u_0$, and *for a disk that yielded completely* ($c = a$, $\sigma = 3\sigma_0$, $u = \sqrt{3}u_0 = 1.73u_0$). The distribution of the residual stresses is shown at the bottom of each figure (the ordinates of the tangential residual stress σ_t are shaded) below the other stress curves that served for their construction; it should be noted that the center portion of the disk is stressed in compression, the maximum value of which in the center of the disk $r = 0$ amounts to $\sigma_r = \sigma_t = -0.095\sigma_0$ and $\sigma_r = \sigma_t = -0.238\sigma_0$, when $c = a/2$ and $c = a$, respectively. When the disk was spun to complete yielding, however, in its peripheral region tensile stresses σ_t of considerable magnitude ($r = a$, $\sigma_t = 0.476\sigma_0$) were produced through the presence of which the value of previous overspeeding to the velocity $u = \sqrt{3}u_0$ becomes questionable. The residual stresses in the latter case (after previous complete yielding) are expressed by the formulas

$$\sigma_r = -\frac{1+3\nu}{8}\sigma_0\left(1 - \frac{r^2}{a^2}\right) = -0.238\sigma_0\left(1 - \frac{r^2}{a^2}\right),$$

$$\sigma_t = -\frac{1+3\nu}{8}\sigma_0\left(1 - \frac{3r^2}{a^2}\right) = -0.238\sigma_0\left(1 - \frac{3r^2}{a^2}\right). \tag{14-12}$$

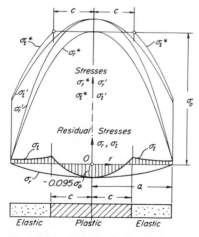

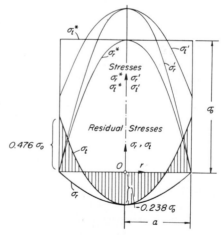

FIG. 14-6. Residual stresses σ_r, σ_t in circular disk of ideally plastic material after overspeed test in which it yielded in region

$$0 \leq r \leq c = a/2.$$

FIG. 14-7. Residual stresses σ_r, σ_t in circular disk after overspeed test in which the entire disk yielded.

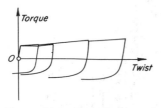

FIG. 14-8. Twisting and untwisting permanently hollow steel cylinders. (*After W. Bader.*)

14-3. Second Method of Evaluating Residual Stresses, Assuming General Law of Deformation for Unloading.

On cyclic loading and unloading, aggregates of crystal grains in solids disclose elastic hysteresis and aftereffects, and for the ductile metals, after a previous yielding and a subsequent unloading, the stress-strain curve, after the stresses change their signs, distinctly departs from a straight unloading line (*the Bauschinger effect*). The simplifying assumption on which the determination of residual stresses was based in the preceding section, namely, that the stresses during unloading may be computed using the linear stress-strain law of elasticity, thus gradually becomes the more invalid, the absolutely greater the stresses were which changed their signs. One may think of improving the former method by postulating for the unloading branches of the stress-strain curves their actual forms made plausible from observations. How this might be done is briefly indicated in the example of the torsion of a round bar by utilizing some observations of W. BADER[1] which he made by twisting and untwisting plastically several thick-walled cylinders of a grade of mild steel which gave him the series of torque-M–twist-θ curves reproduced in Fig. 14-8. From it and from an analogous series of curves obtained for copper that had been prestretched in tension and subsequently tested in compression (see Vol. I, Fig. 3-7, page 20), it is recognized that to each grade of direct cold work belongs or corresponds a branch of unloading, with subsequent cold work in the reversed sense of straining being of a gradually changed but individual shape.

The upper parts of the unloading branches remaining practically straight lines, suppose that we agree to make use of one and the same of these curves for unloading,[2] by shifting it back and forth in the direction of the γ axis in Fig. 14-9, representing the shearing-stress–unit-shear diagram of the metal and using it for the evaluation of the stresses during an unloading process, starting at any point of the virgin curve $\tau^* = f(\gamma)$, supplying, when the angle of untwist θ' is specified, the corresponding values of the system $\gamma' = r\theta'$, τ'. The residual stresses are then $\tau = \tau^* - \tau'$. They have been plotted in Fig. 14-10 for the indicated values of the total angle of twist θ per unit length, showing the shearing stress τ in the cross section of a round bar in its dependence on the ratio r/a (r = variable radius, a = outer radius of

[1] W. BADER, Versuche über die Gleitflächenbildung in bleibend verdrillten Flusseisenstäben und über die in ihnen zurückgebliebenen Eigenspannungen, Dissertation, University of Göttingen, 1927.

[2] Trans. ASME, 1930.

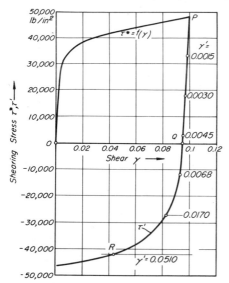

FIG. 14-9. Stress-strain diagram in simple shear for direct and reversed loading.

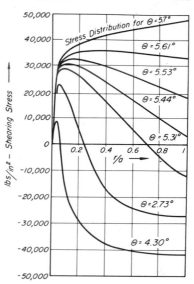

FIG. 14-10. Distributions of shearing stress τ in a round bar under torsion during unloading and subsequent twisting in reversed sense for various angles of twist θ per unit length, using stress-strain diagram shown in Fig. 14-9.

bar). One sees that the sharp corners of the distributions previously obtained by the first method (Sec. 14-2, Figs. 14-2 and 14-3) have now disappeared and that for the greater angles of untwist curves of entirely new shapes for τ are obtained. The method just indicated may be further generalized by considering for each grade of direct plastic twist the corresponding individual curve $\tau' = f(\gamma')$ for unloading.

14-4. Experimental Demonstration of Residual Stresses. By machining down stepwise on a lathe the outer portion of cold-drawn bars of brass and measuring their changes in length carefully in a comparator, the late E. HEYN[1] could show that cold-drawn metal bars contained considerable stresses in the axial direction. Figures 14-11 and 14-12 show the distribution of residual, axial stress that he found in round brass bars drawn from a diameter of 28 to 25 mm, the first reproducing the residual stresses after five days, the second two years after the cold-drawing. If tensile stresses acted in the outer portion, these are partially annihilated by removal of an outer layer; consequently, the compression stresses in the center region of the specimen will decrease, and the bar will expand axially, and vice versa. The former case was observed by Heyn in cold-drawn brass bars, while quenched-steel bars were found to be stressed in their outer portion in compression. In his method of evaluating the axial residual normal stresses, however, Heyn did not take account of the presence of

[1] Metall u. Erz, Halle, p. 411, 1918.

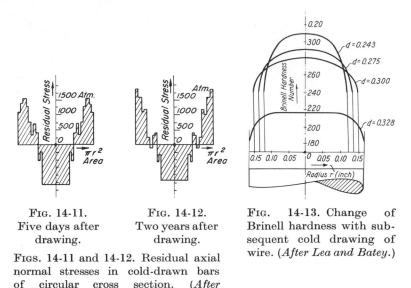

FIG. 14-11.
Five days after
drawing.

FIG. 14-12.
Two years after
drawing.

FIG.   14-13. Change   of
Brinell hardness with subsequent cold drawing of
wire. (*After Lea and Batey.*)

FIGS. 14-11 and 14-12. Residual axial
normal stresses in cold-drawn bars
of circular cross section. (*After
E. Heyn.*)

radial and tangential stresses in such cold-worked bars. The latter were also
taken into consideration by G. SACHS and G. ESPEY[1] who have improved this
method of computation of residual stresses under rotationally symmetric cases.
A method using also the principle of removal o⌐ material has been proposed by
D. ROSENTHAL and J. T. NORTON[2] utilizing electric strain gauges. The latter
authors also applied X-ray diffraction for measuring the residual stresses in the
surface of specimens not requiring a dissection of the test piece.[3]

The residual stresses in cold-drawn round bars are due to nonuniform yielding
when the bars pass through the conical drawing dies and their diameters are
reduced under the high pressures exerted by the dies. LEA and BATEY[4] have
shown that cold-drawn steel wires have a much higher Brinell hardness in their
center region than near their surface. Figure 14-13 reproduces the distribution
of hardness that they measured in the cross section of wires drawn to successively
smaller diameters: $d = 0.328$, 0.300, 0.275, and 0.243 in. Since larger Brinell
hardness numbers correspond to greater amounts of cold work [greater octahedral
unit shears and shearing stresses in the strain-hardening function $\tau_0 = f(\gamma_0)$ of
a ductile metal], one understands why in cold-drawn bars great residual stresses
remain. To remove these stresses the bars and wires must be annealed intermittently.

Concerning the systems of residual stresses that are produced for the purpose
of improving the state of stress in certain highly stressed regions in machine
parts, such as rotating turbine disks under service conditions, the question may
be raised whether these systems of artificially generated, inherent stresses will

[1] The Measurement of Residual Stresses in Metals, Iron Age, vol. 148, pp. 36 and 63,
1941.

[2] A Method of Measuring Tri-axial Residual Stress in Plates (Set Up by Welding
Seams), J. Am. Welding Soc., vol. 24, p. 295, 1945.

[3] Proc. Soc. Exptl. Stress Anal., vol. 1, p. 73, 1943.

[4] Proc. Inst. Mech. Engrs. (London), no. 4, p. 865, 1928.

last indefinitely.   The example reproduced in Fig. 14-12 would seem to indicate that changes with time in the distribution of residual stresses due to excessive cold work may be expected to occur.   If highly prestressed parts are exposed to elevated temperatures over long periods of time, the designer will have to assure himself that the inherent stresses are not subject to subsequent relaxation.

Part IV

THEORY OF PERFECTLY LOOSE AND OF GENERALLY PLASTIC SUBSTANCE

CHAPTER 15

EQUILIBRIUM IN PERFECTLY LOOSE MATERIALS.
GENERALIZATION OF THE CONCEPT OF A
PERFECTLY PLASTIC SUBSTANCE

Furthermore, things which seem to us hard and dense
Must needs be made of particles more hooked
One to another, and be held in union
Welded throughout by branch-like elements.
First in this class diamond stones, inured
To despise blows, stand in the foremost rank,
And stubborn blocks of basalt, and the strength
Of hard iron, and brass bolts which, as they struggle
Against their staples, utter a loud scream.
But things that are liquid and of fluid substance
Must consist rather of smooth round elements;
For the several globules do not hold together:
And you may scoop up poppy seed as easily
As water, which will also, if you spill it,
Glide away with as ready a downward flow.

LUCRETIUS (first century B.C.), "Of Nature of Things"
(*De Rerum Natura*), translated by R. C. Trevelyan,
p. 59, Cambridge University Press, London, 1937.

15-1. The Condition of Slip in Perfectly Loose Material.
Among the various concepts explored in Vol. I, Chap. 15, for formulating
conditions of failure by yielding or fracture in quasi-isotropic, polycrystalline solids, we mentioned a particular case of the MOHR theory of
strength, for which the enveloping curve of the major principal stress
circles consists of two symmetrically inclined straight lines (Vol. I,
page 219), as having a significance if one desires to treat the equilibrium
in loosely aggregated substances such as dry earth or sand. In this
chapter we shall make use of the graphical representation of states of
stress and follow the ideas that OTTO MOHR expressed with such
admirable clarity in a chapter devoted to the theory of idealized

435

FIG. 15-1. OTTO C. MOHR.† (Born Oct. 18, 1835, in Wesselburen, Holstein; died Oct. 2, 1918, in Dresden.) Tablet, dedicated to Otto Mohr's seventieth birthday by eleven professors of mechanics who taught in German and Austrian engineering universities. (*Courtesy Prof. Otto Graf, Stuttgart.*)

granular media in his book in which a collection of his most important investigations in engineering mechanics was published.[1]

Consider an ideal, perfectly loose material made up of loose, round, or polyhedric particles of average size. A heap of sun-dried beach sand piled up in a dune may be an example, among actual materials. A body of such material, exposed to external forces and stressed under the weight of the particles, cannot transmit components of normal stress other than purely compression stresses. To these we shall assign here the positive sign. The components of shear stress in loose sand in a state of equilibrium must satisfy certain inequality conditions. Consider an arbitrary point in the interior of the loose mass, lay a plane section through it, and imagine that the two adjoining portions of mass on the sides of it for an instant are stiffened to a rigid body. The slightest

---

[1] OTTO MOHR, "Abhandlungen aus dem Gebiete der technischen Mechanik," 567 pp., Wilhelm Ernst und Sohn, Berlin, 1st ed., 1905; 2d ed., 1914; cf. Abhandlung VI, Die Lehre vom Erddruck, pp. 236–263.

† His most important investigations in revised form may be found in the selected collection of fourteen of his investigations: Dr. Ing. OTTO MOHR, Geheimer Rat und Professor, Dresden, "Abhandlungen aus dem Gebiete der technischen Mechanik" (quoted in footnote 1), containing reports on the principles of graphostatics, along the ideas of VARIGNON and CULMANN; on geometry of masses and of stress and strain (his graphical methods for representation of the inertia moments of masses distributed in space and of homogeneous states of stress and small strains); his fundamental theory of mechanical strength of solids and of the limiting states of equilibria in ideally loose substances, based on the enveloping curve of the major, principal stress circles (parts of which he published as early as 1882); and his method of tracing with pencil and ruler the elastic lines of beams by constructing funicular lines. Engineers owe to OTTO MOHR many elements that they daily utilize in the design of trusses, bridges, retaining walls, and machine parts.

displacement of one against the other part along the plane section is resisted by a certain force of a frictional nature. It seems reasonable to assume that the shear stress τ_n expressing this frictional resistance per unit area in the contact plane, at the instant when motion (slip) just starts, is proportional to the normal stress σ_n acting across the section and furthermore that $|\tau_n|$, before any slip may occur, nowhere can become greater than a certain fraction μ of the normal stress σ_n in any orientation of the section, so that

$$|\tau_n| \leqq \mu\sigma_n, \tag{15-1}$$

where the subscript n refers to the direction of the external normal to the section. Recalling *Coulomb's law* of sliding solid friction, let us denote by ρ the angle of solid friction by letting

$$\mu = \tan \rho. \tag{15-2}$$

Equilibrium in a loose sand requires, then, that the double inequality be satisfied in it,

$$-\sigma_n \tan \rho < \tau_n < +\sigma_n \tan \rho, \tag{15-3}$$

and, should a surface of slip develop in the mass, that the corresponding inequality sign be replaced by the sign of equality.

Suppose that we trace the three principal stress circles representing a state of stress in a plane figure, using σ_n and τ_n as rectangular coordinates and denoting the principal stresses[1] in algebraic order by $\sigma_1, \sigma_2, \sigma_3$ in an element of material. A point P having the coordinates σ_n, τ_n (Fig. 15-2) will represent the normal and shear stress σ_n, τ_n in a section having the normal n, and P must be situated within one of the curvilinear triangles bounded by the three principal stress circles. Vector $\overline{OP}$ inclined at an angle δ with respect to the σ_n axis represents, in fact, the resultant stress acting in the section n and

$$\tan \delta = \frac{\tau_n}{\sigma_n}. \tag{15-4}$$

[1] Cf. Vol. I, page 97.

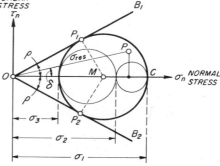

FIG. 15-2. A limiting state of stress represented by its three principal Mohr stress circles.

Since δ can never become greater than the angle of friction ρ, we see that the multitude of all the major principal stress circles having the diameters $\sigma_1 - \sigma_3$, representing the limiting states of stress in the loose material that are just possible before the equilibrium may become disturbed, must be tangent to the two straight lines $\overline{OB_1}$, and $\overline{OB_2}$, inclined at the angle of friction ρ with respect to the σ_n axis. The major circles corresponding to all states of stress prevailing in the loose mass must lie within the angular sector B_1OB_2 and those representing those states in which slip may just start must be tangent to the two Mohr straight-line envelopes $\overline{OB_1}$ and $\overline{OB_2}$. Since

$$\sin \rho = \frac{\sigma_1 - \sigma_3}{\sigma_1 + \sigma_3}, \tag{15-5}$$

we must conclude that the limiting states of stress causing danger of slip are all characterized by a fixed ratio between the major and minor principal stress, namely,

$$\frac{\sigma_1}{\sigma_3} = \frac{1 + \sin \rho}{1 - \sin \rho} = \cotan^2 \left(\frac{\pi}{4} - \frac{\rho}{2} \right). \tag{15-6}$$

The direction of σ_1 in a material element defines *the major pressure direction* in it, and *the two plane sections* in which τ_n/σ_n becomes equal to either $+\tan \rho$ or $-\tan \rho$ (the points P_1 and P_2 in Fig. 15-2) *are called the slip planes*. In a limiting state of equilibrium in a sand heap they define two families of surfaces which, according to Mohr's representation of stress, must always intersect each other along the direction of the intermediate principal stress σ_2 and are called *the surfaces of slip*. To each point in the interior of a sand heap belong, in the limiting state of equilibrium, two surfaces of slip. Suppose that we turn the plane of the section with its normal n around the axis of the intermediate stress σ_2. Point P (σ_n, τ_n) then describes the major stress circle in Fig. 15-3a. Remembering that thereby the normal n to the plane section turns by one-half of the angle PMC and that the positions of point P coinciding with the points C, P_1, and P_2 define the positions of the section across which the major principal pressure σ_1 acts and of the two planes of slip,

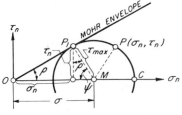

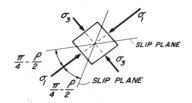

FIG. 15-3a. A major Mohr stress circle.   FIG. 15-3b

respectively, we see that the latter must be inclined toward each other at the acute angle ψ equal to $(\pi/2) - \rho$ and inclined with respect to the major principal pressure σ_1 direction at the equal angles $(\pi/4) - (\rho/2)$ (Fig. 15-3b).

Since the resultant stress σ_{res} that acts across one or the other surface of slip, in a limiting state of equilibrium, is represented in Fig. 15-2 by the two vectors of equal length $\overline{OP}_1 = \overline{OP}_2$, *we note the characteristic property of the equilibria in loose masses*, that at any given point *the resultant stresses σ_{res} are equal to each other across the two surfaces of slip* passing through the point and inclined at the angle of friction ρ with respect to their normals n.

15-2. Homogeneous Plane Stress.   In the engineering applications of the theory describing the distributions of pressure in loose materials one encounters most frequently cases depending on two coordinates x, y.   One important case is concerned with the earth pressures supported by solid retaining walls.   If we denote the components of normal stress by σ_x, σ_y and of shear stress by τ_{xy}, the third normal stress σ_z being of no interest if the displacements occur within the x,y plane, and if we designate by α the angle of inclination of the major principal pressure σ_1 with respect to the x axis and by σ_2 the minor principal pressure, we have for a plane state of stress (Fig. 15-4)

$$\sigma_x = (\tfrac{1}{2})(\sigma_1 + \sigma_2) + (\tfrac{1}{2})(\sigma_1 - \sigma_2)\cos 2\alpha,$$
$$\sigma_y = (\tfrac{1}{2})(\sigma_1 + \sigma_2) - (\tfrac{1}{2})(\sigma_1 - \sigma_2)\cos 2\alpha, \qquad (15\text{-}7)$$
$$\tau_{xy} = (\tfrac{1}{2})(\sigma_1 - \sigma_2)\sin 2\alpha.$$

We may introduce here the mean stress σ and the maximum shearing stress τ_{max}:

$$\sigma = \frac{\sigma_1 + \sigma_2}{2} = \frac{\sigma_x + \sigma_y}{2}, \qquad \tau_{max} = \frac{\sigma_1 - \sigma_2}{2},$$

$$\sigma_x = \sigma + \tau_{max}\cos 2\alpha,$$
$$\sigma_y = \sigma - \tau_{max}\cos 2\alpha, \qquad (15\text{-}8)$$
$$\tau_{xy} = \tau_{max}\sin 2\alpha.$$

Since the condition of slip

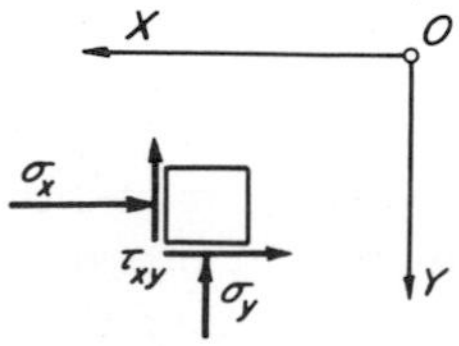

FIG. 15-4

$$\sigma_1 = \frac{1 + \sin\rho}{1 - \sin\rho} \cdot \sigma_2, \qquad (15\text{-}9)$$

using $\sigma_1 + \sigma_2 = 2\sigma$, is expressed also by

$$\sigma_1 = \sigma(1 + \sin\rho),$$
$$\sigma_2 = \sigma(1 - \sin\rho), \qquad (15\text{-}10)$$
$$\tau_{max} = \sigma\sin\rho,$$

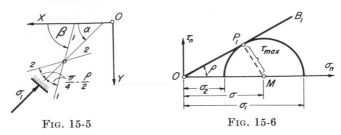

FIG. 15-5   FIG. 15-6

we see that Eqs. (15-8) in *the limiting state of plane stress in loose material* may be expressed by

$$\sigma_x = \sigma(1 + \sin \rho \cos 2\alpha),$$
$$\sigma_y = \sigma(1 - \sin \rho \cos 2\alpha), \tag{15-11}$$
$$\tau_{xy} = \sigma \sin \rho \sin 2\alpha.$$

The acute angle between the two planes of slip $(\pi/2) - \rho$ is bisected by the direction in which the major pressure σ_1 acts (Fig. 15-5). Suppose that we call the plane of slip that makes the angle β

$$\beta = \alpha + \frac{\pi}{4} - \frac{\rho}{2}, \tag{15-12}$$

with the x axis the *first* plane of slip. We may then replace α by β and rewrite Eqs. (15-11) in the alternative form:

$$\sigma_x = \sigma[1 + \sin \rho \sin (2\beta + \rho)],$$
$$\sigma_y = \sigma[1 - \sin \rho \sin (2\beta + \rho)], \tag{15-13}$$
$$\tau_{xy} = -\sigma \sin \rho \cos (2\beta + \rho).$$

Like Eqs. (15-10), they also embody the condition of slip and are valid in any infinitesimal material element in a loose mass in a limiting state of equilibrium. The radius $\overline{MP_1}$ of any major principal stress circle in such a state (such as the circle shown in Fig. 15-6 which is tangent to the straight Mohr envelope $\overline{OB_1}$) represents the maximum shearing stress $\tau_{max} = (\sigma_1 \mp \sigma_2)/2 = \sigma \sin \rho$. By using its value in terms of the components of stress σ_x, σ_y, τ_{xy}, *the condition of slip in a limiting state of equilibrium in loose material* may also be expressed explicitly by

$$(\sigma_x - \sigma_y)^2 + 4\tau_{xy}^2 = (\sigma_x + \sigma_y)^2 \sin^2 \rho = 4\sigma^2 \sin^2 \rho, \tag{15-14}$$

which is identically satisfied by the expressions for σ_x, σ_y, τ_{xy} given in Eqs. (15-11) or (15-13).

15-3. Rankine's Distribution of Stress in Loose Earth under Its Own Weight. Let us now consider the distribution of pressure in loose earth under its own weight in an extended ground, bounded by a plane, horizontal or sloping under a small angle δ, as one of the simplest examples of nonhomogeneous plane stress. The state of stress under a free, plane surface, gently inclined at an angle δ, was treated by RANKINE[1] as early as 1856. Its surfaces of slip are two families of parallel planes that appear in their traces in the x,y plane (assumed as a vertical plane with its origin situated in the free surface plane, with the x,y axes in horizontal and vertical position, the y axis pointing downward) as two families of parallel, *straight* lines of slip. The inclination angle α of the major principal pressure σ_1 in Eqs. (15-10) being independent of x and y, we take $\alpha = $ const in them and, after substituting the values of σ_x, σ_y, τ_{xy} in the two conditions of equilibrium,

$$\frac{\partial \sigma_x}{\partial x} + \frac{\partial \tau_{xy}}{\partial y} = 0, \qquad \frac{\partial \sigma_y}{\partial y} + \frac{\partial \tau_{xy}}{\partial x} = \gamma \qquad (15\text{-}15)$$

($\gamma = $ specific weight of earth), we obtain

$$\frac{\partial \sigma}{\partial x} = -\gamma \frac{\sin \rho \sin 2\alpha}{\cos^2 \rho}, \qquad \frac{\partial \sigma}{\partial y} = \gamma \frac{1 + \sin \rho \cos 2\alpha}{\cos^2 \rho}, \qquad (15\text{-}16)$$

or for the mean pressure σ the value

$$\sigma = \frac{\gamma}{\cos^2 \rho} [y(1 + \sin \rho \cos 2\alpha) - x \sin \rho \sin 2\alpha + c_1]. \qquad (15\text{-}17)$$

If the surface of the ground is horizontal, the major pressure σ_1 in an extended body of earth can be oriented either in a horizontal or in a vertical position. When σ_1 acts in a horizontal direction, $\alpha = 0$, and (after letting $c_1 = 0$) we obtain the equations

$$\sigma = \gamma y \frac{1 + \sin \rho}{\cos^2 \rho} = \frac{\gamma y}{1 - \sin \rho},$$

$$\sigma_x = \sigma_1 = \sigma(1 + \sin \rho) = \frac{1 + \sin \rho}{1 - \sin \rho} \cdot \gamma y = \gamma y \cotan^2 \left(\frac{\pi}{4} - \frac{\rho}{2}\right), \qquad (15\text{-}18)$$

$$\sigma_y = \sigma_2 = \sigma(1 - \sin \rho) = \gamma y,$$

$$\tau_{xy} = 0;$$

and when σ_1 acts in a vertical direction, $\alpha = \pi/2$, we have

$$\sigma = \gamma y \frac{1 - \sin \rho}{\cos^2 \rho} = \frac{\gamma y}{1 + \sin \rho},$$

$$\sigma_x = \sigma_2 = \sigma(1 - \sin \rho) = \frac{1 - \sin \rho}{1 + \sin \rho} \cdot \gamma y = \gamma y \tan^2 \left(\frac{\pi}{4} - \frac{\rho}{2}\right), \qquad (15\text{-}19)$$

$$\sigma_y = \sigma_1 = \sigma(1 + \sin \rho) = \gamma y,$$

$$\tau_{xy} = 0.$$

[1] W. J. M. RANKINE, On the Stability of Loose Earth, Phil. Trans. Roy. Soc. London, vol. 147, 1856–1857. This theory may also be found in RANKINE's textbook, "A Manual of Applied Mechanics," London, 1861.

These two preceding limiting states of plane stress can be visualized by their straight lines of slip and by a simple experiment. Stick a smoothly polished shovel in a vertical position in a flat sandy beach and try to move the blade forward or backward. Paying attention only to what occurs on the front side of the shovel, after scratching away some sand at its rear, we find that, if the shovel is pushed horizontally forward, it will remove a much larger wedge of sand (Fig. 15-7a) than if it is moved in the opposite direction (Fig. 15-7b), releasing in front of it a portion of sand which under its own weight will slip downward by a small amount. We shall also feel that the force required to push the sand forward is considerably greater than the force needed in the second case.

Likewise, if the horizontal pressures σ_x that we computed in Eqs. (15-18) and (15-19) were supported by a perfectly smooth, vertical wall or slab, we would expect when moving the slab toward the sand (Fig. 15-8a) that a much greater force E_1 would be needed than when the slab is withdrawn horizontally, E_2 (Fig. 15-8b). In the theory of earth pressures supported by retaining walls, one calls E_1 *the passive* and E_2 *the active earth pressure*, corresponding to Eqs. (15-18) and (15-19), respectively.

Since the components of stress increase proportionally with the depth y, the resultant force E_1 and E_2 exerted by the horizontal pressures σ_x on a smooth, vertical wall of height h must act at the depth $(\frac{2}{3})h$. For a layer of sand of unit thickness $z = 1$ the resultant, horizontal forces on a vertical wall are equal to:

Resultant of *passive* pressures:

$$E_1 = \frac{\gamma h^2}{2} \cotan^2 \left(\frac{\pi}{4} - \frac{\rho}{2} \right),$$

Resultant of *active* pressures:

$$E_2 = \frac{\gamma h^2}{2} \tan^2 \left(\frac{\pi}{4} - \frac{\rho}{2} \right),$$

having the ratio

$$\frac{E_1}{E_2} = \cotan^4 \left(\frac{\pi}{4} - \frac{\rho}{2} \right). \tag{15-20}$$

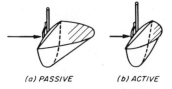

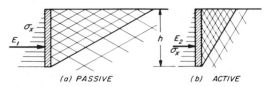

(a) PASSIVE   (b) ACTIVE   (a) PASSIVE   (b) ACTIVE

FIG. 15-7. Sand pressure.

FIG. 15-8. Pressure of a gravitating loose mass on a smooth vertical wall, according to Rankine.

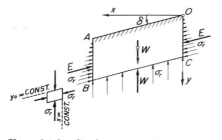

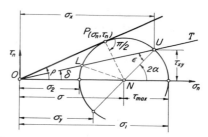

FIG. 15-9. Conjugate sections in a sloping gravitating soil.

FIG. 15-10. Major principal stress circle.

Since E_1 represents an *upper value and E_2 a lower value* of the inner (passive) or (active) resistance of earth due to internal friction, the first and second state of stress have been called the *upper and the lower limiting state of equilibrium in a loose substance*, respectively. The upper equilibrium prevails in earth when the long wedge shown in Fig. 15-8a is to be detached against the inner resistance E_1 due to friction and action of the weight; the lower equilibrium is created behind a wall yielding backward, a little pushed by the forces (E_2) activated in the short wedge shown in Fig. 15-8b. Expressed briefly, in a ground with a horizontal surface, the major, principal pressure σ_1 acts in the upper or the lower equilibrium, in the horizontal or vertical direction, respectively, corresponding to which the slip lines take the characteristic positions indicated in Fig. 15-8a and b.

If the surface of gravitating earth is a plane inclined gently under a small angle δ, the components of stress have invariable values in the planes

$$y - x \tan \delta = y_0 = \text{const} \tag{15-21}$$

parallel to the surface, and we shall not be wrong in assuming that the mean stress $\sigma = (\frac{1}{2})(\sigma_x + \sigma_y)$ increases proportionally with the depth y_0,

$$\sigma = cy_0, \tag{15-22}$$

and that the angle α defining the direction of the principal, major pressure σ_1 also stays invariable. The determination of the constants c and α in the formulas for the stresses

$$\sigma_x, \ \sigma_y = cy_0(1 \pm \sin \rho \cos 2\alpha),$$
$$\tau_{xy} = cy_0 \sin \rho \sin 2\alpha, \qquad \sigma = cy_0, \tag{15-23}$$

is facilitated by the observation already made by O. MOHR that the vertical and the inclined planes $x = \text{const}$ and $y_0 = \text{const}$ (Fig. 15-9) are *conjugate plane sections*, having the property that the *resultant* stresses acting across these two sets of planes in the earth's body are mutually parallel to the other set of planes. This is brought out by tracing a line $\overline{OT}$ in a direction parallel to the free surface plane in Mohr's diagram (Fig. 15-10). Line $\overline{OT}$ intersects the major stress circles, one of which has been traced in the figure, at the points U and L. Obviously, the coordinates of point U or of point L represent the components of stress σ_x and τ_{xy} in the upper or in the lower limiting state of equilibrium, respectively, and the coinciding vectors $\overline{OU}$ or $\overline{OL}$ measure the magnitudes of the resultant stress $\sigma_{\text{res}} = \sqrt{\sigma_x{}^2 + \tau_{xy}{}^2}$ in the vertical sections in the earth body, satisfying the condition of conjugate sections with respect to σ_x, τ_{xy}, namely, that

$$\tan \delta = \frac{\tau_{xy}}{\sigma_x} = \text{const.} \tag{15-24}$$

The latter condition determines the unknown angle α of the principal stress direction. After substituting in it the values of σ_x and τ_{xy} taken from Eqs. (15-23), one obtains

$$\tan \delta = \frac{\sin \rho \sin 2\alpha}{1 + \sin \rho \cos 2\alpha}. \tag{15-25}$$

Considering $\cos 2\alpha$ as the unknown, this is a quadratic equation for $\cos 2\alpha$, from which one computes

$$\cos 2\alpha = \frac{-\sin^2 \delta \pm \cos \delta \cdot \sqrt{\sin^2 \rho - \sin^2 \delta}}{\sin \rho}, \tag{15-26}$$

disclosing that the angle δ under which the earth surface is inclined can never become greater than the angle of internal friction ρ; otherwise the square root would become imaginary. The slopes of a pile of loose sand can never be steeper than the angle of repose ρ.

Suppose that we consider the *upper* limiting state of equilibrium under an embankment rising under the angle δ. Applying the sine theorem to the triangle ONU with the inscribed values of σ_x, τ_{xy}, σ, and τ_{max} and the angles appearing in Fig. 15-10, denoting the angle OUN by $\varepsilon = 2\alpha - \delta$, with $\tau_{\text{max}} = \sigma \sin \rho$, then

$$\sin \varepsilon = \sin (2\alpha - \delta) = \frac{\sigma \sin \delta}{\tau_{\text{max}}} = \frac{\sin \delta}{\sin \rho}, \tag{15-27}$$

thus determining the angles ε and $2\alpha = \varepsilon + \delta$. For the *lower* equilibrium we would likewise have to consider $\triangle ONL$.

There remains evaluation of the constant c. Going back to Eq. (15-17), letting $c_1 = 0$, which gave us the expression for the mean stress σ satisfying the conditions of equilibrium, we find after equating the two expressions on hand for σ,

$$\sigma = c y_0 = c(y - x \tan \rho) = \frac{\gamma[y(1 + \sin \rho \cos 2\alpha) - x \sin \rho \sin 2\alpha]}{\cos^2 \rho}, \tag{15-28}$$

and after using Eqs. (15-25) and (15-27), the two equivalent expressions for the constant c,

$$c = \frac{\gamma[1 + \sin \rho \cos (\varepsilon + \delta)]}{\cos^2 \rho} = \frac{\gamma \cos \delta(\cos \delta + \sin \rho \cos \varepsilon)}{\cos^2 \rho}, \tag{15-29}$$

with which all unknowns have been determined and the stresses σ_x, σ_y, τ_{xy}, etc., after writing in Eqs. (15-23) $2\alpha = \varepsilon + \delta$.

In *horizontal ground* we have $\delta = \varepsilon = 0$ and consequently

$$c = \frac{\gamma(1 + \sin \rho)}{\cos^2 \rho},$$

$$\sigma = \frac{\gamma y(1 + \sin \rho)}{\cos^2 \rho},$$

$$(15\text{-}30)$$

coinciding with the previous expression as given in Eqs. (15-18).

On the other hand, if the *ground drops under the natural slope (the angle of repose)* $\rho = \delta$, for the *lower state of equilibrium* under an embankment $\cos 2\alpha = -\sin \rho = \cos (\pi/2 + \rho)$, the major pressure σ_1 makes an angle $\alpha = (\pi/4) + (\rho/2)$ with the x axis, and the stresses become equal to

$$\sigma_x = \sigma \cos^2 \rho = \frac{\sigma}{2}(1 + \cos 2\rho),$$

$$\sigma_y = \sigma(1 + \sin^2 \rho) = \frac{\sigma}{2}(3 - \cos 2\rho), \qquad (15\text{-}31)$$

$$\tau_{xy} = \frac{\sigma}{2}\sin 2\rho, \qquad \sigma = \gamma(y - x \tan \rho).$$

The first family of slip lines has vertical lines and the second family, the oblique lines dropping under the angle of repose ρ (Fig. 15-11).

In the *upper equilibrium state* under an embankment inclined under an angle $\delta < \rho$ the lines of slip run as illustrated in Fig. 15-12, with the resultant stresses as indicated in it. If the angle δ equals the angle of repose ρ, the major principal pressure σ_1 deviates from the horizontal plane by the angle $\alpha = (\pi/4) - (\rho/2)$. It is hoped that the reader will familiarize himself with these extremely simple details, evidenced by looking at Mohr's diagrams in the preceding examples.

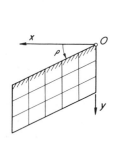

FIG. 15-11. The lines of slip in a ground that is inclined under the natural slope $\delta = \rho$.

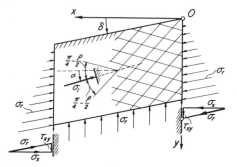

FIG. 15-12. Gravitating loose mass.

A few figures for the angle of friction ρ and the unit weight γ for supposedly cohesionless, freshly piled up, loose masses are listed in Table 15-1, after values claimed by MÜLLER-BRESLAU:[1]

TABLE 15-1

Type of material	Angle of friction ρ, deg	Specific weight γ, kg/m³
Embankment of dry earth	35–40	1,400
Embankment of wet earth	27	1,800
Sand, dry	30–35	1,580–1,650
Sand, wet	25	2,000
Clay, dry	40–45	1,500
Clay, wet	20–25	1,900

15-4. State of Stress in Gravitating, Loose Material Expressed by Polar Coordinates. Using plane polar coordinates r, φ, denoting the radial and tangential normal stresses by σ_r and σ_t, the shear stress by τ_{rt} (taken positive as the arrows indicate in Fig. 15-13), these three components of stress must satisfy the two conditions of equilibrium,

$$\frac{\partial \sigma_r}{\partial r} + \frac{\sigma_r - \sigma_t}{r} + \frac{\partial \tau_{rt}}{r\,\partial \varphi} = \gamma \sin \varphi,$$

$$\frac{\partial \sigma_t}{r\,\partial \varphi} + \frac{2\tau_{rt}}{r} + \frac{\partial \tau_{rt}}{\partial r} = \gamma \cos \varphi,$$

(15-32)

and the limiting condition at which slip may start,

$$(\sigma_r - \sigma_t)^2 + 4\tau_{rt}^2 = (\sigma_r + \sigma_t)^2 \sin^2 \rho = 4\sigma^2 \sin^2 \rho. \qquad (15\text{-}33)$$

With the maximum shear stress $\tau_m = \sigma \sin \rho$ and the mean stress $\sigma = (\sigma_r + \sigma_t)/2$, the latter condition is equivalent to

$$\sigma_1 = (1 + \sin \rho)\sigma, \qquad \sigma_2 = (1 - \sin \rho)\sigma, \qquad (15\text{-}34)$$

where σ_1 and σ_2 denote the major and minor principal pressure. Equations (15-32) have the particular solution

$$\sigma_r = \gamma r \sin^3 \varphi = \frac{\gamma}{2} r \sin \varphi \cdot (1 - \cos 2\varphi),$$

$$\sigma_t = \gamma r \sin \varphi \cos^2 \varphi = \frac{\gamma}{2} r \sin \varphi \cdot (1 + \cos 2\varphi), \qquad (15\text{-}35)$$

$$\tau_{rt} = \gamma r \sin^2 \varphi \cos \varphi = \frac{\gamma}{2} r \sin \varphi \sin 2\varphi.$$

---

[1] H. F. B. MÜLLER-BRESLAU, "Erddruck auf Stützmauern," Alfred Kröner, Leipzig, 1906.

One means of establishing limiting states of equilibria in loose gravitating material consists of
introducing an AIRY stress function $F(r,\varphi)$, by
postulating that the complete solution of Eqs.
(15-32) may be expressed in the form

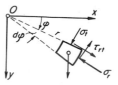

$$\sigma_r = \gamma r \sin^3 \varphi + \frac{F_r}{r} + \frac{F_{\varphi\varphi}}{r^2},$$

FIG. 15-13

$$\sigma_t = \gamma r \sin \varphi \cos^2 \varphi + F_{rr},$$

$$\tau_{rt} = \gamma r \sin^2 \varphi \cos \varphi - \frac{F_{r\varphi}}{r} + \frac{F_\varphi}{r^2}, \qquad (15\text{-}36)$$

$$\sigma = \frac{\gamma}{2} r \sin \varphi + (\tfrac{1}{2}) \Delta F,$$

where the partial derivatives of F have been denoted by the corre-
sponding subscripts r and φ and the Laplacian operator by $\Delta F = F_{rr} + (F_r/r) + (F_{\varphi\varphi}/r^2)$. After substituting the expressions of Eqs. (15-36) in
Eq. (15-33) there results

$$\left(\frac{F_r}{r} + \frac{F_{\varphi\varphi}}{r^2} - F_{rr} - \gamma r \sin \varphi \cos 2\varphi \right)^2 + \left(-\frac{2F_{r\varphi}}{r} + \frac{2F_\varphi}{r^2} + \gamma r \sin \varphi \sin 2\varphi \right)^2$$

$$= (\gamma r \sin \varphi + \Delta F)^2 \sin^2 \rho = 4\sigma^2 \sin^2 \rho, \quad (15\text{-}37)$$

a partial differential equation of second order and of second degree for the
stress function F of which, in a few cases, solutions may be determined.

Another method relies on expressing the three components of stress
σ_r, σ_t, τ_{rt} in a form that satisfies [as the analogous equations (15-11) did
for rectangular coordinates] the condition of slip [Eq. (15-33)] by
letting

$$\sigma_r = \sigma[1 + \sin \rho \cos 2(\varphi - \alpha)],$$

$$\sigma_t = \sigma[1 - \sin \rho \cos 2(\varphi - \alpha)], \qquad (15\text{-}38)[1]$$

$$\tau_{rt} = -\sigma \sin \rho \sin 2(\varphi - \alpha),$$

where α denotes the angle under which the major stress σ_1 is inclined
with respect to the x axis ($\varphi = 0$), and by considering σ and α as two
unknown functions to be determined by the two equilibrium conditions
(15-32). We shall return to this method in Sec. 15-5.

But Eqs. (15-38) now enable us to *split up* the partial, nonlinear
differential equation of hyperbolic type [Eq. (15-37)] *into three separate
equations*, by noting that the two parentheses on the left side represent
$(\sigma_r - \sigma_t)^2$ and $4\tau_{rt}^2$ which can be expressed by Eqs. (15-38). This

---

[1] Equations (15-38) are verified by expressing the three components σ_r, σ_t, τ_{rt},
through σ_x, σ_y, τ_{xy} as given in Eqs. (15-11).

resolves the task into integrating the simultaneous system of three differential equations

$$-\gamma r \sin \varphi \cos 2\varphi + \frac{F_r}{r} + \frac{F_{\varphi\varphi}}{r^2} - F_{rr} = 2\sigma \sin \rho \cos 2(\varphi - \alpha),$$

$$\gamma r \sin \varphi \sin 2\varphi - \frac{2F_{r\varphi}}{r} + \frac{2F_{\varphi}}{r^2} = -2\sigma \sin \rho \sin 2(\varphi - \alpha), \quad (15\text{-}39)$$

$$\gamma r \sin \varphi + \Delta F = 2\sigma$$

for the three unknown functions F, σ, and α which are linear at least for two of them: F and σ.

The same process of linearization may be applied in rectangular coordinates, converting Eqs. (15-11) and the equilibrium conditions into

$$-\gamma y + F_{yy} - F_{xx} = 2\sigma \sin \rho \cos 2\alpha,$$

$$F_{xy} = -\sigma \sin \rho \sin 2\alpha, \quad (15\text{-}40)$$

$$\gamma y + \Delta F = 2\sigma.$$

A few solutions of both groups are readily obtainable.

Two exact solutions that possibly have not been noticed in the abundant literature devoted to problems of earth pressures might be quoted here, solving two instructive cases of some practical interest to engineers. Suppose that the angle α defining the direction of the major pressure σ_1 were a linear function of the polar angle φ and that we assume for the variable angle α

$$\alpha = \frac{\pi}{4} + \frac{\varphi}{2} \quad \text{or} \quad \alpha = \frac{3\pi}{4} + \frac{\varphi}{2} ; \quad (15\text{-}41)$$

furthermore, for the stress function F we assume the form

$$F = r^3 \cdot \phi(\varphi), \quad (15\text{-}42)$$

and by guessing a mean stress σ, compatible with the latter function, we let σ equal

$$\sigma = \gamma r f(\varphi). \quad (15\text{-}43)$$

This allows eliminating the independent variable r in the group of Eqs. (15-39) and converting them into three simultaneous total, linear differential relations for the two unknown functions of the single variable φ, namely, $\phi(\varphi)$ and $f(\varphi)$.

We shall prove now that *they supply the formulas for the exact distribution of stress in the earth under a sharp ridge and a sharp valley*, having plane slopes inclined just under the angle of repose ρ and symmetrically oriented with respect to their vertical axes.

SOLUTION FOR RIDGE:

$$\alpha = \frac{\pi}{4} + \frac{\varphi}{2}.$$

After substituting for

$$\cos 2(\varphi - \alpha) = \sin \varphi, \qquad \sin 2(\varphi - \alpha) = -\cos \varphi,$$

Eqs. (15-39) take the form

$$-3\phi + 0 + \phi'' = \gamma \sin\varphi \cdot (\cos 2\varphi + 2f \sin \rho),$$
$$0 - 4\phi' + 0 = \gamma(-\sin \varphi \sin 2\varphi + 2f \sin \rho \cos \varphi), \qquad (15\text{-}44)$$
$$9\phi + 0 + \phi'' = \gamma(-\sin \varphi + 2f).$$

With the determinant $D = 48$, solving for the variable ϕ, as if ϕ, ϕ', ϕ'' were the unknowns in three linear equations, gives for the function $\phi(\varphi)$

$$\phi = \frac{\gamma}{6} [-\sin \varphi \cos^2 \varphi + (1 - \sin \rho \sin \varphi)f], \qquad (15\text{-}45)$$

and, after eliminating ϕ and ϕ'' from them, there results the differential equation for the function $f(\varphi)$

$$\frac{df}{d\varphi} = \frac{f \cdot \cos \varphi}{\sin \varphi - \sin \rho}, \qquad (15\text{-}46)$$

from which f and the mean stress $\sigma = \gamma r f(\varphi)$ are found equal to

$$\sigma = \gamma r f = \gamma r c(\sin \varphi - \sin \rho), \qquad (15\text{-}47)$$

satisfying the boundary conditions that, for $\varphi = \rho$ and $\varphi = \pi - \rho$. σ vanishes in these two surface planes of the ridge. Since its vertical symmetry axis $\varphi = \pi/2$ coincides with the principal axis $\alpha = \pi/2$, along this line the weight of a thin column of earth requires that σ_r be equal to $\sigma_r = \gamma r$, and the first of Eqs. (15-38) taken for $\varphi = \pi/2$,

$$\sigma_r = \sigma(1 + \sin \rho) = \gamma r c \cos^2 \rho, \qquad (15\text{-}48)$$

defines the integration constant $c = 1/\cos^2 \rho$.

Herewith Eqs. (15-38) expressing *the state of stress under a sharp ridge* of earth take the simple form

$$\sigma_r = \sigma(1 + \sin \rho \sin \varphi),$$
$$\sigma_t = \sigma(1 - \sin \rho \sin \varphi),$$
$$\tau_{rt} = \sigma \sin \rho \cos \varphi, \qquad (15\text{-}49)$$
$$\sigma = \frac{\gamma r(\sin \varphi - \sin \rho)}{\cos^2 \rho},$$

provided that its two plane slopes rest under the angle of repose ρ. The same state of stress is expressed in rectangular coordinates x, y, $r = \sqrt{x^2 + y^2}$ by

$$\sigma_x = \sigma(1 - \sin \rho \sin \varphi) = \sigma\left(1 - \frac{y}{r} \sin \rho\right),$$

$$\sigma_y = \sigma(1 + \sin \rho \sin \varphi) = \sigma\left(1 + \frac{y}{r} \sin \rho\right),$$

$$\tau_{xy} = \sigma \sin \rho \cos \varphi = \sigma \frac{x}{r} \sin \rho, \qquad (15\text{-}50)$$

$$\sigma = \frac{\gamma}{\cos^2 \rho} (y - r \sin \rho).$$

The distribution of stress across the ridge along a horizontal plane $\overline{AB}$ is seen in Fig. 15-14. The orientation of the major principal pressure $\sigma_1 = \sigma(1 + \sin \rho)$ along any circle $r = $ const, traced around the peak O as center, follows the simple rule that all vectors σ_1 converge toward point C situated at the top of the circle (Fig. 15-15).

We may list the explicit expression for the *Airy stress function* $F(r,\varphi)$ that solved the problem in polar and rectangular coordinates:

$$F = r^3 \phi(\varphi) = \frac{\gamma r^3}{6 \cos^2 \rho} [-\cos^2 \rho \sin \varphi \cos^2 \varphi + (\sin \varphi - \sin \rho)(1 - \sin \rho \sin \varphi)],$$

$$F = \frac{\gamma}{6 \cos^2 \rho} [-x^2 y \cos^2 \rho + r^2(y - r \sin \rho)(r - y \sin \rho)]. \qquad (15\text{-}51)$$

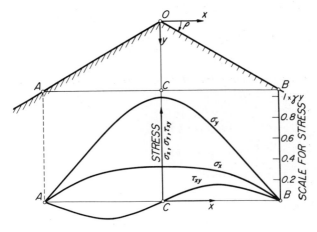

FIG. 15-14. Distribution of stress along a horizontal section AB in the depth y across a ridge of gravitating, loose earth.

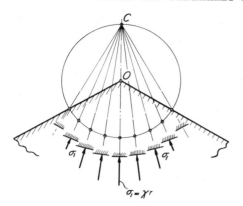

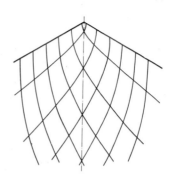

FIG. 15-15. Orientation of major principal pressure σ_1 in loose earth under a ridge.

FIG. 15-16. Lines of slip under a ridge of gravitating earth ($\rho = \pi/6$).

The differential equations for the *lines of slip*,[1]

(1) $$\frac{r\,d\varphi}{dr} = \tan(\beta_1 - \varphi) = \cotan\frac{\rho + \varphi}{2},$$

(2) $$\frac{r\,d\varphi}{dr} = \tan(\beta_2 - \varphi) = \tan\frac{\rho - \varphi}{2}$$

(15-52)

give for their equations

(1) $$r[1 + \cos(\rho + \varphi)] = p = \text{const},$$
(2) $$r[1 - \cos(\rho - \varphi)] = q = \text{const},$$

(15-53)

representing two families of coaxial, confocal and isogonal parabolas with the focus situated at the peak O of the ridge, the constants p and q defining their parameters. The axis of one family coincides with the profile line $\varphi = \rho$ and of the other family with $\varphi = \pi - \rho$, which are the only straight slip lines, the parabolas thus starting with vertical tangents at the points of the profile lines of the ridge (Fig. 15-16). We may add that the preceding relations obviously express the *lower* mode of limiting equilibrium caused by the weight of the mountain.[2]

[1] With the relations:

$$\beta_1 = \alpha + \frac{\pi}{4} - \frac{\rho}{2},$$

$$\beta_2 = \alpha - \frac{\pi}{4} + \frac{\rho}{2},$$

$$\alpha = \frac{\pi}{4} + \frac{\varphi}{2}.$$

[2] One may indeed easily prove that the mean stress σ in a thin sector bordering the right profile line $\varphi = \rho$, when the coordinate r is indefinitely increased, tends to approach the value in Eqs. (15-49) $\sigma = \gamma r \sin(\varphi - \rho)/\cos\rho$ that coincides with the expression of σ in the *lower* Rankine state under an oblique surface plane inclined under the natural slope ρ in Eqs. (15-31).

SOLUTION FOR VALLEY:

$$\underline{\alpha = (3\pi/4) + (\varphi/2)}$$

Supposing that the two plane slopes of a valley are inclined under the angle of repose ρ (Fig. 15-17), we may list the formulas which are the counterpart of those of the ridge as follows:
Distribution of stress in polar coordinates:

$$
\begin{aligned}
\sigma_r &= \sigma(1 - \sin \rho \sin \varphi), \\
\sigma_t &= \sigma(1 + \sin \rho \sin \varphi), \\
\tau_{rt} &= -\sigma \sin \rho \cos \varphi, \\
\sigma &= \frac{\gamma r(\sin \varphi + \sin \rho)}{\cos^2 \rho} ;
\end{aligned}
\tag{15-54}
$$

and expressed in rectangular coordinates:

$$
\begin{aligned}
\sigma_x &= \sigma\left(1 + \frac{y}{r} \sin \rho\right), \\
\sigma_y &= \sigma\left(1 - \frac{y}{r} \sin \rho\right), \\
\tau_{xy} &= -\sigma \frac{x}{r} \sin \rho, \\
\sigma &= \frac{\gamma}{\cos^2 \rho} (y + r \sin \rho).
\end{aligned}
\tag{15-55}
$$

The major pressure $\sigma_1 = \sigma(1 + \sin \rho)$ in the symmetry axis $\varphi = \pi/2$ below the sharp concave corner O of the valley is now oriented in the horizontal direction, and the vectors σ_1 along a circle $r = $ const take the positions indicated in Fig. 15-17 pointing to a point C at the bottom of the circle.   The distribution of stress along a horizontal plane $y = $ const below the valley may be seen in Fig. 15-18.

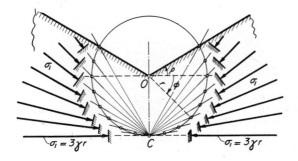

FIG. 15-17. Orientation of the major principal pressure σ_1 under a valley ($\rho = \pi/6$).

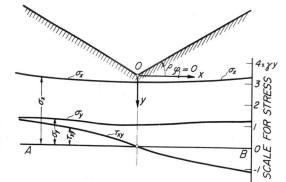

FIG. 15-18. Distribution of stress along a horizontal plane AB in the depth $y = $ const below valley ($\rho = \pi/6$).

The differential equations of the slip lines,

(1) $$\frac{r\,d\varphi}{dr} = -\tan\frac{\varphi + \rho}{2},$$

(2) $$\frac{r\,d\varphi}{dr} = -\cotan\frac{\varphi - \rho}{2},$$ (15-56)

define the system of curves,

(1) $$r[1 - \cos(\varphi + \rho)] = p,$$

(2) $$r[1 + \cos(\varphi - \rho)] = q,$$ (15-57)

representing again two families of confocal, coaxial, isogonal common parabolas, having the corner of the valley O for their focus and their axes oriented along the extensions of the two valley slopes, with the apexes of the parabolas situated, however, within the body of earth, both systems of curves again turning upward at greater values of r (Fig. 15-19)   Their trend indicates that here we have an *upper* state of equilibrium,

We may note that, along the horizontal plane $y = 0$ ($\varphi = 0$ and $\varphi = \pi$) passing through the bottom O of the valley, the stresses defined in Eqs. (15-54) take the values

$$\sigma_r = \sigma_t = \sigma = \frac{\gamma r \sin\rho}{\cos^2\rho},$$

$$\tau_{rt} = \mp\gamma r \tan^2\rho \qquad \text{for } \varphi = \begin{cases} 0 \\ \pi \end{cases},$$ (15-58)

and that the plane $y = 0$ is loaded by a resultant stress σ_{res},

$$\sigma_{res} = \sqrt{\sigma_t^2 + \tau_{rt}^2} = \sigma\sqrt{1 + \sin^2\rho},$$ (15-58a)

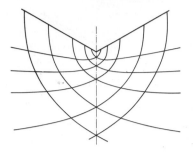

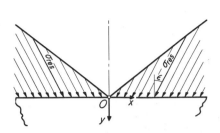

FIG. 15-19. Lines of slip in
earth under a valley ($\rho = \pi/6$).

FIG. 15-20

that increases proportionally with r and is inclined under the same angle
ε with respect to the normals of plane $y = 0$, since

$$\tan \varepsilon = \frac{|\tau_{rt}|}{\sigma_t} = \sin \rho = \text{const.} \qquad (15\text{-}58b)$$

This distributed load is seen in Fig. 15-20. We may consider the block
of earth under the plane $y = 0$ carrying the oblique stresses σ_{res} as a
distributed external load on its surface and conclude that the solution
for the valley developed in the preceding equations also defines the
maximum *pressures, applied obliquely under the angle* ε in parallel
directions that an extended body of loose earth can carry on its plane,
horizontal surface just before slip starts.

**15-5. The F. Kötter Equations of the Theory of Perfectly
Loose Materials.** We have seen that in a limiting state of plane
stress the components of stress σ_x, σ_y, τ_{xy} can be expressed [see Eqs.
(15-13)] by

$$\sigma_x = \sigma[1 + \sin \rho \sin (2\beta + \rho)],$$
$$\sigma_y = \sigma[1 - \sin \rho \sin (2\beta + \rho)], \qquad (15\text{-}59)$$
$$\tau_{xy} = -\sigma \sin \rho \cos (2\beta + \rho),$$

satisfying the condition of slip [Eq. (15-14)]

$$(\sigma_x - \sigma_y)^2 + 4\tau_{xy}^2 = 4\sigma^2 \sin^2 \rho. \qquad (15\text{-}60)$$

The German engineer F. KÖTTER[1] proposed as early as 1903 that the
mean stress σ and the angle β of inclination of the first line of the slip
$\beta = \alpha + (\pi/4) - (\rho/2)$ be considered as the two unknown, dependent
variables to be evaluated from the two conditions of equilibrium valid
in gravitating, loose earth:

$$\frac{\partial \sigma_x}{\partial x} + \frac{\partial \tau_{xy}}{\partial y} = 0, \qquad \frac{\partial \sigma_y}{\partial y} + \frac{\partial \tau_{xy}}{\partial x} = \gamma. \qquad (15\text{-}61)$$

[1] F. KÖTTER, Die Bestimmung des Druckes an gekrümmten Gleitflächen, eine
Aufgabe aus der Lehre vom Erddruck, Ber. Akad. Wiss., Berlin, pp. 229–233,
1903.

If we write temporarily

$$2\beta + \rho = \delta,$$

after substituting the values σ_x, σ_y, τ_{xy} from the Eqs. (15-59) in Eqs. (15-61), the latter take the form

$$\frac{\partial \sigma}{\partial x} + \sin \rho \left(\sin \delta \cdot \frac{\partial \sigma}{\partial x} - \cos \delta \cdot \frac{\partial \sigma}{\partial y} \right) + 2\sigma \sin \rho \left(\cos \delta \cdot \frac{\partial \beta}{\partial x} + \sin \delta \cdot \frac{\partial \beta}{\partial y} \right) = 0,$$

$$\tag{15-62}$$

$$\frac{\partial \sigma}{\partial y} - \sin \rho \left(\sin \delta \cdot \frac{\partial \sigma}{\partial y} + \cos \delta \cdot \frac{\partial \sigma}{\partial x} \right) + 2\sigma \sin \rho \left(-\cos \delta \cdot \frac{\partial \beta}{\partial y} + \sin \delta \cdot \frac{\partial \beta}{\partial x} \right) = \gamma.$$

Let us introduce the arc lengths s_1 and s_2 measured along the first and second lines of slip, respectively, by making use of the partial derivatives:[1]

$$\frac{\partial}{\partial s_1} = \cos \beta \cdot \frac{\partial}{\partial x} + \sin \beta \cdot \frac{\partial}{\partial y},$$

$$\frac{\partial}{\partial s_2} = \sin (\beta + \rho) \cdot \frac{\partial}{\partial x} - \cos (\beta + \rho) \cdot \frac{\partial}{\partial y}.$$

$$\tag{15-63}$$

Then, after multiplying the first and second of Eqs. (15-62) by $\cos \beta$, $\sin \beta$, respectively, and adding and after multiplying the first and second of Eqs. (15-62) by $\sin (\beta + \rho)$, $-\cos (\beta + \rho)$, respectively, and adding, one obtains, using the partial derivatives introduced in Eqs. (15-63), the two equations

$$\frac{1}{\sin \rho} \cdot \frac{\partial \sigma}{\partial s_1} + \frac{\partial \sigma}{\partial s_2} + 2\sigma \left[\cos (\beta + \rho) \cdot \frac{\partial \beta}{\partial x} + \sin (\beta + \rho) \cdot \frac{\partial \beta}{\partial y} \right] = \frac{\gamma \sin \beta}{\sin \rho},$$

$$\tag{15-64}$$

$$\frac{1}{\sin \rho} \cdot \frac{\partial \sigma}{\partial s_2} + \frac{\partial \sigma}{\partial s_1} + 2\sigma \left(-\sin \beta \cdot \frac{\partial \beta}{\partial x} + \cos \beta \cdot \frac{\partial \beta}{\partial y} \right) = -\frac{\gamma \cos (\beta + \rho)}{\sin \rho};$$

these may be further simplified by multiplying the first and second equations by $\sin \rho$, $-\sin^2 \rho$ and adding and by $-\sin^2 \rho$, $\sin \rho$, respectively, and adding, which gives for the two unknown functions σ and β the partial differential equations

$$\cos \rho \cdot \frac{\partial \sigma}{\partial s_1} + 2\sigma \sin \rho \cdot \frac{\partial \beta}{\partial s_1} = \gamma \sin (\beta + \rho),$$

$$\cos \rho \cdot \frac{\partial \sigma}{\partial s_2} - 2\sigma \sin \rho \cdot \frac{\partial \beta}{\partial s_2} = -\gamma \cos \beta.$$

$$\tag{15-65}$$

[1] Recalling that the first and second lines of slip are inclined at the angles

$$\beta_1 = \beta = \alpha + \frac{\pi}{4} - \frac{\rho}{2}, \qquad \beta_2 = \alpha - \frac{\pi}{4} + \frac{\rho}{2} = \beta - \frac{\pi}{2} + \rho$$

with respect to the positive x axis (see Fig. 15-5), α defining the direction in which the major principal pressure σ_1 acts and noting that $\beta + \rho = \pi/2 + \beta_2$.

Here one may change the dependent variable σ by introducing, instead of the mean stress σ, the resultant stress p acting in either of the two sections of slip,

$$p = \sigma \cos \rho \qquad (15\text{-}66)$$

(p may be visualized as the stress expressed by the length $\overline{OP}_1 = p$ in Fig. 15-2),

$$
\frac{\partial p}{\partial s_1} + 2p \frac{\partial \beta}{\partial s_1} \cdot \tan \rho = \gamma \sin (\beta + \rho),
$$

$$
\frac{\partial p}{\partial s_2} - 2p \frac{\partial \beta}{\partial s_2} \cdot \tan \rho = -\gamma \cos \beta,
\qquad (15\text{-}67)
$$

where $\tan \rho$ may be interpreted as the invariable coefficient of internal friction $\mu = \tan \rho$, ρ representing the angle of friction in the loose material. Equations (15-67) are known as *Kötter's equations of the theory of earth pressures*. After multiplying the first and the second equation by the integrating factors $e^{2\mu\beta}$, $e^{-2\mu\beta}$, they may be expressed in symmetric form by

$$
\frac{\partial}{\partial s_1} (pe^{2\mu\beta}) = \gamma e^{2\mu\beta} \sin (\beta + \rho),
$$

$$
\frac{\partial}{\partial s_2} (pe^{-2\mu\beta}) = -\gamma e^{-2\mu\beta} \cos \beta
\qquad (15\text{-}68)
$$

and in a few cases may be integrated, if one can guess how the angle β varies with the coordinates. They have served for constructing the slip-line field behind a rough retaining wall, for computing the pressures exerted by earth on the wall, and also for judging the load-carrying capacity of loose soils in the foundations of buildings.[1]

The methods for establishing solutions, satisfying prescribed boundary conditions in practical applications, are guided by the *Riemannian* principle that, in the realms of hyperbolic-type partial differential equations, the integrals having different analytical forms can be joined smoothly and fitted one to another integral, side by side, along certain

---

[1] In this chapter the limiting states of stress in loose, dry, granular media are discussed with their associated fields of slip as far as they are derivable from enveloping curves in a Mohr diagram. In regard to the vast practical applications of the theory of earth pressures and model and full-scale experiments, the reader must be referred to the books by W. W. SOKOLOWSKY (see pages 154, 476, *op. cit.*); by D. P. KRYNINE, "Soil Mechanics," 511 pp., 2d ed., McGraw-Hill Book Company, Inc., New York, 1947; and GREGORY P. TSCHEBOTARIOFF, "Soil Mechanics, Foundations and Earth Structures," 653 pp., McGraw-Hill Book Company, Inc., New York, 1951. Some older literature by German investigators was also quoted in the author's article, Plastizität und Erddruck, in GEIGER and SCHEEL, "Handbuch der Physik," vol. 6, p. 491, Julius Springer, Berlin, 1928. Instructive tests on cohesionless soils were made by A. CASAGRANDE (references may be found in Tschebotarioff's book quoted above, p. 622).

slip lines, i.e., along one or the other of the "characteristic curves" of the given differential equations (see Vol. I, page 547). The discussions in former years centered around the question of what shapes must be attributed to the lines of slip when they approach a vertical or a slightly inclined, solid, retaining wall having a rough surface and how far this field of bent, curved lines extends behind the wall into the region in which the Rankine field of straight lines of slip prevails. This has been clarified by HANS REISSNER[1] and by THEODOR VON KÁRMÁN,[2] who constructed the field illustrated in Fig. 15-21, by evaluating the integral of KÖTTER's equations (15-67) in the vicinity of the wall supporting a block of loose earth of horizontal surface, by means of stepwise approximations (REISSNER) or series developments (KÁRMÁN). The lines of slip within the wedge of earth ABC (Fig. 15-21) are determined (1) by Eqs. (15-67), (2) by the coefficient of friction valid along the wall, and (3) through the condition that the curvilinear lines of slip along BC must smoothly touch the straight lines of slip of the *lower Rankine state* of equilibrium. This gives for the resultant earth pressure for an angle of friction $\rho = 30°$ the horizontal component

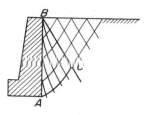

FIG. 15-21. Lines of slip behind a retaining wall.

$$E = 0.81E_R, \tag{15-69}$$

where E_R is the value computed as the active earth pressure,

$$E_R = (\tfrac{1}{2})\gamma h^2 \tan^2 \left(\frac{\pi}{4} - \frac{\rho}{2}\right)$$

from RANKINE's yet undisturbed state (see Sec. 15-3, page 442).[3]

---

[1] H. REISSNER, Zum Erddruck Problem, Sitzber. Berlin. Math. Ges., vol. 23, p. 14, 1924; also Proc. First Intern. Congr. Appl. Mechanics, p. 295, Delft, 1925.

[2] THEODOR VON KÁRMÁN, Über elastische Grenzzustände, Proc. Second Intern. Congr. Appl. Mechanics, p. 23, Zurich, 1927.

[3] According to the formerly much-used so-called *Coulomb theory of earth pressure*, one assumed that the earth would start to slip along a straight line, inclined under an angle φ, traced through the base of the wall, under a resultant force E_c,

$$E_c = (\tfrac{1}{2})\gamma h^2 \frac{\sin (\varphi - \rho) \cotan \varphi}{\cos (\varphi - 2\rho)},$$

prescribing the condition $dE_c/d\varphi = 0$, from which one computed for the critical slope

$$\cotan \varphi = \frac{\sqrt{2}\cos \rho}{1 + \sqrt{2}\sin \rho}$$

and for the horizontal component of E_c the value

$$E_H = E_c \cos \rho = (\tfrac{1}{4})\gamma h^2 \cotan^2 \varphi = \frac{\gamma h^2 \cos^2 \rho}{2(1 + \sqrt{2}\sin \rho)} = 0.79E_R,$$

disclosing that the old Coulomb theory gave a figure very near to the exact one $E = 0.81E_R$.

Realizing the difficulty of expressing in finite terms the stress field behind a retaining wall from his equations (15-67), KÖTTER, in his paper of 1903, proposed determining at least the form of the slip line AC (Fig. 15-21) that originates at the base of the retaining wall A from the condition that the horizontal component E_H of the active earth pressure E becomes an analytic minimum, thus formulating a problem of the calculus of variations. (See the critical remarks in H. REISSNER's papers quoted above.)

15-6. Prandtl's Generalization of the Concept of a Perfectly Plastic Substance. Applications to the Yielding in Solids under Plane Strain, Illustrated by the Corresponding Isogonal Lines of Gliding. Before we proceed further with the discussion of limiting states of equilibria in loose materials, let us bring up a group of related questions, indicated in the title of this section, to which L. PRANDTL called attention in two of his first papers devoted to the subject of plasticity.[1] He based the concept of a *generalized, perfectly plastic substance*, not possessing the property of strain hardening, on MOHR's enveloping curve of the major principal stress circles, having had in mind solids of a quasi-isotropic, polycrystalline structure having a well-defined yield point, in which he could postulate that *its material elements start and continue indefinitely to deform permanently whenever the maximum shearing stress* $\tau_{\max}$ *reaches a sharp limit, dependent on the mean value of the sum of the major and minor principal stresses* σ_1 *and* σ_3:

$$\tau_{\max} = \frac{\sigma_1 - \sigma_3}{2} = f\left(\frac{\sigma_1 + \sigma_2}{2}\right). \tag{15-70}$$

This condition of yielding is particularly suitable for treating two-dimensional cases of the slow flow in those solids in which the yield stresses increase with the mean pressure and within the range of high-compression–normal stresses. In states of plane strain the equations for PRANDTL's generalized plastic substance are practically the same as those which were later proposed for the flow of solids in which not $\tau_{\max}$ but the octahedral shearing stress τ_{oct} was considered as the general measure of a yield stress, assumed to depend on the mean normal stress, $\tau_{\text{oct}} = f(\sigma)$. If one neglects the elastic parts of the strains and if in the boundary of the body the stresses externally imposed on it are prescribed, these two-dimensional plastic states of stress σ_x, σ_y, τ_{xy} are statically already determined[2] through the two equations of equilibrium, the rule of flow [Eq. (15-70)] and the prescribed static boundary

[1] L. PRANDTL, Über die Härte plastischer Körper, Nachr. Ges. Wiss. Göttingen, Math.-physik. Kl., p. 12, 1920; and Über die Eindringungs-festigkeit (Härte) plastischer Baustoffe und die Festigkeit von Schneiden, Z. angew. Math. u. Mech., vol. 1, pp. 15–20, 1921.

[2] Cf. Vol. I, pages 407 and 527.

Fig. 15-22.   Ludwig Prandtl.†
(Born on Feb. 4, 1875, in Freising,
Bavaria; died on Aug. 23, 1953, in
Göttingen.)

† Prandtl was assistant to August Föppl at the Technische Hochschule in Munich, briefly professor in Hanover, then professor at the University of Göttingen, to which he was called to become the director of the Institute of Applied Mechanics, founded by the great mathematician Felix Klein in 1899.   This position he held from 1904 until his death.   Prandtl built the first wind tunnel for aerodynamic investigations (1908) and later the Aerodynamic Institute of the Kaiser Wilhelm Gesellschaft in Göttingen.   He designed the first apparatus, ingeniously utilizing *Töpler's Schlieren method*, for observing the oscillations in supersonic air flow through a DeLaval nozzle (Physik. Z., 1907, p. 23); he defined the conditions under which the laminary boundary layer sticking in a fluid stream along a body detaches itself from it (Über Flüssigkeitsbewegung bei sehr kleiner Reibung, paper read before the Third International Mathematics Congress in Heidelberg, 1904) and proposed the 1/7th power-function speed law when the boundary layer becomes turbulent (Z. angew. Math. u. Mech., vol. 5, p. 136, 1925).   He developed the basic equations for the evaluation of the lift force and drag exerted through the three-dimensional air flow around an aeroplane wing of finite length (Tragflügel-Theorie, pts. 1 and 2, Mitt. Nachr. Kgl. Ges. Wiss. Göttingen, p. 151, 1918, and p. 107, 1919), greatly improving the aerofoil theories previously suggested by F. W. Lanchester (1909), N. Joukowsky (1910), and others.   Whereas his well-known books convey the richness of his own findings in hydro- and aerodynamics—as we have mentioned elsewhere in the text—his contributions to solid mechanics are equally outstanding, beginning with his "membrane soap-film analogy," solving the torsion problem of elastically twisted bars (published in Physik. Z., vol. 4, 1903), in his papers dealing with the mathematical theory of plasticity, his determination of the pressures under which blunt edges of ductile metals yield (1920), his fundamentally important discovery of the hyperbolic sine speed law of deformation which he proposed as early as 1928, and his generalization of the concept of the ideally plastic substance (1921).   Ludwig Prandtl's genius in grasping the essential facts of so many involved problems in engineering mechanics places him among its foremost founders.

conditions.   The two velocity components u and v, assumed to be extremely small, in incompressible material can then be subsequently evaluated from the two equations

$$\frac{\partial u}{\partial x} + \frac{\partial v}{\partial y} = 0,$$

$$\frac{(\partial v/\partial y) - (\partial u/\partial x)}{(\partial u/\partial y) + (\partial v/\partial x)} = \frac{\sigma_y - \sigma_x}{2\tau_{xy}}. \tag{15-70a}$$

Let us choose the simplest type of generalized plastic substance, supposing for it two straight lines inclined at the angles $\pm\rho$ as MOHR envelopes and that the origin O_0 of the σ_n, τ_n system lies in the distance $c = \overline{OO_0}$ from their point of intersection O (Fig. 15-23).   With the symbols inscribed in the figure, *the condition of yielding* [Eq. (15-70)] then takes the form

$$\tau_{\max} = C + \sigma \sin \rho = (c + \sigma) \sin \rho, \tag{15-71}$$

and one sees that *the theories of a loose material* for which the condition of slip was expressed by $\tau_{\max} = \sigma \sin \rho$ (σ referred to the origin O) and of the just-defined simple type of generalized plastic substance (for which σ is measured from the new origin O_0) must be *closely related*.   All that is required to derive the formulas expressing the components of stress for the generalized plastic substance from those valid in loose material is that the normal stresses in the latter, σ_x, σ_y, σ, σ_n, be replaced, after adding the constant c to them, by the stresses $\sigma_x + c$, $\sigma_y + c$, $\sigma + c$, $\sigma_n + c$ to obtain *the stresses in the plastic substance*,

$$c + \sigma_x = (c + \sigma)(1 + \sin \rho \cos 2\alpha),$$

$$c + \sigma_y = (c + \sigma)(1 - \sin \rho \cos 2\alpha), \tag{15-72}$$

$$\tau_{xy} = (c + \sigma) \sin \rho \sin 2\alpha,$$

while the stresses σ_n, τ_n in the glide planes are connected by the linear relation

$$\tau_n = (c + \sigma_n) \tan \rho = k + \sigma_n \tan \rho. \tag{15-73}$$

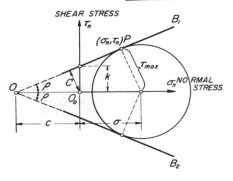

FIG. 15-23. Diagram defining Prandtl's generalized plastic substance.

W. Hartmann[1] remarked that, after substituting the expressions for the stresses [Eqs. (15-72)], the integration of the conditions of equilibrium,

$$\frac{\partial \sigma_x}{\partial x} + \frac{\partial \tau_{xy}}{\partial y} = 0, \qquad \frac{\partial \sigma_y}{\partial y} + \frac{\partial \tau_{xy}}{\partial x} = 0, \qquad (15\text{-}74)$$

is facilitated by introducing a new dependent variable z which he defined by letting

$$c + \sigma = c\mu e^{\mu z} = k e^{\mu z}, \qquad (15\text{-}75)$$

where

$$\mu = \tan \rho, \qquad k = c\mu. \qquad (15\text{-}75a)$$

This gives, then, two differential equations for the two unknowns z and the angle α, defining the direction of the major principal pressure σ_1:

$$\frac{\partial z}{\partial x} \cos 2\alpha + \frac{\partial z}{\partial y} \sin 2\alpha + \sin \rho \cdot \frac{\partial z}{\partial x} + 2 \cos \rho \cdot \frac{\partial \alpha}{\partial y} = 0,$$

$$-\frac{\partial z}{\partial x} \sin 2\alpha + \frac{\partial z}{\partial y} \cos 2\alpha - \sin \rho \cdot \frac{\partial z}{\partial y} + 2 \cos \rho \cdot \frac{\partial \alpha}{\partial x} = 0. \qquad (15\text{-}76)$$

They may be transformed by means of the partial derivatives

$$\frac{\partial}{\partial m} = \cos \alpha \cdot \frac{\partial}{\partial x} + \sin \alpha \cdot \frac{\partial}{\partial y}, \qquad \frac{\partial}{\partial n} = -\sin \alpha \cdot \frac{\partial}{\partial x} + \cos \alpha \cdot \frac{\partial}{\partial y}, \quad (15\text{-}77)$$

taken along the lengths of arc m and n of the first and second principal-stress trajectories running in the directions of the major and minor principal pressures σ_1 and σ_3, into the symmetric form

$$(1 + \sin \rho) \frac{\partial z}{\partial m} + 2 \cos \rho \cdot \frac{\partial \alpha}{\partial n} = 0,$$

$$(1 - \sin \rho) \frac{\partial z}{\partial n} + 2 \cos \rho \cdot \frac{\partial \alpha}{\partial m} = 0. \qquad (15\text{-}78)$$

This plastic state of plane strain creates lines of gliding which may be constructed for the first and the second family of flow lines from

$$\frac{dy}{dx} = \tan \left(\alpha + \frac{\pi}{4} - \frac{\rho}{2} \right),$$

$$\frac{dy}{dx} = \tan \left(\alpha - \frac{\pi}{4} + \frac{\rho}{2} \right), \qquad (15\text{-}79)$$

representing two *isogonal* families of curves traversing each other under the acute angle $(\pi/2) - \rho$.

[1] In a remarkable, regrettably never published doctoral dissertation, submitted to the University of Göttingen, entitled: Über die Integration der Differential Gleichungen des ebenen Gleichgewichtszustandes für den allgemein-plastischen Körper, 1925, Hartmann evolved the general theory dealing with the equilibria of a substance yielding in accordance with Eq. (15-71) and developed many exact solutions of practical interest, including their slip-line patterns that were unknown, to a few of which references will be made below.

The reader is familiar with one special type of generalized, perfectly plastic substance, namely, *the ideally plastic substance*, in which under plane strain $\tau_{max} = k = $ const. For the latter, obviously the two straight-line envelopes in Mohr's diagram (Fig. 15-23) become two parallel lines and $\rho = \mu = 0$, $c = \infty$, but $c \tan \rho = c\mu = k$. A cautious evaluation by HARTMANN showed that

$$\lim_{\rho = 0} (dz) = \frac{d(\sigma_x + \sigma_y)}{2k} = \frac{d\sigma}{k},$$

$$\lim_{\rho = 0} \left(e^{\mu z} - \frac{1}{\sin \rho} \right) = \frac{\sigma}{k}, \tag{15-80}$$

$$\lim_{\rho = 0} (\sin \rho \cdot e^{\mu z}) = 1,$$

and that from Eqs. (15-78) the differential equations valid for the ideally plastic substance for the dependent variables σ and α,

$$\frac{\partial \sigma}{\partial m} + 2k \frac{\partial \alpha}{\partial n} = 0, \qquad \frac{\partial \sigma}{\partial n} + 2k \frac{\partial \alpha}{\partial m} = 0, \tag{15-81}$$

result, creating two *orthogonal* families of flow lines. The last two equations are equivalent to

$$\frac{\partial^2 \sigma}{\partial m^2} = \frac{\partial^2 \sigma}{\partial n^2}, \qquad \frac{\partial^2 \alpha}{\partial m^2} = \frac{\partial^2 \alpha}{\partial n^2} \tag{15-82}$$

or, in terms of the arc lengths s_1 and s_2 measured along the directions of gliding, to

$$\frac{\partial^2 \sigma}{\partial s_1 \partial s_2} = 0, \qquad \frac{\partial^2 \beta}{\partial s_1 \partial s_2} = 0, \tag{15-83}$$

found for the ideally plastic substance by H. HENCKY (1923) and R. VON MISES (1925) and discussed by C. CARATHEODORY and E. SCHMIDT (1923).[1]

But the differential equations (15-78) for the generalized plastic substance have for us now a broader significance than may have appeared heretofore, since they throw some new light on the means of obtaining exact solutions for the limiting states of equilibria in granular materials possessing a limited cohesive strength, a fact that guided us in injecting this theory of PRANDTL's generalized perfectly plastic substance in this chapter which is primarily concerned with equilibria in granular materials.

The difficulties of finding integrals in workable form of the *Kötter equations* (15-67) and (15-68) arise from the presence of the two right-hand terms expressing the influence of the gravity body-force components. In certain applications of the theory of earth pressures one is

[1] Cf. Vol. I, page 545.

concerned with the effects of comparatively high loads or pressures resting on the surface or with judging the equilibrium at great depths where the body forces contribute locally a small fraction to the prevailing values of the stresses.   This led H. REISSNER and W. HARTMANN[1] to put $\gamma = 0$ in *Kötter's equations* within limited regions of the earthy substratum, thus proposing to deal with only the homogeneous parts of Eqs. (15-67) or (15-68),

$$\frac{\partial}{\partial s_1} (pe^{2\mu\beta}) = 0, \qquad \frac{\partial}{\partial s_2} (pe^{-2\mu\beta}) = 0, \qquad (15\text{-}84)$$

closely related to our equations (15-78) which latter differ from the preceding ones through the location of the origins O_0 and O, respectively. In the subsequent section a few examples of solutions are given which may serve to illustrate applications both of the theory of the generalized plastic substance and of earth equilibria, in both cases omitting the gravity body forces.

15-7. Simple Solutions. A. STATE OF ROTATIONAL SYMMETRY. Suppose first that *a body of loose sand* is held in equilibrium *by radial pressures* exerted on two concentric cylinders $r = a$ and $r = b$. The rays of the radii and the circles $r = $ const being the trajectories of principal stress, we distinguish two states of limiting equilibrium depending on whether the radial or the tangential stress, σ_r or σ_t, represents the major principal pressure σ_1. In the first case the greater radial pressure will act on the inner and in the second case on the outer surface of the cylinder $r = a$ and $r = b$. The equilibrium condition

$$\frac{\partial \sigma_r}{\partial r} + \frac{\sigma_r - \sigma_t}{r} = 0 \qquad (15\text{-}85)$$

is satisfied in *the first case*, when $\sigma_r = \sigma_1$, by letting

$$m = \frac{2 \sin \rho}{1 + \sin \rho}, \qquad \begin{aligned} \sigma_r &= \sigma_1 = \sigma(1 + \sin \rho) \\ \sigma_t &= \sigma_2 = \sigma(1 - \sin \rho) \end{aligned}$$

$$\frac{d\sigma}{dr} = -\frac{m\sigma}{r}, \qquad \begin{aligned} \sigma_r &= c_1 r^{-m}(1 + \sin \rho) \\ \sigma_t &= c_1 r^{-m}(1 - \sin \rho) \end{aligned} \qquad (15\text{-}86)$$

$$\sigma = c_1 r^{-m},$$

and in *the second case*, when $\sigma_t = \sigma_1$, by letting

$$n = \frac{2 \sin \rho}{1 - \sin \rho}, \qquad \begin{aligned} \sigma_r &= \sigma_2 = \sigma(1 - \sin \rho) \\ \sigma_t &= \sigma_1 = \sigma(1 + \sin \rho) \end{aligned}$$

$$\frac{d\sigma}{dr} = \frac{n\sigma}{r}, \qquad \begin{aligned} \sigma_r &= c_1 r^n(1 - \sin \rho) \\ \sigma_t &= c_1 r^n(1 + \sin \rho). \end{aligned} \qquad (15\text{-}87)$$

$$\sigma = c_1 r^n,$$

[1] *Op. cit.*

If a pressure p_a acts on the inside of a hole $r = a$, the integration constant c_1 becomes $c_1 = p_a a^m/(1 + \sin \rho)$, $c_1 = p_a a^{-n}/(1 - \sin \rho)$, respectively, but in loose earth p_a may not be evaluated unless some finite, counterbalancing pressure p_b is prescribed on the outside of the cylinder $r = b$.

If the angle of internal friction is $\rho = 30°$, the stresses are as follows: In the first case:

$$m = \tfrac{2}{3}, \qquad \sigma_r = 3\sigma_t = p_a\left(\frac{a}{r}\right)^{2/3},$$

In the second case:

$$n = 2, \qquad \sigma_r = \frac{\sigma}{3} = p_a\left(\frac{r}{a}\right)^2.$$

The pressure head forces the loose material to slip along logarithmic spirals oriented in the two positions shown in Fig. 15-26a and b, corresponding to the stress plots seen in Figs. 15-24 and 15-25.

Secondly, we may express *the mode of complete yielding in a thick-walled cylinder deforming under the law of generalized, perfectly plastic, solid substance* [Eq. (15-71)], after superposing on the former state of stress a uniform, biaxial tensile stress equal to $-c = $ const. A solid cylinder offers us one chance more, namely, of holding either the outer ($r = b$) or inner ($r = a$) surface externally unloaded ($\sigma_r = 0$).

We list the formulas *for the solid cylinder of the Prandtl substance* loaded by an internal pressure p (first case):

Mean stress:
$$\sigma = c_1 r^{-m} - c;$$

Stresses:
$$\sigma_r = c_1(1 + \sin \rho)r^{-m} - c, \qquad \sigma_t = c_1(1 - \sin \rho)r^{-m} - c.$$

Letting σ_r vanish on the outer sruface $r = b$ gives

$$c_1 = \frac{cb^m}{1 + \sin \rho}, \qquad \sigma = c\left[\left(\frac{b}{r}\right)^m \cdot \frac{1}{1 + \sin \rho} - 1\right]$$

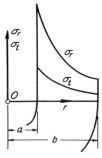

FIG. 15-24

$$\begin{cases} \sigma_r = \sigma_1 = \sigma(1 + \sin \rho) \\ \sigma_t = \sigma_2 = \sigma(1 - \sin \rho) \end{cases}$$

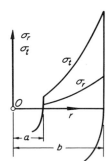

FIG. 15-25

$$\begin{cases} \sigma_r = \sigma_2 = \sigma(1 - \sin \rho) \\ \sigma_t = \sigma_1 = \sigma(1 + \sin \rho) \end{cases}$$

FIGS. 15-24 and 15-25. Stresses of rotational symmetry in loose material.

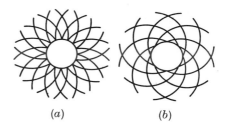

FIG. 15-26. Slip lines in loose material that are logarithmic spirals.

(a)   (b)

and, after prescribing on the inner surface $r = a$, $\sigma_r = p$,

$$\sigma_r = c\left[\left(\frac{b}{r}\right)^m - 1\right], \qquad p = c\left[\left(\frac{b}{a}\right)^m - 1\right],$$

$$\sigma_t = c\left[\frac{1 - \sin\rho}{1 + \sin\rho} \cdot \left(\frac{b}{r}\right)^m - 1\right].$$

(15-88)

But on the outer surface $r = b$, where σ_r vanishes, the tangential stress σ_t just equals the tensile yield strength $-\sigma_y$ of the solid; thus

$$(\sigma_t)_{r=b} = -\frac{2c\sin\rho}{1 + \sin\rho} = -cm = -mk\cotan\rho = -\sigma_y, \qquad (15\text{-}89)$$

showing that, in order to bring the entire cylinder into the plastic stage, a pressure p is required equal to

$$p = \frac{\sigma_y}{m}\left[\left(\frac{b}{a}\right)^m - 1\right] \qquad (15\text{-}90)$$

stressing its wall by

$$\sigma_r = p \cdot \frac{(b/r)^m - 1}{(b/a)^m - 1},$$

$$\sigma_t = p \cdot \frac{(b/r)^m \cdot (1 - \sin\rho)/(1 + \sin\rho) - 1}{(b/a)^m - 1},$$

(15-91)

in contrast to the behavior of loose material also by tensile stresses of substantial magnitudes in the circumferential directions.

The preceding relations must cover also the *ideally plastic substance* yielding under an invariable $\tau_{\max} = k = $ const, for which $\rho = 0$, $m = 0$, $c = \infty$. In this special case the formulas for p, σ_r, and σ_t appear in the indefinite forms $0/0$, but one sees that

$$p = \sigma_y \lim_{m=0} \frac{(b/a)^m - 1}{m} = \sigma_y \ln\frac{b}{a} = 2k \ln\frac{b}{a}$$

and likewise that Eqs. (15-91) take on the values

$$\sigma_r = 2k \ln\frac{b}{r}, \qquad \sigma_t = 2k\left(\ln\frac{b}{r} - 1\right), \qquad (15\text{-}92)$$

in agreement with the well-known relations expressing the state of stress in an ideally plastic cylinder.[1]

[1] Cf. Vol. I, page 441.

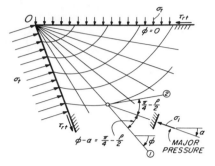

FIG. 15-27. Homogeneous stress along a fan of straight rays.

B. HOMOGENEOUS STRESS ALONG A FAN OF STRAIGHT RAYS. Using polar coordinates r, φ, suppose that the direction of the major principal pressure σ_1 *in loose earth* is inclined along any ray $\varphi = $ const under an invariable angle, the difference of the angles being $\varphi - \alpha = (\pi/4) - (\rho/2) = $ const. The stresses along the group of rays $\varphi = $ const have uniform values, satisfying the condition of slip [Eq. (15-33)], and are expressed by

$$\sigma_r = \sigma(1 + \sin^2 \rho),$$
$$\sigma_t = \sigma \cos^2 \rho, \qquad (15\text{-}93)$$
$$\tau_{rt} = -\sigma \sin \rho \cos \rho.$$

In soil considered weightless over a limited region ($\gamma = 0$), these components are derivable from the AIRY stress function

$$F = \frac{c_0}{2} \cos^2 \rho \cdot r^2 e^{2\mu\varphi} = \frac{(c_0/2)r^2 e^{2\mu\varphi}}{1 + \mu^2}, \qquad (15\text{-}94)$$

giving for the mean stress

$$\sigma = (\tfrac{1}{2})\Delta F = c_0 e^{2\mu\varphi}, \qquad (15\text{-}95)$$

where the constant c_0 measures the intensity of this state of stress and $\mu = \tan \rho$. The lines of slip in the first family coincide with the group of straight lines

$$\varphi = \text{const}, \qquad (\beta_1 = \varphi),$$

and in the second family they are the logarithmic spirals

$$r = Ce^{-\mu\varphi}, \qquad [\beta_2 = \varphi - (\pi/2) + \rho] \qquad \text{(Fig. 15-27).}[1]$$

The corresponding state of stress *in the generalized plastic substance* is expressed by

$$\sigma = c_0 e^{2\mu\varphi} - c,$$
$$\sigma_r = c_0(1 + \sin^2 \rho)e^{2\mu\varphi} - c,$$
$$\sigma_t = c_0 \cos^2 \rho \cdot e^{2\mu\varphi} - c, \qquad (15\text{-}96)$$
$$\tau_{rt} = \sin \rho \cos \rho \cdot (-c_0 e^{2\mu\varphi} + c).$$

In ideally plastic material one derives from the stress function $F = c_1 r^2 \varphi$ the state of stress in a fan,

$$\sigma_r = \sigma_t = 2c_1\varphi, \qquad \tau_{rt} = -c_1, \qquad (15\text{-}97)$$

with the rays $\varphi = $ const and concentric circles $r = $ const as the slip lines.

A thorough examination of the solutions for an elastic-plastic substance, yielding under the TRESCA condition $\tau_{\max} = $ const, for both the states of plane strain ($\varepsilon_z = 0$) and plane stress ($\sigma_z = \tau_{xz} = \tau_{yz} = 0$), in an infinite, elastic–perfectly plastic wedge under uniform surface tractions, prescribing the circumferential normal stress σ_t or the shearing stress τ_{rt} along the straight edges $\varphi = 0$ and $\varphi = \beta$ ($0 < \beta < 2\pi$), may be found in papers by P. M. NAGHDI and

[1] H. REISSNER (see page 457; *loc. cit.*) pointed out that in gravitating, loose material ($\gamma \neq 0$) a fan of *straight* lines of slip converging at a point, as in Fig. 15-27, is impossible.

associates,[1] in which the complete stress–rate-of-strain relations covering the elastic and permanent parts of strain ε', ε'', $\varepsilon = \varepsilon' + \varepsilon''$ of the *Prandtl-Reuss solid* adapted to the *Tresca flow condition* were utilized.

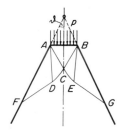

15-8. The Yield Strength of a Blunt Edge. Indentation in Flat Surface of a Semi-infinite Body. When a long, prismatic, solid body with the symmetric section seen in Fig. 15-28 is loaded on its upper, blunted face $\overline{AB}$ by a uniformly distributed, high, normal pressure p of sufficient intensity, a certain region near the short

Fig. 15-28. Blunt edge.

edge $\overline{AB}$ is deformed permanently. PRANDTL[2] solved this case, having in mind materials with sharply defined yield points in tension and compression like some of the ductile metals (mild steels), supposing that the elastic parts of the strains due to the high values of the moduli of elasticity and rigidity are negligible, compared with the permanent parts of strain of still only moderate magnitudes, and by introducing probably for the first time the supposition that the border line of the locally yielded region runs along a last line of gliding of the plasticized area, beyond which the body of the prism stays rigid—a proposition that was later considered by many investigators for solving what they termed the "plastic-rigid" types of problems of plasticity described by W. PRAGER,[3] R. HILL,[4] and others.

PRANDTL distinguished in the plasticized region five distinct areas which he fitted side by side in such a manner that the state of stress changes continuously if one proceeds across the inner boundaries of adjoining zones. He assumed that in the triangle ABC, being pushed downward by the external pressure p, a state of biaxial compression $\sigma_x = \text{const}$, $\sigma_y = p = \text{const}$ acts and likewise that the two triangles ADF and BEG, which are pushed slightly outward from their original positions, are subjected to homogeneous states of equal, simple, uniaxial compression parallel to the two flanks AF and BG, whereas in the two sector areas ACD and BCE there develops the type of homogeneous stress just described in Eqs. (15-96) and (15-97) for a fan, here possessing rays radiating from the corners A and B as the group of straight lines of slip.

[1] P. M. NAGHDI, Stresses and Displacements in an Elastic-Plastic Wedge, J. Appl. Mechanics, vol. 24, pp. 98–104, 1957; see also S. A. MURCH and P. M. NAGHDI, On the Infinite Elastic, Perfectly Plastic Wedge under Uniform Surface Tractions, 16 pp., Univ. Michigan, Eng. Research Inst. Tech. Rept. 11 (Naval Research Project), January, 1958, with further references.

[2] In his two papers of 1920 and 1921 quoted on page 458.

[3] W. PRAGER and P. G. HODGE, "Theory of Perfectly Plastic Solids," 264 pp., John Wiley & Sons, Inc., New York, 1951.

[4] R. HILL, "The Mathematical Theory of Plasticity," 354 pp., Clarendon Press, Oxford, 1950 (see pp. 58 and 128).

Thus the problem of finding the yield strength of the blunted edge, i.e., the pressure p, required to bring simultaneously the five *Riemannian areas* just described to the point of yielding, essentially amounts to evaluating the state of stress in one of the fan-shaped regions, ACD, by making use of Eqs. (15-96) determining the constant c_0, so that along the common boundary of this sector region with the triangle ADF just the uniaxial compression yield strength σ_c (equal to the diameter of the major stress circle representing $\sigma_1 = \sigma_c$, $\sigma_2 = 0$) acts. Then the stresses along the upper boundary line AC define the unknown vertical pressure p active in the triangle ABC.

TABLE 15-2. PRESSURE p EXERTED IN A PARALLEL STRIP UPON THE PLANE SURFACE OF AN EXTENDED BODY ($\vartheta = \pi/2$)

Mohr's angle ρ, deg	ψ, deg	$\mu = \tan \rho$	$\sin \rho$	Pressure p, $p/\sigma_c =$	AF/AB
0	90	0	0	2,571	1
10	80	0.1763	0.1763	3,499	1.572
20	70	0.3640	0.3420	5,194	2.530
30	60	0.5773	0.5000	8,701	4.920
40	50	0.8391	0.6428	17,560	8.462

Denoting by ϑ half the angle of the blunt edge (Fig. 15-28), by ρ the angle of inclination of the straight *Mohr envelope*, by $\mu = \tan \rho$, PRANDTL found for the yield strength p of the prism

$$p = \frac{\sigma_c}{2 \sin \rho} [(1 + \sin \rho)e^{2\mu\vartheta} - 1 + \sin \rho]. \tag{15-98}$$

This converges for the ideally plastic substance yielding under the law $\tau_{max} = \sigma_c/2 = \text{const}$ toward the simple formula

$$p = (1 + \vartheta)\sigma_c. \tag{15-99}$$

An important special case results from taking $\vartheta = \pi/2$, describing what might be termed the *two-dimensional hardness test, in which a uniform normal pressure p is exerted on the plane surface of a body over a long parallel strip.* We reproduce in Table 15-2 values of p, computed

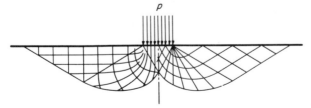

FIG. 15-29. Yielded region in generalized, perfectly plastic substance under concentrated uniform pressure $p = \text{const}$.

by PRANDTL for the generalized plastic
substance, characterized by the friction
angle ρ, $\mu = \tan \rho$, and by the acute
angle $\psi = (\pi/2) - \rho$ under which the surfaces of gliding intersect each other.

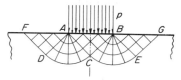

Under these circumstances there results a picture of the penetration of a
rigid stamp into an extended solid body,
bounded by a plane surface, shown in

FIG. 15-30. Concentrated pressure $p = $ const. Lines of gliding
in ideally plastic substance.

Figs. 15-29 and 15-30 for a generalized, perfectly plastic and the ideally
plastic substance, respectively. On the left side of Fig. 15-29 the
trajectories of principal stress and on the right side the lines of gliding[1]
have been traced within the yielded zone which spreads much farther
out along the surface than in the ideally plastic substance (Fig. 15-30),
in which the slip lines meet orthogonally.

A few test results[2] may be listed here which were obtained in compression tests with prisms machined from an annealed mild steel. It
possessed a sharply defined yield stress which was determined in
cylindrical compression specimens at $\sigma_c = 2{,}395 \text{ kg/cm}^2$. The distortion of the sides of one truncated prism having the angle $2\vartheta = 45°$ is
reproduced in Fig. 15-31, indicating that a plateau was raised on each

[1] A similar slip-line field has been constructed by H. REISSNER (see page 457;
loc. cit.) for loose material, neglecting its weight.

[2] Author's: Versuche über die plastischen Formänderungen von keilförmigen
Körpern aus Flusseisen, Z. angew. Math. u. Mech., vol. 1, pp. 20–25, 1921.

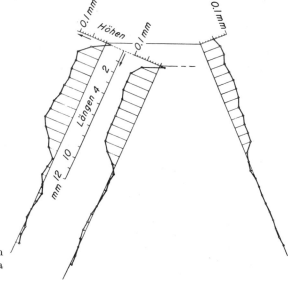

FIG. 15-31. Distortion
of the side planes of a
blunt edge.

side under the blunt edge. Since mild steel behaves like an ideally plastic substance, just after first yielding, in Table 15-3 the observed values of the pressure p causing sudden yielding are compared with those predicted by *Prandtl's formula* [Eq. (15-99)], disclosing a fairly good agreement between tests and theory.

TABLE 15-3. TESTS ON YIELD STRENGTH OF BLUNT EDGES OF MILD STEEL

Wedge angle 2ϑ, deg	45	45	90	90	180
Observed pressure p in smallest cross section that caused sudden yielding, kg/cm^2 .	3,250	3,330	3,850	4,430	5,540
Observed ratio p/σ_c	1.36	1.39	1.61	1.85	2.31
Ratio according to Prandtl formula, $p/\sigma_c = 1 + \vartheta$ . .	1.39	1.39	1.79	1.79	2.57

Mild steel has the peculiarity of showing nicely the LÜDERS' or flow lines. They may be seen in Figs. 15-32 through 15-34 for three of the truncated specimens. They show the expected trend, except near the ends of the prisms, where the state of plane strain is disturbed because of the finite length of the prisms. The width of the plateaux ($AF = BG$ in Fig. 15-28) pushed out on the sides of the compressed width AB agreed fairly well in Figs. 15-31 to 15-34 with the predicted width of the plasticized zone for the ideally plastic substance.

R. HILL and W. PRAGER[1] proposed in their books an altered pattern of the slip lines under the impression of a long die in a semi-infinite body, depicting the plastic-rigid boundary line under the action of a supposedly "perfectly smooth" (frictionless) flat die. The width of the pushed-out zones on both sides of the punch, according to HILL, would be only *one-half* of the width predicted in PRANDTL's slip-line pattern reproduced in Fig. 15-30 and verified in tests. Their fictive pattern has little in common with the actual behavior of a highly ductile metal, such as mild steel, under the concentrated pressure exerted by a hard die. The ever-present large amount of sliding friction in the contact area near the sharp edges of a rigid die and the body yielding under it inevitably causes a very high concentration of the permanent unit shearing strains right at the sharp corners of the die. This makes it understandable that the principal, first *Lüders'* or *flow line ACEG* and *BCDF* in Figs. 15-28 and 15-30 *originates from the sharp corner A* (and *B*). These two flow layers appeared very distinctly in most of the author's tests for the aforementioned reason, convincing him that PRANDTL foresaw an essential feature of the process of localized yielding under concentrated pressures (that was not taken into account in HILL's and PRAGER's flow patterns). PRANDTL's idealized treatment of the complex process of indentation of a metal possessing a sharply defined yield point covers at least one of the important phases of the problem of concentrated pressure.

Granted that one may neglect the elastic strains in both the yielded and unyielded regions, one may raise the question: What evidence, other than by

[1] Cf. HILL, *op. cit.*, Fig. 70(a), p. 254, and PRAGER and HODGE, *op. cit.*, Fig. 58, p. 169; see also Fig. 60, p. 173, illustrating their ideas about the action of a "lubricated" die.

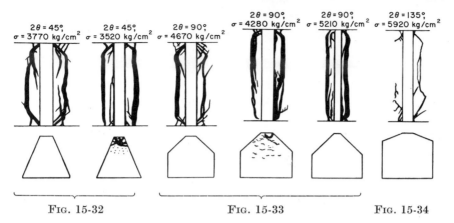

FIG. 15-32   FIG. 15-33   FIG. 15-34

FIGS. 15-32, 15-33, and 15-34. Lüders' flow lines on the side planes of blunt edges of mild steel. 2θ = wedge angle; σ = maximum compression stress to which specimen was loaded in upper contact plane. The view of the patterns of the flow layers is turned up into the narrow compression plane.

observation, has been advanced for the validity of the assumption made by PRANDTL and by quite a number of investigators in these problems of concentrated pressure, namely, *that the border line or surface of a locally yielded zone must run along a line or surface of slip,* the last one of the plasticized region beyond which the body stays *rigid?* When elastically strained portions surround the yielded ones, we have seen in the many cases of partial yielding, described in Vol. I, that their border line or surface does not coincide with the directions of the lines or surfaces of slip but with the surface along which τ_{oct} first reaches its limiting value $\tau_{oct} = (\sqrt{2}/3)\sigma_0$ (σ_0 = yield stress in tension).

It is well known that the phenomenon of the Lüders' lines or sharply visible flow layers in mild steel is caused by an instability of the uniformly, slightly, permanently strained condition of the metal, in contrast to the abrupt flow, concentrated within certain single layers, the favored appearance of which is initiated by slight concentrations of stress. The observations reproduced in Figs. 15-28 and 15-30 through 15-34 were certainly influenced by these circumstances, particularly by the high concentration of stress at the singularities of the state of stress, in the sharp corners of the specimens or the punch. A more precise way of looking at all these facts would be to assume that minute plastic strains were present (below measurable magnitude) in the supposedly "rigid" underground, before the first, distinctly discernible flow layers became visible. One may raise the question whether one should not *preferably investigate rather the gradual growth and the spreading of the yielded zone* under the increasing loads into the elastically resisting underground, instead of postulating ad hoc sudden, "complete" yielding over extended patches of the slip- and flow-line patterns, stopped along the rigid-body boundaries. In view of the difficulties of developing exact solutions of concentrated pressure, the earlier engineering approach still seems inevitable and may at least serve as long as the predicted results are supported by reliable tests.

15-9. Further Isogonal Slip-line Fields. A. ISOGONAL CYCLOIDS. Returning to Eqs. (15-78), consider, according to HARTMANN,

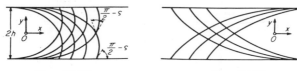

FIG. 15-35   FIG. 15-36

FIGS. 15-35 and 15-36.   The two systems of lines of slip are isogonal cycloids.
(*After W. Hartmann.*)

that the directional angle α of the major principal pressure σ_1 is a
function of the rectangular coordinate y, $\alpha = f(y)$.   Then from Eqs.
(15-76) one deduces, with c, c_1, c_2 as constants,

$$cy = 2\alpha \sin \rho - \sin 2\alpha + c_2,$$
$$z \cos \rho = \cos 2\alpha + cx + c_1, \tag{15-100}$$

with a system of lines of slip in parametric form

$$x = c_0(\mp 2\alpha \cos \rho - 2\alpha) + \text{const},$$
$$y = -c_0[(\pi - 2\alpha) \sin \rho + \sin 2\alpha], \tag{15-101}$$

valid for the parameter α between the limits

$$\frac{\pi}{2} - \rho < 2\alpha < \frac{3\pi}{2} + \rho. \tag{15-101a}$$

Equations (15-101) represent two isogonal families of common *cycloids*,
interwoven as illustrated in Fig. 15-35.   Note that the cycloids have
two parallel straight lines as envelopes.   Equations (15-101) together
with Eqs. (15-72) through (15-75) describe the state of stress within a
parallel strip of the width $2h$, bounded by the two straight envelopes, if
one assigns to the constant c_0 the value

$$c_0 = \frac{2h}{(\pi + 2\rho) \sin \rho + 2 \cos \rho}. \tag{15-101b}$$

In the horizontal symmetry axis $y = 0$ the major pressure σ_1 is oriented
normally to it.   The reader may recall a similar but orthogonal slip-line
pattern,[1] first described by PRANDTL in 1923, for the flow of an ideally
plastic mass squeezed between two rough, parallel compression plates.
Here it flows in the direction opposite to the positive x axis in Fig. 15-35.
We note thus that the preceding equations express this type of flow for
the generalized plastic substance.

On the other hand, if the values of the parameter α are confined between the limits

$$-\frac{\pi}{2} + \rho < 2\alpha < \frac{\pi}{2} - \rho, \tag{15-101c}$$

the cycloids take the positions indicated in Fig. 15-36, corresponding to
a horizontal major pressure acting along the symmetry axis (the x axis)

[1] Cf. Vol. I, Fig. 37-6, page 535.

of the plasticized layer, and this pressure forces the two parallel compression plates apart.[1]

B. NATURAL BOUNDARIES. *If an enveloping surface of the surfaces of slip exists, it forms a natural boundary limiting the domain of a state of plane, plastic strain.* The two aforementioned examples of the flow of a generalized plastic substance are also remarkable because the mathematical relations expressing the stresses cannot be extended analytically beyond the two bodily planes $y = \pm h$ forming the envelopes of the surfaces of slip. These two planes are *natural boundaries* in two senses of the word: confining the plastic mass and prescribing limits in space beyond which the mathematical solution ceases to exist. The latter fact opened up a perspective for finding new exact solutions, as we pointed out in 1924.[2] The condition of flow or slip [Eq. (15-60)] being of second degree in the variable stresses σ_x, σ_y, τ_{xy}, if one resolves its square roots with the $\pm$ sign, two branches of the solution appear, each of which has its mechanical significance, including its appropriate pattern of lines of slip, that must be discussed in a separate x,y plane. This behavior of the solution is reminiscent of that of multiple-valued functions of a complex variable which have been treated by covering the coordinate plane with two or more sheets, representing the individual domains of the function and which branch off along definite "branch lines." The two envelopes of the lines of slip in our last examples behave like two such branch lines of the plastic field, along which two closely related states of plane stress, distinct in physical space, bound each other, while the variable angle α defining the direction of the principal, major pressure σ_1, according to Eqs. (15-101a) and (15-101c) characterizing one and the second domain of the previous solution, changes *continuously*. Since the enveloping line or lines in the slip-line field characterize deeply the ensuing states of plane, plastic strain, *this led to proposing a systematic survey of these states based on the form of these absolute, natural boundaries.*

[1] We may add that in this two-dimensional flow the material moves along stream lines that start vertically near the rigid plates but rapidly bend into horizontal lines along which the velocity components u parallel to the axis increase. In both cases, represented by their slip lines in Figs. 15-35 and 15-36, the plastic mass flows under the plates in the direction of the negative x axis toward one side only under the pressure head acting in this direction. In the first case, obviously, this head is the *passive response* to high pressures created in the mass by the two plates approaching each other, whereas in the second case (Fig. 15-36) it is, in fact, *the active source* for all movements and that drives the plates slightly apart. We may state, using terminology of earth-pressure theory, that behind the two rigid plates a *passive* and *an active pressure* prevails in the first and second case, respectively.

[2] Über die Gleit- und Verzweigungsflächen einiger Gleichgewichtszustände bildsamer Massen und die Nachspannungen bleibend verzerrter Körper, Z. Physik, vol. 30, pp. 106–138, 1924.

We call these branch lines *natural boundaries* because they limit absolutely the domain of flow in the x,y plane and the field of the variables serving to describe the state of stress and plastic strain in the body.   None of the relations connecting them may be extended analytically beyond these envelopes of the slip lines.   This is a unique property of those plastic slip-line fields which have enveloping lines or curves and may be contrasted to the states of plastic strain allowing analytical extension beyond a boundary of a plastic zone.   Whereas both types of flow are based on the postulate of a Mohr envelope of the major principal stress circles in the σ_n, τ_n plane, the apparent paradox of the existence of a peculiar group of solutions possessing natural boundaries is due to the singular fact that *the external stresses along these body boundaries happen to coincide with the values of σ_n, τ_n of points P situated on the two Mohr envelopes,* representing the normal and shear stress in the planes of gliding; a natural body boundary is an infinitely dense aggregation and coincidence of planes of gliding.   Since the Mohr envelope prohibits assuming points P (σ_n, τ_n) on the outside of the sector $B_1 O B_2$ in Fig. 15-22, the maximum, absolute value of the shear stress τ_n in a point P in the Mohr plane under some given value of σ_n (or of the corresponding mean pressure σ) can never become greater than the ordinate of point P situated on the straight lines OB_1 or OB_2. Since no physical states of stress exist outside $B_1 O B_2$, it is now understandable why the domain of flow is limited by an absolute boundary whenever the lines of gliding in one family touch the former.

HARTMANN deserves credit for having systematically surveyed along these otherwise little appreciated trends classes and groups of solutions of the generalized plastic substance, according to the forms of their natural boundaries, and for having developed their slip-line and stress fields.   Lack of space prohibits reviewing them here in detail analytically, but we shall at least describe a few of them through their patterns of slip.

C. A FAMILY OF STRAIGHT LINES OF SLIP ENVELOPING A GIVEN CURVE. Suppose that the curve is continuous and has no inflection points.   Trace its tangents.   They define on one or the other side of their points of tangency one of

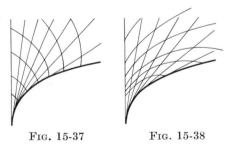

FIG. 15-37   FIG. 15-38

FIGS. 15-37 and 15-38. One family of straight slip lines envelopes a given curve.

the systems of slip in *a plastic domain extending on the convex side of the curve representing its natural boundary.* Together with the isogonal trajectories of the first system, this defines four conjugate singular integrals of Eqs. (15-78) (see in Figs. 15-37 and 15-38 two of the four possible patterns). When the curve shrinks to a point, one obtains the solution which was treated in Eqs. (15-96) for the fan (Fig. 15-27).

D. SLIP LINES ENVELOPING TWO INCLINED STRAIGHT LINES. Suppose that a plastic mass is held under high transversal pressures between two rigid, rough plates while the angle under which they are inclined toward each other is either diminished or increased by a small amount. This will cause a flow in a radial direction inward or outward in the mass with nonuniform radial velocities having a curved velocity profile $u = f(r,\varphi)$ across the circles $r = $ const, because of the high friction exerted by the compression plates retarding the flow. Each family of the lines of slip will be tangent to one of the plates, becoming their envelopes, and the *two inclined planes define two natural boundaries* of the ensuing flow. One may distinguish again four distinct patterns of flow, two of which are sketched

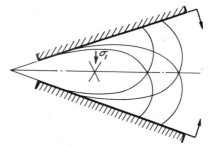

FIG. 15-39

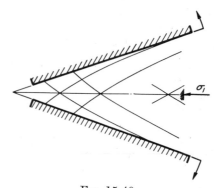

FIG. 15-40

FIGS. 15-39 and 15-40. Slip lines in flow of plastic mass held between tilting plates.

in Figs. 15-39 and 15-40. One case may illustrate what might be expected in the extrusion of a plastic mass driven by a pressure head radially inward while the angle of the two tilted compression plates is slightly diminished.

E. REGION ON THE OUTSIDE OF A CIRCLE OR BOUNDED BY TWO CONCENTRIC CIRCLES. HARTMANN has figured out a variety of cases with one circle or two concentric circles as their natural boundaries which, like the cases in Sec. 15-9D, may be treated by using polar coordinates r,φ (Figs. 15-41 to 15-44).

FIG. 15-41

FIG. 15-42

FIG. 15-43

FIG. 15-44

FIGS. 15-41 and 15-42. Slip lines enveloping circles.

FIGS. 15-43 and 15-44. Slip lines enveloping one circle.

FIG. 15-45. Two loga-rithmic spirals as natu-ral boundaries of flow. (*After W. Hartmann.*)

F. An Interesting, Final Example. As a final example we may mention the flow of a plastic mass between two logarithmic spirals within a trumpet-shaped region (Fig. 15-45).

G. Annex. Somewhat related ideas led Prof. József Jáky, at the Technical Institute of Budapest,[1] to estab-lish the orthogonal slip-line patterns for what he termed *types of completely plastic earth*, identifying it with the ideally plastic substance in which flow occurs under an invariable maximum shearing stress $\tau_{max} = k = $ const but after including the gravity body force γ in the con-ditions of equilibrium. He evaluated the forms of the isobars and curved lines of gliding in plane strain within a wedge $0 \leq \varphi \leq \beta$ in which the two straight edges are loaded by prescribed values of the tangential normal stress $\sigma_t = f_1(r)$, $= f_2(r)$ along $\varphi = 0$ and $\varphi = \beta$ and by a uniform shear stress $\tau_{rt} = $ const and also in a semi-infinite body and claimed to have established fields of gliding in which one family of the lines of slip consisted of a set of non-concentric circles. Among the cases that he investigated was also the slip-line pattern around a tunnel of circular cross section, with a horizontal axis, drilled at a certain depth under the horizontal surface of gravitating, "plastic" earth, after assuming that in the cylindrical hole a normal pressure acts that increases pro-portionally with depth y.

15-10. Extending Mohr's Theory to Cohesive Types of Earth. Plastic Solid Having a Partially Curved Mohr Envelope.

In the escarpments of earth strata consolidated by nature one fre-quently sees short, steep slopes. This has rightly been attributed to the presence of cohesive forces in dry, consolidated earth. Cylindrical specimens of it will withstand uniaxial compression and even tensile stresses of moderate magnitude, disclosing a compression and tensile strength. And this is even truer for plastic distortion in the type of solids treated in Secs. 15-6 through 15-9.

Investigators of earth's equilibria thought long ago that they *might consider cohesive types of earth in Mohr's diagram* (Fig. 15-46) by moving the origin O in the σ_n, τ_n plot of major principal stress circles to the right, to the position O_0, leaving it more or less indefinite where the two straight-line envelopes OB of the stress circles should start, at such points as B_0 or B_1, offering a chance to trace the stress circles $O_0 C$ ($\sigma_1 = \sigma_c$, $\sigma_2 = \sigma_3 = 0$) and $O_0 T$ ($\sigma_1 = \sigma_2 = 0$, $\sigma_3 = -\sigma_t$) of the states of uniaxial compression and tension corresponding to the compression and tensile strength of earth[2] σ_c and σ_t. If they start at the points B_2, this amounts to excluding any finite tensile strength. Figure 15-46 coincides with the one that served to define the generalized plastic

[1] József Jáky, Sur la stabilité des masses de terre complètement plastiques, pts. I–III, Tirage de Müegyetemi Közlemények, Budapest, Müegyetem (Hongrie), C.D.U. 624, 13; pt. I, 1947, pp. 1–23; pt. II, 1948, pp. 1–23; and pt. III, 1948, pp. 1–15 (published in French).

[2] W. W. Sokolowsky, "Statics of Earthy Mediums," 2d ed., 274 pp. (in Russian), Moscow & Leningrad, 1954. (See his fig. 3 on p. 16.)

substance proposed by PRANDTL (Fig. 15-22). We have already mentioned that both theories are closely related to the problems of two-dimensional states of stress, provided that the gravity body forces in the earth are suppressed and that in the boundaries only stresses are prescribed in the solid. If the weight adds little to the already prevailing pressures, the various solutions

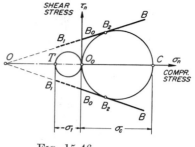

FIG. 15-46

treated in Secs. 15-6 through 15-9 may also be applied (with a few restrictions) to cohesive earth.

We now wish to show briefly that in a few simpler cases *states of equilibria* may be determined *in gravitating, heavy, cohesive types of earth* by availing ourselves of an improved handling of the presence of tensile stresses in such earth having a horizontal or a sloping plane surface, thus considering *a generalized form* of what we termed in Sec. 15-3 *the Rankine states* of limiting equilibria. If tensile stresses are physically allowable, the abrupt ending of the Mohr envelopes at some points situated at the left of B_2, such as B_0 or B_1 in Fig. 15-46, violates the *Alfons Leon rule* that we quoted in Vol. I, page 221, in connection with cleavage and shear fractures, and according to which he ruled out tracing envelopes that cross the σ_n stress axis in the σ_n,τ_n plot of the major stress circles under angles smaller than a right angle. His rule demands—in order to avoid inconsistencies—that the Mohr envelope should cross the σ_n axis at a right angle at its apex.[1]

A satisfactory way of describing limiting states in cohesive earth postulates a curved portion in the MOHR envelope, rounding off the corner of the two straight lines OB—a shape that may well be applicable to the PRANDTL generalized plastic substance for treating plane states of strain. One may think of utilizing for this purpose the branch of a conics section symmetrically oriented with respect to the σ_n axis. Attempting to construct workable expressions for the stresses and for the slip-line field in heavy, gravitating, cohesive earth, let us investigate the two cases in which the Mohr envelope is rounded off by a parabola or an ellipse.

A. THE ARC OF A PARABOLA. *Trace a parabola, bridging the straight lines OB,* which it touches at the points $P_e(\sigma_{ne},\pm\tau_{ne})$, denoting by σ_{ne},τ_{ne} the coordinates at its upper point of tangency. Otherwise using the

---

[1] One may, in fact, trace in Fig. 15-46 such stress circles touching the straight envelopes OB which penetrate into the forbidden region to the left of the ordinates O_0B_0 or TB_1, where physically no states of stress exist—an inconsistency in itself.

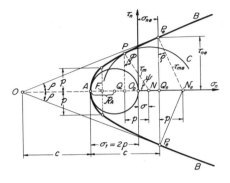

FIG. 15-47. Mohr envelope with blunt corner rounded off by arc of a parabola for describing limiting states of equilibrium in cohesive earth.

former notations, we have for the upper straight part P_eB of the envelope (Fig. 15-47) the equation

$$\tau_n = \tau_{ne} + (\sigma_n - \sigma_{ne}) \tan \rho, \qquad \sigma_{ne} \leqq \sigma_n < \infty, \qquad (15\text{-}102)$$

and for the parabola,

$$\tau_n^2 = 2p(\sigma_t + \sigma_n), \qquad -\sigma_t \leqq \sigma_n \leqq \sigma_{ne}, \qquad (15\text{-}103)$$

both referred to O_0 as origin of the σ_n, τ_n system. If σ and τ_m denote the mean stress and the maximum shearing stress corresponding to a point $P(\sigma_n, \tau_n)$ situated on the parabola $A P_e$ and φ is the angle under which the tangent to the parabola is inclined, the properties of the latter[1] require that the components of stress in the planes of slip also be equal to

$$\sigma_n = \sigma - p = \sigma - \tau_m \sin \varphi,$$
$$\tau_n = p \cotan \varphi = \tau_m \cos \varphi, \qquad (15\text{-}104)$$

and *the tensile strength σ_t equal to twice the parameter p*:

$$\sigma_t = 2p. \qquad (15\text{-}105)$$

A condition of slip equivalent to Eq. (15-103) along the parabolic part of the envelope expressed in terms of the maximum shearing stress τ_m and mean stress σ is

$$\tau_m^2 = p^2 + 2p\sigma \qquad (15\text{-}106)$$

or, explicitly,

$$(\tfrac{1}{4})(\sigma_x - \sigma_y)^2 + \tau_{xy}^2 = p^2 + p(\sigma_x + \sigma_y). \qquad (15\text{-}107)$$

---

[1] The apex $A(\sigma_n = -\sigma_t, \tau_n = 0)$ bisects on the σ_n axis the distance $\overline{OQ_e} = 2c$, and since in a parabola the subnormal $\overline{NQ}$ under any point and the radius of curvature R_A of the parabola at its apex A both equal the parameter p, one sees that the diameter of the major principal stress circle representing a state of uniaxial, simple tension σ_t which has been traced in Fig. 15-47 equals

$$\overline{AO}_0 = \sigma_t = 2R_A = 2p,$$

fixing the location of the origin O_0 in the σ_n, τ_n Mohr system. Furthermore, the subnormals are

$$\overline{NQ} = \tau_m \sin \varphi = p, \qquad \overline{N_eQ_e} = \tau_{ne} \tan \rho = 2c \tan^2 \rho = p$$

and $\overline{AF} = p/2$ locates the focus F of the parabola.

Consider a body of gravitating earth with a horizontal surface. We could distinguish, as we did in Sec. 15-3, an upper and a lower state of equilibrium in it, depending on whether the horizontal (σ_x) or the vertical normal stress (σ_y) represents the major principal stress. Since cohesive earth in the upper limiting state will sustain under the surface plane fairly great compression stresses σ_x and the major principal stress circle of uniaxial compression that passes through the origin O_0 in Fig. 15-47 in most cases will touch the straight parts of the Mohr envelope, so that its parabolic part becomes practically ineffective, *we shall be more interested in the lower state of equilibrium involving tensile stresses near the free surface* and assemble the data for the latter case, postulating σ_y as the major stress, the equilibrium requiring, since the shear stress τ_{xy} vanishes, that $\sigma_y = \gamma y$ (γ = specific weight of earth) taking the y axis in the vertical direction downward.

As long as point $P(\sigma_n, \tau_n)$ moves from the apex A ($\sigma_n = -\sigma_t, \tau_n = 0$ representing the state of stress in the surface plane $y = 0$) to point P_e along the parabolic arc in Fig. 15-47, the angle $\sphericalangle ANP = \psi = (\pi/2) - \varphi$ increases with increasing depth y. Since ψ measures the acute angle under which the two families of lines of slip intersect each other, we see that they are *curved*, in contrast to the RANKINE state that we discussed previously, while y increases to a certain value $y = y_e$ (corresponding to point P_e) beyond which an altered form of a Rankine state prevails, having *straight* lines of slip.

Looking in Fig. 15-47 at the major stress circle PC that touches the parabola at a point P, we may write the equations for the *lower limiting state of equilibrium* expressing the principal stresses σ_x and σ_y, σ_n and the mean stress $\sigma = (\frac{1}{2})(\sigma_x + \sigma_y)$, after letting $\alpha = \pi/2$, $\cos 2\alpha = -1$:

$$\sigma_x = \sigma + \tau_m \cos 2\alpha = \sigma - \tau_m = \gamma y - 2\tau_m = \gamma y - \frac{2p}{\sin \varphi},$$

$$\sigma_y = \sigma - \tau_m \cos 2\alpha = \sigma + \tau_m = \gamma y,$$

$$\sigma = \gamma y - \tau_m = \gamma y - \frac{p}{\sin \varphi}, \qquad \sigma_t = 2p, \tag{15-108}$$

$$\sigma_n = \sigma - p = \gamma y - \frac{(1 + \sin \varphi)p}{\sin \varphi}, \qquad \tau_n = p \cotan \varphi.$$

In order to evaluate σ_x in terms of depth y, substitute the expression for σ_n just obtained and $\tau_n = p \cotan \varphi$ in Eqs. (15-103) of the parabola. With the abbreviating symbol η as a parametric, variable, dimensionless measure of depth (η is always positive) defined by

$$\eta = \sqrt{\frac{2(\sigma_t + \gamma y)}{p}} = \sqrt{4 + \frac{2\gamma y}{p}},$$

$$y = \frac{p}{2\gamma} (\eta^2 - 4), \tag{15-109}$$

we obtain

$$\eta = \frac{1 + \sin \varphi}{\sin \varphi}, \qquad \sin \varphi = \frac{1}{\eta - 1}, \qquad \cos \varphi = \frac{\sqrt{\eta(\eta - 2)}}{\eta - 1},$$

$$\sigma = \gamma y - p(\eta - 1) = \frac{p}{2}\,[(\eta - 1)^2 - 3],$$

$$\sigma_x = \gamma y - 2p(\eta - 1) = \frac{p\eta}{2}\,(\eta - 4)$$

$$= \gamma y - 2p \left[\sqrt{\frac{2(\sigma_t + \gamma y)}{p}} - 1 \right],$$

(15-110)

where the parameter p of the parabola [Eq. (15-103)] is

$$p = 2c \tan^2 \rho = \text{const.}$$

The preceding formulas cease to be valid at the end point of the parabola P_e, where φ becomes equal to ρ and the variable $\eta = \eta_e$ becomes equal to

$$\eta_e = \frac{1 + \sin \rho}{\sin \rho}, \qquad (15\text{-}111)$$

to which a certain depth y_e will correspond in the earth, namely,

$$y_e = \frac{p}{2\gamma}\,(\eta_e^2 - 4), \qquad (15\text{-}112)$$

below which the altered RANKINE state of stress with straight lines of slip starts. The stresses in the surface $y = 0$, $\eta = 2$ attain the values $\sigma_x = -\sigma_t = -2p$, $\sigma_y = 0$ of *the tensile strength σ_t of the earth.*

The slip lines in the layer $0 \leqq y \leqq y_e$ are easily constructed from the differential equation of the first family,

$$\frac{dy}{dx} = \tan\left(\frac{\pi}{2} + \frac{\varphi}{2}\right) = \tan\left(\frac{3\pi}{4} - \frac{\varphi}{2}\right)$$

$$= \frac{1 + \sin \varphi}{\cos \varphi}, \qquad (15\text{-}113)$$

or in terms of $\eta = (1 + \sin \varphi)/\sin \varphi$ from

$$\frac{d\eta}{dx} = \frac{\gamma}{p \cdot \sqrt{\eta(\eta - 2)}}, \qquad (15\text{-}114)$$

which gives, after integration for the slip line that passes through the origin $x = y = 0$, $\eta = 2$, the equation

$$x = \frac{p}{2\gamma}\,\{(\eta - 1)\sqrt{\eta(\eta - 2)} - \ln\,[\eta - 1 + \sqrt{\eta(\eta - 2)}]\},$$

$$y = \frac{p}{2\gamma}\,(\eta^2 - 4). \qquad (15\text{-}115)$$

All lines of the first family being congruent to it and those of the second family being the image pictures of the first family reflected on the y axis, this then solves their evaluation.   The two systems touch each other in the normal direction to the free surface plane $y = 0$.   If the horizontal forces holding the block of heavy, cohesive earth are a trifle smaller than the limiting values that we computed for σ_x in Eqs. (15-110), the earth will crumble and tensile cleavage cracks will start to open up along the curves defined by Eqs. (15-115).

Figures 15-48 and 15-49 illustrate the form of the Mohr envelope and the slip-line field for the case when the angle of friction is taken

$$\rho = \frac{\pi}{6} = 30° \qquad [c = (\tfrac{3}{4})\sigma_t = (\tfrac{3}{2})p],$$

corresponding to which,

$$\eta_e = \frac{1 + \sin \rho}{\sin \rho} = 3, \qquad y_e = (\tfrac{5}{4})\frac{\sigma_t}{\gamma} = (\tfrac{5}{2})\frac{p}{\gamma},$$

the curved portions of the slip lines running over the interval $2 \leqq \eta \leqq 3$, $0 \leqq y \leqq y_e$ within which the acute angle ψ, under which the two families of lines of slip intersect each other, increases from $\psi = 0$ at the surface $y = 0$ to $\psi = 60°$ at the depth y_e.

Because of the postulate of stronger earth being able to carry tensile normal stresses up to the limit σ_t, the preceding analysis—it is believed—supports the physically plausible fact that *a plateau of such earth can be kept in equilibrium by much smaller lateral forces and stresses σ_x*, which may prevent it from crumbling and disintegrating under its own weight, than the forces that are required to hold noncohesive earth.

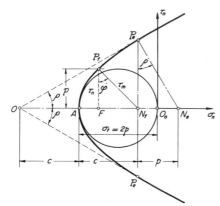

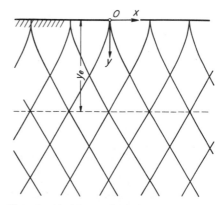

Fig. 15-48. Mohr envelope (part parabola, part straight) for $\rho = \pi/6$.

Fig. 15-49. Lines of slip for lower state of equilibrium under horizontal plane in cohesive earth ($\rho = \pi/6$).

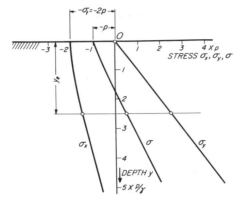

FIG. 15-50. Stresses plotted versus depth y for lower state of equilibrium under horizontal plane in cohesive earth using Mohr envelope shown in Fig. 15-48 ($\rho = \pi/6$).

It suffices finally to give the values of the stresses σ_x and σ_y in the region below the plane $y = y_e$ that conform with *an altered Rankine "lower" state of equilibrium*:

$$\sigma_x = \frac{\gamma y(1 - \sin\rho)}{1 + \sin\rho} + \frac{2\gamma y_e \sin\rho}{1 + \sin\rho} - \frac{2p}{\sin\rho}, \qquad (y \geqq y_e),$$

$$\sigma_y = \gamma y. \tag{15-116}$$

Figure 15-50 reproduces the distribution of the stresses σ_x, σ_y in the ground derived from the Mohr envelope represented in Fig. 15-48.

In this connection certain systems of parallel cracks in the earth's crust should be mentioned to which the Canadian geologist J. D. MOLLARD, of Regina, Canada, called attention recently.[1] In photographs of the earth's surface taken from airplanes at high altitudes over Canada, also over many other regions, he was able, by applying refined methods of interpretation, to detect most remarkably regular, fine patterns of parallel surface cracks (otherwise not discernible). These cracks were found in the *nonconsolidated, sedimentary surface layers* covering the solid rock bases of several hundred feet thickness over vast areas in Saskatchewan and Manitoba, frequently in several, parallel systems of straight lines several miles in length, intersecting each other at angles of varying magnitude. Among the various causes which were considered, Mollard advanced one explanation that seems rather plausible, namely, that these parallel systems of straight cracks might have been caused during the geologic periods by earthquakes, not of local but of distant origin, traveling over the continents in straight wavefronts that shook the cohesive, upper, sedimentary layers, breaking them in the parallel systems of tensile cracks in vertical

---

[1] J. D. MOLLARD *and associates*, "A Study of Aerial Mosaics in Southern Saskatchewan and Manitoba," Saskatchewan Geological Society meeting, Apr. 25, 1957; reprinted in Oil in Canada, Aug. 5, 1957 (with many figures of the crack patterns).

orientation at regular intervals, not unlike the way in which a stress coat cracks upon a strained metal.   Although it is beyond the scope of this book to delve into the effects of ruptures by earthquakes, it seems that this interesting example of the formation of these *regularly spaced tensile cracks* on a grand scale *in nature*, in thick, sedimentary layers of cohesive earth, should be mentioned in connection with the subjects treated in this chapter.

A smooth, continuously curved Mohr envelope such as the parabola of Eq. (15-103) may well define *a generalized plastic substance in which the yield resistance to shear increases substantially with the mean normal stress* in the compression range.   In a manner analogous to the preceding computations, one could evaluate states of plane strain by basing the equations of flow on a *condition of plasticity expressed by an ordinary parabola*[1] in the variables σ_n, τ_n,

$$\tau_n^2 = \sigma_t^2 + \sigma_t \sigma_n, \tag{15-117}$$

the constant $\sigma_t = 2p$ representing the yield stress in simple tension (p = parameter of the parabola) and which one may now assume to be valid over the entire range of the variable σ_n: $-\sigma_t \leq \sigma_n < \infty$.   This is equivalent to postulating that the relation connecting the maximum shearing stress τ_m and the mean compression stress $\sigma = (\frac{1}{2})(\sigma_x + \sigma_y)$,

$$\tau_m^2 = p^2 + 2p\sigma, \tag{15-118}$$

is also an ordinary parabola, prescribing in plane strain the condition of yielding

$$(\tfrac{1}{4})(\sigma_x - \sigma_y)^2 + \tau_{xy}^2 = p^2 + p(\sigma_x + \sigma_y). \tag{15-119}$$

By combining it with the two conditions of equilibrium for the components of stress,

$$\frac{\partial \sigma_x}{\partial x} + \frac{\partial \tau_{xy}}{\partial y} = 0, \qquad \frac{\partial \sigma_y}{\partial y} + \frac{\partial \tau_{xy}}{\partial x} = 0, \tag{15-120}$$

in which terms containing the body forces are omitted, the three flow stresses σ_x, σ_y, τ_{xy} may be evaluated.[2]

[1] C. TORRE in several remarkable papers made extensive use of a *parabola* for expressing the Mohr envelope of limiting states of equilibria in solids.   In his paper Der Spannungszustand in einem schweren Erdkörper, Sitz. Akad. Wiss. Wien, Math.-naturw. Kl., vol. 156, nos. 9 and 10, p. 583, 1947 (also Österr. Ing. Arch., vol. 1, p. 36, 316, 1946–1947), he assumed, however, the parabola

$$\tau_n^2 = 2p\sigma_n, \qquad (0 < \sigma_n < \infty) \tag{15-117a}$$

by excluding any tensile normal stresses in cohesive earth and evaluated the slip-line pattern for the case that we illustrated in Fig. 15-49.

[2] For large values of the mean stress σ the slip lines tend to become perpendicular families of straight lines as in an ideally plastic material.   This occurred in the state of stress in cohesive earth at great depths y in TORRE's example quoted in the preceding footnote.

B. THE ARC OF AN ELLIPSE.   *Secondly, suppose that an arc of an ellipse bridges the tensile range of the stresses in the Mohr envelope* which, owing to two constants available in its equation, allows describing a broader variation in the mechanical properties of an earthy substance than a parabola.   Consider the *lower* state of equilibrium and of stress in a mountain of cohesive earth having a plane surface rising under the angle δ.   The running coordinates σ_n, τ_n of a point $P(\sigma_n, \tau_n)$ of the Mohr envelope satisfy the equations of the ellipse,

$$\tau_n^2 = ps\left(2 - \frac{s}{a}\right) , \qquad (0 \leq s \leq s_e), \qquad (15\text{-}121)$$

(p = parameter; a = major semiaxis of the ellipse) and of the upper straight portion,

$$\tau_n = \tau_{ne} + (s - s_e) \tan \rho, \qquad (s_e \leq s < \infty), \qquad (15\text{-}122)$$

where we wrote for $\sigma_t + \sigma_n$,

$$s = \sigma_t + \sigma_n, \qquad s_e = \sigma_t + \sigma_{ne}, \qquad (15\text{-}123)$$

the subscript e attached to the variables referring to the points $P_e(\sigma_{ne}, \pm \tau_{ne})$ at which the ellipse touches the straight parts of the envelope (Fig. 15-51).

We have seen that the vertical and the inclined planes parallel to the surface,

$$x = \text{const}, \qquad y - x \tan \delta = y_0 = \text{const},$$

respectively, are conjugate stress planes in the earth body, having the reciprocal property that their resultant stresses are parallel to the other set of plane sections.   Thus in any vertical section in the earth body

$$\tan \delta = \frac{\tau_{xy}}{\sigma_x} , \qquad (15\text{-}124)$$

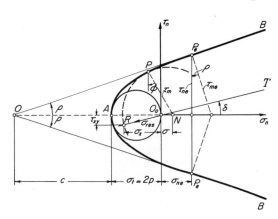

FIG. 15-51. Mohr diagram utilizing arc of ellipse P_eAP_e on blunt end.

and, if we trace in Fig. 15-51 the line $\overline{O_0 T}$ through the origin O_0, inclined at the angle δ of the free slope, the two components of stress σ_x and τ_{xy} appear as the abscissas and ordinates of point R at which the major stress circle that touches the envelope at point $P(\sigma_n,\tau_n)$ intersects the line $O_0 T$, the resultant stress σ_{res} acting across a plane $x = \text{const}$ being represented by the vector $\overline{O_0 R} = \sigma_{\text{res}}$.

If φ denotes the angle of inclination of the tangent to the ellipse and c the distance $\overline{OA} = c$, since the radius of curvature R_A of an ellipse at the apex A of its major semiaxis a equals the parameter p (the ordinate above its focus F) and the length of the subnormal is equal to $\tau_m \sin \varphi = \tau_n \, d\tau_n/d\sigma_n$, we have, after differentiating Eq. (15-121), the relations

$$\tau_m \sin \varphi = p\left(1 - \frac{s}{a}\right), \qquad \frac{d\tau_n}{ds} = \tan \varphi = \sqrt{\frac{p}{a}} \cdot \frac{a-s}{\sqrt{s(2a-s)}} \qquad (15\text{-}125)$$

and also

$$\frac{1}{a} + \frac{1}{c} = \frac{1}{s_e}, \qquad c = \tau_{ne} \cotan \rho - s_e, \qquad (15\text{-}126)$$

defining the major ellipse axis and the parameter p,

$$a = \frac{cs_e}{c - s_e}, \qquad p = R_A = \frac{\sigma_t}{2}, \qquad (15\text{-}127)$$

and again the rule, as in the case of the parabola, that the tensile strength of the earth σ_t equals twice the parameter p:

$$\sigma_t = 2p. \qquad (15\text{-}128)$$

We presume that in inclined ground the mean stress $\sigma = (\frac{1}{2})(\sigma_x + \sigma_y)$ varies proportionally with depth y_0:

$$\sigma = -\frac{\sigma_t}{2} + \gamma y_0 = -p + \gamma y_0 = -p + \gamma(y - x \tan \delta). \qquad (15\text{-}129)$$

Using the symbol $\eta = \gamma y_0/p$ to denote a dimensionless depth variable,

$$\eta = \frac{\gamma}{p}(y - x \tan \delta), \qquad (15\text{-}130)$$

we have for the mean stress σ

$$\sigma = p(\eta - 1) \qquad (15\text{-}131)$$

and, since on the other hand

$$\sigma = \sigma_n + \tau_n \tan \varphi = s\left(1 - \frac{p}{a}\right) - p, \qquad (15\text{-}132)$$

by equating both expressions for the relation connecting the variable s with the dimensionless depth η,

$$\eta = s\left(\frac{1}{p} - \frac{1}{a}\right). \qquad (15\text{-}133)$$

Likewise for the maximum shearing stress τ_m we have the two expressions

$$\tau_m^2 = \frac{p}{a}\left[s(2a-s)+\frac{p}{a}(a-s)^2\right] = \frac{p^2 a}{a\sin^2\varphi + p\cos^2\varphi}, \quad (15\text{-}134)$$

$$\tau_m^2 = p^2\left(1+2\eta-\frac{p\eta^2}{a-p}\right). \quad (15\text{-}135)$$

By combining the equations for the three components of stress,

$$\sigma_x = \sigma + \tau_m\cos 2\alpha,$$
$$\sigma_y = \sigma - \tau_m\cos 2\alpha, \quad (15\text{-}136)$$
$$\tau_{xy} = \tau_m\sin 2\alpha,$$

with the condition of conjugate sections [Eq. (15-124)], we find for the directional angle α of the major principal stress σ_1 the condition

$$\sin(2\alpha - \delta) = \frac{\sigma\sin\delta}{\tau_m}. \quad (15\text{-}137)$$

Suppose that we denote the difference of angles $2\alpha - \delta$ by an angle ε or let

$$2\alpha = \delta + \varepsilon. \quad (15\text{-}138)$$

Then we can evaluate ε from Eq. (15-137) with the help of the formulas that we developed for σ and τ_m from

$$\sin\varepsilon = \frac{\sigma\sin\delta}{\tau_m} = \frac{p(\eta-1)\sin\delta}{\tau_m}$$
$$= (\eta-1)\sin\delta\cdot\sqrt{\frac{a\sin^2\varphi + p\cos^2\varphi}{a}} \quad (15\text{-}139)$$

and can compute *the state of stress in the body of the sloping mountain of cohesive earth* in its lower state of equilibrium from the formulas

$$\sigma_x = \sigma\left[1 + \frac{\sin\delta\cos(\varepsilon+\delta)}{\sin\varepsilon}\right],$$

$$\sigma_y = \sigma\left[1 - \frac{\sin\delta\cos(\varepsilon+\delta)}{\sin\varepsilon}\right]$$

$$\tau_{xy} = \frac{\sigma\sin\delta\sin(\varepsilon+\delta)}{\sin\varepsilon}, \quad (15\text{-}140)$$

$$\sigma = p(\eta-1),$$

$$\tau_m = \frac{p(\eta-1)\sin\delta}{\sin\varepsilon} = p\cdot\sqrt{2\eta+1-\frac{p\eta^2}{a-p}},$$

where
$$\sin\varepsilon = \frac{(\eta-1)\sin\delta}{\sqrt{2\eta+1-[p\eta^2/(a-p)]}}. \quad (15\text{-}141)$$

In *the free surface plane* of the mountain we have to take $\eta = 0$, $\sin \varepsilon = -\sin \delta$, $\varepsilon = \pi + \delta$, $\alpha = (\pi/2) + \delta$, giving for the state of stress under the free surface plane the formulas

$$\sigma_x = -p(1 + \cos 2\delta),$$
$$\sigma_y = -p(1 - \cos 2\delta),$$
$$\tau_{xy} = -p \sin 2\delta, \qquad\qquad\qquad (15\text{-}142)$$
$$\sigma = -p, \qquad \tau_m = p,$$

coinciding with those of a state of *simple tension*, $\sigma_1 = 0$, $\sigma_2 = -\sigma_t = -2p$ parallel to the plane $y_0 = 0$, $y = x \tan \delta$, disclosing that, in the lower state of equilibrium of the mountain, the earth is stressed in this plane to the tensile strength σ_t that it can just sustain.

Equation (15-141) ceases to be valid at a certain, greater depth $\eta = \eta_e$, corresponding to point $P_e(\sigma_{ne}, \tau_{ne})$ in the Mohr diagram (Fig. 15-51), where φ becomes equal to the slope ρ of the straight part of the envelope. By combining

$$\sigma_e = s_e - 2p + \tau_{me} \sin \rho = p(\eta_e - 1) \qquad (15\text{-}143)$$

with the value of τ_{me} obtained for $\varphi = \rho$ in Eq. (15-134), one finds the depth η_e equal to

$$\eta_e = \frac{a - p}{p}\left[1 - \frac{1}{\sqrt{1 + (p/a)\cotan^2 \rho}}\right] \qquad (15\text{-}144)$$

and, from Eq. (15-139),

$$\sin \varepsilon_e = \sin (2\alpha_e - \delta) = (\eta_e - 1) \sin \delta \sin \rho \cdot \sqrt{1 + \frac{p}{a}\tan^2 \rho}. \quad (15\text{-}145)$$

In the region below the oblique plane $\eta = \eta_e$, where the straight part $\overline{B_e B}$ of the Mohr envelope becomes effective, again an *altered lower Rankine* state of equilibrium prevails in the earth and one verifies easily, by looking at Fig. 15-52, that when $\eta_e \leq \eta < \infty$, for the variable angle ε, the condition[1]

$$\sin \varepsilon = \frac{\sigma \sin \delta}{\tau_m} = \frac{p(\eta - 1) \sin \delta}{[p(\eta + 1) + c] \sin \rho} \qquad (15\text{-}146)$$

is prescribed.   From this one sees that, if η approaches infinity,

$$[\sin \varepsilon]_{\eta = \infty} = \frac{\sin \delta}{\sin \rho}, \qquad (15\text{-}146a)$$

the angle $(\varepsilon)_{\eta = \infty}$ and the direction of the major principal stress $(\alpha)_{\eta = \infty} = (\frac{1}{2})[(\varepsilon)_{\eta = \infty} + \delta]$ both tend to become invariable.

[1] Trace in Fig. 15-52 $\overline{O_0 T}$ inclined under the angle δ with respect to the σ_n axis. It intersects the major stress circle tangent to the straight envelope OB at the points R and S. Angle ε appears as the $\sphericalangle TSN$ and in the triangle $O_0 NS$ $O_0 N \sin \delta = NS \sin (\pi - \varepsilon)$ or $\sigma \sin \delta = \tau_m \sin \varepsilon$, which is Eq. (15-146) in the text. The coordinates of point R supply the values σ_x, τ_{xy}. $O_0 R$ and $O_0 S$ represent the resultant stresses in the conjugate sections.

Thus we note that in both regions, above and below the plane $\eta = \eta_e = (\gamma/p)(y - x \tan \delta)$, the lines of slip remain curved. They straighten out only at great depths η, slowly approaching their straight asymptotes when $\eta \to \infty$.

In the Rankine region $\eta > \eta_e$ the distribution of stress may be evaluated from Eqs. (15-140), using, however, Eq. (15-146) for $\sin \varepsilon$.

Over the entire range $0 < \eta < \infty$ the only component of stress that varies strictly linearly with depth η is the mean stress σ. This is illustrated by Fig. 15-53 in which the stresses σ_x, σ_y, τ_{xy}, and σ are plotted versus depth η for the special case in which the angle of inclination δ of the mountain just *equals* the angle of internal friction ρ for which $\delta = \rho = \pi/6 = 30°$ is assumed. The curves for σ_x, σ_y, τ_{xy} tend to approach very slowly the rays of their asymptotes emanating from point C ($\eta = 1$), indicated by thin dashed lines.

The lines of slip were not evaluated, their differential equations not being easily integrable. But Fig. 15-54 reproduces their probable shapes with a limited accuracy (constructed from the field of their isoclinics) near the mountain slope. The first family sloping to the left tends to bend toward the vertical lines and the second family toward the lines $\eta = $ const dropping under the angle $\delta = \rho = 30°$ in very great depths η, this conforming to the rules of a lower Rankine state of equilibrium under a plane inclined under *the natural angle of repose ρ* (see Fig. 15-11, page 445) of gravitating earth.

Figure 15-54 may illustrate to a certain extent in those surfaces of slip that tend to bend downward, toward the valley (second family), the instantaneous form of *the profile of a mountain slide along which a*

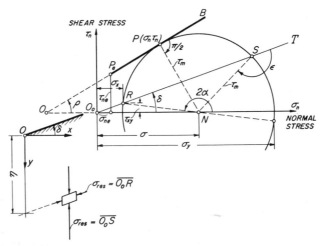

FIG. 15-52. Mohr diagram for altered Rankine lower limiting state of equilibrium in cohesive earth ($\eta > \eta_e$).

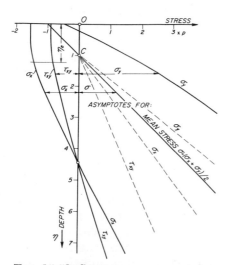

FIG. 15-53. Stresses σ_x, σ_y, σ, and τ_{xy} plotted versus depth η under an inclined surface plane ($\delta = \rho = \pi/6$) of gravitating cohesive earth.

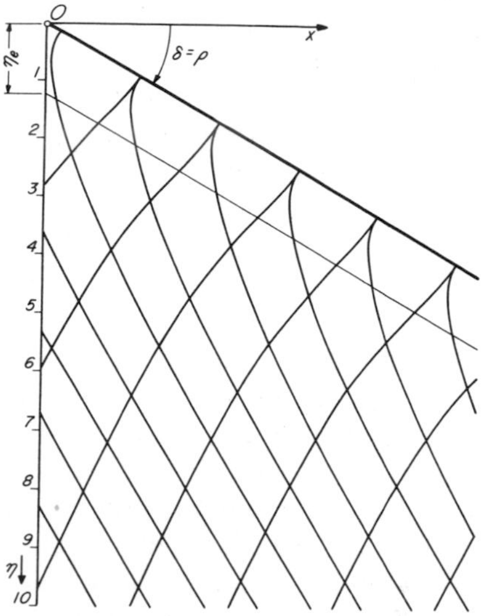

FIG. 15-54. Slip lines in gravitating cohesive earth under an inclined surface plane ($\delta = \rho = \pi/6$).

stronger type of earth would break off along a fracture surface, starting in perpendicular direction to the free surface plane, wherever a local weakness near it initiates the first tensile cracks.

A final remark: The foregoing relations do not become invalid if one assumed that the free surface plane of a mountain were more steeply inclined toward the horizontal plane than the angle of friction ρ prescribes for the upper limit of its slope δ, that is, if one traced the line RO_0T in Figs. 15-51 and 15-52 at an angle $\delta > \rho$, greater than the angle of inclination of the straight part $\overline{P_eB}$ of the Mohr envelope. The corresponding states of stress are stable within a layer under the free surface plane in a certain, limited region, namely, as long as the line RO_0T has not crossed the envelope AP_eB. In other words, an escarpment of cohesive earth may stand up steeper than the angle of repose ρ. This is verified by the steep slopes that one not infrequently sees on the uppermost sides of large cinder piles deposited near highways. But we have to bear in mind that our statement does not hold for the parts buried at greater depths, where the altered RANKINE state of equilibrium prevails and where no slip line of the family dropping to the right side in Fig. 15-54 can stand up under angles greater than ρ.

15-11. Powdery or Porous Elastic Material Containing a Fluid. Bewetted clay or porcelain earth is highly deformable. The easy formability of wet clays has been utilized by man since prehistoric times for making pottery and bricks.   Finely granular materials can behave in a highly plastic manner if the voids between the solid particles are partially filled with a fluid, and it is well known that their easy formability is due to the capillary action of the fluid, to the surface tension in the fluid films anchored between the solid particles, and to the capillary underpressure in the droplets binding them together, creating an apparent cohesion.   According to TERZAGHI, this is present even in fairly dry clay, owing to the minutest quantities of adsorbed water films of near-molecular thickness and to the submicroscopic, lamellar shape of the solid particles of colloidal size sticking together in fine clays but which, in the plastic state, are easily movable along each other when more pore water is present, acting like a lubricant to facilitate their relative displacements.   A layer of natural clay saturated with water will shrink in its volume under a vertical pressure carried continuously with time, because it will lose its pore water which may escape through evaporation on the surface or percolate away into the unloaded regions. Thus the pore-water pressure w is a function of space and time, constituting the main problems involved in constructing foundations of buildings on such soils, aimed at predicting the amounts of subsidence during the long times required for the consolidation of water-containing soils.   Since the mechanical behavior of wet, formable clays cannot be analyzed without engaging in consideration of the flow of fluids through porous media, a discussion of these questions must remain outside the scope of this volume.   It suffices to refer to the outstanding work by KARL TERZAGHI, who based the treatments of the slow processes of consolidation of clay on *an ingenious analogy* that he established between the *Fourier differential equation for the conduction of heat:*

$$Q = -k\frac{\partial \theta}{\partial x}, \qquad \frac{\partial \theta}{\partial t} = a^2 \frac{\partial^2 \theta}{\partial x^2}, \qquad (15\text{-}147)$$

and *the movement of the pore water percolating slowly through the voids in a layer of clay* loaded by external pressure:

$$Q = -k\frac{\partial w}{\partial x}, \qquad \frac{\partial w}{\partial t} = b^2 \frac{\partial^2 w}{\partial x^2}, \qquad (15\text{-}148)$$

where the quantities represent

Q the amount of heat	Q the volume of water, cm/sec
flowing, circulating per unit of area and time	
k the conductivity of heat	k the permeability in soil, $cm^4/(kg\ sec)$
θ the temperature	w the pressure in pore water, kg/cm^2 in technical units (T.S.)

and utilized in $Q = -k\partial w/\partial x$ the *Darcy law*, according to which the quantity of circulating ground water Q per unit of time is proportional to the gradient of the pore-water pressure[1] w.

The problems of earth foundations supporting buildings have been treated in an equally remarkable way by MAURICE A. BIOT, who in a series of papers[2] gave consideration, apart from the thermohydrodynamical analogy just mentioned, to the elasticity of the skeleton of a porous but elastically responding material containing a compressible fluid by introducing stress-strain relations in the form

$$\sigma_x = 2Ne_x + Ae + Q\varepsilon, \dots,$$

$$\sigma = Qe + R\varepsilon, \qquad\qquad (15\text{-}149)$$

$$\tau_{yz} = N\gamma_{yz}, \dots ;$$

$e_x, \dots, \gamma_{yz}, \dots$ are the strain components; e is the dilatation of volume in the solid; ε is the elastic dilatation of the pore fluid; A, N, Q, R are elasticity constants; the $\sigma_x, \dots, \tau_{yz}, \dots$, represent the forces acting on the solid part of the faces of a unit cube of bulk material, while σ is the force applied to the fluid part, $\sigma = -fp$; p is the pressure in the fluid and f is the coefficient of porosity.

In regard to the two-dimensional *plane-strain problem*, this led Biot, after making use of the equilibrium and compatibility conditions and of *Darcy's law* for the fluid pressure σ, to the sum of two functions σ satisfying, respectively, the two equations (Δ is the Laplacian operator),

$$K\Delta\sigma = b\frac{\partial\sigma}{\partial t}, \qquad \Delta\sigma = 0, \qquad (15\text{-}150)$$

[1] Cf. KARL TERZAGHI, "Erdbaumechanik auf bodenphysikalischer Grundlage," 391 pp., F. Deuticke's Verlag, Leipzig, Vienna, 1925, and "Theoretical Soil Mechanics," 510 pp., John Wiley & Sons, Inc., New York, 1943; TERZAGHI and RALPH B. PECK, "Soil Mechanics in Engineering Practice," John Wiley & Sons, Inc., New York, 1948; also Proc. First Intern. Congr. Appl. Mechanics, p. 288, Delft, 1925, and papers by his collaborators A. CASAGRANDE, R. E. FADUM, RALPH B. PECK, and others. (Cf. R. B. PECK, Eng. Stat. Bull. 429, 60 pp., Univ. Illinois, 1955, and O. K. FROELICH, "Druckverteilung im Baugrunde," Springer-Verlag, Vienna, 183 pp., 1934.)

[2] M. A. BIOT, General Theory of Three Dimensional Consolidation, J. Appl. Phys., vol. 12, pp. 155–165, 1941, also p. 426 (under a rectangular load); General Solutions of the Equations of Elasticity and Consolidation for a Porous Material, J. Appl. Mechanics, vol. 23 (Trans. ASME, vol. 78), p. 91, 1956; The Elastic Coefficients of the Theory of Consolidation, J. Appl. Mechanics, December, 1957; Linear Thermodynamics and the Mechanics of Solids, Proc. U.S. Natl. Congr. Appl. Mechanics, June 11, 1958, in Providence, R.I. (with extensive bibliography).

and after introducing a stress function $F(x,y)$ expressing

$$\sigma_x + \sigma = \frac{\partial^2 F}{\partial y_2},$$

$$\sigma_y + \sigma = \frac{\partial^2 F}{\partial x^2}, \qquad\qquad (15\text{-}151)$$

$$\tau_{xy} = -\frac{\partial^2 F}{\partial x\,\partial y},$$

to the sum of two functions F satisfying, respectively, the two equations

$$K\,\Delta F = b\,\frac{\partial F}{\partial t}, \qquad \Delta\Delta F = 0, \qquad (15\text{-}152)$$

where the integrals of the two differential equations not containing the time derivatives represent the initial state of stress upon sudden application of the external loads.   The constant K therein is

$$K = \frac{(A + 2N)R - Q^2}{A + 2N + R + 2Q}, \qquad (15\text{-}153)$$

and the constant b appears in *Darcy's law* which was expressed here in an alternative form by letting

$$\frac{\partial\sigma}{\partial x} = -b\,\frac{\partial}{\partial t}\,(u_x - U_x), \qquad \frac{\partial\sigma}{\partial y} = -b\,\frac{\partial}{\partial t}\,(u_y - U_y), \qquad (15\text{-}154)$$

the right-hand difference representing the displacement components of the fluid relative to the solid frame in their time derivatives, thus the relative fluid velocity components, the latter two relations serving for evaluation of the settlement of a ground of porous soil under a given external load over an extended period of time.

Whereas in the preceding theories the gravity forces in the fluid itself percolating through the voids of the earth layers could be neglected, it must be pointed out that petroleum geologists are concerned with including them when judging the flow of fluids (oil or water) or gas through porous media deep underground.   This led M. KING HUBBERT[1]

[1] See a recent, most instructive, historically critical review in his paper *Darcy's Law and the Field Equations of the Flow of Underground Fluids*, presented before the Darcy Centennial Hydrology Symposium of the International Association of Hydrology held in Dijon, France, Sept. 20–26, 1956 (Shell Development Company, Exploration and Production Division, Houston, Tex., Bull. 5, Publ. 104, pp. 24–59, 1957).   HENRY DARCY in his book "Les Fontaines publiques de la ville de Dijon," published in 1856, described his experiments made in a 10-ft-high hollow cylinder filled with sand, through which he let water percolate under greater and smaller pressure differences, arriving at the conclusion that the rate

to introduce DARCY's law in an amended vector form,

$$\mathbf{Q} = \frac{Nd^2}{\mu}(\boldsymbol{\gamma}_0 - \text{grad } \mathbf{w}) = c\mathbf{F}, \qquad (15\text{-}154a)$$

in which he also included in the seepage flow the gravity force $\boldsymbol{\gamma}_0$ besides the pressure gradient grad $\mathbf{w}$, considering both incompressible and compressible fluids, by letting $\gamma_0 = \rho g$ (ρ is mass per unit volume) and by postulating laminar flow of a viscous fluid.   In his flow equation, N represents a dimensionless form factor, d a characteristic length, μ the viscosity of the fluid, $c = N\, d^2\rho/\mu$ the permeability of the system, and $\mathbf{F}$ the impelling force per unit of mass acting upon the fluid driven through the porous medium.

Hubbert's equation is thus amenable to the migration of petroleum and natural gas through water-saturated, porous underground environment, aiming at establishing the field equations for the fluid motion around deep oil wells.   When several immiscible fluids are considered, then the impelling forces F_1, F_2, . . . for each separate fluid of different densities $\rho_1, \rho_2, \ldots$ will differ among themselves in magnitude and direction but will all fall in the same vertical plane and must be added as vectors to the gravity vector, their geometric sum defining the resultant force vector $\mathbf{F}$ at every point in the ground.

Whereas in the previous equations attention is focused on the slow percolation of ground water through the voids of porous media, causing settlement, and the differential equations are of the type describing phenomena or processes of diffusion in space in dependence on time, *another question has been raised* in connection with deep-well drilling by petroleum geologists *that is concerned with the yield and fracture strength of the denser-type, stronger, sedimentary rocks*, such as limestones or consolidated sandstones encountered at greater depths underground *in which the pores are invariably saturated and filled with fluid*, ground water or oil or both.   In solid rocks surrounding the hole of a deep petroleum well triaxial states of stress are generated while one can assume that the liquid entrapped in the pores, since it cannot escape, takes on high hydrostatic pressures which under normal conditions may be of the order of one-third of the total overburden pressure due to the weight of the rocks.

---

of flow was given by

$$Q = -k(p_2 - p_1)/l$$

($p_2 - p_1$, pressure difference; height l of column of sand).

Concerning the movements of liquids entrapped in the pore spaces of solids or sand, see books by MORRIS MUSKAT, The Flow of Homogeneous Fluids through Porous Media (International Series in Pure and Applied Physics, with an introductory chapter by R. D. WYCKOFF), 763 pp., 1937, and "Physical Principles of Oil Production," 922 pp., 1949, both McGraw-Hill Book Company, Inc., New York.

An interesting question thus arises, namely, how does the *pressure p of the fluid entrapped in the pores of solid rocks influence their triaxial compression strength underground*, as compared with the yield or fracture stresses that one observes in *dry samples* in which the voids are filled with air, while one subjects the rock specimens in the standard manner under confining lateral pressures (after enclosing them in metal foils or plastic jackets) to axial compression in laboratory tests.

The effects of pore pressure of an entrapped fluid on the triaxial strength of sedimentary rocks have been investigated by L. H. ROBINSON, JR.,[1] at the Humble Oil and Refining Company in Houston, Texas, who subjected cylindrical specimens having ¾ in. diameter and 1½ in. height, saturated with distilled water and covered by a plastic jacket, in the interior of a pressure chamber to a confining pressure p_c and axial compression between a piston projecting into the chamber and an anvil.   The pore pressure p was exerted by pumping water through a central hole of the piston and anvil toward the plane ends of the specimen.   To start with, the confining and the pore pressure p_c and p were set; they were held invariable during the test, and the axial load was adjusted to a value such that the rock sample initially carried a uniform hydrostatic pressure, $\sigma_1 = \sigma_2 = \sigma_3 = p_c$, not having any effect on it beyond an irrelevant elastic decrease of volume.   In order to avoid leakage of the pore fluid around the plastic jacket, the pore pressure p had to be $p \leq p_c$.   With the increase of the axial compression stress σ_a beyond p_c the rock cylinder started to deform permanently by ε_a. The compression stress-strain diagrams $\sigma_a - p_c = f(\varepsilon_a)$ which were recorded at sufficiently high values of the confining pressure p_c are reminiscent in their character of the THEODOR VON KÁRMÁN experiments observed for marble;[2] at small values of the pore pressure p the rock yields not unlike a ductile metal, but as p increases and the pressure difference $p_c - p$ decreases beyond a certain value ($p_c - p = 5,000$ lb/in.[2] for Indiana limestone while p_c was set to the value $p_c = 10,000$ lb/in.[2]), the mode of failure changes from malleable to brittle, occurring at much smaller axial loads $\sigma_a - p_c$ than the yield point corresponding to vanishing pore pressure $p = 0$.   The important result of these tests was that the presence of a pore fluid held under a high pressure p approaching the value of the confining pressure p_c embrittled the rocks. When the difference $p_c - p$ was smaller than the critical value, the rocks broke in brittle fashion along oblique planes, as in simple, uniaxial compression.   It is interesting that the pore fluid under these

[1] Effects of Pore and Confining Pressures on Failure Characteristics of Sedimentary Rocks, presented at 33d annual meeting of the Society of Petroleum Engineers of American Institute of Mining, Metallurgical and Petroleum Engineers, Houston, Tex., Oct. 5, 1958; J. Petrol. Technol.
[2] Cf. Vol. I, page 240.

circumstances acted as a lubricant squeezed between the shear crevices, greatly facilitating the transgression and relative slip of the two parts in the broken specimen along the shear fracture plane, in spite of the high normal stress pressing the former together, with the consequence that the axial load $\sigma_a - p_c$ dropped rapidly, as from an upper to a lower yield point.

While ROBINSON did not construct the Mohr enveloping curve of the major principal stress circles associated with the first appreciable yielding, this has been done for rocks by M. KING HUBBERT and DAVID G. WILLIS,[1] and in an extensive series of triaxial compression tests covering many sedimentary rocks tested, however, in dry condition by JOHN HANDIN and REX V. HAGER, JR.[2] The first-mentioned investigators confirmed an interpretation of similar tests made by DOUGLAS MCHENRY[3] on concrete, by stating that rock cylinders containing a pore fluid of pressure p behave in first approximation not unlike jacketed but dry rock cylinders in regard to the Mohr envelope; if one replaces its equation $\tau_n = F(\sigma_n)$, describing the limiting states of stress causing first yielding in *dry*, solid rocks, by the equation $\tau_n = F(S_n - p)$ referring to the same rocks saturated with pore fluid of pressure p, the latter equation defines in a first approximation the behavior of *wet* rocks, where τ_n, σ_n are the components of shear and normal stress in the surfaces of slip or gliding in the dry, and τ_n, S_n, those in the wet rock (postulating that $\sigma_n = S_n - p$). While this over-simplifies the more complex conditions prevalent in fluid-saturated rocks, because the stress-strain curves $\sigma_a - p_c = f(\varepsilon_a)$ in the latter case are not congruent to those derived for dry rocks in the tests by Robinson (the former disclosed sharp peaks and drops from an upper to a lower load within the critical range of $p_c - p$ of embrittlement, whereas dry rocks deform in more continuous manner), it may serve for judging a few phenomena encountered at great depths in drilling techniques.

The conditions of yielding and fracture, the afterflow through creep in dry natural rocks, and their behavior when the pore spaces in them were filled with fluid under an interstitial pressure, *in tests under combined stress at normal and high temperatures*, were reviewed in a

---

[1] Mechanics of Hydraulic Fracturing, Shell Development Company, Houston, Tex., J. Petrol. Technol., vol. 9, June, 1957.

[2] Experimental Deformation of Sedimentary Rocks under Confining Pressure. Tests at Room Temperature on Dry Samples, Bull. Am. Assoc. Petrol. Geologists, vol. 41, no. 1, p. 50, January, 1957, reporting stress-strain curves and Mohr enveloping curves for many types of anhydrites, dolomites, limestones, Yule marble, sandstones, and shales.

[3] The Effect of Uplift Pressure on the Shearing Strength of Concrete, 3e Congrès des Grands Barrages, Stockholm, 1948, vol. I.

Symposium on Rock Deformation in thirteen papers[1] to which brief reference is made in the following:

1. While rocks such as marble, dolomite, granite, and basalt, under triaxial stress and moderate confining pressure, at normal temperature may sustain moderate plastic straining (in cylindrical samples a few per cent axial strain) before fracturing, at elevated temperatures up to 800°C the ductility of these rocks was found to increase considerably. They can be deformed by 10 to 15 per cent or more axial strain under materially reduced differential (axial minus lateral) flow stress, yielding by intracrystalline glide.   Hard, dry granite and basalt under a confining pressure of 5,000 atm are still only slightly ductile at 300°C, but at 500°C they flow under a differential, axial stress of 1,100 atm beyond 15 per cent axial strain without breaking.   But the most ductile of rocks, Yule marble, could be strained by 1,500 per cent in extension at 800°C under a confining pressure of 5,000 atm.

2. The transition from brittle to plastic behavior for Solenhofen limestone in its dependence on temperature (up to 700°C) and confining and interstitial (pore-fluid) pressure was recorded in 115 triaxial tests (by HUGH C. HEARD) in stress-strain curves.   In order to produce an axial plastic strain equal to $\varepsilon = 10$ per cent, the differential (axial minus lateral) stress of 6,500 atm (kg/cm^2) at 20°C had to be reduced to 1,800 atm at 600°C in dry limestone under a confining pressure held at $p_c = 3,000$ atm $=$ const—these stress-strain curves being reminiscent of those of a strain-hardening ductile metal.   In contrast, the presence of interstitial (pore-water) pressure p strongly reduced the ductility, from a strain $\varepsilon = 10$ per cent at $p = 610$ atm to $\varepsilon = 3$ per cent at $p = 940$ atm pore pressure, while the confining pressure p_c was held at $p_c = 1,100$ atm $=$ const, the temperature at $\theta = 150$°C $=$ const, and the differential flow stress showed *a distinct hump*, an "upper yield stress," and premature fractures occurred, disclosing clearly an embrittlement in consequence of the pore-water pressure p.

3. Afterflow (creep) tests were made under axial compression and lateral confining pressure on limestone, by adding increments of axial

---

[1] Geol. Soc. Am. Mem. 79, 381 pp., edited by DAVID GRIGGS and JOHN HANDIN, with a foreword by M. KING HUBBERT, Waverly Press, Baltimore, Md., Mar. 1, 1960.   This symposium, with the partial support of the Exploration and Production Research Division of the Shell Development Company, Houston, Tex., was held in November, 1956, at the University of California in Los Angeles, Calif., and contains, apart from the papers devoted to the related questions pertaining to plastic and creep deformation of rocks indicated above in the text, investigations on reorientation of anisotropic, constituent minerals in rocks due to a stress field, the recrystallization in the structure of rocks, and also experiments on compaction and cementation of loose sand through pressure and concepts concerning the mechanism of seismic faulting and of fracture caused by earthquakes which lack of space prohibits abstracting here.

load and allowing it subsequently to relax gradually over time intervals of 3 hr at room temperature (by EUGENE C. ROBERTSON).   Since in these afterflow tests the differential stress was allowed to change, they did not lend themselves to a precise determination of the creep-speed law.

4. Torsion tests on Yule marble in the plastic range under confining pressure and at temperatures from 24° to 300°C were made by JOHN HANDIN, D. V. HIGGS, and J. K. O'BRIEN, which led to results similar to those by R. BÖKER[1] in 1914.   As expected, ductility was enhanced by an increase of temperature; permanent twists of as much as 1.6 radians per cm have been observed.

Although the time rate of permanent straining in these flow tests made in elaborately designed machines was comparatively very great, it is believed that the observed values of flow stresses required to deform the hardest types of rocks at high temperatures throw an instructive light on the conditions under which deeply buried rock strata in the earth's outer, solid shell were slowly deformed during the long geologic epochs of time.

15-12.   The Elastic Response of Loose, Granular Materials. That an aggregation of loose, polyhedric or rounded solid particles, on loading by three unequal principal pressures within permissible limits, discloses elastic compressibility and elastic shear strains in the bulk mass has not escaped the attention of the investigators of the possible modes of deformation of earthy substances since old times.   It suffices to remember that dilatational and shear waves in earthquakes are transmitted through sand and the nonconsolidated, uppermost layers of the earth's crust.   This led a group of elasticians to develop recently a special mechanics of granular materials, based on *new idealized models*, by assuming that these bodies are *made up of equal, elastic spheres in elastic contact* with each other and grouped preferably in one of the denser modes of closely, regularly packed layers of the spheres, in the hope that one may describe their equilibria and types of oscillations if one knows precisely how two spheres touching each other react in their contact area when a force P is transmitted normally and a force T is transmitted tangentially between them.

These developments became possible after R. D. MINDLIN[2] succeeded in enriching the mathematical theory of elasticity in 1949 with his exact solution describing the distribution of the tangential stresses in the elliptic contact area of a pair of convex elastic bodies held pressed together by an invariable normal force P while one of the bodies exerts on the other an additional, gradually increasing force T in the tangential direction across the contact area, thus extending HEINRICH HERTZ's

[1] Cf. Vol. I, page 242, Fig. 17-6.
[2] R. D. MINDLIN, Compliance of Elastic Bodies in Contact, J. Appl. Mechanics, vol. 16, no. 3, pp. 259–268, September, 1949.

well-known solution of 1881 of the normal stress distribution produced by a normal force P to adding a tangential force T also transmitted through the contact area. Excluding first slip, MINDLIN found that there is no change in the normal components of traction across the contact surface, that the tangential tractions in it are everywhere parallel to the applied force T, that the contours of equal shear stresses are ellipses, homothetic (coaxial and similar) with the elliptic boundary, and that the magnitude of these tractions rises from one-half the average at the center of the contact surface to infinity along its edge.

In the case of two elastic spheres of equal radii the points remote from the contact plane (the two centers of the spheres) are displaced by an amount $\delta = (2 - \nu)T/4Ga$ (G modulus of rigidity; ν Poisson's ratio; a radius of the flattened contact circle), all points of the contact circle are displaced as in a rigid body parallel to δ (and to the force T), and the shear stresses τ are also parallel but axially distributed symmetrically and increase with the distance ρ from the center as

$$\tau = \frac{T}{2\pi a \cdot \sqrt{a^2 - \rho^2}} \qquad (15\text{-}155)$$

without limit toward the edge of the contact circle $\rho = a$—supposing that no slip occurred—whereas the normal stresses σ according to HERTZ's solution vary as the ordinates of a semiellipsoid of revolution:

$$\sigma = \frac{3P}{2\pi a^2} \cdot \sqrt{1 - \frac{\rho^2}{a^2}} \cdot \qquad (15\text{-}156)$$

In consequence of the trend of the surface tractions τ [Eq. (15-155)], a redistribution of the latter must occur, beginning right from the smallest values of the tangential force resultant T, because of the fact that no value τ greater than the friction caused by the Hertzian distribution of normal stresses σ [Eq. (15-156)] can exist in the contact surface. Supposing that *Coulomb's friction law* $\tau = \mu\sigma$ is valid, the surface tractions will be reduced to their Coulomb values,

$$\tau = \mu\sigma = \frac{3\mu P}{2\pi a^2} \sqrt{1 - \frac{\rho^2}{a^2}}, \qquad a' \leqq \rho \leqq a, \qquad (15\text{-}157)$$

within the annulus in which *slip between the adjoining material points* of the two spheres *has penetrated* from the outer radius $\rho = a$ to an inner radius $\rho = a'$. By prescribing the condition that the two spheres stick together without any slip inside the circle $\rho = a'$, MINDLIN and C. CATTANEO[1] independently found that the tractions τ take on the values

$$\tau = \frac{3\mu P}{2\pi a^2} \left[\sqrt{1 - \frac{\rho^2}{a^2}} - \frac{a'}{a} \sqrt{1 - \frac{\rho^2}{a'^2}} \right] \qquad \text{for } 0 \leqq \rho \leqq a' \quad (15\text{-}158$$

[1] C. CATTANEO, Sul contatto di due corpi elastici: distribuzione locale degli sforzi, Atti accad. naz. Lincei, Rendi., ser. 6, vol. 27, p. 342, 1938.

and that the boundary $\rho = a'$ of the no-slip zone in the contact is given by

$$a' = a\left(1 - \frac{T}{\mu P}\right)^{\frac{2}{3}}. \qquad (15\text{-}159)$$

The distribution of the surface tractions σ and τ may be seen in Fig. 15-55. K. L. JOHNSON[1] has verified the relationship between the displacement δ and the tangential force T in tests with two spheres pressed together and loaded by an increasing lateral load T as predicted in this theory,

$$\delta = \frac{3(2 - \nu)\mu P}{8Ga}\left[1 - \left(1 - \frac{T}{\mu P}\right)^{\frac{2}{3}}\right],$$

$$(15\text{-}160)$$

finding an excellent agreement.

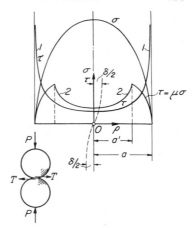

FIG. 15-55. Contact of two elastic spheres under normal (P) and tangential (T) force. Normal stresses σ and tangential tractions τ in contact area. Curve 1 for τ when no slip occurs; curve 2 for τ after slip penetrated in annulus from circle $\rho = a$ to circle $\rho = a'$. (*According to Mindlin and Deresiewicz.*)

Whereas these condensed relations reproducing briefly the results of elaborate developments related to those which have served to solve the NAVIER equations of the theory of elasticity [Cf. Eq. (25-21) on page 392 in Vol. I] by means of potential functions of the CERRUTI-BOUSSINESQ type are straightforward and remarkable also because of their great simplicity, time will have to be allowed to pass before their utilization for handling the static problems in an assembly of very numerous, equal or nonequal, elastic spheres (gravitating or nongravitating, with or without a pore fluid) and representing the new mechanical models of granular media possessing a pronounced elasticity will become more evident. Attempts in this direction have been summarized by H. DERESIEWICZ in a commendable report[2] in which the reader will find a thorough discussion of a variety of regular modes of dense packings of equal, elastic spheres; the theory of the contact of a pair and of many spheres arranged in layers, subjected to normal and oblique forces; an analysis of hysteresis loops for cyclic loading of pairs or arrays of spheres; the response of the latter to rapid oscillations; and the influence

[1] K. L. JOHNSON, Surface Interaction between Elastically Loaded Bodies under Tangential Forces, Proc. Roy. Soc. (London), Ser. A, vol. 230, pp. 531–548, 1955.

[2] H. DERESIEWICZ, Mechanics of Granular Matter, 89 pp., Columbia Univ., Civil Eng. & Mechanics Dept., Tech. Rept. 25 (Naval Research Project), February, 1957, with an extended list of references covering, among others, Mindlin's and his own work.

of the hydrostatic pressure on the speed of propagation of sound predicted by the theory and recorded in experiments by H. BRANDT (1955) in sandstone (dry and saturated with oil). A majority of these investigations originated in Professor Mindlin's Institute at Columbia University in New York.

15-13. Rotationally Symmetric States of Limiting Equilibrium in Loose, Gravitating Material. A. ROTATIONALLY SYMMETRIC STATE ANALOGOUS TO RANKINE'S DISTRIBUTION IN LOOSE EARTH UNDER ITS OWN WEIGHT. Assuming the z axis directed vertically upward in an extended, otherwise undisturbed ground, two states of axial, vertical compression confined through the presence of lateral, uniform pressures parallel to the planes $z = $ const can prevail that are analogous to the two RANKINE distributions which were described in Sec. 15-3 under a horizontal surface. Supposing that the radial, tangential, and axial normal stresses σ_r, σ_t, σ_z are principal pressures everywhere in a limiting state of axially symmetric equilibrium, a fixed ratio of the major (σ_1) and minor (σ_3) principal stresses, according to Eq. (15-6), requires that

$$\frac{\sigma_1}{\sigma_3} = \frac{1 + \sin \rho}{1 - \sin \rho} = \cotan^2 \left(\frac{\pi}{4} - \frac{\rho}{2} \right), \qquad (15\text{-}161)$$

and one sees at once that one may distinguish (1) *an upper limiting state* when the major pressure σ_1 acts in the vertical direction,

$$\sigma_z = \sigma_1 = \gamma(h - z), \qquad \sigma_r = \sigma_t = \sigma_3 = \sigma_z \tan^2 \left(\frac{\pi}{4} - \frac{\rho}{2} \right),$$
$$(15\text{-}162)$$

and (2) *a lower limiting state* when it acts in any horizontal direction,

$$\sigma_z = \sigma_3 = \gamma(h - z), \qquad \sigma_r = \sigma_t = \sigma_1 = \sigma_z \cotan^2 \left(\frac{\pi}{4} - \frac{\rho}{2} \right),$$
$$(15\text{-}163)$$

both types representing laterally confined, axial, vertical compressions. Any plane passing through a point $P(r,z)$ inclined at an angle with respect to the vertical direction, in

Case 1: $\qquad\qquad\qquad (\pi/4) - (\rho/2)$

Case 2: $\qquad\qquad\qquad (\pi/4) + (\rho/2)$

is a plane of slip. These planes envelop around point P a circular cone of vertical axis with an acute or obtuse apex angle $(\pi/2) - \rho$, $(\pi/2) + \rho$, respectively (Fig. 15-56). If the point $P(r,z)$ is moved along a circle $r = $ const around the z axis as center, the individual cones radiating out from the points P will envelop two new circular cones 1 and 2 which we may interpret as the major surfaces of slip related to the circle $r = $ const.

The upper limiting state (1) may be illustrated by an example of *subsidence of loose gravel overlaying an abandoned mine excavation* in which the roofs were allowed to crumble, permitting gravel to trickle down into the empty mine chamber, detaching a funnel along which the material sinks down.   This circular cone of apex angle $(\pi/2) - \rho$, with its point located at depth h at the center O of the disturbance, demarks with its base in the circle ss of radius $r_0 = h \tan [(\pi/4) - (\rho/2)]$ the zone of subsidence on the free surface $z = h$ within which ground-level changes might be expected to occur.   It may be instructive to evaluate the components of normal and shear stress σ_n and τ_n that will just hold in place the weight

$$W = (\tfrac{1}{3})\gamma\pi h^3 \tan^2 \left(\frac{\pi}{4} - \frac{\rho}{2}\right)$$

of the inverted cone of height h, namely,

$$\sigma_n = \frac{\sigma_z \cos^2 \rho}{1 + \sin \rho} = \frac{\gamma(h - z)(1 + \cos 2\rho)}{2(1 + \sin \rho)} ,$$

$$\tau_n = - \frac{\sigma_z \sin \rho \cos \rho}{1 + \sin \rho} = - \frac{\gamma(h - z) \sin 2\rho}{2(1 + \sin \rho)} ,$$

and one confirms that their vertical components integrated over the area of the funnel mantle just holds the weight W in balance (Fig. 15-57).

B. Equilibrium Expressed in Terms of Cylindrical Coordinates r, z.   Suppose that two of the principal axes lie in the meridian planes passing through the z axis and that the state of stress is defined by the three components of normal stress σ_r, σ_t, σ_z and the shear stress τ_{rz} with their positive arrows as indicated in Fig. 15-58.   In regard to the types of the surfaces of slip compatible with axial symmetry, a variety of cases is possible, depending on whether the major (σ_1) and minor (σ_3) principal stresses both lie in the meridian planes or only one of them and the other coincides with σ_t.   Confining the discussion to the first case, one class of solutions for loose material is characterized by two families of isogonal surfaces of slip which are *surfaces of revolution;* this is based

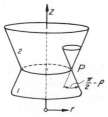

Fig. 15-56

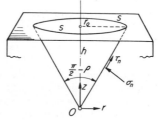

Fig. 15-57. Zone of sub-sidence SS.

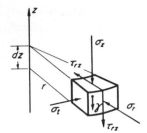

FIG. 15-58

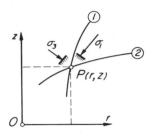

FIG. 15-59. First and second lines of slip (1, 2), assuming that σ_t is intermediate principal stress σ_2.

on the supposition that the circumferential normal stress σ_t acts as the *intermediate* principal stress σ_2 ($\sigma_1 > \sigma_2 > \sigma_3$) at any point of the stress field[1] (Fig. 15-59).

The states of equilibrium in loose, gravitating material must satisfy the two conditions of equilibrium,

$$\frac{\partial(r\sigma_r)}{\partial r} - \sigma_t + r\frac{\partial \tau_{rz}}{\partial z} = 0, \qquad (15\text{-}164)$$

$$r\frac{\partial \sigma_z}{\partial z} + \frac{\partial}{\partial r}(r\tau_{rz}) = -\gamma r, \qquad (15\text{-}165)$$

and the condition of slip,

$$4\tau_{max}^2 = (\sigma_z - \sigma_r)^2 + 4\tau_{rz}^2 = \sin^2 \rho \cdot (\sigma_z + \sigma_r)^2, \qquad (15\text{-}166)$$

with the understanding that in these *three* equations for the *four* unknown components of stress the magnitude of the tangential normal stress σ_t may be permitted to take any value situated between the limits of the inequalities:

$$\sigma_3 = (\tfrac{1}{2})(\sigma_r + \sigma_z)(1 - \sin \rho) < \sigma_t < (\tfrac{1}{2})(\sigma_r + \sigma_z)(1 + \sin \rho) = \sigma_1.$$
$$(15\text{-}167)$$

Since the unknown σ_t appears only in the first of the three equations, we may avail ourselves of the liberty of searching for triples σ_r, σ_z, τ_{rz} that will satisfy only the two equations (15-165) and (15-166) and use Eq. (15-164) for computing from it

$$\sigma_t = \frac{\partial}{\partial r}(r\sigma_r) + r\frac{\partial \tau_{rz}}{\partial z}, \qquad (15\text{-}168)$$

[1] If this supposition does not hold, the surfaces of slip generally become greatly involved, resembling helical surfaces except in the case of a circular cylinder held in equilibrium by radial pressures σ_r exerted uniformly on the inner and outer surfaces $r = a$ and $r = b$, while $\sigma_z = \sigma_2$ is the intermediate principal stress (recalling the case treated in Sec. 15-7A) when the surfaces of slip are the cylinders erected with their generatrices above two logarithmic spirals.

in order to ascertain that the inequality (15-167) is not being violated. We note the peculiar property of these axially symmetric states of stress in loose material: that it suffices to satisfy as a fourth relation an inequality for one of the unknown components of stress, namely, σ_t. The presence of the gravity body-force term $-\gamma r$ in Eq. (15-165) makes it, however, difficult to find exact solutions. We shall be able to illustrate one or two groups of solutions only after omitting the right-hand term $-\gamma r$ in Eq. (15-165).

Suppose that we try to express the stresses σ_r, σ_z, τ_{rz} in the form

$$\sigma_r = \sigma_0 c_r e^{\zeta},$$
$$\sigma_z = \sigma_0 c_z e^{\zeta}, \qquad\qquad (15\text{-}169)$$
$$\tau_{rz} = \sigma_0 c_{rz} e^{\zeta},$$

denoting by σ_0 an arbitrary constant stress (for which we may take the unity of stress 1 kg/cm^2); by c_r, c_z, c_{rz}, three dimensionless constants; and by ζ, a function of the cylindrical coordinates r, z. After substituting Eqs. (15-169) in Eqs. (15-165) and (15-166) we obtain the partial differential equation of first order for the unknown function ζ (letting $\gamma = 0$),

$$c_z \frac{\partial \zeta}{\partial z} + c_{rz} \frac{\partial \zeta}{\partial r} = -\frac{c_{rz}}{r}, \qquad\qquad (15\text{-}170)$$

and a quadratic equation relating the three constants c_r, c_z, c_{rz},

$$(c_z - c_r)^2 + 4c_{rz}^2 = \sin^2 \rho \cdot (c_z + c_r)^2, \qquad\qquad (15\text{-}171)$$

in which we may choose c_z, c_r freely and from which c_{rz} is found equal to

$$c_{rz} = \pm(\tfrac{1}{2})\sqrt{2c_r c_z(1 + \sin^2 \rho) - (c_r^2 + c_z^2)\,\cos^2 \rho}. \qquad (15\text{-}171a)$$

Equation (15-170) is solved[1] by

$$\zeta(r,z) = \ln \frac{a}{r} + f(m), \qquad m = \frac{c_{rz}z - c_z r}{a}. \qquad (15\text{-}172)$$

Thus with the exponential factor

$$e^{\zeta} = e^{\ln (a/r) + f(m)} = \frac{a}{r} e^{f} \qquad\qquad (15\text{-}173)$$

we have the group of equations for the stresses σ_r, σ_z, τ_{rz} satisfying in weightless, loose material the two equations (15-165) and (15-166):

$$\sigma_r = \sigma_0 c_r \frac{a}{r} e^{f},$$

$$\sigma_z = \sigma_0 c_z \frac{a}{r} e^{f}, \qquad\qquad (15\text{-}174)$$

$$\tau_{rz} = \sigma_0 c_{rz} \frac{a}{r} e^{f},$$

---

[1] By letting $c_{rz}\, dz = c_z\, dr$ gives $c_{rz}z - c_z r = ma$ (m is a variable parameter, a an arbitrary length) and after adding to $\zeta = f(m)$ the particular integral $\ln (a/r)$ of Eq. (15-170), $f(m)$ being an arbitrary function of m.

with two arbitrary constants c_r, c_z and the arbitrary function $f(m) = f[c_{rz}(z/a) - c_z(r/a)]$ covering a variety of possible limiting states of equilibrium.

We may also evaluate from Eq. (15-168), using Eqs. (15-174), the tangential stress σ_t, obtaining

$$\sigma_t = \sigma_0(c_{rz}^2 - c_r c_z)e^f \cdot \frac{df}{dm} = -\frac{\sigma_0}{4}(c_r + c_z)^2 \cos^2 \rho \cdot e^f \cdot \frac{df}{dm},$$

$$(15\text{-}175)$$

and must note, in order to avoid the disturbing minus sign on the extreme right side (i.e., that σ_t shall not become a tensile stress), that functions $f(m)$ having only a negative derivative, $df/dm < 0$, are permissible. With these premises the inequality (15-167) takes the form

$$1 - \sin \rho < (c_r + c_z)\frac{r}{2a}\cos^2 \rho \cdot \left|\frac{df}{dm}\right| < 1 + \sin \rho, \qquad (15\text{-}176)$$

restricting the range and space region within which the stress field may be applied.

Simple cases result by taking $f = -m$ or $f = -\ln m$, etc., the distributions of stress are homologous along the families of parallel circular cones $c_{rz}z - c_z r = ma$, the three stresses σ_r, σ_z, τ_{rz} differing at corresponding points of the cones by a factor.

C. EQUILIBRIUM EXPRESSED IN SPHERICAL COORDINATES R, φ. Assuming axial symmetry around the axis $\varphi = 0$ oriented vertically upward (Fig. 15-60) and postulating conditions analogous to those elucidated in Sec. 15-13B, we have for the four unknown components of stress σ_R, σ_T, σ_t, τ_{RT}, presuming that σ_t acts as the intermediate principal stress σ_2, $\sigma_t = \sigma_2$, three equations:

$$\frac{\partial \sigma_R}{\partial R} + \frac{\partial \tau_{RT}}{R\,\partial \varphi} + \frac{1}{R}(2\sigma_R - \sigma_T - \sigma_t + \tau_{RT}\cot \varphi) = -\gamma \cos \varphi,$$

$$\frac{\partial \sigma_T}{R\,\partial \varphi} + \frac{\partial \tau_{RT}}{\partial R} + \frac{1}{R}[(\sigma_T - \sigma_t)\cot \varphi + 3\tau_{RT}] = \gamma \sin \varphi, \qquad (15\text{-}177)$$

$$4\tau_{max}^2 = (\sigma_R - \sigma_T)^2 + 4\tau_{RT}^2 = \sin^2 \rho \cdot (\sigma_R + \sigma_T)^2;$$

furthermore, for the inequality for σ_t, we have

$$\sigma_3 = (1 - \sin \rho)(\tfrac{1}{2})(\sigma_R + \sigma_T) < \sigma_t < (1 + \sin \rho)(\tfrac{1}{2})(\sigma_R + \sigma_T) = \sigma_1.$$

$$(15\text{-}178)$$

The procedure for handling these relations could follow the scheme described in Sec. 15-13B after eliminating first the stress σ_t from the first two equations. Since there is little hope of finding integrals of a general type, we shall confine ourselves to stating two simple, special solutions.

(1). *Hollow spheres under internal pressure*, neglecting gravity body force. Supposing $\gamma = 0$, that σ_R and σ_T are principal stresses, and that τ_{RT} vanishes, from symmetry conditions the two circumferential stresses must equal each other, $\sigma_t = \sigma_T$; since the remaining unknown stresses σ_R and σ_T depend only on the radial distance R, but not on the polar angle φ, we have the two equations

$$R \frac{d\sigma_R}{dR} + 2(\sigma_R - \sigma_T) = 0, \qquad (15\text{-}179)$$

$$\sigma_R = \frac{1 + \sin \rho}{1 - \sin \rho} \cdot \sigma_T, \qquad (15\text{-}180)$$

in the second of which we assume that the radial stress $\sigma_R = \sigma_1$ represents the major principal stress. Denoting by m the constant

$$m = \frac{4 \sin \rho}{1 + \sin \rho}, \qquad (15\text{-}181)$$

the state of stress in a hollow sphere $R \geq R_0$, in which an internal pressure p acts, is given by

$$\sigma_R = p \left(\frac{R_0}{R}\right)^m, \qquad \sigma_T = \frac{1 - \sin \rho}{1 + \sin \rho} \cdot \sigma_R = \left(1 - \frac{m}{2}\right)\sigma_R. \quad (15\text{-}182)$$

(2). *Spherical small cavity held under static pressure p_0 situated deep under a layer of gravitating, loose material.* One might be interested in evaluating the maximum pressure in the cavity p_0 causing the first disturbances to appear on the surface of the ground. The state of stress around and in the vicinity of the vertical axis passing through the center O of the cavity may be approximately determined by tracing a sphere around O tangent to the surface (Fig. 15-61), by replacing the vertical

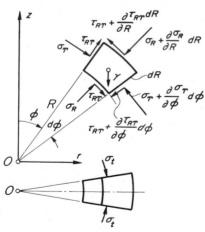

FIG. 15-60

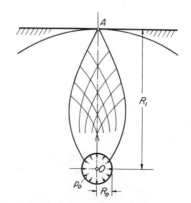

FIG. 15-61. A spherical cavity held under static pressure p_0 in the depth R_1 underground in gravitating loose material.

gravity field through vectors converging toward the center O of the cavity and of uniform magnitude, and solving the problem for this sphere loaded by a uniform, radially converging field of body forces.

This amounts to adding a right-hand term equal to $-\gamma R$ to Eq. (15-179),

$$R\frac{d\sigma_R}{dR} + 2(\sigma_R - \sigma_T) = -\gamma R, \qquad (15\text{-}183)$$

and to combining with Eq. (15-180). If R_0 denotes the radius of the cavity and R_1 the distance of its center O from the earth's surface, the boundary condition $R = R_1, \sigma_R = 0$ and Eqs. (15-183) and (15-180) are satisfied by

$$\sigma_R = \frac{\gamma}{m+1}\left(\frac{R_1^{m+1}}{R^m} - R\right),$$

$$\sigma_T = \left(1 - \frac{m}{2}\right)\sigma_R, \qquad (15\text{-}184)$$

giving for the maximum pressure p_0 that might be exerted inside the cavity, just causing the first disturbance to appear on the earth's surface, the value

$$R = R_0, \qquad \sigma_R = p_0 = \frac{\gamma R_1}{m+1}\left[\left(\frac{R_1}{R_0}\right)^m - \frac{R_0}{R_1}\right]. \qquad (15\text{-}185)$$

Figure 15-61 illustrates the body of loose material in a vertical section, bounded by two logarithmic spirals in its profile, starting at point A, that will be lifted up slightly by the pressure p_0.

If, for example, the friction angle of the loose material is $\rho = 30°$, the exponent m is $m = \frac{4}{3}$ and the pressure is

$$p_0 = (\tfrac{3}{7})\gamma R_1\left[\left(\frac{R_1}{R_0}\right)^{4/3} - \frac{R_0}{R_1}\right], \qquad (15\text{-}186)$$

and if, for example, the depth of the cavity $R_1 = 100 R_0$ is a hundred times its radius R_0, the pressure is approximately $p_0 = 200\gamma R_1$, or equal to 200 times the static pressure γR_1 of a column of undisturbed earth under its own weight, disclosing the formidable resistance of a frictional nature exerted by the rubbing along the surface of slip indicated in the sketch in Fig. 15-61. The distribution of the stresses σ_R and σ_T along the vertical axis may probably not be far from the exact one and on the safe side.

Part V

CREEP OF METALS AT ELEVATED TEMPERATURES

CHAPTER 16

CREEP OF METALS AT
ELEVATED TEMPERATURES

If you should think that the primordial atoms
Can stay still, and by staying still give birth
To new motions of things, then far astray
You wander from true reasoning . . .

And all those particles that congregating
In denser union, collide and rebound
Through minute intervals, being entangled
By their own close-locked shapes, these atoms form
The strong substance of rocks, and stubborn lumps
Of iron, and all other things like these.
Then of the rest a smaller number roam
Through the great void, and leaping far apart
Recoil afar over huge intervals.

LUCRETIUS (*De Rerum Natura*, p. 46)

16-1. Variables of State. The raising of temperatures and pressures in steam and gas turbines in and around the parts admitting hot steam or burning fuels and the building of single units with greatly increased capacities of power for achieving improved thermodynamic efficiencies have brought about the development of new construction metals and alloys that can withstand severe service conditions under high temperatures.   These recent trends make the design of vital parts in machines converting heat into mechanical power or serving other purposes in industry greatly dependent on a better knowledge of the mechanical strength of metallic parts of construction exposed to prolonged action of stress at elevated temperatures.

Since the operating lives of machines in plants are far longer than the time usually allowed for determining the strength of laboratory samples of the metals to be used, it is necessary to give much thought to the skillful extrapolation of the test results in order to predict the slow permanent deformations or the creep of metals to be expected over prolonged times and to estimate the stresses causing fracture at high temperatures.

Whereas at normal temperature the yield or flow stress σ in a tensile

509

test increases in a ductile metal with the permanent part ε'' of strain and a function $\sigma = F(\varepsilon'')$ may characterize the strain hardening of the metal, if the testing temperature θ is raised to higher values, the flow stress σ is found to increase both with the permanent strain ε'' and with the permanent rate of strain $d\varepsilon''/dt = \dot{\varepsilon}''$ and the ductile metals are said to disclose, apart from strain hardening, also a generally viscous behavior. Whether a unifying function (an equation of state), expressing the flow stress σ for uniaxial states of stress and strain in finite terms of ε'' and $\dot{\varepsilon}''$,

$$\sigma = F(\varepsilon'', \dot{\varepsilon}''), \tag{16-1}$$

at a given temperature θ exists is by no means clear a priori.   It would postulate that the yield strength σ under normal stresses of a metal deformed to a prescribed permanent strain ε'' that is reached at a given rate of permanent strain $\dot{\varepsilon}''$ should be independent of the various paths of loading or straining along which the metal may be deformed.

During the past 20 to 30 years a vast number of observations have been assembled in long-time, tensile, creep and creep-to-fracture tests in which (1) tensile specimens were held under invariable loads and temperatures and the creep curves $\varepsilon'' = f(t)$ in function of the time t recorded over periods of a few weeks or months.   Besides these *standard long-time creep tests* tensile bars have also been subjected to (2) *constant-rate-of-stretching tests* by extending specimens under uniform speeds of stretching and (3) by observing the drop of load with time t while the total elongation ε [sum of the elastic (ε') and the permanent or creep strain (ε'')] $\varepsilon = \varepsilon' + \varepsilon'' = (\sigma/E) + \varepsilon'' = \text{const}$ was held at an invariable value, i.e., by running *relaxation tests*, while in all these conventional types of tensile tests the temperature θ was held invariable.   Furthermore, (4) the creep elongation has been observed while σ was held invariable but the temperature θ fluctuated slowly with time t between an upper and lower value, (5) tests have been made under combined stress by subjecting hollow cylinders to biaxial states of stress, and (6) bending or torsion tests have been made on prismatic bars.

Notwithstanding the complexity of the thermal phenomena taking place in polycrystalline metals exposed to long-time action of stress at high temperatures,[1] causing changes in the atomic structure within the

[1] R. W. BAILEY and A. M. ROBERTS, Testing of Materials for Service in High Temperature Steam Plant, Proc. Inst. Mech. Engrs. (London), vol. 122, p. 209, 1932, pointed out as early as 1932 that plain carbon steels undergo a conspicuous change in their structure in the carbides, the lamellae of which are spheroidized, transformed into globules through long exposure to elevated temperature.   The reader may find detailed information on the structural changes and the behavior of metals in F. H. NORTON, "The Creep of Steel at High Temperatures," McGraw-Hill Book Company, Inc., New York, 1929, and H. J. TAPSELL, "Creep of Metals," 279 pp., Oxford University Press, London, 1931; also in Creep and Fracture

grains and in the grain-boundary substance, attempts have not ceased to correlate the experimental results obtained in these aforementioned various types of tests with each other and to deduce from them mechanical rules of more general validity on which a working theory of creep of metals may be based.

In the pure, stable, polycrystalline metals, at temperatures comparatively not greatly elevated (in their pronounced strain-hardening range), one may not go far astray by assuming that in uniaxial tension or compression the yield or flow stress σ will increase by a differential $d\sigma$ if the permanent strain ε'' and rate of strain $\dot\varepsilon''$ are increased by the differentials $d\varepsilon''$ and $d\dot\varepsilon''$:

$$d\sigma = \frac{\partial\sigma}{\partial\varepsilon''}\,d\varepsilon'' + \frac{\partial\sigma}{\partial\dot\varepsilon''}\,d\dot\varepsilon''. \tag{16-2}$$

The ratio $\partial\sigma/\partial\varepsilon''$ measures *the rate of strain hardening* under invariable rate of strain $\dot\varepsilon'' = $ const, and $\partial\sigma/\partial\dot\varepsilon''$ measures *the viscosity of the metal* at a strain $\varepsilon'' = $ const while the temperature θ is held invariable and the elastic strain changes by $d\varepsilon' = d\sigma/E$.

Likewise in an element subjected to a triaxial state of stress, we may assume that

$$d\tau_0 = \frac{\partial\tau_0}{\partial\gamma_0''}\,d\gamma_0'' + \frac{\partial\tau_0}{\partial\dot\gamma_0''}\,d\dot\gamma_0'' \tag{16-3}$$

in terms of the octahedral variables of the shearing stress τ_0, permanent unit shear γ_0'', and rate of shear $\dot\gamma_0''$. In both differential relations the time t as a variable is supposed not to appear explicitly.

---

of Metals at High Temperatures, Proc. Symposium Natl. Phys. Lab., Teddington, May 31–June 2, 1954, 420 pp., Her Majesty's Stationery Office, London, containing 22 papers devoted to deformation and creep in simple and complex materials and to the theory of fracture.

Compare also W. E. BARDGETT, Comparative High Temperature Properties of British and American Steels, and R. W. BAILEY, A Critical Examination of Procedures Used in Britain and the United States to Determine Creep Stresses for the Design of Power Plants for Long Life at High Temperatures, 19 pp., papers presented before the Institution of Mechanical Engineers, Dec. 4, 1953, London, and at the ASME Annual Meeting, New York, 1953. BAILEY elucidates therein four procedures for extrapolating creep data: (1) to plot the relation on double logarithmic scales between stress σ and time t and to extrapolate to working life t_s (service time) in order to obtain permissible working stress σ_s; (2) to plot stress σ versus minimum creep rate $\dot\varepsilon_{min}$ on double log scales, favored in the United States; (3) to represent stress causing rupture, likewise versus time. (4) The reliability of adopting a working stress as the test stress and of using temperature to accelerate creep is urged by BAILEY, who discouraged procedures 1 and 2 which make working temperature the test temperature. For details supporting his views the reader must be referred to his paper. Concerning principles of extrapolating creep data, compare also ground-laying papers by P. G. McVETTY (J. Appl. Mechanics, 1932; Mech. Eng., March, 1934, p. 1490; Trans. ASME, 1943; Proc. ASTM, 1943).

The yield strength in a ductile metal is raised through previous cold work for subsequent stressing in the same sense.   But a cold-worked metal may lose its strength through exposure to a sufficiently high temperature during a sufficiently long time through annealing or recrystallization.   The yield stress σ and the octahedral shearing stress τ_0 as a measure of the yield strength thus are subject to deterioration through prolonged action of heat.   This might be expressed precisely by adding a third term on the right sides of Eqs. (16-2) and (16-3), namely, $(\partial\sigma/\partial t)\, dt$, $(\partial\tau_0/\partial t)\, dt$, respectively, the differential ratios $\partial\sigma/\partial t$, $\partial\tau_0/\partial t$ measuring the time rates of decay of yield strength σ and τ_0, which manifest themselves concurrently with the rates of strain hardening $\partial\sigma/\partial\varepsilon''$, $\partial\tau_0/\partial\gamma_0''$, the latter being positive, the former negative.[1]   On the other hand, if the structure of a metal is such that a pure thermal action raises its strength as the time t elapses—such metals are said to age-harden—the effects of both rates will add up.   Whereas at moderately elevated temperatures it thus suffices to assume that τ_0 depends on the two strain variables γ_0'' and $\dot\gamma_0''$, according to Eq. (16-3), in a group of equally important cases, namely, when gradual softening or age hardening must be taken into consideration, Eq. (16-3) must be amended and expressed in the form

$$d\tau_0 = \frac{\partial\tau_0}{\partial\gamma_0''}\, d\gamma_0'' + \frac{\partial\tau_0}{\partial\dot\gamma_0''}\, d\dot\gamma_0'' + \frac{\partial\tau_0}{\partial t}\, dt \qquad (16\text{-}4)$$

by assuming that τ_0 depends on the three independent variables γ_0'', $\dot\gamma_0''$, and the time t.   We shall draw some instructive conclusions from Eq. (16-4) in subsequent sections.[2]

[1] R. W. Bailey in one of his fundamental papers, Physical Properties of Metals and the Design of Plant for High-temperature Service, read before the North-western Branch, Institution of Mechanical Engineers (London), April, 1927 (abridged in Engineering, vol. 124, pp. 44–46, 1927), is credited with having expressed his concept of this type of creep as "the outward manifestation of the balance in the destruction of strain hardening by thermal influence and its recreation by further slip"—a thought P. G. McVetty used to express to the author that creep is "a balance between the opposing forces of strain hardening and annealing" (see his paper Creep of Metals at Elevated Temperatures—the Hyperbolic Sine Relation between Stress and Creep Rate, ASME Meeting, Davenport, Iowa, April, 1943).

[2] It is well known that the creep strength in a metal may be improved by alloying small amounts of another, structurally related metal with it, for example, by adding a few ounces of silver per ton to pure (oxygen-free) copper and likewise that the creep strength may appreciably be raised in commercially pure copper or aluminum by cold-working, prestretching, or rolling them cold to a moderate degree before they are subjected to continuous stressing at moderately elevated temperatures.   The electrical industry makes extensive use of both methods of improving the creep strength in the windings conducting heavy electric currents in the rotors of generators.

When in the preceding remarks we spoke of relatively low, intermediate, and high values of the temperature θ, we had in mind *Paul Ludwik's homologous temperature* θ/θ_m, expressing the ratio of the absolute temperature θ to that at the melting point θ_m, recalling that polycrystalline metals not having allotropic transformations and their alloys behave in a somewhat comparable manner mechanically at the same homologous ratio θ/θ_m. The material constants or parameter embodied in the partial derivatives in Eq. (16-4) are to be considered dependent on θ/θ_m. Functions expressing their variation with the temperature have been proposed on empirical and physical grounds.

Apart from the technical applications, the mechanical theory of the creep of metals may offer some interesting insights into another group of problems that should at least be mentioned here. Polycrystalline, nonmetallic, solid (brittle) substances can be forced continuously to deform permanently without fracturing, i.e., can be brought to the plastic stage, and one should expect that they will also disclose the phenomena of slow creep under prolonged exposure to stress at elevated temperatures, not unlike the ductile metals. These conditions prevail at greater depths in the natural rocks, in the solid, upper parts of the earth's crust, if one gives due consideration to the *geothermal gradient* ever present in the earth's outer mantle in which the temperature rises by 3°C with every hundred meters depth, on an average. Thus the theory of the creep of metals may throw an important light on the closely related laws of the slow creep of the natural rocks and *on some fundamental questions in geomechanics*, such as the slow processes of the deformation in the earth's deeper strata, associated with the building up of the high mountain ranges over the long geologic epochs; the shift of the continental blocks due to the attraction of the moon, facilitated through the enhanced mobility of the rock layers at depths of 40 to 50 km where high temperatures of the order of 1200° to 1500°C must prevail; and other problems in geomechanics.

16-2. Correlating Behavior of Metals Stressed in Uniaxial Tension in Various Types of Tests. A. RATE OF STRAIN HARDENING AND OF INCREASE OF FLOW STRESS WITH RATE OF PERMANENT

The massive copper bars of the windings, embedded in axial grooves of the steel rotors, tend to expand because of the evolution of heat through current losses, raising their temperature, while the high centrifugal forces press them against the rotor bodies. Since the thermal expansion of copper is much greater than that of steel, the friction along the contact surfaces tends to prevent the differential expansion of the copper rods relative to the steel rotor, with the result that considerable compression stresses are built up in the long copper conductors in their axial direction, causing them at the prevailing temperatures continuously to shorten permanently and to creep in compression during the service time of the generators.

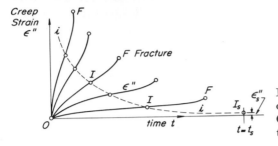

FIG. 16-1.   Long-time creep curves $\varepsilon'' = f(t)$. Curve ii, locus of inflection points I.

STRAIN.   The common method of determining at an elevated service temperature θ the stress σ that will produce in metal a maximum allowable permanent deformation ε_s'' in a prescribed service time t_s is to subject several specimens to long-time creep tests, under loads σ_l per unit area held invariable, and to observe the dependence of the permanent strain ε'' on the time t in the creep curves $\varepsilon'' = f(t)$.   Under the higher loads σ_l, the curves distinctly show an inflection point I (Fig. 16-1) but at the lower loads they usually straighten out over a considerable time.   Denoting rates of strain $d\varepsilon/dt = \dot{\varepsilon}$ by $u = \dot{\varepsilon}$, for convenience, one may distinguish in the creep curves taken at low loads a primary, secondary, and ternary range, in which the rate of permanent strain $u'' = \dot{\varepsilon}''$ first decreases, then remains approximately at its minimum value u_m'' (minimum creep rate), and starts again to increase, respectively, with time t.   One may base the design on an estimation of the load stress σ_l under which the ordinate of the locus of the inflection points I at service time t_s just reaches the allowable permanent strain ε_s'', presuming that the inflection point I marks the beginning of localized necking in the tension bar.   This demands extrapolation of the lower creep curves $\varepsilon'' = f(t)$, recorded over a limited time of testing, beyond their observed range up to the service time t_s.   The uncertainty arising from this extrapolation can be bridged over only if one has established some plausible functional relation connecting the stress σ with the minimum creep rate[1] u_m''.   We shall attempt to indicate how this may be achieved by excluding first the phenomenon of gradual softening of the metal with time t.

The total strain ε being the sum of the elastic and permanent part ε' and ε'',

$$\varepsilon = \varepsilon' + \varepsilon'' = \frac{\sigma}{E} + \varepsilon'', \qquad (16\text{-}5)$$

[1] This amounts to replacing the creep curves in the lower part of Fig. 16-1, approaching those expected in service, by straight lines inclined under the minimum creep rate u_m'', neglecting the curved portion of the primary creep range (Fig. 16-2).

the total rate of strain $u = d\varepsilon/dt = \dot{\varepsilon}$ likewise being the sum of

$$u = \frac{d\varepsilon}{dt} = u' + u'' = \frac{1}{E}\frac{d\sigma}{dt} + u'', \qquad (16\text{-}6)$$

where ε, ε'' and u, u'' express conventional strains and rates of strain referred to an original gauge length l_0 in a tensile specimen, $\varepsilon' = \sigma/E$ being considered small, let us denote *the rate of strain hardening $\partial\sigma/\partial\varepsilon''$* and *the rate of increase of yield or flow stress σ with rate of permanent strain u'' $\partial\sigma/\partial u''$* by the abbreviating symbols ψ and ϕ:

$$\psi = \frac{\partial\sigma}{\partial\varepsilon''}, \qquad \phi = \frac{\partial\sigma}{\partial u''}. \qquad (16\text{-}7)$$

We may state one fundamental concept on which the theory of creep and flow of metals at elevated temperatures may be based by postulating the differential relation [Eq. (16-2)]:

$$d\sigma = \psi\, d\varepsilon'' + \phi\, du'', \qquad (16\text{-}8)$$

assuming at a given temperature first, in general, that ψ and ϕ may or may not vary with the independent variables ε'' and u'' but that they do not depend on the variable time t explicitly.

We may use casually Eq. (16-8) also *when the conventional strain ε'' tends to increase to semifinite values,* but in such cases we have to distinguish the load stress σ_l per unit of the original area and the true stress σ, the latter taken per unit of actual area and in incompressible material equal to

$$\sigma = (1 + \varepsilon'')\sigma_l, \qquad (16\text{-}9)$$

giving for the rate of strain hardening ψ the second expression

$$\psi = \frac{\partial\sigma}{\partial\varepsilon''} = \sigma_l + (1 + \varepsilon'')\frac{\partial\sigma_l}{\partial\varepsilon''}. \qquad (16\text{-}10)$$

This indicates that at the maximum load in a tensile test, at the "ultimate strength" $\sigma_{l,\max}$, $\partial\sigma_l/\partial\varepsilon'' = 0$, a critical value of rate of strain hardening ψ_c,

$$\psi_c = \sigma_{l,\max}, \qquad (16\text{-}11)$$

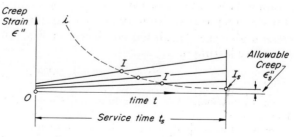

FIG. 16-2.   Idealized creep in lower range of loads σ_l, replacing creep curves $\varepsilon'' = f(t)$ by straight lines
$\varepsilon'' = \varepsilon_0 + u_m''t.$

is reached, below which a tensile bar cannot be expected to stretch uniformly, and an instability of equilibrium due to local necking occurs—a relation which the French engineer M. CONSIDÈRE[1] utilized in 1888 to propose a geometric construction for defining ψ_c from the equivalent equation

$$\psi_c = \frac{d\sigma}{d\varepsilon''} = \frac{\sigma}{1 + \varepsilon''} = \sigma_{l,\,\max}. \tag{16-11a}$$

Allowing for unrestricted creep strains ε'', the long-time creep test should thus strictly conform to the condition of holding the *load* $\sigma_l = $ const (not the stress $\sigma = $ const). After differentiating Eq. (16-9) with respect to the time t, this amounts to putting $d\sigma_l/dt = 0$ in

$$\frac{d\sigma}{dt} = \sigma_l u'' + (1 + \varepsilon'')\frac{d\sigma_l}{dt} = \sigma_l u''. \tag{16-12}$$

Since, from Eq. (16-8),

$$\frac{d\sigma}{dt} = \psi \cdot u'' + \phi \frac{du''}{dt}, \tag{16-13}$$

by combining both, the differential equation for the rate of creep $u'' = d\varepsilon''/dt$ under an invariable load $\sigma_l = $ const is obtained,

$$\phi \frac{du''}{dt} + (\psi - \sigma_l)u'' = 0, \tag{16-14}$$

defining the creep-time curves $\varepsilon'' = f(t)$ and indicating that, due to

$$\frac{du''}{dt} = -\frac{(\psi - \sigma_l)u''}{\phi}, \tag{16-15}$$

the creep rates u'' will decrease first, as long as $\psi > \sigma_l$; reach a minimum value $u''_{\min}$ when $\psi = \sigma_l$; and subsequently increase after $\psi < \sigma_l$, disclosing that the creep curves $\varepsilon'' = f(t)$ under loads σ_l approaching the ultimate strength $\sigma_{l,\,\max}$ [at which, according to Eq. (16-11), $\sigma_{l,\,\max} = \psi_c$] will possess an inflection point I ($du''/dt = 0$) and a primary ($du'' < 0$) and ternary ($du'' > 0$) range like those depicted in Fig. 16-1. Point I marks the point at which necking sets in in the specimen.

On the contrary, however, as long as the load σ_l in a tensile specimen is a good deal smaller than the ultimate strength $\sigma_{l,\,\max}$ (in the stress-strain curves run at low rates $u'' = $ const, comparable to the expected slowest creep rates), we may ignore Eq. (16-15) and *describe long-time creep* under the stipulated condition of Eq. (16-8) combined with Eq. (16-6) by letting in

$$\frac{d\sigma}{dt} = E(u - u'') = \psi u'' + \phi \frac{du''}{dt} \tag{16-16}$$

[1] M. CONSIDÈRE, "Die Anwendung von Eisen und Stahl bei Constructionen," Vienna, 1888. See Vol. I, page 71, Fig. 8-2, for the tangent traced to the *true* stress $\sigma = $ func(ε'') curve above the load maximum $\sigma_{l,\max}$.

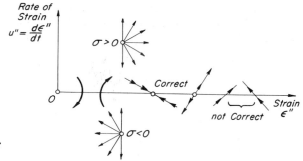

FIG. 16-3.   Rules for hodographs.

the $(true)$ stress $\sigma = const, d\sigma/dt = 0, u = u''$. Supposing that upon application of a stress σ the variables of state had the initial values $\varepsilon_0{''}$, $u_0{''}$ at time $t = 0$, the strain ε'' will start to increase under the action of σ by small amounts while the rates of strain u'' decrease with the creep strains ε'' according to the differential equation

$$\frac{du''}{u'' \, dt} = \frac{du''}{d\varepsilon''} = -\frac{\psi}{\phi} \tag{16-17}$$

which $determines \ the \ small \ afterflow \ or \ creep \ under \ invariable \ stress \ \sigma.$

Suppose that we interpret the three interrelated variables of state σ, ε'', $u'' = \dot{\varepsilon}''$ as the rectangular coordinates of a point P in space, by plotting σ as ordinate above ε'', u'' represented in a horizontal plane.   A specific path of loading or straining is then represented by a space curve in the system ε'', u'', σ and may be evaluated from the differential relation [Eq. (16-8)] and the condition characterizing the sequence of loading or straining, i.e., the type of tensile test to be considered, by integrating Eq. (16-8) along the prescribed path.   We note that the projection on the ε'', u'' plane of the space curve described by point P represents $the \ hodograph \ d\varepsilon''/dt = u'' = \varphi(\varepsilon'') \ of \ the \ path \ of \ straining.$[1]

Equation (16-17) obviously defines the differential equation of $the \ family \ of \ hodograph \ lines$ (Fig. 16-4) $for \ the \ sequences \ of \ straining \ under \ the \ condition \ \sigma = const$, and one sees that the theory of the long-time creep tests and curves $\varepsilon'' = f \ (t)$, in regard to a clear method of extrapolating such curves, hinges on the plausible functions that may express

[1] The hodographs must conform to certain rules. If a positive (tensile) stress σ prevails over an extended period of time t, the rate of permanent strain $u'' = d\varepsilon''/dt$ must stay positive, and the strain ε'' can only increase. In the positive quadrant ($u'' > 0$) a hodograph line approaching the ε'' axis must end on it inclined at an obtuse angle and one originating from it must start at an acute angle. It makes no sense to let a hodograph line transgress through the ε'' axis from the positive to the negative quadrant of u'', except at a right angle (Fig. 16-3).

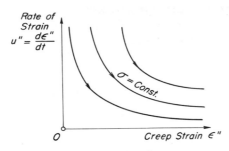

FIG. 16-4. Hodograph of creep tests made under invariable stress $\sigma = $ const.

the two quantities ψ and ϕ in terms of the variables of state ε'', u''. The task of establishing reliable expressions for ψ and ϕ from experimental evidence will concern us in the following subsections.

B. UTILIZING THE STRESS SURFACE. We have mentioned that at a prescribed temperature $\theta = $ const in some cases the dependence of the tensile flow stress σ on the variables ε'' and u'' may be expressed by a unifying function in finite terms or a stress surface (Fig. 16-5):

$$\sigma = F(\varepsilon'', u''). \tag{16-18}$$

The condition for the existence of such *an equation of state* is that $d\sigma$ in Eq. (16-8) *be a complete differential* of the variables ε'' and u'' or that

$$\frac{\partial \psi}{\partial u''} = \frac{\partial \phi}{\partial \varepsilon''}. \tag{16-19}$$

If a stress surface exists, the long-time creep tests under invariable stress are obviously *the contour lines* $\sigma = $ const *of the stress surface F.* The hodograph lines $u'' = \varphi(\varepsilon'')$ are the projections of the contour lines on the ε'', u'' plane, representing $\sigma = F(\varepsilon'', u'')$, in the manner of a geographic topographic map. Stress surfaces F, if they may be postulated, are useful tools for visualizing the interdependence of various sequences of loading or straining in a metal.

Suppose, for example, that

$$\psi = \psi(\varepsilon''), \qquad \phi = \phi(u''), \tag{16-20}$$

amounting to assuming that the rate of strain hardening in a metal is independent of the speed of deformation u'' and the speed law independent of the plastic strain ε''. Then Eq. (16-17) can be integrated by separation of the variables, and an equation of state exists having the form

$$\sigma = F_1(\varepsilon'') + F_2(u''), \tag{16-21}$$

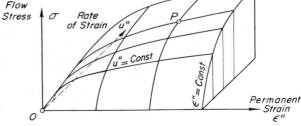

FIG. 16-5. Stress surface $\sigma = F(\varepsilon'', u'')$.

the ordinates of the stress surface F being the sum of the ordinates of two cylindrical surfaces. If $\psi = 0$, $F_1 = 0$; this represents a generally viscous substance which may or may not have a yield point.

If an equation in analytical form for Eq. (16-18) is not known, we may conceive of tentatively tracing graphically a topographic picture of a stress surface S_t in a block diagram, as shown in Fig. 16-5, erected for the tensile tests above the positive quadrant $\varepsilon'' \geqq 0$, $u'' \geqq 0$, by utilizing a series of constant rate $u'' = \text{const}$ profiles which were determined experimentally. From a sequence of uniaxial compression tests a surface of yielding for compression S_c may likewise be defined in a second block diagram below the negative quadrant $\varepsilon'' \leqq 0$, $u'' \leqq 0$, having negative ordinates for the stress σ. For a group of ductile metals one may assume that these two stress surfaces S_t and S_c comply with the rule

$$S_t \cdots \sigma_t = F(\varepsilon'',u''), \qquad S_c \cdots \sigma_c = -F(-\varepsilon'',-u''). \qquad (16\text{-}22)$$

For a ductile cast iron this rule would certainly not hold, the flow stresses σ_c in compression being much greater in their absolute values than σ_t in tension at equal deformations and speeds.[1]

C. CONSIDERING A PURE SPEED LAW $\sigma = g(u'')$. It is appropriate to list first a few speed laws that have intuitively been proposed for expressing the dependence of the yield or flow stress σ on the rate of permanent strain $u'' = d\varepsilon''/dt = \dot{\varepsilon}''$ for solids, including the metals, over certain ranges of temperature, excluding first the phenomenon of strain hardening, letting $\psi = \partial\sigma/\partial\varepsilon'' = 0$ in Eq. (16-8). This reverts to assuming *a generally viscous substance* that flows with the instantaneous rate of strain u'' whenever a stress σ acts according to a speed law,

$$\sigma = g(u'') \qquad \text{or} \qquad u'' = h(\sigma), \qquad (16\text{-}23)$$

expressing a stress surface, namely, a cylinder above the ε'',u'' plane of coordinates in the ε'', u'', σ space, with the generatrices parallel to the ε''

---

[1] As to the profiles of the block diagram S_t in the regions bordering the ε'' and the u'' axes, the ordinates of the stress surface σ may or may not vanish along these axes. If $\sigma = F(\varepsilon'',u'')$ terminates along the ε'' axis in a finite profile, this amounts to assuming what might be termed the stress-strain curve of an infinitely slow tensile test. Strong metals at low temperatures approach this condition when they are strained extremely slowly ($u'' \sim 0$). The contour lines $\sigma = \text{const}$ terminate in this case on the ε'' axis under obtuse angles; *creep stops* at any stress $\sigma = \text{const}$ *at a finite creep limit*.

On the contrary, at sufficiently elevated temperatures, the stress surface dips down quite steeply toward the ε'' axis, ending along it. The contour lines $\sigma = \text{const}$ tend on their approach to the ε'' axis to become parallel lines, never intersecting it; creep ε'' progresses at small rates u'' indefinitely and never stops. Looking, on the other hand, at the region bordering the u'' axis, a finite profile along it illustrates the case of a metal that has been cold-worked previous to testing and, if σ vanishes along the u'' axis, on the contrary, of a very soft metal in the fully annealed state (soft, annealed copper).

axis.   Equation (16-23) is equivalent to postulating *a coefficient of viscosity* that varies with the rate of strain u'' and is identical with the quantity ϕ introduced in Eqs. (16-7) and (16-8):

$$\phi = \frac{d\sigma}{du''} = \frac{dg}{du''}.\qquad(16\text{-}24)$$

For metals that behave alike in uniaxial compression and in tension (yielding at the same absolute values of σ with the same absolute values of u'') mechanical reasons make it imperative that the speed law $\sigma = g(u'')$ should be an odd function of u''.   We list a few speed laws that have been proposed on experimental evidence.

1. In the early days of assembling data on creep of metals, investigators favored *a power function* for expressing the dependence of stress σ on the minimum creep rate u'':

$$\sigma = \sigma_0 \left(\frac{u''}{u_0}\right)^n,\qquad (0 \leqq n \leqq 1),\qquad (u'' \geqq 0).\dagger\qquad(16\text{-}25)$$

A power function speed law has the well-known defect that the quantity ϕ measuring the viscosity

$$\phi = \frac{d\sigma}{du''} = n\sigma_0 u''^{\,n-1} \cdot u_0^{-n}$$

at vanishing values of σ and u'' becomes infinite (except for $n = 1$), which is physically objectionable.

2. *The logarithmic speed law*

$$\sigma = \sigma_0 \ln \frac{u''}{u_0},\qquad(16\text{-}26)$$

first proposed by PAUL LUDWIK[1] in 1909, has been verified in the ductile metals tested at normal or low temperatures under faster rates of stretching.   Equation (16-26) loses its sense when u'' approaches the value of u_0, but it may alternatively be expressed within the positive range of rates of strain u'' as follows:

$$\sigma = \sigma_2 \frac{u''}{u_2} \cdots 0 \leqq u'' \leqq u_2,$$

$$\sigma = \sigma_2 \left(1 + \ln \frac{u''}{u_2}\right) \cdots u_2 \leqq u'',\qquad(16\text{-}27)[2]$$

supplying at vanishing u'' the finite viscosity $\phi = \sigma_2/u_2$.

---

† If the exponent n is an irrational number and the formula has to be extended into the compression range ($\sigma < 0$, $u'' < 0$), one may write $\sigma = -\sigma_0(-u''/u_0)^n$ with σ_0, u_0 as positive constants.

[1] Cf. Vol. I, page 21, where tests by CASSEBAUM (1911), DEUTLER (1932), and other German investigators are quoted.

[2] This function [Eqs. (16-27)] is made up by the tangent to a logarithmic curve drawn from the origin and the part of the latter beyond the point of tangency situated at $u'' = u_2$, $\sigma = \sigma_2$.

3. *Ludwig Prandtl's hyperbolic sine speed law,*

$$u'' = u_1 \sinh \frac{\sigma}{\sigma_1} , \qquad (16\text{-}28)$$

is, as we have mentioned on several occasions in this book, deeply rooted in the mechanism of slip in the atomic lattices in polycrystalline solid substances, responsible for the generally viscous bahavior prevalent in the ductile metals and becoming more pronounced with a rise of temperature. Whereas PRANDTL announced this law as early as 1913 in his lecture courses at the University of Göttingen, he proposed it as a generalization of LUDWIK's logarithmic speed law in his fundamental paper of 1928 and also made use of it in some of his last papers devoted to the flow of what he termed "normally viscous" solid or fluid substances through cylindrical tubes (see page 368; *loc. cit.*).[1]

Extensive studies based on the EYRING absolute rate theory, applied to mechanical models of organic materials, plastic compounds, to the creep of limestone, alabaster, etc., may be found in four reports by MERVIN B. HOGAN, The Engineering Application of the Absolute Rate Theory, Univ. Utah, Bull. 26, 1951; 58, 1952; 59, 1952; and 62, 1953. The last report of 220 pages summarizes his investigations and lists an extensive bibliography.

The hyperbolic sine law was suggested years ago by the author, merely for practical reasons, as a means of extrapolating the results of the standard long-time creep tests to service times. Equation (16-28) gives for large values of the flow stress σ

$$u'' = \frac{u_1}{2} e^{\sigma/\sigma_1} \qquad \text{or} \qquad \sigma = \sigma_1 \ln \frac{2u''}{u_1} ;$$

when this is compared with the logarithmic speed law [Eq. (16-26)], one sees that the material constants u_1, σ_1 introduced in Eq. (16-28) are expressed in terms of those appearing in Eq. (16-26) by

$$u_1 = 2u_0, \qquad \sigma_1 = \sigma_0. \qquad (16\text{-}29)$$

We shall also set up comparisons of the power function speed laws with Eq. (16-28) in Sec. 16-2G below.

Small creep under a constant stress σ increases under any of the three speed laws (1, 2, 3) with time t at a uniform rate $u'' = $ const to be

---

[1] L. PRANDTL, Ein Gedankenmodell zur kinetischen Theorie der festen Körper, Z. angew. Math. u. Mech., vol. 8, pp. 85–106, 1928 (cf. Vol. I, page 57). The hyperbolic sine law was independently introduced by H. EYRING and his collaborators, S. GLASSTONE and K. J. LAIDLER, in their work on diffusion and viscosity of fluids, "The Theory of Rate Processes," 611 pp., McGraw-Hill Book Company, Inc., New York, 1941. See also H. EYRING, Viscosity, Plasticity and Diffusion as Examples of Absolute Reaction Rates, J. Chem. Phys., vol. 4, p. 283, 1936.

evaluated from the preceding relations for $u'' = h(\sigma) = $ const:

$$\varepsilon'' = \varepsilon_0'' + u''t = \varepsilon_0'' + h(\sigma) \cdot t, \tag{16-30}$$

using, for example, in the case of Eq. (16-28)

$$u'' = h(\sigma) = u_1 \sinh \frac{\sigma}{\sigma_1} . \tag{16-31}$$

If an allowable creep ε_s'' is accumulated at a prescribed service time t_s, for *the permissible minimum creep rate u_m''* this gives the value

$$u_m'' = \frac{\varepsilon_s'' - \varepsilon_0''}{t_s} \tag{16-32)[1]}$$

and hence *for the allowable stress σ*, after inverting the hyperbolic sine function [Eq. (16-31)],

$$\sigma = \sigma_1 \ln \left[\frac{u_m''}{u_1} + \sqrt{1 + \left(\frac{u_m''}{u_1}\right)^2} \right]. \tag{16-33}$$

We list *the laws of relaxation* corresponding to the three aforementioned speed laws (1, 2, 3). We denote the initial values at time $t = 0$, when relaxation of stress starts, by the subscript i. The condition that the total strain ε at any time shall remain constant,

$$\varepsilon = \frac{\sigma}{E} + \varepsilon'' = \frac{\sigma_i}{E} + \varepsilon_i'' = \varepsilon_i = \text{const}, \qquad \frac{d\sigma}{dt} = -E\frac{d\varepsilon''}{dt} = -Eu'', \tag{16-34}$$

prescribes for relaxation with $u'' = h(\sigma)$:

$$\frac{d\sigma}{dt} = -Eh(\sigma), \qquad t = \frac{1}{E}\int_\sigma^{\sigma_i} \frac{d\sigma}{h(\sigma)} . \tag{16-35}$$

The stress σ decreases with time t according to the following laws of relaxation.

(1). *For the power function speed law* [Eq. (16-25)],

$$\sigma = \frac{\sigma_i}{[1 + (1 - n)(Eu_0/n\sigma_i)(\sigma_i/\sigma_0)^{1/n} \cdot t]^{n/(1-n)}} . \tag{16-36}$$

This becomes indeterminate when the exponent n equals unity, $\sigma = \sigma_0 u''/u_0$, reverting to the viscoelastic substance for which the stress decreases with time t according to MAXWELL's relaxation law:

$$\sigma = \sigma_i e^{-t/t_r}, \qquad t_r = \frac{\sigma_0}{Eu_0} . \tag{16-37}$$

---

[1] Tacitly presuming that the height of the intercept ε_0'' at time $t = 0$ is known either from creep-data interpolation or from other sources. How ε_0'' may be estimated will be indicated in Sec. 16-2I below where cases of sudden loading and unloading will be considered.

The constant t_r of the dimension of time has been called the *Maxwell relaxation time* for uniaxial tension, t_r being also equal to $t_r = 3\mu/E$; the ratio $\sigma_0/u_0 = 3\mu$ equals three times the common coefficient of viscosity μ as expressed in $\tau = \mu \, d\gamma/dt$.

(2). *Using the logarithmic law* [Eqs. (16-27)] one obtains two branches of the curves representing the drop of the stress σ with time t tangent to each other:

$$\sigma = \sigma_i - \sigma_2 \ln\left(1 + \frac{t}{t_e - t_0}\right) \cdots 0 \leq t \leq t_0, \qquad u_2 \leq u'', \qquad (16\text{-}38a)$$

$$\sigma = \sigma_2 e^{-t/(t_e - t_0)} \cdots t_0 \leq t, \qquad 0 \leq u'' < u_2, \qquad (16\text{-}38b)$$

where the constants t_0 and t_e are equal to

$$t_e = \frac{\sigma_2}{Eu_2}, \qquad t_0 = t_e[1 - e^{-(\sigma_i - \sigma_2)/\sigma_2}] \qquad (16\text{-}38c)$$

and the constant t_0 denotes the time required to reach the transition value of stress $\sigma = \sigma_2$ at which the linear law $\sigma = \sigma_2 u''/u_2$ changes smoothly to the logarithmic law $\sigma = \sigma_2[1 + \ln(\mu''/u_2)]$.

(3). *For the hyperbolic sine speed function* [Eq. (16-28)] one obtains from Eq. (16-35), with $u'' = h(\sigma) = u_1 \sinh(\sigma/\sigma_1)$ and with the constant $t_e = \sigma_1/Eu_1$,

$$t = \frac{1}{Eu_1} \int_\sigma^{\sigma_i} \frac{d\sigma}{\sinh(\sigma/\sigma_1)} = -t_e \ln \frac{\tanh(\sigma/2\sigma_1)}{\tanh(\sigma_i/2\sigma_1)} \qquad (16\text{-}39)$$

or if we let the constant time t_r equal

$$t_r = -t_e \ln \tanh \frac{\sigma_i}{2\sigma_1}$$

$$(16\text{-}40)$$

and
$$\frac{t + t_r}{t_e} = -\ln \tanh \frac{\sigma}{2\sigma_1},$$

after inversion,[1] we find that, vice versa, the initial stress σ_i at time $t = 0$ is

$$\sigma_i = -\sigma_1 \ln \tanh \frac{t_r}{2t_e} \qquad (16\text{-}40a)$$

and that the stress σ will drop with time according to

$$\sigma = -\sigma_1 \ln \tanh \frac{t + t_r}{2t_e}. \qquad (16\text{-}41)$$

---

[1] Using the reciprocal relations,

$$y = -\ln \tanh \frac{x}{2}, \qquad x = -\ln \tanh \frac{y}{2}. \qquad (16\text{-}40b)$$

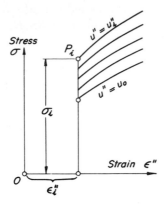

FIG. 16-6. ψ varies with ε'' and u''.

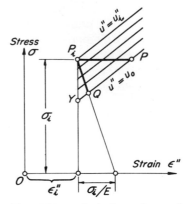

FIG. 16-7. ψ is independent of ε'' and u''.

This law of relaxation of stress is also expressed alternatively from Eq. (16-39) by[1]

$$\tanh \frac{\sigma}{2\sigma_1} = e^{-t/t_e} \cdot \tanh \frac{\sigma_i}{2\sigma_1}, \qquad (16\text{-}42)$$

reverting back at small values of σ/σ_1 to the MAXWELL and at large values of σ/σ_1 to the relaxation function [Eq. (16-38b)].

This then *correlates* the straight lines $\varepsilon_s'' = \varepsilon_0'' + u_m'' t_s$ of *the creep tests* under the allowable stress $\sigma = g(u_m'')$ held at an invariable value with *the behavior under relaxation* of stress for the three important pure speed laws $\sigma = g(u'')$ listed earlier, disregarding strain hardening.

D. ALLOWING FOR A UNIFORM RATE OF STRAIN HARDENING, $\psi = \partial\sigma/\partial\varepsilon'' = $ const. In a cylindrical bar of a stronger metal, held loaded under a constant tensile stress or subjected to a relaxation test at a moderately elevated temperature, the permanent strain ε'' increases but little. Supposing that the metal has been deformed to an initial state characterized by the variables of state σ_i, ε_i'', u_i'', one may trace in the σ, ε'' plane the profiles of the constant-rate tensile tests $u'' = $ const in the neighborhood of point $P_i(\varepsilon_i'', u_i'', \sigma_i)$ (Fig. 16-6). They will be crowded in a narrow band of nearly parallel stress-strain curves the slopes of which define the rate of strain hardening $\psi = \partial\sigma/\partial\varepsilon''$ of the metal. If the permanent strain ε'' changes but little during the subsequent distortion, it will be permissible to assume that $\psi = $ const in the neighborhood of point P_i, i.e., that the curves $u'' = $ const are a

[1] Cf. author's: The Creep of Metals under Various Stress Conditions, in "Applied Mechanics," THEODOR VON KÁRMÁN Anniversary Volume, p. 237, 1941, where tests made by G. H. HEISER on K-20 steel at 1100°F in 1939 were also quoted, verifying Eq. (16-42).

family of parallel straight lines inclined under the slope ψ = const (Fig. 16-7). An afterflow or creep under an invariable stress σ_i = const traces the horizontal line $\overline{P_iP}$ and a relaxation test $\varepsilon' + \varepsilon'' = (\sigma/E) + \varepsilon''$ = const, the steeply dropping line $\overline{P_iQ}$ in Fig. 16-7, representing these special sequences of loading. Let us evaluate them by making use of speed laws 2 and 3 of Sec. 16-2C as follows:

Supposing ψ = const and the *validity of the logarithmic speed law* (2) in the form given in Eq. (16-26) for which $\phi = \sigma_0/u''$, we have

$$\frac{d\sigma}{dt} = \psi u'' + \phi \frac{du''}{dt} = \psi u'' + \frac{\sigma_0 \, du''}{u'' \, dt}, \qquad (16\text{-}43)$$

for the long-time creep test σ = const,

$$\frac{du''}{dt} = -\frac{\psi u''^2}{\sigma_0}, \qquad (16\text{-}44)$$

and for relaxation of stress,

$$\frac{du''}{dt} = -\frac{(E + \psi)u''^2}{\sigma_0}, \qquad (16\text{-}45)$$

two differential equations, differing only in one constant factor on the right sides; since the initial conditions are the same (at time $t = 0$, σ_i, ε_i'', u_i''), their integrals have the identical forms with the appended constants t_c and t_r: for the creep curve,

$$\underline{\underline{\varepsilon'' - \varepsilon_i'' = \frac{\sigma_0}{\psi} \ln\left(1 + \frac{t}{t_c}\right),}} \qquad t_c = \frac{\sigma_0}{\psi u_i''} = \frac{\sigma_0 e^{-(\sigma_i/\sigma_0)}}{\psi u_0}, \qquad (16\text{-}46)$$

and for the relaxation test,

$$\varepsilon'' - \varepsilon_i'' = \frac{\sigma_0}{E + \psi} \ln\left(1 + \frac{t}{t_r}\right), \qquad t_r = \frac{\sigma_0}{(E + \psi)u_i''} = \frac{\sigma_0 e^{-(\sigma_i/\sigma_0)}}{(E + \psi)u_0},$$

$$\underline{\underline{\sigma_i - \sigma = \frac{\sigma_0 E}{E + \psi} \ln\left(1 + \frac{t}{t_r}\right).}} \qquad\qquad (16\text{-}47)$$

We note the interesting facts that, when the rate of strain hardening ψ remains invariable, (1) the creep $\varepsilon'' - \varepsilon_i''$ under constant stress $\sigma = \sigma_i$ = const progresses along a similar time function as the stress difference $\sigma_i - \sigma$ in relaxation, as indicated in Figs. 16-8 and 16-9 (except when $\psi = 0$), and (2) the differential equations (16-44) and (16-45) have the same form as the dynamic equation for the motion of a material point along a straight line which is slowed down by an air resistance proportional to the square of the velocity.[1]

---

[1] It must, however, be remembered, that Eqs. (16-46) and (16-47) become invalid when the rate of permanent strain u'' tends to approach the value u_0. If this has to be anticipated, the logarithmic speed law should be formulated in accordance with its alternative form expressed by Eqs. (16-27) and the integration carried out using the two function branches $0 < u'' < u_2$ and $u_2 < u''$.

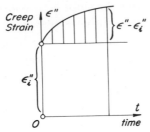

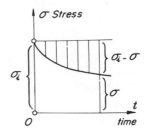

FIG. 16-8. Creep curve.   FIG. 16-9.   Relaxation
                                 curve.

The validity of the creep-time curves expressed by Eq. (16-46) was neatly verified by EVAN A. DAVIS in several series of tensile tests made with copper specimens.   In one series *the slow afterflow (creep) in copper rods* was observed at room temperature by subjecting them to *gentle, tensile impact tests*, through hanging equal weight increments at the end of a horizontal lever arm in equal time intervals, raising the load instantaneously by equal steps, and recording the subsequent creep strains ε'' during 10-min or 24-hr time intervals between each step.[1] Figure 16-10 reproduces the sequences of loading in three copper rods that were previously annealed at 650°C for ½ hour: curve 1 for continuous loading, line 2 for loading in steps of 24 hr, and line 3 for 10-min intervals. The afterflow or creep strain ε'' plotted above the logarithms of time t disclosed well-defined straight lines (not reproduced here), verifying the logarithmic time function [Eq. (16-46)] and thus the speed law $\sigma = \sigma_0 \ln (u''/u_0)$, $\phi = \partial\sigma/\partial u'' = \sigma_0/u''$.

In a second series, bars of softly annealed copper were first cold-worked in tension to the permanent strains ε_l'' under the load stresses σ_l given below[2] and the creep strain $\varepsilon'' = f(t)$ subsequently recorded on semilogarithmic plots up to 3 to 5 hr, under the loads $\sigma_l = $ const in Fig. 16-11, again disclosing well-defined straight lines.   The corresponding afterflow and creep curves $\varepsilon'' = f(t)$ may be seen in Fig. 16-12.

For a third, broad series of long-time creep and relaxation tests made at elevated temperatures on oxygen-free copper, see Sec. 16-8.

Let us evaluate now *the long-time creep curve* $\varepsilon'' = f(t)$ under invariable stress $\sigma = \sigma_i = $ const and *the function expressing the variation of stress σ with time t for relaxation also for the case of the hyperbolic sine*

[1] Cf. E. A. DAVIS and A. NADAI, The Creep of Metals, II, J. Appl. Mechanics, March, 1936.

[2] Test no.	1	2	3	4	5	6
Strain ε_l'', per cent . .	1.56	3.90	4.85	6.15	8.05	10.6
Load stress σ_l, lb/in.[2] .	10,195	14,460	16,085	17,600	19,640	22,010

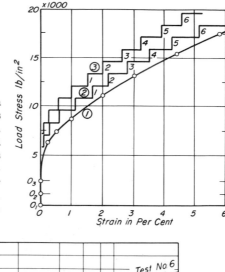

FIG. 16-10. Stress-strain relation for various tensile tests of copper. Curve 1, stress-strain curve for continuous loading. Curve 2, loading in steps of 24-hr duration. Curve 3, loading in steps of 10-min duration.

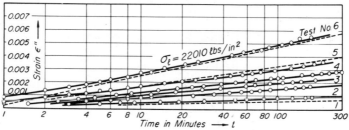

FIG. 16-11. Creep (afterflow) of copper at room temperature under invariable stress $\sigma_l = $ const. The copper bars were prestretched to the permanent strain ε_l'' and load stress σ_l given in the footnote and the afterflow subsequently observed under $\sigma_l = $ const. (*Tests by Evan A. Davis.*)

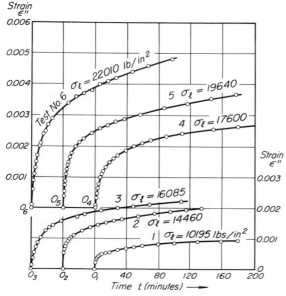

FIG. 16-12. Creep (after-flow) of copper at room temperature under in-variable stress $\sigma_l = $ const. (*Tests by E. A. Davis.*)

527

speed law [speed law 3; Eq. (16-28)] *while the metal strain-hardens under a uniform rate* $\psi = \partial\sigma/\partial\varepsilon'' = $ const. This stipulates that a stress surface of flow exists of the form

$$\sigma = \sigma_\psi + \sigma_\phi \tag{16-48}$$

in which the part due to strain hardening is assumed,

$$\sigma_\psi = \psi\varepsilon'' \tag{16-49}$$

and the part dependent on rate of strain u'',

$$\sigma_\phi = \sigma_1 \ln\left[\frac{u''}{u_1} + \sqrt{1 + \left(\frac{u''}{u_1}\right)^2}\right], \tag{16-50}$$

is equivalent to

$$u'' = \frac{d\varepsilon''}{dt} = u_1 \sinh\frac{\sigma_\phi}{\sigma_1} \tag{16-50a}$$

with ψ, σ_1, u_1 as known material constants. We suppose that the stress is instantaneously applied.

Denoting again the initial values of the variables of state at time $t = 0$ by the subscript i, if the metal has been cold-worked previously to a strain ε_i'', the initial values upon loading are $\sigma = \sigma_i$, $\varepsilon'' = \varepsilon_i''$, and

$$u_i'' = u_1 \sinh\frac{\sigma_i - \sigma_y}{\sigma_1},$$

while, owing to the previous prestretching, the metal possesses a finite yield stress $\sigma_y = \psi\varepsilon_i'' = \overline{RY}$ at zero rate of strain $u'' = 0$ (Fig. 16-13). If the metal was originally in its virgin (annealed soft) condition, we put $\sigma_y = 0$.

The two aforementioned sequences of straining situated on the stress surface [Eq. (16-48)], initiating at point $P_i(\sigma_i, \varepsilon_i'', u_i'')$, are defined through their *hodograph curves* in the ε'', u'' plane originating at point ε_i'', u_i'', namely, for *the long-time creep sequence* under invariable stress $\sigma = \sigma_i = $ const, by

$$\sigma = \sigma_\psi + \sigma_\phi = \sigma_i = \text{const},$$

$$\psi\varepsilon'' + \sigma_1 \ln\left[\frac{u''}{u_1} + \sqrt{1 + \left(\frac{u''}{u_1}\right)^2}\right] = \sigma_i, \tag{16-51}$$

and for *the relaxation path* along which the strain is held invariably at value $\varepsilon' + \varepsilon'' = $ const or $\sigma_i - \sigma = E(\varepsilon'' - \varepsilon_i'')$, after writing therein $\sigma = \sigma_\psi + \sigma_\phi$ and using Eqs. (16-49) and (16-50), by

$$(E + \psi)\varepsilon'' + \sigma_1 \ln\left[\frac{u''}{u_1} + \sqrt{1 + \left(\frac{u''}{u_1}\right)^2}\right] = \sigma_i + E\varepsilon_i'' = \text{const}. \tag{16-52}$$

These two similar differential equations are easily integrated for the above-mentioned initial conditions by changing the dependent variable u'' through a new variable w of dimensionless form, made dependent on the viscous part σ_ϕ of stress σ carried at time t, by means of the substitution

$$w = \frac{\sigma_\phi}{\sigma_1} = \ln\left[\frac{u''}{u_1} + \sqrt{1 + \left(\frac{u''}{u_1}\right)^2}\right], \qquad (16\text{-}53)$$

equivalent to letting

$$u'' = \frac{d\varepsilon''}{dt} = u_1 \sinh w. \qquad (16\text{-}53a)$$

Looking at Figs. 16-13 and 16-14, reproducing in a projection onto the ε'',σ plane of the rectangular coordinates ε'', u'', σ in the two straight, thick lines $P_i P P_\infty$ and $P_i Q Q_\infty$ the projections of the paths of the long-time creep test $\sigma = $ const and the relaxation test $\varepsilon = $ const, one sees that the viscous parts σ_ϕ of stress σ, indicated under the moving points P and Q in the figures, decrease linearly with the strain ε'', and hence the new dimensionless variable $w = \sigma_\phi/\sigma_1$ takes on the values:
For the creep test:

$$w = \frac{\sigma_i - \psi\varepsilon''}{\sigma_1},$$

For the relaxation test:

$$w = \frac{\sigma - \psi\varepsilon''}{\sigma_1} \qquad (16\text{-}54)$$

or

$$w = \frac{1}{\sigma_1}[\sigma_i + E\varepsilon_i'' - (E + \psi)\varepsilon''],$$

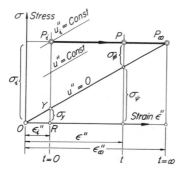

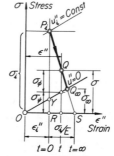

FIG. 16-13. Creep path $\overline{P_i P_\infty}$. For a solid having a uniform rate of strain hardening $\psi = $ const.

FIG. 16-14. Relaxation path $\overline{P_i Q_\infty}$. For a solid having a uniform rate of strain hardening $\psi = $ const.

both assuming at time $t = 0$ the same initial value

$$w_i = \frac{\sigma_i - \psi\varepsilon_i''}{\sigma_1} = \frac{\sigma_i - \sigma_y}{\sigma_1} . \qquad (16\text{-}54a)$$

Equations (16-51) and (16-52) are thereby transformed into

$$\frac{dw}{dt} = -k_c \sinh w, \ -k_r \sinh w, \qquad (16\text{-}55)$$

with the constants

$$k_c = \frac{\psi u_1}{\sigma_1}, \qquad k_r = \frac{(E + \psi)u_1}{\sigma_1} \qquad (16\text{-}56)$$

(the subscripts c and r referring to the cases of creep and relaxation) having the integral

$$k_c t, \ k_r t = -\int_{w_i}^{w} \frac{dw}{\sinh w} = -\ln \frac{\tanh (w/2)}{\tanh (w_i/2)}, \qquad (16\text{-}57)$$

respectively. This may be inverted in the manner described in Sec. 16-2C, using Eqs. (16-40b) and two constant times t_c, t_r, defined by putting

$$k_c t_c, \ k_r t_r = -\ln \tanh \frac{w_i}{2} = -\ln \tanh \frac{\sigma_i - \sigma_y}{2\sigma_1},$$

$$k_c(t_c + t), \ k_r(t_r + t) = -\ln \tanh \frac{w}{2}, \qquad (16\text{-}58)$$

with the final result, after reverting back to the original variables ε'' and σ, that *the creep curve* $\varepsilon'' = f(t)$ *under invariable stress* $\sigma = \sigma_i = \text{const}$ is expressed by

$$\varepsilon'' - \varepsilon_i'' = \frac{\sigma_1}{\psi} \ln \frac{\tanh [k_c(t_c + t)/2]}{\tanh (k_c t_c/2)} \qquad (16\text{-}59)$$

and that the stress σ and strain ε'' vary with time t *in a relaxation sequence under invariable strain* $\varepsilon = \varepsilon_i = \text{const}$ as

$$\sigma_i - \sigma = E(\varepsilon'' - \varepsilon_i'') = \frac{\sigma_1 E}{E + \psi} \ln \frac{\tanh [k_r(t_r + t)/2]}{\tanh (k_r t_r/2)}. \qquad (16\text{-}60)$$

A glance at Figs. 16-13 and 16-14 discloses that, in a metal which strain-hardens under a uniform rate $\psi = \text{const}$, creep stops as time t increases indefinitely, at *a finite creep limit* (at point P_∞)

$$t = \infty, \qquad \varepsilon_\infty'' - \varepsilon_i'' = \frac{\sigma_i - \sigma_y}{\psi} = P_i P_\infty, \qquad (16\text{-}61)$$

and likewise that *the stress* σ *in a relaxation sequence drops* from its initial value σ_i *to a finite end value* (point Q_∞)

$$t = \infty, \qquad \sigma_\infty = \frac{\psi\sigma_i + E\sigma_y}{E + \psi}, \qquad (16\text{-}62)$$

(σ_∞ is the ordinate of point Q_∞ in Fig. 16-14), thus indicating that the accrued amount of creep at the creep limit and the total drop of stress in relaxation are reduced with an increase of the rate of strain hardening ψ.

This relaxation (and likewise this creep) law to which we were led may conspicuously be expressed in terms of the two differences of stress to be designated by s and s_i,

$$s = \sigma - \sigma_\infty, \qquad s_i = \sigma_i - \sigma_\infty, \qquad (16\text{-}63)$$

after using the abbreviating symbols for the constants,

$$t_e = \frac{\sigma_1}{Eu_1}, \qquad c = 1 + \frac{\psi}{E}, \qquad k_r = \left(1 + \frac{\psi}{E}\right)\frac{Eu_1}{\sigma_1} = \frac{c}{t_e}, \qquad (16\text{-}63a)$$

as follows:

$$\tanh \frac{cs}{2\sigma_1} = e^{-(ct/t_e)} \cdot \tanh \frac{cs_i}{2\sigma_1}, \qquad (16\text{-}64)$$

having in terms of cs, cs_i, ct precisely the form of the relaxation Eq. (16-42) we obtained in Sec. 16-2C by postulating a pure hyperbolic sine speed law (disregarding strain hardening) in terms of σ, σ_1, t.

Equation (16-64) *brings out clearly the effect of a finite rate of strain hardening* ψ = const *upon the relaxation process*, and we may note the interesting result[1] that the stress s versus time t *relaxation curves for a series of values of the parameter c consist of a family of geometrically similar curves* if they are plotted in a system t,s of coordinates. In fact, in terms of the coordinates x and y, Eq. (16-64) represents a single, basic equation of a curve:

$$x = \frac{ct}{t_e}, \qquad y = \frac{cs}{2\sigma_1}, \qquad \tanh y = e^{-x}\tanh y_i \qquad (16\text{-}65)$$

which needs only to be traced. All relaxation curves s versus t are similar to it.

This then solves creep and relaxation progressing under the speed law $u'' = u_1 \sinh (\sigma_\phi/\sigma_1)$ and at an invariable rate of strain hardening ψ = const.

Figure 16-15 illustrates the trend of decrease of stress with time for a non-strain-hardening metal ($\psi = 0$, $c = 1$) for four initial values of stress at $t = 0$: $\sigma_i/2\sigma_1 = \frac{1}{2}$, 1, $\frac{3}{2}$, 2.6. The lowest curve practically follows the Maxwell relaxation law [Eq. (16-37)] of a viscoelastic substance with invariable viscosity, while the uppermost curve indicates very much faster initial rates of decrease of stress. In Fig. 16-16 one sees the influence of strain hardening on relaxation, at the ratio rates $\psi/E = 0.1, 0.3, 0.5$, the last value representing a high rate of hardening.

---

[1] Conforming to what we found for the case of the logarithmic speed law in comparing Eqs. (16-46) and (16-47) and Figs. 16-8 and 16-9.

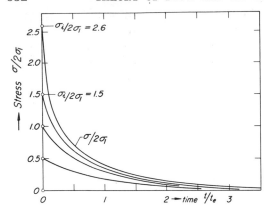

Fig. 16-15. Relaxation of stress. For pure hyperbolic sine speed law from four initial values of stress σ_i: $\sigma_i/2\sigma_1 = 0.5, 1, 1.5, 2.6$ when no strain hardening is assumed $(\psi = 0, c = 1)$.

The greater ψ/E is in the shorter a time the final minimum asymptotic value σ_∞ is reached, and the smaller a drop in stress is to be expected.

E. CONSTANT-STRAIN-RATE TEST. Suppose that a tensile specimen is stretched by displacing its heads under an invariable relative velocity so that the total extension per unit of length ε increases uniformly with the time t with the rate of strain $u = d\varepsilon/dt = $ const:

$$\varepsilon = \varepsilon' + \varepsilon'' = \frac{\sigma}{E} + \varepsilon'' = ut. \qquad (16\text{-}66)$$

Equating the rate of increase of stress $d\sigma/dt = E(u - u'')$ with the value expressed in Eq. (16-13) gives the relation

$$\phi\,\frac{du''}{dt} + (E + \psi)u'' = Eu = \text{const}, \qquad (16\text{-}67)$$

from which the rate of permanent strain $u'' = d\varepsilon''/dt$, the permanent part of strain $\varepsilon'' = \int u''\,dt$, and the stress $\sigma = E(\varepsilon - \varepsilon'') = E(ut - \int u''\,dt)$ as functions of the time t (or strain $\varepsilon = ut$) may be

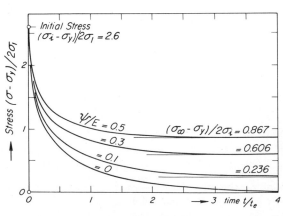

Fig. 16-16. Relaxation of stress. Influence of invariable rate of strain hardening $\psi = $ const on relaxation of stress progressing under hyperbolic sine speed law $u'' = u_1 \sinh (\sigma_\phi/\sigma_1)$. Curves of stress ratio $(\sigma - \sigma_y)/2\sigma_1$ versus time ratio t/t_e plotted for values $\psi/E = 0, 0.1, 0.3, 0.5$ and for same initial stress σ_i corresponding to $(\sigma_i - \sigma_y)/2\sigma_1 = 2.6$. $(\sigma_y = \psi\varepsilon_i''$ is initial yield stress, $t_e = \sigma_1/2u_1$.)

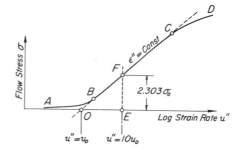

FIG. 16-17. Speed law:
$\sigma = g(u'')$ represented
on semilogarithmic plot.

evaluated; i.e., *the stress-strain curves σ in terms of the total strain ε may be derived for metallic bars stretched at uniform rates of strain $u = \text{const}$.*[1]

Since constant-rate tests are easily made over a wide range of speeds, they lend themselves to checking the validity of the assumptions on which the theory of deformations of ductile metals at elevated temperatures may be based. The ideal way of doing this would consist, in fact, of comparing a set of stress-strain curves which were obtained by holding the rate of permanent strain $u'' = d\varepsilon''/dt = \text{const}$, not the total rate $u = d\varepsilon/dt = \text{const}$. While at small strains ε or ε'' this is not feasible practically, a satisfactory picture of the combined effects of strain hardening and of the speed of stretching may be obtained by replotting the observed flow stress σ above the permanent strains ε'' and, after having also computed the actual permanent rates of strain u'' along each curve $u = \text{const}$, representing the true variation of $\sigma = g(u'')$ with permanent rate $u'' = \dot\varepsilon''$ at prescribed values of $\varepsilon'' = \text{const}$.

The experiences gathered in this manner in flow tests made with stable metals at normal and at elevated temperatures of moderate magnitude invariably led to the conclusion that *in the curves $\sigma = g(u'')$,* at freely chosen values $\varepsilon'' = \text{const}$, traced in a semilogarithmic plot, three more or less distinctly distinguishable ranges appear:

1. At very slow rates u'', with decreasing u'', they approach asymptotically $\sigma = 0$.

2. In an intermediate range covering many cycles of the log scale ($\overline{BC}$ in Fig. 16-17) they are straight lines.

3. For very great speeds of stretching u'', approaching those of high-velocity impact tests, they become slightly concave toward the horizontal axis (CD).

[1] The reader should note incidentally that Eq. (16-67) at a vanishing rate $u = 0$ supplies a second form of the differential equation valid for the relaxation of stress; also that the slope $d\sigma/d\varepsilon$ under which a constant-rate–stress-strain curve (true stress σ plotted versus total strain ε) rises cannot be considered as a good measure of the rate of strain hardening in a ductile metal since $d\sigma/d\varepsilon$ would not vanish (as $\psi = \partial\sigma/\partial\varepsilon''$ does) in a generally viscous substance (not possessing the ability to strain-harden) pulled at $u = d\varepsilon/dt = \text{const}$.

The fact interests us here that the points corresponding to the rates observed in the standard long-time creep tests $\sigma = $ const fit the curve and appear usually to the left of its knee B.[1]

The simplest function $\sigma = g(u'')$ that follows a trend like ABC in Fig. 16-17 and is compatible with the observations within the low and intermediate range of u'' is

$$u'' = u_1 \sinh \frac{\sigma}{\sigma_1}. \qquad (16\text{-}68)$$

It was also suggested, as previously mentioned, as a means for extrapolating the long-time creep curves $\varepsilon'' = f(t)$ to service times t_s. Suppose that the straight portion $\overline{BC}$ (Fig. 16-17) of the speed law $\sigma = g(u'')$, at the small prescribed strain ε'' that interests us, has been located from a few constant-rate and creep tests. The two material parameters $u_1 = 2u_0$, $\sigma_1 = \sigma_0$, defining the hyperbolic sine function in Eq. (16-68) and its equivalent expression for large values of u'', σ, namely, the logarithmic function [Eq. (16-26)] $\sigma = \sigma_0 \ln (u''/u_0)$, are then supplied by reading the abscissa $u'' = u_0$ on the log scale at point O at which the extension of line $\overline{BC}$ intersects the horizontal axis and through the slope of $\overline{BC}$, by reading the length $\overline{EF}$ of the ordinate erected one cycle of the log scale apart from the point O [$\overline{EF} = \sigma = \sigma_0 \ln (u''/u_0) = 2.303\sigma_0 \log 10 = 2.303\sigma_0$].

[1] Extensive series of constant-rate-of-strain tests have been carried out by EVAN A. DAVIS and M. J. MANJOINE at the Westinghouse Research Laboratories, covering a wide range of speeds, by stretching tensile specimens either in a 10-ton AMSLER machine or in a high-speed machine utilizing the kinetic energy of a flywheel for making rapid tests (see a view of it in Vol. I, Fig. 3-9, page 23). The piston of the Amsler machine was kept in a fixed position by means of an electric contact device operating the oil pump and served only for measuring the axial load by means of an Amsler pendulum-manometer while the other head was moved by a screw drive at a constant, adjustable velocity.

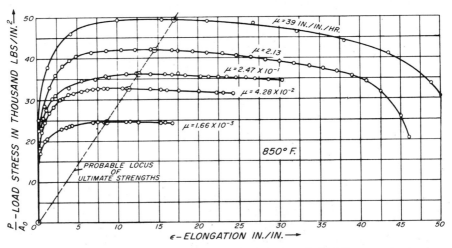

FIG. 16-18. Stress-strain diagrams for 0.35% carbon steel (K-20) at constant rates $u = d\varepsilon/dt = $ const.

These simple facts were utilized for constructing on a large scale a *hyperbolic sine chart*[1] for the convenience of designers of high-temperature equipment. In this chart the affine family of densely spaced curves $u'' = u_1{}^* \sinh(\sigma/\sigma_1)$ for a fixed value of the parameter u_1, namely, $u_1 = u_1{}^* = 0.2$ per hr, was traced by plotting these curves for the values $\sigma_1 = 0.1, 0.2, \ldots$ up to $\sigma_1 = 200$ semilogarithmically over the speed range $0.001 < u'' < 1,000$ per hr. The point[2] $u'' = u_1{}^*$, $\sigma = 0$ was designated as "target." This chart actually represents the complete double-parameter family of curves

$$u = u_1 \sinh \frac{\sigma}{\sigma_1}$$

since a change from $u_1{}^*$ to any value of u_1 requires a horizontal shift of the log scale by the amount $\log(u_1/u_1{}^*)$.

The procedure of finding the two unknown material parameters u_1, σ_1, representing a series of actual observations,

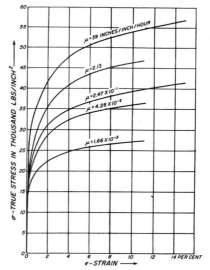

FIG. 16-19. Stress-strain curves for 0.35% carbon steel (K-20). $u = d\varepsilon/dt = $ const, 850°F.

consists of marking the observed points (u'',σ) on transparent paper laid over the chart and moving the loose sheet horizontally until the test points fall nearest to one of the curves of the chart. The desired value of u_1 is read on the movable log scale just over the "target" (the point $u_1{}^*$ on the chart) and σ_1 on the line of the chart that best fitted the observed points (u'',σ).

A group of constant-strain-rate tensile tests[3] *made with an annealed 0.35% carbon steel at* 850°F = 454°C is reproduced in Figs. 16-18 through 16-20. In these tests a range of speeds of stretching from $u = d\varepsilon/dt = 0.00166$ up to $u = 39$ in./in.-hr or 1 to 23,500 was covered, but after including the long-time creep tests quoted in the footnote, the velocities varied over an interval 1 to 10^8. The stress-strain diagrams of load per unit of area plotted above the strain ε are seen in Fig. 16-18. The dependence of the (true) flow stress σ on the total strain ε is reproduced in Fig. 16-19 for the five inscribed rates u held invariable in each test. These

[1] Cf. P. G. McVETTY and A. NADAI, Hyperbolic Sine Chart for Estimating Working Stresses of Alloys at Elevated Temperatures, 46th Annual Meeting of American Society for Testing Materials, June, 1943. Also P. G. McVETTY, Interpretation of Creep Tests, same ASTM Meeting, 1943, and Creep of Metals at Elevated Temperatures, the Hyperbolic Sine Relation between Stress and Creep Rate, ASME Meeting, Davenport, Iowa, April, 1943.

[2] Obviously only one of the curves needs to be evaluated, because of the affine relation requiring multiplication of its ordinates σ by constant factors for tracing all the other curves.

[3] Cf. EVAN A. DAVIS and A. NADAI, Constant Strain-rate Tests on 0.35 C steel K-20 at 850°F, ASME Annual Meeting, 1936. This steel, known as K-20 steel, was especially prepared on behalf of the Joint Research Committee (ASME, ASTM) for cooperative high-temperature tests among various laboratories (see Preprint 25, p. 17, appendix II, ASTM, 1936; also Trans. ASME, vol. 58, p. 97, 1936, Research Paper 58-4). Long-time creep curves for this steel at 850°F were recorded by H. C. CROSS and F. B. DAHLE, Battelle Memorial Institute, Columbus, Ohio, at 800 lb/in.² over 9,620 hr and at 7,500 lb/in.² over 8,690 hr duration.

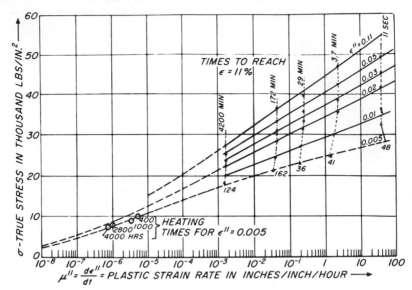

FIG. 16-20. Stress-strain-rate curves for 0.35% carbon steel (K-20) at 850°F. $u'' = d\varepsilon''/dt =$ plastic strain rate in inches per inch per hour.

curves $\sigma = f(\varepsilon)$ disclose pronounced strain hardening and effect of speed of deformation; the flow stresses σ at the fastest rate were twice as high as in the slowest test. After applying the required corrections, the flow stresses σ were replotted above the logarithms of the *plastic* rates of strain $u'' = d\varepsilon''/dt$ for given amounts of $\varepsilon'' =$ const in Fig. 16-20.

It is important to note that the four points taken from the Battelle long-time creep tests (with values of the order of $u'' = 10^{-6}$ per hr) fitted quite well the lowest line corresponding to $\varepsilon'' = 0.005$. While the shortest test had a duration of less than 1 min and the longest constant-rate test lasted 5 days, the points at $u'' = 10^{-6}$ taken from the Battelle creep tests corresponded to a heating time of 4000 hr (one-half year). In this especially prepared steel, not the slightest change of hardness or sign of aging could be detected after continuous exposure to 850°F over one-half year. The straight lines representing $\sigma = g(u'')$ at $\varepsilon' =$ const in Fig. 16-20 spoke definitely for the validity of $\sigma = \sigma_0 \ln (u''/u_0)$ over a wide range of u'' in this steel at 850°F. An interesting fact in these constant-rate tests worth mentioning is that the ultimate strength $\sigma_{l,max}$ increased approximately proportionally with the strain ε_m at which the load maximum occurred (see Fig. 16-18).

The uncertainty involved in an extrapolation of the standard long-time creep curves $\varepsilon'' = f(t)$ to service time t_s can thus be relieved in nonaging metals behaving in a stable manner by locating the straight-line portion of $g(u'')$ at values $\varepsilon'' =$ const approaching the permissible creep ε_s'' in plots such as Fig. 16-20, to be based on a few constant-rate tests or by making use of the hyperbolic sine chart.

F. CREEP OF SEMIFINITE MAGNITUDE. Although the parts of machines exposed to high temperature must be designed under the condition that the creep strains in them remain of a small order of magnitude, it is perhaps instructive to extend our considerations to creep strains of semifinite order, by supplementing a few remarks which were made in this regard in Sec. 16-2A on page 515.   It will be sufficient for our present purpose to neglect entirely the elastic, reversible parts of strain and to assume that ε and $u = d\varepsilon/dt$ represent conventional strains and rates of strain of a permanent nature and that the load σ_l per unit of original area and the true stress σ per unit of actual area in a tensile bar of incompressible material are related by

$$\sigma_l = \frac{\sigma}{1 + \varepsilon}. \tag{16-69}$$

Suppose that *a stress surface* of regular shape exists,

$$\sigma = F(\varepsilon,u), \tag{16-70}$$

in which the plane sections $\varepsilon = $ const and $u = $ const have monotonously increasing ordinates σ with the increasing values of u and ε along which the slopes $\partial\sigma/\partial u$ and $\partial\sigma/\partial\varepsilon$ gradually decrease, respectively.   To this stress surface $\sigma = F(\varepsilon,u)$ correspond the load stresses

$$\sigma_l = \frac{F(\varepsilon,u)}{1 + \varepsilon}. \tag{16-71}$$

With ordinates σ_l, erected above the ε,u plane smaller than σ, this represents *a second, the load stress surface*, also characterizing the material.   To avoid any ambiguity let us add that both surfaces σ and σ_l are supposed to rise steeply inward from the ε and u axes into the positive quadrant from values $\sigma = 0$ and $\sigma_l = 0$ along these axes.

The long-time creep tests in which the *load* σ_l is held invariable obviously trace the family of contour lines $\sigma_l = $ const on the load stress surface σ_l [Eq. (16-71)].   Their hodograph lines in the ε,u plane are defined by assigning fixed values to σ_l in Eq. (16-71), which with $u = d\varepsilon/dt$ expresses the differential equation of the long-time creep curves $\varepsilon = f(t)$.   Upon sudden application of the load, creep starts with a high rate $u = u_i$, but the initial strain ε_i will be quite small and we may as well neglect ε_i.

In a constant-rate test, on the other hand, in Eq. (16-71) we have to assign to the rate of strain a fixed value $u = u_r = $ const and obtain in the vertical sections of the load stress surface the stress-strain diagrams.   Suppose that at the prescribed rate u_r the load σ_l reaches its maximum value $\sigma_{l,\,\mathrm{max}}$ (the ultimate strength) at a certain strain $\varepsilon = \varepsilon_r$ (Fig. 16-21).

We may draw a conclusion in regard to the magnitudes of the minimum creep rate u_{min} and of the strain $\varepsilon = \varepsilon_c$ at which the former is reached in a long-time creep

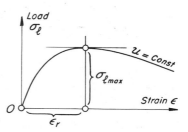

Fig.16-21. Stress-strain diagram.

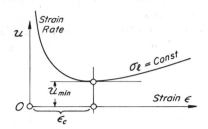

FIG. 16-22. Hodograph.

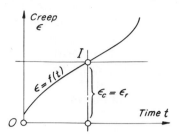

FIG. 16-23. Creep curve.

test under an invariable load $\sigma_l = $ const. If the two stress surfaces
[Eqs. (16-70) and (16-71)] exist and if we choose the load σ_l in the creep
test equal to the ultimate strength $\sigma_{l, \max}$ that we observed at the uniform rate of stretching $u = u_r$, then

$$u_{\min} = u_r, \qquad \varepsilon_c = \varepsilon_r, \qquad (16\text{-}72)$$

*the minimum creep rate $u_{\min}$ equals the rate u_r necessary to produce a load
maximum $\sigma_{l, \max}$ equal to the load $\sigma_l = $ const held invariable in the creep
test*, and, furthermore, the strain ε_c at which the inflection point I is
reached in it equals the strain ε_r, corresponding to the ultimate strength
(Figs. 16-21 through 16-23). The reason is simple, because

$$d\sigma = \frac{\partial \sigma}{\partial \varepsilon}\, d\varepsilon + \frac{\partial \sigma}{\partial u}\, du \qquad (16\text{-}73)$$

is a complete differential and the two sequences of straining $\sigma_l = $ const
and $u = u_r = $ const lie in two perpendicular planes, demarking two
plane curves situated on the load stress surface σ_l [Eq. (16-71)] being
tangent to each other at the same point $\varepsilon = \varepsilon_c = \varepsilon_r$, $u_r = u_{\min}$,
$\sigma_l = \sigma_{l, \max}$.

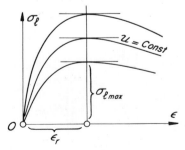

FIG. 16-24. Stress-strain diagrams.

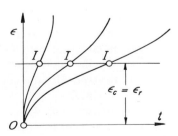

FIG. 16-25. Creep curves
$\varepsilon = f(t)$.

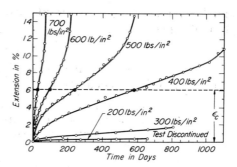

FIG. 16-26. Tensile long-time creep tests by J. McKeown on lead at room temperature.

An interesting example may illustrate this further. Suppose that the equation of the stress surface has the product form

$$\sigma = f_1(\varepsilon) \cdot f_2(u). \tag{16-74}$$

The load maxima $\sigma_{l,\,\max}$, when $u = u_r = $ const, must then occur when

$$\frac{\partial \sigma_l}{\partial \varepsilon} = \frac{\partial}{\partial \varepsilon}\left(\frac{\sigma}{1 + \varepsilon}\right) = f_2(u_r) \cdot \frac{d}{d\varepsilon}\left[\frac{f_1(\varepsilon)}{1 + \varepsilon}\right] = 0 \tag{16-75}$$

for a value $\varepsilon = \varepsilon_r$ satisfying the condition

$$\frac{df_1(\varepsilon)}{d\varepsilon} = \frac{f_1(\varepsilon)}{1 + \varepsilon}. \tag{16-76}$$

We note that all *the load maxima $\sigma_{l,\,\max}$ in the stress-strain diagrams recorded at uniform various speeds of stretching $u = u_r$ occur at the same value of strain $\varepsilon = \varepsilon_r$* and hence all the creep curves $\varepsilon = f(t)$ will have their inflection points I at this strain $\varepsilon = \varepsilon_c = \varepsilon_r = $ const, as indicated in Figs. 16-24 and 16-25.

It is noteworthy that these conditions may have prevailed in a series of long-time creep tests published by J. McKeown,[1] made with lead at room temperature, covering the long testing periods of 3 years and remarkable also for the fairly large creep strains amounting to 15 per cent, reproduced in Fig. 16-26. The horizontal dotted line in it, indicating the locus of the inflection points J at the constant height $\varepsilon_r = \varepsilon_c$, has been added by the author.

An example of the product form of a stress surface [Eq. (16-73)] would be

$$\sigma = \sigma_0\left(\frac{\varepsilon}{\varepsilon_0}\right)^m \cdot \left(\frac{u}{u_0}\right)^n \tag{16-77}$$

($\sigma_0, \varepsilon_0, u_0, n, m$ being material constants). The strain ε_r at which all the

[1] J. Inst. Metals, vol. 60, p. 201, 1937.

load maxima $\sigma_{l,\,max}$ in constant-rate tests occur, computed from Eq.
(16-76), is equal to

$$\varepsilon_r = \frac{m}{1-m}\,, \tag{16-78}$$

and this is also the strain ε_c at which the minimum creep rates u_{min} are
reached in constant-load tests.

G. Comparing Power Function with Hyperbolic Sine Speed Law.
Recalling that in the early days of creep testing investigators favored utilizing
a power function for expressing the dependence of the minimum creep rate
$u'' = \dot{\varepsilon}''$ on the flow stress σ,

$$u'' = u_2\left(\frac{\sigma}{\sigma_2}\right)^m \tag{16-79}$$

($m > 1$, u_2, σ_2 are constants), it may be instructive to set up a comparison of
the latter function with the function

$$u'' = u_1 \sinh \frac{\sigma}{\sigma_1} \tag{16-80}$$

by searching for the power function that lies nearest to the hyperbolic sine
function at a given point of the latter. This amounts to constructing the
osculating power function

$$x = cy^m \tag{16-79a}$$

to the function

$$x = \sinh y, \tag{16-80a}$$

letting $x = u''/u_1$, $y = \sigma/\sigma_1$ so that, at a given point (u_0'',σ_0), $x_0 = u_0''/u_1$,
$y_0 = \sigma_0/\sigma_1$, common to both, they have equal derivatives. The constants c
and m have to be chosen equal to

$$c = y_0^{-m} \sinh y_0 = \left(\frac{\sigma_1}{\sigma_0}\right)^m \sinh \frac{\sigma_0}{\sigma_1}\,, \tag{16-81}$$

$$m = y_0 \coth y_0 = \frac{\sigma_0}{\sigma_1} \coth \frac{\sigma_0}{\sigma_1}\,, \tag{16-82}$$

$$u_2 = u_1\left(\frac{\sigma_2}{\sigma_0}\right)^m \sinh \frac{\sigma_0}{\sigma_1}\,, \tag{16-81a}$$

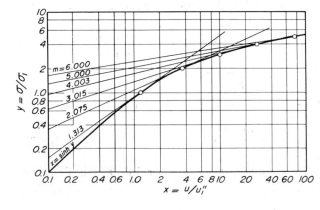

Fig. 16-27. Comparison
of hyperbolic sine creep
law with power function
laws used for extrapo-
lating creep data.

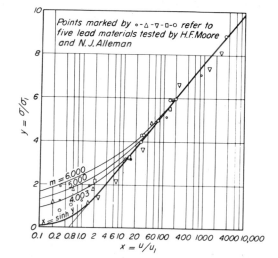

FIG. 16-28. Hyperbolic sine creep law compared with power function laws and with lead tests by H. F. Moore and K. J. Alleman.

and the power function equal to

$$u'' = u_2 \left(\frac{\sigma}{\sigma_2}\right)^m = u_1 \sinh \frac{\sigma_0}{\sigma_1} \cdot \left(\frac{\sigma}{\sigma_0}\right)^m = u_1 c y^m. \tag{16-83}$$

This has been shown in two figures. In the double-logarithmic plot in Fig. 16-27 the curve traced with a thick line represents Eq. (16-80a). For small values of x and y it tends to approach an asymptote inclined at 45°. Since power functions appear as straight lines in double-log plots, Eqs. (16-79a) are represented in Fig. 16-27 by the tangents to the former curve which were traced in the following points:

$$y_0 = \quad 1 \qquad 2 \qquad 3 \qquad 4 \qquad 5 \qquad 6$$
$$x_0 = \quad 1.175 \quad 3.627 \quad 10.02 \quad 27.29 \quad 74.20 \quad 201.7$$

The corresponding values of the exponent m computed from Eq. (16-82) were

$$m = \quad 1.313 \quad 2.075 \quad 3.015 \quad 4.003 \quad 5.000 \quad 6.000$$

Figure 16-27 brings out the deviation of the osculating power functions from the hyperbolic sine speed law.

Figure 16-28 shows the same conditions represented in our semilogarithmic plot. The power functions appear here as curves, and the hyperbolic sine law $x = \sinh y$ as a very slowly rising curve that suddenly turns into an inclined straight line.

We have utilized Fig. 16-28 to represent an extensive series of long-time creep tests $\sigma = $ const which were carried out by Prof. H. F. MOORE[1] and K. J. ALLEMAN at the University of Illinois on lead, by transferring their sets of observed pairs of values u_m'', σ into the values[2] $x = u_m''/u_1$, $y = \sigma/\sigma_1$. Although some points at the small rates appear somewhat scattered, the majority of the observations

[1] Univ. Illinois Bull., vol. 39, no. 48, 1932.
[2] Author's paper in the anniversary volume dedicated to STEPHEN TIMOSHENKO's sixtieth birthday, pp. 155–170, The Macmillan Company, New York, 1938.

are fairly well distributed along the line representing the hyperbolic sine speed law, particularly at the higher creep rates.[1]

H. ALLOWING FOR VARIABLE RATE OF STRAIN HARDENING $\psi = \partial\sigma/\partial\varepsilon''$ AND VARIABLE VISCOSITY $\phi = \partial\sigma/\partial u''$.

Let us conceive a stress surface $\sigma = F(\varepsilon'', u'')$ that describes qualitatively at least the way in which most ductile metals are seen to flow, namely, that they strain-harden at rates $\psi = \partial\sigma/\partial\varepsilon''$ decreasing with strain ε'' and increasing with rate of strain $u'' = \dot{\varepsilon}''$, and that they resist deformation with viscosity rates $\phi = \partial\sigma/\partial u''$ increasing with ε'' but decreasing with u''.

Presuming that ε'' represents a small permanent strain so that in a bar subjected to tension the change of the area of the cross sections is not appreciable, a stress surface expressed by a double power function

$$\sigma = c\varepsilon''^{m} \cdot u''^{n}, \qquad (0 \leq m, n \leq 1), \qquad (16\text{-}84)$$

complies with these rules, having the rates of strain hardening ψ and of change of yield stress σ with rate of strain (viscosity) ϕ:

$$\psi = \frac{\partial\sigma}{\partial\varepsilon''} = mc\varepsilon''^{m-1} \cdot u''^{n} = m\frac{\sigma}{\varepsilon''},$$

$$\phi = \frac{\partial\sigma}{\partial u''} = nc\varepsilon''^{m} \cdot u''^{n-1} = n\frac{\sigma}{u''}. \qquad (16\text{-}85)$$

---

[1] Our observations on stable metals (steel, copper) have indicated that at low temperatures the yield stress increases according to the logarithmic speed law [Eq. (16-26)] at higher extension rates prevalent in constant-strain-rate tests, while the linear speed range (σ proportional to u'') in the speed law $u'' = u_1 \sinh (\sigma/\sigma_1)$, when σ, u'' tend to become zero, is still beyond the order of observable quantities. It is known that at low temperatures the flow in ductile metals is due to slip in the crystal grains. Our observations of the K-20 steel in the temperature range of 450° to 550°C make it to a certain degree probable that the mechanism of distortion at the latter, elevated temperatures, while the logarithmic speed law is active, is similarly due to slip in the grains. But at the higher temperatures the linear speed range (σ proportional to u'') also becomes gradually observable. This linear relation expresses the behavior of matter in the fluid state. This tends to suggest that with the decreasing strain rates probably the mechanism of flow in solids changes gradually.

Recent investigations conducted on single crystals of pure lead, tin, and crystal aggregates of lead and its alloys, particularly by H. F. MOORE at the University of Illinois (*op. cit.*), also H. F. MOORE, B. B. BETTY, and C. W. DOLLINS (Univ. Illinois Bull., vol. 32, no. 23, 1935); by J. N. GREENWOOD in Australia (GREENWOOD and C. W. ORR, Proc. Australasian Inst. Mining & Metallurgy, no. 109, 1938); by J. McKEOWN (J. Inst. Metals, vol. 60, p. 201, 1937), B. CHALMERS (*ibid*, p. 293, 1937), and K. HANFFSTENGEL and H. HANEMANN (Z. Metallk., vol. 30, p. 41, 1938) have brought out the fact that the intracrystalline mechanism of the creep in metals is far from being of a uniform or simple nature. Apart from slip and twinning, the irregular change of the position of the atoms in the lattices (*Platzwechsel*), recrystallization, localized *Platzwechsel* along the grain boundaries, and the opening up and distortion of the grain boundary substance have been noticed, having a profound effect on the shapes of the simultaneously recorded creep curves. It is beyond the scope of this book to go into their analysis, and the reader must be referred to books on the solid state authored by physicists and metallurgists.

The differentials $d\sigma, d\varepsilon'', du''$ satisfy the equation

$$\frac{d\sigma}{\sigma} = m\,\frac{d\varepsilon''}{\varepsilon''} + n\,\frac{du''}{u''}\,, \qquad (16\text{-}86)$$

giving for creep under invariable stress, $\sigma = \text{const}, d\sigma = 0$, the differential equation of the strain path,

$$\frac{du''}{d\varepsilon''} = -\,\frac{mu''}{n\varepsilon''}\,, \qquad (16\text{-}87)$$

and for the hodograph lines $\sigma = \text{const}$ the general hyperbolas

$$cu''^n \cdot \varepsilon''^m = c\left(\frac{d\varepsilon''}{dt}\right)^n \cdot \varepsilon''^m = \sigma = \text{const}, \qquad (16\text{-}88)$$

from which (with the initial condition at time $t = 0,\ \varepsilon_i'',\ u_i'',\ \sigma_i$), after integrating, *the creep curves* $\varepsilon'' = f(t)$ *under invariable stress* σ_i take on the equation

$$\varepsilon'' = \varepsilon_i''\left(\frac{t_c + t}{t_c}\right)^{n/(m+n)}, \qquad (16\text{-}89)$$

where t_c denotes the constant time:

$$t_c = \frac{n\varepsilon_i''}{(m+n)u_i''}\,. \qquad (16\text{-}89a)$$

One sees from

$$\varepsilon''^{m+n} = \left(\frac{m+n}{n}\right)^n \cdot \frac{\sigma_i}{c} \cdot (t_c + t)^n \qquad (16\text{-}90)$$

that small creep proceeds proportionally with the $1/(m+n)$th power of stress σ_i and the $n/(m+n)$th power of the time $t_c + t$.   Creep never stops.   If $m = n$, the creep curves are ordinary *parabolas*:

$$\varepsilon''^2 = 2\left(\frac{\sigma_i}{c}\right)^{1/m} \cdot (t_c + t), \qquad t_c = \frac{\varepsilon_i''}{2u_i''}\,. \qquad (16\text{-}91)$$

The double power stress surface [Eq. (16-84)] has been utilized for the practical treatment of the slow creep in bending at high temperatures in comparative tensile and bending tests on cast chromium-nickel bars by EVAN A. DAVIS.[1] After having determined the exponent n in tensile constant-rate tests at 1500°F and 1652°F, prismatic bars were subjected to states of pure bending at each of these two temperatures by keeping them loaded under an invariable bending moment over a period of one week[2] and recording the deflection w as a function of the time t from which the creep bending strains within the uniformly bent

---

[1] Creep of Metals at High Temperature in Bending, J. Appl. Mechanics, March, 1938.
[2] One-thousand-hour tests in bending of cantilevers were made on aluminum by R. G. STURM, C. DUMONT, and F. M. HOWELL, A Method of Analyzing Creep Data, J. Appl. Mechanics, June, 1936.

gauge length having a uniform radius of curvature were evaluated, assuming that the cross sections remained planes.[1]   Using *the theory of plastic bending, but here based on the postulate of the double power stress surface* satisfying Eq. (16-84), the bending creep strains ε'' in the extreme fibers of the cross sections should supply a set of parallel lines on the double logarithmic ε'',t plot, corresponding to the bending moments M held at invariable values.   This was fairly well confirmed by these bending tests, indicating that a stress surface such as Eq. (16-74) may serve practical purposes in metals.[2]

For relaxation of stress, while the total elongation ε is held at its initial value ε_i, after combining

$$\sigma + E\varepsilon'' = \sigma_i + E\varepsilon_i'' = E\varepsilon_i = \text{const} \qquad (16\text{-}92)$$

with Eq. (16-84), one obtains

$$t = \left(\frac{c}{E}\right)^{1/n} \cdot \int_{\varepsilon_i''}^{\varepsilon''} \varepsilon''^{m/n} \cdot (\varepsilon_i - \varepsilon'')^{-1/n}\, d\varepsilon''; \qquad (16\text{-}93)$$

after evaluating the integral in a first approximation,[3] *the evanescing stress σ is found to relax* with the $[-n/(1-n)]$th power of $t + t_r$:

$$\sigma = \sigma_i \left(\frac{t_r}{t_r + t}\right)^{n/(1-n)}, \qquad t_r = \frac{n\sigma_i}{(1-n)E} \cdot \left(\frac{c}{\sigma_i}\right)^{1/n} \cdot \varepsilon_i^{m/n} \qquad (16\text{-}94)$$

Equation (16-94) fails when $n = 1$, that is, for a substance having the ordinary type of viscosity $\phi = c\varepsilon''^m$ that increases with ε'', in which case, by going back to Eq. (16-84), $\sigma = c\varepsilon''^m u''$, one verifies easily that the stress relaxes according to

$$t = \frac{c\varepsilon_i^m}{E}\left[\ln\frac{\sigma_i}{\sigma} - \frac{m(\sigma_i - \sigma)}{E\varepsilon_i}\right] \qquad (16\text{-}95)$$

or, after neglecting the rather small second term in the brackets, according to

$$\sigma = \sigma_i e^{-Et/c\varepsilon_i^m}.$$

This then takes some account of variable viscosity ϕ and rates of strain hardening ψ in creep and relaxation.

I. CREEP RECOVERY.   The various assumptions utilized in the preceding sections are inadequate for the treatment of a phenomenon that is associated with a sudden unloading, after creep strains have progressed for a prolonged time, namely, creep recovery at elevated temperature in metals.   Bars that were loaded in tension for a long

---

[1] G. H. MacCullough, An Experimental and Analytical Investigation of Creep in Bending, Trans. ASME, vol. 55, 1933.

[2] The defect of a power function in the region of very small rates of strain u'' (see Sec. 16-2C, page 520) has little effect on these states of bending.

[3] By letting

$$z = 1 - \frac{\varepsilon''}{\varepsilon_i} = \frac{\sigma}{E\varepsilon_i}, \qquad z_i = \frac{\sigma_i}{E\varepsilon_i}$$

in the integrand and developing it in powers of the small quantity z, one can express the integral precisely through a series, but it suffices to let

$$\int_z^{z_i} (1 - z)^{m/n} \cdot z^{-1/n} \cdot dz \simeq \int_z^{z_i} z^{-1/n}\, dz = \frac{n}{1-n}\left(z^{-(1-n)/n} - z_i^{-(1-n)/n}\right).$$

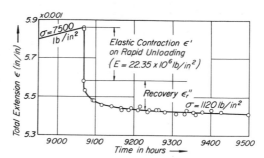

FIG. 16-29. Creep recovery of 0.35% C steel at 842°F after unloading from 7,500 to 1,120 lb/in.² stress. (*Tests by P. G. McVetty and K. R. Waugh, East Pittsburgh, Pa., 1939.*)

time disclose after sudden unloading, apart from their instantaneous elastic contraction, a gradually developing further permanent shortening through which a certain portion of the former creep extension is being slowly recovered. These recovery strains are pronounced in high polymers, but they have definitely been observed in metals. Two nice examples of the gradual recovery of a portion of sustained creep, observed by P. G. McVetty[1] after sudden unloading in tensile tests made with an 0.35% C steel at 842°F over a period of 700 hr and an ATV steel at 1000°F over a period of 2,100 hr, may be seen in Figs. 16-29 and 16-30.[2] The recovery in the second bar amounted to nine-tenths of the elastic contraction ε' upon unloading.

It has been pointed out in Sec. 4-1C that a gradual recovery of permanent strain is traceable analytically by assuming two additively

[1] Permission to reproduce these unpublished results on creep-recovery tests is gratefully acknowledged to P. G. McVetty in Pittsburgh. The tests were made by him and K. R. Waugh in 1939.

[2] The 0.35% C steel bar had been subjected to a long-time creep test under a stress $\sigma = 7,500$ lb/in.² over a period of 9,070 hr during which it elongated by a total extension of 0.00587. Then the bar was quickly unloaded to a stress $\sigma = 1,120$ lb/in.², contracted elastically by $\varepsilon' = 0.00029$, and subsequently contracted permanently by $\varepsilon_r'' = 0.00019$ after 700 hr had passed.

The ATV steel sustained a stress $\sigma = 20,000$ lb/in.² for 8,600 hr. Upon unloading to $\sigma = 1,120$ lb/in.² it contracted elastically by $\varepsilon' = 0.000921$ and subsequently contracted permanently, showing a recovery strain $\varepsilon_r'' = 0.000800$ after an additional 2,100 hr had passed.

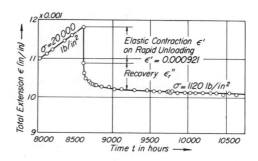

FIG. 16-30. Creep recovery of ATV steel at 1000°F after unloading from 20,000 to 1,120 lb/in.² stress. (*Tests by P. G. McVetty and K. R. Waugh, East Pittsburgh, Pa., 1939.*)

connected parts σ' and σ'' in the stress σ, one carried elastically and the other required to overcome the internal resistance of a viscous nature opposing any change of strain with time in a substance.

In generalizing our earlier assumptions, suppose that the part σ' is proportional to the recoverable strain ε, $\sigma' = E\varepsilon$, but that the part σ'' is a known function $\sigma'' = g(u)$ of the rate of strain $u = d\varepsilon/dt$, thus postulating, as far as the strain ε of a recoverable nature is concerned, existence of a *stress surface*:

$$\underline{\underline{\sigma = \sigma' + \sigma'' = E\varepsilon + g(u).}} \qquad (16\text{-}96)$$

Let us evaluate the response ε when a stress is suddenly applied, subsequently held invariable for a time, and then suddenly released, by assuming as an example for the part $\sigma'' = cu^n$ a power function of the rate u, giving the differential equation for ε,

$$E\varepsilon + c\left(\frac{d\varepsilon}{dt}\right)^n = \sigma = \text{const}, \qquad (0 < n < 1), \qquad (16\text{-}97)$$

having, after sudden loading, the integral

$$\varepsilon = \varepsilon_1 - \frac{\varepsilon_1}{[1 + (1 - n)(E/n\sigma)(\sigma/c)^{1/n} \cdot t]^{n/(1-n)}}, \qquad (16\text{-}98)$$

and upon release of σ, after sudden unloading, the solution

$$\varepsilon = \frac{\varepsilon_1}{[1 + (1 - n)(E/n\sigma)(\sigma/c)^{1/n} \cdot t]^{n/(1-n)}}, \qquad (16\text{-}99)$$

disclosing the time-delayed growth of the former and gradual evanescence of the latter strain, exhibiting a full recovery of the previously attained value $\varepsilon_1 = \sigma/E$ [Fig. 16-31, time t after unloading in Eq. (16-99) being counted from the new origin O_1]. The time function in Eq. (16-99) is reminiscent of the one found in Eq. (16-36) for the relaxation of a stress σ for a power function speed law, and, by looking at the dashed lines in Fig. 16-31, we may state that the phenomenon of recovery

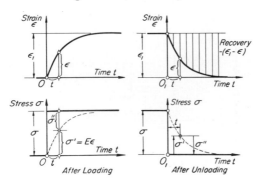

Fig. 16-31. Time-delayed response of strain ε in recovery-sensitive material.

brings about a relaxation of the viscous part of stress σ'' upon sudden loading and of the elastic part of stress σ' upon sudden unloading.[1]

The time-delayed generation of strain ε may likewise be evaluated for other types of speed laws $\sigma'' = g(u)$, such as the logarithmic or the hyperbolic sine laws, but we shall refrain from developing the corresponding responses of ε. What seems more important is that the preceding recoverable strains may be tied to the general theory of creep of metals, by making use of what we called *the concept of a composite, firmoviscous, and viscoelastic, recovery-sensitive substance* (in Sec. 4-1D), for which we postulated a combined principle of superposing three distinct types of strain associated with two additive types of stress:

$$\varepsilon = \varepsilon' + \varepsilon'' + \varepsilon''', \qquad \sigma = \sigma' + \sigma''. \tag{16-100}$$

By generalizing our earlier-made assumptions, denoting the corresponding rates of strain by

$$u = \frac{d\varepsilon}{dt} = \dot{\varepsilon} = \dot{\varepsilon}' + \dot{\varepsilon}'' + \dot{\varepsilon}''' = u' + u'' + u''', \tag{16-101}$$

let $\varepsilon' = \sigma/E$ be the elastic and ε'' the permanent (usual creep) strain and now, however, identify the recoverable type of strain [designated in Eqs. (16-96) above by simply writing for it the symbol ε] with the strain ε''' in Eqs. (16-100), reserving the symbol ε in it for the *total* strain. We may then specify that the substance be generally viscous by postulating a general speed law for the stress σ,

$$\sigma = g(u''), \qquad u'' = h(\sigma), \tag{16-102}$$

and likewise, as we did in the preceding theory of recovery, that the part of stress σ'' be a known (other) function of the rates u''' designated by

$$\sigma'' = g_r(u'''); \tag{16-103}$$

we may avail ourselves of the freedom of letting the part of stress σ' be either $\sigma' = E\varepsilon'''$ or more generally $\sigma' = E_r\varepsilon'''$ (E_r thus need not equal Young's modulus of elasticity E), these assumptions now reverting back to postulating the part-stress surface,

$$\sigma = \sigma' + \sigma'' = E_r\varepsilon''' + g_r(u'''), \tag{16-104}$$

controlling the recoverable strains ε''' and rates $u''' = \dot{\varepsilon}'''$.

---

[1] A generalized *Kelvin unit* mentioned in Sec. 4-1, page 170, consisting of an elastic spring and a dashpot joined parallel, the latter responding under the general speed law $\sigma'' = g(u)$, depicts this behavior in a mechanical model: On sudden loading the spring exerts its initial full force on the dashpot.

For a long-time creep test under an invariable stress $\sigma = \text{const}$ the latter equation obviously defines the recoverable strain ε'''; since the part ε'' of the strain increases uniformly with the time t, $\varepsilon'' = u''t = h(\sigma) \cdot t$, the total strain ε varies according to the function of time,

$$\varepsilon = \varepsilon' + \varepsilon'' + \varepsilon''' = \frac{\sigma}{E} + h(\sigma) \cdot t + \varepsilon''', \qquad (16\text{-}105)$$

where now ε''' is the integral of Eq. (16-104) satisfying the initial condition upon sudden loading $t = 0$, $\sigma' = \varepsilon''' = 0$. This gives creep curves $\varepsilon = f(t)$ such as the one shown in Fig. 16-32, approaching asymptotically straight lines BA, inclined under the slopes $u'' = d\varepsilon''/dt = h(\sigma)$ and increasing with the stress $\sigma = \text{const}$. We note that now *there appears in the curves* $\varepsilon = f(t)$ *a primary creep (curved) stage* due to the recoverable strain parts ε''', causing an "upset" just equal to the elastic strain $\varepsilon' = \varepsilon_0 = \sigma/E$ if $E_r = E$, but otherwise equal to $\varepsilon_0 = \sigma/E_r$. *Upon sudden unloading* from a point A in Fig. 16-32 which is already situated on the straight asymptote $\overline{AB}$, the indicated *strain recovery appears* (shaded ordinates) tending toward the value ε_0.

The double superposition principle [Eqs. (16-100)] also may be applied *to amend the theory of relaxation of stress* by introducing in the condition of holding the total strain ε at the fixed value $\varepsilon = \varepsilon_i = \text{const}$,

$$\varepsilon = \frac{\sigma}{E} + \varepsilon'' + \varepsilon''' = \varepsilon_i, \qquad (16\text{-}106)$$

for the variable flow stress σ either the expression $\sigma = g(u'') = g(\dot{\varepsilon}'')$, based on the speed law Eqs. (16-102), or $\sigma = \sigma' + \sigma''$, the condition that controlled the evolution of the *recoverable* parts ε''' of strain according to Eq. (16-104). This gives, respectively,

$$\frac{g(\dot{\varepsilon}'')}{E} + \varepsilon'' + \varepsilon''' = \varepsilon_i,$$

$$\frac{1}{E}[E_r\varepsilon''' + g_r(\dot{\varepsilon}''')] + \varepsilon'' + \varepsilon''' = \varepsilon_i,$$

or two simultaneous differential equations of symmetrical form, interrelating the two parts of strain ε'' and ε''':

$$\varepsilon''' = \varepsilon_i - \varepsilon'' - \frac{g(\dot{\varepsilon}'')}{E},$$

$$\qquad\qquad (16\text{-}107)$$

$$\varepsilon'' = \varepsilon_i - \left(1 + \frac{E_r}{E}\right)\varepsilon''' - \frac{g_r(\dot{\varepsilon}''')}{E},$$

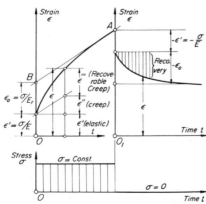

FIG. 16-32. Strain ε in composite, recovery-sensitive substance.

either of which supplies, through Eq. (16-104),

$$\sigma = g(\dot{\varepsilon}'') = E_r\varepsilon''' + g_r(\dot{\varepsilon}'''), \qquad (16\text{-}108)$$

the time function under which the flow stress σ relaxes with the time t.

It is appropriate to recall that, while the elastic strain $\varepsilon' = \sigma/E$ and the creep rate $u'' = d\varepsilon''/dt = h(\sigma)$ depend solely on the instantaneous value of the stress σ carried in the material, on the other hand the recoverable part ε''' of strain ε, the rate of strain $u''' = d\varepsilon'''/dt$, and consequently the part $\sigma'' = g_r(u''')$ of the stress σ require a time until they can fully develop or may have been produced *prior* to the actual deformation that one desires to describe. From a heuristic viewpoint, therefore, it is important to note that our double principle of superposing three distinct types of strain $\varepsilon = \varepsilon' + \varepsilon'' + \varepsilon'''$ with two types of stress $\sigma = \sigma' + \sigma''$ makes it possible to consider the effects of previous stages in the loading or straining process upon the actual sequence of deformation, i.e., *to include the prior history of loading or straining.*

This is exemplified by the different types of relaxation curves, representing the decline of stress σ with time t, that one observes, depending on the different ways in which the initial load has been brought up to its value $\sigma = \sigma_i$ at time $t = 0$, prior to letting a bar relax in stress. One sees immediately, upon looking at the condition of relaxation, according to which the sum of the three rates of strain $u' = \dot{\sigma}/E$, u'', u''' at any instant must vanish, that the stress σ decreases at the rate

$$\frac{d\sigma}{dt} = -E(u'' + u''') = -E[h(\sigma) + u''']. \qquad (16\text{-}109)$$

Hence, the initial rate of drop of stress $(d\sigma/dt)_{t=0}$ at starting time $t = 0$ of relaxation in a recovery-sensitive solid must certainly depend, apart from the initial, given value of $h(\sigma_i)$, on the value of $(u''')_{t=0}$ at time $t = 0$. *If the initial stress $\sigma = \sigma_i$ is suddenly applied* and the specimen left to relax, then at time $t = 0$, $\varepsilon''' = 0$, the part stress $\sigma' = E_r\varepsilon''' = 0$ vanishes and hence the part stress $\sigma'' = \sigma_i = g_r(u''')$ takes on its maximum possible value σ_i with the corresponding *greatest*, initial, positive rate $(u''')_{t=0}$. On the other hand, suppose that *the specimen was kept loaded* under the initial stress σ_i *for a long time* prior to letting it relax. A glance at the left part of Fig. 16-32 shows that in this case the rate u''' at point A vanished and that, at the start of relaxation, $(u''')_{t=0} = 0$, $(d\sigma/dt)_{t=0} = -Eh(\sigma_i)$. Thus we see from Eq. (16-109) that *in a recovery-sensitive solid, upon sudden loading to $\sigma = \sigma_i$, the stress σ starts to drop initially from its value σ_i at a much faster rate $(d\sigma/dt)_{t=0}$ than in a solid in which no recovery strains ε''' are active*, but if the load σ was gradually increased prior to relaxation, the absolute value of $(d\sigma/dt)_{t=0}$ will become smaller, depending on the initial value of $(u''')_{t=0}$ under which the specimen starts to relax.   As the time t advances, the stress σ in a composite solid may overtake the values of declining stress corresponding to a recovery-nonsensitive substance, the former relaxing at later times at higher stresses and at slower rates with time than the latter.[1]

In summing up these reflections, it may be stated that the double principle of superposition [Eqs. (16-100)] (1) serves to define what we called a composite solid in a stable condition, exhibiting three additive parts of strain: an elastic, a generally viscous, permanent type, and a semipermanent, recoverable part of the total strain, and (2) allows one to take account of *the anelastic aftereffect of the history of prior loading modes.*[2]

For historical evidence it is remarked that the anelastic aftereffects were discovered by the German physicist WILHELM WEBER in Göttingen around 1835, long before engineers became interested in the creep of metals.   Half a century later they inspired the great Austrian theoretical physicist LUDWIG BOLTZMANN (1874) in Vienna and the great Italian mathematician VITO VOLTERRA (1909) in Rome to ingenious treatments by means of definite integrals for analyzing these phenomena of imperfect elasticity, the latter appropriately designated as *phenomena possessing hereditary characteristics.*

The first investigators of anelastic aftereffects were greatly puzzled by observing that a thin filament of supposedly elastic material which was held for a longer time twisted under a constant torque, then unloaded and, after a short while subsequently twisted in the opposite direction for a short time; after it was finally left unloaded, it would untwist permanently by a small amount from the second load, but after a certain time had elapsed, it would retwist itself a little in the direction in which it was originally distorted by the first torque.   Such behavior evidenced by inanimate material, comparable to *memory of the various past actions* to which it had been subjected, was considered an unusual property that one would not expect to observe in inanimate objects.

Our composite, recovery-sensitive, generally viscoelastic substance discloses this effect, as Figs. 16-33a and 33b may illustrate.   Suppose that a specimen has passed through the two sequences of loading indicated in the upper part of Fig. 16-33a.   Below it has been traced the variation of the total strain ε with time t caused by each of the two

---

[1] Cf. Sec. 4-1D and also Sec. 16-8 below where relaxation tests with copper are discussed.

[2] The reader may find a critical review, parts of which are along the lines of the above section, in F. K. G. ODQUIST (Stockholm), Engineering Theories of Metallic Creep, 12 pp., a paper presented at the Symposium of Plasticity held in honor of Prof. ARTURO DANUSSO in Varenna, Italy, in September, 1956.

loads, independently, in curves $OABC$ and $DEFG$, respectively, in accordance with the preceding synthesis of deformation. By adding algebraically the strain ordinates ε of positive extensions and negative compressions, corresponding to the first, tensile and the second, compression stresses, obviously the response along the jagged curve results, reproduced in Fig. 16-33b, in which the last branch FG represents the anelastic aftereffect after cessation of the second load. This verifies, under the required conditions to be stipulated, that the specimen lastly contracts from the effect of the second compression load but later again extends a trifle, in memory of the first, tensile load. We shall treat similar aftereffects in Sec. 16-7 below.

J. THE INFLUENCE OF TIME ON CHANGE OF YIELD STRENGTH AT ELEVATED TEMPERATURE. As was mentioned in Sec. 16-1, the first investigators of the creep of metals advanced the idea that, while the continuous permanent deformation observed as creep strain hardens a metal, this is simultaneously being opposed by the cumulative effect of exposure of the solid to an elevated temperature that softens it and enhances its deformability. Let us give a little thought as to how the

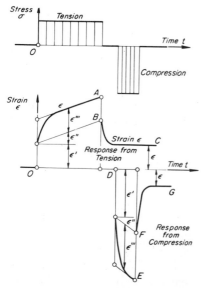

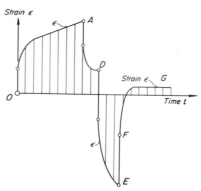

FIG. 16-33a. Variation of total strain ε with time t caused independently by a steady tensile and a steady compression load.

FIG. 16-33b. Response of total, resultant strain $\varepsilon = \varepsilon' + \varepsilon'' + \varepsilon'''$ in composite, recovery-sensitive, viscoelastic substance after having been loaded first by tensile and later by compression stresses. The branch FG represents the resultant total anelastic effect after cessation of second load.

deterioration of the yield strength in metals with time, due to prolonged action of heat, may phenomenologically be susceptible to mechanical treatment.

It seems reasonable to expect that, while the tensile flow stress σ will depend on the permanent strain ε'' and rate of strain $u'' = \partial \varepsilon''/\partial t$, in the so-called intermediate range of temperature, when a gradual softening of a metal with time becomes appreciable, the material parameters entering in the functional relation expressing a stress surface—if such an equation of state in finite terms should exist—will be dependent on the time t; thus we may assume that

$$\sigma = F(\varepsilon'', u'', t). \tag{16-110}$$

In any case, with time t as a third, independent variable besides ε'' and u'', let us presume that the differential of flow stress $d\sigma$ equals

$$d\sigma = \frac{\partial \sigma}{\partial \varepsilon''} d\varepsilon'' + \frac{\partial \sigma}{\partial u''} du'' + \frac{\partial \sigma}{\partial t} dt \tag{16-111}$$

or, if we denote the partial derivatives by the three abbreviating symbols

$$\psi = \frac{\partial \sigma}{\partial \varepsilon''}, \qquad \phi = \frac{\partial \sigma}{\partial u''}, \qquad \chi = \frac{\partial \sigma}{\partial t}, \tag{16-112}$$

that $d\sigma$ equals

$$d\sigma = \psi \, d\varepsilon'' + \phi \, du'' + \chi \, dt. \tag{16-113}$$

Here $\chi = \partial \sigma/\partial t$ expresses *the rate of change of the yield strength of the metal with time*: if $\chi < 0$, a rate of softening; and if $\chi > 0$, a time rate of hardening (if the metal should age-harden). The various fundamental tests considered in previous sections may be discussed if Eq. (16-113) can be integrated along their prescribed pathways.

In a long-time creep test under $\sigma = $ const, $d\sigma = 0$, after solving Eq. (16-113) for

$$\frac{du''}{dt} = -\frac{\psi u'' + \chi}{\phi}, \tag{16-114}$$

one sees, since $\psi u''$ is always positive and χ negative in the softening range of temperature, that the balance of the two right-hand terms in the last equation determines the sign of du''/dt, of the rate of change of the creep rate u'', along the ideas expressed by R. W. BAILEY and P. G. McVETTY.[1] The creep rate u'' will decrease first, because of the large initial values of u'', but will increase later, reaching its *minimum value* $u''_{\min}$ in the inflection point I (Figs. 16-1 and 16-34) of the creep curve $\varepsilon'' = f(t)$, when $du''/dt = 0$:

$$u''_{\min} = \left(\frac{d\varepsilon''}{dt}\right)_{\min} = -\frac{\chi}{\psi}, \tag{16-115}$$

provided that $\chi < 0$.

[1] See page 512 (*loc. cit.*).

One sees from Eq. (16-113) that a primary and ternary portion in the creep curves may become evident even in *a non-strain-hardening* ($\psi = 0$), *generally viscous solid if the viscosity ϕ is dependent on time,* increasing first with time to a maximum value and subsequently decreasing while the strains ε'' remain small. Taking in Eq. (16-113) $\sigma = $ const, $d\sigma = 0$, $\psi = 0$, one sees that

$$\frac{du''}{dt} = -\frac{\chi}{\phi} \tag{16-116}$$

may vanish if, at some time $t = t_1$, $\chi(t_1) = 0$. This may happen in a perfectly viscous substance for which

$$\sigma = \phi(t) \cdot u'', \tag{16-117}$$

if the viscosity $\phi = \partial\sigma/\partial u''$ varies with the time t according to a curve like the one traced in Fig. 16-34a. Since such a substance possesses a time rate of change of yield strength or hardness $\chi(t)$,

$$\chi(t) = \frac{\partial\sigma}{\partial t} = \frac{d\phi}{dt} \cdot u'' = \phi'(t) \cdot u'', \tag{16-118}$$

and for it along the creep curves $\sigma = $ const, after Eq. (16-116),

$$\frac{du''}{dt} = -\frac{u''\phi'(t)}{\phi(t)}, \tag{16-119}$$

this will vanish when at the time $t = t_1$, $\phi'(t_1) = 0$, namely, when the viscosity ϕ passes through its analytic maximum at which χ changes its sign with $\phi'(t)$. This solid would be said to harden first and to soften thereafter.

Suppose that the viscosity ϕ varied with time t according to the function

$$\phi = \frac{\phi_1}{1 + \alpha(t - t_1)^2}, \tag{16-120}$$

(α, ϕ_1, t_1 are constants), ϕ being, at time $t = 0$, $\phi = \phi_0 = \phi_1/(1 + \alpha t_1^2)$ and

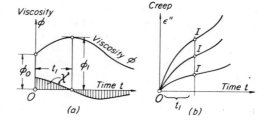

FIG. 16-34. (a) Time-dependent viscosity.
(b) Creep curves.

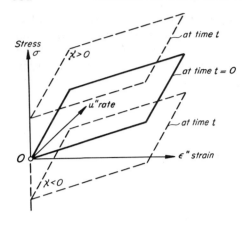

FIG. 16-35. The stress surface is a plane $\sigma = \psi\varepsilon'' + \phi u'' + \chi t$.

$\phi_1 = \phi_{\max}$ the maximum reached at $t = t_1$. The time rate of change of resistance of material χ, using $\sigma = \phi \cdot u''$,

$$\chi = \frac{\partial \sigma}{\partial t} = \frac{d\phi}{dt} \cdot u'' = -\frac{2\alpha\sigma(t - t_1)}{1 + \alpha(t - t_1)^2},$$

varies as indicated by the curve with shaded ordinates in Fig. 16-34a, and the creep curves under invariable stress[1] $\sigma = $ const,

$$\varepsilon'' = \frac{\sigma}{3\phi_1}[\alpha t^3 - 3\alpha t_1 t^2 + 3(1 + \alpha t_1^2)t],$$

are represented by a family of affine curves (Fig. 16-34b), having all their inflection points at the same time t_1 at which the minimum creep rates are equal to $u_{\min} = \sigma/\phi_1$.

Returning to Eq. (16-113), its applicability in this amended form, which includes the time rate of change of resistance to flow $\chi = \partial\sigma/\partial t$ here proposed, has seldom, if at all, been considered by experimentors on creep of metals; thus unfortunately little is known about the magnitude of χ and about the variation of the rate of strain hardening $\psi = \partial\sigma/\partial\varepsilon''$ and viscosity $\phi = \partial\sigma/\partial u''$ with time t.

To visualize the quantitative influence of χ on the flow of a solid, consider the *simplest ideal, viscoplastic, strain-hardening substance*, characterized by the property that for it *the three* fundamental rate expressions ψ, ϕ, χ *are universal constants* in an equation of state that is a linear function of the three independent variables ε'', u'', t:

$$\sigma = \psi\varepsilon'' + \phi u'' + \chi t. \qquad (16\text{-}121)$$

At time $t = 0$ this stress surface is represented by the oblique plane having the slopes ψ and ϕ traced by thick lines in Fig. 16-35. As time t progresses, this plane rises or sinks with the uniform velocity χ, depending on the sign of χ. If $\chi > 0$, the substance hardens; if $\chi < 0$, it softens with time. If the time t is measured from the instant at which the ordinate above the origin O should equal some given value $\sigma = \sigma_0$, this may be interpreted as the initial yield stress of the substance. Thus by adding a constant σ_0 on the right side of Eq. (16-121),

---

[1] Author's paper: Strainhardening and Softening with Time in Reference to Creep and Relaxation in Metals, Trans. ASME, vol. 74, no. 3, pp. 403–413, April, 1952.

material having a finite yield stress σ_0 at time $t = 0$ might be included, and—to follow terminology used by the rheologists—in this case the substance may be also characterized as a *generalized ideal Bingham solid*, having apart from elasticity ($\varepsilon' = \sigma/E$) a constant viscosity ϕ, linear strain hardening, and a *yield value σ_y equal to $\sigma_0 + \chi t$* that increases or decreases due to age hardening or softening with time t. A sequence of loading or straining is represented by a curve traced by a point $P(\varepsilon'',u'',\sigma)$ on the obliquely inclined plane [Eq. (16-121)] while it rises or sinks uniformly with the velocity χ. But if the orbit or path of P intersects the vertical (ε'',σ) plane in Fig. 16-35, the point P rests in its last position indefinitely in the ε'', u'', σ space.

Let us now evaluate creep under invariable stress σ = const and relaxation of stress from an initial stress σ_1 while $\sigma + E\varepsilon'' = \sigma_1 + E\varepsilon_1'' = $ const, both sequences to be based on the stress surface [Eq. (16-121)]. Letting σ = const gives, with $u'' = d\varepsilon''/dt$, the linear differential equation of first order for the creep strain ε'',

$$\frac{d\varepsilon''}{dt} + \frac{\psi}{\phi}\,\varepsilon'' = \frac{\sigma - \chi t}{\phi}\,, \qquad (16\text{-}122)$$

and for the relaxation of stress the equation for $(\sigma_1 - \sigma)/E$:

$$\frac{d}{dt}\frac{\sigma_1 - \sigma}{E} + \frac{E + \psi}{\phi}\cdot\frac{\sigma_1 - \sigma}{E} = \frac{\sigma_1 - \chi t}{\phi}\,. \qquad (16\text{-}123)$$

Since both equations have for their dependent variables ε'' and $(\sigma_1 - \sigma)/E$ the same form and since the initial conditions $t = 0$, $\varepsilon'' = 0$, and $t = 0$, $\sigma_1 - \sigma = 0$, respectively, are similar also, their integrals will be expressed by similar functions of the time t. Equation (16-22) gives, with the abbreviations

$$t_0 = \frac{\phi}{\psi}\,, \qquad \alpha = \frac{\chi\phi}{\psi\sigma}\,, \qquad (16\text{-}124)$$

for *the equation of the long-time creep curves*,

$$\varepsilon'' = \frac{\sigma}{\psi}\left[-\alpha\frac{t}{t_0} + (1 + \alpha)(1 - e^{-t/t_0})\right], \qquad (16\text{-}125)$$

and for the creep rate,

$$u'' = \frac{d\varepsilon''}{dt} = \frac{\sigma}{\phi}[-\alpha + (1 + \alpha)e^{-t/t_0}]. \qquad (16\text{-}126)$$

The creep curves start under the same slope σ/ϕ at the origin O (Fig. 16-36) and, when χ is negative ($\alpha < 0$, when the material softens), approach a group of straight lines as asymptotes radiating from the point $t = t_0 = \phi/\psi$, $\varepsilon'' = \sigma/\psi$.

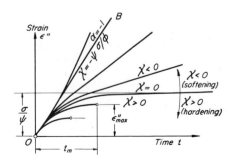

FIG. 16-36. Creep curves showing influence of time rate of change of flow resistance $\chi = \partial\sigma/\partial t$ on shape of creep curves for same value of invariable stress σ = const.

When χ vanishes, a creep limit $\varepsilon'' = \sigma/\psi$ appears; when χ is positive ($\alpha > 0$, age hardening), the creep curves end abruptly at a finite time $t_m = t_0 \ln (1 + 1/\alpha)$ and strain $\varepsilon''_{max} = (\sigma - \chi t_m)/\psi$, as is indicated in Fig. 16-36.   When the rate of softening equals $\chi = -\psi\sigma/\phi$, $\alpha = -1$, *the creep curve is a straight line* $\overline{OB}$ as for a purely viscous substance; in fact, in this special case the sum of the first and last term in Eq. (16-121) vanishes, $\psi\varepsilon'' + \chi t = \psi(\varepsilon'' - \sigma t/\phi) = 0$, the increase in plastic resistance is just annulled by the decrease in yield strength due to softening, and thus $\varepsilon'' = \sigma t/\phi = u''t$.

Likewise *for relaxation* we obtain from Eq. (16-123), after now designating by:

$$t_0 = \frac{\phi}{\psi + E}, \qquad \alpha = \frac{\chi\phi}{\sigma_1(\psi + E)}, \qquad (16\text{-}127)$$

a relation perfectly analogous to Eq. (16-125), namely,

$$\frac{\sigma_1 - \sigma}{E} = \frac{\sigma_1}{\psi + E}\left[-\alpha\frac{t}{t_0} + (1 + \alpha)(1 - e^{-t/t_0}) \right]. \qquad (16\text{-}128)$$

The stress σ relaxes according to

$$\sigma = \sigma_1 + \frac{E\sigma_1}{\psi + E}\left[\alpha\frac{t}{t_0} - (1 + \alpha)(1 - e^{-t/t_0}) \right] \qquad (16\text{-}129)$$

at the rate

$$\frac{d\sigma}{dt} = \frac{E\sigma_1}{\phi}[\alpha - (1 + \alpha)e^{-t/t_0}], \qquad (16\text{-}130)$$

σ starting to drop at $t = 0$ with the same rate $(d\sigma/dt)_{t=0} = -E\sigma_1/\phi$ for all values of χ or α.

Because of the perfect analogy between the corresponding relations with respect to creep and relaxation, *the stress-time curves characterizing relaxation of stress for the various values of the rate of change of flow resistance* $\chi = \partial\sigma/\partial t$ *are represented* in Fig. 16-37 *by the mirror images of the long-time creep curves* reproduced in Fig. 16-36, after reflecting the latter along the same axis [keeping in mind the different definitions attributed to the respective parameters t_0 and α in Eqs. (16-124) and (16-127)].

Thus when $\chi = 0$, ($\alpha = 0$), that is, in a strain-hardening, viscoelastic material which neither softens nor hardens with time, the stress

$$\sigma = \frac{\sigma_1}{\psi + E}(\psi + Ee^{-t/t_0}) \qquad (16\text{-}131)$$

drops to a finite value $\sigma_2 = \sigma_1\psi/(\psi + E)$, which is, however, reached asymptotically with $t \to \infty$, whereas when $\chi > 0$ (hardening), the relaxation curves end abruptly after finite times.   But when $\chi < 0$ (softening), all relaxation curves end after finite times with a vanishing value of stress, and when

$$\chi = -\frac{(\psi + E)\sigma_1}{\phi}, \qquad \alpha = -1,$$

the strange case of a *straight* relaxation line ($S\overline{B}$ in Fig. 16-37) occurs, ending at the time $t = \phi/E$.

Although it is realized that the mechanism of creep or relaxation, embracing the change of the yield strength in the ductile metals with time at elevated

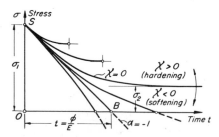

FIG. 16-37. Relaxation curves for various rates of change of flow resistance $\chi = \partial\sigma/\partial t$ for same initial stress σ_1.

temperatures, will follow more involved relations than the ones deduced from the three-term linear equation of state (16-113), the hope may be expressed that the preceding simple rules under which the idealized viscoplastic substance was seen to deform may prove helpful for clarifying the concepts upon which further, more realistic attempts in the indicated directions might be based.

It seems appropriate at this stage, in summarizing our conclusions concerning the phenomenon of the occurrence of an inflection point and a minimum creep rate in the long-time creep tests, to list three independent causes which became apparent for it:

1. Under an invariable load σ_l, in the course of continuous extension, the critical value of rate of strain hardening $\psi_c = \partial\sigma/\partial\varepsilon'' = \sigma_{l,\,\mathrm{max}}$ may be reached [Eq. (16-11)], below which a tensile bar cannot be expected to stretch uniformly and the equilibrium becomes unstable. An equivalent statement is that this instability, marking the beginning of local necking, coincides with the instant at which the gradually decreasing creep rate becomes just equal to the rate necessary to produce that load maximum $\sigma_{l,\,\mathrm{max}}$ in a constant-rate test which equals the invariable load σ_l of the creep test.

2. Whereas these conditions are encountered primarily under creep strains of *semifinite magnitudes*, a minimum creep rate u''_{min} with the accompanying instability is caused *under quite small creep strains ε''* through the action of heat if the yield strength σ of a metal deteriorates gradually owing to a negative rate of change of flow stress $\chi = \partial\sigma/\partial t$ and this latter becomes equal to $\chi = -\psi u''$, defining the critical minimum creep rate $u''_{\mathrm{min}} = -\chi/\psi$ [Eq. (16-115)].

3. In a non-strain-hardening viscous substance whose viscosity $\phi = \partial\sigma/\partial u''$ varies with time, the instability may occur at the instant when ϕ reaches an analytic maximum [Eq. (16-119)].

16-3. Creep under Alternating Stress Superposed on Constant Stress. Leaving aside the phenomenon of fatigue associated with creep under oscillating loads of high frequencies, let us consider the creep in a metal bar kept at an elevated temperature loaded under a tensile stress σ of which the part σ_c stays constant while a certain fraction of load changes periodically at a comparatively *low* frequency ω between the amplitudes $\pm\sigma_a$:

$$\sigma = \sigma_c + \sigma_a \sin \omega t. \tag{16-132}$$

Suppose that the creep rates $u = d\varepsilon/dt$ vary with stress σ according to the hyperbolic sine speed law:

$$u = u_0 \sinh \frac{\sigma}{\sigma_0}, \tag{16-133}$$

with u_0, σ_0 as known constants. If the load were invariable, $\sigma = \sigma_c =$ const, the bar would creep with the uniform rate

$$u_c = u_0 \sinh \frac{\sigma_c}{\sigma_0}. \tag{16-134}$$

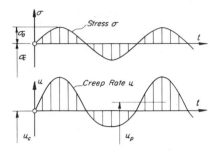

FIG. 16-38. Creep under oscillating stress.

But under the stress σ [Eq. (16-132)] the creep rates u will oscillate between the maximum and minimum values,

$$u_{\max} = u_0 \sinh \frac{\sigma_c + \sigma_a}{\sigma_0},$$

$$u_{\min} = u_0 \sinh \frac{\sigma_c - \sigma_a}{\sigma_0}, \qquad (16\text{-}135)$$

in a periodic function like the one in Fig. 16-38 in which the crest heights are greater than the valley depths measured from the horizontal line $u = u_c = \text{const}$, with the consequence that *the average creep rate* with which the bar stretches over the time of one cycle,

$$u_p = \frac{u_0}{2\pi} \int_0^{2\pi} \sinh \frac{\sigma_c + \sigma_a \sin \theta}{\sigma_0} \, d\theta, \qquad (16\text{-}136)$$

becomes greater than u_c.   Hence, the ratio $u_p/u_c > 1$ is expressed by

$$\frac{u_p}{u_c} = \frac{1}{2\pi \sinh (\sigma_c/\sigma_0)} \int_0^{2\pi} \sinh \frac{\sigma_c + \sigma_a \sin \theta}{\sigma_0} \, d\theta; \qquad (16\text{-}137)$$

since the second term in the integrant,

$$\sinh \frac{\sigma_c}{\sigma_0} \cosh \frac{\sigma_a \sin \theta}{\sigma_0} + \cosh \frac{\sigma_c}{\sigma_0} \sinh \frac{\sigma_a \sin \theta}{\sigma_0},$$

does not contribute to the integral, the ratio u_p/u_c equals

$$\frac{u_p}{u_c} = \frac{1}{2\pi} \int_0^{2\pi} \cosh \frac{\sigma_a \sin \theta}{\sigma_0} \, d\theta. \qquad (16\text{-}138)$$

If we denote $x = \sigma_a/\sigma_0$, this integral is recognized as the definition of BESSEL's function of imaginary argument ix of zero order, expressed in the form of a definite integral, namely,[1]

$$\frac{1}{2\pi} \int_0^{2\pi} \cosh (x \sin \theta) \, d\theta = \frac{1}{2\pi} \int_0^{2\pi} \cos (ix \sin \theta) \, d\theta = J_0(ix), \qquad (16\text{-}139)$$

[1] PAUL SCHAFHEITLIN, "Die Theorie der Besselschen Funktionen," p. 30, Teubner, Berlin, 1908. Bessel's function $J_0(ix)$ is given in E. JAHNKE and E. EMDE's tables; a few values are

$x =$	0	1	2	3	4	$\cdots$
$J_0(ix) =$	1	1.266	2.280	4.881	11.30	$\cdots$

the series development of which is

$$J_0(ix) = \sum_{n=0}^{\infty} \frac{(ix/2)^{2n}}{(n!)^2}$$
$$= 1 + \left(\frac{x}{2}\right)^2 + \frac{1}{(1 \cdot 2)^2}\left(\frac{x}{2}\right)^4 + \frac{1}{(1 \cdot 2 \cdot 3)^2}\left(\frac{x}{2}\right)^6 + \ldots, \quad (16\text{-}140)$$

disclosing that this even function of x increases monotonically with x.

Thus a metal bar loaded in tension under a stress σ_c, on which a sinusoidally varying stress $\sigma_a \sin \omega t$ is superposed, creeps according to the hyperbolic sine speed law $u = u_0 \sinh (\sigma/\sigma_0)$ at a faster rate u_p than the rate $u_c = u_0 \sinh (\sigma_c/\sigma_0)$ with which it would stretch under invariable stress $\sigma_c = $ const, namely, at the rate

$$u_p = u_c J_0\left(i \frac{\sigma_a}{\sigma_0}\right) \sim u_c\left[1 + \frac{1}{4}\left(\frac{\sigma_a}{\sigma_0}\right)^2\right], \quad (16\text{-}141)$$

where it suffices to take the first two terms of the series if the amplitude of the oscillating part of stress $\sigma_a < \sigma_0$.

Our evaluation of the rate of creep u_p was based on the hypothesis that the instantaneous values of the stress σ determine the rate u with which the metal creeps also under periodically changing stresses σ, that is, that the two material constants u_0 and σ_0 retain the values that they possess under steady loads. Unfortunately, very little reliable information has been substantiated or become available on the question of whether a large number of slow oscillations superposed on a comparatively small steady load σ_c may have an influence on the values of the constants u_0 and σ_0 defining the speed law

$$u = u_0 \sinh \frac{\sigma}{\sigma_0} .†$$

TAPSELL and associates[1] developed a formula for u_p, somewhat in line with the ideas just described but based on the power function speed law, that did not offer the possibility of an integration in closed form and found for a 0.26 C steel at 400°C that the experimental points grouped themselves in proper relation to those predicted for fixed creep strains by the theory. In regard to further tests on the effects of cyclic stressing and also of periodically changing temperatures superposed on a steady stress or temperature, respectively, and how they

† A few creep tests under conditions simulating the assumptions described above, made on a 14S-T aluminum alloy at 400°F up to fracture, by M. J. MANJOINE, Effect of Pulsating Loads on the Creep Characteristics of Aluminum Alloy 14S-T, Proc. ASTM, vol. 49, p. 788, 1949, confirmed at least at the higher values of the steady part of stress σ_c that the rate u_p was greater than u_c at a ratio $\sigma_a/\sigma_c = 0.1$, but at small values of σ_c creep appeared retarded ($u_p < u_c$) and lack of isotropy and rapid strain hardening encountered in this alloy may have disturbed these latter observations. J. GREENWOOD and J. NEILL, The Influence of Vibrations on the Creep of Lead, Proc. ASTM, vol. 49, p. 834, 1949, recorded a considerable increase of the creep rate u_p under superposed oscillatory stresses and that the lead recrystallized much more rapidly when $\sigma_a \sin \omega t$ was present.

[1] H. J. TAPSELL, P. G. FORREST, and G. R. TREMAIN, Creep Due to Fluctuating Stresses at Elevated Temperatures, Engineering, vol. 170, p. 189, Aug. 25, 1950.

influence the time to fracture, reference must be made to a valuable survey by S. S. MANSON, G. SACHS, and W. F. BROWN of these questions, reviewed in detail for the Joint ASTM-ASME Committee on effects of temperature on the properties of metals.[1]

16-4. Steady Creep under General States of Stress. We shall attempt to outline a theory of creep in metals for general states of stress, by laying emphasis on that ideal type of creep flow in which at any locality in a stressed body the state of stress unequivocally determines the time rates of change of the permanent unit components of strain. Presuming that equilibrium prevails, we shall assume that the external loads acting on a body are held at invariable values and that, after they were applied, a sufficiently long period of time has elapsed for the rates of permanent strain and shear to adjust to their characteristic minimum rates of creep corresponding to the components of stress. Expressed in other words, while at the instant of application of the external forces the strains are first purely elastic, it takes a certain time until the permanent rates of strain adjust themselves to their minimum values and the initially elastic state of stress readjusts itself to the new equilibrium state under which steady creep progresses indefinitely under uniform, time-independent rates of strain. Leaving aside this readjustment period, we shall be concerned only with the steady stage of slow creep distortion, making it unnecessary to include the elastic parts of strain which subsequently remain invariable with time anyway.

To avoid misinterpretations and to state this more precisely, this first-range, simplified theory of steady creep, also of relaxation of stress under general equilibrium states of stress, in this section, Sec. 16-5, and in several applications listed in Sec. 16-6 presumes: (1) a one-to-one functional interdependence between stress and the time rates of (small) permanent strain, supposing what we termed "generally viscous behavior" in solids; (2) that it excludes the phenomenon of strain hardening, the time effects of prolonged exposure to heat producing strain aging or softening in materials; and (3) that it ignores the phenomenon of creep recovery (anelastic effects), since it leaves aside the primary creep period under invariable stressing, being unable to follow up the changes occurring during the transition period of time between the purely elastic state of stress and strain upon sudden loading and the final steady stage of creep developed while the external loads are held invariable. If some of these excluded cases are to be considered, the reader is referred to the paragraphs in which they were defined. In the example of relaxation of stress in a hollow cylinder [see Sec. 16-6A (1) and (2)], however, the elastic strains must be considered besides the permanent ones.

[1] The Effect of Cyclic Heating and Loading on the Creep, Stress-rupture, and Fatigue Properties of Metals at Elevated Temperatures, 52 pp., 58 curve sheets, and 5 tables, June, 1957.

Using rectangular coordinates x, y, z; denoting the components of normal and shear stress by σ_x, σ_y, σ_z, τ_{yz}, τ_{zx}, τ_{xy}; the creep strains and unit shears, to be assumed as quite small, by ε_x, ε_y, ε_z, γ_{yz}, γ_{zx}, γ_{xy}; the equally small rates of strain by the symbols u, $u_x = \dot{\varepsilon}_x$, $u_y = \dot{\varepsilon}_y$, $u_z = \dot{\varepsilon}_z$ and of shear by the symbol v, $v_{yz} = \dot{\gamma}_{yz}$, $v_{zx} = \dot{\gamma}_{zx}$, $v_{xy} = \dot{\gamma}_{xy}$; and the components of the velocity vector by w_x, w_y, w_z, we have for the rates of creep and shear

$$u_x = \frac{\partial w_x}{\partial x}, \qquad u_y = \frac{\partial w_y}{\partial y}, \qquad u_z = \frac{\partial w_z}{\partial z},$$

$$(16\text{-}142)$$

$$v_{yz} = \frac{\partial w_y}{\partial z} + \frac{\partial w_z}{\partial y}, \qquad v_{zx} = \frac{\partial w_z}{\partial x} + \frac{\partial w_x}{\partial z}, \qquad v_{xy} = \frac{\partial w_x}{\partial y} + \frac{\partial w_y}{\partial x},$$

and the continuity relation expressing incompressibility with regard to the permanent rates of strain is

$$u_x + u_y + u_z = \frac{\partial w_x}{\partial x} + \frac{\partial w_y}{\partial y} + \frac{\partial w_z}{\partial z} = 0. \qquad (16\text{-}143)$$

When a material element is permanently deformed, the rates of shear $v = \partial\gamma/\partial t$ at any instant are proportional to the corresponding shearing stresses τ, independent of the orientation of the planes of shear or of slip:

$$v = \frac{\partial\gamma}{\partial t} = \frac{\tau}{\mu}, \qquad (16\text{-}144)$$

where *the viscosity* of the metal μ depends in any locality on the state of stress.

Assuming likewise the rates of strain produced by a single, tensile normal stress σ_x proportional to it,

$$u_x = \frac{\partial\varepsilon_x}{\partial t} = -2u_y = -2u_z = \frac{\sigma_x}{\phi}, \qquad (16\text{-}145)$$

since the maximum rate of shear and maximum shearing stress are $u_x - u_y = (\tfrac{3}{2})u_x$, $\tau_{\max} = \sigma_x/2 = \phi u_x/2 = (\tfrac{3}{2})\mu u_x$, obviously the measure of viscosity ϕ is

$$\phi = 3\mu. \qquad (16\text{-}146)$$

Consequently, when σ_x, σ_y, σ_z act simultaneously, they produce the rates of strain

$$u_x = \frac{\partial w_x}{\partial x} = \frac{1}{3\mu}\left(\sigma_x - \frac{\sigma_y + \sigma_z}{2}\right),$$

$$u_y = \frac{\partial w_y}{\partial y} = \frac{1}{3\mu}\left(\sigma_y - \frac{\sigma_z + \sigma_x}{2}\right), \qquad (16\text{-}147)$$

$$u_z = \frac{\partial w_z}{\partial z} = \frac{1}{3\mu}\left(\sigma_z - \frac{\sigma_x + \sigma_y}{2}\right),$$

and to these come the relations for the shearing stress components:

$$v_{yz} = \frac{\partial w_y}{\partial z} + \frac{\partial w_z}{\partial y} = \frac{\tau_{yz}}{\mu}, \ldots \qquad (16\text{-}148)$$

The preceding six relations may be condensed to one equation if one makes use of the deviatoral part of the stress tensor symbolically expressed by D_σ, as defined in Vol. I, Eq. (14-46), page 163, and denotes the deviator of rates of strain by D,

$$D_\sigma = 2\mu D, \qquad (16\text{-}149)$$

equivalent to stating that

$$
\begin{aligned}
\sigma_x - \sigma &= 2\mu u_x, & \tau_{yz} &= \mu v_{yz}, \\
\sigma_y - \sigma &= 2\mu u_y, & \tau_{zx} &= \mu v_{zx}, \\
\sigma_z - \sigma &= 2\mu u_z, & \tau_{xy} &= \mu v_{xy},
\end{aligned}
\qquad (16\text{-}150)
$$

where σ denotes the mean stress $\sigma = (\tfrac{1}{3})(\sigma_x + \sigma_y + \sigma_z)$.

Assuming in the steady stage of small creep for the general measures of the intensity of stress and rate of creep distortion the octahedral shear stress τ_{oct} and rate of shear $v_{\text{oct}} = \partial\gamma_{\text{oct}}/\partial t$ defined by

$$
\begin{aligned}
\tau_{\text{oct}}^2 &= \frac{1}{9}\left[(\sigma_1 - \sigma_2)^2 - (\sigma_2 - \sigma_3)^2 + (\sigma_3 - \sigma_1)^2\right], \\
v_{\text{oct}}^2 &= \frac{4}{9}\left[(u_1 - u_2)^2 + (u_2 - u_3)^2 + (u_3 - u_1)^2\right],
\end{aligned}
\qquad (16\text{-}151)
$$

where σ_1, σ_2, σ_3 and u_1, u_2, u_3 are the principal stresses and rates of strain, we shall postulate that τ_{oct} is a known function of v_{oct}:

$$\tau_{\text{oct}} = f(v_{\text{oct}}). \qquad (16\text{-}152)[1]$$

Since, according to Eq. (16-144), any $\tau = \mu v$, this speed law defines *the viscosity* μ in the material,

$$\mu = \frac{\tau_{\text{oct}}}{v_{\text{oct}}} = \frac{f(v_{\text{oct}})}{v_{\text{oct}}}, \qquad (16\text{-}153)$$

[1] That the speed law postulated in Eq. (16-152) is valid in the steady stage of creep in solids is based, apart from creep tests under combined stresses, on the observations on creep values obtained *in tests made in axial compression* which disclosed essentially the main features of those found in *tensile tests*, thus proving that the fundamental law is controlled by the behavior under pure or simple shear. See papers on creep in compression by C. S. LANDAU and A. R. EDWARDS, Aeronaut. Research Lab. of Australia, Met. Note 6, January, 1957; also H. T. GREENAWAY, *ibid.*, SM 195, June, 1952; A. H. SULLY, Prod. Eng., vol. 24, no. 4, p. 150, April, 1953; and N. P. ALLEN and W. E. CARRINGTON, J. Inst. Metals, vol. 82, p. 525, July, 1954.

while the six components of stress must satisfy the three conditions of equilibrium:

$$\frac{\partial \sigma_x}{\partial x} + \frac{\partial \tau_{xy}}{\partial y} + \frac{\partial \tau_{xz}}{\partial z} = 0, \dots \qquad (16\text{-}154)$$

The six components of rate of strain $u_x, \dots, v_{yz}, \dots$ may be eliminated after substituting their expressions from Eqs. (16-150) in the three compatibility conditions of the form

$$\frac{\partial^2 u_x}{\partial y^2} + \frac{\partial^2 u_y}{\partial x^2} = \frac{\partial^2 v_{xy}}{\partial x\, \partial y}, \dots, \qquad (16\text{-}155)$$

supplying three equations containing the six stress components and the viscosity μ. Together with the three equilibrium conditions [Eqs. (16-154)] and the speed law of Eq. (16-153), these represent seven equations for the seven aforementioned unknowns, but their general treatment is prohibitive unless a workable expression for the speed law is available and symmetry conditions in special states of stress simplify the two equations (16-151) for $\tau_{\text{oct}}, v_{\text{oct}}$ in terms of the stresses and rates of strain.

16-5. Steady Creep in Plane Strain. In two-dimensional flow parallel to the x,y plane ($w_z = u_z = v_{yz} = v_{zx} = 0$), in incompressible material $u_y = -u_x$, since $\sigma_z = (\frac{1}{2})(\sigma_x + \sigma_y)$, $\tau_{yz} = \tau_{zx} = 0$, the three nonvanishing rates of strain and shear are

$$u_x = -u_y = \frac{1}{4\mu}(\sigma_x - \sigma_y), \qquad v = \frac{\tau}{\mu}, \qquad (16\text{-}156)$$

where we wrote $v_{xy} = v$, $\tau_{xy} = \tau$. The three unknown components of stress σ_x, σ_y, τ must satisfy the two conditions of equilibrium,

$$\frac{\partial \sigma_x}{\partial x} + \frac{\partial \tau}{\partial y} = 0, \qquad \frac{\partial \sigma_y}{\partial y} + \frac{\partial \tau}{\partial x} = 0, \qquad (16\text{-}157)$$

and the condition of compatibility

$$\frac{\partial^2 u_x}{\partial y^2} + \frac{\partial^2 u_y}{\partial x^2} = \frac{\partial^2 v}{\partial x\, \partial y}, \qquad (16\text{-}158)$$

which with Eqs. (16-156) takes the form

$$\left(\frac{\partial^2}{\partial y^2} - \frac{\partial^2}{\partial x^2} \right) \left(\frac{\sigma_x - \sigma_y}{4\mu} \right) = \frac{\partial^2}{\partial x\, \partial y} \left(\frac{\tau}{\mu} \right). \qquad (16\text{-}159)$$

The octahedral shearing stress τ_{oct} and rate of shear v_{oct} in a state of plane strain differ in their expressions only by a numerical factor from those of the maximum shearing stress τ_{max} and maximum rate of shear v_{max}, respectively, which are

$$\tau_{oct}^2 = \frac{2}{3}\left[\frac{(\sigma_x - \sigma_y)^2}{4} + \tau^2\right]$$

$$= \frac{2}{3}\tau_{max}^2, \qquad (16\text{-}160)$$

$$v_{oct}^2 = \frac{2}{3}(4u_x^2 + v^2)$$

$$= \frac{2}{3}v_{max}^2, \qquad (16\text{-}161)$$

and one verifies after substituting the values of u_x and v from Eq. (16-156) in the last equation that, indeed,

$$\tau_{oct} = \mu v_{oct}, \qquad \tau_{max} = \mu v_{max}. \qquad (16\text{-}162)$$

We have now to introduce the speed law relating τ_{oct} to the rate of shear v_{oct}. Suppose, for illustration, that the speed law $\tau_{oct} = f(v_{oct})$ were expressible by a power function:

$$\tau_{oct} = cv_{oct}^m, \qquad (0 < m \leq 1). \qquad (16\text{-}163)$$

This is equivalent to stating that *the material possesses a viscosity μ* that varies with the intensity of stress according to the function

$$\mu = c^{1/m}\tau_{oct}^{-(1-m)/m} = c^{1/m}\left[\frac{2}{3}\left(\frac{(\sigma_x - \sigma_y)^2}{4} + \tau^2\right)\right]^{-(1-m)/2m} \qquad (16\text{-}164)$$

If this expression for μ is substituted in the compatibility condition [Eq. (16-159)], then for the three unknown components of stress σ_x, σ_y, τ three equations have been established determining steady creep flow in plane strain, namely,

$$\left(\frac{\partial^2}{\partial y^2} - \frac{\partial^2}{\partial x^2}\right)\left((\sigma_x - \sigma_y)[(\sigma_x - \sigma_y)^2 + 4\tau^2]^{(1-m)/2m}\right)$$

$$= 4\frac{\partial^2}{\partial x\,\partial y}\left(\tau \cdot [(\sigma_x - \sigma_y)^2 + 4\tau^2]^{(1-m)/2m}\right) \qquad (16\text{-}165)$$

and the two equilibrium equations (16-157). The latter may be satisfied by an Airy stress function $F(x,y)$ by letting

$$\sigma_x = \frac{\partial^2 F}{\partial y^2} = F_{yy}, \qquad \sigma_y = \frac{\partial^2 F}{\partial x^2} + F_{xx}, \qquad \tau = -\frac{\partial^2 F}{\partial x\,\partial y} = -F_{xy}, \qquad (16\text{-}166)$$

and one sees that Eq. (16-165) prescribes for $F(x,y)$ the fourth-order, nonlinear, partial differential equation

$$\left(\frac{\partial^2}{\partial y^2} - \frac{\partial^2}{\partial x^2}\right)\left((F_{yy} - F_{xx})[(F_{yy} - F_{xx})^2 + 4F_{xy}^2]^{(1-m)/2m}\right)$$

$$+ 4\frac{\partial^2}{\partial x\,\partial y}\left(F_{xy}[(F_{yy} - F_{xx})^2 + 4F_{xy}^2]^{(1-m)/2m}\right) = 0. \qquad (16\text{-}167)$$

If the power exponent m equals unity, $m = 1$, this last equation reduces to the linear, biharmonic, partial differential equation of fourth order:

$$\Delta\Delta F = F_{xxxx} + 2F_{xxyy} + F_{yyyy} = 0, \qquad (16\text{-}168)$$

valid for the purely viscous substance, having invariable viscosity $\mu = \text{const}$, in agreement with the theory developed for it in Vol. I, Eq. (26-23), page 399.

If the exponent in the speed law $m = \frac{1}{3}$, an interesting special case occurs in that the exponent $(1 - m)/2m$ appearing in Eq. (16-167) becomes equal to unity, which may possibly permit further treatment, in spite of leaving the equation of higher than first degree. In this special case the viscosity of the substance μ is inversely proportional to the square of τ_{oct} or τ_{max}. If $m = \frac{1}{2}$, μ varies inversely with the first power of τ_{oct}.

16-6. Rotationally Symmetric Cases of Creep. A. Radial Flow in a Hollow Cylinder. (1) *Steady creep in hollow cylinder under internal pressure.* In case that rotational symmetry prevails, the evaluation of steady creep in states of plane strain becomes very simple. Following the outline of theory presented in the preceding section, consider the creep in a hollow cylinder having closed ends and stressed by an internal pressure $p = \text{const}$, held invariable. The axial rate of strain vanishes in this case, $u_z = 0$, and, if w denotes the radial velocity in the radial distance r; u_r, u_t the permanent rates of strain; and σ_r, σ_t the normal stresses in the radial and circumferential directions, we have in incompressible material

$$u_r = \frac{dw}{dr}, \qquad u_t = \frac{w}{r}, \qquad u_z = 0,$$

$$u_r = -u_t = -\frac{\sigma_t - \sigma_r}{4\mu} = -\frac{c_1}{r^2}, \qquad (16\text{-}169)$$

having satisfied the compatibility condition

$$\frac{d(ru_t)}{dr} = u_r, \qquad (16\text{-}170)$$

with c_1 as integration constant. Furthermore,

$$\tau_{\text{oct}} = \sqrt{\frac{2}{3}}\,\tau_{\text{max}} = \frac{\sigma_t - \sigma_r}{\sqrt{6}},$$

$$v_{\text{oct}} = \sqrt{\frac{2}{3}}\,v_{\text{max}} = \sqrt{\frac{2}{3}}\,(u_t - u_r) = \sqrt{\frac{2}{3}} \cdot \frac{2c_1}{r^2}; \qquad (16\text{-}171)$$

after introducing the speed law, using Eqs. (16-163) and (16-164) with c as a material constant,

$$\tau_{\text{oct}} = cv_{\text{oct}}^m, \qquad \mu = c^{1/m} \tau_{\text{oct}}^{-(1-m)/m} = c^{1/m} \left(\frac{\sigma_t - \sigma_r}{\sqrt{6}} \right)^{-(1-m)/m}, \qquad (16\text{-}172)$$

one deduces from the two expressions for

$$\sigma_t - \sigma_r = \sqrt{6} \cdot c^{1/(1-m)} \cdot \mu^{-m/(1-m)},$$
$$\sigma_t - \sigma_r = \frac{4\mu c_1}{r^2}, \qquad\qquad (16\text{-}173)$$

that the viscosity μ in the hollow cylinder must amount to

$$\mu = c \left[\sqrt{\frac{3}{2}} \cdot \frac{r^2}{2c_1} \right]^{1-m}. \qquad (16\text{-}174)$$

After substituting this value of μ in the condition of equilibrium,

$$\frac{d\sigma_r}{dr} = \frac{\sigma_t - \sigma_r}{r} = \frac{4\mu c_1}{r^3} = \frac{2mC_1}{r^{2m+1}}, \qquad (16\text{-}175)$$

where C_1 was written for the combination of constants,

$$C_1 = \left(\frac{3}{2} \right)^{(1-m)/2} \cdot \frac{c}{m} \cdot (2c_1)^m, \qquad (16\text{-}176)$$

one obtains for the radial stress

$$\sigma_r = -C_1 r^{-2m} + C_2, \qquad (16\text{-}177)$$

C_1, C_2 representing two integration constants which are determined in a cylinder of inner and outer radii a and b from the conditions $r = a$, $\sigma_r = -p$, and for $r = b$, $\sigma_r = 0$, with the result that the radial and tangential stresses σ_r and σ_t in the steady stage of creep are found equal to

$$\sigma_r = -\frac{pa^{2m}}{b^{2m} - a^{2m}} \left(\frac{b^{2m}}{r^{2m}} - 1 \right),$$
$$\sigma_t = \frac{d(r\sigma_r)}{dr} = \frac{pa^{2m}}{b^{2m} - a^{2m}} \left[-(1 - 2m) \frac{b^{2m}}{r^{2m}} + 1 \right], \qquad (16\text{-}178)$$

and the axial stress σ_z is equal to:

$$\sigma_z = \frac{\sigma_r + \sigma_t}{2} = -\frac{pma^{2m}b^{2m}}{(b^{2m} - a^{2m})r^{2m}}. \qquad (16\text{-}179)$$

The mean value of the axial stress $\bar{\sigma}_z$ over the tube wall turns out to be independent of the exponent m, namely,

$$\bar{\sigma}_z = \frac{pa^2}{b^2 - a^2}, \qquad (16\text{-}180)$$

as required in a tube with closed ends.

The stress formulas [Eqs. (16-178)] disclose that, when the exponent $m = \frac{1}{2}$, the steady tangential stresses σ_t are *uniformly* distributed over the tube wall, that $\sigma_t =$ const, and the practically important result that, when $0 < m < \frac{1}{2}$, the absolutely *greatest tensile*, circumferential, normal *stress σ_t occurs at the outside surface $r = b$* of the cylinder. Since in Eqs. (16-178), C_1 equals

$$C_1 = \frac{pa^{2m}b^{2m}}{b^{2m} - a^{2m}}, \qquad (16\text{-}181)$$

by equating this with the former expression for C_1 given in Eq. (16-176), this determines the constant c_1 appearing in the creep rate $u_t = c_1/r^2 = w/r$ and thereby *the uniform, steady, radial velocity w* with which *the hollow cylinder* expands in the bore $r = a$:

$$w = \frac{c_1}{a} = \left(\frac{2}{3}\right)^{(1-m)/2m} \cdot \left(\frac{mC_1}{c}\right)^{1/m} \cdot \frac{1}{2a}. \qquad (16\text{-}182)$$

When the exponent in the power function speed law is $m = 1$, Eqs. (16-178) coincide with the Lamé formulas for the purely viscous substance $\mu =$ const.

The reader will recognize *the complete analogy* between the preceding relations describing the steady state of creep in a hollow cylinder, based on the monotonic speed law

$$\tau_{\text{oct}} = f(v_{\text{oct}}) = cv_{\text{oct}}^m \qquad (16\text{-}183)$$

and those which were developed *for the plastic flow in a cylinder of a strain-hardening metal* in Vol. I, page 450, yielding under the monotonic strain-hardening function

$$\tau_{\text{oct}} = f(\gamma_{\text{oct}}) = c\gamma_{\text{oct}}^m, \qquad (16\text{-}184)$$

valid in both cases for the fully developed stage (steady creep, complete yielding) of flow. The analogy results from the fact that the rates of strain and shear in the first case,

rates of strain: $u_r,\ u_t,\ v,\ v_{\text{oct}}$, velocity w,

and the permanent strains and shears in the second case,

strains: $\varepsilon_r,\ \varepsilon_t,\ \gamma,\ \gamma_{\text{oct}}$, displacement ρ,

are expressed, respectively, in terms of the radial velocity w or the displacement ρ and of the components of stress by similar formulas.

(2). *Relaxation of stress in a hollow cylinder.* Assume a long, heavy-walled metal cylinder that has been slightly expanded radially, elastically by shrink-fitting on a rigid shaft, exerting a certain pressure in its contact surface. If this assembly is held at a moderately elevated temperature, the ensuing creep strains cause a gradual evanescence of the press-fit pressure p and of the stresses σ_r, σ_t in the cylinder, while the small radial enlargement ρ_a of the inner radius $r = a$ remains constant, changing from an elastic to a permanent enlargement. EVAN A. DAVIS[1] solved this relaxation problem for a cylinder in which a state of plane strain prevails, characterized by the conditions that the axial strain vanishes, $\varepsilon_z = 0$, that the solid is strictly incompressible with respect to any elastic or permanent part of strain, and that it deforms in a generally viscous manner, possessing a viscosity μ that varies with the intensity of stress according to a power function speed law [Eq. (16-172)].

In a radially expanded cylinder of a strictly incompressible substance, the small, radial enlargements ρ of the radii r obviously are proportional to the enlargement ρ_a of the inner radius a and inversely proportional to r,

$$\rho = \sqrt{r^2 + 2a\rho_a + \rho_a^2} - r \cong r\left[\sqrt{1 + \frac{2a\rho_a}{r^2}} - 1\right] \cong \frac{\rho_a a}{r},$$

independently of the laws of deformation that prevail for the elastic parts of strain and for the permanent rates of strain and from the elapsed time t. Since the radial displacements ρ do not change with time, the radial velocities w,

$$w = \frac{\partial \rho}{\partial t} = \frac{\partial \rho_a}{\partial t} \cdot \frac{a}{r} = 0,$$

vanish at all times t and radii r, and all material points in the cylinder of a totally incompressible substance during relaxation stagnate in their positions taken in the initial, elastic state, namely,

$$\rho = \rho_i = \frac{a^2 b^2 p_i}{2G(b^2 - a^2)r}, \qquad (0 \leqq t < \infty),$$

where the subscript i refers to the time $t = 0$.

Denoting the sum and difference of stress by the abbreviating symbols s and S, designating the two, unknown, dependent variables,

$$s = \sigma_t + \sigma_r, \qquad S = \sigma_t - \sigma_r,$$

the initial, purely elastic state of stress in the cylinder at the beginning of relaxation, at time $t = 0$, is expressed by the LAMÉ formulas

$$\sigma_r = -\frac{a^2 p_i}{b^2 - a^2}\left(\frac{b^2}{r^2} - 1\right) \qquad S_i = \frac{2a^2 b^2 p_i}{(b^2 - a^2)r^2}$$

$$\sigma_t = \frac{a^2 p_i}{b^2 - a^2}\left(\frac{b^2}{r^2} + 1\right), \qquad s_i = \frac{2a^2 p_i}{b^2 - a^2},$$

creating the radial displacements

$$\rho = \frac{(\sigma_t - \sigma_r)r}{4G} = \frac{S_i r}{4G} = \rho_a \frac{a}{r}, \qquad \rho_a = \frac{S_i r^2}{4Ga} = \frac{ab^2 p_i}{2(b^2 - a^2)G}.$$

[1] Relaxation of a Cylinder on a Rigid Shaft, ASME Annual Meeting, Paper 59-A-31, 1959.

Affix one and two primes to the symbols representing the elastic and the permanent part of the time rates of strain denoted by $u = \partial \varepsilon / \partial t$. Remembering that the radial velocity $w = 0$ vanishes throughout the cylinder, one sees that the total rates of strain

$$u_t = u_t' + u_t'' = \frac{w}{r} = 0,$$

$$u_r = u_r' + u_r'' = \frac{\partial w}{\partial r} = 0$$

must vanish at all points at all times t and, after substituting therein the stress–rate-of-strain relations valid in the generally viscoelastic substance,

$$u_t' = -u_r' = \frac{1}{4G} \cdot \frac{\partial(\sigma_t - \sigma_r)}{\partial t} = \frac{1}{4G} \frac{\partial S}{\partial t},$$

$$u_t'' = -u_r'' = \frac{\sigma_t - \sigma_r}{4\mu} = \frac{S}{4\mu},$$

that either of the conditions $u_r = 0$ or $u_t = 0$ supplies for the determination of the unknown stress difference $S = \sigma_t = \sigma_r$ the partial differential equation

$$\frac{\partial S}{\partial t} + \frac{G}{\mu} \cdot S = 0.$$

Under the power function speed law [Eq. (16-172)] equivalent to supposing

$$\tau_{\text{oct}} = \tau_0 \left(\frac{v_{\text{oct}}}{v_0} \right)^m, \qquad (0 \leqq m \leqq 1),$$

with τ_0, v_0, m as material constants, with the rate of permanent shear $v_{\text{oct}} = u_t'' - u_r''$ and $\tau_{\text{oct}} = (\sigma_t - \sigma_r)/\sqrt{6} = S/\sqrt{6}$, the viscosity μ equals

$$\mu = \frac{\tau_{\text{oct}}}{v_{\text{oct}}} = \frac{\tau_0^{1/m}}{v_0} \left(\frac{S}{\sqrt{6}} \right)^{-(1-m)/m}.$$

One deduces that, after substituting this value of μ in the partial differential equation for S and integrating, using the initial condition that, for $t = 0$, $S = S_i = 2a^2b^2 p_i/(b^2 - a^2)r^2$, the unknown stress difference S in its dependence on the variables r and t is determined by

$$S = \sigma_t - \sigma_r = \frac{S_i}{(1 + [(1/m) - 1] \cdot (Gv_0/\tau_0^{1/m}) \cdot S_i^{(1-m)/m} t)^{m/(1-m)}}.$$

It is worth noting that this function is built perfectly analogously to the formula obtained for the relaxation under a *simple, uniaxial tension*

σ [Eq. (16-36), page 522] by postulating a speed law $\sigma = \sigma_0(u''/u_0)^m$, namely,

$$\sigma = \frac{\sigma_i}{(1 + [(1/m) - 1] \cdot (Eu_0/\sigma_0^{1/m}) \cdot \sigma_i^{(1-m)/m} t)^{m/(1-m)}},$$

the former expression being obtained from the latter by writing, instead of the quantities

$$E, u_0, \sigma_0, \sigma, \sigma_i,$$

the quantities

$$G, v_0, \tau_0, S, S_i.$$

The second unknown, the stress sum $s = \sigma_t + \sigma_r$, is prescribed through the condition of equilibrium of the stresses σ_r, σ_t,

$$\frac{\partial(r\sigma_r)}{\partial r} - \sigma_t = 0,$$

which in terms of the variables S and s takes the form of the partial differential equation

$$r^2 \frac{\partial s}{\partial r} = \frac{\partial}{\partial r}(r^2 S).$$

In order to integrate it, for the sake of simplicity let

$$n = \frac{m}{1-m} \quad (0 < n < \infty), \qquad c_0 = \frac{2a^2 b^2 p}{b^2 - a^2}, \qquad C = \frac{G v_0 c_0^{1/n}}{n \tau_0^{(n+1)/n}};$$

then

$$S = \frac{c_0}{(r^{2/n} + Ct)^n}, \qquad r^2 S = \frac{c_0}{(1 + Cr^{-2/n}t)^n}$$

and

$$\frac{\partial s}{\partial r} = \frac{2Cc_0 t}{r(r^{2/n} + Ct)^{n+1}},$$

from which

$$s = \sigma_t + \sigma_r = 2Cc_0 t \int \frac{dr}{r(r^{2/n} + Ct)^{n+1}} + f(t). \qquad (16\text{-}185)$$

The integral may be evaluated in closed form when n is an integer, $n = 0, 1, 2, \ldots$, or when $m = 0, \frac{1}{2}, \frac{2}{3}, \ldots$, and the arbitrary function $f(t)$ is defined through the boundary condition that, for $r = b$, on the outer, free surface of the cylinder $\sigma_r = 0$ or that for $r = b$

$$s_b = S_b = (\sigma_t)_{r=b}.$$

For further details as to examples of the distribution of the radial and tangential stresses σ_r, σ_t at prescribed times t in cylinders for which $b/a = 4$, and the curves along which the press-fit pressure p decays with time t, the reader is referred to the paper by DAVIS quoted above.

B. Stresses around a Cylindrical Cavity.   In an extended body let a uniform stress $\sigma_r = \sigma = $ const act when r tends to increase indefinitely.   If the body contains a cylindrical cavity of radius $r = r_1$, one finds in the steady stage of creep following the power function speed law [Eq. (16-183)] that the radial and tangential stresses are now given by the formulas

$$\sigma_r = \sigma\left[1 - \left(\frac{r_1}{r}\right)^{2m}\right],$$

$$\sigma_t = \sigma\left[1 + (2m - 1)\left(\frac{r_1}{r}\right)^{2m}\right].$$

Around the surface of the cylindrical cavity the tangential stress being equal to $r = r_1$, $\sigma_t = 2m\sigma$, we note that the ratio

$$k = \frac{\sigma_t}{\sigma} = 2m \qquad (16\text{-}186)$$

will be greater than unity, as long as the exponent m of the power function speed law is $\frac{1}{2} < m < 1$, and that *a stress concentration under steady creep occurs measured by the factor* $k = 2m$ under these circumstances.   Since in an *elastic* body, upon applying the stress σ, k equals $k = 2$, after the redistribution of the stresses in the body due to creep, the *stress-concentration factor has been reduced to the value* $k = 2m$ smaller than 2, *except* in the case when $m = 1$, in *a purely viscous substance*, when $k = 2$ remains unchanged.

The uniform, steady, radial velocity w with which the cavity expands is given by

$$r = r_1, \qquad w = \left(\frac{2}{3}\right)^{(1-m)/2m} \cdot \frac{r_1}{2} \cdot \left(\frac{m\sigma}{c}\right)^{1/m}. \qquad (16\text{-}187)$$

The distribution of the radial and tangential stresses σ_r, σ_t may be seen in Fig. 16-39 for a few values of m.   When $m = \frac{1}{2}$, the tangential stresses σ_t are redistributed in a uniform manner over the body,

$$\sigma_r = \sigma\left(1 - \frac{r_1}{r}\right), \qquad \sigma_t = \sigma = \text{const},$$

and, when $m < \frac{1}{2}$, σ_t becomes even smaller than σ.

C. Concentration of Stress around a Circular Hole in a Thin, Plane Disk in a Steady Stage of Creep or in a Plastic State of Stress While the Disk Is Stretched Uniformly.   Supposing that an infinite sheet of equal thickness is loaded on its periphery by a uniform tensile stress $\sigma = $ const, this creates a state of plane stress in which the axial stress σ_z vanishes.

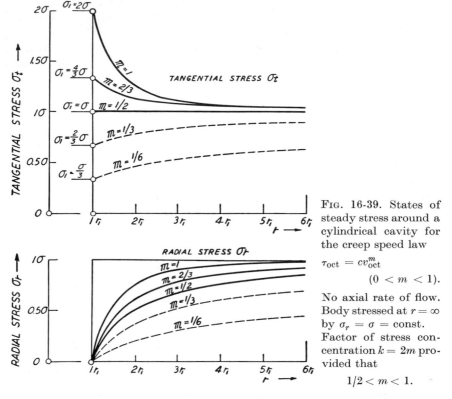

FIG. 16-39. States of steady stress around a cylindrical cavity for the creep speed law

$$\tau_{oct} = c v_{oct}^{m}$$

$$(0 < m < 1).$$

No axial rate of flow. Body stressed at $r = \infty$ by $\sigma_r = \sigma = $ const. Factor of stress concentration $k = 2m$ provided that

$$1/2 < m < 1.$$

The evaluation of the radial and tangential stresses σ_r and σ_t *in a stage of steady creep* is a little more involved than in the preceding cases, and we shall state only the formulas for the distribution of stress in parametric form, using a parameter ω, defined by letting

$$\omega = \frac{\sigma_t - \sigma_r}{\sigma_{t,}},$$

ω varying when $r_1 < r < \infty$ as $1 \geqq \omega \geqq 0$, postulating[1] the power

[1] Cf. Author's paper: On the Creep of Solids at Elevated Temperatures, J. Appl. Phys., vol. 8, pp. 418–432, June, 1937. Since the octahedral shearing stress τ_{oct} in a state of plane stress of radial symmetry equals

$$\tau_{oct} = \tfrac{1}{3} \sqrt{2(\sigma_t^2 - \sigma_t \sigma_r + \sigma_r^2)}$$

while at $r = r_1$, $\sigma_r = 0$ and at $r = \infty$, $\sigma_r = \sigma_t = \sigma$, we see that τ_{oct} at both ends of the interval $r_1 < r < \infty$ equals $\tau_{oct} = \sqrt{2} \cdot \sigma_t/3$. We availed ourselves of postulating this last expression for τ_{oct} over the entire disk, a simplification that is equivalent to replacing the short arc of the plasticity ellipse by a secant situated very near to the ellipse.

function creep law $\tau_{\text{oct}} = cv_{\text{oct}}^m$ $(0 \leqq m \leqq 1)$:

$$\sigma_r = \sigma(1 - \omega)\left[1 + \frac{(1 - 3m)\omega}{1 + 3m}\right]^{2m/(1-3m)},$$

$$\sigma_t = \sigma\left[1 + \frac{(1 - 3m)\omega}{1 + 3m}\right]^{2m/(1-3m)} \qquad (16\text{-}188)$$

$$\left(\frac{r_1}{r}\right)^{3m+1} = \omega^{m+1}\left[\frac{1 + 3m + (1 - 3m)\omega}{2}\right]^{4m/(1-3m)}$$

At the circumference of the hole $r = r_1$, by letting $\omega = 1$, the formula for $\sigma_t = k\sigma$ leads to a *factor of stress concentration*

$$k = \left(\frac{2}{1 + 3m}\right)^{2m/(1-3m)}, \qquad (16\text{-}188a)$$

giving for the exponents m the values of k:

$m =$	1	$\frac{2}{3}$	$\frac{1}{2}$	$\frac{1}{3}$	$\frac{1}{4}$	$\frac{1}{5}$	$\frac{1}{6}$	0
$k =$	2	1.72	1.56	1.40	1.31	1.25	1.21	1

which differ little from the approximate expression

$$k \sim m + 1, \qquad (16\text{-}188b)$$

as may be seen in Fig. 16-41. The two extreme cases $m = 1$, $k = 2$, and $m = 0$, $k = 1$ obviously correspond to a *purely viscous material* (viscosity $\mu = $ const) and to *the ideally plastic substance* [yielding under the invariable yield stress $\tau_{\text{oct}} = (\sqrt{2}/3)\sigma_0 = $ const, σ_0 yield stress in tension], respectively. Figure 16-40 illustrates the distribution of radial and tangential stress around the circular hole due to steady creep in an infinite sheet.

B. BUDIANSKY and O. L. MANGASARIAN[1] have developed along somewhat similar trends of thoughts exact relations expressing the factor of stress concentration k for the case when the material of the perforated, infinite sheet is in *the completely plastic stage* of yielding, deforming under uniaxial stress, however, according to a three-parametric strain-hardening curve originally proposed by RAMBERG and OSGOOD,[2]

$$\varepsilon = \frac{\sigma}{E}\left[1 + \frac{3}{7}\left(\frac{\sigma}{\sigma_1}\right)^{n-1}\right], \qquad (n \geqq 1) \qquad (16\text{-}188c)$$

(σ_1 is a nominal yield stress constant), and by postulating what they termed a "deformation theory of flow" (not utilizing incremental plastic stress-strain

[1] Plastic Stress Concentration at a Circular Hole in an Infinite Sheet Subjected to Equal Biaxial Tension, Office of Naval Research Contract Nonr 1866(02), Tech. Rept. 3, 16 pp., Harvard University, Division of Engineering and Applied Physics, December, 1958.

[2] WALTER RAMBERG and WILLIAM B. OSGOOD, Description of Stress Strain Curves by Three Parameters, Natl. Advisory Comm. Aeronaut., Tech. Note 902, 1943.

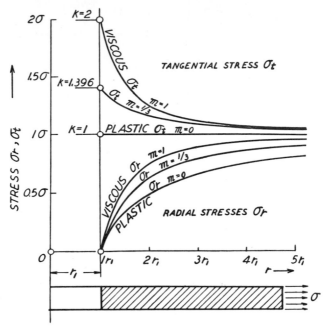

Fig. 16-40. Stresses around hole in disk in viscous ($m = 1$), in creeping ($1 > m > 0$), and in plastic ($m = 0$) substance. Stress concentration factor: $k = [2/(1 + 3m)]^{2m/(1-3m)}$

relations), finding for the plastic stress concentration factor k at the bore $r = r_1$, when the ratio σ_∞/σ_1 (σ_∞ is the stress σ at $r = \infty$) tends to approach infinity, the remarkable expression solely dependent on their power exponent n:

$$k = \left(\frac{n + 3}{2n}\right)^{(n+3)/(n^2+3)} \cdot e^{\pi(n-1)/\sqrt{3}(n^2+3)}. \qquad (16\text{-}188d)$$

This corresponds to the situation in which the elastic strains are negligible compared with the plastic strains, i.e., when the uniaxial stress-strain (the plastic

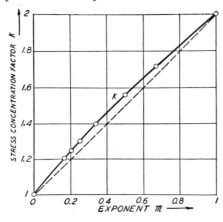

Fig. 16-41. Factor of stress concentration

$k = [2/(1 + 3m)]^{2m/(1-3m)}$

plotted *versus* exponent m of speed law $\tau_{\text{oct}} = cv_{\text{oct}}^m$ for disk with hole.

strain-hardening function) curve obeys a pure power law $\varepsilon = c_0 \sigma^n$. For purely elastic behavior, when $n = 1$, k equals 2.

Since for a pure power function law the plastic distribution of stress, as was shown by A. A. ILYUSHIN,[1] varies linearly, proportionally with the applied, external loading (with the stress σ_∞ at $r = \infty$), with all stresses at various points in the disk retaining a constant ratio to each other, the factor of stress concentration k turns out to be independent of the applied stress, conforming with Eqs. (16-188) found by the author for steady creep and Eq. (16-188d) developed for plastic flow. But if the three-parametric flow function [Eq. (16-188c)] is fully valid, the stress concentration factor k varies (while the exponent n is held constant) also with the external load σ_∞, between the values $2 > k > 1$, and the evaluation of k corresponding to prescribed ratios σ_∞/σ_1 becomes rather complex, requiring numerical integrations by a digital computer. It has not been ascertained how closely the two analytic expressions [Eqs. (16-188a) and (16-188d)] derived independently for a pure power function law of deformation check with each other.

D. CREEP IN REVOLVING DE LAVAL TURBINE DISK. In the body of the well-known solid *de Laval steam turbine wheel of equal strength*, not having a central aperture and carrying a heavy rim to which the blades are attached, the radial and tangential stresses take on uniform values $\sigma_r = \sigma_t = \sigma = $ const under the action of the centrifugal body forces. If h denotes the variable thickness of the disk, h_0 the value of h at the axis of revolution $r = 0$, r the variable radius, ω the angular velocity, γ the specific weight of material, g the acceleration of gravity, the condition of equilibrium

$$\frac{d}{dr}(rh\sigma_r) - h\sigma_t = -\frac{\gamma\omega^2 h r^2}{g},$$ (16-189)

by letting $\sigma_r = \sigma_t = \sigma = $ const and $c = \gamma\omega^2/g\sigma$,

$$\frac{dh}{dr} = -crh$$ (16-189a)

determines the exponential profile of the disk of equal strength:

$$h = h_0 e^{-cr^2/2}.$$ (16-190)

Since in the steady stage of creep the peripheral and radial rates of creep are equal to

$$u_r = u_t = \frac{\sigma}{6\mu} = \text{const},$$ (16-190a)

one sees that a de Laval rotating wheel creeps under any speed law at half the rate with which a tensile bar would stretch under the same stress σ, namely, $u = \sigma/3\mu$.

E. CREEP IN ROTATING DISK OF UNIFORM THICKNESS. The rapidly turning disks running at the high admission temperatures in steam turbines may suffer permanent displacements in the radial directions because of the slow creep in the stressed metal. Their designers wish to ascertain that such disks will not expand in their plane by excessive amounts, because the wheels usually run with quite small radial

[1] The Theory of Small Elastic-plastic Deformations, Priklad. Math. i Mekhan., vol. 10, pp. 347–356, 1946.

clearances in the steel casing. If parts of their rim should come in contact with the stationary parts of the turbine, the heat evolved through the sliding friction would cause dangerous overheating when the disk started to rub against the casing wall. The evaluation of radial distortion due to creep has therefore attracted various investigators.

For simplicity's sake let us assume a disk of uniform thickness having a central aperture, supposing that both cylindrical surfaces at the inside and outside radii r_1 and r_2 are unloaded. While in a thin disk $\sigma_z = 0$, the rates of creep are

$$u_r = \frac{dw}{dr} = \frac{1}{6\mu}(2\sigma_r - \sigma_t),$$

$$u_t = \frac{w}{r} = \frac{1}{6\mu}(2\sigma_t - \sigma_r), \qquad \text{(16-191)}$$

$$u_z = -u_r - u_t.$$

Most investigators assumed a power function creep-speed law by postulating it either in terms of the octahedral shear stress and rate of shear τ_{oct}, v_{oct},

$$\tau_{oct} = \mu v_{oct} = c v_{oct}^m, \qquad (0 < m \leq 1), \qquad \text{(16-192)}$$

corresponding to which the viscosity equals

$$\mu = c v_{oct}^{m-1} = c^{1/m}(\tau_{oct})^{(m-1)/m}. \qquad \text{(16-192a)}$$

With the abbreviating symbol

$$x = \frac{\sigma_r}{\sigma_t}, \qquad \text{(16-193)}$$

since

$$\tau_{oct}^2 = \frac{2}{3}(\sigma_r^2 - \sigma_r\sigma_t + \sigma_t^2) = \frac{2\sigma_t^2(x^2 - x + 1)}{3}, \qquad \text{(16-194)}$$

$$v_{oct}^2 = 4(u_r^2 + u_r u_t + u_t^2),$$

the rates of strain become equal to

$$u_r = \frac{dw}{dr} = \left(\frac{\sigma_t}{c}\right)^{1/m} \cdot \frac{2x-1}{6}\left[\frac{2(x^2 - x + 1)}{3}\right]^{(1-m)/2m},$$

$$u_t = \frac{w}{r} = \left(\frac{\sigma_t}{c}\right)^{1/m} \cdot \frac{2-x}{6}\left[\frac{2(x^2 - x + 1)}{3}\right]^{(1-m)/2m}. \qquad \text{(16-195)}$$

Or, alternatively, in terms of the maximum shearing stress

$$\tau_{max} = \frac{\sigma_t}{2}$$

and maximum rate of unit shear

$$v_{max} = u_t - u_z = 2u_t + u_r,$$

the rates of strain will amount to, when $\tau_{max} = cv_{max}^m$,

$$u_r = \frac{dw}{dr} = \left(\frac{\sigma_t}{2c}\right)^{1/m} \cdot \frac{2x-1}{3},$$

$$u_t = \frac{w}{r} = \left(\frac{\sigma_t}{2c}\right)^{1/m} \cdot \frac{2-x}{3}, \qquad \text{(16-196)}$$

corresponding to which

$$\mu = c^{1/m}\left(\frac{\sigma_t}{2}\right)^{(m-1)/m}, \qquad \sigma_t = 2c\left(\frac{3u_t}{2-x}\right)^m. \qquad \text{(16-197)}$$

One or the other group of Eqs. (16-195) or (16-196) has to be combined with the conditions of equilibrium and of compatibility:[1]

$$\frac{d(r\sigma_r)}{dr} - \sigma_t = -\gamma\frac{\omega^2 r^2}{g}, \qquad \text{(16-198)}$$

$$\frac{d(ru_t)}{dr} - u_r = 0. \qquad \text{(16-199)}$$

Using the maximum shearing stress theory and as the two dependent variables the functions x and y defined by

$$x = \frac{\sigma_r}{\sigma_t}, \qquad y = \sigma_t^{1/m} = \frac{3(2c)^{1/m} \cdot u_t}{2-x}, \qquad \text{(16-200)}$$

from Eqs. (16-196), (16-198), and (16-199) the two, simultaneous differential equations for x and y are deduced:

$$\frac{d}{dr}(rxy^m) - y^m = -\frac{\gamma\omega^2 r^2}{g}, \qquad \text{(16-201)}$$

$$\frac{d}{dr}[(2-x)y] + \frac{3(1-x)y}{r} = 0. \qquad \text{(16-202)}$$

The boundary conditions prescribe that for $r = r_1$ and $r = r_2$ the function x should vanish.

We indicate a method of integration by successive approximations. Upon closer examination, one sees that the tangential stress σ_t in the disk varies little with r. By integrating the equilibrium condition of Eq. (16-201) between the limits r_1 and r_2 at which $\sigma_r = 0$, $x = 0$, one computes the exact mean values of $\bar{\sigma}_t$ and $\bar{y}$,

$$\bar{\sigma}_t = (\bar{y})^m = \frac{\displaystyle\int_{r_1}^{r_2}\sigma_t\,dr}{r_2 - r_1} = \frac{\gamma\omega^2(r_2^3 - r_1^3)}{3g(r_2 - r_1)} = \frac{\gamma\omega^2}{3g}(r_1^2 + r_1 r_2 + r_2^2), \quad \text{(16-203)}$$

[1] A method of integration by means of successive numerical approximations has been worked out in the paper by A. M. WAHL, G. O. SANKEY, M. J. MANJOINE, and E. SHOEMAKER, Creep Tests of Rotating Disks at Elevated Temperature and Comparison with Theory, J. Appl. Mechanics, vol. 21, pp. 225–235, 1954, in which expressions were developed utilizing both the criteria based on the octahedral and the maximum shearing stress theories, respectively. In this paper also numerous references to work on the creep of rotating disks, including wheels of variable thickness (by R. W. BAILEY, F. K. G. ODQUIST, and others), may be found.

and after replacing the variable y by its mean value $\bar{y}$ just evaluated, one gets, after integrating Eq. (16-201) between the limits r_1 and r, in first approximation for the unknown function x the expression

$$x = \frac{\sigma_r}{\bar{\sigma}_t} = 1 - \frac{r_1}{r} - \frac{r^3 - r_1^3}{(r_1^2 + r_1 r_2 + r_2^2)r} . \tag{16-204}$$

By substituting the latter value of x in Eq. (16-202) and after multiplying it with the integrating factor $1/(2 - x)$, the second differential equation, namely, Eq. (16-202),

$$\frac{d[y(2 - x)]}{y(2 - x)} = -\frac{3(1 - x)\,dr}{(2 - x)r} = \frac{du_t}{u_t}, \tag{16-205}$$

may then be integrated between the limits r_1 and r, supplying the first approximate expression for the second unknown function y, giving

$$y = \sigma_t^{1/m} = \frac{2y_1 \varphi(r)}{2 - x}, \tag{16-206}$$

where y_1 is the value of y for $r = r_1$ and

$$\varphi(r) = e^{-3\int_{r_1}^{r} \frac{(1-x)\,dr}{(2-x)r}} . \tag{16-207}$$

Since from Eq. (16-197)

$$u_t = \frac{2 - x}{3}\left(\frac{\sigma_t}{2c}\right)^{1/m} = \frac{(2 - x)y}{3(2c)^{1/m}} = (u_t)_{r_1} \cdot \varphi(r) \tag{16-208}$$

and for $r = r_1, x = x_1 = 0$,

$$(u_t)_{r_1} = u_{t1} = \frac{2y_1}{3(2c)^{1/m}},$$

the integration constant y_1 is found equal to

$$y_1 = (\sigma_{t1})^{1/m} = \frac{3(2c)^{1/m}u_{t1}}{2}$$

and the unknown rate of strain u_{t1} may be evaluated from the condition

$$\int_{r_1}^{r_2} \sigma_t\,dr = 2c(3u_{t1})^m \cdot \int_{r_1}^{r_2}\left[\frac{\varphi(r)}{2 - x}\right]^m dr = \frac{\gamma\omega^2}{3g}(r_2^3 - r_1^3) \tag{16-209}$$

by graphical integration.

Thus the state of stress in a rotating disk of uniform thickness in the steady stage of creep is expressed in a first approximation by the formulas

$$\sigma_r = \bar{\sigma}_t \cdot x = \bar{\sigma}_t\left[1 - \frac{r_1}{r} - \frac{r^3 - r_1^3}{(r_1^2 + r_1 r_2 + r_2^2)r}\right],$$

$$\sigma_t = y^m = 2c\left[\frac{3u_{t1}\varphi(r)}{2 - x}\right]^m, \tag{16-210}$$

and the disk creeps with the radial velocity

$$w = ru_t = \frac{r(2 - x)y}{3(2c)^{1/m}} = ru_{t1}\varphi(r). \tag{16-211}$$

By repeating the process with the preceding expressions the latter may be improved further.

In Fig. 16-42 the distribution of the radial and tangential stresses σ_r and σ_t is reproduced for a steel disk of 2.5 in. inside diameter, 12 in. outside diameter, and 1 in. thickness at a turning speed of 15,000 rpm after the computations reported in the paper quoted in the footnote on page 577, the three curves referring to the values of the exponent $n = 1/m = 6, 8, 9$ of the creep-speed law [Eq. (16-192)] and using the value for the constant c that was determined in tensile creep tests for a 12% chrome steel at 1000°F on specimens machined from one of the disks.[1]

With the development of high-strength–creep-resistant alloys the allowable stresses have increased as compared with the flow stresses at the same elevated temperature. Since under these circumstances the height ε_0 of the intercept of the backward extended straight portion $\varepsilon = \varepsilon_0 + u_{min} \cdot t$ of the creep curves increases and the primary curved portion of the latter covers a longer fraction of the service time t_s, this stimulated FOLKE K. G. ODQUIST[2] *to include the primary period of creep* (usually omitted in the theory) in the evaluation of the states of stress in rotating disks. He proposed writing generalized stress–rate-of-strain relations which would also cover the first, curved parts of the creep lines which he utilized in evaluating the distribution of stress in a rotating disk of uniform thickness by means of successive approximations. This amounted to dealing with this problem in a somewhat analogous manner to the spreading of the plastic zone in a par-

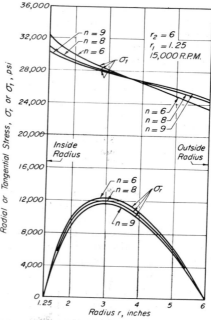

FIG. 16-42. Stress distribution along radius of rotating disk for various values of $n = 1/m$ (maximum shear theory assumed under speed law $\tau_{max} = cv_{max}^m$).

tially elastic and yielding disk, by distinguishing two zones, in one of which the primary creep prevails, while in the other the steady stage of creep has already been reached. Thus gradually a redistribution of stress takes place as a consequence of primary creep. The theory is involved, and since, after a sufficient time has elapsed, the steady stage of creep establishes itself over the disk, one may as well base the evaluation of the creep distortions on the latter,[3] by

[1] In the high-speed spin tests made on several disks over a period of 900 hr, the creep on the inside and outside diameters was intermittently measured and compared with the values predicted by the calculations based on the criteria of the octahedral and the maximum shearing stress theories. The comparisons suffered under the pronounced anisotropy of the forged billets, but an acceptable agreement was obtained between the average results of the measured creep distortion in the spin tests at 1000°F and the deformation predicted by the maximum shearing stress criterion of flow.

[2] Influence of Primary Creep on Stresses in Structural Parts, Trans. Roy. Inst. Technol. Stockholm, no. 66, 1953, paper read before Eighth International Congress of Applied Mechanics, Istanbul, 1952.

[3] With the steady increase of the number of theoretical investigations concerned with the various phases of the problems arising from the design of revolving turbine disks for high-temperature service, lack of space prohibits reporting further on them. The reader may find the concepts reviewed in the papers by F. K. G. ODQUIST, Recent Advances in Theories of Creep of Engineering Materials, Appl. Mechanics Revs., vol. 7, p. 517, 1954, and by A. M. WAHL, Stress Distributions in Rotating Disks Subjected to Creep, J. Appl. Mechanics, vol. 24, p. 299, 1957 (containing design data for disks of uniform and variable thickness in which the temperature is constant or may increase toward the periphery).

attempting to take account of the initial strain ε_0.   On the other hand, it would seem worthwhile to extend the theory for the evaluation of the stresses and permanent distortions in rotating disks by introducing the concept of a composite, recovery-sensitive substance along the lines indicated in Sec. 16-2I in Eqs. (16-106) and (16-108), possibly permitting the treatment of the relaxation of the contact pressures holding the massive hub of the disk shrunk onto the shaft.

F. PLASTIC DEFORMATION IN ROTATING CYLINDERS OF STRAIN-HARDENING METAL.   Recalling the analogy mentioned in Sec. 16-6A, it scarcely need be said that the states of stress previously developed by postulating a power function speed law active in steady creep in cylinders and disks apply just as well to the corresponding cases in a strain-hardening metal which yields completely in these bodies under a monotonic power function deformation law—it is understood—provided that the elastic parts of strain are neglected and the permanent strains remain small.

The aforementioned analogy justifies listing one more case that has been treated by EVAN A. DAVIS and F. M. CONNELLY[1] for a long metal cylinder, solid or hollow (a-inner, b-outer radius), rotating around its axis with angular speed ω so high that the entire cylinder yields completely.   Suppose that the metal yields under an idealized deformation law by assuming that *the octahedral shearing flow stress τ_{oct} is a linear function of the permanent, small, octahedral unit shear γ_{oct}*

$$\tau_{oct} = \tau_1 + \tau_2\gamma_{oct} \tag{16-212}$$

(τ_1, τ_2 are positive constants; $\gamma_{oct} > 0$) and that the cylinder is not constrained from contracting in the axial direction by a uniform axial strain $\varepsilon_z = -\varepsilon_0 =$ const, equivalent to the condition for the axial normal stress σ_z:

$$\int_a^b \sigma_z r\, dr = 0. \tag{16-213}$$

In incompressible material the radial, permanent displacement ρ must be equal to

$$\rho = \frac{\varepsilon_0}{2}\left(r + \frac{3k^2}{r}\right), \tag{16-214}$$

where k represents a constant length.   Hence the radial and tangential permanent strains are

$$\varepsilon_t = \frac{\rho}{r} = \frac{\varepsilon_0}{2}\left(1 + \frac{3k^2}{r^2}\right),$$
$$\varepsilon_r = \frac{d\rho}{dr} = \frac{\varepsilon_0}{2}\left(1 - \frac{3k^2}{r^2}\right); \tag{16-215}$$

the stress-strain relations are expressed by

$$\sigma_t - \sigma_r = 2\phi\varepsilon_0\frac{k^2}{r^2},$$
$$\sigma_r - \sigma_z = \phi\varepsilon_0\left(1 - \frac{k^2}{r^2}\right), \tag{16-216}$$
$$\sigma_z - \sigma_t = -\phi\varepsilon_0\left(1 + \frac{k^2}{r^2}\right);$$

[1] Stress Distribution and Plastic Deformation in Rotating Cylinders of Strain-hardening Material, J. Appl. Mechanics, vol. 26, p. 25, March, 1959.   In this paper two ideal, linear strain-hardening laws are considered by assuming that either $\tau_{oct} = \tau_1 + \tau_2\gamma_{oct}$ or $\tau_{max} = \tau_1 + \tau_2\gamma_{max}$.   The distributions of stress are of interest to designers of steam turbines for judging the safety of their heavy long rotors in case of overspeeding beyond the plastic limit.

and the octahedral shear stress τ_{oct} and unit shear γ_{oct} become

$$\tau_{\text{oct}} = \frac{\sqrt{2} \cdot \epsilon_0 \phi}{3r^2} \sqrt{r^4 + 3k^4},$$

$$\gamma_{\text{oct}} = \frac{\sqrt{2} \cdot \epsilon_0}{r^2} \sqrt{r^4 + 3k^4},$$

(16-217)

showing that the modulus of plasticity ϕ must be taken equal to

$$\phi = \frac{3\tau_{\text{oct}}}{\gamma_{\text{oct}}} = \frac{3r^2 \tau_1}{\sqrt{2} \cdot \epsilon_0 \sqrt{r^4 + 3k^4}} + 3\tau_2.$$

(16-218)

After substituting the expression for $\sigma_r - \sigma_x$ given in the first of Eqs. (16-216), by using the value of ϕ just obtained in the equilibrium condition [Eq. (16-198)] and integrating, the radial stress σ_r is found equal to

$$\sigma_r = C_1 - \frac{\gamma\omega^2 r^2}{2g} - 3\epsilon_0 \tau_2 \frac{k^2}{r^2} - \sqrt{\frac{3}{2}} \cdot \tau_1 \ln \frac{\sqrt{r^4 + 3k^4} + \sqrt{3} \cdot k^2}{r^2}, \quad (16\text{-}219)$$

and the normal stresses σ_t and σ_z may be computed from Eqs. (16-216). Since in a freely rotating, hollow cylinder, σ_r in Eq. (16-219) must be zero for $r = a$ and $r = b$, for the integration constant C_1 two expressions are obtained in terms of a or b, prescribing a first functional relation between the unknown strain ε_0 the length k, and ω, and finally Eq. (16-213) supplies a second relation connecting the two unknowns ε_0 and k. Because of the complexity of these two, simultaneously valid equations determining for any prescribed angular velocity ω the values of ε_0 and k, we shall not reproduce them here, since they were solved only numerically in the quoted paper for several values of the rotational speed.

In summing up, we see that, while the cylinder revolves at increasing speeds, the plastic state of stress changes gradually with increasing values of the circumferential stress σ_t at the inner bore and throughout the cylinder, as a consequence of the postulated strain-hardening function $\tau_{\text{oct}} = \tau_1 + \tau_2\gamma_{\text{oct}}$. In Fig. 16-43 the distribution of stress may be seen in an example in a long cylinder having the inner and outer radii $a = 1$ in., $b = 4$ in., the material constants $\tau_1 = 20,000$ lb/in.², $\tau_2 = 100,000$ lb/in.², the comparatively low speed factor $\gamma\omega^2/2g = 4,059$, and axial strain $\varepsilon_0 = 0.01$.

In a solid, revolving cylinder of linearly

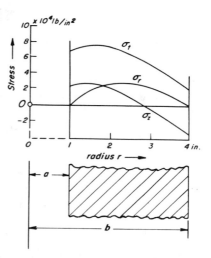

FIG. 16-43. Distribution of stress in a hollow rotating cylinder completely yielding under deformation law

$$\tau_{\text{oct}} = \tau_1 + \tau_2\gamma_{\text{oct}}.$$
$$\tau_1 = 2 \times 10^4, \qquad \tau_2 = 10^5 \text{ lb/in.}^2,$$
$$\varepsilon_0 = 0.01, \qquad \gamma\omega^2/2g = 4,059.$$

(*After E. A. Davis and F. M Connelly.*)

hardening metal the constant k is zero, $\varepsilon_r = \varepsilon_t = \varepsilon_0/2 = $ const, the stresses are equal to

$$\sigma_r = \sigma_t = \frac{\gamma\omega^2(b^2 - r^2)}{2g},$$

$$\sigma_z = \sigma_r - \phi\varepsilon_0 = \sigma_r - 3\left(\frac{\tau_1}{\sqrt{2}} + \tau_2\varepsilon_0\right), \qquad (16\text{-}220)$$

$$\tau_{oct} = \frac{\sqrt{2}\phi\varepsilon_0}{3} = \tau_1 + \sqrt{2}\tau_2\varepsilon_0,$$

the octahedral flow stress τ_{oct} has this uniform value at every point of the cylinder because $\gamma_{oct} = \sqrt{2}\varepsilon_0 = $ const is independent of r, and one verifies easily that the absolute value of the contraction $\varepsilon_z = -\varepsilon_0$ in the axial direction increases with the angular velocity of rotation ω as

$$\varepsilon_0 = \frac{\gamma\omega^2 b^2}{12g\tau_2} - \frac{\tau_1}{\sqrt{2}\tau_2}, \qquad (16\text{-}221)$$

supplying for the radial expansion of a solid cylinder yielding under the centrifugal forces the value

$$\rho = \varepsilon_t r = \frac{\varepsilon_0 r}{2} \qquad (16\text{-}222)$$

except when $\varepsilon_0 = 0$.

Since ε_0 must be positive, the formula for ε_0 furnishes for $\varepsilon_0 = 0$ the smallest speed ω_{min} with which a solid cylinder must rotate in order that the plastic state should spread over the entire cylinder, when, namely,

$$\frac{\gamma\omega_{min}^2 b^2}{g} = \frac{12\tau_1}{\sqrt{2}} \qquad (16\text{-}223)$$

and τ_{oct} takes on the value $\tau_{oct} = \tau_1 = $ const in it. The latter formula and the corresponding ones for $\sigma_r = \sigma_t$, $\sigma_z = \sigma_r - (3\tau_1/\sqrt{2})$ coincide with those which were derived for an ideally plastic, solid, rotating cylinder in Vol. I, page 484, for the case $\varepsilon_z = 0$ in non-strain-hardening material.

We may add the final remark that the preceding states of stress for a material yielding under the linear strain-hardening rule

$$\tau_{oct} = \tau_1 + \tau_2\gamma_{oct}$$

express also *the distributions of stress in a viscous solid* having the yield value τ_1 and deforming under the *Bingham law*

$$\tau_{oct} = \tau_1 + \mu v_{oct} \qquad (16\text{-}224)$$

if we replace the constant τ_2 by an invariable coefficient of viscosity μ, the plasticity modulus ϕ by 3μ, the unit shear γ_{oct} by the rate of shear v_{oct}, and the displacement ρ by the velocity $\dot{\rho}$. The derived expressions thus also furnish those in rotating cylinders of a *Bingham solid*.

16-7. Anelastic Aftereffects of Sequences of Steady and of Transient Loading or Straining. A. SYNTHESIS OF AFTER-EFFECTS.

Under anelastic aftereffect (in German terminology called *elastische Nachwirkung*) the observation is understood that, after a load of moderate magnitude is held invariable for a time, supposedly elastic solids tested at normal temperature are seen slowly to deform gradually by small strains, beyond the initially recorded elastic, reversible strains.[1] Although the term is vague, we shall use it in this section, by attempting to *define the various types of aftereffects* into which these may be resolved, after specifying the properties of solids to which they are to be applied.

Solids creep under stress at elevated temperatures, and since slow, small creep prevails to some extent also at normal and even at low temperatures, one type of aftereffect is due to creep.   In the strain-hardening ductile metals the yield or flow stress is dependent on both the plastic strain and the rate of permanent deformation.   A soft metal will disclose a small, plastic *afterflow* after it has been brought up to a load under which it yielded, when the load is maintained at such a level for some time.   The anelastic aftereffects under steady load are associated with the fundamental property of the solid state of matter that one or the other fraction of small permanent strain must grow with the time t whenever a stress acts, since it may cause a permanent rate of deformation.

We have seen[2] that, apart from the permanent strains associated with creep or plasticity or both just mentioned, small permanent parts of strain ε''' of a recoverable nature are observed and traceable analytically by considering the total, uniaxial, normal stress $\sigma = \sigma' + \sigma''$ as made up of two additive parts: $\sigma' = E_r \varepsilon'''$ proportional to the recoverable part ε''' of the total strain and the part $\sigma'' = g_r(u''')$ dependent on the rate $u''' = d\varepsilon'''/dt = \dot{\varepsilon}'''$,

$$\sigma = \sigma' + \sigma'' = E_r \varepsilon''' + g_r(\dot{\varepsilon}'''). \tag{16-225}$$

The small, conventional, total strain ε is then regarded as the sum of the types of strain to be considered.

In generalizing our former assumptions in respect to ε, we stipulate that the total strain ε has an *elastically* reversible part $\varepsilon' = \sigma/E$, *a first, plastic part* ε_p'', increasing monotonously with the flow stress σ along a strain-hardening function $\varepsilon_p'' = h_p(\sigma)$; *a second, permanent part* ε'' of a *viscous* nature, the rates of which $u'' = d\varepsilon''/dt = \dot{\varepsilon}'' = h(\sigma)$ comply with

---

[1] See an extensive, historically critical review of these phenomena in HERBERT LEADERMAN, "Elastic and Creep Properties of Filamentous Materials and Other High Polymers," 278 pp., the Textile Foundation, Washington, D.C., 1943. Elastic aftereffects were first described by WILHELM WEBER (Göttingen) in 1835 who discovered them on twisting and untwisting the filaments of silk or glass on which galvanometer mirrors were suspended.   The elder R. KOHLRAUSCH (Poggendorf's Ann. Physik, 1847, 1854), his son F. KOHLRAUSCH (*ibid.*, 1863, 1866, 1876), J. HOPKINSON [Proc. Roy. Soc. (London), 1878] were some of the first to describe their rules of formation.   (Quoted from Leaderman's extensive bibliography.)

[2] Sec. 16-2I; also Sec. 4-1D.

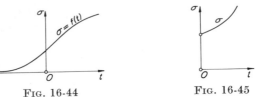

FIG. 16-44 FIG. 16-45

FIGS. 16-44 and 16-45. Problem of transient loading.

a given speed function $u'' = h(\sigma)$; and *lastly a recoverable, semipermanent part ε'''*, the law of variation of which is defined in Eq. (16-225).

Supposing a solid in which these four types of strain prevail being quite continuously loaded gradually from $\sigma = 0$ at distant, past time $t = -\infty$ under the stress $\sigma = \sigma(t) = f(t)$ increasing monotonously[1] (Fig. 16-44), the plastic strain ε_p'' takes on at time t the value

$$\varepsilon_p''(t) = h_p(\sigma); \tag{16-226}$$

the viscous strain ε'', the value

$$\varepsilon''(t) = \int_{-\infty}^{t} u'' \, dt = \int_{-\infty}^{t} h(\sigma) \, dt; \tag{16-227}$$

and the total strain ε, the value

$$\varepsilon = \varepsilon' + \varepsilon_p'' + \varepsilon'' + \varepsilon''',$$
$$\varepsilon(t) = \frac{\sigma(t)}{E} + h_p(\sigma) + \int_{-\infty}^{t} h(\sigma) \, dt + \varepsilon'''(t), \tag{16-228}$$

where $\varepsilon'''(t)$ obviously is the integral of the differential equation (16-225) after substituting in it $\sigma = \sigma(t) = f(t)$, the part sum $\varepsilon_p'' + \varepsilon''$ representing the permanent, irrecoverable strain accrued at time t.

Equation (16-228) does not lose its validity if at some fixed time $t = t_1$ the solid *is suddenly unloaded* from $\sigma_1 = f(t_1)$ to $\sigma = 0$. While $t > t_1$, the term $\varepsilon_1' = \sigma_1/E$ has to be left out and the permanent strain

$$\varepsilon_{p1}'' + \varepsilon_1'' = h_p(\sigma_1) + \int_{-\infty}^{t_1} h(\sigma) \, dt \tag{16-229}$$

remains unchanged. After unloading, the branch of the ε curve results as an aftereffect

$$t > t_1, \qquad \varepsilon(t) = \varepsilon_{p1}'' + \varepsilon_1'' + \varepsilon''', \tag{16-230}$$

where ε''' must now satisfy

$$t > t_1, \qquad g_r(\dot\varepsilon''') + E_r\varepsilon''' = 0, \tag{16-231}$$

defining the recovery of strain after sudden release of stress.

[1] Restricting $\sigma = f(t)$ to a monotonously increasing load function is not essential but serves to avoid the necessity of considering stagnating plastic strains ε_p'', stopping growth whenever $d\sigma/dt$ temporarily becomes negative.

If the solid is kept loaded over a limited time interval t beginning with $t = 0$ (Fig. 16-45) the lower limit $t = -\infty$ in the integrals appearing in the preceding equations is replaced by $t = 0$.

Although details of simple synthesis of terms ε'' and ε''' have been worked out in several examples in the preceding sections, supplying in the sum of strains $\varepsilon'' + \varepsilon'''$ the corresponding anelastic aftereffects, it seems appropriate at this stage of their present analysis to pay *attention to two special sequences* of loading and straining.

(1). *Steady load*, $\sigma = $ const, beginning at the time $t = 0$.   On applying the stress $\sigma = $ const, the elastic and plastic strains $\varepsilon' = \sigma/E$ and $\varepsilon_p'' = h_p(\sigma)$ remain stationary, and the total strain $\varepsilon(t)$ becomes equal to

$$\varepsilon(t) = \frac{\sigma}{E} + h_p(\sigma) + h(\sigma) \cdot t + \varepsilon''', \qquad (16\text{-}232)$$

where ε''' as the solution of Eq. (16-225), after assigning to σ a constant value

$$g_r(\dot{\varepsilon}''') + E_r\varepsilon''' = \sigma = \text{const}, \qquad (16\text{-}233)$$

obviously defines *the unit-recoverable strain response under steady stress* which we symbolically denote by

$$\underline{\underline{\varepsilon''' = \frac{\sigma}{E}\,\psi(t),}} \qquad (16\text{-}234)$$

satisfying the initial condition at time $t = 0$, $\psi(0) = 0$.

(2). *Steady strain*, $\varepsilon = $ const.   After sudden loading at time $t = 0$ to an initial strain $\varepsilon = \varepsilon_i = $ const held fixed, the initial stress σ_i is defined by

$$\varepsilon_i = \frac{\sigma_i}{E} + h_p(\sigma_i), \qquad (16\text{-}235)$$

the plastic part $\varepsilon_p'' = h_p(\sigma_i)$ remains stationary since the stress $\sigma(t)$ starts to drop, and the subsequent release of stress during relaxation is governed by the simultaneous differential equations for the strains ε'' and ε''' which were given in Eqs. (16-107):

$$\varepsilon''' = \varepsilon_i - \varepsilon'' - \frac{g(\dot{\varepsilon}'')}{E},$$

$$\varepsilon'' = \varepsilon_i - \left(1 + \frac{E_r}{E}\right)\varepsilon''' - \frac{g_r(\dot{\varepsilon}''')}{E}, \qquad (16\text{-}236)$$

where g, g_r symbolize the inverse functions of $h(\sigma)$, $h_r(\sigma)$.   With the initial value at time $t = 0$, $\sigma(0) = \sigma_i$ to be computed from Eq. (16-235) and with ε''' determined from Eqs. (16-236), then Eq. (16-225) supplies $\sigma(t)$ or *the unit relaxation function*, to be denoted symbolically by

$$\underline{\underline{\sigma = \sigma_i\phi(t),}} \qquad (16\text{-}237)$$

satisfying the initial condition $t = 0$, $\phi(0) = 1$.

Whereas the aftereffects caused during the progress of *prescribed, transient, uniaxial loading or straining*, while the stress $\sigma = \sigma(t)$ or strain $\varepsilon = \varepsilon(t)$ increases in a continuous manner with time t, are thus straightforwardly computable from the corresponding ordinary differential equations by establishing their integrals, we have mentioned in Sec. 16-2I that the first originators of a mathematical theory of the anelastic aftereffects (LUDWIG BOLTZMANN, VITO VOLTERRA, and others) expressed the aftereffects in terms of certain definite integrals, in the integrants of which they intuitively made use of the derivatives with respect to time θ either of the *unit recoverable strain response* $\psi(t - \theta)$ or of the *unit relaxation function* $\phi(t - \theta)$, where θ denotes the intermediate time at which $\sigma(\theta)$ or $\varepsilon(\theta)$ acted along their prescribed transient traces.

B. THE RICHARD BECKER, LUDWIG BOLTZMANN, AND VITO VOLTERRA INTEGRALS. In following this scheme, let us utilize the aforeintroduced two fundamental functions $\psi(t)$ and $\phi(t)$, defined in Eqs. (16-234) and (16-237), by posting (1) *the problem of transient stress:* given the stress $\sigma = \sigma(t)$ as a function of time t, find the strain $\varepsilon = \varepsilon(t)$; and (2) *the inverse problem of transient strain:* given the strain $\varepsilon = \varepsilon(t)$ as a function of time t, determine the stress $\sigma = \sigma(t)$ that produced it.

(1). *In conceiving the direct problem*, suppose that a specimen is being loaded over an extended period of time $-\infty < t$ from an unstrained condition by gradually increasing continuously the stress σ from value zero along the given function of time $\sigma = \sigma(t) = f(t)$ (Fig. 16-44), excluding any discontinuous changes in σ. The solid may take on an elastic strain $\varepsilon' = \sigma/E$, a plastic distortion ε_p'' along a strain-hardening curve $\varepsilon_p'' = h_p(\sigma)$ solely dependent on σ, a viscous strain ε'' the rates $u'' = \dot{\varepsilon}'' = h(\sigma)$ of which depend on the instantaneous values of σ in accordance with a given, general speed law $h(\sigma)$, and a permanent strain of recoverable nature ε''' of unit response $\psi(t)$, which per unit of a steady stress $\sigma = $ const is a known function $\psi(t)$ of t, according to Eq. (16-234).

In order to compute the total strain $\varepsilon(t)$ evolved at a *fixed* time $t = \overline{OB}$ (Fig. 16-46), consider an *intermediate* time $\theta = \overline{OA}$ at which the stress has the value $\sigma(\theta) = \overline{AP}$. According to the superposition principle [Eq. (16-228)], the strain $\varepsilon(t)$ at time $t = \overline{OB}$ is

$$\varepsilon(t) = \frac{\sigma(t)}{E} + h_p(\sigma) + \int_{\theta = -\infty}^{\theta = t} h[\sigma(\theta)]\, d\theta + \varepsilon'''(t). \qquad (16\text{-}238)$$

In order to compute $\varepsilon'''(t)$, we shall make use of the unit-response recoverable-strain function $\psi(t)$, defined in Eq. (16-234), referred to a unit of stress held invariable, but we must remember that the function ψ may or may not contain the variable stress $\sigma(\theta)$ as a parameter. Suppose that the stress $\sigma(\theta)$ at intermediate time θ were increased by the differential $d\sigma = d\sigma(\theta)$. Since this increment of load acts as a *steady stress* $d\sigma$ during the period of time $t - \theta$, it will produce in general the differential of strain $d\varepsilon'''$ at time t:

$$d\varepsilon'''(t) = \frac{1}{E}\left[d\sigma \cdot \psi(t - \theta) + \sigma \cdot \frac{\partial \psi(t - \theta)}{\partial \sigma}\, d\sigma\right], \qquad (16\text{-}239)$$

where the second term takes care of the fact that ψ may also contain σ as a variable parameter.

Consequently *the total anelastic aftereffect* consisting of the last two terms in Eq. (16-238), at time t, will amount to the definite integral

$$\varepsilon'' + \varepsilon''' = \int_{\theta = -\infty}^{\theta = t} \left\{ h[\sigma(\theta)] + \frac{1}{E}\frac{d\sigma(\theta)}{d\theta}\left[\psi(t - \theta) + \sigma(\theta)\frac{\partial \psi(t - \theta)}{\partial \sigma}\right]\right\} d\theta \tag{16-240}$$

with inclusion also of the accumulated strains ε'' of a viscous nature.

As to the part strain,

$$\varepsilon'''(t) = \frac{1}{E}\int_{\theta = -\infty}^{\theta = t}\left[\psi(t - \theta) + \sigma(\theta)\frac{\partial \psi(t - \theta)}{\partial \sigma}\right] d\sigma(\theta), \qquad (16\text{-}241)$$

this can also be expressed in a second, equivalent form:[1]

$$\varepsilon'''(t) = \frac{1}{E}\int_{\theta = -\infty}^{\theta = t} \sigma(\theta)\left[\frac{d\sigma(\theta)}{d\theta}\cdot\frac{\partial \psi(t - \theta)}{\partial \sigma} - \frac{\partial \psi(t - \theta)}{\partial \theta}\right] d\theta. \tag{16-242}$$

Let us now write the equation for the total strain $\varepsilon(t)$ caused by a transient stress $\sigma(t)$ after disregarding the strains of plastic and viscous nature (letting $\varepsilon_p'' = \varepsilon'' = 0$) and after postulating that the function $\psi(t - \theta)$ does not depend on σ, that is, when $\partial \psi/\partial \sigma = 0$. The total strain evolved is then expressed in the simpler form by

$$\varepsilon(t) = \frac{\sigma(t)}{E} - \frac{1}{E}\int_{\theta = -\infty}^{\theta = t} \sigma(\theta)\frac{d\psi(t - \theta)}{d\theta} d\theta \qquad (16\text{-}243)$$

or, after changing the integration variable from the *current* time θ to the *past* time $t' = t - \theta$, by

$$\varepsilon(t) = \frac{\sigma(t)}{E} + \frac{1}{E}\int_{t' = 0}^{t' = \infty} \sigma(t - t')\frac{d\psi(t')}{dt'} dt', \qquad (16\text{-}244)$$

with this latter integral extended from *present* time ($t' = 0$) backward into the *past* oblivion ($t' = \infty$). The last definite integral in Eq.

[1] Since by partial integration

$$\int_{-\infty}^{t} \psi(t - \theta)\, d\sigma(\theta) = \left[\psi(t - \theta)\sigma(\theta)\right]_{-\infty}^{t} - \int_{-\infty}^{t} \frac{\partial \psi(t - \theta)}{\partial \theta} \cdot \sigma(\theta)\, d\theta,$$

where the term within the brackets cancels out.

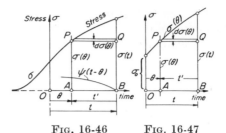

FIG. 16-46   FIG. 16-47

FIGS. 16-46 and 16-47. Problem of transient loading.

(16-244) coincides with one RICHARD BECKER postulated in his evaluation of aftereffects covering past history of loading.[1]

While in the preceding two equations $\sigma(t)$ is known and $\varepsilon(t)$ the function to be determined, mathematically inclined readers may conversely consider the two equations as symbolizing also the solution of the inverse problem of transient straining, requiring determination of the *unknown* function $\sigma(t)$, appearing before and behind the sign of a definite integral, thus from an integral equation.

Returning to Eq. (16-242), if the transient load starts to act at time $t = 0$ *beginning with a finite value* $\sigma = \sigma_0$ and while $t > 0$, $\sigma = \sigma(t)$ (Fig. 16-47) further increases continuously with time, the definite integral expressing $\varepsilon'''(t)$ as given in Eq. (16-242), because of the discontinuous growth of the load at time $t = 0$ from $\sigma = 0$ to $\sigma = \sigma_0$, has to be amended.   One shows easily that the recoverable part of strain $\varepsilon'''(t)$ is to be evaluated from the integral

$$\varepsilon'''(t) = \frac{1}{E} \int_{\theta=0}^{\theta=t} \left\{ [\sigma(\theta) - \sigma_0] \frac{d\sigma}{d\theta} \cdot \frac{\partial \psi(t - \theta)}{\partial \sigma} - \sigma(\theta) \frac{\partial \psi(t - \theta)}{\partial \theta} \right\} d\theta. \quad (16\text{-}245)$$

If $\psi(t - \theta)$ does not contain the parameter σ this reduces to *Becker's equation* for total strain $\varepsilon = \varepsilon' + \varepsilon'''$:

$$\varepsilon(t) = \frac{1}{E} \left[\sigma(t) - \int_{\theta=0}^{\theta=t} \sigma(\theta) \frac{d\psi(t - \theta)}{d\theta} d\theta \right], \qquad t \geq 0. \quad (16\text{-}245a)$$

[1] Elastische Nachwirkung und Plastizität, Z. Physik, vol. 33, no. 3, pp. 183–213, 1925.   Becker assumed that a stress $\sigma(\theta)$ causes the greater aftereffect ε''' the longer it persists and that it becomes smaller, the farther back in time the stress acted in the past, letting the increment of aftereffect $d\varepsilon'''(t)$ accrued at fixed time t be proportional to the value of stress $\sigma(\theta)$, to the time of its action $d\theta$, and to a function $\varphi(t - \theta) = \varphi(t')$ declining with age $t' = t - \theta$, postulating

$$d\varepsilon'''(t) = \frac{1}{E} \sigma(\theta)\varphi(t - \theta) d\theta.$$

Becker's function, in fact, coincides with $\varphi(t') = d\psi(t')/dt'$, with the derivative with respect to time t' of our unit-recovery response function $\psi(t')$.

(2). *In conceiving the inverse problem*[1] *of finding stress $\sigma(t)$ that deforms a solid along given, continuously rising, transient straining path $\varepsilon(t)$,* we impose—in order to avoid dealing with two strains ε'' and ε''' interrelated by two nonlinear differential equations [Eqs. (16-236)]—the omission of plastic and viscous strains, putting $\varepsilon_p'' = \varepsilon'' = 0$, confining the total strain ε to the sum of elastic $\varepsilon' = \sigma/E$ and semipermanent, recoverable strain ε''', $\varepsilon = \varepsilon' + \varepsilon'''$. This amounts to prescribing in regard to the elementary *relaxation process* under steady strain $\varepsilon = \varepsilon_i = \sigma_i/E = $ const, for the semipermanent part of strain ε''' constituting aftereffect, the differential equation

$$g_r(\dot{\varepsilon}''') + (E + E_r)\varepsilon''' = E\varepsilon_i = \sigma_i, \qquad (16\text{-}246)$$

solution of which supplies for the stress $\sigma(t)$ declining with time t,

$$\sigma(t) = E(\varepsilon_i - \varepsilon''') = \sigma_i - E\varepsilon''' = \sigma_i\phi(t,\varepsilon_i), \qquad (16\text{-}247)$$

defining in $\phi(t,\varepsilon_i)$ the unit relaxation response per unit of initial stress σ_i satisfying the condition for $t = 0$, $\phi(0,\varepsilon_i) = 1$.

It is here tacitly assumed that the function $\phi(t,\varepsilon_i)$ in general may contain ε_i as a variable parameter. The omission of plastic and viscous strains by letting $\varepsilon_p'' = \varepsilon'' = 0$ still leaves space for dealing with fairly general types of solid substances with examples of which we were previously concerned when we postulated a power function [Eq. (16-36)] or the hyperbolic sine speed law [Eqs. (16-41) and (16-42)].[2]

[1] The inverse problem figured prominently in work by LUDWIG BOLTZMANN, Zur Theorie der elastischen Nachwirkung, Sitzber. Akad. Wiss. Wien, Math.-naturw. Kl., vol. 70, p. 275, 1874; also Poggendorf's Ann. Physik, vol. 7, p. 624, 1876; by E. WIECHERT, Gesetze der elastischen Nachwirkung, Wiedemann's Ann. Physik u. Chem., vol. 50, pp. 335, 546, 1893; by VITO CARLO VOLTERRA, Rend. accad. dei Lincei, vol. 21, ser. 5, 1912; "Lecons sur les équations intégrales et integro-differentielles," Gauthier-Villars, Paris, 1913; "Theory of Functionals, Integral- and Integro-differential Equations," Blackie & Sons, Ltd., Glasgow, 1930 (selectively quoted from papers by his son, ENRICO VOLTERRA, referred to below). From the very extensive literature on this subject are further selectively quoted: K. BENNEWITZ (Z. Physik, 1920, 1924); H. FROMM, "Nachwirkung und Hysteresis," Handbuch der physikalischen und technischen Mechanik, Vol. 4, pt. 1, pp. 436–457, 504–550, Verlag von Johann Ambrosius Barth, Leipzig, 1931; ALFRED M. FREUDENTHAL, "Inelastic Behavior of Engineering Materials and Structures," 587 pp., John Wiley & Sons, Inc., New York, 1950; BERNHARD GROSS, "Mathematic Structure of Theories of Viscoelasticity," 74 pp., Hermann & Cie, Paris, 1953; also Rheologische Verteilungsfunktionen, Kolloid-Z., vol. 131, p. 161, 1853; C. ZENER. "Elasticity and Anelasticity," p. 60, University of Chicago Press, Chicago, 1948; also Metals Technol., p. 1992, 1946.

[2] This solid for which the *Boltzmann-Volterra integrals* are to be developed in Eqs. (16-248) and (16-250) can be visualized by a mechanical model of the type mentioned in Sec. 4-1 (footnote on page 170) complying with the rule $\varepsilon = \varepsilon' + \varepsilon''' = (\sigma/E) + \varepsilon'''$, if a generalized *Kelvin unit*, an elastic spring and dashpot joined parallel, the latter moving under a general speed law $\sigma'' = g_r(\dot{\varepsilon}''')$, is attached in series to an additional elastic spring representing the term $\varepsilon' = \sigma/E$.

Suppose first that the unit response $\phi(t)$ is a pure function of time t not dependent on ε_i. Proceed in a manner analogous to the way in which the integrals in Eqs. (16-243) and (16-244) were developed, and now increase the strain $\varepsilon(\theta)$ at intermediate time θ by the differential $d\varepsilon(\theta)$ (Fig. 16-48). The parallel strip of length $t - \theta$ and height $d\varepsilon(\theta)$ represents an elementary relaxation process causing a response in declining stress $d\sigma(t)$ at the fixed time t according to Eq. (16-247). Letting $d\sigma_i = E\, d\varepsilon_i = E\, d\varepsilon(\theta)$,

$$d\sigma(t) = E\phi(t - \theta)\, d\varepsilon(\theta),$$

transient straining $\varepsilon(t)$ creates the stress

$$\sigma(t) = E \int_{\theta=-\infty}^{\theta=t} \phi(t - \theta) \frac{d\varepsilon(\theta)}{d\theta}\, d\theta, \tag{16-248}$$

an integral that after partial integration may also be expressed in the two forms

$$\sigma(t) = E\left[\varepsilon(t) - \int_{\theta=-\infty}^{\theta=t} \varepsilon(\theta) \frac{d\phi(t - \theta)}{d\theta}\, d\theta \right], \tag{16-249}$$

$$\sigma(t) = E\left[\varepsilon(t) + \int_{t'=0}^{t'=\infty} \varepsilon(t - t') \frac{d\phi(t')}{dt'}\, dt' \right], \tag{16-250}$$

in which the integral extends over current time θ or retroactive, past time $t' = t - \theta$, respectively, *being known as the Boltzmann-Volterra integral* in the theory of anelastic aftereffects.

Let us state once more BECKER's equation (16-244) *for transient stressing,*

$$E\varepsilon(t) = \sigma(t) + \int_{t'=0}^{t'=\infty} \sigma(t - t') \frac{d\psi(t')}{dt'}\, dt', \tag{16-251}$$

so that the reader will notice the remarkable, reciprocal symmetry in building up the last two equations and realize the simple rule through which the two definite integrals in Eqs. (16-250) and (16-251) are converted into each other, one inverted into the other, vice versa, if they are applied to the corresponding functions $\varepsilon(t)$ and $\sigma(t)$ in both places: One has to interchange $E\varepsilon$ and ϕ with σ and ψ. If one considers ε in Eq. (16-250) as the unknown, this integral equation for ε is solved by

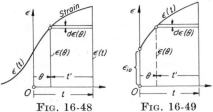

FIG. 16-48   FIG. 16-49

FIGS. 16-48 and 16-49. Inverse problem.

FIG. 16-50. LUDWIG BOLTZMANN. (Born Feb. 20, 1844, in Vienna; died Sept. 5, 1906, in Duino, by committing suicide.) He was professor of physics at the Universities of Graz, Vienna, Munich, and Leipzig. His collected papers were published in 1909. (*Photo courtesy of Dr. Enrico Volterra, Austin, Tex.*)

FIG. 16-51. VITO VOLTERRA. (Born May 3, 1860, in Ancona; died Oct. 11, 1940, in Rome.) He was professor of mathematics at the Universities of Pisa, Turin, and, from 1900 to 1931, of Rome; was dismissed under the Fascist regime, later knighted by King George of England. (*Photo courtesy of Dr. Enrico Volterra, Austin, Tex.*)

Eq. (16-251), and vice versa for σ. The bond of relationship between the two definite integrals is anchored to the two fundamental unit functions $\psi(t)$ and $\phi(t)$, precisely, to their time derivatives $d\psi/dt$ and $d\phi/dt$, and the knowledge of $\psi(t)$ and $\phi(t)$ hinges on having solved ε''' *for steady stress* $\sigma =$ const from

$$g_r(\dot{\varepsilon}''') + E_r \varepsilon''' = \sigma = \text{const},\qquad(16\text{-}252)$$

defining the unit response function $\psi(t)$ by

$$\varepsilon''' = \frac{\sigma}{E}\,\psi(t),\qquad \psi(0) = 0,\qquad(16\text{-}253)$$

and *for steady strain* $\varepsilon = \varepsilon_i = \sigma_i/E =$ const from Eqs. (16-246) and (16-247), defining the unit relaxation function $\phi(t)$,

$$\sigma(t) = \sigma_i \phi(t),\qquad \phi(0) = 1,\qquad(16\text{-}254)$$

in both parent differential equations (16-252) and (16-246) using in the

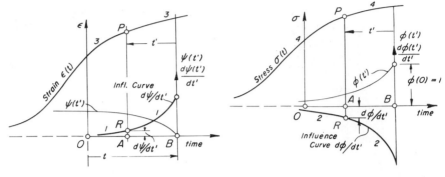

FIG. 16-52

FIG. 16-53. Influence-curves $d\psi/dt'$, $d\phi/dt'$ serving to compute Becker-Boltzmann integrals.

term $g_r(\dot{\varepsilon}''')$ the speed function that characterizes the evolution of after-effects.[1]

The two derivatives $d\psi/dt'$, $d\phi/dt'$ playing the role of "influence-functions" within the integrants have been called the *nuclei* in the theory of integral equations. From a resumé by ENRICO VOLTERRA who devoted parts of his papers[2] to the work of his father, one of the founders of this theory, it appears that the elder, VITO VOLTERRA, designated the quantities $d\psi(t')/dt'$ and $-d\phi(t')/dt'$ as the *hereditary nuclei*, or memory functions, in the definite integrals and the latter as their "functionals" in his theory of phenomena having hereditary characteristics.

If straining starts at time $t = 0$, beginning discontinuously with a finite, initial strain ε_i, upon sudden loading (Fig. 16-49), the stress $\sigma(t)$ must be evaluated from either of the expressions

$$\sigma(t) = E\left[\varepsilon_i\phi(t) + \int_0^t \phi(t-\theta)\frac{d\varepsilon(\theta)}{d\theta}\,d\theta\right],$$

$$\sigma(t) = E\left[\varepsilon(t) - \int_0^t \varepsilon(\theta)\frac{d\phi(t-\theta)}{d\theta}\,d\theta\right],$$

(16-255)

[1] Figures 16-52 and 16-53 depict the expected shape of the "*influence-curves*" 11 and 22 representing the derivatives $d\psi/dt'$ and $d\phi/dt'$ in their relative position to the curves $\varepsilon(t-t')$ (33, given strain ε) and $\sigma(t-t')$ (44, given stress σ) at a fixed time $t = OB$. One sees that the integrants in the two definite integrals could graphically or numerically be evaluated pointwise by multiplying the ordinates AR of the influence-curves 11 or 22 with the ordinates AP of the ε or σ curves. The process is to be repeated for other values of fixed time $t = OB$, after simply shifting curves 11 and 22 into their corresponding new positions.

[2] Vibrations of Elastic Systems Having Hereditary Characteristics, J. Appl. Mechanics, vol. 17, p. 363, 1950, and On Elastic Continua with Hereditary

where the term $E\varepsilon_i\phi(t)$ in the first line obviously represents the elementary relaxation curve that would result if the suddenly applied strain ε_i had persisted alone over the time $0 < \theta < t$.

Secondly, in the previously, first excluded, general case, when the unit response function $\phi(t,\varepsilon_i)$ also contains the variable parameter ε_i, we give *the solution of the inverse problem* prescribing the strain path $\varepsilon(t)$, beginning with a finite value at $t = 0$, $\varepsilon = \varepsilon_{i0}$ (conforming with Fig. 16-49) that requires the stress

$$\sigma(t) = E\varepsilon(t) + E\int_{\theta=0}^{\theta=t} \varepsilon(\theta)\left[\frac{d\varepsilon(\theta)}{d\theta}\cdot\frac{\partial\phi(t-\theta,\varepsilon_i)}{\partial\varepsilon_i} - \frac{\partial\phi(t-\theta,\varepsilon_i)}{\partial\theta}\right]d\theta. \quad (16\text{-}256)$$

This coincides in the case that $\phi(t-\theta)$ does not depend on ε_i, that is, for $\partial\phi/\partial\varepsilon_i = 0$, indeed, with the second of Eqs. (16-255).

This then sums up a brief survey of the theory of anelastic aftereffects, following somewhat along the classical lines of expressing them in terms of definite integrals *but laying emphasis on the basic speed law* [Eq. (16-225)] *and on the two fundamental unit functions* $\psi(t)$, $\phi(t)$ evolving from it. Let us illustrate their usefulness, constituting in their derivatives hereditary nuclei in the interior of these integrals.

C. APPLICATIONS IN EXAMPLES

EXAMPLE 1. Consider first the simplest type of composite, viscoelastic, recovery-sensitive solid, complying with the *linear* speed relations

$$\sigma = 3\mu\dot{\varepsilon}'' = Et_e\dot{\varepsilon}'', \qquad t_e = \frac{3\mu}{E},$$

$$\sigma = E_r(\varepsilon''' + t_r\dot{\varepsilon}'''), \qquad t_r = \frac{3\mu_r}{E_r},$$

with the material constants E, E_r, μ, μ_r, t_e, t_r. We found [Eq. (4-34)] that under a steady stress $\sigma = $ const the strain ε equals

$$\varepsilon = \varepsilon' + \varepsilon'' + \varepsilon''' = \frac{\sigma}{E}\left[1 + \frac{t}{t_e} + \frac{E}{E_r}(1 - e^{-t/t_r})\right]$$

with the third term in it defining the unit recovery function

$$\psi(t) = \frac{E}{E_r}(1 - e^{-t/t_r}).$$

Find the strain response $\varepsilon(t)$ if the stress σ increases as an exponential function of time t,

$$\sigma = \sigma_0 e^{\omega t},$$

with σ_0, ω as given constants.

Characteristics, *ibid.*, vol. 18, p. 273, 1951, containing interesting applications to complex phenomena involving internal, dynamic friction in rapidly oscillating elastic bodies, experiments on plastics and rubberlike materials for determining the form of the hereditary functions, and extension of theory to three-dimensional dynamics in elastic continua.

An increase of stress $d\sigma(\theta)$ at an intermediate time θ produces the increment of strain

$$d\varepsilon = \frac{d\sigma(\theta)}{E}\left[1 + \frac{t - \theta}{t_e} + \psi(t - \theta)\right],$$

and the transient load $\sigma = \sigma_0 e^{\omega \theta}$, the total strain $\varepsilon(t)$ at time t:

$$\varepsilon(t) = \frac{\sigma(t)}{E} + \frac{1}{E}\int_{\theta = -\infty}^{\theta = t}\left[\frac{t - \theta}{t_e} + \psi(t - \theta)\right]d\sigma(\theta)$$

or

$$\varepsilon(t) = \frac{\sigma(t)}{E} + \frac{1}{E}\int_{\theta = -\infty}^{\theta = t}\sigma(\theta)\left[\frac{1}{t_e} - \frac{d\psi(t - \theta)}{d\theta}\right]d\theta.$$

The *Becker integral* in this last equation is easily evaluated after substituting in it $\sigma(\theta) = \sigma_0 e^{\omega \theta}$ and

$$\frac{d\psi(t - \theta)}{d\theta} = -\frac{E e^{-(t-\theta)/t_r}}{E_r t_r},$$

giving

$$\varepsilon(t) = \left[1 + \frac{1}{\omega t_e} + \frac{E}{E_r(1 + \omega t_r)}\right]\frac{\sigma_0 e^{\omega t}}{E},$$

with the interesting result that in this solid each of the three parts of strain (the elastic ε', the viscous ε'', and the recoverable ε''', corresponding to the three terms within the brackets) increases with the same time factor $e^{\omega t}$ as the stress itself, as is indicated by the triple family of affine curves in Fig. 16-54 and that if, in the last equation, one writes for $\varepsilon = \varepsilon_0 e^{\omega t}$, $\sigma_0 e^{\omega t} = \sigma(t)$, it also solves the inverse problem for the transient strain ε.

EXAMPLE 2. For an exercise, verify *Becker's integral* expressing the total aftereffect for $t > t_1$,

$$\varepsilon''(t) + \varepsilon'''(t) = \frac{1}{Et_e}\int_{\theta = 0}^{\theta = t_1}\sigma(\theta)\,d\theta + \frac{e^{-(t-t_1)/t_r}}{E_r t_r}\int_{\theta = 0}^{\theta = t_1}\sigma(\theta)e^{-(t_1 - \theta)/t_r}\,d\theta,$$

in a solid that complies with the same, linear speed relations that were stipulated in Example 1, but assume that the transient stress $\sigma(t)$ acted during a limited time $0 \leq t \leq t_1$ and was released at time t_1.

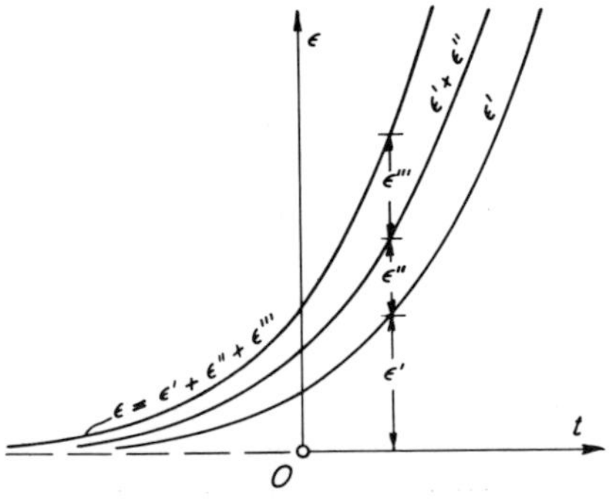

One sees from the preceding equation that, if the load was held invariable at $\sigma = \sigma_0 = $ const over the interval of time $0 \leq t \leq t_1$ and thereafter suddenly released, an aftereffect

$$\varepsilon''(t) + \varepsilon'''(t) = \frac{\sigma_0 t_1}{Et_e}$$

$$+ \frac{\sigma_0}{E_r}e^{-t/t_r}(e^{t_1/t_r} - 1), \qquad t > t_1,$$

results.

FIG. 16-54. Development of elastic (ε'), viscous (ε''), and recoverable (ε''') parts of strain ε.

EXAMPLE 3. Assuming that the strain ε has two parts, an elastic strain $\varepsilon' = \sigma/E$ and a semipermanent strain ε''', $\varepsilon = \varepsilon' + \varepsilon'''$, and that the aftereffect

ε''' develops similarly as in Example 1 under a *linear* speed law $\sigma'' = g_r(\dot{\varepsilon}''') = 3\mu_r\dot{\varepsilon}''' = E_r t_r \dot{\varepsilon}'''$, compare *the hereditary nuclei* (memory functions) in the two definite integrals expressing the aftereffects to be observed in the direct problem (transient stress is given) and in the inverse problem (transient straining is prescribed).

Obviously, the unit recovery function associated with steady stress is the one defined in Example 1:

$$\psi(t) = \frac{E}{E_r}(1 - e^{-t/t_r}),$$

but the elementary relaxation process under steady strain $\varepsilon = \varepsilon_i = \sigma_i/E = $ const, being controlled by the differential equation

$$\dot{\varepsilon}''' + \frac{\varepsilon'''}{T} = \varepsilon_i\left(\frac{1}{T} - \frac{1}{t_r}\right) = \text{const}, \qquad T = \frac{t_r}{1 + E/E_r},$$

supplies, through

$$\sigma = \sigma_i - E\varepsilon''' = \sigma_i\phi(t),$$

the unit relaxation function $\phi(t)$:

$$\phi(t) = \frac{T}{t_r} + \left(1 - \frac{T}{t_r}\right)e^{-t/T}.$$

Thus the hereditary nuclei for the direct problem are

$$-\frac{d\psi(t-\theta)}{d\theta} = \frac{E}{E_r t_r}e^{-(t-\theta)/t_r}$$

and for the inverse problem,

$$+\frac{d\phi(t-\theta)}{d\theta} = \left(\frac{1}{T} - \frac{1}{t_r}\right)e^{-(t-\theta)/T}.$$

Therefore the direct problem is solved by Eq. (16-245a):

$$\varepsilon(t) = \frac{\sigma(t)}{E} + \frac{1}{E_r t_r}\int_0^t e^{-(t-\theta)/t_r}\cdot\sigma(\theta)\,d\theta, \qquad t \geq 0,$$

and the inverse problem, using Eq. (16-255), by

$$\sigma(t) = E\left[\varepsilon(t) - \left(\frac{1}{T} - \frac{1}{t_r}\right)\int_0^t e^{-(t-\theta)/T}\cdot\varepsilon(\theta)\,d\theta\right], \qquad t \geq 0,$$

the corresponding aftereffects being expressed by a BECKER and a BOLTZMANN-VOLTERRA integral, respectively, multiplied by the factors preceding each. If the functions $\sigma(\theta)$ or $\varepsilon(\theta)$ appearing behind the integral signs are considered as the unknowns, each of the two preceding integral equations is directly resolved by the other equation.

EXAMPLE 4. For the type of solid in which the total strain equals $\varepsilon = \varepsilon' + \varepsilon'''$, suppose that the aftereffect strain ε''' under a steady stress $\sigma = $ const increases with time t along a logarithmic function

$$\varepsilon''' = \frac{\sigma}{E_r}\ln\left(1 + \frac{t}{t_r}\right) = \frac{\sigma}{E}\psi(t),$$

defining the unit response

$$\psi(t) = \frac{E}{E_r}\ln\left(1 + \frac{t}{t_r}\right).$$

This is equivalent to postulating for the part stress $\sigma'' = g_r(\dot{\varepsilon}''')$ of $\sigma = \sigma' + \sigma''$, a *logarithmic speed law*, namely, of the form

$$\sigma'' = \sigma - E_r\varepsilon''' = \sigma\left(1 + \ln\frac{E_r t_r\dot{\varepsilon}'''}{\sigma}\right),$$

showing that the above assumed time functions, expressing ε''' and ψ, in fact satisfy the two nonlinear differential equations under steady stress $\sigma = \text{const}$:

$$\frac{d\varepsilon'''}{dt} = \frac{\sigma}{E_r t_r}e^{-E_r\varepsilon'''/\sigma}, \qquad \frac{d\psi}{dt} = \frac{E}{E_r t_r}e^{-E_r\psi/E}.$$

Since the hereditary nucleus equals

$$-\frac{d\psi(t-\theta)}{d\theta} = \frac{E}{E_r(t_r + t - \theta)},$$

Becker's equation (16-245a),

$$\varepsilon(t) = \frac{\sigma(t)}{E} + \frac{1}{E_r}\int_{\theta=0}^{\theta=t}\frac{\sigma(\theta)\,d\theta}{t_r + t - \theta}, \qquad t \geqq 0,$$

solves the transient loading problem for a solid in which the part of stress σ'' dependent on the rate of strain $\dot{\varepsilon}'''$ is a logarithmic function of it. This is noted because the memory function appearing in the above integral has frequently figured in the classical work on aftereffects.

The corresponding relaxation and inverse problem for this type of solid, however, becomes more involved. Under steady strain $\varepsilon = \sigma_i/E = \text{const}$ relaxation requires the integration of

$$\frac{d\sigma}{dt} = -\frac{\sigma}{\alpha t_r}e^{-\alpha(\sigma_i - \sigma)/\sigma}, \qquad \alpha = \frac{E_r}{E},$$

showing that the asymptote $d\sigma/dt = 0$ in any case coincides with the t axis, $\sigma = 0$. By using $s = \alpha\sigma_i/\sigma$ (when $0 \leqq t < \infty$, $\alpha \leqq s < \infty$) as a new variable, this equation transforms into

$$\frac{ds}{dt} = \frac{e^\alpha}{\alpha t_r}\cdot se^{-s},$$

giving

$$t = t_r\alpha e^{-\alpha}\int_\alpha^s \frac{e^s\,ds}{s} = t_r\alpha e^{-\alpha}\left(\ln\frac{s}{\alpha} + \frac{s-\alpha}{1.1} + \frac{s^2-\alpha^2}{2.2!} + \frac{s^3-\alpha^3}{3.3!} + \cdots\right),$$

where the infinite power series which converges better as the series of the exponential function e^s may serve well for numerically evaluating s, the stress $\sigma = \sigma_i\phi(t)$, and the unit relaxation function $\phi(t) = \alpha/s$ in their dependence on the time t, particularly for computing smaller values of s and greater values of σ and of $\phi(t)$.

Since an analytical expression in closed form for $\phi(t)$ does not become readily available, one may, however, set up for $\phi(t)$ a finite sum of terms,

$$\phi(t) = \sum_{n=0}^{m} a_n e^{-nt/t_r}, \qquad (n = 0, 1, \ldots, m),$$

and may compute the constants a_n in it from the conditions that the curve corresponding to this finite sum of terms passes through a few discrete points (ϕ_k, t_k) which one has chosen so that they satisfy the infinite power series through which t was expressed above. When the constant α is a small quantity, by neglecting all terms in the power series, putting $e^\alpha = 1$, in first approximation,

$$s = \frac{\alpha \sigma_i}{\sigma} = \frac{\alpha}{\phi(t)} = \alpha e^{t/\alpha t_r},$$

$$\phi(t) = e^{-t/\alpha t_r} = e^{-Et/E_r t_r},$$

may be taken, supplying with the hereditary nucleus

$$\frac{d\phi(t - \theta)}{d\theta} = \frac{E}{E_r t_r} e^{-E(t-\theta)/E_r t_r}$$

the solution of the inverse problem for transient straining $\varepsilon(t)$ after Eq. (16-254):

$$\sigma(t) = E\varepsilon(t) - \frac{E^2}{E_r t_r} \int_{\theta=0}^{\theta=t} \varepsilon(\theta) e^{-E(t-\theta)/E_r t_r} \, d\theta.$$

EXAMPLE 5. Supposing a solid in which the total strain $\varepsilon = \varepsilon' + \varepsilon'''$, assume now for the part stress $\sigma'' = g_r(\dot{\varepsilon}''') = c(\dot{\varepsilon}''')^n$ a power function of rate of strain $\dot{\varepsilon}'''$. With reference to Sec. 16-2I, Eq. (16-98), in which this speed law was considered for any exponent n $(0 < n < 1)$, in order to avoid carrying some irrelevant constants, let us use in this example the speed law $\sigma'' = c\sqrt{\dot{\varepsilon}'''}$, taking $n = \frac{1}{2}$. Under a steady stress $\sigma = $ const imposed at time $t = 0$ we found that the strain ε''', after Eq. (16-98), should increase with time $t > 0$ as follows:

$$\varepsilon''' = \frac{\sigma}{E_r}\left(1 - \frac{c^2}{c^2 + E_r \sigma t}\right) = \frac{\sigma}{E} \psi(t).$$

Since the unit response

$$\psi(t - \theta) = \frac{E}{E_r}\left[1 - \frac{c^2}{c^2 + E_r \sigma \cdot (t - \theta)}\right]$$

belongs to the class of functions $\psi(t - \theta, \sigma)$ dependent also on the stress σ as a variable parameter, we have

$$\frac{\partial \psi}{\partial \theta} = -\frac{Ec^2 \sigma}{[c^2 + \sigma E_r(t - \theta)]^2},$$

$$\frac{\partial \psi}{\partial \sigma} = \frac{Ec^2(t - \theta)}{[c^2 + \sigma E_r(t - \theta)]^2};$$

hence the *total anelastic aftereffect* $\varepsilon'''(t)$ under a transient stress $\sigma(\theta)$ that begins to act with the finite value σ_0 at time $t = 0$, according to Eq. (16-245), at time t will be expressed by the integral

$$\varepsilon'''(t) = c^2 \int_{\theta=0}^{\theta=t} \frac{(t - \theta)(\sigma - \sigma_0)(d\sigma/d\theta) + \sigma^2}{[c^2 + \sigma E_r(t - \theta)]^2} \, d\theta,$$

in the integrant of which the abbreviated symbol σ stands for the value of stress $\sigma(\theta)$ at intermediate time θ. One verifies that for a steady stress $\sigma(\theta) = \sigma_0 = $ const the integral indeed reduces to the value $\varepsilon''' = \sigma\psi(t)/E$ given in the first equation in this example.

It is hoped that these five examples have further clarified the usefulness of constructing the two unit functions $\psi(t)$ and $\phi(t)$ from several basic speed laws that figure prominently in the observed behavior of actual, elastically imperfect, solid materials and illustrate their applicability in the evaluation of aftereffects by means of definite integrals.

16-8.   The Influence of Temperature.   It is impossible to abstract in a limited space rules of general validity covering the variation of the yield strength and creep properties over a broad range of temperatures in the ductile metals.   We shall confine ourselves to illustrating how the temperature affects the parameters entering in the function expressing the hyperbolic sine speed law and some properties characterizing the tensile behavior of metals, basing the comparison on a few, selected series of reliable tests.   It has naturally long been known that an increase (decrease) of the absolute temperature T may cause the same change in the yield strength—generally speaking—as a certain decrease (increase) in the speed of deformation or of the permanent rate of strain u causes, the influences of the two variables T and u on the response of the yield or flow stress σ being opposite to each other.

Concerning the deformation speed law

$$u = u_0 \sinh \frac{\sigma}{\sigma_0} , \qquad\qquad (16\text{-}257)$$

where $u = d\varepsilon/dt$ represents the minimum permanent strain rate in long-time creep tests under invariable stress σ, an extensive series of tests by EVAN A. DAVIS[1] has supplied the following important results for pure, *oxygen-free copper:*

1. At room temperature this copper does not reach a minimum creep rate in 3,500 hr testing time; commercial copper not within a year.

2. Around 80°C a minimum rate becomes discernible, and as the temperature is increased the time required to reach a minimum creep rate is decreased.   An example is reproduced in the creep curves observed at 165°C in Fig. 16-55.

3. The hyperbolic sine law [Eq. (16-257)] fits the data of tests run at temperatures between $\theta = 80°C$ and $235°C$ very well, as is illustrated in Fig. 16-56 by five curves in which the stresses σ were plotted versus the logarithms of the minimum rates of strain u at the indicated five

[1] Creep and Relaxation of Oxygen-free Copper, J. Appl. Mechanics, June, 1943.

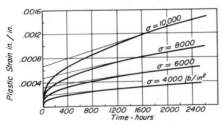

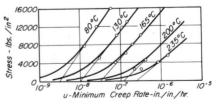

FIG. 16-55.   Long-time creep of oxygen-free copper at 165°C. (*Tests by Evan A. Davis.*)

FIG. 16-56. Stress–creep-rate relations for oxygen-free copper.

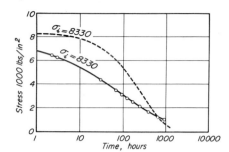

FIG. 16-57. Relaxation of oxygen-free copper at 235°C.

temperatures θ = const, the curves approaching at greater rates u inclined straight lines corresponding to $\sigma = \sigma_0 \ln (2u/u_0)$.

4. The material constant σ_0 varies linearly, decreasing with the temperature θ.

5. Likewise the material constant u_0 decreases with the temperature θ. The intercepts of the straight asymptotes in Fig. 16-56 at $\sigma = 0$ furnish the value of $u_0/2$ read on the logarithmic scale. A relation based on the so-called reaction rate theory,[1] claimed in physics of the solid state,

$$u_0 = Ae^{-B/T} \qquad (16\text{-}258)$$

(T = absolute temperature, A, B = constants) did not fit these tests well.

6. The relaxation of stress σ with time t, while the length in the copper bars was held invariable, is shown in an example in Fig. 16-57 on a semilogarithmic plot. The dashed curve in this figure represents the relaxation of stress σ according to the pure hyperbolic sine speed law as derived in Sec. 16-2C in Eq. (16-41) or (16-42) in which, however, no account was taken of any strain hardening nor of recovery of strain and of the finite intercepts ε_0 of the backward extended straight portions of the creep lines $\varepsilon = \varepsilon_0 + u_{min}t$. The observed stress curve in Fig. 16-57 drops first at a much steeper rate $d\sigma/dt$ than the simple theory predicts in the dashed curve and subsequently runs flatter than it.

7. Upon sudden unloading, the creep curves disclosed a pronounced recovery of strain.

Davis emphasized the importance of including in a theory of relaxation the phenomenon of recovery of plastic strain; his opinion is supported by his tests and the outline of a theory which was indicated in Sec. 16-2I in Eqs. (16-106) through (16-108) and allowed us qualitatively to predict that in a recovery-sensitive solid the stress should start to drop initially at a much faster rate than in a solid in which no parts of permanent strain are recovered.

---

[1] W. KAUZMANN, Flow of Solid Metals from the Standpoint of the Chemical Rate Theory, Metals Technol., June, 1941; also Trans. AIME, vol. 143, pp. 57–83, 1941.

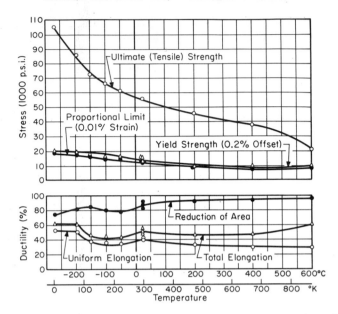

Fɪɢ. 16-58. The effect of temperature on the tensile properties of annealed commercially pure nickel.

The concepts in regard to the influence of temperature on yielding, creep, and the conditions of fracture have been greatly clarified by extending the range of testing temperatures to extremely low temperatures approaching zero degree absolute. E. T. Wᴇssᴇʟ deserves credit for having developed special equipment for making tensile tests with metal bars under controlled rates of strain within an air chamber in which testing temperatures down to 4.2°K (absolute temperature) could be maintained[1] and for having expressed the mechanical behavior of metals over wide ranges of the temperature. In the following, Wᴇssᴇʟ's extensive series of tensile tests are reviewed by reproducing in Figs. 16-58 to 16-66 his observations taken from his papers.

For the face-centered-cubic metal *nickel* (Fig. 16-58) and the closed-packed-hexagonal metal *zirconium* (Fig. 16-59) the conventional 0.2 per cent offset in the rising part of the stress-strain curve (the conventional,

[1] E. T. Wᴇssᴇʟ, Tension Testing Apparatus for the Temperature Range of −320°F to −452°F (77°K to 4.2°K); ASTM Bull. 211, January, 1956. The apparatus designed at the Westinghouse Research Laboratories in Pittsburgh consists of an inner and an outer double *Dewar flask* of cylindrical form. In the inner flask, in its lower open Dewar cylinder, liquid helium and in the outer double cylinder, liquid nitrogen could circulate. A good summary of Wᴇssᴇʟ's investigations may be found in his paper: Some Exploratory Observations of the Tensile Properties of Metals at Very Low Temperatures; Trans. ASME, vol. **49**, Preprint 3, 26 pp., 1956, quoting 28 references to earlier work.

so-called "yield strength") rises comparatively little with a lowering of temperature, in contrast to the metals having a body-centered-cubic lattice, such as, for example, *an alloy steel* (SAE 4340 type, quenched and tempered, Fig. 16-60), in which the proportional limit and the 0.2 per cent yield strength increased steeply when the absolute temperature T was lowered to 4.2°K.   The variation with T is reproduced for the 0.2 per cent yield strength σ_y, the ultimate strength $\sigma_{l,\max}$ (load maximum), reduction of area at fracture $q = (A_0 - A_f)/A_0$, and uniform elongation ε_m at load maximum $\sigma_{l,\max}$ for these three metals in Fig. 16-58 (annealed, commercial nickel), Fig. 16-59 (annealed zirconium), and Fig. 16-60 (the aforementioned alloy steel), the latter disclosing the very steep rise of the flow stresses required to deform such a steel at very low temperatures.

Figure 16-61 offers a glance at the behavior characterizing metals of body-centered-cubic structure in the stress-strain diagrams of *niobium*[1] stretched under the same strain rate of $u = d\varepsilon/dt = 0.001$ per sec at seven temperatures.   The greatest ductility appears around room temperature, 25°C; a substantial rise in yield and ultimate strength

---

[1] E. T. WESSEL and D. D. LAWTHERS, The Ductile-to-brittle Transition in Niobium, Meeting of Electrochemical Society, Washington, D.C., May, 1957.

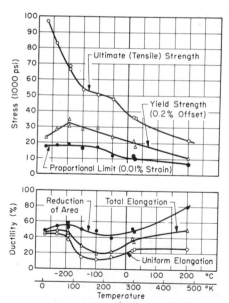

FIG. 16-59. The effect of temperature on the tensile properties of annealed zirconium.

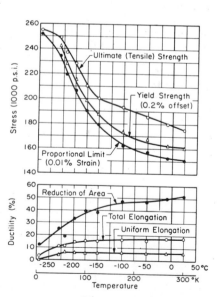

FIG. 16-60. The effect of temperature on the tensile properties of an alloy steel (SAE 4340 type) in the quenched and tempered condition.

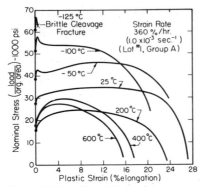

FIG. 16-61. The effect of temperature on the stress-strain curves of annealed niobium.

occurs around 300°C, accompanied by loss of ductility at the temperatures $+400°C$ to $+600°C$ (tentatively attributed to strain aging). The ultimate ($\sigma_{l,\max}$) strength disclosed a marked dip at 200°C and increased again with decreasing temperature. Below $-50°C$ an upper yield stress appeared which at $-100°C$ even surpassed the load maximum, and at $-125°C$ this metal broke right after the drop from the upper yield point in a brittle cleavage fracture.

The effect of temperature on the conventional tensile properties of *mild steel (ship plate)*[1] is reproduced in Fig. 16-63, showing the well-known dip around 100°C and hump around 250°C of the ultimate strength $\sigma_{l,\max}$ attributed to strain aging. The instructive series of stress-strain curves for this mild steel recorded at eight temperatures below 0°C under the uniform rate of strain $u = 0.00208$ per sec is seen

[1] E. T. WESSEL, "A Tensile Study of Brittle Failure in Ship-plate," ASTM 59th Annual Meeting, 1956. During the last war hundreds of cases of severe damage occurred in the hulls of ships, in their decks and welded steel bodies, through sudden cracking, with such disastrous consequences that entire ships broke into two pieces. Almost all failures occurred when the air temperatures were near or below freezing.

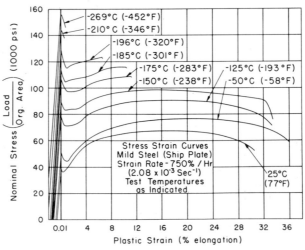

FIG. 16-62. The effect of test temperature on the stress-strain curves of mild steel (ship plate).

in Fig. 16-62, disclosing distinctly the variation of the phenomenon of the drop from the upper to the lower yield point which was sharply pronounced from room temperature to the lowest temperature of 4°K. The upper yield stress increases in this interval to *four times* its value at 25°C.   At −269° and −200°C brittle cleavage fracture occurs right during the initial drop of load, but in the range from −196° to −160°C mild steel is capable of sustaining some plastic extension up to 14 per cent before the cleavage fracture suddenly sets in.   A third type of failure occurs between −160° and −50°C while the elongations increase up to 30 per cent strain and necking develops.   The failure initiates with a fibrous (shear) fracture in the center of the minimum cross section of the neck, spreading to what appeared as a finely faceted fracture surface over the entire section.   The usual "cup and cone" fracture known at room temperatures was not observed at and below −50°C.   The number of shear facets increased with increasing temperature in the fracture plane, starting from a small fibrous dot in the center of the area at −160°C and increasing all over it above −50°C.[1]

A very interesting observation worth mentioning is the appearance of densely distributed, fine serrations in the stress-strain diagrams of those metals that retain a remarkably high ductility at the lowest temperature of 4.2°K of liquid helium.   After the flow stresses σ_l and $\sigma = (1 + \varepsilon)\sigma_l$ have gradually risen due to strain hardening, at 4.2°K *very regular serrations were seen developing in the stress-strain curve* with increasing amplitudes and decreasing frequencies (Figs. 16-64 through 16-66) while the magnitude of the permanent strain accompanying each drop of the load increases with the total mean extension ε.   These diagrams are reminiscent of the jagged curves observed by MISS C. F. ELAM for a quenched aluminum alloy and in Armco iron and by M. J. MANJOINE for mild steel[2] (stretched very slowly at 200°C), considered as a manifestation of pronounced strain aging within the successively

---

[1] The latter observations about the mode in which an aggregate of ferrite crystals breaks in mild steel agree perfectly with those made by HARMER E. DAVIS and associates at the University of California in Berkeley in 1946, who found that the relative proportion between the number of cleavage to shear facets in the central portion of the fracture surface increases with lowering of the temperature.   See Vol. I, page 185.

Lack of space prohibits enumerating the practically important observations by WESSEL on the effects of sharp, circumferential notches in tensile tests on fracture at low temperatures; in view of the vast amount of work that has been devoted to this field covering elevated temperatures, the reader must be referred in the latter respect to the extensive Literature Survey on the Notch-sensitivity of High Temperature Alloys, prepared by G. SACHS and W. F. BROWN, JR., with the assistance of J. G. SESSLER, for the Joint ASTM-ASME Committee on the effect of temperature on the properties of metals, June, 1957, with elaborate curve sheets and tables.

[2] Cf. Vol. I, pages 314–316.

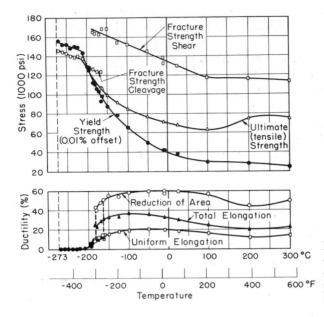

FIG. 16-63. The effect of temperature on the conventional tension properties of mild steel (ship plate).

forming, discrete flow layers that could distinctly be detected on the unevenly jagged surface of the specimens. But age hardening as a slow process of internal diffusion of atom groups fails to explain the appearance of serrated stress-strain curves at such a low temperature as $4.2°K$. There is, however, little doubt that they are caused also by the formation of many, discrete flow (LÜDERS') layers in which the plastic distortion is instantaneously concentrated. In other words, the regular mode of *smooth yielding under a uniform axial strain ε* accompanied by uniform lateral contractions $\varepsilon_c = -1 + (1 + \varepsilon)^{-1/2}$ *is inhibited* in the group of metals that still discloses a remarkably high

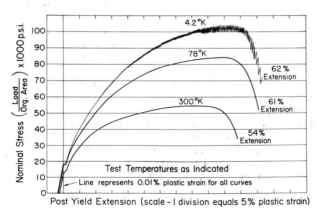

FIG. 16-64. The effect of temperature on the stress-strain curves of commercially pure nickel in the annealed condition.

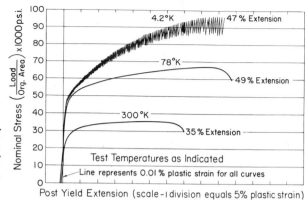

FIG. 16-65. The effect of temperature on the stress-strain curves of arc-remelted zirconium in the annealed condition.

ductility and sufficient tensile strength at temperatures approaching the absolute zero. For a tentative explanation of this strange phenomenon reference is made to the heat shocks accompanying localized yielding within thin layers—to the "adiabatic" formation of discrete flow (Lüders') layers—at extremely low temperatures which was considered in Sec. 13-7.

Concerning the data that have been assembled covering the values of the intercept ε_0 and of the minimum creep rate u_m defining creep ε with time t along idealized straight lines $\varepsilon = \varepsilon_0 + u_m t$ and the times t_r at which rupture is to be expected in tensile tests carried out under invariable loads σ_l per unit of area of the original cross section for metals and alloys in their dependence on the temperature θ, the best that can be done is to record ε_0, u_m for various loads $\sigma_l = $ const and temperatures $\theta = $ const in plots of ε_0 and σ_l versus log u_m and of σ_l versus the logarithms of rupture time (log t_r) and attempt to extrapolate the curves

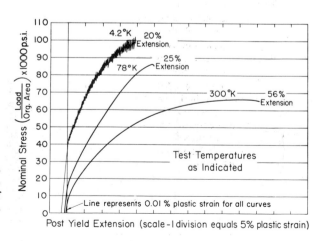

FIG. 16-66. The effect of temperature on the stress-strain curves of beta brass in the annealed condition.

to service time t_s.   The attempts to deduce functional relations from cross plots using temperature θ as a variable parameter, however, have seldom furnished clear-cut forms of such functions over a wider range of θ or of more general validity.[1]

M. J. MANJOINE found in extensive series of creep-fracture tests for various Cr-Ni steels that the curves representing the load stress σ_l above the rupture time t_r in double logarithmic plots tended to become, at greater values of $t_r = 10^3$ to 10^4 hr, a set of *parallel* straight lines, permitting an extrapolation to service times t_s of the order of 10^5 hr within the temperature range 650° to 1100°C and to conclude that the exponent m in the tentatively assumed power function

$$\sigma_r = \sigma_1 \left(\frac{t_r}{t_1}\right)^m,$$

expressing the tensile rupture stress σ_r as a function of the rupture time t_r (σ_1, t_1 are material constants at a given temperature) in a first approximation, was independent of temperature.

We may mention that certain *ceramic oxide bodies*[2] have a marked superiority in both strength and creep characteristics at around 1420° to 1500°C above the best available high-strength–temperature-resistant metal alloys, reaching a short-time tensile strength equal to 180,000 lb/in.^{2} (12,600 kg/cm^2), and have been used successfully in jet-engine and gas-turbine parts.

[1] F. R. LARSON and J. MILLER, A Time-Temperature Relationship for Rupture and Creep Stresses, Trans. ASME, vol. 74, no. 5, p. 765, 1952, represent the $\log \sigma_l$ by an inclined straight line $\log \sigma_l = \log \sigma_0 - cp$, plotted above a variable parameter $p = T(20 + \log t_r)$ (T = absolute temperature; σ_0, c are constants) in creep-rupture tests.   On the other hand, S. S. MANSON and A. M. HAFERD, A Linear Time-Temperature Relation for Extrapolation of Creep and Stress-rupture Data, Natl. Advisory Comm. Aeronaut., Tech. Note 2890, 1953, propose a time-temperature parameter $q = (T - T_a)/\ln (t_r/t_a)$ which is a function $q = f(\sigma_l)$ singly dependent on the stress σ_l (T_a, t_a are constants), claiming that if one plots $\log t_r$, the logarithms of rupture time t_r versus the absolute temperature T, there results a pencil of rays converging at the point (T_a, $\log t_a$), each ray referring to a given stress σ_l = const.   Empirical relations based on parameters such as p or q—it seems—do not offer an insight into the complex phenomenon of creep-rupture behavior at high temperatures in view of the fact that tensile bars of ductile metals stretched under an invariable load σ_l = const elongate nonuniformly and neck down considerably before they break, hence are deformed under stresses that vary considerably over the gauge length.

[2] BURDICK, MORELAND, and GELLER, Strength and Creep Characteristics of Ceramic Bodies at Elevated Temperatures, Natl. Advisory Comm. Aeronaut., Tech. Note 1561, 1950.

Part VI

OUTLINE OF SELECTED PROBLEMS IN GEOMECHANICS

CHAPTER 17

OUTLINE OF SELECTED PROBLEMS IN GEOMECHANICS

17-1. Geometry of Simple Faults

Nobody will believe it. One will call me a fool.
Arnold Escher (1839).

BERTRAND's vision and the perception of BERTRAND, SCHARDT, LUGEON of overthrusted sheets, "Nappes de recouvrement," the so-called Decken-theory were correct. It spread in triumphal conquest since 1898 from West to East, converting the science of alpine geology. Nothing comparable ever happened in our science. "Impossible, unthinkable, a nonsense, one pulls the ground beneath our feet away—so cried out many people and even today some."

ALBERT HEIM. "Geologie der Schweiz," vol. II, third part, "The Swiss Alps," A. Introduction: History of the Geology of the Swiss Alps, I. The development of our knowledge about the evolution of the Alps, p. 16, Chr. Herm. Tauchnitz, Leipzig, 1920.

The evolution of prominent features of the earth's surface—in the high continental mountain ranges, in long, extended swellings, in the great deeps of the ocean floors, on a grand scale—and the evidences of plastic distortion and disruption of the rock strata attracting the attention of naturalists have inspired mechanically inclined observers to describe the states of stress and strain in the upper, solid parts of the earth's crust and of the relative motions involved therein. While the phenomena of long-time formation and of plastic distortion of the rock strata are studied in geology and the short-time, dynamic actions in seismology, it was thought that a few selected questions concerning the equilibrium states within the earth's upper shell which are amenable to a limited, mechanical analysis may be listed in this last chapter, because they are closely related to problems treated in this book, as, for example, the theory of earth pressures or of the viscoelastic bending of slabs floating on semifluid substratum.

A first step in this direction should be briefly to acquaint the reader with geometric terminology used in geology, describing the effects of

FIG. 17-1. ALBERT HEIM.† Born Apr. 12, 1849, in Zurich; died Aug. 31, 1937, in Zurich. This portrait is reproduced from the Hundredth Anniversary Volume: "Eidgenössische Technische Hochschule 1855–1955," 723 pp., Buchverlag der Neuen Zürcher Zeitung, Zurich, 1955.

finite strains that were localized within one or two narrow layers and acted either simultaneously or transgressed at different times in oblique directions through parallel sedimentary rock strata.   Traces of homogeneous or variable, permanent strains of finite magnitude are seen in innumerable examples in nature.   They may become measurable by the distortions suffered by the remnants of the bones of fossil animals.[1] A beautiful example observed by ALBERT HEIM can be seen in Fig. 17-2. The broken spine of the fossil fish clearly indicates that the rock in

[1] Old-time Swiss paleontologists (H. Wettstein, 1886) thought that the different forms and sizes in which they saw the skeletons of the fossil fish *Lepidopus* belonged to different species of it, giving them a variety of different names, until ALBERT HEIM pointed out that not the species were different, but only the principal strains by which the rocks had been deformed.

† Swiss geologist, author of the monumental book "Geologie der Schweiz," vol. 1, "Molasseland und Juragebirge," 704 pp., 1919; vol. 2, "Die Schweizer Alpen," 976 pp., 1922, Christian Hermann Tauchnitz, Leipzig.   This most complete treatise on the geology of the *Swiss Alps* contains many profiles with the minutest details through the folded chains of the Swiss Jura ranges and through the main massifs of the Alps in Switzerland, traced by Heim's hand and by his son ARNOLD HEIM (who became his successor in the chair at the Swiss Federal Institute of Technology in Zurich), in conjunction with his life-long studies in the field and most careful explorations of the mechanical causes of the folding and the phenomena of deformation in the stratigraphy of the Alps.   *Albert Heim emphasized* more than seventy years ago *the plastic distortion of the rocks* under mountain chains, long before the first laboratory tests were made proving the continuous, plastic deformability of natural rocks under confining pressures. He was a marvelous lecturer who during his lectures would sketch from free hand on the blackboard pictures of mammoths, fossil fishes, or the tracings made by prehistoric man, discovered on the walls of caves, with the utmost perfection, as the author remembers vividly from a course which he attended in 1902.   Albert Heim was one of the greatest geologists of all times; his beautiful, patriarchal features disclose the greatness of his humble character.

which it was found embedded was deformed by plastic flow, the arrow pointing in the direction in which the principal extension acted. Geologists call a sudden discontinuity in the parallel layering of rocks a *fault* (Fig. 17-3) and speak of *folds* if the original equidistant layering has undergone gradual distortion, the thickness of the layers (measured perpendicularly to their boundaries) having become variable.   For example, in the *middle limb* of the *recumbent fold* (Fig. 17-4) it is the smallest, while in the *vault* or *trough* it is much larger than in the *upper* or *lower limbs*.   As W. Schmidt[1] pointed out long ago, such wavy distortions need not be considered as a "bending" or "arching" action but are merely the *consequence of a shearing strain of variable intensity* that transgressed at an inclined direction through the formerly parallel strata.   Faults, if they are not de facto shear fractures, comprise a layer of finite thickness b within which the relative displacement u of part A (Fig. 17-5) with respect to part B of the mountain is a function $u = f(y)$ of the coordinate y measured perpendicularly to the fault

[1] Walter Schmidt, "Tektonik und Verformungslehre," 208 pp., Verlagsbuchhandlung Gebrüder Bornträger, Berlin, 1932.

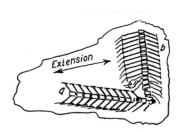

Fig. 17-2. Fossil-fish remains deformed together with rock in which they were embedded. The two pieces a and b of the broken spine of a fossil fish belonged to the same skeleton of *Lepidopus*. Being buried at a different angle to the main direction of the plastic extension (marked with arrows), they appear distorted by different amounts. Tertiary rocks, Alps. (*According to Albert Heim, "Geologie der Schweiz," pt.* **3**, *p.* 88, *Tauchnitz, Leipzig, 1920.*)

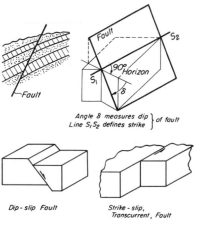

Angle δ measures dip } of fault
Line S_1S_2 defines strike }

Dip-slip Fault   Strike-slip, Transcurrent, Fault

Fig. 17-3. Faults.

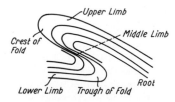

Upper Limb

Middle Limb

Crest of Fold

Lower Limb   Trough of Fold   Root

Fig. 17-4.   Recumbent fold. (*According to A. Heim, "Geologie der Schweiz," pt.* **3**, *p.* 8, *Tauchnitz, Leipzig,* 1920.)

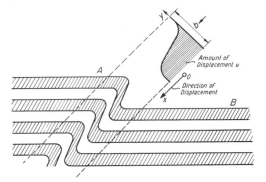

FIG. 17-5. Simple shearing displacements in a strip crossing strata at an angle.

plane, creating a simple shearing strain of variable intensity:

$$\gamma = \frac{\partial u}{\partial y} = \frac{df}{dy}.$$

Leaving aside confusing fault nomenclature used by mining engineers, the maximum value of the unit shearing strain γ as just defined measures the degree of specific distortion within a fault. Strongly localized simple shears γ in faults that have suffered a large slip may greatly change the crystalline structure of the affected rocks. The extreme consequences of such motions lead to the familiar slaty cleavage, pronounced anisotropy with respect to fracture strength, densely laminated structure, schistosity, etc.[1]

Pebbles, round mud pellets, and small, fossil marine animals that originally had a spherical form with a pronounced radial structure (*oölites*) have been utilized by geologists as a welcome means for quantitatively determining *Cauchy's strain ellipsoid* in the size and orientation of its principal strain axes in plastically deformed, strongly folded rock strata in which the fossils were found embedded. They served ERNST CLOOS[2] in his extensive, careful studies of the mechanism of folding in the Appalachian Mountains.

[1] The hard garnets in the eastern Alps, according to W. SCHMIDT, embedded in such severely sheared rocks are seen in rotated positions (Fig. 17-6). They have literally been turned as rigid balls within the plastic rock.

[2] Cf. ERNST CLOOS, Oölite Deformation in the South Mountain Fold, Maryland, Bull. Geol. Soc., vol. 58, pp. 843–918, September, 1947; Geology of the South Mountain Anticlinorium, Maryland, 28 pp., Johns Hopkins Univ. Studies in Geology, no. 16, pt. 1, 1950; and several papers in "The Physical Features of Washington County," 331 pp., Department of Geology, Maryland, 1951. These small *oölites* of originally spherical form of 1 mm diameter in strongly folded rocks were distorted to three-axial ellipsoids, the major, principal strain in them amounting to $\varepsilon_1 = 1$ and more. The strongly contorted folds in these parts of the Appalachians disclose many signs of severe changes in their structure, striation, cleavages in fan-shaped orientation parallel to the major, positive strain in the vaults of the folds, etc.

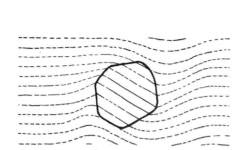

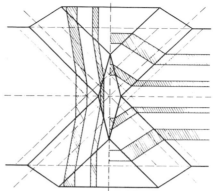

FIG. 17-6. Rotation of laminar markings in rock around and within garnet inclusion. (*According to W. Schmidt.*)

FIG. 17-7. Sketch showing result of two simultaneous shearing displacements of equal amount in two perpendicular strips.

Two idealized examples of disturbance caused in regular stratification through simple shear layers may be instructive to note.   In Fig. 17-7 it is assumed that the distortion is localized within two layers of slip running perpendicularly to each other, under $\gamma =$ const, the same amount of uniform, simple shear, under the action of two horizontal compression forces while both layers were simultaneously produced, displacing on the right side horizontal, and on the left side vertically standing rock strata.   Figure 17-8 shows two similar layers inclined, as one may expect in natural rocks, under angles smaller than 45° with respect to the horizontal thrust and under the assumption that slip layer I formed first and layer II at a later time, this resulting in the contorted profile of the formerly horizontal (partially shaded) strata.

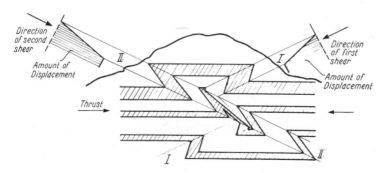

FIG. 17-8. Sketch showing distortion of horizontal strata as result of two consecutive shearing displacements acting in two different directions I and II.

If the unit simple shear γ is variable in each slip layer and one forms after the other, there results the picture seen in Fig. 17-9 with partially curved strata lines.   To the untrained eye such distorted profiles in stratification in normal cross sections at a first glance appear mysterious while in truth they may have a simple kinematic history.

This brings us to the extreme case of considering a large relative slip between two adjoining mountain masses in an *overthrust fault*.   It created a sensation among geologists when ARNOLD ESCHER VON DER LINTH in 1839 discovered that the tops of many high peaks in the central Swiss Alps are made up of geologically much older rocks than the ones in the strata at the bases of the mountains and when he spoke of *Klippen* in reference to these mountain peaks in which he saw "exotic" blocks.   In his imagination he drew two huge, recumbent folds, the *Glarner Doppelfalte*, across the mountains of the Canton Glarus, with their limbs clasped together in horizontal position over a distance of 40 km and with their vaults opposing and touching each other, leaving the two upper-fold limbs passing through the air above the mountains, assuming that they were washed away through the action of erosion. His bold ideas, expressed during the years 1840 to 1850, of the Klippen and of the spectacular *alpine overthrusts* through which rock layers of 1,000 to 2,000 meters thickness were pushed over substratum by distances of many kilometers laid the foundation of the so-called "Decken" theory, of the *alpine nappes* (overthrust sheets), accepted soon thereafter by the leading Swiss geologists ALBERT HEIM (pupil of

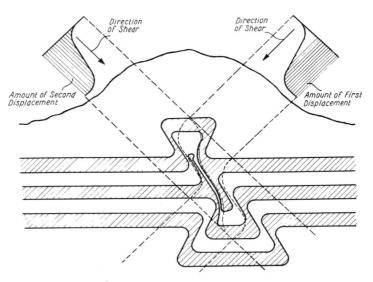

FIG. 17-9. The distortions of a set of parallel strata (layers) as a result of two consecutive shearing displacements acting in two intersecting directions.

Alb. Heim, Geologie der Schweiz   Verlag von Chr. Herm. Tauchnitz, Leipzig

ARNOLD ESCHER V. D. LINTH

1807—1872

Gez. 1870 von Alb. Heim

FIG. 17-10. ARNOLD ESCHER VON DER LINTH. Portrait drawn in 1870 by the hand of ALBERT HEIM.

Arnold Escher), his son ARNOLD HEIM, by MAURICE LUGEON,[1] HANS SCHARDT, and others. ALBERT HEIM wrote in 1878: "It is irrevocable that in the Alps in fact flat overlaying folds (sheets) of the earth's crust exist, which extend over enormous distances and have brought about a total inversion of the succession of rock strata over many hundred square kilometers, that the mountain peaks consist of the oldest and the valleys are cut through the youngest rock strata." The genial MARCEL BERTRAND[2] of France straightened out in 1884 the concept of

[1] Sur la tectonique de la nappe de Morcle et ses conséquences, Eclogae 1912, Compt. rend., vol. 155, Nov. 30, 1912; also vol. 158, June 29, 1914. The great French-Swiss geologist first rejected the Decken theory (1894) but in 1896 avowed himself as one of the converted followers of M. BERTRAND and showed in his classical papers, Les grandes nappes de recouvrement des Alpes du Chablais et de la Suisse, Bull. soc. géol. France, 1901, and Sur la formation des Alpes franco-suisse, ibid., 1904, that overthrusts were also instrumental in the mechanisms elsewhere, in the Austrian Alps, the Carpathians, and the Apennines.

[2] Bull. soc. géol. France, 1884.

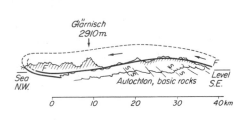

Fig. 17-11. Schematic representation of *Glarner fold* in section through the Glärnisch Mountain. *FF*, the overthrust fault. The details of the nappes were omitted; *ss*, secondary faults. (*After Arnold Heim,* 1910; *reproduced from Albert Heim, "Geologie der Schweiz," vol. 2, no. 3, Fig.* 66, *p.* 265, 1920.)

A. Escher's *Glarner double fold.* In his vision he saw a *single*, huge fold that had been pushed from south to north, covering by a blanket sheet 40 km in length the younger strata in the Canton Glarus along a gently waved single overthrust fault (*FF* in Fig. 17-11, reproduced after Arnold Heim's schematic representation of 1910).

A plausible way of looking at the nappes in the Alps, it seems, is seeing in them the old surface sheets of a long, wavy elevation—a geoanticline—on the gently inclined slopes of which they slipped down under the action of their weight. Suppose that in a remote time past this wavy elevation had risen up to the profile in a vertical section tentatively assumed by the smooth, averaging curve *ABC* in Fig. 17-12, representing one-half of the original anticline which had a total width of 250 to 350 km and the steepest slope inclined at an angle α. In the absence of orogenic, additional, driving, horizontal forces, after a crack opened up at the top of the surface sheet, a nappe can start to slip downhill on the inclined plane, provided that the friction coefficient μ of rock on rock is

$$\mu \leqq \tan \alpha. \tag{17-1}$$

If the height[1] of the anticline is $H = 8$ km, its width $w = 240$ km,

[1] In guessing the height $H = 8$ km ample allowance was given to denudation through erosion, no peak in the central Swiss Alps presently reaching up to more than 5,000 m. The thickness h of the nappe, irrelevant as far as the condition of slip is concerned, in Fig. 17-12 was arbitrarily assumed equal to $h = 2,000$ m.

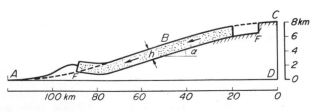

Fig. 17-12. Hypothetically hanging alpine overthrust in early stage of detachment along thrust fault *FF*, postulating that a geoanticline initiated it.

estimating the maximum slope to be $\tan \alpha = 0.1$, a nappe can form unless $\mu < 0.1$.

From an impressive synopsis on overthrust faulting, presented by M. KING HUBBERT and WILLIAM W. RUBEY,[1] it is noted that long overthrusts have been discovered and investigated in many places in the Rocky Mountains and elsewhere in North America, along which entire mountain chains were found displaced horizontally near the Canadian border, in Wyoming, Nevada, etc. It is most interesting that the initial thickness of the displaced, old, huge blocks of rock was tentatively guessed to reach an order of $h = 8,000$ m in some places (see preceding footnote), that the dips of the fault planes (angle of inclination α) were found very small, and that, according to the opinions of such expert geologists as HUBBERT, DALY, and WILLIS, these North American overthrusts, in contrast to the alpine Decken, are thought to have originated along the flanks of shallow *geosynclines*.

This brings us to the *mechanical paradox of large overthrusts* expounded in the paper by HUBBERT and RUBEY. To it the physicist M. S. SMOLUCHOWSKI[2] first called attention in 1909. While the factual evidence of nappes is established beyond any doubt, it was difficult to reconcile the high values of the coefficient of friction μ observed in sliding experiments of dry rock on rock amounting to $\mu \sim 0.3 = \tan \rho$ (angle of friction $\rho = 17°$) with the values of the angles α approaching a small fraction of ρ under which the faults dip. Furthermore one easily sees also that the average, orogenic compression stresses σ_x required to push extended, thick rock sheets many miles long on nearly horizontal fault planes would reach values that no rock could withstand without shattering to pieces. The necessity confronting geologists for finding a property in the rocks adjoining the fault that would reduce materially the frictional resistance to sliding was soon recognized. Two suggestions lay at hand:

1. One was that the nappes were sliding on a thin layer of highly plastic rock. Old ALBERT HEIM thought that a thin layer of rocksalt underlying the western and northern "Prealps" toward the arch of the

---

[1] See Role of Fluid Pressure in Mechanics of Overthrust Faulting, Bull. Geol. Soc. Am., pt. I, vol. 70, February, 1959. Probably the first discovery in America was made by R. G. McCONNELL (1887) in the Canadian Rockies; BAILEY WILLIS (1902) and R. A. DALY (1912) found a horizontal bodily movement along the *Lewis* overthrust in Montana which they estimated to be between 8 and 40 miles. J. GILLULY (1957) recognized in central Nevada a minimum horizontal displacement of 50 miles in rocks having been shifted in a plate of initial thickness as great as 5 miles; C. R. LONGWELL (1922) found in the Muddy Mountains (Nevada) that a block of Paleozoic strata of 2,500 ft thickness had overridden its base for a distance of 15 miles (quoted from the Hubbert and Rubey paper).

[2] Some Remarks on the Mechanics of Overthrusts, Geol. Mag., new ser., p. 204, 1909.

Jura Mountain chains acted as a lubricant, since rocksalt is known to be highly plastic and to be present in many places under these regions;[1] the spectacular folding of the Jura chains (see Fig. 10-30, page 332) supported his views.

2. The second suggestion was that the rocks in a few kilometers depth deformed by creep because of the increasing temperatures with depth.

That water acted as a lubricant has been suggested, but its presence in the contact surface of solid, dry, unsaturated rock pieces does not reduce the coefficient of friction. An exception may be wet clays which in thin layers facilitate gliding, but such layers do not exist in the upper, crystalline rocks in the high Alps.

HUBBERT and RUBEY[2] are to be credited with having greatly clarified the mechanical behavior of fluid-filled porous, solid rocks, saturated with fluid, under the condition that its pressure reaches high values that are comparable with the total, vertical compression stress S_z due to the overburden of the column of rock under its own weight. While this normal stress S_z is the sum of the part σ_z transmitted through the solid skeleton of the rock (if its pores were empty) and of the pressure p of the pore fluid,

$$S_z = \sigma_z + p, \tag{17-2}$$

the critical shear stress τ_{crit} required to slide the block of a nappe acts as if no fluid were present, and the small surface roughnesses of the solid framework would be held pressed together wherever they could contact each other. Hence, the limiting value of the shear stress is computable from the friction law, being associated with the stress σ_z carried through the solid frame of the rock,

$$\tau_{\text{crit}} = \mu\sigma_z = \mu(S_z - p), \tag{17-3}$$

from which it becomes evident that, even though the coefficient of friction μ may have the high values of dry sliding friction, the shear stress τ_{crit} may be substantially reduced with the increasing values of the fluid pore pressure p.

The preceding formulas apply to gravitational sliding on an inclined plane. Under orogenic, horizontal compression forces σ_x, however, this is the maximum principal stress and is greater than S_z, and the pressure p may be raised until it approaches the value of S_z. The observations gathered from deep oil wells (compare the end of Sec. 15-11) support these conclusions and have, according to HUBBERT and RUBEY, shown that fluid pressures p of the order of $p = 0.9S_z$ occur in geosynclinal basins at depths of several kilometers. In conclusion, it may be stated

[1] Or was present ages ago before the ground water leached it out.
[2] *Loc. cit.*

that some of the North American overthrust faults developed along the gently dropping slopes of wide geosynclinal basins at the bottom of which conditions are particularly favorable for causing sliding, because of the accumulation of

FIG. 17-13. Idealized section through a flat geosyncline ABC, showing detachment of a plate of rocks starting to slip down, causing local upfolding at front edge B. (*After Hubbert and Rubey.*)

ground and pore water under high pressures, as exemplified by the low-angle overthrusts in western Wyoming (Fig. 17-13).

17-2. The Pressure in the Interior of the Earth. In the uppermost parts of the earth's crust, near its surface, the principal stresses differ from one another from point to point in the strata of rocks because of the local disturbances in their equilibrium under their weight. But, below this surface zone, the state of equilibrium soon becomes approximately hydrostatic with increasing depths, and is characterized by equal pressures acting in all directions at points situated in horizontal planes. This precludes long-time action, causing the slow permanent deformation of bunches of rock strata, as exemplified in the processes of slow mountain building in which very small differences between the pressures in the horizontal and vertical directions are active over prolonged times, to be referred to in Secs. 17-6 and 17-7. Leaving the questions of mountain folding aside, it was thought that it may interest readers to obtain by simple means some exact information concerning the order of magnitude of the pressures p built up in the interior of the earth under its gravity field.[1] An estimation of the pressures implies knowledge of how the density of mass ρ of the rocks varies with depth. To express the condition of equilibrium to be satisfied by the hydrostatic pressures p, it will be permissible in a first approximation to neglect the flattening of the earth, namely, the ellipticity e of the meridians, and also the centrifugal accelerations due to the earth's rotation around the polar axis. The ellipticity e expressed by the ratio of the difference of the radii a and b of the equator and in the polar axis to a, $e = (a - b) : a$, has the small value of $e = \frac{1}{297}$, and the centrifugal force per unit of mass at the equator decreases the gravitational acceleration there by only about 0.35 per cent. By neglecting these two small effects, we may deal with a purely radial field of density distribution ρ and gravity g, considering ρ and g as

---

[1] Whereas, according to the KANT-LAPLACE theory, the earth in its initial stage was in the fluid state and during its existence as a separate body, estimated at around 3,000 million years, was in a process of gradual cooling, more recently opinions have been advanced that its original mass has accrued through the aggregation of cosmic dust and meteorite particles as an *initially cold, solid* mass that became gradually hot in its interior owing to the work of gravity and to the presence of radioactive components in the rocks and that it is presently warming up or passing through a semisteady, thermal stage.

pure functions of the radial distance x from the center of the earth assumed to be a sphere (standing still).

In these directions we have to rely on the fundamental data gathered during the past 60 years in seismology, expecting, since the classical determination of the mean density ρ_m of the earth by MASKELYNE (1774) and CAVENDISH (1799) gave the value equal to $\rho_m = 5.52$ and the rocks on the surface have an average density of $\rho = 2.7$, that ρ must increase greatly in the deep regions around the center of the sphere. On reasoning on density, E. WIECHERT (1896) concluded that the earth probably possesses an iron core surrounded by a (silicate) mantle of lighter rocky material. Seismologists (BENO GUTENBERG, C. F. RICHTER, and others) have constructed by intricate integration methods the travel-time curves for earthquake waves and thus evaluated the velocities of propagation of the two principal types of waves in the interior of the earth: the longitudinal (dilatational) and transverse (distortional, shear) waves (designated by them briefly as P and S waves).[1] The present status of the knowledge of the distribution of seismic velocities across the earth leads to the two curves[2] shown in Fig. 17-14, disclosing

[1] BENO GUTENBERG (ed.), "Internal Constitution of the Earth," 2d ed., 439 pp., Dover Publications, New York, 1951. See in this book fig. 16, p. 276, velocity of P waves and fig. 42, p. 409, velocity curves of dilatational (P) and transverse (S) waves.

[2] H. E. LANDSBERG (ed.), "Advances in Geophysics," vol. 3, 578 pp., Academic Press, Inc., New York, 1956. See in it an article by J. A. JACOBS, The Interior of the Earth, fig. 1, p. 187, showing P and S velocity curves. The cross section of the earth traced in Fig. 17-15 has been based on JACOBS's article.

The displacement u parallel to the x axis of a plane wave in an extended, elastic continuum satisfies the wave equation

$$\frac{\partial^2 u}{\partial t^2} = c^2 \frac{\partial^2 u}{\partial x^2}, \tag{17-4}$$

the velocity of propagation c for the (rotational) *waves of distortion* (shear, transverse, S waves) being equal to

$$c = c_s = \sqrt{\frac{G}{\rho}} \tag{17-5}$$

and for the (irrotational) waves of dilatation (P waves) equal to

$$c = c_d = \sqrt{\frac{2G(1 - \nu)}{\rho(1 - 2\nu)}} = \sqrt{\frac{2K(1 - \nu)}{\rho(1 + \nu)}} \tag{17-6}$$

(ρ density; G modulus of rigidity; K bulk modulus; ν Poisson's ratio).

If Poisson's ratio were taken as $\nu = \frac{1}{4}$ (a value held probable by B. GUTENBERG over greater portions of the earth's interior, but excepting the regions near the outer surface and close around its center), then the ratio of the velocities of the dilatational (c_d) to the transverse waves (c_s) at any depth equals

$$c_d : c_s = \sqrt{\frac{2(1 - \nu)}{1 - 2\nu}} = \sqrt{3} = 1.73. \tag{17-7}$$

Otherwise this last relation may serve well for an evaluation of ν.

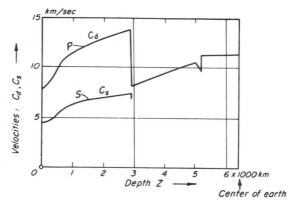

Fig. 17-14. Seismic velocities: c_d of dilatational, longitudinal waves (P), c_s of transverse, shear waves (S) in earth plotted above depth z. (*After J. A. Jacobs.*)

the geomechanically important facts (1) that the velocities of the dilatational waves P suffer a very strong discontinuity at a depth $z = 2{,}898$ km, defining the lower boundary of the mantle; (2) that a second, very distinct discontinuity in the curve of the P waves still occurs at the great depth $z = 5{,}121$ km; and (3) that the distortional (shear) S waves are unable to penetrate below the depth $z = 2{,}898$ km, making it highly probable that the latter depth marks the outer surface of a dense core in a fluid condition (since transverse, distortional waves are not transmitted through a fluid).

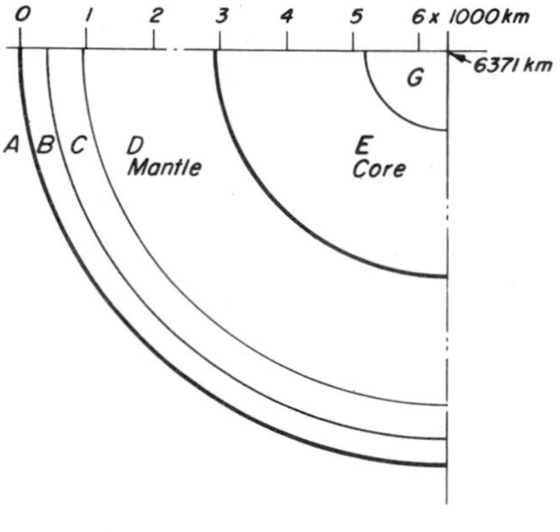

Based on this aforementioned evidence, a cross section through the earth was traced in Fig. 17-15. Seismologists believe that they have located a distinct surface as the lower boundary of the uppermost crust, supposing that its thickness varies between 30 to 50 km under the continents, representing at its bottom a granitic-basaltic layer on which the sedimentary upper strata rest, while the thickness of the corresponding (basaltic) layer is not much more than 5 km under the oceanic basins. (This layer designated by A by Jacobs could not be shown in Fig. 17-15.) He distinguishes three zones in the rock mantle: B, C, D, corresponding to the breaks in the slopes of

Fig. 17-15. Mantle and core of earth. Outer crust 30 to 40 km thick. (A, not shown.) Mantle: (B) outer $z = 40$–413 km; (C) intermediate, 413–984 km; (D) lower, 984–2,898 km. Core: (E) outer, 2,898–4,982; (G) inner, 4,982–6,371 km. After K. E. Bullen and J. A. Jacobs, using velocities of earthquake waves and their travel-time integration by B. Gutenberg.

the velocity curves of Fig. 17-14.   The outer boundary of the *core* is demarked sharply at $z = 2{,}898$ km depth.   The earth's core may consist of two parts E and G (neglecting a thin shell F between them, indicated in the velocity of P waves).   Its outer part E is supposed to be in a molten condition; whether or not the inner part G is fluid is a matter of dispute.

But herewith evidence based on reliably observed quantities at great depths ends.   In the expressions for wave velocities c_s and c_d [Eqs. (17-5) and (17-6)] the same ratio of the two unknowns, of the modulus of rigidity G and the density ρ, appears.   Granted that one may postulate an averaging value for Poisson's number ν ($\nu = \frac{1}{4}$, as mentioned in the footnote on page 620), the expressions for c_s and c_d may serve to ascertain the value of G/ρ, if their observed values at any point do not contradict each other.   It has been pointed out in previous chapters that the values of the moduli E, G, and K depend to a lesser degree on the mean pressure p but considerably on the temperature θ and that the compressibility of such important rocks as granites and gabbros seems not to vary appreciably around pressures p of the order of 12,000 atm (see Fig. 17-17 in Sec. 17-3 below).   In view of the fact that the composition and the properties of the rocks at the depth below the upper crust are unknown and that (apart from the geothermal gradient $d\theta/dz$ near the surface) little is known or has been reliably established concerning the temperatures θ prevailing in the interior of the earth, where they must increase to very high values, one has to admit that an evaluation of the density ρ and of the moduli E, G, and K at great depths still poses difficult problems, leaving a range for speculation to which we cannot refer here.

For estimating the pressure p in the interior of the earth, there remains the alternative of making ad hoc assumptions about the distribution of the density ρ by assigning to the structure of concentric mantle shells plausibly chosen values of ρ or by postulating a simple, averaging function $\rho = f(x)$ of the radial distances $x = a - z$ (radius of earth: $a = 6{,}371$ km, z is depth) and of computing the corresponding variation of the pressures p with x.   The potential ϕ of a gravitating mass m situated at distance r from the origin or the mechanical work done when a mass equal to unity descends from an infinite distance to m is equal to

$$\phi = \frac{fm1}{r},$$

where f is the constant of gravitational attraction.   The gravitational potential ϕ_1 at a point P situated on the surface $x = r$ of a spherical mass of variable density $\rho =$ function (x) hence is

$$\phi_1 = \frac{4\pi f}{r} \int_0^r \rho x^2 \, dx. \tag{17-8}$$

Since, on the other hand, the potential inside a hollow spherical shell of radius x and thickness dx is constant, equal to the potential at its surface, namely,

$$d\phi_2 = \frac{f\,dm}{x} = 4\pi f\rho x\,dx,$$

$$(17\text{-}9)$$

therefore the potential ϕ at an inner point P $(x < a)$ of a material sphere of radius a having a variable density ρ is

$$\phi = \dot{\phi}_1 + \phi_2 = 4\pi f\left(\frac{1}{r}\int_0^r \rho x^2\,dx + \int_r^a \rho x\,dx\right).$$

$$(17\text{-}10)$$

Furthermore, the gravity acceleration g at the same point P $(x = r)$ is

$$g = -\frac{\partial\phi}{\partial r} = \frac{4\pi f}{r^2}\int_0^r \rho x^2\,dx,$$

$$(17\text{-}11)$$

giving, if the total mass of the earth is denoted by M and its mean density by ρ_m, for the gravity acceleration $g = g_a$ on the surface $r = a$ of the sphere

$$g_a = \frac{4\pi f}{a^2}\int_0^a \rho x^2\,dx = \frac{Mf}{a^2} = \frac{4}{3}\pi f a\rho_m,$$

$$(17\text{-}12)$$

defining the gravitational constant,

$$f = \frac{g_a a^2}{M} = \frac{3g_a}{4\pi a\rho_m},$$

$$(17\text{-}13)$$

while the equilibrium of the forces on a small element of mass inside the gravitating sphere requires that the pressure p must satisfy the condition

$$\frac{\partial p}{\partial r} = -g\rho.$$

$$(17\text{-}14)$$

This last equation combined with Eq. (17-11) suffices for computing the pressure p at the radial distance r from the center of the earth, provided that the distribution of density $\rho =$ function (x) is known.

Let us now consider three cases:

Case 1. *Sphere having homogeneous density* $\rho = \rho_m =$ const. In it the gravity acceleration $g = g_a r/a$, after Eq. (17-11), is proportional to r, and we obtain from Eq. (17-14) for the pressure

$$p = p_0\left(1 - \frac{r^2}{a^2}\right), \qquad p_0 = \frac{g_a\rho_m a}{2} = \frac{\gamma_a a}{2},$$

$$(17\text{-}15)$$

where $\gamma_a = g_a\rho_m$ obviously represents the weight of unit volume (specific weight) of the substance composing the sphere of invariable density, as measured on its surface $r = a$, and p_0 is the pressure at its center $r = 0$. Suppose that this sphere had a radius a and density ρ_m equal to the mean radius $a = 6{,}371$ km and the mean, physically observable density of our planet $\rho_m = 5.52$. Then the unit volume of its substance at its surface $r = a$ would weigh $\gamma_a = 5{,}520$ kg/m^3 = 0.00552 kg/cm^3. The maximum pressure p_0 at the center of this gravitating sphere of uniform density would be equal to

$$p_0 = \frac{\gamma_a a}{2} = \frac{0.00552 \times 6.371 \times 10^8}{2},$$

$$p_0 = 1{,}758{,}400 \text{ atm,} \tag{17-16}$$

equal to 1.76 million terrestrial atmospheres (1 atm being approximately 1 kg/cm^2 or 14.2 lb/in.^{2}).

Case 2. Parabolic density distribution. In an attempt to take some account of the increase of the density ρ with depth, suppose that ρ varies with x according to the function

$$\rho = \rho_0 - (\rho_0 - \rho_a)\frac{x^2}{a^2}, \tag{17-17}$$

denoting by ρ_a and ρ_0 the density at the surface $x = a$ and at the center $x = 0$. Under this assumption, the mean density ρ_m is given by

$$\rho_m = \frac{2\rho_0 + 3\rho_a}{5}. \tag{17-18}$$

With $\rho_a = 3$, $\rho_m = 5.50$, this gives at the center of the sphere the density $\rho_0 = 9.25$. The distribution of the gravity acceleration g and the pressure p is easily computed from Eqs. (17-11) and (17-14). There results at the center $x = 0$ of the sphere a value of the pressure p

$$p = \frac{2\rho_0(\rho_0 + \rho_a) + \rho_a^2}{5\rho_m^2}\, p_0 = 1.56 p_0,$$

$$p = 2{,}740{,}000 \text{ atm,} \tag{17-19}$$

where the constant $p_0 = g_a \rho_m a/2$ denotes the pressure at the center of a homogeneous sphere of uniform density ρ_m [Eq. (17-15)]. The variation of density ρ, gravity acceleration g, and pressure p with depth is shown in Fig. 17-16.

Case 3. Sphere having a heavy metal core and a silicate mantle. We have seen that, from seismic evidence, a sharp discontinuity of the earthquake velocities v_d and v_s has been located at a depth of 2,898 km (see Fig. 17-14) or at a radius of about $x = 0.545a$. Neglecting other discontinuities that we indicated formerly, let us suppose that, according to E. WIECHERT's early hypothesis, an outer silicate mantle of lower density surrounds a much heavier core of perhaps nickel and iron (the constituents of a certain class of meteorites) in the earth and, for

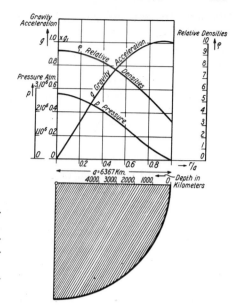

Fig. 17-16. Variation of density ρ, of gravity acceleration g, and of pressure p in interior of earth, assuming parabolic distribution of density ρ.

simplicity's sake, that the densities ρ_0 in the inner core and ρ_1 in the mantle are uniform. In this sphere composed of two parts, having hypothetically the invariable densities ρ_0 and ρ_1, we may evaluate ρ_0, ρ_1 by specifying two conditions, namely, (1) that their mean density be equal to the true value $\rho_m = 5.50$ in the earth and (2) that the moment of inertia of the composite sphere around a central axis be equal to the correct value I for the earth taken around the polar axis, as it was determined astronomically from the 25,740-year-long period of the precession of the equinoxes, due to the moment of the gravitational attractions of the sun exerted on the excess of mass in the bulge around the equator of the earth's ellipsoid (precession of axis of rotation of a gyroscope). Now the moment of inertia of a ball of uniform density ρ is

$$I_0 = \frac{8\pi\rho a^5}{15} = \frac{2Ma^2}{5} = 0.400Ma^2, \tag{17-20}$$

whereas the actual moment of inertia of the earth around the polar axis is[1]

$$I = 0.334Ma^2. \tag{17-21}$$

Suppose that the metallic-core sphere extends to half the earth's mean radius a, so that the separation of core and mantle lies at $x = a_1 = a/2$ (allowing ourselves use of the latter instead of the value $x = 0.545a$

[1] H. Jeffreys, "The Earth," 3d ed., p. 145, Cambridge University Press, London, 1952.

claimed by seismology). Then we have, on the basis of density distribution,

$$\alpha^3 \rho_0 + (1 - \alpha^3)\rho_1 = \rho_m, \tag{17-22}$$

denoting by α the ratio $\alpha = a_1/a$, and furthermore, from the condition in respect to the inertia moment [Eqs. (17-20) and (17-21)],

$$\alpha^5 \rho_0 + (1 - \alpha^5)\rho_1 = (5/2) \times 0.334\rho_m. \tag{17-23}$$

Taking $\alpha = 1/2$, $\rho_m = 5.50$, we obtain from the last two equations for the mean density of the metallic core $\rho_0 = 14.0$ and in the rock mantle $\rho_1 = 4.28$, and there results at the earth's center a pressure equal to

$$p_{max} = \frac{\rho_0^2 + \rho_0\rho_1 + 2\rho_1^2}{4\rho_m^2} p_0, \tag{17-24}$$

$$p_{max} = 2.42p_0 = 4,230,000\text{-atm.}$$

We list in Table 17-1 a few values of the density ρ and pressure p which were computed by much more refined, elaborate physical methods by K. E. BULLEN and adjusted by B. GUTENBERG.[1]

TABLE 17-1.   DENSITY AND PRESSURES IN THE INTERIOR OF THE EARTH

Depth z, km	Radius x, km	Density ρ, gr/cm^3	Pressure p, bars $\times$ 10^6
mantle:			
0	6,370	2.76	0
400	5,970	4.06	0.15
1,000	5,370	4.41	0.40
2,900	3,470	5.57	1.33
core:			
2,900	3,470	9.74	1.33
4,982	1,388	12.00	3.19
6,370	0	17.9	3.92

A comparison of the values of the densities ρ_0 and ρ_1 and of the maximum pressure p_{max} just computed with the figures listed in Table 17-1 shows that our third, simple model of the earth, having a heavy core and a lighter mantle of uniform densities appropriately determined, reproduces in good approximation several features which characterize

[1] *Op. cit.*, table 81, p. 359. The pressures p in Table 17-1 are given in units of *bars*. Since one international bar equals 0.9869 atm and 1 atm equals 1.033 kg (weight)/cm^2, the pressures in the table have to be multiplied by $0.987 \times 1.033 = 1.020$ in order to convert them to the engineering unit of one kilogram (weight) per square centimeter.

the interior of the earth according to the best methods with which its gravity field has been investigated: The value of the maximum pressure p_{max} just computed from Eq. (17-24) differs by $+9$ per cent from the one quoted in Table 17-1, while our figure for the mean density in the core $\rho_0 = 14$ is only by 6 per cent greater than the mean value $\rho_0 = 13.2$ computed from the table. The exceptionally high density $\rho_{max} = 17.9$ at the center $x = 0$ of the earth's supposedly metallic core points to conditions of heavy matter highly densified elastically under the tremendous pressure of the order of 4 million atm. Concerning the magnitude of the high temperature θ prevailing in this region, opinions regrettably differ greatly.[1]

17-3. Elastic Compressibility of Rocks. The compressibility of natural rocks has been thoroughly investigated in the Geophysical Laboratory in Washington, D.C., by L. H. Adams and his collaborators[2] at hydrostatic pressures up to 12,000 bars (12,240 kg/cm^2) and for selected minerals up to 40,000 bars. The compressibility β was defined here as

$$\beta = -\frac{dv}{v_0 dp}, \tag{17-25}$$

the diminution in volume for an increment of 1 bar pressure divided by the volume v_0 at a standard pressure and temperature. Thus a compressibility of 1×10^{-6} means a volume change of one-millionth for 1 bar increase in pressure p. The reciprocal of compressibility β measures the bulk modulus K:

$$K = -v_0 \frac{dp}{dv}. \tag{17-26}$$

As a rule, the compressibility β for natural rocks decreases with pressure p, first, at low pressures, rapidly and then, above 2,000 to 4,000 atm, very gradually, as the curves in Fig. 17-17 illustrate for various granites and gabbros; the shaded bands enclose the variation between the types of these rocks. A few values of compressibility β, modulus of rigidity G, bulk modulus K in bars per square centimeter, and density ρ are reproduced in the Table 17-2, as found by Adams and Williamson for some igneous rocks.

While one would expect that the elastic decrease of volume with pressure at great depths in the earth is opposed by the dilatation of volume due to the increasing temperatures θ, according to Adams, regrettably very little is known from experiments about the effect of temperature. Based on theoretical considerations, utilizing the velocities v_d and v_s of dilatational and transverse waves in combination with a hypothetically assumed distribution of the density ρ,

---

[1] In Beno Gutenberg's latest book "Physics of the Earth's Interior," 240 pp., International Geophysics Series, vol. 1, Academic Press, Inc., 1959, New York, curves proposed lately by nine named investigators are reproduced (in fig. 6.1, p. 144, of this book) for the distribution of the temperature $\theta = F(x)$ in the interior of the earth. The uncertainties of the concepts on which these nine curves were based are illustrated by the maximum values of θ in which they culminated, varying between $\theta_{max} = 2800°$ and $6000°C$.

[2] L. H. Adams and E. D. Williamson, The Compressibility of Minerals and Rocks at High Pressures, J. Franklin Inst., vol. 195, p. 475, 1923; L. H. Adams and R. E. Gibson, Proc. Natl. Acad. Sci. U.S., vol. 15, p. 713, 1929; L. H. Adams, Elastic Properties of Materials of the Earth's Crust, in B. Gutenberg (see page 620, *op. cit.*, p. 50).

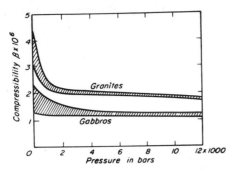

FIG. 17-17. Compressibility of granites, gabbros, and diabases as a function of pressure. (*After L. H. Adams.*)

B. GUTENBERG[1] has traced a curve representing the variation of the bulk modulus K with depth across the interior of the earth (Fig. 17-18) along which it increases from $K = 1.2 \times 10^{12}$ at depth $z = 50$ km to the incredibly high value of $K = 1.56 \times 10^{13}$ dynes/cm^2 = 1.56×10^7 bars $\sim 1.60 \times 10^7$ kg/cm^2 at the center of the earth's supposedly fluid core, *thirteen times* the value of K at moderate depth.[2]

HUGHES and McQUEEN[3] recently succeeded in measuring the densities of two gabbros and a dunite rock at several pressures in the high range from 150 to 750 kilobars, between 148,000 and 740,000 atm (1 kilobar = 986.9 atm), in dynamic tests by subjecting small pellets of these rocks (¾ in. in diameter, ¼ in. in height) to a shock front generated through the detonation of a high-explosive charge under an aluminum plate above which the pellets were placed. These valuable tests clarify the behavior of rocks compressed adiabatically under high pressures which were formerly not reached by artificial means, proving that the heavy dunite rock of initial density $\rho_i = 3.25$ g/cm^3 is compressed to a density $\rho = 4.9$ g/cm^3 at 720 kilobars pressure and the gabbros of $\rho_i = 3.00$ are compressed to $\rho = 5.0$ g/cm^3 at 750 kilobars; furthermore, that gabbros undergo a polymorphic transformation in their crystalline structure at a pressure of 150 kilobars, changing discontinuously into a more dense and less compressible rock. Figure 17-19

TABLE 17-2

Rock	Pressure p, bars	Compressibility, $\beta \times 10^6$	G, bars/cm^2	K, bars/cm^2	Density ρ
Granite	2,000	2.12	260,000	470,000	2.61
	10,000	1.88	290,000	530,000	2.66
Gabbro	2,000	1.49	360,000	670,000	3.05
	10,000	1.20	450,000	830,000	3.08
Dunite	2,000	0.93	590,000	1,800,000	3.38
	10,000				3.41

[1] *Ibid.*, fig. 30, p. 377.

[2] K. E. BULLEN, Compressibility Pressure Hypothesis and the Earth's Interior, Monthly Notices, Roy. Astron. Soc., Geophys. Suppl. 5, p. 355, 1949, advanced the hypothesis that, above a certain pressure, K becomes independent of the chemical composition of matter, increasing with density ρ as

$$K = a_0 + a_1\rho + a_2\rho^2,$$

where a_0, a_1, a_2 are universal constants.

[3] DARRELL S. HUGHES and ROBERT G. McQUEEN, Density of Basic Rocks at Very High Pressures, Trans. Am. Geophys. Union, vol. 39, pp. 959–965, October, 1958. They determined the wave velocity in the shock front and the particle velocity from observation and computed the mass density ρ and shock pressure p from the dynamic equations.

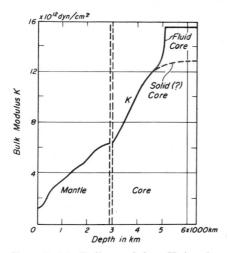

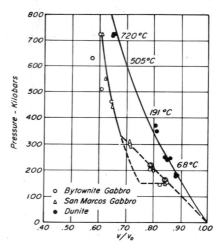

FIG. 17-18. Bulk modulus K in the interior of the earth. (*After B. Gutenberg.*)

FIG. 17-19. Pressure-volume curves of dunite and gabbros. (*After D. S. Hughes and R. G. McQueen.*)

reproduces the curves of the pressure p plotted above the ratio of the volume v to the normal volume v_0 for these rocks. They may serve for the evaluation of their bulk modulus K, using either Eq. (17-26) or, in view of the great decrease of volume $v_0 - v$, more precisely from

$$K = -v \frac{dp}{dv}. \tag{17-27}$$

The tests by HUGHES and McQUEEN greatly support the facts brought out in the theory of the constitution of the mantle and core of the earth and that the inner core is probably composed of the metals iron and nickel, the volumes of which under the pressures of cosmic magnitude approaching four million atmospheres in the center of the earth are elastically compressed to less than one-half of their normal values.

17-4. The Weight of the Continents. As stated, geologic and seismic observations indicate that the crust of the earth under the large continental tablelands is composed of lighter types of rocks (apart from the uppermost sedimentary layers, of granites and basalts), reaching down to depths varying from 30 to 50 km, having an average, mean specific weight of about $\gamma = 2,700$ kg/m³, and that this assembly of light rocks[1] is underlain by the rock mantle of the earth, consisting of distinctly heavier rocks, the specific weight of which near the contact surface with the crust has been estimated at $\gamma = 3,200$ kg/m³.

---

[1] The assembly of light rocks making up the continental tablelands is called by geologists *sial* (abbreviating silica and aluminum as abundant constituents) and the heavier rocks of the mantle underlying the former are called *sima* (silica, magnesium).

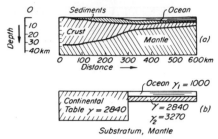

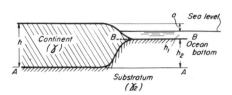

FIG. 17-20. (*a*) Cross section through continental shelf, off Cape May, N.J., to actual scale, deduced from seismic and gravity evidence. (*After Maurice Ewing and Frank Press, 1955.*) (*b*) Idealized section. Specific weights: ocean, $\gamma_1 = 1,000$ kg/m³; sediments, $\gamma = 2,300$ kg/m³; crust, $\gamma = 2,840$ kg/m³; mantle, $\gamma_2 = 3,270$ kg/m³.

FIG. 17-21. Continental rock slab floating on heavier substratum.

The rocks making up the floors of the oceanic basins, on the other hand, are supposed to consist of a heavier type than those found in the continental massifs. Whereas the genial ALFRED WEGENER[1] in his theory of continental drift assumed that in the beds of the oceans the rock mantle (sima) is evidenced, MAURICE EWING[2] and his collaborators in their extensive, recent deep-sea explorations found conclusively that on the ocean floors a comparatively thin, unconsolidated sedimentary layer less than 1 km thick covers a solid layer of basaltic rock 5 km thick, similar to that assumed to exist near the bottom of the continental crusts, of specific weight $\gamma = 2,800$ kg/m³, and that this basaltic layer rests on the earth's mantle (sima) of $\gamma = 3,200$ kg/m³.

The mathematical determination of the state of internal stress in limited portions of or over the entire, outer, solid, spherical shell of the earth is one of the central, major problems of geomechanics but poses considerable difficulties. The reasons for this are, first that the grand, secular system of the external, bodily forces that activates the crustal, diurnal elastic strains and has deformed permanently and displaced parts of the spherical outer crust over the geologic epochs of time could not yet be defined with acceptable certainty, and secondly, that it is

[1] A. WEGENER, "Die Enstehung der Kontinente und Ozeane," 231 pp., 4th ed., Friedr. Vieweg und Sohn, Brunswick, Germany, 1929.

[2] MAURICE EWING and FRANK PRESS, Geophysical Contrasts between Continents and Ocean Basins, Geol. Soc. Am., Special Paper 62, 1955; also Seismic Measurements in Ocean Basins, Sears Foundation, J. Marine Research, vol. 14, no. 4, pp. 417–422, 1955. An instructive profile through the continental shelf off the eastern shores of the United States constructed to actual scale from seismic and gravity evidence by EWING and PRESS may be seen in Fig. 17-20, disclosing clearly how the subcontinental crust tapers out gradually toward the Atlantic Ocean.

little known how the combined effects of the hydrostatic pressures p and temperatures θ which increase to high values at greater depths influence the elasticity, viscosity, and the plastic behavior of rocks at greater depths in the crust.   Geophysicists have struggled to decipher some of these involved, interrelated conditions in the deeper interior of the earth, in the mantle and core.   But as far as the state of stress in the outer crust is concerned, they have contented themselves mostly with considering only hydrostatic equilibrium governed by *the principle of isostacy*, by accepting the hypothesis that the weight of any narrow vertical column of mass reaching down into the heavier substratum is supported by the buoyancy pressure exerted by the latter, that the columns of rock float like a pack of pencils held in vertical positions in the substratum.[1]

This hypothesis fails to take account of the *long-time interaction* between the vertical columns, of the bending and shearing stresses that may act across the vertical sections in those parts of the continental shell which participate actively in viscoplastic deformation during the slow processes of mountain building or of the formation of deep-sea trenches.[2]   But when the *instantaneous* conditions of equilibria over greater areas in the continents are considered, it seems adequate.

To describe in the simplest way the equilibrium of a continental slab of light rocks floating on heavier substratum, suppose that the rocks in the continent have a uniform, average specific weight $\gamma = 2{,}600$ kg/m^3 and in the substratum $\gamma_2 = 3{,}100$ kg/m^3.   We shall not err much in further simplifying the findings of the quoted suboceanic explorations by assuming with WEGENER that the substance beneath the bottom of the oceans is the same as the substratum beneath the continents, having the specific weight γ_2.   If $\gamma_1 = 1{,}000$ kg/m^3 designates the specific weight of water, the hydrostatic pressure p along the horizontal, lower boundary plane $\overline{AA}$ of the continental slab (Fig. 17-21) due to its weight equals the pressure beneath the ocean floor in this plane:

$$p = h\gamma = h_1\gamma_1 + h_2\gamma_2, \qquad (17\text{-}28)$$

where h, h_1, h_2 denote the thickness of the continental table, the mean depth of the oceans (taken to be about 5 km), and the height of the ocean floor $\overline{BB}$ above the plane $\overline{AA}$.

Given the mean elevation a of the continent above sea level, $a = h - h_1 - h_2$, the thickness h of the continental slab must equal

$$h = \frac{h_1(\gamma_2 - \gamma_1) + a\gamma_2}{\gamma_2 - \gamma}. \qquad (17\text{-}29)$$

[1] The alternative ways of considering columns of different densities but equal weights (J. H. PRATT, 1854), of equal density but different heights (G. B. AIRY, 1855), of stratified columns with density increasing with depths and varying heights (W. HEISKANEN, 1931) are elucidated in detail by REGINALD ALDWORTH DALY, "Strength and Structure of the Earth," 434 pp., Prentice-Hall, Inc., Englewood Cliffs, N.J., 1940 (see in it fig. 3-4, p. 48), elaborating on the history of isostacy and gravity anomalies.

[2] The disciples of isostacy, in fact, equivocally reported finding some *gravity anomalies* associated with the regions of high mountain chains (the Alps) or at sea, above the deep ocean troughs, proving that simple unilateral equilibrium of weights is insufficient for handling cases where bending of the crust is involved.

The first term on the right side of this equation defines the thickness h_0 of a continent whose upper surface is flush with sea level ($a = 0$). With $\gamma_2 = 3.1$, $\gamma_1 = 1$, $\gamma = 2.6 \times 1,000$ kg/m^3, and $h_1 = 5$ km, we obtain

$$h_0 = \frac{h_1(\gamma_2 - \gamma_1)}{\gamma_2 - \gamma} = \frac{5 \times (3.1 - 1.0)}{3.1 - 2.6} = 21 \text{ km.} \qquad (17\text{-}30)$$

Equation (17-29) elucidates the fact emphasized by PRATT, AIRY, the geologists DALY, HEIM, and others that under the high mountain ranges and terraces of high altitude the continental slabs dip much more deeply into the substratum than elsewhere, provided that isostatic equilibrium has had sufficient time to establish itself.   A few values of the thickness h may illustrate this

Mean elevation a of continent above sea level, km	Thickness of continental slab, $h = h_0 + a\gamma_2/(\gamma_2 - \gamma)$, km
0	21
0.7	25.3
3	39.6
5	52
7	64.4

The value $a = 0.7$ km corresponds to the mean elevation 700 m above sea level of all lands, and $h = 25.3$ km represents the mean thickness of all continents on the earth.   The figures indicate that the roots of the high mountain massifs are deeply embedded in the heavy substratum of the mantle of the earth and show why the celebrated experiment of PRATT in the plains of India south of the Himalaya Mountains gave a negative answer, namely, that the plumb line did not deviate northward toward the towering mountain peaks, since the weights of the columns of rock above the plane of isostatic compensation (the plane $\overline{AA}$ in Fig. 17-21) are the same under the peaks as elsewhere.

With these ideas, let us conceive a simple, static model of a mechanism that could illustrate the slow process activating mountain building.   There is ample evidence that during past geologic epochs great parts of the continents have drifted and been displaced relatively to each other in tangential directions to the earth's surface above the heavier rock mantle.   If certain greater portions of the upper crust were displaced more or less as rigid bodies, they must have exerted forces through the more deformable parts on the adjoining less deformed regions. As a simple case, suppose that a parallel strip of continent received parallel, horizontal, normal force resultants P of sufficient magnitude as external compression forces.   Since the temperature θ increases by 3°C with every hundred meters of depth, under a continental plateau of 3 km elevation having an initial thickness of $h \sim 40$ km at this depth, it reaches a value of $\theta \sim 1200$°C, approaching the melting point of granites or basalts under atmospheric pressure.   Should these high temperatures prevailing near the base of the continental slab not have a profound effect on the deformability of the deeply buried layers of rocks in spite of the presence of hydrostatic pressures p of the order of 10,000 or more atmospheres?   Rocks, like the ductile metals, continuously deform permanently at these high temperatures under steady stress.   In the case of the broad parallel strip of crust under the long-time action of the external, horizontal compression forces P per unit of width, a state of plane strain σ_x, σ_y, τ_{xy} develops that is superposed on the state of hydrostatic pressures p of gravitational origin, and a system of long-time, permanent creep strains ε_x, ε_y, γ_{xy} accrues, causing the originally rectangular cross section of the parallel strip of continent to deform into a body, as indicated in the sketch Fig. 17-22, having two symmetrical bulges, AEB upward and $A'E'B'$ downward in its vertical profile. To account for this symmetric distortion, it suffices to assume that the temperatures θ near the middle plane EE' were a trifle higher than along AA' and BB', perhaps because of an extremely slow convective current of mass and heat rising from the interior of the mantle. Such convection currents in vortical form may be parts of the secular, gradual cooling of the earth and have been considered by many investigators. While the gentle, wavy anticline rises slowly in its crest E by the height H above the ground plane, this is isostatically balanced through the formation of the downward bulge of a geosyncline in which the trough E' sinks by the corresponding amount H_2:

$$H_2 = \frac{\gamma}{\gamma_2 - \gamma} H = \frac{2.6}{3.1 - 2.6} H = 5.2H. \qquad (17\text{-}31)$$

Looking at the position of the horizontal force resultant P, one sees that around the middle section EE', besides the compression strains ε_x due to P, bending stresses and creep strains must develop. If, for example, the ground rose at the crest E by $H = 3$ km, the trough E' is submerged by $H_2 = 15.6$ km into the heavy substratum, and the rocks along the symmetry axis EE' suffered a mean, permanent compression strain ε_x in a horizontal direction approximately equal to $\varepsilon_x = -0.47$ (47 per cent) in excess of that in the border sections AA' and BB'. The variation of the hydrostatic pressure p and temperature θ with depth may be inspected in Fig. 17-22, where the maximum values of p, θ at the bottom points A' and E' are inscribed. In the absence of reliable information about the function expressing the viscosity $\mu = f(p,\theta)$ of rocks, no attempts are made to estimate the distribution of the stresses σ_x, σ_y, τ_{xy}, except to state that their values in the hot, lower portions of the slab are expected to be small compared with the pressures p in these regions and that the horizontal normal stresses σ_x will take on their largest values in the cold upper parts of the slab, thus causing the well-known, spectacular effects of mountain raising (folding, shear fracturing in faults, overthrust faulting of the uppermost rock strata), whereas the true origin of all these phenomena is seated deep down in the hot regions that can yield smoothly without disruption while the adjoining rigid blocks of continent exert their secular action in pushing a more deformable band of it together. In order to supply the volume of rocks swallowed by the bulges, the horizontal width $(\overline{AB})$ of the

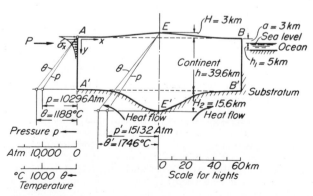

FIG. 17-22. Mountain building. In the upper surface AB of a continental block a gentle, flat anticline AEB rises while the lower boundary plane $A'B'$ is being deformed into a geosyncline $A'E'B'$, the trough of which is submerged into the substratum. p pressures; θ temperatures.

compressed zone must have been shortened by many tens of kilometers during the early times of this process. As time progresses, the rates of deformation tend to slow down toward a semisteady stage of culmination in the profiles of the two bulges, namely, when the flow from both sides has only to replenish the loss of masses along the upper bulge exposed to denudation by erosion. At this stage the mountains cease to grow in height, and the shortening of the breadth of the compressed zone becomes practically unobservable. Some of these facts seem in good agreement with what one sees in the active belts of the high mountains of comparatively young Tertiary age, while some of the Caledonian, old-age, obliterated mountains have long ago passed through these stages.[1]

In contrast to the process of elevation of mountains through horizontal compression force resultants P, there are depressions in the level of the continents and particularly deep troughs in the ocean bottoms known as *rift valleys*, the German *Grabens* (in the valley of the Rhine, in the Red Sea and its extension southward in the African graben of many hundred miles in length, in the most spectacular deep-sea trenches discovered by M. EWING in the Atlantic and Pacific Oceans, etc.). It is presumed that these depressed regions in the earth's crust owe their existence to *tensile force resultants* P that acted superposed on the hydrostatic pressures p. Along the flanks of rift valleys one frequently sees in the upper, loose sedimentary strata steeply inclined, old faults dipping toward the valley,[2] supporting the view that at moderate depths the ground permanently yielded horizontally, under tensile forces P. If, for example, the valley floor sank by $b = 0.5$ km in a continent of mean elevation $a = 0.7$ km and thickness $h = 25.3$ km, the latter decreased under the graben to

$$h' = h - \frac{b\gamma_2}{\gamma_2 - \gamma} = 25.3 - \frac{0.5 \times 3.1}{0.5} = 22.2 \text{ km.} \qquad (17\text{-}32)$$

In the gently sloping sides of the great, suboceanic trenches circumscribing the earth in which valleys of 3 to 5 km depth below the mean ocean floor level have been located by undersea echo soundings, the steeply dipping shear-fault fractures must still occur frequently since most of the numerous, strong submarine earthquakes are known to have their epicenters in these apparently still quite active regions of the earth's crust.

17-5. The Origin of the Rocksalt Domes

At the Beginning was Rhythm. HANS VON BÜLOW

The great rocksalt domes of the Gulf Coastal Plains and in other places are outstanding geologic features because of their genesis and because they represent in their regular shapes perhaps the most beautiful examples of the formation of large bodies underground that owe their

[1] Although, as J. GESZTI (Zusammenschub der Erdrinde, Gerlands Beitr. Geophys., vol. 21, no. 1, 1929) rightly pointed out, a comparison of a severely folded chain of mountains, like the Alps, with a folded tablecloth gives a very incomplete picture of the formation process of a chain of mountains, the smoothing out of the tablecloth folds can at least demonstrate that the earth's crust under the folded mountains during their initial stage of formation was shortened by distances of many tens of kilometers, as claimed by geologists.

[2] The classical example of a fault trough traversed by steep faults is the rift valley of the Rhine (*Rheingraben*). The elevated sides along its flanks that have not participated in the subsidence are known as *Horsts*.

Fig. 17-23. Stages of formation of rocksalt domes of German type. (*According to E. Seidl.*) 1. Brittle strata (*Bunt-Sandstein*). 2. Highly plastic rocksalt layer. 3. Underlying solid strata. *S*, rocksalt dome or stock.

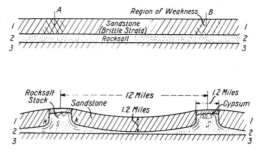

existence to an almost perfectly radially symmetric flow of a plastic substance in nature. Rocksalt lies deposited in vast beds between brittle sedimentary layers of rock[1] from which the salt rose in many places into huge, vertical, elliptic or nearly circular cylinders of 8,000 to 12,000 ft diameter and 12,000 ft and more in height during the geologic ages. Much of the knowledge about these salt domes is due to the exploratory work of petroleum geologists, since experience has shown that the uppermost oil-bearing strata in the oil fields of Texas are reachable at the least depths near the cylindrical boundary of the salt domes.

Suppose that the lighter salt, having a specific weight $\gamma_s = 2{,}150$ kg/m³, lies under horizontal strata of consolidated, brittle rocks of specific weight $\gamma = 2{,}400$ to $2{,}600$ kg/m³ (Fig. 17-23) and that the latter have in a few spots a density a trifle less or have been weakened through faults of orogenic origin (two such spots are marked in Fig. 17-23 by crosshatching in A and B). The equilibrium of the lighter salt under these spots will be unstable and, since it is a highly plastic material, the least differences in pressure will produce movement within the salt. Because of its high deformability as compared with the rigid strata, it will tend to flow radially toward the centers A or B, bending and

---

[1] A bed of rocksalt between sedimentary layers exists in many places, in parts of the northern states, the Gulf states, in the north German plains, under the Alps, around the Carpathian Mountains, etc. Great areas of the present continents once were covered by shallow sea water like the Gulf of Mexico. When the land again rose across or around them, land bridges formed, closing the connections with the oceans, and inland seas were created that evaporated later, during the Permian age, leaving the salt deposited on their former floors. This salt layer was subsequently covered by loose sediments that consolidated to solid rocks. Concerning the geologic history of the inland sea that covered parts of the present Gulf Coastal Plains, refer to the instructive Genesis of Salt Domes of Gulf Coastal Plain by MICHEL T. HALBOUTY and GEORGE C. HARDIN, JR. (Bull. Am. Assoc. Petrol. Geologists, vol. 40, pp. 737–746, 1956) where it is stated that one cubic mile of sea water contains around 140 million tons of dissolved salt and other solids. Thus an inland sea 1 km = 1,000 m deep left, after it dried out, a salt layer 14 m thick on the ground, roughly estimated.

uplifting the overlying crust that will start to show a small bulge.   As
time progresses, the latter may be eroded away, which gives a new
impetus to motion: Since the heavier, washed-away masses are being
replenished by the lighter salt from below, the degree of the initial
instability must tend to increase and the salt will rise at a faster rate,
thus gradually building up the domes indicated in Fig. 17-23.

ERICH SEIDL[1] who investigated the *Salzhorste* in the Magdeburg-
Halberstadt basin, from which salt is quarried in Germany, advanced
these ideas, attributing the accumulation of salt in these large bodies
underground to its high capability of deforming plastically and radially,
flowing toward the places of least pressure.   This theory of the genesis
of the German *Salzhorste*, based on plastic flow, has been accepted by
American geologists for the formation of the Gulf Coast salt domes.
While the former extend 1 to 2 miles in diameter and are rooted deeply,
and the sedimentary layers in and around their vertical profiles appear
folded, strongly bent up in remarkable concordance with the salt (or
KCl, German *Kali*) squeezed up from below, the American counterparts,
the piercement domes along the Gulf Coast, are much more regularly

[1] ERICH SEIDL, "Die Permische Salzlagerstätte im Graf Moltke Schacht,"
p. 104 and "Schürfen, Belegen und Schachtabteufen auf deutschen Salzhorsten,"
p. 209, published by Preussische Geologische Landesanstalt, Berlin, 1914, 1921.

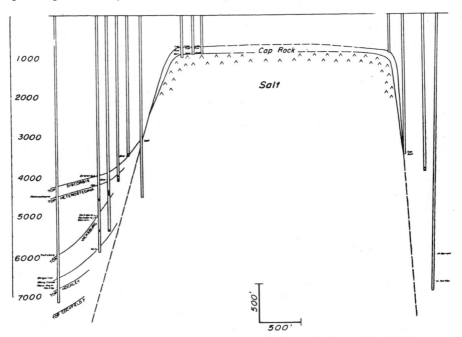

FIG. 17-24. Vertical section through Pierce Junction salt dome, Harris County,
Texas.

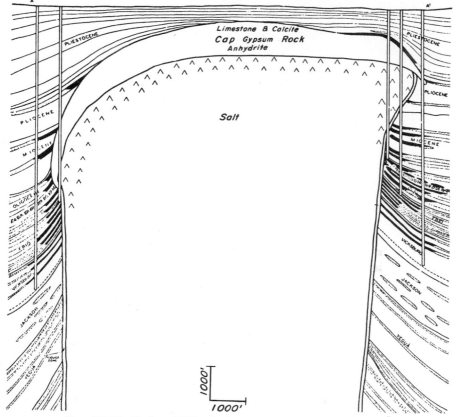

FIG. 17-25. Barbers Hill salt dome, Chambers County, Tex.

formed, having risen in cylinders of circular or oval cross sections with nearly vertical surfaces and a rounded cap. Leaching by the ground water has produced a *cap rock* layer of calcite, anhydrite, and light gypsum that covers the top of the dome. The characteristic vertical sections of two salt domes are reproduced in Figs. 17-24 and 17-25 for the Pierce Junction (Harris County) and Barbers Hill (Chambers County) domes of Texas,[1] the latter being covered by cap rock 1,000 ft thick and disclosing an *overhang* in its right upper corner. The dimensions of both are quite impressive: heights as far as explored, 7,000 and 11,000 ft; diameters, 6,000 and 8,000 ft. One of the mechanically most remarkable features (clearly established through the deep oil wells

[1] The author gratefully acknowledges permission to reproduce the vertical sections of these two salt domes from AUBREY H. RABENSBURG, president, and RALPH E. TAYLOR, vice-president, of the Houston Geology Society (1957). Further thanks are due to LEON H. ROBINSON, JR., Humble Oil & Refining Company; and to PAUL WEAVER, Houston, Tex., for having supplied the details mentioned in the text above.

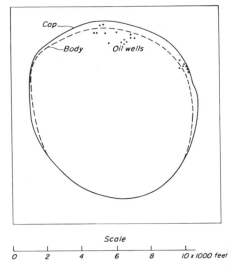

Fig. 17-26. Circumference of cap and body of Barbers Hill salt dome in Texas projected on horizontal plane. Oil wells only partially shown. (*After Judson, Murphy, and Stamey*, 1932.)

drilled in the vicinity of the dome) is the regular, upward-tilted position of the bent neighboring rock strata as they approach the vertical wall of the dome, clearly proving that it pierced its way through them. Thanks to the band of densely spaced shallow and deep oil wells, a map has been traced[1] (Fig. 17-26) showing the circumference of Barbers Hill dome in the cap (overhang) and below it; quite a number of the wells pierced the overhang, locating first the salt and below it the oil-bearing layers. It is presumed that the brittle strata lying initially above the cap of the rising salt dome are broken up through the arching action, being weakened around the upper edge, and that this contributes to the overhang that gradually develops; the ground-water seepage through the faults then also facilitates a sidewise, lateral flow in the salt and the formation of the overhang in the mushroom-shaped upper part of the dome, while the bulged-up brittle strata above the cap are eroded away. The formation of a dome in gradual stages is further illustrated in the self-explanatory sketches of Fig. 17-27a. In the sedimentary layers flanking the Boling salt dome, a fault was located in the shale S through the oil wells that penetrated the same layer twice. This fault formed at an earlier stage of the growing dome, when its cap pushed up the fault, at a time when the youngest (Miocene) layers were not yet all deposited[2] (Fig. 17-27b).

[1] Sidney A. Judson, P. C. Murphy, and R. A. Stamey, Overhanging Cap Rock and Salt at Barbers Hill, Bull. Am. Assoc. Petrol. Geologists, vol. 16, pp. 469–483, 1932.

[2] After Michel T. Halbouty and George C. Hardin, New Exploration Possibilities on Piercement-type Salt Domes, Bull. Am. Assoc. Petrol. Geologists, vol. 38, p. 1725, 1954.

Finally we may mention that the crystalline and flow structure of the rocksalt has most carefully been investigated in the interior of two of the larger salt domes (Grand Saline near Dallas and Jefferson Island dome in Louisiana) by ROBERT BALK,[1] whose untimely death in an airplane crash in 1955 was a great loss for the science of geomechanics.   Since in both of these domes salt is being mined and high chambers are excavated, BALK could describe their internal structure, finding large-scale lineation dominantly in steep, near-vertical direction and limbs of small, open and closed folds, proving that the mechanism of their deformation and propulsion fully conformed with the preceding details of their history of growth.   He found almond-shaped halite crystals oriented vertically with their maximum elongations, alignment of inclusions in the same direction, and many other signs of deformation in the salt fabric, proving that the vertical movements in these salt domes withstand a comparison with the state of flux characterizing the flow of formerly molten lava through the vents of volcanos and the phenomena of distortion in granite massifs that have been studied by geologists

---

[1] ROBERT BALK, Structure of Grand Saline Salt Dome, Bull. Am. Assoc. Petrol. Geologists, vol. 33, pp. 1791–1829, 1949; Salt Structure of Jefferson Island Salt Dome, *ibid.*, vol. 37, pp. 2435–2474, 1953.

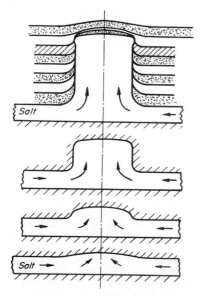

FIG. 17-27a. Rise of a salt dome.

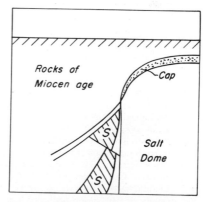

FIG. 17-27b. Boling salt dome. A fault located in flanking sedimentary layer (shale S). (*After Halbouty and Hardin*, 1954.)

FIG. 17-28. ROBERT BALK.† (Born May 31, 1899, in Reval, Estonia; died Feb. 19, 1955, in a plane crash near Albuquerque, N. Mex.) Photograph from "Memorial to Robert Balk" by ERNST CLOOS.

(cf. Sec. 17-6D).   According to BALK, the temperatures at the base of the salt domes that have risen from 2,500 ft below the earth's surface may be estimated to exceed 300°C, a value that must be considered as high for salt melting at 804°C, conditions under which quite small differences of pressure are sufficient to produce permanent strains through long-time action (creep).

In conclusion, it is evident that the magnificent effects of the formation of the great salt domes are due to the instability of the equilibrium in a parallel layer of light salt buried deep under heavier rocks.   If their average weight is locally a little less or their strength has been weakened locally through faults, the highly, plastically deformable salt

---

† Descendant of German immigrants to Estonia, ROBERT BALK grew up in Düsseldorf; while he was studying geology under HANS CLOOS in Breslau, he became interested in the granites of the Silesian mountains and the Bavarian Forest.   In 1924 Balk came to the United States, taught at Hunter College, Mt. Holyoke College (1935), and was professor at the University of Chicago (1947), from where he soon moved to the Bureau of Mines, Socorro, N. Mex.   Through his vast field work of geologic mapping of quadrangles in the northeastern states (Adirondacks) he became thoroughly familiar with the structural and petrological details in igneous rocks, granite domes, the processes of inclusion, foliation, cleavages, and disintegration of glaciated cliffs.   He was an artist in drawing exquisite sketches, a passionate lover of the beauties in nature, who would send his hand-drawn landscapes of the western desert country that he loved so much as Christmas cards to his friends.   He studied the gneisses on the New England Coast as thoroughly as the internal flow structure of the Grand Saline salt dome, near Dallas, Texas, or the fabric of quartzites near thrust faults.   The science of geology suffered a great loss in his untimely death, which occurred a few minutes after he boarded a plane in Socorro, on his way to Washington to attend a National Research Council meeting, that crashed into a mountain near Albuquerque, N. Mex., in foggy weather.   See "Memorial to Robert Balk," by his friend ERNST CLOOS, Baltimore, Proc. Geol. Soc. Am., July, 1956, p. 93.

starts to flow toward the centers of these regions and to rise there.   The elevated temperatures prevailing in these depths facilitate the flow.[1]

17-6.   Traces of Flow in the Structure of Rocks.   Flow phenomena analogous to the ones just described are well known in the motion of igneous rocks, in the domes of granites.   It may be instructive for the nongeologist readers to acquaint themselves with the various traces of motion that have been observed, often on a grand scale, in nature.

A. THE STREAKS AND VEINS IN GRANITES.   On the basis of the comprehensive investigations by HANS CLOOS,[2] ROBERT BALK, and others on the large granitic blocks (*Plutons*) explored in the Riesengebirge in Germany, in the Yosemite Valley, the Sierra Nevada mountains in California, the Adirondacks, etc., on granites that have been pushed up while gradually cooling in molten, large, cohesive masses, it has been observed that certain impurities and fine, solid particles are regularly arranged (Fig. 17-30a). These bands, the *Schlieren* or streaks, discernible through their color, tend to deceive one into thinking that a kind of stratification exists in granite.   They are small particles of higher melting point that floated in the granite when it was still in the fluid state.   H. CLOOS has shown that these thin streaks form large, flat arches, concave downward, which cling to the sedimentary rock surface along the "contact" with it where they are steeply inclined, while inside and on the exposed top of the granitic mass at some distance from the contact surface these streaks of fine particles may run for miles in the parallel, approximately horizontal position (Fig. 17-30b) in which they were originally suspended in the fluid masses.   Along the boundary zones with the rigid neighboring rocks the friction reduced the velocities of the slowly rising, fluid granite, producing the characteristic arches of the Schlieren.   Upon further cooling, after the top

[1] Concerning tests on the plastic behavior of rocksalt, dry and bewetted, the reader is referred to R. HOUWINK, "Elasticity, Plasticity and Structure of Matter," 376 pp., Cambridge University Press, London, 1937, in which various investigations by A. F. JOFFÉ, A. W. STEPANOW, A. SMEKAL, M. POLANYI, F. ZWICKY, and others are reviewed.   A few creep tests of impure rocksalt, of rather short duration, were described by KARL-HEINZ HÖFER, Proc. Intern. Strata Control Congress, Leipzig, p. 49, 1938.

[2] HANS CLOOS, "Einführung in die Tektonische Behandlung magmatischer Erscheinungen: Granit Tektonik," pt. I: Das Riesengebirge in Schlesien, 194 pp., 1925, and "Bau und Bewegung der Gebirge in Nord Amerika, Skandinavien und Mitteleuropa," Fortschritte der Geologie, 87 pp., vol. 7, 1928, both published by Verlagsbuchhandlung Gebrüder Bornträger, Berlin; ERNST CLOOS, Der Sierra Nevada–Pluton, Geolog, Rundschau, vol. 22, pp. 372–384, 1931; ROBERT BALK, Structural Geology of the Adirondack-Anorthosite, a Structural Study of the Problem of Magmatic Differentiation, Mineral. u. petrog. Mitt., vol. 41, pp. 308–432, 1931, printed in English by Akademische Verlagsgesellschaft m.b.H., Leipzig; also Geology of the Newcomb Quadrangle (in the Adirondacks), 106 pp., N.Y. State Museum Bull. 290, 1932.

FIG. 17-29. HANS CLOOS.† (Born Nov. 8, 1886, at Magdeburg, died Sept. 26, 1951, at Bonn.) Photograph from "Memorial to Hans Cloos" by ROBERT BALK.

layers became solid, the pressure in the still molten granite bulged the solid crust upward, subjecting it to tensile stresses and burst it into many cracks normal to the arch.   In the marginal region along the contact of granite with the sedimentary rocks, a grandiose system of *aplitic veins*, called *Fiederspalten* by H. CLOOS, in fanshaped orientation opened up which also split the surrounding rocks.   The marginal veins are filled up with magma or products of recrystallization and are inclined with respect to the steep contact surface (see Fig. 17-31).   Since along the side walls tangential shear stresses τ acted on account of the friction that opposed the outflow of the granite, the principal stresses $\sigma_1 = +\tau$, $\sigma_2 = -\tau$ corresponding to the system of shear stresses τ were inclined at angles of 45° to the side wall, and the direction normal to the tensile principal stresses $\sigma_1 = +\tau$ indeed coincides with the planes of the cracks in which the aplitic veins formed and are seen in Fig. 17-31.

† Assistant professor of geology, Marburg, 1914, professor in Breslau, 1919, and in Bonn, 1925, HANS CLOOS studied extensively the granite tectonics all over the earth, in Europe, Africa, on three trips to the United States, in the Sierra Nevada, exploring the structural characteristics of granitic blocks with a keen sense for the mechanical problems involved in their generation and in the mechanism of formation of magmatic masses.   His careful explorations led him to new concepts about the formation of "Grabens."   His great interest in the phenomena of plastic distortion and of fractures in the earth's crust inspired him to experiments in an apparatus in his institute at the University in Bonn in which he studied the formation of cracks in the shear zones originating in the edges of transcurrent faults, in small-scale model tests made with soft clay.   He spoke German, English, Norwegian, and French fluently, and even Malayan and Hottentot.   He had an aesthetic sense for harmony and symmetry of form, drawing by hand sketches like those of ALBERT HEIM.   He wrote several outstanding monographs and published more than 80 papers (listed in the "Memorial to Hans Cloos" by his faithful pupil Dr. Robert Balk, Proc. Geol. Soc. Am., June, 1953, p. 87, from which some of the preceding notes are quoted).

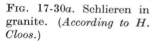

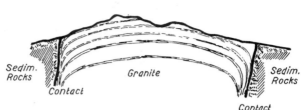

FIG. 17-30a. Schlieren in granite. (*According to H. Cloos.*)

FIG. 17-30b. Arches formed by Schlieren in a granitic mass. Vertical section showing also regions of contact of granitic mass with Tertiary rock. (*According to H. Cloos.*)

B. JOINTING. This is another phenomenon that is frequently observed in granites and basalts (and in some sedimentary rocks). Cliffs are seen dissected through three parallel systems of fine faults, not infrequently normal to each other, that appear as cleavage planes and become conspicuous through the action of erosion or glaciation (water freezing along the planes of the joints or initial planes of weakness splits them further apart). Two examples are seen in Figs. 17-32 and 17-33, after observations by ROBERT BALK[1] in foliated gneiss.

Jointing may probably be an effect of a combination of various causes, such as the thermal contraction of volume during the process of gradual cooling of an igneous rock from the molten to the solid state, the generation of a regular field of tensile thermal stresses during the cooling process, and the slow flow in a cooling magmatic mass while it attained a higher degree of viscosity and the suspended feldspar or mica flakes oriented themselves in parallel directions, thus creating an anisotropy in the over-all structure relative to the tensile strength with

[1] Disintegration of Glaciated Cliffs, J. Geomorphology, vol. 2, pp. 305–334, 1939.

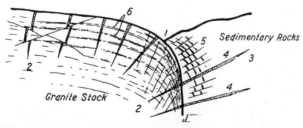

FIG. 17-31. The vertical section through the region of contact of a granitic stock (left) with sedimentary rocks (right). (*According to H. Cloos.*) 1. Surface of contact. 2. Granite stock. 3. Sediments in greatly disturbed order. 4. Aplitic veins. 5. Marginal surfaces of slip. 6. Streaks, or Schlieren, in granite.

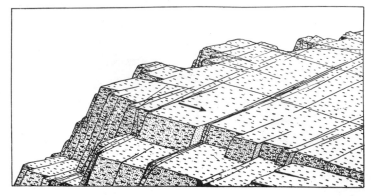

FIG. 17-32. Joints in a cliff of rocks having lineation (longitudinal inclusions parallel to arrow). The gently inclined joint planes of exfoliation coincide with the lamellar inclusions. (*Drawn by Robert Balk*.)

which the solidified rock resisted the thermal stresses or the mountain-building forces at a later time. In the beautifully jointed gneisses along the Maine coast one suspects that fatigue through periodic tide loads may have been active, apart from the anisotropy of such rocks disclosing lineation, foliation, etc. The hexagonally cleaving columns of black basalts in the remnants of the vents of long-extinct volcanoes are a classical example of jointing, the basalt having been split upon cooling in joints into vertically erect columns having regular hexagons in their cross sections.

Suppose that a pack of parallel layers of a brittle rock were separated by thin sheets of sand (representing the weak, layered inclusions in a rock of igneous origin) which are unable to transmit shearing stresses of nominal value and subject the pack to bending subsequently in two

FIG. 17-33. Joints in foliated gneiss in New England. (*After Robert Balk*.)

FIG. 17-34. *Boudinage* in folded rocks. Fold with quartzite bed between shaly layers. The former is broken into fragments by tension joints which are filled with quartz veins; arrows indicate relative movement.

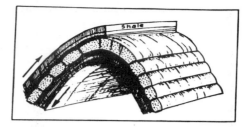

perpendicular directions.   A pack of dusty playing cards of a flexible, elastic, brittle material like thin mica sheets would be a model of this system.   When such a system is bent first in one direction and perhaps later in a perpendicular direction, the rock layers will slip one above the other and bend individually as if they had no neighbors, until they start to break into two systems of perpendicular joints (the third system of joints runs along the sand layers).   Possibly some such conditions may be responsible for the jointing in three mutually normal directions in rocks in nature.   A strange, extreme case of rock distortion of this kind, known as *boudinage*[1] (from the French word *boudin*, for sausage) is reproduced in Fig. 17-34.   The striking patterns of vertical, parallel cracks, the traces of which intersect in oblique parallelograms, the "aerial mosaics" described by J. D. MOLLARD (see Sec. 15-10), may be a last example of large-scale jointing worth mentioning.

C. PARALLEL TENSION CRACKS CAUSED BY MOVEMENT ALONG A TRANSCURRENT FAULT.   Whereas tensile and bending stresses of thermal or long-time, orogenic origin have a prominent part in the genesis of rectangular joints, comparatively short parallel cracks have been seen as a consequence of shearing strains generated above a long, vertical or very steeply dipping shear, a *transcurrent fault*, in which deeper underground one flank slipped in a horizontal direction with respect to the other flank.   Such short tension cracks are frequently seen after an earthquake[2] (Fig. 17-35).   A model test made by W. RIEDEL in an apparatus[3] utilizing wet

[1] ERNST CLOOS, Boudinage, Trans. Am. Geophys. Union, vol. 38, p. 626, 1947.

[2] JOHN P. BUWALDA and PIERRE ST. AMAND, The Recent Arvin-Tehachapi, Southern California, Earthquake, Science, vol. 116, p. 645, 1952.   This was one of the strongest earthquakes since the San Francisco earthquake of 1906 that shook the district around the southern end of the San Joaquin Valley on July 21, 1952, causing cracks to open up in the alluvium, locally 1 to 3 ft wide, kinking a railroad track by 8 ft horizontally, etc.

[3] The two wooden boards A and B (Fig. 17-36) are covered with a layer of wet, plastic clay C.   The surface of the clay must be heavily wetted with water in order to nullify in it the capillary attraction exerted on the clay particles by the water films in the interior of the cohesive, plastic mass.   If the rigid plate B is displaced in the direction SS, a *wedge-shaped shear zone develops* in the clay layer in which the plastic distortion is concentrated under shearing stresses τ that act parallel and perpendicularly to the straight line SS.   There results a system of tensile cracks in the surface (within the strip of width b) inclined at 45° to SS and normal to the principal tensile stresses $\sigma_1 = \tau$ of the states of simple shear $\sigma_1 = \tau$, $\sigma_2 = -\tau$.   Besides these tension cracks 11, there is formed yet a second system of stepped shearing fractures parallel to the lines 33 (inclined at 12°), as shown in the right sketch.   It is noted that, if the surface of the clay is not wetted, only the shear cracks will occur, the tensile strength of the clay apparently being greater than its shearing strength.

FIG. 17-35. Typical *en échelon* tension cracks, seen in perspective view on the gently rising slope of a hill, which formed during the Arvin-Tehachapi earthquake in California on July 21, 1952.

clay reproduces the conditions under which such a system of short, parallel tension surface cracks is generated. Suppose that along a transcurrent fault a strike-slip occurs in an essentially horizontal direction, starting at great depth from the epicenter of an earthquake, and that the upper edge or front of the vertical fault just reaches a line corresponding to the line SS in the model apparatus (Fig. 17-36). The horizontal, strike-slip displacement along the vertical fault puts a wedge-shaped zone radiating upward under high shearing stresses, with the consequence, since loose alluvium possesses a very low tensile strength, that the earth's surface in the highly sheared, narrow zone breaks into obliquely oriented, stepped tension cracks above the transcurrent main fault in the manner illustrated in Fig. 17-36.

D. Ordered Arrangement of Feldspar Tablets in an Extinct Volcano.

Many of the Tertiary volcanic cones in western Europe consist of trachyte, a rather porous igneous rock that contains many greenish-yellow, flat, oblong-shaped tablets, the so-called *sanidine* inclusions, feldspar crystals, about 2 by 3 in. and ½ in. thick. A conspicuous trachyte cone is the *Drachenfels* on the right shore of the Rhine, opposite to Bonn, which served as a quarry for the stones from which the magnificent Cologne Cathedral was built in the Middle Ages.

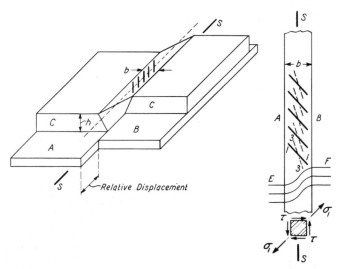

FIG. 17-36. System of cracks produced on surface of a plastic clay resting on two rigid plates A and B which have been displaced tangentially relative to each other. (*According to W. Riedel.*)

FIG. 17-37. Ideal section through the *Drachenfels* on the Rhine. (*According to field observations gathered by H. Cloos.*) The curves connect the most preferred directions along which the plate-shaped Sanidine-inclusions were oriented in the trachyte.

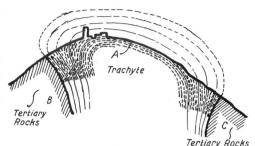

HANS and ERNST CLOOS,[1] upon inspecting this trachytic cone, found that the flat sanidine tablets are not lying in random directions in the magma from which they once crystallized but are in preferred orientations.   While in a vertical section through the cone the plates near the highest point of the mountain (at A in Fig. 17-37) are situated with the middle plane of their two longest axes normal to the plane of the vertical profile, approximately horizontally, near the contact (B, C) with the adjoining sedimentary rocks, the tablets stand in vertical position with their longest axis and parallel to the contact surface.   The curves traced in Fig. 17-37 indicate this schematically, the longest axis of the oblong sanidine pebbles being tangent to the curves.   Oblong, rigid bodies embedded in a viscoplastic, deformable matrix would orient themselves into positions in which they exert the least resistance to the flow.   The dashed curves represent the direction of the maximum principal permanent strain during the last stage of flow in the volcanic mass after it cooled below its melting temperature and became a highly viscoplastic solid.

This motion of a volcanic mass in its viscoplastic stage, pressed upward through a volcanic vent with an approximately circular cross section, was further studied in model tests by W. RIEDEL.[2]   Figure 17-38 shows the distortion pattern of an initially square net of lines in a meridian plane of the volcanic mass, and Fig. 17-39 shows the orientation of the axes of principal, permanent strain.   While it is seen that a certain portion of mass remained dead—did not participate in the motion near the corners of the pressure chamber—the distortion pattern in the

[1] Die Quellkuppe des Drachenfels am Rhein, ihre Tektonik und Bildungsweise, Z. Vulkanologie, vol. 11, p. 33, 1927.

[2] Das Aufquellen geologischer Schmelzmassen als plastischer Formänderungsvorgang, Neues Jahrb. Mineralogie, Beilage 67, Abt. B, p. 151, 1929.   This was done by pressing out a plastic mass (plasticine) by means of a piston through a long cylindrical orifice.   To make the deformation visible, a device was used to deform the mass within a longitudinally split wooden pressure container, both halves of which were smeared with the mass.   Before the split cylinder was assembled, a square net was scratched on the two plane surfaces of the mass and these were covered with talcum dust.   The two halves of the form were then fitted together and tightened by screws.   After a test, the two halves were opened and the distortion of the network photographed.   From it the principal strains and their orientation in the meridian plane were numerically determined.

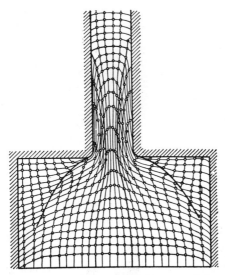 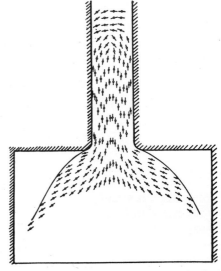

Fig. 17-38. Network of lines used for determining principal strain directions in a slowly moving plastic mass squeezed up through a narrow opening.

Fig. 17-39. The orientation of the maximum principal strain directions in a plastic mass pressed through a channel, visualizing the upward movement of a cooling volcanic mass through the neck of a volcano. (*According to W. Riedel.*)

narrow volcanic neck clearly discloses the influence of friction of the solid side walls in retarding the flow. The contour lines of maximum-strain direction in the upper part of the neck show a great resemblance to the curves along which the plate-shaped sanidine crystals were aligned in the Drachenfels (Fig. 17-37). But it is also noted that these phenomena in cooling volcanic masses rising through vents and wide fissures between solid rock massifs are reminiscent of the flow of hot metals in the technical processes of extrusion, that certainly throw a useful light on the former.

In this broadly termed analogy might be included a number of structural changes that have been studied in rocks by the mineralogists, on the one hand, and in metals by the metallurgists on the other. In terminology proposed by mineralogists, W. Schmidt[1] calls a structure like that of volcanic rocks having Schlieren, or streaks (cf. Sec 17-6A), an "actively" regulated structure, since these elements (suspensions) owe their positions to the situation which they had while the rock was still in its fluid, forming stage. In contrast, according to him, the remarkable, parallel arrangement of the axes of the quartz crystals in certain alpine rocks is an example of a "passively" oriented structure. W. Schmidt found that the axes of small quartz crystal grains in the rocks of the Alps, in

[1] Walter Schmidt, Gefügesymmetrie und Tektonik, Jahrb. geol. Bundesanstalt (Austria), p. 407, 1926; also Gesteinsumformung, Denkschr. Naturhist. Museums, Vienna, vol. 3, 1925. Concerning regulation of rock structures, see also K. A. Redlich, K. von Terzaghi, and R. Kampe, "Ingenieurgeologie," 708 pp., J. Springer, Berlin, 1929, and Bruno Sander, "Gefügekunde der Gesteine," 352 pp., J. Springer, Verlag, Vienna, 1930.

regions of many square kilometers extent, all showed a preferred, common position with respect to the compass directions.   He attributed this to the severe plastic cold deformation to which the rock strata were subjected through mountain orogeny.   To this "passively" reoriented rock structure corresponds the well-known, preferred position into which the axes of the lattice of the crystallites is brought in severely cold-rolled copper sheets.   Thus the fluidal structure of cold-worked metals conforms in many respects to phenomena which the mineralogists have independently described.

17-7.   Alfred Wegener's Continental-drift Theory

> He lies now in the land for the explorations of which he gave so many years of his life, that attracted him always through his scientific problems and the greatness of its Nature . . . .   He went out there into the Winternight and succumbed to its strains.   But through his high ideals his death is blessed.
>
> ELSE WEGENER
> (Alfred Wegener's letzte
> Grönlandfahrt, 1932.)

Geologic observations in the high mountain ranges and elsewhere have supplied convincing proof that large parts of the great, continental tablelands moved relatively to each other and to their base during the past history of the earth.   It appears appropriate to list in this section first a few details, believed to be significant from the geomechanical viewpoint, describing forms of marginal contour lines between land and sea and the trend of high ranges of mountains and of deep sea trenches, as they appear to an objective observer on a globe map of the earth. ALFRED WEGENER around 1910 advanced the idea[1] that the geographical continental massifs as we now know them once were joined together in a single, primeval block of land and that the latter split apart into several pieces, perhaps during the beginning of the Eocene or Tertiary geologic period, some 20 to 60 million years ago.

[1] He states on page 1 of the first edition of his book "Die Entstehung der Kontinente und Ozeane," 94 pp., Friedr. Vieweg und Sohn, Brunswick, 1915, that the impressive congruence of the shore lines of Brazil's projecting easternmost, convex corner with the concavel ines of the Gulf of Guinea in Africa initiated in his mind around 1910 the idea that these shores of South America and Africa were once joined together, a fact that he expounded in two papers published in Petermanns Mitt., pp. 185, 253, 305, 1912, and in Geol. Rundschau, vol. 3, pp. 276–292, 1912.   A fourth edition of his book, 220 pp., appeared in 1929; an English edition was published by Methuen & Co., Ltd., London, in 1924.   A separation of the continent of North America from Greenland after the former drifted away westward from the latter was independently postulated by F. B. TAYLOR, Bearing of Tertiary Mountain Belt on the Origin of the Earth's Plan, Bull. Geol. Soc. Am., vol. 21, no. 2, pp. 179–226, 1910.
    A fit of the continents, somewhat like the one reproduced after Wegener's reconstructed world map in Fig. 17-41, was envisaged by H. B. BAKER as early as 1911 (according to A. L. DuToIT, "Our Wandering Continents," Oliver & Boyd, Ltd., Edinburgh and London, 1937).

FIG. 17-40. ALFRED WEGENER, professor of meteorology and geophysics at the University in Graz, Austria, from 1924.† (Born Nov. 1, 1880, in Berlin; died November, 1930, in Greenland.)

Eozän

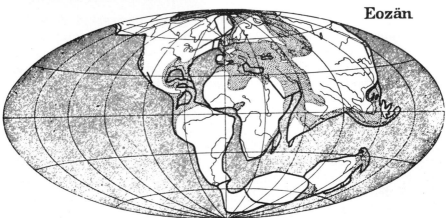

FIG. 17-41. Map of world in Eocene epoch, drawn by Wegener. The finely black-dotted areas in Europe, Africa, and Asia were at that time covered by inland seas.

† ALFRED WEGENER was professor at the Universities in Marburg (1921) and Hamburg (up to 1924) and took part in the Danemark (1906–1908) and T. P. Koch (1912–1913) expeditions to Greenland. In the summer of 1929 he explored the best means of access through the deeply glaciated slopes to the ice-covered plateau of this island. On Apr. 1, 1930, he left Copenhagen with 20 scientific participants for his last expedition to Greenland, sponsored by the Notgemeinschaft der deutschen Wissenschaft, Berlin, primarily for the purpose of exploring by echo soundings the thickness of the ice covering Greenland. During the summer of 1930, with his men, he established in the middle of Greenland, on its barren glaciers, at an altitude of 3,000 m and 400 km east of the Umanak Fjord, the station "Eismitte." On a return sledge trip from this place, he and a companion lost their lives in the icy wilderness through exposure and overexertion in November, 1930. His body was found later and buried in the glacier ice.

The photograph and the preceding notes were taken from FRITZ LOEWE and ELSE WEGENER, "Alfred Wegener's letzte Grönlandfahrt," F. A. Brockhaus, Leipzig, 1932, 304 pp., 125 illustrations, with prefaces by Kurt and Else Wegener, and 26 communications.

Envisage from a mechanical viewpoint the following trends in a few physiographical features pertaining to the form of seashore lines characterizing the two main land massifs, *Eurasia*[1] and the two *Americas*:

1. The singularly impressive congruence of the shore line around the easternmost, convex, projecting corner of South America with the reentrant, concave corner of Africa, which fit together over an arc length of 4,000 to 5,000 km as perfectly on the globe as two corresponding cardboard pieces in a gigantic jigsaw puzzle.[2]

2. From Eurasia four large peninsulas, Africa, Arabia, India, Thailand-Malaya, all project in a southward direction.

3. The Adriatic, the Red Sea, the Persian Gulf, and the Strait of Malacca with their axes run approximately in parallel directions from northwest to southeast.

4. The long, narrow land tongue of Central America extends from

---

[1] Along fundamental viewpoints accepted by geologists, one considers certain shallow inland seas, such as the North, Baltic, and Red Seas, the Gulf of Mexico, the Hudson Bay, and also the Mediterranean, the Black Sea, and the Persian Gulf, as more or less gentle dips of the continents, geosynclines, flooded by sea water, in contrast to the three deep seas—the Atlantic, Pacific, and Indian Oceans—by assigning the former areas covered by shallow inland seas to the continents.   With this in mind, the continent of Africa is considered a part of the largest, compact land massif, namely, *Eurasia*, on the earth.

Whereas dry lands cover 30 per cent and the deep sea 70 per cent of the earth's surface, two-thirds of the area of the continents (21.3 per cent of the total surface) rises to elevations 0 to 1 km high above sea level, but 40.8 per cent of the total earth's surface lies below water 4 km or more deep (after A. WEGENER's and H. WAGNER's "hypsometric" curve, disclosing that the continental plateaux rise to 4.5 km average height above the average abyssal floor plains of the oceans).

[2] With regard to this fit, reference of an adverse nature must be made by quoting HAROLD JEFFREYS' well-known book "The Earth, Its Origin, History and Physical Constitution," Cambridge University Press, London.   In its second edition (1929), p. 322, and also in its third edition (1952), p. 349, one reads the assertion: "Perhaps the best-known argument for continental drift is the alleged fit of South America into the angle of Africa.   On a moment's examination of a globe this is seen to be really a misfit by about 15°.   The coasts along the arms could not be brought within hundreds of kilometers of each other without distortion.   The width of the shallow margins of the ocean lend no support to the idea that the forms have been greatly altered by denudation and deposition; . . .".   Fortunately, S. WARREN CAREY, Wegener's South America-Africa Assembly, Fit or Misfit?, Geol. Mag. vol. 92, pp. 196–201, 1955, took occasion to object vigorously to such false assertions, from the authoritative side, after rechecking the fit of the two shore lines, using rigorous methods of careful mapping for comparison, on a globe and by means of azimuthal, stereographic projection, after allowing for the narrow, marginal continental shelves at the 2,000 m depth line, halfway down the continental slope.   Briefly, suffice it to say, that *not the least proof for an appreciable misfit* has been detected in the carefully constructed map traced by CAREY.   JEFFREYS compared the shore contours in a superficial way, and his statements are unfounded.

North America and likewise the Malayan peninsula from Asia in a
southeastern direction, and both gradually bend eastward in association with an arch of islands, the chain of which seems to trail an apparent westward motion of the continents like a tail that is attached to
the latter.

5. The great, nearly equilateral triangles of South America and
Greenland point with their tips southward.

6. The contour of the southernmost tip of South America, including
Tierra del Fuego, bends distinctly eastward.

7. The highest mountain chains on the earth may be grouped in two
main systems: (a) the Cordilleras (Andes, Rockies) running in an
essentially south-north direction and (b) the band of Pyrennees, the
Alps, Carpathians, the Caucasian, and Himalayan Mountain ranges,
running roughly in a west-east direction encircling great parts of the
globe.

After allowing for nearby submerged portions of former dry land in
the continental shelves, it strikes one's imagination that some of the
aforementioned regularities of preferred orientation of the present
contour lines of land might be the consequences of a grand-scale
common pattern in the process of splitting up the primeval land mass
into large chunks that moved apart above the heavier substratum
underlying them and were subsequently permanently distorted.
While the two sides of the initial, huge crack in the upper crust which
presently are the east and west coast lines of the South Atlantic Ocean
remained well preserved, WEGENER presumed that other parts of the
crack system have undergone considerable changes since the separation, and he assembled an impressive list of arguments of geophysical,
geologic, paleontologic, paleoclimatic, and other nature supporting his
theory, details of which must remain outside the scope of this book
devoted to mechanical phenomena.   We only reproduce in Fig. 17-41
a reconstruction of a world map due to WEGENER, roughly showing the
position of the continents in early *Eocene* times in the beginning stage of
their separation.   The darkened areas in the upper middle of this map
(utilizing, for convenience, an arbitrarily drawn net of meridian and
latitude circles) represent shallow inland seas; the rest of the dark areas
represent deep sea.   A. WEGENER,[1] E. ARGAND,[2] and A. L. DuToit[3]
place the archaic continent "Gondwanaland" (present Antarctica,
Australia, the southern tip of India, and the East Indian Archipelago)

[1] The paleoclimatic arguments are enumerated by W. KÖPPEN and A. WEGENER
in "Die Klimate der geologischen Vorzeit," 265 pp., Verlagsbuchhandlung
Gebrüder Bornträger, Berlin, 1924, in which the distribution of the arid desert and
the tropical humid zones and the position of the glaciated polar caps during the
Carboniferous epoch (265 million years ago) are analyzed, leading these authors to
the conclusion that the North Pole of the earth at that time was located somewhere near the Hawaiian Islands in the present Pacific and that the equator

to the east side of Africa at the young Carboniferous epoch, prior to separation.[4]   These keen ideas of a separation and dislocation of the continents met first with many dissenting opinions, but as the years passed their opponents became fewer and fewer in spite of a few inherent difficulties that have not yet been resolved.[5]

Confining ourselves to drawing a few conclusions based on the fore-going observations, we consider it significant that the east and west flanks of parts of the primeval crack that separated South America from Africa are still so well preserved over a length of 4,000 to 5,000 km, with wrinkles and details fitting into each other, after a lapse of time since the early Tertiary (Eocene) epoch estimated at 20 to 60 million years. This induces the thought that the primeval continental shell broke up rapidly at this remote time, that the fractures perhaps started at a point situated somewhere in the southern hemisphere, south of Africa, from which three huge cracks of a brittle nature radiated northward.   Two of them, converging at an angle approximately equal to 25°, became the boundaries of the large equilateral triangle of the continent of South America.   Furthermore, a system of impulsive forces, of tensile normal stresses tangent to the earth's surface, superposed on the hydrostatic pressures due to the weights of the rocks, burst the original, hollow, spherical shell crust—a gigantic fracturing process to which nothing comparable ever occurred in the continental plateau of Eurasia since it existed—while the northern extensions of the three primordial cracks probably required a longer time for their development, were slowed down through plastic distortion in the adjoining regions, and were gradually obliterated, so that the old, original shore lines in the North Atlantic Ocean, east and west, between the present northern latitudes 30° and 60° are not as sharply recognizable.   Various physiographic details concerning the inland seas make it probable that in the wake of

---

passed through northern Europe, at an era long prior to the separation of the continents.

[2] E. ARGAND, La tectonique de l'Asie, 13th Geol. Congress, Liege, 1924, analyzing the magnificent "lemuric" (East Indian) pushing together of the crust in a south-north direction that created the high Himalayas and the mountain belts in the Caucasus, the Alps, etc., during the Tertiary ages.

[3] A. L. DuToit, op. cit., envisaged in the Carboniferous epoch a somewhat more northern position of the parts of Gondwanaland than that postulated by Wegener.

[4] A team from Victoria University, Wellington, New Zealand, under V. B. BULL discovered recently (see Sci. News Letter, vol. 76, Nov. 14, 1959) in Antarctica dolerite rocks of the same type and old age as those found in Tasmania, in Australia.   Bull states that this is a striking, new proof that Antarctica and Australia were once joined together along the coast of Tasmania (as parts of the vanished, archaic continent "Gondwanaland").

[5] See Theory of Continental Drift, a Symposium on the Origin and Movement of Land Masses, as proposed by A. WEGENER, with communications of 14 authors, 240 pp., American Association of Petroleum Geologists, London, 1928.

the first impulsive action a steady system of tensile stresses of smaller intensity prevailed a long time in western Eurasia, directed parallel to the line bisecting the reentrant corner of the Gulf of Guinea.   This could possibly explain the formation of the conspicuous depressions (rift valleys) of the Adriatic, the Red Sea, and the Persian Gulf, the long axes of which are nearly perpendicular to the direction of the tensile stresses just mentioned.

An examination of the initial $(A_0B_0C_0)$ and present (ABC) positions of the corners of the *great, spherical triangle South America* in Fig. 17-42 leaves no doubt that this part of the New World, apart from having drifted essentially westward (its center of gravity G moved roughly by one-eighth of the circumference of a great circle, 40,000 km, by 5,000 km west), *turned continuously clockwise* by an angle of about 25° around an axis normal to the sphere passing through G.   The nature of the system of body forces that during the millions of years drove the great, triangular, spherical shell ABC gently forward against the frictional forces exerted from the interior of the earth is obscure.   Neither has the second, clockwise rotation that was superposed on the general westward drift ever been determined, nor the positions of the true, momentaneous axes of the instantaneous, combined, infinitesimal, resultant rotations.

One first consequence of this secular motion has been recognized, namely, the great frontal resistance that it encountered, normal to the leading, frontal, long edge AB.   All geologists agree that the westward drift of both American continents—of trapezoid-shaped North and triangular-shaped South America—created on their frontal, leading, western edges the great frontal pressures that have pushed up the Rocky Mountains and the Andes Mountain ranges through horizontal compression and folded them along the west coast of both Americas.

A second, geomechanically interesting conclusion may also be added.   While the solid, large, triangular, heavy, spherical shell of South America drifted slowly westward, turning clockwise, the hot, semifluid, viscous base exerted drag forces

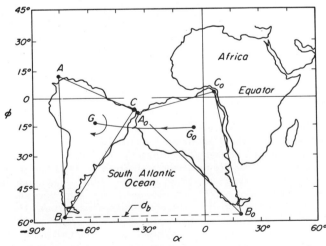

FIG. 17-42. Westward drift of South America (Mercator-projection).

along its surface, tangential shearing stresses τ everywhere in the lower contact sphere, in opposite direction to the relative glide velocities v, increasing with v according to a shear speed law $\tau = f(v)$, valid at the high hydrostatic pressures $p = h\gamma$, due to the weight of the overlying rock strata and temperature θ, prevailing at the depth h at the base of the continent. Referring to Fig. 17-42, denote the relative glide velocities at the corners C (corner of Brazil) and B (tip of South America) by v_C and v_B. While point C has practically moved on the equator a distance $C_0C = d_C = 5,000$ km, by looking at an earth globe we have estimated roughly that the southern tip of South America, point B, in fact traveled the distance[1] $B_0B = d_B = 7,000$ km from its initial position B_0. For guessing the order of magnitude of these two travel velocities, suppose in first, rough approximation that both rates were uniform and, with

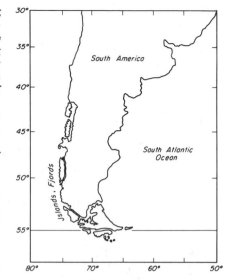

FIG. 17-43. Tip of South America bends eastward.

WEGENER, that the time since the separation of the continents, since early Eocene, amounted to, say, $t = 60$ million years. This gives for *the travel velocities* of *the corner of Brazil* (point C)

$$v_C = \frac{d_C}{t} = \frac{5 \times 10^3}{6 \times 10^7} = 8.3 \times 10^{-5} \text{ km/year} = 8.3 \text{ cm/year}$$

and of *the southernmost tip of South America* (point B)

$$v_B = (\tfrac{7}{5})v_C = 11.6 \text{ cm/year},$$

both surely small velocities, but this brings out the expected, interesting fact, due to the superposed clockwise rotation, that the great triangle of South America until more recently drifted west *in its narrow tip B with the fastest rate prevailing in this continent, just in the region where its vertical cross sections are the weakest.*

We believe that these simple kinematic facts are beautifully supported by the physiographical contour lines. It has always impressed us to note that the tip and *narrowest southern end of South America is distinctly, strongly bent eastward* (Fig. 17-43), reminding us of the permanently, plastically, sidewise deflected end of a long, slender cantilever beam having converging sides distorted by lateral loads. Since this narrow end of the beam moved with the greatest velocities relatively to the viscous substratum, the shearing drag that kept it loaded sidewise was the greatest at its weakest end. No wonder that

---

[1] The distance d_B and orbit B_0B traveled by point B appear distorted on the Mercator's projection used for convenience in Fig. 17-42.

the cantilever was permanently bent so distinctly eastward.   The
wrinkles on the east side, carrying the maximum compression stresses,
likewise the hundreds of narrow fjords and small, detached islands on
the west side, where the high, tensile bending stresses "cracked" up the
beam, speak impressively for the aforementioned plastic bending
distortion of it—and indirectly beautifully prove the truth of the
continental-drift theory.

Quite a number of impressive arguments of a similar nature may be
enumerated in favor of the dislocation and localized distortion that the
continent of North America has made evident, but lack of space prohibits describing them here.   In these "reconstructions" of the initial
contour lines of both Americas we have to bear in mind that on the
west side they initially looked quite different from their present forms
because the great frontal resistance encountered on their journey

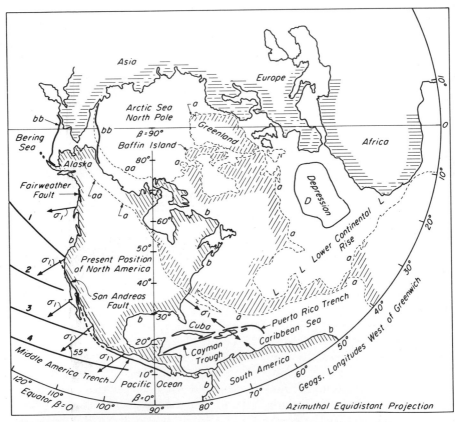

FIG. 17-44. Westward drift of North America.   Azimuthal equidistant projection.   Shoreline contours *aa*, just after separation of North America from
Eurasia.   Shoreline contours *bb*, present position.

westward pushed each continent together horizontally on these sides and raised their upper levels, deforming them by lateral compression. We have to content ourselves with presenting without comments, only Fig. 17-44, sketched in azimuthal, equidistant projection by the author, somewhat along WEGENER's ideas, to illustrate the hypothetical early position of North America, indicated by the dashed contours *aa*, and its present position by the lines *bb*. The curve circumscribing the depression *DD* utilizes a beautiful physiographic map of the topography below the Atlantic Ocean published recently by BRUCE C. HEEZEN,[1] based on the contours of the "lower continental rise" *LL*, showing that quite wide strips along the shores are submerged parts of the adjacent continental massifs or were once a wide land bridge *LL* that connected North with South America. It is presumed that some of its remnants are the Caribbean Islands and Lesser Antilles and that this region, as it trailed the westward movement of the trapezoidal slab of North America, was subjected to a severe shearing distortion parallel to the line *LL*. The thick lines 1, 2, . . . in the present situation represent deep trenches in the Pacific and near Puerto Rico, owing their existence to orogenic movements of the major continental massif; the thick lines *bb* are steep submarine escarpments, demarking a shallow undersea platform: the former land bridge that joined Alaska with Siberia.[2] If further proof for the continental-drift motion were needed, it should be noted how well the contours of Greenland, of Baffin Island, and of the flat lands in the northeastern corner of North America fit in their backward, displaced, early position geographically, and structurally, with the eastern shores of Scandinavia and the British Isles (see Fig. 17-44).

On the other hand, seismic and slip observations along transcurrent faults leave no doubt that the western part of the large North American continental slab *presently moves slowly* and intermittently along its curved boundary line, running roughly parallel to the West Coast over 6,000 to 8,000 km, *in a southward direction* relative to the Pacific Basin— a secular motion that might perhaps be roughly described as an

[1] BRUCE C. HEEZEN, MARIE THARP, and MAURICE EWING, The Floors of the Oceans, I, The North Atlantic, Geol. Soc. Am. Spec. Paper 65, 122 pp., April, 1959; see plates 20, 22 therein.

[2] DAVID M. HOPKINS, Cenozoic History of the Bering Land Bridge, Science, vol. 129, p. 1919, 1959, recently assembled impressive proofs that this land bridge existed for at least 50 million or more years, and that the submarine Bering Sea platform *bb* establishes geologic evidence of the structural continuity of western Alaska with Asia, as indicated in the narrow band of land *aa* that hypothetically once connected both continents along the thick, dashed lines *aa*. Again, the sidewise bulged-out thick lines *bb* are a striking proof of plastic, axial compression through which the narrow band *aa* widened while it axially shortened owing to the westward drift of North America.

anticlockwise rotation of the entire continent,[1] interrupted spasmodically by periods of temporary stagnation.   One might be inclined to surmise that the westward drift of the northern slab has halted, at least for the time being, and that the character of the secular motion for unknown reasons changed during our times.

In this respect other signs of local distortion are of interest, namely, the submarine *deep sea troughs and trenches* that have been discovered near the west shores of both Americas.   One group approaches the western continental shelf with their axes inclined to the coast.[2]   Another extends over a length of 5,500 km, running in the Pacific Ocean at the foot of the west side of South America (the Edwards, Richards, Haekel troughs, reaching down to depths of 6.2, 7.6, 5.5 km, respectively) that has recently been explored[3] and described as a long submarine depression and valley bordering the continental shelf, significantly located on the west side of South America, whereas no trenches have been found on its east side.   This grand system of straight, long, deep valleys embedded in the floor of the Pacific, so near to the continental shelves, it seems to us, proves that the vast Pacific Basin presently exerts tensile normal stresses on both Americas, whereas the two trenches crossing the Caribbean Sea in an east-west direction (the Cayman and Puerto Rico troughs—the latter represents the greatest depth of 8.4 km yet discovered in the Atlantic Ocean) might be interpreted as a phenomenon akin to the oblique necking in a wide, flat, tensile metal bar (cf. Vol. I, page 316, Figs. 19-25 to 19-28), exhibiting a permanently, plastically distorted tension-shear zone through which tensile forces originating in the slabs of North and South America are transmitted, oriented as the arrows σ_1 across the Caribbean trough show in the map in Fig. 17-44.   Geological evidence seems to support this assumption.

If the postulates of ALFRED WEGENER's keen ideas are correct that a single, compact tableland massif existed for a long time on one side of the surface of the earth prior to the origin of the continents, then *two major events of cataclysmic nature* must have occurred (440 million years apart) in geomechanical history: (1) *the birth of the Pacific Basin* and

---

[1] Parts of the boundary curve coincide with two well-known, long transcurrent faults: the *San Andreas* and the *Fairweather Faults* (see Fig. 17-44) in California and Alaska along which earthquakes frequently occurred.   In the great San Francisco earthquake of 1906 one side of the San Andreas fault moved in places 21 ft horizontally, relative to the other side.   In a violent quake on July 20, 1958, the continental (east) side slipped in regard to the Pacific (west) side in the Fairweather Fault by 22 ft southward, triggering a landslide that produced a huge wave of 1,700 ft crest height in the Lituya Bay (Alaska).   Cf. DON TOCHER and DON J. MILLER, Science, vol. 129, p. 394, 1959.

[2] HENRY W. MENARD, Deformation of the Northeastern Pacific Basin, Bull. Geol. Soc. Am., vol. 66, pp. 1149–1198, 1955, reported the discovery of four "fracture zones" 1,400 to 3,300 miles long, reaching down to a 6 to 6.2 km depth (see the thick lines 1, . . . , 4 in Fig. 17-44), which the author has interpreted as caused by combined tension and shear stresses and associated with the principal tension direction σ_1, approximately normal to the west coast of North America.

[3] By M. EWING, B. C. HEEZEN, J. G. HACOCK, and J. L. WORZEL (1955).   These authors recognize in the latter deep trenches tension zones in which the crust underlying the Pacific floor locally became appreciably thinner through plastic flow, an opinion with which the author fully concurs.

(2) *the origin of the continents.*   Whereas the hypothesis of the existence of a primeval land massif that blanketed only less than one-half of the earth's surface since the beginning of the geologic time scale, some 500 million years ago, while the oldest and more recent sedimentary rocks were formed from land debris, has enjoyed acceptance in geology, it cannot be claimed that agreement has been reached as to what bodily force systems—impulsive, steady, or fluctuating—acted on the material elements of the outer, thin, spherical shell of light rocks prior to and later, during and after the separation of the continents.   In order to explain localized distortions in the earth's crust, various attempts were made recently to derive bodily force systems from thermal convection currents,[1] rising from and sinking back slowly to the hot interior of the earth.   But they are not suitable for explaining the aforementioned impulsive events.   Slow underground vortical streams of heavy matter could not have dug out the vast Pacific Basin nor later break up impulsively the other, residual half of the rock shell.   We hold onto bodily force systems that were akin in both cataclysms, of cosmic origin, and such that they developed at two critical times a general instability of equilibrium in the uppermost, solid rock shell.

Supposing that on the entire surface of the fluid earth ball the first, substantial, as yet comparatively thin layer of the lightest granitic rocks had solidified, SIR GEORGE HOWARD DARWIN envisaged more than 60 years ago the fundamental fact that one-half of this solid rock shell, still in archaic times, had disappeared on one side of the globe. In his classical book "The Tides and Kindred Phenomena in the Solar System" (3d ed., 1910), in which he treated in a popular manner but very generally many problems in cosmology, he reviewed his theory of the tidal oscillations of a fluid, revolving sphere of heavy matter, pointing out that tidal friction was instrumental in slowing down the speed of rotation of the earth around its axis, presupposing that the length of the solar day, the period of one revolution, increased continuously in those early times.   After having evaluated the period of the fundamental mode of the small, lateral, free oscillations of a gravitating, nonrevolving sphere having a uniform density equal to the mean density $\rho = 5.5$ of the earth, which he found to be equal to one of our present hours plus 34 minutes, he concluded that, at a time when the period of one forced, semidiurnal solar tide caused by the attractions of the sun on the turning fluid earth, equaling one-half of a solar day, became just equal to the period of free oscillations, the tides became unstable.   In remote times past, when the solar day was 3 hr and 8 min

---

[1] Convective vortices were proposed in a variety of forms: "roller cells" having rectangular streamlines with rounded corners, fancy octahedral arrangement, etc.; even "random forces," without elucidating their nature, were made responsible for causing continental drift in preferred directions.

long, the tides disrupted the light granitic solid rock shell on the side turned toward the sun which pulled away the detached light masses that became the moon, leaving the unerasable huge scar on the face of the earth that became the Pacific Basin.[1]

DARWIN's hypothesis of the origin of the moon is supported through the following observations:

1. Its mean density $\rho_m = 3.3$ is of the right order of magnitude. With due regard to the elastic compressibility of rocks under the pressures in the interior of a gravitating sphere of homogeneous matter and size of the moon, having the radius 1,738 km, one would expect that its mean density ρ_m should be perhaps 8 to 10 per cent greater than the density ρ_s of the rocks from which it is made up.   While the density of the rocks in the earth's crust is only $\rho = 2.7$, it seems quite probable that it was initially somewhat higher, $\rho_s = 3.0$, in the early times before sedimentation started.

2. Geologists have found no important "planetesimal" material of extraterrestrial origin in massive accumulation in the earth's outer crust (quoting B. Gutenberg).   The scarce, heavy, iron-nickel meteorites that have reached the earth's surface, having a density around 8, preclude that the moon aggregated from such planetesimal substances.

3. The volume of the moon equals reasonably well the volume of the abyssal depression in the Pacific Basin that was left as a scar on one side of the earth, after this part of the solid crust was scraped up.

[1] Allowing for the increase of the density ρ with depth in the interior of the earth, DARWIN revised the value of the length of the solar day at which resonance causing the instability of the tides occurred and estimated its critical value at 4 hr.

HAROLD JEFFREYS, successor in the chair once held by G. H. DARWIN, in the third edition of his quoted book, "The Earth," 1952 (see p. 235 in it), expressed the opinion that DARWIN's theory of fluidal oscillations is inadequate for explaining the expulsion of the moon because it presupposes small tide amplitudes and because the particle velocities of the tidal waves normal to the surface of the sphere fall short of the values required to throw up masses that would not return to the parent body.   But it seems to us that these objections are mitigated if DARWIN's theory is amended.   According to ideas proposed first in the planetesimal hypotheses by FOREST RAY MOULTON and THOMAS CHROWDER CHAMBERLIN and later by SIR J. H. JEANS, planets are born when two hot stars pass so close to one another that the enormous tides raised on one of them are pulled out by the gravitational attractions of the other into a long protuberance of matter spurting out into space.   The attractions of an extraneous, heavenly body, comparable perhaps in size and mass with the earth, on passing not very far from it in an orbit in which it would not otherwise upset the order of our solar system, might have pulled out from the earth the solid crust masses that became the moon.

Since it must remain outside the scope of this book to discuss cosmologic theories, we must content ourselves with accepting the statements that (1) an impulsive event of cosmic origin created the Pacific Basin, (2) in early geologic time the earth turned much faster around its axis, and (3) the moon circled much nearer around the earth than in our present times.

4. The circumference of the Pacific Ocean is still an active zone, penetrated by frequent volcanic activity and through transcurrent faults, in contrast to the relatively quiet coasts of the Atlantic Ocean.

Let us conjecture and envisage tentatively, in contrast to the promulgators of thermal convection currents, that *the second phenomenon, the origin of the continents*, placed by WEGENER for good reasons some 440 million years later, at a time when the Pacific grounds had long been filled up with deep sea water, was likewise of an impulsive but of a far less violent nature and that in it also tide-generating body forces were involved in which only the attractions of the moon played a role. The heavy substratum on which the lighter, continental slab Eurasia and the solid, granitic floor of the Pacific rested had long solidified.   Consequently, the outer spherical rock shell lost one of its degrees of freedom of motion and if periodic, *solid* bodily tide forces were excited in it, then they caused essentially small, tangential movements as in an elastic solid, a *sidewise, elastic, periodic wabbling motion* in the tangential directions relative to the very hot substratum.   Since the solid spherical shell could transmit longitudinal, elastic oscillations like dilatational earthquake waves, a chance still existed that the former, forced, solid-tidal and the latter, free, longitudinal, elastic oscillations could come to resonance while the solar day gradually was getting longer.   Our contention is then that this might have caused the impulsive separation, the origin of the continents, at a time when the moon possibly described a much closer orbit around the earth than now.   The velocity of propagation of a dilatational elastic wave c sweeping along a straight bar being equal to

$$c = \sqrt{\frac{E}{\rho}} \, ,$$

the period of the longitudinal oscillations in an elastic bar of length l having both ends fixed, unmovable, amounts to

$$T = \frac{2l}{c} = 2l \cdot \sqrt{\frac{\rho}{E}} \, .$$

Supposing that such a bar is wrapped around the equator of the earth, taking for the length l half of the circumference of a major global circle, namely, $l = \pi R$, it would take for a dilatational wave to run once around the earth equator $2\pi R = 40,000$ km, the time period

$$T = 2\pi R \cdot \sqrt{\frac{\rho}{E}} \, ,$$

or, after assuming for the specific weight of the rocks $\gamma = \rho g = 0.0028$ kg/cm³ and for Young's modulus of rock elasticity the somewhat low value $E = 150,000$ kg/cm^2 (taking some account of the average high temperature in the rock shell of granite) corresponding to which the wave velocity is $c = \sqrt{E/\rho} = \sqrt{Eg/\gamma} = 2.294$ km/sec $= 2,294$ m/sec, the period of one full oscillation is found equal to

$$T = \frac{2\pi R}{c} = \frac{40,000}{2.294} = 17,430 \text{ sec,}$$

$$T = 290.5 \text{ min} = 4.85 \text{ hr.}$$

This is a long oscillation period. Hence the particle velocities in the rock shell relative to the underlying semifluid substratum and the damping through the viscous drag of the latter in those early geologic epochs were comparatively quite small.

We may then conjecture, along GEORGE DARWIN's assumptions in regard to fluid tides, that these solid tides consisting of longitudinal oscillations of the solid crust may have likewise produced an instability in the crust at a time when the "day" or period of one revolution of the earth *relative* to the motion of the moon was 9.7 hr, equal to twice the period T of the slow free, lateral, tangential oscillations of the outer rock shell, impelling them to resonance. We are aware of the uncertainty whether our planet in the early Eocene epoch, 60 million or more years ago, turned as fast around its polar axis as this primitive survey of the fundamental, elastic, sidewise oscillation mode in its crust led us to conclude. Some refinements of the theory of the elastic shell deformations may be found in Sec. 17-8.

In summing up, convincing evidence has been assembled by the work of geologists, seismologists, oceanographers, and particularly by MAURICE EWING and his collaborators that (1) the continental massifs are, in fact, rock slabs of some 35 to 40 km minimum thickness where their surface is flush with sea level and correspondingly thicker under their elevated portions, having a specific weight varying between 2,650 to 2,900 kg/m^3 and consisting near their base of basaltic rock; (2) that the ocean deep-sea floors are, apart from a thin sedimentary cover, a rock shell of basalt ($\gamma = 2,900$ kg/m^3) only about 5 km thick; (3) that both the continents and the thin submarine basaltic layer are underlain by the mantle of the earth (peridotite rock, $\gamma = 3,300$ kg/m^3);[1] and (4) that impressive geomechanical evidence, based on the fit of shore-line contours, the identity of the composition of the rock strata including their geologic age and direction of folding on the corresponding shore lines of the presently widely separated continents that were formerly joined, and the orientation of the main mountain-chain and deep-sea

---

[1] H. H. HESS, The Deeper Structure of the Atlantic, Proc. Roy. Soc. (London), ser. A, vol. 222, pp. 341–348, 1954.

trench systems, apart from the many arguments of a nonmechanical nature, speaks convincingly for WEGENER's continental-drift hypothesis.

17-8. The Mid-Atlantic Ridge. The extensive deep-sea explorations by MAURICE EWING and his associates brought out a most remarkable feature in the sub-Atlantic floor topography: the *Mid-Atlantic Ridge* (to be abbreviated M.A.R.),[1] a very gently rising, long, submarine mount that runs with the maximum elevation of its crest line along a curve midway between the east and west shores of the Atlantic Ocean practically over half of the circumference of the earth.[2] A roughly sketched map reproduces it in Fig. 17-45. The gentle rise of the M.A.R. from the abyssal deep-sea plains (in many places having a depth of 3,000 fathoms, or 5,500 meters) to a broad, submarine mount with elevations culminating 3,700 meters above the former and extending along the median line of the Atlantic basin over an arc line nearly 20,000 km long is considered by naturalists as one of the great wonders in the realms of the physiography of the earth's surface, stirring the imagination that its origin was tied closely to the genesis of the Atlantic Ocean.[3]

A striking phenomenon in the M.A.R. is a deep notch running parallel with its crest line—strange as it may seem, *a rift valley on top of a high mountain*—in places 15 to 30 miles wide and having a jagged, rough floor, bordered by steep escarpments rising up to side peaks 1.3 to 1.8 km high above the rift valley. We shall see below that their steep, flanking planes might be considered as the faces of long, gently inclined blocks or strata of rocks that slid downhill on both sides of the high

[1] The first references to the existence of an upswelling in the middle region of the Atlantic Ocean basin date back more than 80 years. The first echo soundings taken from the German research vessel *Meteor* under WEGENER's direction also located the mount in the North Atlantic.

[2] This submarine mount explored in the North and South Atlantic extends beyond their realms into the Indian and South Pacific Oceans over a total length of more than 40,000 miles (according to M. EWING and B. C. HEEZEN, unpublished information).

[3] See the impressive details of these explorations by the members of the Lamont Geological Observatory in a series of papers by MAURICE EWING, C. H. ELMENDORF, D. B. ERICSON, BRUCE C. HEEZEN, FRANK PRESS, IVAN TOLSTOY, and others, and the monograph quoted in the next footnote. From six instructive, vertical, trans-Atlantic profiles recorded by echo soundings taken from the vessel *Atlantis* by B. C. HEEZEN (Geol. Soc. Am., Spec. Paper 65, plate 22, 1959) the profile through the narrowest width across a line between *Brazil* and *Africa* is reproduced with exaggerated heights in Fig. 17-46, disclosing that the mount rises over one-third, $b = 500$ nautical miles $= 928$ km, of the total width, a distance $d = 1,650$ nautical miles $= 3,060$ km between shores. Remarkably, the breadth b of the mount in the other profiles increases proportionally with the distance d between the shores while the crest maintains approximately a mean elevation of 3,700 meters above the abyssal deep-sea plains.

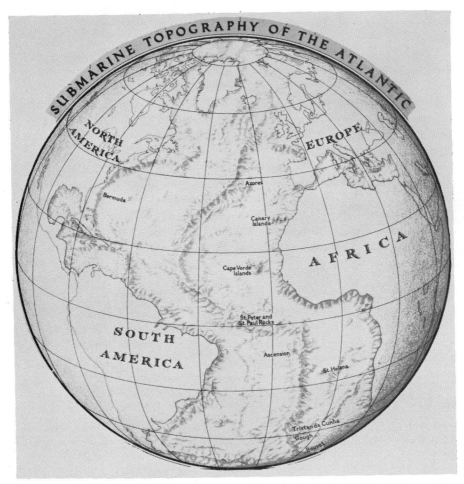

FIG. 17-45. The Mid-Atlantic Ridge.   (*After a map of the National Geographic Society, Washington, D.C., 1955.*)

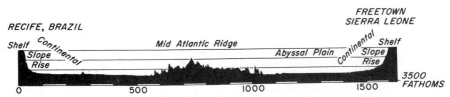

FIG. 17-46. *Transatlantic profile showing Mid-Atlantic Ridge* in a vertical section between the easternmost corner of *Brazil* (South America) and the *Gulf of Guinea* (Africa).   Evaluated by echo soundings by BRUCE C. HEEZEN, MARIE THARP, and MAURICE EWING, The Floors of the Oceans, I, the North Atlantic, Geol. Soc. Am., Spec. Paper 65, 122 pp., plate 22, April, 1959.   Vertical exaggeration of scale 40:1.

submarine mount not unlike the "nappes" in the high central massifs of the Swiss Alps.[1]

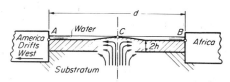

FIG. 17-47. Welling up of substratum into Mid-Atlantic mount.

The singularly unique coincidence of the axis of the long Mid-Atlantic Mount and of the rift valley running along its crest with the median line of the Atlantic basin leaves no doubt that the submarine mount was created through *the peculiar thermal conditions that developed in the wake of the westward drift* of both Americas within and underneath the newly formed rock bottom of the ocean during the Tertiary age. Looking at the schematic sketch of Fig. 17-47, envisage that between the trailing rear edge A (both Americas) and the edge B (Eurasia) a deep gap widened into which the hot masses of rocks rose up from the earth's interior. Obviously, while the trailing edge A had traveled for a long time a long distance $d = \overline{AB}$ and the westward drift of point A became more stagnant, general cooling in the newly formed rock bottom in the oceanic basin progressed from both its marginal sides A and B toward the middle region which stayed warm the longest. Under it a slowly rising, up-welling stream of hot magmatic material established itself with streamlines bending east and west of the characteristic stagnation point, as indicated by the arrows in Fig. 17-47.[2]

While the cold ends A and B of the bottom slab ceased to get thicker, new matter still entered into the middle portion of the ocean bed because of the buoyancy of the hot up-welling current. One gathers from the deep-sea explorations[3] that E. C. BULLARD measured the quantity of escaping heat flow 7×10^{-6} cal/cm^2 sec in the rift valley floor on top of the M.A.R., which he found significantly about *six times greater* than in places in the abyssal deep-sea floor plains in the eastern Atlantic, namely, 1.2×10^{-6} cal/cm^2 sec, observations that lend strong support to our preceding statements.

[1] BRUCE C. HEEZEN, MARIE THARP, and MAURICE EWING, The Floors of the Oceans, I, The North Atlantic, Geol. Soc. Am., Spec. Paper, 122 pp., Apr. 11, 1959, and also H. H. HESS (*loc. cit.*) state that, among the various working theories that they termed as speculative for explaining the origin of the M.A.R., the most probable one attributes it to the intrusion of porous, comparatively light, volcanic lavas that rose up through innumerable faults and fissures through the ocean floor and built the mount.

[2] Leaving aside speculative reflections concerning the early times, just after separation of the primeval continent, and about the effects of down-rushing water into the huge crack with its extremely hot bottom, geologists (H. H. HESS, *loc. cit.*) presume that during the archaic epochs probably much less oceanic water existed on earth than later.

[3] HEEZEN, THARP, and EWING, *op. cit.*, p. 103, and E. C. BULLARD, Proc. Roy. Soc. (London), ser. A, vol. 222, p. 408, 1954.

Since according to the indicated observational evidence the rise of the mount may be the result of a large-scale, long-time, slow intrusion of quantities of basaltic magma from the earth's deeper mantle into the surface rock layers, associated with extensive vulcanism and faulting, it seems difficult to explain the slow, secular bending up of the M.A.R. through a mechanically describable, simpler-type process of deformation. Because of the considerably higher mean temperatures prevailing in the middle third of the basin floor width, one could think of *thermal stresses* that became active within the suboceanic crust, embedded during the late, stagnating stage of the westward drift between the axially, lengthwise-fixed, immovable heads A and B of the rock slab, namely, axial, compression force resultants in an east-west direction and bending stresses under the bulged-up parts of the mount, presupposing that the latter two systems of thermal stresses were superposed on the hydrostatic pressures due to the weights of the rocks. In material possessing the property of general viscoelasticity, the temporary action of these thermal stresses should permanently bend upward the warmer middle third of the ocean-basin crust. These attractive concepts are, however, upset through the process of *relaxation* that must take place in material sensitive to rate-of-permanent-strain-dependent distortion, on account of which any elastic strain due to thermal volume dilatation changes gradually to permanent strain while the stress evanesces with time. Remembering that the temperature increases and the viscosity consequently decreases considerably with depth in the ocean floor, one would expect that the bending stresses would relax much faster at greater depths than in the uppermost rock layers. One may therefore conjecture that the thermal, positive, tensile, bending stresses which take on their greatest values just under the top of the bulged-up submarine mount persisted for a long time, while it slowly grew in height, and the negative, compression bending stresses soon practically evanesced because the latter are absolutely much smaller and the temperatures much higher at great depths (see Fig. 17-48). We believe that the deep-sea explorations made probable that this hypothetical prevalescence of tensile surface bending stresses might have caused those normal fissures (tensile cracks) on top of the M.A.R., which weakened the equilibrium of the surface rock layers until they started to slip downhill along the steepest slopes, opening up the spectacular rift valley. Remembering KING HUBBERT's theory of slip along gently inclined overthrust faults (Sec. 17-1), it is herewith noted that the conditions for a gravitational slip of packages of rock along the steepest slopes must have approached the critical stage: conditions were particularly favorable on the sides of the mount because of

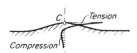

FIG. 17-48. Hypothetical bending-stress distribution in mount.

the complete saturation of the rocks with pore water of very high pressure, reducing the critical frictional shear stress that could hold them in position—the coincidence of these circumstances thus supplying a plausible explanation for the strange phenomenon of the deep Mid-Atlantic rift valley running along almost the entire crest line of the M.A.R., including the numerous wrinkles in its slopes.

Lastly, we note that a narrow belt comprising the epicenters of the majority of submarine earthquakes recorded since 1910 in the North Atlantic precisely follows the median trench or rift valley, as may be seen in Fig. 17-49,[1] proving that this region represents a relatively *quite active zone of concentrated, submarine distortion* in the earth's crust.

The foregoing reflections, formulated in primitive, nonexact form, are offered in the hope that perhaps they may at least inspire younger investigators to analyze with improved mechanical means the unique phenomenon of the origin and genesis of the Mid-Atlantic Ridge, pave the way for understanding the forces activating prominent motions in the upper solid crust of our planet, and convince people to regard the rise and existence of this mount as a further argument—little appreciated as yet, it seems—proving indirectly the correctness of WEGENER's continental-drift theory.

17-9. Stress and Strain in the Outer Solid Rock Shell of the Earth. A. SYSTEM OF BODILY FORCES ACTIVE IN OUTER, HOLLOW, SPHERICAL SOLID ROCK SHELL. Anybody standing on the summit of a salient mountain who has been impressed by the inspiring view of the nearby and more distant jagged ridges rising up in a vast horizon to a sea of peaks—for example, by the view from the summit of the Gorner Grat on the glaciated massif of the Monte Rosa group and the commanding pyramid of the Matterhorn in the Alps of the Wallis in Switzerland, or from the Fall River Pass in the Rockies in Colorado—has been moved to reflections about the origin of the high mountain chains of the earth and about the forces of nature that must have built them. The idea that the high mountain chains may have been lifted up from the plains through forces which must have acted deep under their hidden roots must have occurred to many an observer and lover of nature. The mechanically minded may have asked themselves the question: What kind of a force field pushed up and folded the rock layers and brought them to their elevated positions? Since mountain building has been going on in places concurrently with simultaneous sinking of the crust in broad belts in other localities, an inescapable conclusion in meditations of this kind is the thought that, in the evolution of the earth's long

---

[1] C. H. ELMENDORF and B. C. HEEZEN, Oceanographic Information for Engineering Submarine Cable Systems, Bell System Tech. J., vol. 36, no. 5, pp. 1047–1093, 1957. A second active belt runs through the Caribbean Sea.

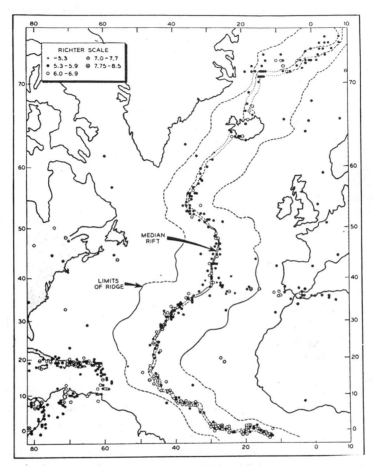

Fɪɢ. 17-49. *Mid-Atlantic Ridge and rift valley.* Earthquake epicenters in the North Atlantic Ocean basin after seismic observations from 1910 to 1956, according to C. H. Eʟᴍᴇɴᴅᴏʀꜰ and Bʀᴜᴄᴇ C. Hᴇᴇᴢᴇɴ. (Earthquake magnitudes after the Richter scale.)

history, the layers in the upper rock crust were continuously kept stressed, strained permanently, pushed together in some regions and stretched out in others, but not in a uniform manner; that in these manifestations on a grand scale a system of bodily forces in the deeply rooted distortion phenomena was and is still active; and that one of the fundamental questions in geology is of a mechanical nature, requiring, first, prima-facie definition of these bodily forces and, secondly, an analysis of the equilibrium states of stress and strain that they generate in the comparatively thin outer shell of solid rocks supported by the heavier, deeper substratum.

Thin curved shells of uniform thickness bound by two parallel surfaces of revolution are common elements in engineering construction.
In the applications the cases of primary importance are fairly rigid,
curved, metallic shells in which the lateral displacements of points of the
middle surface, i.e., the deflections of the shell in its strained condition,
remain small quantities compared with its thickness.   Stable states of
the equilibria of the stresses in such shells of elastic material, loaded
under extraneous forces of rotational symmetry, particularly, in
cylindrical, conical, and spherical shells, loaded by uniform gas or fluid
pressure or forces uniformly distributed along parallel circles, have been
investigated extensively by fairly simple means.[1]

In the mechanical problems of the outer, solid rock shell of the earth
little, if any, use has been made of these general developments, except
perhaps under greatly oversimplified assumptions, such as that the
whole body of the earth under the thin solid crust would behave either
as a homogeneous, incompressible fluid or a homogeneous, elastic,
gravitating sphere of uniform density and temperature.   The thought
having been expressed in previous sections that considerable shifting of
great parts of solid land relative to each other and to the earth's heavier
mantle has taken place, one might expect that these facts should throw
a guiding light on the origin of the grand changes in the positions of the
continental tablelands and of the phenomena of localized distortion
therein.   Leaving aside elucidation of some of the force fields proposed
at variance in textbooks, mostly found deficient in one respect or
another, we shall hold onto embodying a single, primary, bodily force
field in the theory of a thin, spherical, elastic shell of uniform thickness
that will represent for us the outer, solid rock shell of the earth, namely,
the force field of the tide-generating, gravitational accelerations exerted
primarily by the attractions of the moon, and endeavor to construct by
the simplest means solutions of the equations of equilibrium, expressing
the distributions of the stresses, of the elastic and permanent strains
over extended regions within the earth's outer, solid shell, and the
tangential and normal components of the small displacements of its
points.

This field of bodily forces seems to us adequate to explain several,
general, over-all trends observed in the secular distortion of the rock
shell and to derive values of stress and strain based on a unifying point
of view, with due consideration of the mobility of the outer crust as a

---

[1] Among the pioneers of the general theory of distorted, curved, elastic shells,
stretched in their middle surface and deflected to finite amounts while bent by
moments, might be cited A. E. H. LOVE, HANS REISSNER, ERNST MEISSNER,
ERIC REISSNER, and J. J. STOKER, among many unnamed investigators.   Shells
and flat plates of a yielding material in the plastic state have been treated by A.
ILYUSHIN, W. W. SOKOLOWSKY, and by others.

whole, as well as of parts thereof, in consequence of the rapid decrease of the strength properties of rocks with increase of temperature with depth.[1]

In the elementary theory of thin, curved, elastic shells, one assumes that in any normal section of infinitesimal width, the normal and shearing stresses, whose directions are parallel to the nearby plane tangent to the middle surface of the shell, vary linearly with the distance of a point from this surface. The stresses may be composed additively of a part uniformly distributed over the normal section and the remaining part which is then proportional to the distance from the curved middle surface. The former, the "membrane stresses," have a normal and a shear force per unit of width of the section as resultants, both of which lie in the plane tangent to the middle surface of the shell. The latter, the "bending stresses," balance the bending and twisting moments per unit of width which the shell may transmit. The latter components of stress usually have significant values only near the edges of open shells or near singularities of stress. In the thin rock shell of the earth, which is a closed shell of uniform curvature, we can neglect the bending stresses entirely. We shall, therefore, be concerned in the following *only with the membrane stresses*,[2] omitting consideration of localized bending effects and writing the terms of the hydrostatic state of pressures increasing with depths due to the weights of the rocks (presuming that the latter terms may be superposed, if needed, on the forces otherwise to be considered).

The state of stress in the solid spherical rock shell depends on *the bodily forces with which the moon attracts the elements of mass*. Denote by $r_0 = (\frac{1}{2})(r_1 + r_2)$ the mean radius and by ρ_0 the mean density of the

---

[1] The terms the *rock shell* or the *solid crust*, hereafter used synonymously, are meant to designate the complex of outermost, lighter rock layers underground within a spherical shell whose thickness h is considered small ($h = 50$ km), compared with the mean, outside, global radius $r_1 = 6,370$ km of the earth. The solid state is meant to apply to material within this shell having definable moduli of elasticity and rigidity E and G, of comparable magnitude to or smaller than those of the stronger rocks known on the surface when they are stressed over prolonged periods of time. With due consideration of the temperatures θ, increasing with depth to a value $\theta_2 = 1500°C$ in the lower contact sphere of radius $r_2 = 6,320$ km with the heavy substratum, the moduli E, G under static conditions are much smaller than those usually guessed from the velocity of propagation of dilatational and shear earthquake waves. Assuming Poisson's ratio $\nu = 0.25$, in consolidated rocks the mean values $E = 65,000$ kg/cm^2, $G = 26,000$ kg/cm^2 seem appropriate. Within the radii $r_2 \leq r \leq r_1$ the rock shell is supposed to withstand either elastic or permanent, deviatoral strains or both.

[2] A good review of the exact LOVE-MEISSNER theory and of the simplified theory of curved elastic shells of rotational symmetry may be found in J. W. GECKELER's article in H. GEIGER and KARL SCHEEL, "Handbuch der Physik," vol. 6, pp. 231–265, Julius Springer, Berlin, 1928.

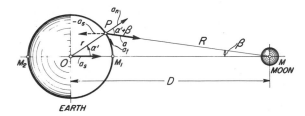

FIG. 17-50. Tide-
generating acceleration
exerted by moon.

shell.   On an element of mass, situated at a point P in the interior of
the earth, having the polar coordinates $r = \overline{OP}$ and α' with respect to
the axis $\overline{OM}$ connecting the centers of the earth O and moon M (Fig.
17-50), if it were free to move relatively to the earth, is impressed the
gravitational acceleration $\mathbf{a} - \mathbf{a}_s$; $\mathbf{a}$ expresses the acceleration at point
$P(r,\alpha')$ exerted by the moon and $\mathbf{a}_s$ at the center of the earth O.   We
shall resolve the relative acceleration $\mathbf{a} - \mathbf{a}_s$ at point P into a normal
and tangential component a_n and a_t and likewise the bodily attraction
force per unit volume into its normal and tangential components
$\gamma_n = a_n\rho$ and $\gamma_t = a_t\rho$.   At a point situated in the middle surface
$r = r_0$ of the rock shell, where the density ρ equals ρ_0, $\gamma_n = a_n\rho_0$ and
$\gamma_t = a_t\rho_0$, according to the theory of fluid equilibrium tides,[1] the latter
components of *the resultant bodily attraction force γ* per unit volume are
expressed by the functions of the polar angle α':

$$\gamma_n = a_n\rho_0 = \frac{\gamma_0}{4}\,(1 + 3\cos 2\alpha'),$$

$$\gamma_t = a_t\rho_0 = \frac{3\gamma_0}{4}\sin 2\alpha',$$

where the constant γ_0 obviously represents the greatest value of γ_n that
occurs in the shell at the point nearest to the moon, namely, at $r = r_0$,
$\alpha' = 0$.   Now let

   $g_e = 9.81$ m/sec², mean gravity acceleration in shell

   $r_e = r_1 = 6{,}370$ km, outer radius of earth sphere

   $r_m = 1{,}738$ km, radius of moon

   $\rho_e = 5.52$ g/cm³ (cgs system), mean density of earth

   $\rho_m = 3.34$ g/cm³, mean density of moon

   $D = 384{,}400$ km, mean distance between centers of earth and moon.

Then from tidal theory the bodily-attraction-force constant γ_0 per unit
volume which was introduced above is known to equal the expression

$$\gamma_0 = 2\rho_0 g_e \cdot \frac{r_0\rho_m}{r_1\rho_e} \cdot \left(\frac{r_m}{D}\right)^3.$$

[1] Cf. HORACE LAMB, "Hydrodynamics," p. 267, Dover Publications, New York,
1945.

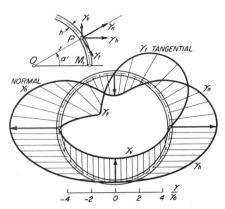

$$\gamma_h = \gamma_0 \cos \alpha', \qquad \gamma_v = -\frac{\gamma_0}{2} \sin \alpha'.$$

FIG. 17-51.   Components of tide-generating body forces in rock shell of earth.

It will be convenient also to resolve *the resultant bodily force* γ into the components γ_h and γ_v in the directions parallel to the line connecting the centers of the earth and moon ($\overline{OM}$ in Fig. 17-50) and perpendicularly to it, taken positive as indicated in Fig. 17-51. We have

Figure 17-51 reproduces the distribution of the two equivalent groups of components of bodily forces γ_n, γ_t and γ_h, γ_v along the middle surface of the rock shell.

B. EVALUATION OF ELASTIC STATE OF STRESS AND STRAIN IN THE OUTER, HOLLOW, SPHERICAL, SOLID ROCK SHELL OF THE EARTH. Based on elementary shell theory, two simple, idealized cases will be considered.

Case 1. *In the shell the bodily tidal attraction forces are solely active.* As can be seen from the preceding formulas, the system of the resultant, solid-tidal, bodily forces γ holds its own equilibrium within the thin, hollow, closed, spherical rock shell; since we did not include the state of hydrostatic pressures due to the weights of the rocks,[1] no external reaction forces are needed to support the hollow shell, and it may be considered to be floating freely in space. In this rotationally symmetrically loaded shell, obviously the principal directions of stress are known a priori. They coincide for the principal stress σ_1 with the great circles ("meridians" with respect to the position of the moon) which converge at the two "poles" M_1 and M_2 (Fig. 17-52) in which the moon stands at the zenith and the nadir and for the principal stress σ_2 with the

---

[1] It is presumed that the state of stress caused by the bodily forces originating from the earth's own gravitational field, if so required, may be superposed on the states of stress considered in the text. In homogeneous, perfectly elastic, solid rock settled under its own weight ($\rho_0 g_e = \gamma_r$ per unit volume), taking $\varepsilon_x = \varepsilon_y = 0$, there prevails the state of stress

$$\sigma_x = \sigma_y = -\frac{3vp}{1 + v} = -\frac{v\gamma_r z}{1 - v}, \qquad \sigma_z = -\gamma_r z,$$

with the mean pressure

$$p = -\frac{\sigma_x + \sigma_y + \sigma_z}{3} = \frac{(1 + v)\gamma_r z}{3(1 - v)}.$$

Only in an incompressible solid ($v = \frac{1}{2}$) does a state of pure hydrostatic pressures $\sigma_x = \sigma_y = \sigma_z = -p = -\gamma_r z$ persist.

"parallel circles" around M_1, M_2. The elementary proposition of finding the membrane stresses σ_1 and σ_2 requires writing their two conditions of equilibrium for an infinitesimal element of the shell, as reproduced in two views in Fig. 17-52, which may conveniently be expressed for the components of force in the directions normal to the shell element and parallel to the axis $\overline{OM}_1$, $\alpha' = 0$ as follows:

$$\sigma_1 + \sigma_2 = \gamma_n r_0 = \frac{\gamma_0 r_0}{4}(1 + 3\cos 2\alpha'),$$

$$\frac{d}{d\alpha'}(\sigma_1 \sin^2 \alpha') = \gamma_h r_0 \sin \alpha' = \frac{\gamma_0 r_0}{2}\sin 2\alpha',$$

from which
$$\sigma_1 = \frac{\gamma_0 r_0}{2} = \text{const},$$

$$\sigma_2 = \frac{\gamma_0 r_0}{4}(3\cos 2\alpha' - 1),$$

presuming that the third principal stress σ_3 in the direction normal to the rock shell vanishes, $\sigma_3 = 0$, and indicating that the meridian circles are strained by a uniform tensile stress $\sigma_1 = $ const and the two polar caps around the "poles" $M_1(\alpha' = 0)$ and $M_2(\alpha' = \pi)$ along the parallel circles ($\alpha' = $ const) are strained by tensile stresses σ_2, whereas the equatorial belt carries compression stresses σ_2 along the parallel circles.

Supposing elastic rocks, the principal strains ε_1 and ε_2 are equal to

$$\varepsilon_1 = \frac{1}{E}(\sigma_1 - \nu\sigma_2) = \frac{\gamma_0 r_0}{4E}(2 + \nu - 3\nu\cos 2\alpha'),$$

$$\varepsilon_2 = \frac{1}{E}(\sigma_2 - \nu\sigma_1) = \frac{\gamma_0 r_0}{4E}(-1 - 2\nu + 3\cos 2\alpha').$$

After combining these equations with the well-known kinematic relations of the theory of spherical shells expressed in terms of the

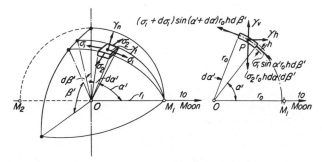

Fig. 17-52. Principal stresses σ_1 and σ_2 in an element of the outer solid rock shell of the earth.

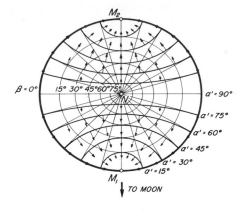

FIG. 17-53. Tangential displacements u in solid shell in stereographic projection.

components of displacement u and v in tangential and normal direction (u is positive in the direction in which α' increases),

$$\varepsilon_1 = \frac{1}{r_0}\left(v + \frac{du}{d\alpha'}\right), \qquad \varepsilon_2 = \frac{1}{r_0}(v + u \cot \alpha'),$$

and, eliminating v, there results for u the differential equation

$$\frac{du}{d\alpha'} - u \cot \alpha' = \frac{3(1 + v)\gamma_0 r_0^2}{2E} \sin^2 \alpha',$$

from which

$$u = -\frac{3(1 + v)\gamma_0 r_0^2}{4E} \sin 2\alpha'$$

and

$$v = \frac{(2 + v)\gamma_0 r_0^2}{4E}(1 + 3 \cos 2\alpha').$$

Whereas u vanishes at the poles M_1 and M_2 and on the circle $\alpha' = \pi/2$, the deflection v has its greatest, positive value at M_1 and M_2 and smallest, negative value on the circle $\alpha' = \pi/2$. The hollow, solid, spherical rock shell is distorted into an elongated ellipsoid of revolution with the major axis pointing toward the moon. The distribution of the elastic tangential displacements u is shown in a stereographic projection for the northern hemisphere in Fig. 17-53.[1]

---

[1] The effect of the tidal attractions of the moon on the elastic distortion of the outer solid rock shell, hypothetically suspended freely in space and assumed to have a uniform thickness $h = 100$ km and the mean radius $r_0 = 6,320$ km, is illustrated by quoting that its greatest elastic deflection at the two poles $\alpha' = 0$ and $\alpha' = \pi$ was estimated equal to $v_{\max} = 45.5$ m in the bulged-out regions, $v_{\min} = -22.75$ m in the flattened portions at $\alpha' = \pm\pi/2$, and the absolutely greatest tangential displacement equal to $u_{\max} = 19.8$ m. The maximum membrane stress in the shell amounts to $\sigma_2 = 0.20$ kg/cm² around the equator $\alpha' = \pi/2$, whereas at the apex $\alpha' = 0$, $\sigma_1 = \sigma_2 = -0.10$ kg/cm².

Case 2. The material elements of the thin, outer, solid, hollow, spherical rock shell sustain elastic displacements in the tangential directions, remaining in sliding contact with the rock mantle sphere of the earth.[1] Suppose that, apart from the bodily force system γ defined by its normal and tangential components γ_n, γ_t or its horizontal and vertical components γ_h, γ_v,

$$\gamma_n = \frac{\gamma_0}{4}(1 + 3\cos 2\alpha'), \qquad \gamma_h = \gamma_0 \cos \alpha',$$

$$\gamma_t = \frac{3\gamma_0}{4}\sin 2\alpha', \qquad \gamma_v = -\frac{\gamma_0}{2}\sin \alpha',$$

corresponding to *the resultant bodily forces*

$$\gamma = \frac{\gamma_0}{2}\sqrt{\frac{5 + 3\cos 2\alpha'}{2}},$$

a certain distributed load $p = f(\alpha')$ acts in the radial directions in the contact surface of the rock shell with the substratum, so that the *normal components of displacement, the deflections v of the shell, vanish, v = 0.* This is equivalent to assuming that the material elements of the shell wabble elastically to and fro in its middle surface r_0 = const when the moon describes its orbit around the earth, moving only in tangential directions, and that this freedom of sliding motion of the material elements of the rock shell relative to the mantle core due to the prevailing high temperatures and consequently small viscosity values is not inhibited.[2]

After including the normal, distributed load p we now have for the

[1] In author's: Stress and Strain in the Outer Solid Shell of the Earth, Trans. Am. Geophys. Union, vol. 33, pp. 247–276, April, 1952, this case has been considered in a less satisfactory way, namely, by neglecting the part of stress σ' to be introduced below in the text—the assumption $\sigma' = 0$ need *not* be made because it leads to implausible values of the elastic strains $\bar{\varepsilon}_x$, $\bar{\varepsilon}_y$ near the equatorial region $\beta = 0$ of the shell—a defect in former theory that is being straightened out through the present theory.

[2] B. GUTENBERG states on page 145 of his latest book (see footnote, page 627) that the upper rock mantle of the earth, at depths between 60 and 200 km, may locally be in a near-molten condition, this being supported by a minimum in the velocity of earthquake waves and through the correlation of belts of earthquake foci located at the depths just mentioned and the belts of the active volcanoes.

Thus our assumption of an increased mobility of the substratum underlying the upper solid rock shell and our postulate that the viscosity μ of the rocks attains comparatively low values in this critical region respectively to the long-time permanent deformation phenomena in the outer crust is significantly conceded by the authoritative opinion of seismologists; quoting B. GUTENBERG, "That the viscosity and the resistance to plastic flow have a minimum in the upper portion of the earth's mantle."

two conditions of equilibrium:

$$\sigma_1 + \sigma_2 = \left(\gamma_n + \frac{p}{h}\right)r_0 = \frac{\gamma_0 r_0}{4}(1 + 3\cos 2\alpha') + \frac{pr_0}{h},$$

$$\frac{d}{d\alpha'}(\sigma_1 \sin^2 \alpha') = \left(\gamma_0 + \frac{p}{h}\right)\frac{r_0 \sin 2\alpha'}{2}.$$

These have to be combined with the stress-strain relations expressing the elasticity law for the principal strains ε_1 and ε_2. With reference to the formulas listed for ε_1 and ε_2 in Sec. 17-9B(1), after letting $v = 0$ and neglecting the normal stress in a thin solid shell that acts in the normal directions to it, putting $\sigma_3 = 0$, in accordance with the theory of a thin spherical shell, we have now

$$\varepsilon_1 = \frac{1}{r_0} \cdot \frac{du}{d\alpha'} = \frac{1}{E}(\sigma_1 - v\sigma_2),$$

$$\varepsilon_2 = \frac{u \cotan \alpha'}{r_0} = \frac{1}{E}(\sigma_2 - v\sigma_1);$$

hence

$$\sigma_1 = \frac{E}{(1 - v^2)r_0}\left(\frac{du}{d\alpha'} + vu \cotan \alpha'\right),$$

$$\sigma_2 = \frac{E}{(1 - v^2)r_0}\left(v\frac{du}{d\alpha'} + u \cotan \alpha'\right).$$

Letting the constant

$$c_0 = \frac{(1 - v)r_0^2 \gamma_0}{E},$$

$$\sigma_1 + \sigma_2 = \frac{r_0 \gamma_0}{c_0}\left(\frac{du}{d\alpha'} + u \cotan \alpha'\right),$$

the withholding pressure p is found equal to

$$p = \frac{\gamma_0 h}{c_0}\left(\frac{du}{d\alpha'} + u \cotan \alpha'\right) - \frac{\gamma_0 h}{4}(1 + 3\cos 2\alpha').$$

After substituting this value of p in the second condition of equilibrium, the differential equation for the tangential displacement u is obtained,

$$L(u) = (1 + v)\left(u + \frac{3c_0}{4}\sin 2\alpha'\right),$$

where $L(u)$ denotes a second-order linear differential operator,

$$L(u) = \frac{d^2 u}{d\alpha'^2} + \frac{du}{d\alpha'}\cotan \alpha' + u(1 - \cotan^2 \alpha'),$$

which is closely related to one more general such operator which the late ERNST MEISSNER[1] of Zurich introduced in the theory of thin shells of rotational symmetry.

[1] Vierteljahresschr. naturforsch. Ges. Zürich, vol. 60, p. 23, 1915. See also W. FLÜGGE, "Statik und Dynamik der Schalen," 238 pp., Julius Springer, Berlin, 1934; see p. 153.

If we let $u = -u_0 \sin 2\alpha'$, then

$$L(u) = 4u_0 \sin 2\alpha';$$

we see that this is a particular integral of the above differential equation which also satisfies the prescribed boundary conditions at $\alpha' = 0, u = 0$ and $\alpha' = \pi/2, du/d\alpha' = 0$ and thus represents the sought-for solution of our shell problem, provided that the integration constant u_0 is chosen equal to

$$u_0 = \frac{3(1 + \nu)c_0}{4(5 + \nu)} = \frac{3(1 - \nu^2)r_0^2\gamma_0}{4(5 + \nu)E}.$$

We may note that the corresponding "hold-down load" p that keeps the rock shell flush on its concave side in contact with the earth's mantle sphere, impeding its uplifting, namely,

$$p = -p_0(1 + 3\cos 2\alpha') = -\frac{4p_0\gamma_n}{\gamma_0}, \qquad p_0 = \frac{(2 + \nu)\gamma_0 h}{5 + \nu},$$

turns out to be proportional to the normal component γ_n of the tidal body forces exerted by the gravitational attractions of the moon, the values of p having the opposite sign of the γ_n.[1]

Using the preceding functions u and p, the two principal stresses σ_1 and σ_2 acting in the solid rock shell may be expressed in the symmetric form

$$\sigma_1 = -\frac{2\sigma_0}{1 + \nu}[\nu + (2 + \nu)\cos 2\alpha'] = \sigma + \sigma',$$

$$\sigma_2 = -\frac{2\sigma_0}{1 + \nu}[1 + (1 + 2\nu)\cos 2\alpha'] = \sigma - \sigma',$$

where the constant σ_0 denotes

$$\sigma_0 = \frac{3(1 + \nu)\gamma_0 r_0}{8(5 + \nu)},$$

$\sigma = (\tfrac{1}{2})(\sigma_1 + \sigma_2)$ is the mean stress, and the terms

$$\pm\sigma' = \pm(\tfrac{1}{2})(\sigma_1 - \sigma_2)$$

represent a state of pure shear; thus

$$\underline{\underline{\sigma = -\sigma_0(1 + 3\cos 2\alpha'),}} \qquad \underline{\underline{\sigma' = \frac{(1 - \nu)\sigma_0}{1 + \nu}(1 - \cos 2\alpha'),}}$$

$$\underline{\underline{\sigma_1 = \sigma + \sigma', \qquad \sigma_2 = \sigma - \sigma'.}}$$

These four stresses (taking $\nu = 0.375$, $r_0 = 6.32 \times 10^8$ cm, $\gamma_0 = 3.12 \times 10^{-10}$ kg/cm³, $\sigma_0 = 0.0189$ kg/cm²) have been plotted above the

[1] The curve in the upper part of Fig. 17-51 with its radially plotted ordinates $\gamma_n = f(\alpha')$ may represent a polar graph of the inverted withholding loads $-p$ in the appropriate scale. While at the poles $\alpha' = 0$ and $\alpha' = \pi$ the load equals $p = -4p_0$, in the circle $\alpha' = \pi/2, p = 2p_0$; the former is a tensile and the latter a compression normal stress.

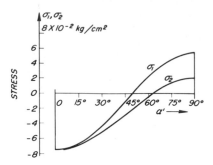

FIG. 17-54. Principal stresses σ_1 and σ_2 in solid shell.

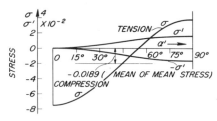

FIG. 17-55. Mean stress $\sigma = (\sigma_1 + \sigma_2)/2$ and stress σ' in solid shell.

polar angle α' in Figs. 17-54 and 17-55, disclosing that the solid rock shell around the poles M_1, $M_2(\alpha' = 0, \alpha' = \pi)$, in two broad caps, is now stressed in compression and in an equatorial belt by tensile stresses, the former being predominant.[1] This is understandable in the absence of any normal deflections v, since the combined effects of the normal forces p and of γ_n bring the shell practically back to its initially unstrained form, whereas the tangentially directed body forces γ_t push the elements of material elastically toward the two poles M_1 and M_2.

The trajectories of principal stress corresponding to σ_1 and σ_2 again consist of the family of great circles $\beta' = $ const emanating from the diametrically opposite points M_1 and M_2 as poles, in the zenith and nadir of which stands the moon, and of the group of parallel circles $\alpha' = $ const, both of which, for the sake of brevity of expression, we shall call *moon meridians* and *moon parallels* on the earth's sphere.[2]

The principal stress trajectories are conveniently mapped in stereographic projection. This is shown for the northern hemisphere in Fig. 17-56 in which the bunch of rays radiating from the North Pole N and the concentric circles (both shown by thin lines) are the circles of geographic longitude (earth meridians) $\alpha = $ const and of latitude $\beta = $ const. Suppose that the moon stands above a point M_1 chosen at some initial time $t = 0$ on the earth's equator $\beta = 0$ at longitude $\alpha = 0$. Then the familiar group of orthogonal circles drawn in a little heavier lines in Fig. 17-56 represents the "moon meridians" $\beta' = $ const, radiating from the moon poles $M_1(\alpha' = 0)$ and $M_2(\alpha' = \pi)$, and the circles orthogonal to them represent the "moon parallels," both families defining the principal stress trajectories of σ_1 and σ_2.

---

[1] The meridian stress σ_1 vanishes when $\cos 2\alpha' = -\nu/(2 + \nu) = -0.158$ for $\alpha' = 49°33'$ and the stress σ_2 vanishes when $\cos 2\alpha' = -1/(1 + 2\nu) = -0.572$ for $\alpha' = 62°25'$. The mean stress σ vanishes for $\alpha' = 54°44'$.

[2] Although the angle α' (see Fig. 17-51) being measured from the "pole" $M_1(\alpha' = 0)$ in fact is the complement of the angle which is usually called angle of latitude.

We have now to take account of two motions: the rotation of the earth around its polar axis and the motion of the moon around the earth, in consequence of which obviously the system of the stress trajectories (moon meridians and parallels) continuously changes its relative position with respect to the system of geographic meridians and parallels. The moon circles uniformly around the earth approximately at the invariable distance D in a plane that is slightly inclined at a small angle with respect to the plane of the ecliptic in which the earth moves around the sun. Suppose for convenience that the moon remains in the ecliptic. This intersects the earth's sphere at any instant in a great circle inclined under the angle $\delta = 23°30'$ with respect to the earth's equator $\beta = 0$, and we may, without losing generality, presume that at time $t = 0$ it just passes through point M_1 above which the moon stands in Fig. 17-56. This permits us to represent at this initial time the ecliptic in Fig. 17-56 as the circle traced as a dashed line $M_1E_1M_2E_2$, complying with the requirement that it be inclined at $\delta = 23°30'$ toward the equator $\beta = 0$. Consider this circle *fixed in stellar space* as representing in the figure the path of the moon or of point M_1 at which the radius vector drawn from the center of the earth to the moon pierces the surface of the earth. Then it takes point M_1, marking the position of the moon, to circumnavigate once the ecliptic circle the time t_s equal to *the sidereal month* $t_s = 27$ days 7 hr 43 min $= 27{,}322$ solar days or a quarter month $(t_s/4)$ to travel in Fig. 17-56 the arc length M_1E_1 to reach its *farthest*

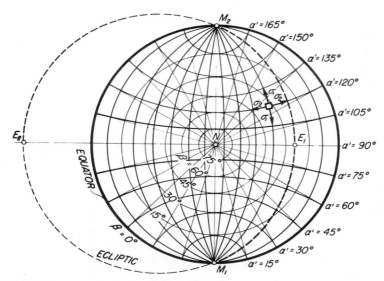

FIG. 17-56. Stereographic representation of the trajectories of principal stress in the solid earth shell caused by the attraction of the moon. Northern hemisphere, position of moon at M_1 in equator.

northern declination (the "summer solstice" E_1 if this point were referred to the sun). Whereas the trajectories of stress σ_1, σ_2 were plotted in Fig. 17-56 at the instant $t = 0$ when the moon just culminated above point M_1 situated on the earth's equator $\beta = 0$, their position at time $t = t_s/4$ is shown in Fig. 17-57 at the instant when M_1 reaches its farthest northern declination, when M_1 coincides with the summer solstice E_1, with the moon meridians radiating from this latter point.[1]

While point M_1 moves with an invariable *absolute* peripheral velocity $\mathbf{w}_a$($|w_a| = r_e \omega_m$) on the ecliptic circle fixed in space and while the earth turns with the angular speed ω_e around its axis, *an observer on earth participating in the latter motion with the vehicular velocity* $\mathbf{w}_v$ ($|w_v| = r_e \omega_e \cos \beta$, β = geographic latitude of instantaneous position of point M_1) sees point M_1 recede with the *relative velocity*

$$\mathbf{w}_r = \mathbf{w}_a - \mathbf{w}_v$$

in a near-*westward* direction.

Hence, when M_1 just crosses the earth's equator $\beta = 0$, as indicated in Fig. 17-56, M_1 moves with the component w_1 of relative velocity in a westward direction,

$$w_1 = r_e(\omega_e - \omega_m \cos \delta)$$

($\delta = 23° 30'$ angle of ecliptic and equator), and when M_1 passes through E_1, its farthest northern declination, indicated in Fig. 17-57, just moving in the latitude circle $\beta = \delta$, the westward relative velocity of M_1 is equal to

$$w_2 = r_e(\omega_e \cos \delta - \omega_m).$$

Suppose in a first approximation that we neglect the small relative oscillatory movements of the moon pole M_1 in the north-south direction. *We may then assume that the path of M_1 on earth coincides practically with the equator $\beta = 0$ and state that M_1 moves on it with the mean, invariable relative velocity w westward:*

$$w = (\tfrac{1}{2})(w_1 + w_2) = \frac{r_e}{2}(1 + \cos \delta)(\omega_e - \omega_m) = 0.96 r_e(\omega_e - \omega_m).$$

---

[1] If we denote the length of time of one solar day by $T_s = 24$ hr $= 86,400$ sec and of *one sidereal day* by $T_s' = 86,164.09$ sec (time elapsed between two consecutive fix-star passages through the geographic stellar meridian or the time in which the earth completes one revolution around its axis in stellar space), furthermore by ω_e the angular speed of rotation of the earth and by ω_m the angular velocity with which the radius vector drawn from the earth to the moon turns uniformly in stellar space, then obviously we have:
For the earth's revolutions:

$$\omega_e = 2\pi/T_s' = 7.29212 \times 10^{-5} \text{ per sec,}$$

For the motion of the moon along the ecliptic circle:

$$\omega_m = 2\pi/t_s = 2.6616 \times 10^{-6} \text{ per sec,}$$

the vector ω_m being inclined to vector ω_e at the angle $\delta = 23°30'$ and both turning velocities in Figs. 17-56 and 17-57 are directed anticlockwise, eastward.

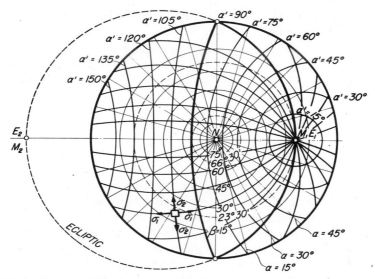

FIG. 17-57. Stereographic representation of the trajectories of principal stress in the solid earth shell caused by the attraction of the moon. Northern hemisphere, position of moon at M_1 in farthest northern declination.

For the purpose to be elucidated below, it will suffice to assume *that the pattern of principal stress trajectories* seen in Fig. 17-56 *revolves on earth and its rock shell westward around the center point with a mean, uniform, relative angular speed*

$$\omega = \frac{w}{r_e} = 0.96(\omega_e - \omega_m) = 6.745 \times 10^{-5} \text{ per sec}$$

or that an observer placed on the moon sees the earth uniformly revolving, completing one full turn eastward in the time

$$T = \frac{2\pi}{\omega} = 93{,}200 \text{ sec,}$$

which is 6,800 sec = 1 hr 53 min 20 sec longer than the solar day $T_s = 24$ hr $= 86{,}400$ sec.

Natural rocks having viscoelastic properties under long-time action of stress, this is perhaps an appropriate place to ask *what types and magnitudes of permanent strains must accrue in the solid rock shell* under the system of fluctuating stresses σ_1 and σ_2 that sweeps continuously through the shell over long geologic times. Single out an arbitrary point $P(\alpha,\beta)$ on the northern hemisphere having geographic longitude α and latitude β. During the time period T the principal stresses σ_1, σ_2 at point $P(\alpha,\beta)$ vary in their values and directions, periodically describing two complete cycles of their oscillations. We may express the state of plane stress defined by the principal stresses σ_1, σ_2, $\sigma_3 = 0$ at point P of the solid rock shell,

$$\sigma_1 = \sigma + \sigma', \qquad \sigma_2 = \sigma - \sigma',$$

by means of the components of normal stress σ_x, σ_y and shear stress τ_{xy} that act in the direction of the geographic latitude ($\beta = $ const) and longitude ($\alpha = $ const) circle by

$$\sigma_x = \sigma + \sigma' \cos 2\phi, \qquad \sigma = -\sigma_0(1 + 3 \cos 2\alpha'),$$
$$\sigma_y = \sigma - \sigma' \cos 2\phi,$$
$$\tau_{xy} = \sigma' \sin 2\phi, \qquad \sigma' = \frac{(1 - \nu)\sigma_0}{1 + \nu}(1 - \cos 2\alpha'),$$

where ϕ denotes the angle under which the moon meridian $M_1 P$ or the principal stress σ_1 crosses at some given time t at point P ($\alpha = \omega t$, β) the latitude circle $A'PB'$, $\beta = $ const, as shown in Fig. 17-58.

Supposing that the revolving rock shell under the prolonged action of these stresses σ_x, σ_y, τ_{xy} (we neglect, as already stated, the normal stress $\sigma_z = \sigma_3$ in the direction normal to the shell which has the small mean value $\sigma_z = p/2$ over the shell thickness h, letting $\sigma_z = 0$) responds with the permanent strains ε_x'', ε_y'', ε_z'', γ_{xy}'' of a purely viscous nature, these will continuously increase at the following rates of strain:

$$\dot{\varepsilon}_x'' = \frac{1}{3\mu}\left(\sigma_x - \frac{\sigma_y}{2}\right) = \frac{1}{6\mu}(\sigma + 3\sigma' \cos 2\phi),$$

$$\dot{\varepsilon}_y'' = \frac{1}{3\mu}\left(\sigma_y - \frac{\sigma_x}{2}\right) = \frac{1}{6\mu}(\sigma - 3\sigma' \cos 2\phi),$$

$$\dot{\varepsilon}_z'' = -\frac{(\sigma_x + \sigma_y)}{6\mu} = -\frac{\sigma}{3\mu},$$

$$\dot{\gamma}_{xy}'' = \frac{\tau_{xy}}{\mu} = \frac{\sigma' \sin 2\phi}{\mu},$$

where for the coefficient of viscosity μ an average, low, mean value is presumed to be effective, taking into consideration the rapid decrease of μ with increasing depths z on account of the increasing temperatures θ below ground in the rock shell $0 \leq z \leq h$ of thickness h.

We desire to express the left-hand quantities in the two preceding groups of relations in terms of the geographic coordinates α (longitude) and β (latitude) as the independent variables. This requires evaluation of the two yet unknown angles α' and ϕ in terms of α and β on the rotating earth. Looking at an octant of the northern hemisphere of the earth, turning with the angular speed $\omega = 6.745 \times 10^{-5}$ per sec anticlockwise relatively with respect to the position of the moon in Fig. 17-58, supposed to stand fixed above point M_1, the position of the earth being defined at the time t by its relative "hour angle" $\alpha = \omega t$ of the

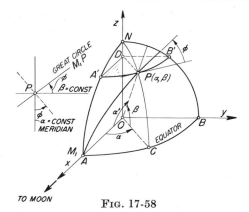

Fig. 17-58

geographic meridian (CPN) passing through point $P(\alpha,\beta)$, one shows
easily that there correspond to α, β an angle α' ($\sphericalangle M_1OP$) of moon
meridian M_1P and an angle ϕ under which it intersects the parallel
circle $\beta =$ const $(A'PB')$ which may be evaluated from the simple
formulas[1]

$$\cos \alpha' = \cos \alpha \cos \beta, \qquad \tan \phi = \cotan \alpha \cdot \sin \beta.$$

[1] In the triangular pyramid $APCO$ with the apex angles α', β, α, in fact,
the direction cosines of

edge $\overline{OP}$ being equal to $a_x = \cos \alpha'$, $a_y = \sqrt{\cos^2 \beta - \cos^2 \alpha'}$, $a_z = \sin \beta$;

edge $\overline{OC}$ being equal to $c_x = \cos \alpha$, $c_y = \sin \alpha$, $c_z = 0$,

by the cosine theorem,

$$\cos \beta = a_xc_x + a_yc_y + a_zc_z, \qquad a_yc_y = \cos \beta - a_xc_x,$$

or $$(\cos^2 \beta - \cos^2 \alpha') \sin^2 \alpha = (\cos \beta - \cos \alpha \cos \alpha')^2,$$

from which one deduces the formula $\cos \alpha' = \cos \alpha \cos \beta$.

Assigning likewise to the tangents to the parallel $\beta =$ const and grand circle
M_1P at point P, enclosing the unknown angle ϕ, the direction cosines b_x, b_y, b_z
and d_x, d_y, d_z, respectively, with the positive directions in these two straight lines
chosen in the sense of increasing longitude α, one ascertains by trigonometry that

$$b_x = -\sin \alpha, \qquad d_x = -\sin \alpha'$$
$$b_y = \cos \alpha, \qquad d_y = \sin \alpha \cos \beta \cotan \alpha'$$
$$b_z = 0, \qquad d_z = \sin \beta \cotan \alpha';$$

after substituting these values in

$$\cos \phi = b_xd_x + b_yd_y + b_zd_z$$

there result the equivalent formulas for

$$\cos \phi = \frac{\sin \alpha}{\sin \alpha'}, \qquad \tan \phi = \cotan \alpha \cdot \sin \beta,$$

$$\cos 2\phi = \frac{1 - \cos^2 \alpha \cdot (2 - \cos^2 \beta)}{1 - \cos^2 \alpha \cos^2 \beta}, \qquad \sin 2\phi = \frac{\sin 2\alpha \cdot \sin \beta}{1 - \cos^2 \alpha \cos^2 \beta}.$$

With the help of these and the formulas for $\cos 2\phi$, $\sin 2\phi$ listed in the footnote, one obtains in terms of the two geographic variables α and β for the stresses σ, σ':

$$\sigma = -2\sigma_0(3\cos^2\alpha\cos^2\beta - 1)$$
$$= -\sigma_0[3(1 + \cos 2\alpha)\cos^2\beta - 2],$$

$$\sigma' = \frac{2(1 - \nu)\sigma_0}{1 + \nu}(1 - \cos^2\alpha\cos^2\beta)$$
$$= \frac{(1 - \nu)\sigma_0}{1 + \nu}[2 - (1 + \cos 2\alpha)\cos^2\beta],$$

$$\sigma'\cos 2\phi = \frac{2(1 - \nu)\sigma_0}{1 + \nu}[1 - \cos^2\alpha \cdot (2 - \cos^2\beta)],$$

$$\sigma'\sin 2\phi = \frac{2(1 - \nu)\sigma_0}{1 + \nu}\sin 2\alpha\sin\beta.$$

To avoid involvements due to dealing with different values of Poisson's ratio in the elastic and the permanent range of strains, suppose that we accept in the preceding equations the value $\nu = \frac{1}{2}$, postulated in the stress–permanent-rate-of-strain relations valid *for incompressible material.* The stresses in the solid rock shell are then expressed by

$$\sigma = -\sigma_0(3\cos^2\beta - 2 + 3\cos 2\alpha\cos^2\beta),$$

$$\sigma' = \frac{\sigma_0}{3}(2 - \cos^2\beta - \cos 2\alpha\cos^2\beta),$$

$$\sigma_x = \frac{2\sigma_0}{3}[3 - 4\cos^2\beta - \cos 2\alpha \cdot (1 + 4\cos^2\beta)]$$

$$\sigma_y = \frac{2\sigma_0}{3}[3 - 5\cos^2\beta + \cos 2\alpha \cdot (1 - 5\cos^2\beta)]$$

$$\tau_{xy} = \frac{2\sigma_0}{3}\sin 2\alpha\sin\beta,$$

where the constant σ_0 is equal to

$$\sigma_0 = \frac{3(1 + \nu)\gamma_0 r_0}{8(5 + \nu)} = \frac{9\gamma_0 r_0}{88}.$$

Glancing back at the stress–viscous-rate-of-strain relations, after substituting in them the afore-listed expressions of the stresses σ_x, σ_y, τ_{xy}, one sees that, if one integrates these relations with respect to the time t over the period $T = 93{,}200$ sec of one earth's revolution or multiples thereof, the oscillating parts of the stresses varying as $\cos 2\alpha$ or $\sin 2\alpha$ with $\alpha = \omega t$ do not contribute to the formation of the permanent strains ε_x'', ε_y'', τ_{xy}''. In order to evaluate the long-time permanent distortion of the solid rock shell, we need to consider only the steady, time-independent parts of stress. Designating the latter by placing a bar above the symbols, *the steady, time-independent part of the elastic state of stress in the revolving outer, solid earth shell* is therefore expressed in the simple form

$$\bar{\sigma} = (\tfrac{1}{2})(\bar{\sigma}_x + \bar{\sigma}_y) = \sigma_0(2 - 3\cos^2\beta) = \frac{\sigma_0}{2}(1 - 3\cos 2\beta),$$

$$\bar{\sigma}_x = 2\sigma_0(1 - \tfrac{4}{3}\cos^2\beta) = \frac{2\sigma_0}{3}(1 - 2\cos 2\beta),$$

$$\bar{\sigma}_y = 2\sigma_0(1 - \tfrac{5}{3}\cos^2\beta) = \frac{\sigma_0}{3}(1 - 5\cos 2\beta),$$

$$\bar{\tau}_{xy} = 0,$$

and this causes the elastic strains

$$\bar{\varepsilon}_x = -\frac{u}{r_0}\tan\beta = \frac{1}{E}\left(\bar{\sigma}_x - \frac{\bar{\sigma}_y}{2}\right) = \frac{\sigma_0}{2E}(1 - \cos 2\beta),$$

$$\bar{\varepsilon}_y = \frac{du}{r_0\, d\beta} = \frac{1}{E}\left(\bar{\sigma}_y - \frac{\bar{\sigma}_x}{2}\right) = -\frac{\sigma_0}{E}\cos 2\beta,$$

$$\bar{\varepsilon}_z = -\bar{\varepsilon}_x - \bar{\varepsilon}_y = \frac{-\sigma_0}{2E}(1 - 3\cos 2\beta),$$

and time rates of permanent strain, built up according to the perfectly analogous group of relations,

$$\dot{\varepsilon}_x'' = -\frac{w}{r_0}\tan\beta = \frac{1}{3\mu}\left(\bar{\sigma}_x - \frac{\bar{\sigma}_y}{2}\right) = \frac{\sigma_0}{6\mu}(1 - \cos 2\beta),$$

$$\dot{\varepsilon}_y'' = \frac{\partial w}{r_0\, \partial\beta} = \frac{1}{3\mu}\left(\bar{\sigma}_y - \frac{\bar{\sigma}_x}{2}\right) = -\frac{\sigma_0}{3\mu}\cos 2\beta,$$

$$\dot{\varepsilon}_z'' = -\dot{\varepsilon}_x'' - \dot{\varepsilon}_y'' = -\frac{\sigma_0}{6\mu}(1 - 3\cos 2\beta),$$

where u denotes the elastic displacement and $w = \partial u''/\partial t$ the velocity of flow or time rate of permanent displacement, both in tangential direction to the middle surface of the spherical, hollow, rock shell. From the kinematic side of the preceding two groups of relations, one sees that

$$u = -\frac{\sigma_0 r_0}{2E}\sin 2\beta, \qquad w = -\frac{\sigma_0 r_0}{6\mu}\sin 2\beta,$$

that all points in the middle shell surface move exactly southward in the northern hemisphere, except on the equator $\beta = 0$ and at the North Pole $\beta = \pi/2$; furthermore that the circumferential elastic strain $\bar{\varepsilon}_x = 0$ and rate of permanent strain $\dot{\varepsilon}_x'' = 0$, both in the direction of the earth equator $\beta = 0$, vanish on it as one should expect.

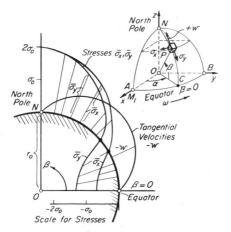

FIG. 17-59. Polar graph of steady normal stresses $\bar{\sigma}_x$ and $\bar{\sigma}_y$ acting in direction of geographic parallel (β = const) and meridian circles (α = const) in thin solid shell of the earth.

The distribution of the rotationally symmetric, steady stresses $\bar{\sigma}_x$, $\bar{\sigma}_y$ just derived and illustrated in Fig. 17-59 discloses that a broad equatorial zone is stressed in compression, whereas the two large polar caps beyond it are stressed very nearly under biaxially equal tensions increasing toward the poles $\beta = \pm\pi/2$ to the maximum values $\bar{\sigma}_x = \bar{\sigma}_y = 2\sigma_0$.†

During the time $T = 93{,}200$ sec of one full revolution of the earth the permanent strains ε_x'', ε_y'' increase by the amounts

$$\varepsilon_x'' = \frac{\sigma_0 T}{6\mu}\,(1 - \cos 2\beta),$$

$$\varepsilon_y'' = -\,\frac{\sigma_0 T}{3\mu}\,\cos 2\beta,$$

along the equator $\beta = 0$ by

$$\varepsilon_x'' = 0, \qquad \varepsilon_y'' = -\,\frac{\sigma_0 T}{3\mu}\,,$$

and at the poles $\beta = \pm\pi/2$ by

$$\varepsilon_x'' = \varepsilon_y'' = \frac{\sigma_0 T}{3\mu}\,.$$

If the values of the viscosity μ in their dependence on the pressure p of the weights of overlying rock and on the temperature θ underground that prevailed during past geologic epochs were better known, one could estimate the mean value $\bar{\mu}$ of the viscosity μ over the thickness h of the outer, solid, spherical rock shell at past times in the history of the earth and speculate about the accrued amounts of permanent strain during each long geologic epoch of time.

We may thus state that *the gravitational body forces* γ_0 *exerted by the moon tend to displace extremely slowly material in both hemispheres toward the equatorial region* where it is gradually piled up and accumulated in a broad belt, held under steady compression stresses $\bar{\sigma}_y$ in the

† The normal stress $\bar{\sigma}_y$ that acts in the direction of the earth meridians vanishes on the parallels $\beta = \pm 39° \, 15'$ (on which $\cos 2\beta = \frac{1}{5}$) and takes on the value $\bar{\sigma}_y = -4\sigma_0/3$ on the equator, whereas the normal stress $\bar{\sigma}_x$ that acts in the direction of the parallel circles vanishes on $\beta = \pm 30°$ and equals $\bar{\sigma}_x = -2\sigma_0/3$ on the equator. The strain $\bar{\varepsilon}_y$ and rate of strain $\dot{\varepsilon}_y''$ in the north-south direction both vanish on the parallels $\beta = \pm 45°$ along which the velocity of viscous flow maintains its absolutely greatest value $|w_{\max}| = \sigma_0 r_0/6\mu$.

north-south direction between the parallels $\beta = \pm 39°15'$, this slow flow being supported at the expense of substance drawn from the polar regions. Certain physiographical trends in the continents lend support to the aforementioned facts brought out in the preceding, primitive theory of long-time, slow, permanent distortion of the solid outer rock shell: a good portion of the highest, extensive plateaus of the earth is to be found in Central Asia (Tibet); the majority of the principal, highest mountain ranges in the eastern hemisphere (the Himalayas, Caucasian, Carpathian Ranges, the Alps, Pyrenees, Atlas Mountains, etc.) run primarily in the east-west direction—admitting exceptions to the rule. In this respect one has to keep in mind many additional geologic factors that influenced mountain building and folding on earth outside the scope of our considerations and the fact that the moon during the earlier phases of these phenomena probably circled around the earth at a much closer distance than presently, also remembering that the separation of the primeval continents according to WEGENER's ideas caused its own, typical effects unrelated to those which were here described.

In conclusion, a few words may be said in regard to *the small oscillations of an elastic, periodic nature* that the points of the solid shell describe relative to the earth's interior. Their magnitude was found to be proportional to the sine of twice the moon-latitude angle α' and their directions pointing always toward the position M_1 of the moon, i.e., at a point $P(\alpha,\beta)$ on earth, inclined under the angle $\pi + \phi$ with respect to the positive sense of the parallel circle $\beta = $ const. Letting these tangential displacements

$$u = -u_0 \sin 2\alpha',$$

we find their amplitude equal to

$$u_0 = \frac{3(1 - \nu^2)r_0\gamma_0}{4(5 + \nu)E} = \frac{3r_0\gamma_0}{28E},$$

the factor $\frac{3}{28}$ resulting for Poisson's ratio $\nu = \frac{1}{2}$. The components of the vector $\mathbf{u}$, in the direction of the geographic parallel u_p and meridian u_m of point P,

$$u_p = u \cos \phi, \qquad u_m = u \sin \phi,$$

may easily be evaluated by making use of the angular relations stated in the footnote on page 683, and one finds that

$$u_p = -u_0 \sin 2\alpha \cos \beta,$$

$$u_m = -\frac{u_0}{2}(1 + \cos 2\alpha)\sin 2\beta,$$

indicating that the path which a point $P(\alpha,\beta)$ of the solid shell describes, owing to the elastic oscillations, is *a small ellipse*, presuming that the moon stays at the earth's equator, as assumed in Fig. 17-58:

$$\frac{u_p^2}{a^2} + \frac{(u_m + b)^2}{b^2} = 1,$$

$$a = u_0 \cos \beta,$$

$$b = u_0 \sin \beta \cos \beta.$$

These ellipses are plotted in Fig. 17-60 for six geographic latitudes β. The ellipse collapses to a straight path at the equator $\beta = 0$, and the North Pole $\beta = \pi/2$ remains at rest, each ellipse being circumscribed twice during the time T of one earth's revolution. If, however, the plane of the actual orbit of the moon had been considered, that nearly coincides with the ecliptic plane in which the earth moves, the curves described by the elastic oscillations would have been of a more complicated form, the pole would not have remained at rest, and a point on the equator would have moved in a loop.

A few words, lastly, about *the viscous drag* that must retard slightly this elastic wiggling of the outer, solid rock shell, changing the relative orbits above the semifluid core of the earth's mantle to coils of densely spaced small loops. As the solid shell wobbles back and forth relative to the earth's interior in the planes of the horizons, there results a drag in the more mobile, hot, underlying magma of a viscous nature, and shearing stresses are transmitted onto the shell below the contact surface of both. Since the only source able to supply the energies lost through the viscous drag, apart from the comparatively very small

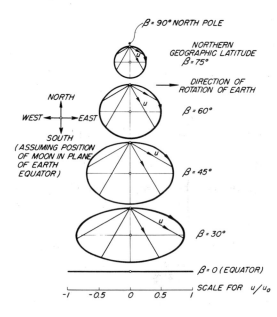

FIG. 17-60. Tangential displacements u of points of the solid earth shell relative to fluid magma substratum. The vectors u represent the horizontal displacements caused by the attraction of the moon at the given geographic latitudes β in the northern hemisphere during the revolutions of the earth. Position of the moon is assumed in plane of earth equator $\beta = 0$.

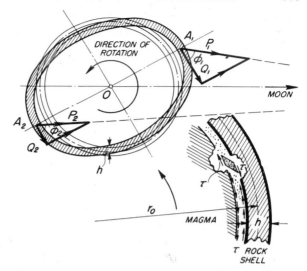

Fig. 17-61. Forces ex-
plaining westward drift
of solid shell of earth.

amounts of elastic strain energy stored in the solid shell, is the kinetic
energy of rotation of the earth's interior mass, the friction through
which the magma resists the wiggling solid crust must retard the
rotational angular speed of the earth.   This results in a certain moment
around an axis which perhaps may be situated not too far from the
earth's polar axis (coinciding with the latter when the moon stands over
the earth's equator).   According to the law of action and reaction, a
resultant couple of equal magnitude but of opposite direction must act
on the solid shell itself, in the direction in which the earth turns in space.
This seems paradoxical or absurd: if the outer, solid rock shell should
slide as a huge brake shoe on the earth's core, the friction that it exerts
builds up an "inner moment," whereas no external force can be found
that supports the brake shoe at an external point.

The classical theory of tidal friction by G. Darwin (1910) explains
the apparent paradox.   There exists an external couple of forces that
balances the internal frictional moment originating in the drag of the
magma core.   It is supplied by the difference of the two attractional
force resultants P_1 and P_2 exerted by the moon on the two bulges A_1
and A_2 of the rock shell, supposing that it took on the elastically,
slightly elongated ellipsoidal form in the tilted position indicated in
Fig. 17-61.[1]   The tangential component Q_1 of the resultant attraction

[1] Although our detailed analysis in this section considered elastic tidal shell
distortions of a type in which no normal deflections v, only tangential displacements u and $v = 0$, were postulated, a certain, instantaneously prevailing
condensation in matter density in the two earth's caps nearest to and farthest
from the moon over a quarter quadrant of the shell in two bulges, like those in
Fig. 17-61, of computable amplitude is evidenced, intensified by a slow viscous
flow and permanent accumulation of matter in the equatorial region.

force P_1 originating at point A_1 is, in fact, slightly larger than the tangential component Q_2 of the resultant force P_2 at point A_2 (both resultants P_1 and P_2 pointing toward the moon) for two reasons: (1) because $P_1 > P_2$, owing to NEWTON's law of gravitation, and (2) because the angle ϕ_1 is smaller than the angle ϕ_2, $\phi_1 < \phi_2$.   Therefore

$$Q_1 = P_1 \cos \phi_1 > P_2 \cos \phi_2 = Q_2,$$

and *an external moment* $(Q_1 - Q_2)r_0$ *results, tending to turn the solid shell relatively to the core* in the opposite direction in which both the shell and core revolve, provided that the two bulged regions A_1 and A_2 moved out from the axis connecting the centers of the earth and moon (on which they would lie had no frictional forces been at play) into the new, tilted, retarded positions A_1 and A_2 in which they are seen in Fig. 17-61.   We note that the tidal moment $(Q_1 - Q_2)r_0$, accompanied by the shear stresses τ indicated in the side sketch, turns the solid rock shell with an extremely small velocity around the core, *thus causing the westward drift, supplying the force system once sought by Wegener.*

Reflecting again on action and equal reaction, one sees, on the other hand, that, if one applies the inverted forces P_1 and P_2 as reactions $-P_1$ and $-P_2$, by transferring the latter to the center of the moon, pointing toward the points A_1 and A_2 on earth, they must have *the effect on the moon of moderately changing its motion around the earth,*   As shown in schematized Fig. 17-62 illustrating tilted positions of masses m_1 and m_2, concentrated at points A_1 and A_2 (representing bulges in the solid rock shell) on earth, the gravitational reaction forces $-P_1$, $-P_2$ with which masses m_1 and m_2 attract the moon combine in their force triangle to a resultant R at the center of the moon C_m.   Since force $-P_1$ originating in the nearer mass m_1 pulls the moon *forward* more than force $-P_2$ exerted by the farther mass m_2 tends to *retard* it, the effect of both results in a small total force in a direction tangential to the orbit of the moon that *accelerates its motion* slightly, whereas the centripetal component of resultant R is practically the same compared with the situation (not shown in the figure) in which m_1 and m_2 were on the axis C_eC_m connecting the centers of the earth and moon (in the positions that they would have taken in the absence of friction).

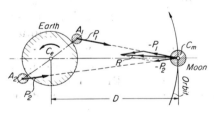

FIG. 17-62.   Gravitational reaction forces $-P_1$, $-P_2$ applied to moon, caused by elastic distortion of earth's rock shell in presence of tidal, solid, viscous friction.   They constrain moon to increase its distance D from the earth.

The presence of tidal, solid friction thus causes three effects: (1) it retards the rotation of both the earth's core and outer rock shell, (2) it causes the slow westward drift of the shell relative to the core, and (3) it increases the distance $D = C_e C_m$ of the moon from the earth, forcing it to move slightly away from the earth—in agreement with DARWIN's theory of tidal, fluid friction. This *third effect is deemed particularly significant*, remembering that the intensity of the tide-generating body forces γ_0, exerted by the moon on the earth, varies inversely with the third power of the distance D, so that when in early, geologic epochs this distance once equaled one-half, one-third, . . . of its present value, the attractions onto and the tidal elastic distortions produced thereby in the solid rock shell were greater than at present[1] by a factor equal to 8, 27, ...

It is hoped that the last sections devoted to geomechanics on the border line of engineers' theories of thin, elastic, spherical shells may induce readers to further contemplations in this interesting field.

[1] G. DARWIN pointed out clearly in 1910 in his admirable book devoted to the tides quoted on page 659 that the effectiveness of fluid- or solid-tidal phenomena increases *even faster* than just stated with the decrease of distance D of the moon from the earth, because of a further intensification of the attractions exerted by the moon on the masses already heaped up in the tide mounts or bulges. In order to understand these circumstances, suppose that the form of solid-tide height were not affected by an approach of the moon's orbit. Then, by the same reasoning, the attractions on the masses concentrated within the bulged-out regions would have been intensified by a factor equal to 8, 27, . . . at distances of one-half, one-third, . . . of present D. Hence, the over-all effect was an increase of the elastic bulge amplitude by the factor 64, 729, . . . , in past geologic epochs when the moon circled much closer to the earth.

These last remarks along G. DARWIN's ideas may perhaps also serve the purpose of weakening certain arguments that one could read in statements (by A. E. SCHEIDEGGER, "Principles of Geodynamics," p. 132, Springer-Verlag, Berlin, Vienna, 1958, and by others), asserting that the solid-tidal forces exerted by the action of the moon on the earth are much too small and inadequate to be considered as the bodily forces that could have caused the effects of mountain building on earth and the drift of the continents. It suffices to keep in mind that these forces were incomparably stronger and intensified in remote, geologic times past, on account of the closer positions of the moon to the earth.

AUTHOR INDEX

SUBJECT INDEX